THE PEARSON CUSTOM LIBRARY FOR THE
BIOLOGICAL SCIENCES

Microbiology: An Introduction

Custom Edition
Manchester Community College

PEARSON

Senior Vice President, Editorial: Patrick F. Boles
Senior Sponsoring Editor: Natalie Danner
Development Editor: Jill Johnson
Executive Marketing Manager: Nathan L. Wilbur
Operations Manager: Eric M. Kenney
Production Manager: Jennifer Berry
Art Director: Renée Sartell
Cover Designer: Kristen Kiley

Cover Art: Courtesy of Michael R. Martin, Darryl Johnson, Photodisk, DK Images, and Prentice-Hall, Inc.

This special edition published in cooperation with Pearson Learning Solutions.

Printed in the United States of America.

V092

Please visit our website at *www.pearsonlearningsolutions.com.*

Attention bookstores: For permission to return unused stock, contact us at *pe-uscustomreturns@pearson.com.*

Pearson Learning Solutions, 501 Boylston Street, Suite 900, Boston, MA 02116
A Pearson Education Company
www.pearsoned.com

ISBN 10: 1-256-56476-1
ISBN 13: 978-1-256-56476-8

Laboratory Safety: General Guidelines

1. Notify your instructor immediately if you are pregnant, color blind, allergic to any insects or chemicals, taking immunosuppressive drugs, or have any other medical condition (such as diabetes, immunologic defect) that may require special precautionary measures in the laboratory.

2. Upon entering the laboratory, place all books, coats, purses, backpacks, etc. in designated areas, not on the bench tops.

3. Locate and, when appropriate, learn to use exits, fire extinguisher, fire blanket, chemical shower, eyewash, first aid kit, broken glass container, and cleanup materials for spills.

4. In case of fire, evacuate the room and assemble outside the building.

5. Do not eat, drink, smoke, or apply cosmetics in the laboratory.

6. Confine long hair, loose clothing, and dangling jewelry.

7. Wear shoes at all times in the laboratory.

8. Cover any cuts or scrapes with a sterile, waterproof bandage before attending lab.

9. Wear eye protection when working with chemicals.

10. Never pipet by mouth. Use mechanical pipeting devices.

11. Wash skin immediately and thoroughly if contaminated by chemicals or microorganisms.

12. Do not perform unauthorized experiments.

13. Do not use equipment without instruction.

14. Report all spills and accidents to your instructor immediately.

15. Never leave heat sources unattended.

16. When using hot plates, note that there is no visible sign that they are hot (such as a red glow). Always assume that hot plates are hot.

17. Use an appropriate apparatus when handling hot glassware.

18. Keep chemicals away from direct heat or sunlight.

19. Keep containers of alcohol, acetone, and other flammable liquids away from flames.

20. Do not allow any liquid to come into contact with electrical cords. Handle electrical connectors with dry hands. Do not attempt to disconnect electrical equipment that crackles, snaps, or smokes.

21. Upon completion of laboratory exercises, place all materials in the disposal areas designated by your instructor.

22. Do not pick up broken glassware with your hands. Use a broom and dustpan and discard the glass in designated glass waste containers; never discard with paper waste.

23. Wear disposable gloves when working with blood, other body fluids, or mucous membranes. Change gloves after possible contamination and wash hands immediately after gloves are removed.

24. The disposal symbol indicates that items that may have come in contact with body fluids should be placed in your lab's designated container. It also refers to liquid wastes that should not be poured down the drain into the sewage system.

25. Leave the laboratory clean and organized for the next student.

26. Wash your hands with liquid or powdered soap prior to leaving the laboratory.

27. The biohazard symbol indicates procedures that may pose health concerns.

The caution symbol points out instruments, substances, and procedures that require special attention to safety. These symbols appear throughout this manual.

Measurement Conversions

Metric to American Standard	American Standard to Metric

Length

1 mm = 0.039 inches	1 inch = 2.54 cm
1 cm = 0.394 inches	1 foot = 0.305 m
1 m = 3.28 feet	1 yard = 0.914 m
1 m = 1.09 yards	1 mile = 1.61 km

Volume

1 mL = 0.0338 fluid ounces	1 fluid ounce = 29.6 mL
1 L = 4.23 cups	1 cup = 237 mL
1 L = 2.11 pints	1 pint = 0.474 L
1 L = 1.06 quarts	1 quart = 0.947 L
1 L = 0.264 gallons	1 gallon = 3.79 L

Mass

1 mg = 0.0000353 ounces	1 ounce = 28.3 g
1 g = 0.0353 ounces	1 pound = 0.454 kg
1 kg = 2.21 pounds	

Temperature

To convert temperature:

$$°C = \ (F - 32) \qquad °F = \quad + 32$$

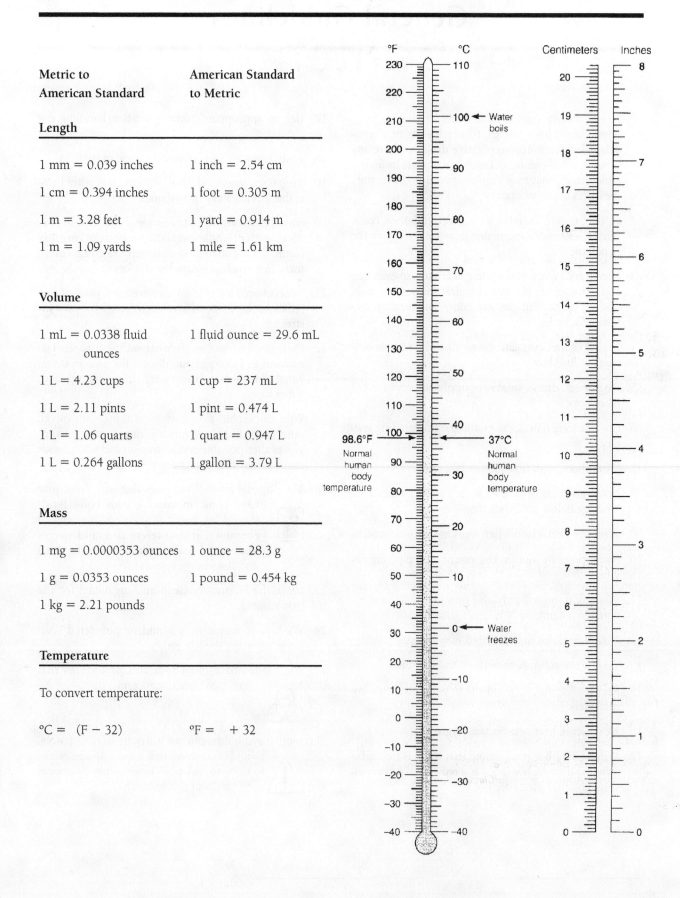

Table of Contents

MasteringMicrobiology®

Dear Student:

In this course you will be using MasteringMicrobiology®, an online tutorial and homework program that accompanies your textbook. *If you have joined a MasteringMicrobiology course before and can still log in*: Save time by following the guide for joining another course by following the guide for joining another course (available from www.masteringmicrobiology.com > Tours & Training > Getting Started) instead of this page.

What You Need:
- ✓ **A valid email address**
- ✓ **A student access code**
  (Comes in the Student Access Code Card/Kit that may have been packaged with your new textbook or that may be available separately in your school's bookstore. Otherwise, you can purchase access online at www.masteringmicrobiology.com.)
- ✓ **The ZIP or other postal code for your school:** _____
- ✓ **A Course ID:** _____ (Provided by your instructor)

1. Register
- Go to www.masteringmicrobiology.com and click **Students** under **Register**.
- To register using the student access code inside the MasteringMicrobiology Student Access Code Card/Kit, select **Yes, I have an access code**. Click **Continue**.

  –OR– *Purchase access online*: Select **No, I need to purchase access online now**. Select your textbook, whether you want access to the eText, and click **Continue**. Follow the on-screen instructions to purchase access using a credit card. The purchase path includes registration, but the process is a bit different from the steps printed here.

- **License Agreement and Privacy Policy:** Click **I Accept** to indicate that you have read and agree to the license agreement and privacy policy.
- Select the appropriate option under "Do you have a Pearson Education account?" Continue to give the requested information until you complete the process. The **Confirmation & Summary** page confirms your registration. This information will also be emailed to you for your records. You can either click **Log In Now** or return to www.masteringmicrobiology.com later.

2. Log In
- Go to www.masteringmicrobiology.com.
- Enter your Login Name and Password that you specified during registration and click **Log In**.

3. Join Your Instructor's Online Course and/or Open Self-Study Resources
Upon first login, you'll be asked to do one or more of the following:
- **Join a Course** by entering the **MasteringMicrobiology Course ID** provided by your instructor. If you don't have a Course ID now, you can return to join the MasteringMicrobiology course later. When you join a course, you may also be asked for a Student ID (follow on-screen instructions).
- **Explore the Study Area** or **Launch Your eText**, if these resources are available for your textbook.

To Access MasteringMicrobiology Again Later
Simply go to www.masteringmicrobiology.com, enter your Login Name and Password, and click **Log In**.

After you have joined a course: You can open any assignments from the **Assignments Due Soon** area or from the **Assignments** page. For self-study, click **eText** or **Study Area**, if these options are available.

Support
Access Customer Support at www.masteringmicrobiology.com/support, where you will find:
- System Requirements
- Answers to Frequently Asked Questions
- Registration Tips & Tricks video
- Additional contact information for Customer Support, including Live Chat

Juergen Berger/Photo Researchers

The Microbial World and You

Visualize microbiology and check your understanding with a pre-test at www.masteringmicrobiology.com.

The overall theme of this text is the relationship between microbes (very small organisms that usually require a microscope to be seen) and our lives. This relationship involves not only the familiar harmful effects of certain microorganisms, such as disease and food spoilage, but also their many beneficial effects. In this chapter we introduce you to some of the many ways microbes affect our lives. Microbes have been fruitful subjects of study for many years. We begin by introducing you to how organisms are named and classified, followed by a short history of microbiology that reveals how much we have learned in just a few hundred years. We then discuss the incredible diversity of microorganisms and their ecological importance, noting how they maintain balance in the environment by recycling chemical elements such as carbon and nitrogen among the soil, organisms, and the atmosphere. We also examine how microbes are used in commercial and industrial applications to produce foods, chemicals, and drugs (such as antibiotics); and to treat sewage, control pests, and clean up pollutants. We will discuss microbes as the cause of such diseases as avian (bird) flu, West Nile encephalitis, mad cow disease, diarrhea, hemorrhagic fever, and AIDS. We will also examine the growing public health problem of antibiotic-resistant bacteria. *Staphylococcus aureus* bacteria on human nasal epithelial cells are shown in the photograph. These bacteria live harmlessly on skin or inside the nose. Misuse of antibiotics allows the survival of bacteria with antibiotic-resistant genes such as methicillin-resistant *S. aureus* (MRSA). As illustrated in the Clinical Case, an infection caused by these bacteria is resistant to antibiotic treatment.

From Chapter 1 of *Microbiology: An Introduction*, Eleventh Edition. Gerard J. Tortora, Berdell R. Funke, Christine L. Case.

Microbes in Our Lives

LEARNING OBJECTIVE

1 List several ways in which microbes affect our lives.

For many people, the words *germ* and *microbe* bring to mind a group of tiny creatures that do not quite fit into any of the categories in that old question, "Is it animal, vegetable, or mineral?" **Microbes,** also called **microorganisms,** are minute living things that individually are usually too small to be seen with the unaided eye. The group includes bacteria, fungi (yeasts and molds), protozoa, and microscopic algae. It also includes viruses, those noncellular entities sometimes regarded as straddling the border between life and nonlife. You will be introduced to each of these groups of microbes shortly.

We tend to associate these small organisms only with major diseases such as AIDS, uncomfortable infections, or such common inconveniences as spoiled food. However, the majority of microorganisms actually help maintain the balance of living organisms and chemicals in our environment. Marine and freshwater microorganisms form the basis of the food chain in oceans, lakes, and rivers. Soil microbes help break down wastes and incorporate nitrogen gas from the air into organic compounds, thereby recycling chemical elements between the soil, water, life, and air. Certain microbes play important roles in *photosynthesis*, a food- and oxygen-generating process that is critical to life on Earth. Humans and many other animals depend on the microbes in their intestines for digestion and the synthesis of some vitamins that their bodies require, including some B vitamins for metabolism and vitamin K for blood clotting.

Microorganisms also have many commercial applications. They are used in the synthesis of such chemical products as vitamins, organic acids, enzymes, alcohols, and many drugs. For example, microbes are used to produce acetone and butanol, and the vitamins B_2 (riboflavin) and B_{12} (cobalamin) are made biochemically. The process by which microbes produce acetone and butanol was discovered in 1914 by Chaim Weizmann, a Russian-born chemist working in England. With the outbreak of World War I in August of that year, the production of acetone became very important for making cordite (a smokeless form of gunpowder used in munitions). Weizmann's discovery played a significant role in determining the outcome of the war.

The food industry also uses microbes in producing, for example, vinegar, sauerkraut, pickles, soy sauce, cheese, yogurt, bread, and alcoholic beverages. In addition, enzymes from microbes can now be manipulated to cause the microbes to produce substances they normally do not synthesize, including cellulose, digestive aids, and drain cleaner, plus important therapeutic substances such as insulin. Microbial enzymes may even have helped produce your favorite pair of jeans (see the box on the next page).

Though only a minority of microorganisms are **pathogenic** (disease-producing), practical knowledge of microbes is necessary for medicine and the related health sciences. For example, hospital workers must be able to protect patients from common microbes that are normally harmless but pose a threat to the sick and injured.

Today we understand that microorganisms are found almost everywhere. Yet not long ago, before the invention of the microscope, microbes were unknown to scientists. Thousands of people died in devastating epidemics, the causes of which were not understood. Entire families died because vaccinations and antibiotics were not available to fight infections.

We can get an idea of how our current concepts of microbiology developed by looking at a few historic milestones in microbiology that have changed our lives. First, however, we will look at the major groups of microbes and how they are named and classified.

CHECK YOUR UNDERSTANDING

✔ Describe some of the destructive and beneficial actions of microbes. 1*

Naming and Classifying Microorganisms

LEARNING OBJECTIVES

2 Recognize the system of scientific nomenclature that uses two names: a genus and a specific epithet.

3 Differentiate the major characteristics of each group of microorganisms.

4 List the three domains.

---

* The numbers following Check Your Understanding questions refer to the corresponding Learning Objectives.

Clinical Case: A Simple Spider Bite?

Andrea is a normally healthy 22-year-old college student who lives at home with her mother and younger sister, a high school gymnast. She is trying to work on a paper for her psychology class but is having a hard time because a red, swollen sore on her right wrist is making typing difficult. "Why won't this spider bite heal?" she wonders. "It's been there for days!" She makes an appointment with her doctor so she can show him the painful lesion. Although Andrea does not have a fever, she does have an elevated white blood cell count that indicates a bacterial infection. Andrea's doctor suspects that this isn't a spider bite at all, but a staph infection. He prescribes a β-lactam antibiotic, cephalosporin. Learn more about the development of Andrea's illness on the following pages.

What is staph? Read on to find out.

Designer Jeans: Made by Microbes?

Denim blue jeans have become increasingly popular ever since Levi Strauss and Jacob Davis first made them for California gold miners in 1873. Now, companies that manufacture blue jeans are turning to microbiology to develop environmentally sound production methods that minimize toxic wastes and the associated costs.

Stone Washing?

A softer denim, called "stone-washed," was introduced in the 1980s. Enzymes, called cellulases, from *Trichoderma* fungus are used to digest some of the cellulose in the cotton, thereby softening it and giving the stone-washed appearance. Unlike many chemical reactions, enzymes usually operate at safe temperatures and pH. Moreover, enzymes are proteins, so they are readily degraded for removal from wastewater.

Fabric

Cotton production requires large tracts of land, pesticides, and fertilizer, and the crop yield depends on the weather. However, bacteria can produce both cotton and polyester with less environmental impact. *Gluconacetobacter xylinus* bacteria make cellulose by attaching glucose units to simple chains in the outer membrane of the bacterial cell wall. The cellulose microfibrils are extruded through pores in the outer membrane, and bundles of microfibrils then twist into ribbons.

Bleaching

Peroxide is a safer bleaching agent than chlorine and can be easily removed from fabric and wastewater by enzymes. Researchers at Novo Nordisk Biotech cloned a mushroom peroxidase gene in yeast and grew the yeasts in washing machine conditions. The yeast that survived the washing machine were selected as the peroxidase producers.

Indigo

Chemical synthesis of indigo requires a high pH and produces waste that explodes in contact with air. However, a California biotechnology company, Genencor, has developed a method to produce indigo by using bacteria. Researchers identified a gene from a soil bacterium, *Pseudomonas putida*, for conversion of the bacterial by-product indole to indigo. This gene was put into *Escherichia coli* bacteria, which then turned blue.

Bioplastic

Microbes can even make plastic zippers and packaging material for the jeans. Over 25 bacteria make polyhydroxyalkanoate (PHA) inclusion granules as a food reserve. PHAs are similar to common plastics, and because they are made by bacteria, they are also readily degraded by many bacteria. PHAs could provide a biodegradable alternative to conventional plastic, which is made from petroleum.

Precision Graphics

E. coli bacteria produce indigo from tryptophan.

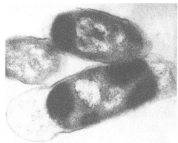

Indigo-producing *E. coli* bacteria.

0.3 μm

TEM

Precision Graphics

Nomenclature

The system of nomenclature (naming) for organisms in use today was established in 1735 by Carolus Linnaeus. Scientific names are latinized because Latin was the language traditionally used by scholars. Scientific nomenclature assigns each organism two names—the **genus** (plural: *genera*) is the first name and is always capitalized; the **specific epithet** (**species** name) follows and is not capitalized. The organism is referred to by both the genus and the specific epithet, and both names are underlined or italicized. By custom, after a scientific name has been mentioned once, it can be abbreviated with the initial of the genus followed by the specific epithet.

Scientific names can, among other things, describe an organism, honor a researcher, or identify the habitat of a species. For example, consider *Staphylococcus aureus* (staf-i-lō-kok′kus ô′rē-us), a bacterium commonly found on human skin. *Staphylo-* describes the clustered arrangement of the cells; *coccus* indicates that they are shaped like spheres. The specific epithet, *aureus*, is Latin for golden, the color of many colonies of this bacterium. The genus of the bacterium *Escherichia coli* (esh-ē-rik′-ē-ä kō′lī or kō′lē) is named for a scientist, Theodor Escherich, whereas its specific epithet, *coli*, reminds us that *E. coli* live in the colon, or large intestine. **Table 1** contains more examples.

CHECK YOUR UNDERSTANDING

✔ Distinguish a genus from a specific epithet. 2

Types of Microorganisms

Here is an overview of the major groups used to classify and identify microorganisms.

Bacteria

Bacteria (singular: **bacterium**) are relatively simple, single-celled (unicellular) organisms. Because their genetic material is not

TABLE 1 Making Scientific Names Familiar

Use a word roots guide to find out what the name means. The name will not seem so strange if you translate it. When you encounter a new name, practice saying it out loud. The exact pronunciation is not as important as the familiarity you will gain.

Following are some examples of microbial names you may encounter in the popular press as well as in the lab.

	Pronunciation	Source of Genus Name	Source of Specific Epithet
Salmonella enterica (bacterium)	sal-mōn-el′lä en-ter′i-kă	Honors public health microbiologist Daniel Salmon	Found in the intestines (*entero-*)
Streptococcus pyogenes (bacterium)	strep-tō-kok′kŭs pī-äj′en-ēz	Appearance of cells in chains (*strepto-*)	Forms pus (*pyo-*)
Saccharomyces cerevisiae (yeast)	sak-ă-rō-mī′ses se-ri-vis′ē-ī	Fungus (*-myces*) that uses sugar (*saccharo-*)	Makes beer (*cerevisia*)
Penicillium chrysogenum (fungus)	pen-i-sil′lē-um krī-so′jen-um	Tuftlike or paintbrush (*penicill-*) appearance microscopically	Produces a yellow (*chryso-*) pigment
Trypanosoma cruzi (protozoan)	tri-pa-nō-sō′mä krūz′ē	Corkscrew- (*trypano-*, borer; *soma-*, body)	Honors epidemiologist Oswaldo Cruz

enclosed in a special nuclear membrane, bacterial cells are called **prokaryotes** (prō-kar′e-ōts), from Greek words meaning prenucleus. Prokaryotes include both bacteria and archaea.

Bacterial cells generally appear in one of several shapes. *Bacillus* (bä-sil′lus) (rodlike), illustrated in **Figure 1a**, *coccus* (kok′kus) (spherical or ovoid), and *spiral* (corkscrew or curved) are among the most common shapes, but some bacteria are star-shaped or square. Individual bacteria may form pairs, chains, clusters, or other groupings; such formations are usually characteristic of a particular genus or species of bacteria.

Bacteria are enclosed in cell walls that are largely composed of a carbohydrate and protein complex called *peptidoglycan*. (By contrast, cellulose is the main substance of plant and algal cell walls.) Bacteria generally reproduce by dividing into two equal cells; this process is called *binary fission*. For nutrition, most bacteria use organic chemicals, which in nature can be derived from either dead or living organisms. Some bacteria can manufacture their own food by photosynthesis, and some can derive nutrition from inorganic substances. Many bacteria can "swim" by using moving appendages called *flagella*.

Archaea

Like bacteria, **archaea** (är′kē-ä) consist of prokaryotic cells, but if they have cell walls, the walls lack peptidoglycan. Archaea, often found in extreme environments, are divided into three main groups. The *methanogens* produce methane as a waste product from respiration. The *extreme halophiles* (*halo* = salt; *philic* = loving) live in extremely salty environments such as the Great Salt Lake and the Dead Sea. The *extreme thermophiles* (*therm* = heat) live in hot sulfurous water, such as hot springs

at Yellowstone National Park. Archaea are not known to cause disease in humans.

Fungi

Fungi (singular: **fungus**) are **eukaryotes** (yū-kar′ē-ōts), organisms whose cells have a distinct nucleus containing the cell's genetic material (DNA), surrounded by a special envelope called the nuclear membrane. Organisms in the Kingdom Fungi may be unicellular or multicellular. Large multicellular fungi, such as mushrooms, may look somewhat like plants, but unlike most plants, fungi cannot carry out photosynthesis. True fungi have cell walls composed primarily of a substance called *chitin*. The unicellular forms of fungi, *yeasts*, are oval microorganisms that are larger than bacteria. The most typical fungi are *molds* (**Figure 1b**). Molds form visible masses called *mycelia*, which are composed of long filaments (*hyphae*) that branch and intertwine. The cottony growths sometimes found on bread and fruit are mold mycelia. Fungi can reproduce sexually or asexually. They obtain nourishment by absorbing solutions of organic material from their environment—whether soil, seawater, freshwater, or an animal or plant host. Organisms called *slime molds* have characteristics of both fungi and amoebas.

Protozoa

Protozoa (singular: **protozoan**) are unicellular eukaryotic microbes. Protozoa move by pseudopods, flagella, or cilia. Amebae (**Figure 1c**) move by using extensions of their cytoplasm called *pseudopods* (false feet). Other protozoa have long *flagella* or numerous shorter appendages for locomotion

Juergen Berger/Photo Researchers

Biophoto Associates/Photo Researchers

Andrew Syred/Photo Researchers

Stephen Durr

NIBSC/Photo Researchers

Figure 1 Types of microorganisms.
NOTE: Throughout the text, a red icon under a micrograph indicates that the micrograph has been artificially colored. (**a**) The rod-shaped bacterium *Haemophilus influenzae,* one of the bacterial causes of pneumonia. (**b**) *Mucor,* a common bread mold, is a type of fungus. When released from sporangia, spores that land on a favorable surface germinate into a network of hyphae (filaments) that absorb nutrients. (**c**) An ameba, a protozoan, approaching a food particle. (**d**) The pond alga *Volvox.* (**e**) Several human immunodeficiency viruses (HIVs), the causative agent of AIDS, budding from a CD4+ T cell.

 How are bacteria, archaea, fungi, protozoa, algae, and viruses distinguished on the basis of cellular structure?

called *cilia.* Protozoa have a variety of shapes and live either as free entities or as *parasites* (organisms that derive nutrients from living hosts) that absorb or ingest organic compounds from their environment. Some protozoa, such as *Euglena,* are photosynthetic. They use light as a source of energy and carbon dioxide as their chief source of carbon to produce sugars. Protozoa can reproduce sexually or asexually.

Algae

Algae (singular: **alga**) are photosynthetic eukaryotes with a wide variety of shapes and both sexual and asexual reproductive forms (**Figure 1d**). The algae of interest to microbiologists are usually unicellular. The cell walls of many algae, are composed of a carbohydrate called *cellulose.* Algae are abundant in freshwater and salt water, in soil, and in association with plants. As photosynthesizers, algae need light, water, and carbon dioxide for food production and growth, but they do not generally require organic compounds from the environment. As a result of photosynthesis, algae produce oxygen and carbohydrates that are then utilized by other organisms, including animals. Thus, they play an important role in the balance of nature.

Viruses

Viruses (**Figure 1e**) are very different from the other microbial groups mentioned here. They are so small that most can be seen only with an electron microscope, and they are acellular (not cellular). Structurally very simple, a virus particle contains a core made of only one type of nucleic acid, either DNA or RNA. This core is surrounded by a protein coat, which is sometimes encased by a lipid membrane called an envelope. All living cells have RNA *and* DNA, can carry out chemical reactions, and can reproduce as self-sufficient units. Viruses can reproduce only by using the cellular machinery of other organisms. Thus, on the one hand, viruses are considered to be living only when they multiply within host cells they infect. In this sense, viruses are parasites of other forms of life. On the other hand, viruses are not considered to be living because they are inert outside living hosts.

Multicellular Animal Parasites

Although multicellular animal parasites are not strictly microorganisms, they are of medical importance and therefore will be discussed in this text. Animal parasites are eukaryotes. The two major groups of parasitic worms are the flatworms and the roundworms, collectively called **helminths**. During some stages of their life cycle, helminths are microscopic in size. Laboratory identification of these organisms includes many of the same techniques used for identifying microbes.

CHECK YOUR UNDERSTANDING

✔ Which groups of microbes are prokaryotes? Which are eukaryotes? 3

Classification of Microorganisms

Before the existence of microbes was known, all organisms were grouped into either the animal kingdom or the plant kingdom. When microscopic organisms with characteristics of animals and plants were discovered late in the seventeenth century, a new system of classification was needed. Still, biologists could not agree on the criteria for classifying these new organisms until the late 1970s.

In 1978, Carl Woese devised a system of classification based on the cellular organization of organisms. It groups all organisms in three domains as follows:

1. Bacteria (cell walls contain a protein–carbohydrate complex called peptidoglycan)
2. Archaea (cell walls, if present, lack peptidoglycan)
3. Eukarya, which includes the following:
   - Protists (slime molds, protozoa, and algae)
   - Fungi (unicellular yeasts, multicellular molds, and mushrooms)
   - Plants (mosses, ferns, conifers, and flowering plants)
   - Animals (sponges, worms, insects, and vertebrates)

CHECK YOUR UNDERSTANDING

✔ What are the three domains? 4

A Brief History of Microbiology

LEARNING OBJECTIVES

5   Explain the importance of observations made by Hooke and van Leeuwenhoek.

6   Compare spontaneous generation and biogenesis.

7   Identify the contributions to microbiology made by Needham, Spallanzani, Virchow, and Pasteur.

8   Explain how Pasteur's work influenced Lister and Koch.

9   Identify the importance of Koch's postulates.

10 Identify the importance of Jenner's work.

11 Identify the contributions to microbiology made by Ehrlich and Fleming.

12 Define *bacteriology*, *mycology*, *parasitology*, *immunology*, and *virology*.

13 Explain the importance of microbial genetics and molecular biology.

The science of microbiology dates back only 200 years, yet the recent discovery of *Mycobacterium tuberculosis* (mī-kō-bak-ti′rē-um tü-bėr-ku-lō′sis) DNA in 3000-year-old Egyptian mummies reminds us that microorganisms have been around for much longer. In fact, bacterial ancestors were the first living cells to appear on Earth. Although we know relatively little about what earlier people thought about the causes, transmission, and treatment of disease, we know more about the history of the past few hundred years. Let's look now at some key developments in microbiology that have spurred the field to its current technological state.

The First Observations

One of the most important discoveries in biology occurred in 1665. After observing a thin slice of cork through a relatively crude microscope, an Englishman, Robert Hooke, reported to the world that life's smallest structural units were "little boxes," or "cells," as he called them. Using his improved version of a compound microscope (one that uses two sets of lenses), Hooke was able to see individual cells. Hooke's discovery marked the beginning of the **cell theory**—the theory that *all living things are composed of cells*. Subsequent investigations into the structure and function of cells were based on this theory.

Though Hooke's microscope was capable of showing large cells, it lacked the resolution that would have allowed him to see microbes clearly. The Dutch merchant and amateur scientist Anton van Leeuwenhoek was probably the first actually to observe live microorganisms through the magnifying lenses of more than 400 microscopes he constructed. Between 1673 and 1723, he wrote a series of letters to the Royal Society of London describing the "animalcules" he saw through his simple, single-lens microscope. Van Leeuwenhoek made detailed drawings of "animalcules" he found in rainwater, in his own feces, and in material scraped from his teeth. These drawings have since been identified as representations of bacteria and protozoa (Figure 2).

CHECK YOUR UNDERSTANDING

✔ What is the cell theory? 5

The Debate over Spontaneous Generation

After van Leeuwenhoek discovered the previously "invisible" world of microorganisms, the scientific community of the time became interested in the origins of these tiny living things. Until the second half of the nineteenth century, many scientists and philosophers believed that some forms of life could arise spontaneously from nonliving matter; they called this hypothetical process **spontaneous generation.** Not much more than 100 years ago, people commonly believed that toads, snakes, and mice could be born of moist soil; that flies could emerge from manure;

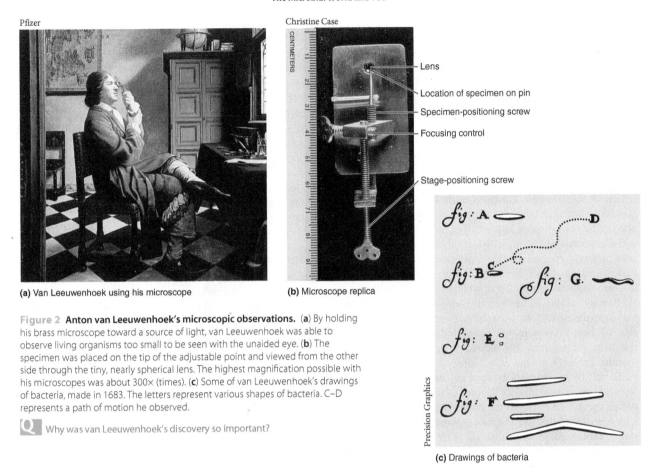

Pfizer

Christine Case

— Lens

— Location of specimen on pin

— Specimen-positioning screw

— Focusing control

— Stage-positioning screw

CENTIMETERS

Precision Graphics

(a) Van Leeuwenhoek using his microscope

(b) Microscope replica

(c) Drawings of bacteria

Figure 2 Anton van Leeuwenhoek's microscopic observations. **(a)** By holding his brass microscope toward a source of light, van Leeuwenhoek was able to observe living organisms too small to be seen with the unaided eye. **(b)** The specimen was placed on the tip of the adjustable point and viewed from the other side through the tiny, nearly spherical lens. The highest magnification possible with his microscopes was about 300× (times). **(c)** Some of van Leeuwenhoek's drawings of bacteria, made in 1683. The letters represent various shapes of bacteria. C–D represents a path of motion he observed.

Q Why was van Leeuwenhoek's discovery so important?

and that maggots (which we now know are the larvae of flies) could arise from decaying corpses.

Evidence Pro and Con

A strong opponent of spontaneous generation, the Italian physician Francesco Redi set out in 1668 to demonstrate that maggots did not arise spontaneously from decaying meat. Redi filled two jars with decaying meat. The first was left unsealed; the flies laid their eggs on the meat, and the eggs developed into larvae. The second jar was sealed, and because the flies could not lay their eggs on the meat, no maggots appeared. Still, Redi's antagonists were not convinced; they claimed that fresh air was needed for spontaneous generation. So Redi set up a second experiment, in which he covered a jar with a fine net instead of sealing it. No larvae appeared in the gauze-covered jar, even though air was present. Maggots appeared only when flies were allowed to leave their eggs on the meat.

Redi's results were a serious blow to the long-held belief that large forms of life could arise from nonlife. However, many scientists still believed that small organisms, such as

van Leeuwenhoek's "animalcules," were simple enough to be generated from nonliving materials.

The case for spontaneous generation of microorganisms seemed to be strengthened in 1745, when John Needham, an Englishman, found that even after he heated nutrient fluids (chicken broth and corn broth) before pouring them into covered flasks, the cooled solutions were soon teeming with microorganisms. Needham claimed that microbes developed spontaneously from the fluids. Twenty years later, Lazzaro Spallanzani, an Italian scientist, suggested that microorganisms from the air probably had entered Needham's solutions after they were boiled. Spallanzani showed that nutrient fluids heated *after* being sealed in a flask did not develop microbial growth. Needham responded by claiming the "vital force" necessary for spontaneous generation had been destroyed by the heat and was kept out of the flasks by the seals.

This intangible "vital force" was given all the more credence shortly after Spallanzani's experiment, when Anton Laurent Lavoisier showed the importance of oxygen to life. Spallanzani's observations were criticized on the grounds that there was not enough oxygen in the sealed flasks to support microbial life.

The Theory of Biogenesis

The issue was still unresolved in 1858, when the German scientist Rudolf Virchow challenged the case for spontaneous generation with the concept of **biogenesis,** the claim that living cells can arise only from preexisting living cells. Because he could offer no scientific proof, arguments about spontaneous generation continued until 1861, when the issue was finally resolved by the French scientist Louis Pasteur.

With a series of ingenious and persuasive experiments, Pasteur demonstrated that microorganisms are present in the air and can contaminate sterile solutions, but that air itself does not create microbes. He filled several short-necked flasks with beef broth and then boiled their contents. Some were then left open and allowed to cool. In a few days, these flasks were found to be contaminated with microbes. The other flasks, sealed after boiling, were free of microorganisms. From these results, Pasteur reasoned that microbes in the air were the agents responsible for contaminating nonliving matter.

Pasteur next placed broth in open-ended, long-necked flasks and bent the necks into S-shaped curves (Figure 3). The contents of these flasks were then boiled and cooled. The broth in the flasks did not decay and showed no signs of life, even after months. Pasteur's unique design allowed air to pass into the flask, but the curved neck trapped any airborne microorganisms that might contaminate the broth. (Some of these original vessels are still on display at the Pasteur Institute in Paris. They have been sealed but, like the flask shown in Figure 3, show no sign of contamination more than 100 years later.) **8**

Pasteur showed that microorganisms can be present in nonliving matter—on solids, in liquids, and in the air. Furthermore, he demonstrated conclusively that microbial life can be destroyed by heat and that methods can be devised to block the access of airborne microorganisms to nutrient environments. These discoveries form the basis of **aseptic techniques,** techniques that prevent contamination by unwanted microorganisms, which are now the standard practice in laboratory and many medical procedures. Modern aseptic techniques are among the first and most important concepts that a beginning microbiologist learns.

Pasteur's work provided evidence that microorganisms cannot originate from mystical forces present in nonliving materials. Rather, any appearance of "spontaneous" life in nonliving solutions can be attributed to microorganisms that were already present in the air or in the fluids themselves. Scientists now believe that a form of spontaneous generation probably did occur on the primitive Earth when life first began, but they agree that this does not happen under today's environmental conditions.

CHECK YOUR UNDERSTANDING

✔ What evidence supported spontaneous generation? 6

✔ How was spontaneous generation disproved? 7

The Golden Age of Microbiology

The work that began with Pasteur started an explosion of discoveries in microbiology. The period from 1857 to 1914 has been appropriately named the Golden Age of Microbiology. During this period, rapid advances, spearheaded mainly by Pasteur and Robert Koch, led to the establishment of microbiology as a science. Discoveries during these years included both the agents of many diseases and the role of immunity in preventing and curing disease. During this productive period, microbiologists studied the chemical activities of microorganisms, improved the techniques for performing microscopy and culturing microorganisms, and developed vaccines and surgical techniques. Some of the major events that occurred during the Golden Age of Microbiology are listed in Figure 4.

Fermentation and Pasteurization

One of the key steps that established the relationship between microorganisms and disease occurred when a group of French merchants asked Pasteur to find out why wine and beer soured. They hoped to develop a method that would prevent spoilage when those beverages were shipped long distances. At the time, many scientists believed that air converted the sugars in these fluids into alcohol. Pasteur found instead that microorganisms called yeasts convert the sugars to alcohol in the absence of air. This process, called **fermentation,** is used to make wine and beer. Souring and spoilage are caused by different microorganisms called bacteria. In the presence of air, bacteria change the alcohol into vinegar (acetic acid).

Pasteur's solution to the spoilage problem was to heat the beer and wine just enough to kill most of the bacteria that caused the spoilage. The process, called **pasteurization,** is now commonly used to reduce spoilage and kill potentially harmful bacteria in milk as well as in some alcoholic drinks. Showing the connection between food spoilage and microorganisms was a major step toward establishing the relationship between disease and microbes.

The Germ Theory of Disease

As we have seen, the fact that many kinds of diseases are related to microorganisms was unknown until relatively recently. Before the time of Pasteur, effective treatments for many diseases were discovered by trial and error, but the causes of the diseases were unknown.

The realization that yeasts play a crucial role in fermentation was the first link between the activity of a microorganism and physical and chemical changes in organic materials. This discovery alerted scientists to the possibility that microorganisms might have similar relationships with plants and animals—specifically, that microorganisms might cause disease. This idea was known as the **germ theory of disease.**

Disproving the Theory of Spontaneous Generation

According to the theory of spontaneous generation, life can arise spontaneously from nonliving matter, such as dead corpses and soil. Pasteur's experiment, described below, demonstrated that microbes are present in nonliving matter—air, liquids, and solids.

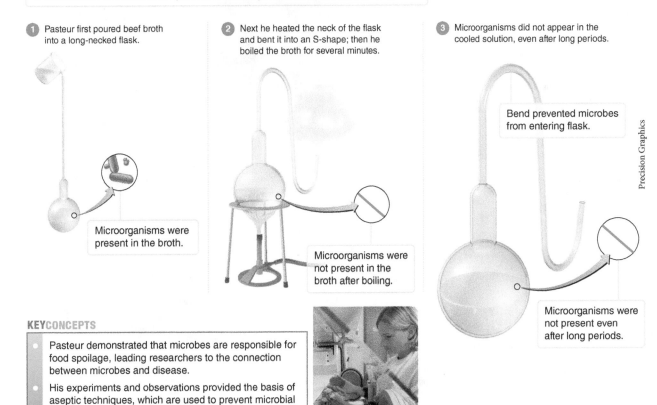

1 Pasteur first poured beef broth into a long-necked flask.

Microorganisms were present in the broth.

2 Next he heated the neck of the flask and bent it into an S-shape; then he boiled the broth for several minutes.

Microorganisms were not present in the broth after boiling.

3 Microorganisms did not appear in the cooled solution, even after long periods.

Bend prevented microbes from entering flask.

Microorganisms were not present even after long periods.

Precision Graphics

KEYCONCEPTS

- Pasteur demonstrated that microbes are responsible for food spoilage, leading researchers to the connection between microbes and disease.

- His experiments and observations provided the basis of aseptic techniques, which are used to prevent microbial contamination, as shown in the photo at right.

TEK Image/SPL/Alamy

The germ theory was a difficult concept for many people to accept at that time because for centuries disease was believed to be punishment for an individual's crimes or misdeeds. When the inhabitants of an entire village became ill, people often blamed the disease on demons appearing as foul odors from sewage or on poisonous vapors from swamps. Most people born in Pasteur's time found it inconceivable that "invisible" microbes could travel through the air to infect plants and animals or remain on clothing and bedding to be transmitted from one person to another. Despite these doubts scientists gradually accumulated the information needed to support the new germ theory.

In 1865, Pasteur was called upon to help fight silkworm disease, which was ruining the silk industry throughout Europe.

Years earlier, in 1835, Agostino Bassi, an amateur microscopist, had proved that another silkworm disease was caused by a fungus. Using data provided by Bassi, Pasteur found that the more recent infection was caused by a protozoan, and he developed a method for recognizing afflicted silkworm moths.

In the 1860s, Joseph Lister, an English surgeon, applied the germ theory to medical procedures. Lister was aware that in the 1840s, the Hungarian physician Ignaz Semmelweis had demonstrated that physicians, who at the time did not disinfect their hands, routinely transmitted infections (puerperal, or childbirth, fever) from one obstetrical patient to another. Lister had also heard of Pasteur's work connecting microbes to animal diseases. Disinfectants were not used at the time, but Lister knew

1665	Hooke—First observation of cells
1673	van Leeuwenhoek—First observation of live microorganisms
1735	Linnaeus—Nomenclature for organisms
1798	Jenner—First vaccine
1835	Bassi—Silkworm fungus
1840	Semmelweis—Childbirth fever
1853	DeBary—Fungal plant disease

1857	Pasteur—Fermentation
1861	Pasteur—Disproved spontaneous generation
1864	Pasteur—Pasteurization
1867	Lister—Aseptic surgery
1876	*Koch—Germ theory of disease
1879	Neisser—*Neisseria gonorrhoeae*
1881	*Koch—Pure cultures
	Finley—Yellow fever
1882	*Koch—*Mycobacterium tuberculosis*
	Hess—Agar (solid) media
1883	*Koch—*Vibrio cholerae*
1884	*Metchnikoff—Phagocytosis
	Gram—Gram-staining procedure
	Escherich—*Escherichia coli*
1887	Petri—Petri dish
1889	Kitasato—*Clostridium tetani*
1890	*von Bering—Diphtheria antitoxin
	*Ehrlich—Theory of immunity
1892	Winogradsky—Sulfur cycle
1898	Shiga—*Shigella dysenteriae*
1908	*Ehrlich—Syphilis
1910	Chagas—*Trypanosoma cruzi*
1911	* Rous—Tumor-causing virus (1966 Nobel Prize)

GOLDEN AGE OF MICROBIOLOGY

1928	*Fleming, Chain, Florey—Penicillin
	Griffith—Transformation in bacteria
1934	Lancefield—Streptococcal antigens
1935	*Stanley, Northrup, Sumner—Crystallized virus
1941	Beadle and Tatum—Relationship between genes and enzymes
1943	*Delbrück and Luria—Viral infection of bacteria
1944	Avery, MacLeod, McCarty—Genetic material is DNA
1946	Lederberg and Tatum—Bacterial conjugation
1953	*Watson and Crick—DNA structure
1957	*Jacob and Monod—Protein synthesis regulation
1959	Stewart—Viral cause of human cancer
1962	*Edelman and Porter—Antibodies
1964	Epstein, Achong, Barr—Epstein-Barr virus as cause of human cancer
1971	*Nathans, Smith, Arber—Restriction enzymes (used for recombinant DNA technology)
1973	Berg—Genetic engineering
1975	Dulbecco, Temin, Baltimore—Reverse transcriptase
1978	Woese—Archaea
	*Mitchell—Chemiosmotic mechanism
1981	Margulis—Origin of eukaryotic cells
1982	*Klug—Structure of tobacco mosaic virus
1983	*McClintock—Transposons

1988	*Deisenhofer, Huber, Michel—Bacterial photosynthesis pigments
1994	Cano—Reported to have cultured 40-million-year-old bacteria
1997	*Prusiner—Prions

Precision Graphics

Images from the History of Medicine (NLM)

Louis Pasteur (1822–1895)
Demonstrated that life did not arise spontaneously from nonliving matter.

KRUIF, Paul de. Mikrobenjäger. Orell Füssli, Zürich, 1927

Robert Koch (1843–1910)
Established experimental steps for directly linking a specific microbe to a specific disease.

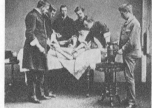

Performing an 1871 surgery in the Lister Surgery Theatre, Edinburgh, Scotland

Joseph Lister (1827–1912)
Performed surgery under antiseptic conditions using phenol. Proved that microbes caused surgical wound infections.

Rockefeller Archive Center

Rebecca C. Lancefield (1895–1981)
Classified streptococci according to serotypes (variants within a species)

Figure 4 **Milestones in microbiology, highlighting those that occurred during the Golden Age of Microbiology.** An asterisk (*) indicates a Nobel laureate.

Q Why do you think the Golden Age of Microbiology occurred when it did?

that phenol (carbolic acid) kills bacteria, so he began treating surgical wounds with a phenol solution. The practice so reduced the incidence of infections and deaths that other surgeons quickly adopted it. Lister's technique was one of the earliest medical attempts to control infections caused by microorganisms. In fact, his findings proved that microorganisms cause surgical wound infections.

The first proof that bacteria actually cause disease came from Robert Koch in 1876. Koch, a German physician, was Pasteur's young rival in the race to discover the cause of anthrax, a disease that was destroying cattle and sheep in Europe. Koch discovered rod-shaped bacteria now known as *Bacillus anthracis* (bä-sil′lus an-thrā′sis) in the blood of cattle that had died of anthrax. He cultured the bacteria on nutrients and then injected samples of the culture into healthy animals. When these animals became sick and died, Koch isolated the bacteria in their blood and compared them with the originally isolated bacteria. He found that the two sets of blood cultures contained the same bacteria.

Koch thus established **Koch's postulates,** a sequence of experimental steps for directly relating a specific microbe to a specific disease. During the past 100 years, these same criteria have been invaluable in investigations proving that specific microorganisms cause many diseases.

Vaccination

Often a treatment or preventive procedure is developed before scientists know why it works. The smallpox vaccine is an example. On May 4, 1796, almost 70 years before Koch established that a specific microorganism causes anthrax, Edward Jenner, a young British physician, embarked on an experiment to find a way to protect people from smallpox.

Smallpox epidemics were greatly feared. The disease periodically swept through Europe, killing thousands, and it wiped out 90% of the American Indians on the East Coast when European settlers first brought the infection to the New World.

When a young milkmaid informed Jenner that she couldn't get smallpox because she already had been sick from cowpox—a much milder disease—he decided to put the girl's story to the test. First Jenner collected scrapings from cowpox blisters. Then he inoculated a healthy 8-year-old volunteer with the cowpox material by scratching the person's arm with a pox-contaminated needle. The scratch turned into a raised bump. In a few days, the volunteer became mildly sick but recovered and never again contracted either cowpox or smallpox. The process was called *vaccination,* from the Latin word *vacca,* meaning cow. Pasteur gave it this name in honor of Jenner's work. The protection from disease provided by vaccination (or by recovery from the disease itself) is called **immunity.**

Years after Jenner's experiment, in about 1880, Pasteur discovered why vaccinations work. He found that the bacterium that causes fowl cholera lost its ability to cause disease (lost its *virulence,* or became *avirulent*) after it was grown in the laboratory for long periods. However, it—and other microorganisms with decreased virulence—was able to induce immunity against subsequent infections by its virulent counterparts. The discovery of this phenomenon provided a clue to Jenner's successful experiment with cowpox. Both cowpox and smallpox are caused by viruses. Even though cowpox virus is not a laboratory-produced derivative of smallpox virus, it is so closely related to the smallpox virus that it can induce immunity to both viruses. Pasteur used the term *vaccine* for cultures of avirulent microorganisms used for preventive inoculation.

Jenner's experiment marked the first time in a Western culture that a living viral agent—the cowpox virus—was used to produce immunity. Physicians in China had immunized patients from smallpox by removing scales from drying pustules of a person suffering from a mild case of smallpox, grinding the scales to a fine powder, and inserting the powder into the nose of the person to be protected.

Some vaccines are still produced from avirulent microbial strains that stimulate immunity to the related virulent strain. Other vaccines are made from killed virulent microbes, from isolated components of virulent microorganisms, or by genetic engineering techniques.

CHECK YOUR UNDERSTANDING

- Summarize in your own words the germ theory of disease. 8
- What is the importance of Koch's postulates? 9
- What is the significance of Jenner's discovery? 10

The Birth of Modern Chemotherapy: Dreams of a "Magic Bullet"

After the relationship between microorganisms and disease was established, medical microbiologists next focused on the search for substances that could destroy pathogenic microorganisms without damaging the infected animal or human. Treatment of disease by using chemical substances is called **chemotherapy.** (The term also commonly refers to chemical treatment of noninfectious diseases, such as cancer.) Chemicals produced naturally by bacteria and fungi to act against other microorganisms are called **antibiotics.** Chemotherapeutic agents prepared from chemicals in the laboratory are called **synthetic drugs.** The success of chemotherapy is based on the fact that some chemicals are more poisonous to microorganisms than to the hosts infected by the microbes.

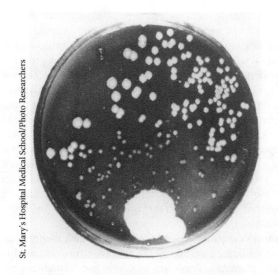

St. Mary's Hospital Medical School/Photo Researchers

Figure 5 **The discovery of penicillin.** Alexander Fleming took this photograph in 1928. The colony of *Penicillium* mold accidentally contaminated the plate and inhibited nearby bacterial growth.

Q Why do you think penicillin is no longer as effective as it once was?

The First Synthetic Drugs

Paul Ehrlich, a German physician, was the imaginative thinker who fired the first shot in the chemotherapy revolution. As a medical student, Ehrlich speculated about a "magic bullet" that could hunt down and destroy a pathogen without harming the infected host. He then launched a search for such a bullet. In 1910, after testing hundreds of substances, he found a chemotherapeutic agent called *salvarsan,* an arsenic derivative effective against syphilis. The agent was named salvarsan because it was considered to offer salvation from syphilis and it contained arsenic. Before this discovery, the only known chemical in Europe's medical arsenal was an extract from the bark of a South American tree, *quinine,* which had been used by Spanish conquistadors to treat malaria.

By the late 1930s, researchers had developed several other synthetic drugs that could destroy microorganisms. Most of these drugs were derivatives of dyes. This came about because the dyes synthesized and manufactured for fabrics were routinely tested for antimicrobial qualities by microbiologists looking for a "magic bullet." In addition, *sulfonamides* (sulfa drugs) were synthesized at about the same time.

A Fortunate Accident—Antibiotics

In contrast to the sulfa drugs, which were deliberately developed from a series of industrial chemicals, the first antibiotic was discovered by accident. Alexander Fleming, a Scottish physician and bacteriologist, almost tossed out some culture plates that had been contaminated by mold. Fortunately, he took a second look at the curious pattern of growth on the contaminated plates. Around the mold was a clear area where bacterial growth had been inhibited (**Figure 5**). Fleming was looking at a mold that could inhibit the growth of a bacterium. The mold was later identified as *Penicillium notatum* (pen-i-sil′lē-um nō-tā′tum), later renamed *Penicillium chrysogenum* (krĭ-so′jen-um), and in 1928 Fleming named the mold's active inhibitor *penicillin.* Thus, penicillin is an antibiotic produced by a fungus. The enormous usefulness of penicillin was not apparent until the 1940s, when it was finally tested clinically and mass produced.

Since these early discoveries, thousands of other antibiotics have been discovered. Unfortunately, antibiotics and other chemotherapeutic drugs are not without problems. Many antimicrobial chemicals are too toxic to humans for practical use; they kill the pathogenic microbes, but they also damage the infected host. For reasons we will discuss later, toxicity to humans is a particular problem in the development of drugs for treating viral diseases. Viral growth depends on life processes of normal host cells. Thus, there are very few successful antiviral drugs, because a drug that would interfere with viral reproduction would also likely affect uninfected cells of the body.

Another major problem associated with antimicrobial drugs is the emergence and spread of new strains of microorganisms that are resistant to antibiotics. Over the years, more and more microbes have developed resistance to antibiotics that at one time were very effective against them. Drug resistance results from genetic changes in microbes that enables them to tolerate a certain amount of an antibiotic that would normally inhibit them. For example a microbe might produce chemicals (enzymes) that inactivate antibiotics, or a microbe might undergo changes to its surface that prevent an antibiotic from attaching to it or entering it.

The recent appearance of vancomycin-resistant *Staphylococcus aureus* and *Enterococcus faecalis* (en-te-rō-kok′kus fe-kā′lis) has alarmed health care professionals because it indicates that some previously treatable bacterial infections may soon be impossible to treat with antibiotics.

CHECK YOUR UNDERSTANDING

✔ What was Ehrlich's "magic bullet"? **11**

Modern Developments in Microbiology

The quest to solve drug resistance, identify viruses, and develop vaccines requires sophisticated research techniques and correlated studies that were never dreamed of in the days of Koch and Pasteur.

The groundwork laid during the Golden Age of Microbiology provided the basis for several monumental achievements during the twentieth century (**Table 2**). New branches of microbiology were developed, including immunology and virology. Most recently, the development of a set of new methods called recombinant DNA technology has revolutionized research and practical applications in all areas of microbiology.

Bacteriology, Mycology, and Parasitology

Bacteriology, the study of bacteria, began with van Leeuwenhoek's first examination of tooth scrapings. New pathogenic

TABLE **2** Selected Nobel Prizes Awarded for Research in Microbiology

Nobel Laureates	Year of Presentation	Country of Birth	Contribution
Ronald Ross	1902	England	Discovered how malaria is transmitted
Selman A. Waksman	1952	Ukraine	Discovered streptomycin
Hans A. Krebs	1953	Germany	Discovered chemical steps of the Krebs cycle in carbohydrate metabolism
John F. Enders, Thomas H. Weller, and Frederick C. Robbins	1954	United States	Cultured poliovirus in cell cultures
Joshua Lederberg, George Beadle, and Edward Tatum	1958	United States	Described genetic control of biochemical reactions
Frank Macfarlane Burnet and Peter Brian Medawar	1960	Australia Great Britain	Discovered acquired immune tolerance
César Milstein, Georges J. F. Köhler, and Niels Kai Jerne	1984	Argentina Germany Denmark	Developed a technique for producing monoclonal antibodies (single pure antibodies)
Susumu Tonegawa	1987	Japan	Described the genetics of antibody production
J. Michael Bishop and Harold E. Varmus	1989	United States	Discovered cancer-causing genes called oncogenes
Joseph E. Murray and E. Donnall Thomas	1990	United States	Performed the first successful organ transplants by using immunosuppressive agents
Edmond H. Fisher and Edwin G. Krebs	1992	United States	Discovered protein kinases, enzymes that regulate cell growth
Richard J. Roberts and Phillip A. Sharp	1993	Great Britain United States	Discovered that a gene can be separated onto different segments of DNA
Kary B. Mullis	1993	United States	Discovered the polymerase chain reaction to amplify (make multiple copies of) DNA
Peter C. Doherty and Rolf M. Zinkernagel	1996	Australia Switzerland	Discovered how cytotoxic T cells recognize virus-infected cells prior to destroying them
Peter Agre and Roderick MacKirron	2003	United States	Discovered water and ion channels in plasma membranes
Aaron Ciechanover, Avram Hershko, and Irwin Rose	2004	Israel Israel United States	Discovered how cells dispose of unwanted proteins in proteasomes
Barry Marshall and J. Robin Warren	2005	Australia	Discovered that *Helicobacter pylori* causes peptic ulcers
Andrew Fire and Craig Mello	2006	United States	Discovered RNA interference (RNAi), or gene silencing, by double-stranded RNA
Harald zur Hausen	2008	Germany	Discovered that human papilloma viruses cause cervical cancer
Françoise Barré-Sinoussi and Luc Montagnier	2008	France	Discovered human immunodeficiency virus (HIV)
Venkatraman Ramakrishnan, Thomas A. Steitz, and Ada E. Yonath	2010	India United States Israel	Detailed study of the structure and function of ribosomes

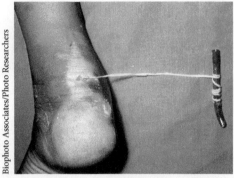

(a) Rod of Asclepius, symbol of the medical profession.

(b) A parasitic guinea worm (*Dracunculus medinensis*) is removed from the subcutaneous tissue of a patient by winding it onto a stick. This procedure may have been used for the design of the symbol in part (a).

Figure 6 Parasitology: the study of protozoa and parasitic worms.

Q How do you think parasitic worms survive and live off a human host?

bacteria are still discovered regularly. Many bacteriologists, like Pasteur, look at the roles of bacteria in food and the environment. One intriguing discovery came in 1997, when Heide Schulz discovered a bacterium large enough to be seen with the unaided eye (0.2 mm wide). This bacterium, named *Thiomargarita namibiensis* (thī'o-mä-gär-e-tä na'mib-ē-èn-sis), lives in the mud on the African coast. *Thiomargarita* is unusual because of its size and its ecological niche. The bacterium consumes hydrogen sulfide, which would be toxic to mud-dwelling animals.

Mycology, the study of fungi, includes medical, agricultural, and ecological branches. Recall that Bassi's work leading up to the germ theory of disease focused on a fungal pathogen. Fungal infection rates have been rising during the past decade, accounting for 10% of hospital-acquired infections. Climatic and environmental changes (severe drought) are thought to account for the tenfold increase in *Coccidioides immitis* (kok-sid-ē-oi'dēz im'mi-tis) infections in California. New techniques for diagnosing and treating fungal infections are currently being investigated.

Parasitology is the study of protozoa and parasitic worms. Because many parasitic worms are large enough to be seen with the unaided eye, they have been known for thousands of years. It has been speculated that the medical symbol, the rod of Asclepius, represents the removal of parasitic guinea worms (Figure 6). Asclepius was a Greek physician who practiced about 1200 B.C. and was deified as the god of medicine.

The clearing of rain forests has exposed laborers to previously undiscovered parasites. Previously unknown parasitic diseases are also being found in patients whose immune systems have been suppressed by organ transplants, cancer chemotherapy, or AIDS.

Bacteriology, mycology, and parasitology are currently going through a "golden age" of classification. Recent advances in **genomics,** the study of all of an organism's genes, have allowed

scientists to classify bacteria and fungi according to their genetic relationships with other bacteria, fungi, and protozoa. These microorganisms were originally classified according to a limited number of visible characteristics.

Immunology

Immunology, the study of immunity, dates back in Western culture to Jenner's first vaccine in 1796. Since then, knowledge about the immune system has accumulated steadily and expanded rapidly. Vaccines are now available for numerous diseases, including measles, rubella (German measles), mumps, chickenpox, pneumococcal pneumonia, tetanus, tuberculosis, influenza, whooping cough, polio, and hepatitis B. The smallpox vaccine was so effective that the disease has been eliminated. Public health officials estimate that polio will be eradicated within a few years because of the polio vaccine.

A major advance in immunology occurred in 1933, when Rebecca Lancefield proposed that streptococci be classified according to serotypes (variants within a species) based on certain components in the cell walls of the bacteria. Streptococci are responsible for a variety of diseases, such as sore throat (strep throat), streptococcal toxic shock, and septicemia (blood poisoning). Her research permits the rapid identification of specific pathogenic streptococci based on immunological techniques.

In 1960, interferons, substances generated by the body's own immune system, were discovered. Interferons inhibit replication of viruses and have triggered considerable research related to the treatment of viral diseases and cancer. One of today's biggest challenges for immunologists is learning how the immune system might be stimulated to ward off the virus responsible for AIDS, a disease that destroys the immune system.

Virology

The study of viruses, **virology,** originated during the Golden Age of Microbiology. In 1892, Dmitri Iwanowski reported that the organism that caused mosaic disease of tobacco was so small that it passed through filters fine enough to stop all known bacteria. At the time, Iwanowski was not aware that the organism in question was a virus. In 1935, Wendell Stanley demonstrated that the organism, called tobacco mosaic virus (TMV), was fundamentally different from other microbes and so simple and homogeneous that it could be crystallized like a chemical compound. Stanley's work facilitated the study of viral structure and chemistry. Since the development of the electron microscope in the 1940s, microbiologists have been able to observe the structure of viruses in detail, and today much is known about their structure and activity.

Recombinant DNA Technology

Microorganisms can now be genetically modified to manufacture large amounts of human hormones and other urgently needed medical substances. In the late 1960s, Paul Berg showed that fragments of human or animal DNA (genes) that code for important proteins can be attached to bacterial DNA. The resulting hybrid was the first example of **recombinant DNA.** When recombinant DNA is inserted into bacteria (or other microbes), it can be used to make large quantities of the desired protein. The technology that developed from this technique is called **recombinant DNA technology.** Its origins can be found in two related fields. The first, **microbial genetics,** studies the mechanisms by which microorganisms inherit traits. The second, **molecular biology,** specifically studies how genetic information is carried in molecules of DNA and how DNA directs the synthesis of proteins.

Although molecular biology encompasses all organisms, much of our knowledge of how genes determine specific traits has been revealed through experiments with bacteria. Through the 1930s, all genetic research was based on the study of plant and animal cells. But in the 1940s, scientists turned to unicellular organisms, primarily bacteria, which have several advantages for genetic and biochemical research. For one thing, bacteria are less complex than plants and animals. For another, the life cycles of many bacteria last less than an hour, so scientists can cultivate very large numbers of bacteria for study in a relatively short time.

Once science turned to the study of unicellular life, rapid progress was made in genetics. In 1941, George W. Beadle and Edward L. Tatum demonstrated the relationship between genes and enzymes. DNA was established as the hereditary material in 1944 by Oswald Avery, Colin MacLeod, and Maclyn McCarty. In 1946, Joshua Lederberg and Edward L. Tatum discovered that genetic material could be transferred from one bacterium to another by a process called conjugation. Then, in 1953, James Watson and Francis Crick proposed a model for the structure and replication of DNA. The early 1960s witnessed a further explosion of discoveries relating to the way DNA controls protein synthesis. In 1961, François Jacob and Jacques Monod discovered messenger RNA (ribonucleic acid), a chemical involved in protein synthesis, and later they made the first major discoveries about the regulation of gene function in bacteria. During the same period, scientists were able to break the genetic code and thus understand how the information for protein synthesis in messenger RNA is translated into the amino acid sequence for making proteins.

CHECK YOUR UNDERSTANDING

✔ Define *bacteriology, mycology, parasitology, immunology,* and *virology.* 12

✔ Differentiate microbial genetics from molecular biology. 13

Microbes and Human Welfare

LEARNING OBJECTIVES

14   List at least four beneficial activities of microorganisms.

15   Name two examples of biotechnology that use recombinant DNA technology and two examples that do not.

As mentioned earlier, only a minority of all microorganisms are pathogenic. Microbes that cause food spoilage, such as soft spots on fruits and vegetables, decomposition of meats, and rancidity

of fats and oils, are also a minority. The vast majority of microbes benefit humans, other animals, and plants in many ways. For example, microbes produce methane and ethanol that can be used as alternative fuels to generate electricity and power vehicles. Biotechnology companies are using bacterial enzymes to break down plant cellulose so that yeast can metabolize the resulting simple sugars and produce ethanol. The following sections outline some of these beneficial activities.

Recycling Vital Elements

Discoveries made by two microbiologists in the 1880s have formed the basis for today's understanding of the biogeochemical cycles that support life on Earth. Martinus Beijerinck and Sergei Winogradsky were the first to show how bacteria help recycle vital elements between the soil and the atmosphere. **Microbial ecology,** the study of the relationship between microorganisms and their environment, originated with the work of these scientists. Today, microbial ecology has branched out and includes the study of how microbial populations interact with plants and animals in various environments. Among the concerns of microbial ecologists are water pollution and toxic chemicals in the environment.

The chemical elements carbon, nitrogen, oxygen, sulfur, and phosphorus are essential for life and abundant, but not necessarily in forms that organisms can use. Microorganisms are primarily responsible for converting these elements into forms that plants and animals can use. Microorganisms, primarily bacteria and fungi, return carbon dioxide to the atmosphere when they decompose organic wastes and dead plants and animals. Algae, cyanobacteria, and higher plants use the carbon dioxide during photosynthesis to produce carbohydrates for animals, fungi, and bacteria. Nitrogen is abundant in the atmosphere but in that form is not usable by plants and animals. Only bacteria can naturally convert atmospheric nitrogen to a form available to plants and animals.

Sewage Treatment: Using Microbes to Recycle Water

Our society's growing awareness of the need to preserve the environment has made people more conscious of the responsibility to recycle precious water and prevent the pollution of rivers and oceans. One major pollutant is sewage, which consists of human excrement, waste water, industrial wastes, and surface runoff. Sewage is about 99.9% water, with a few hundredths of 1% suspended solids. The remainder is a variety of dissolved materials.

Sewage treatment plants remove the undesirable materials and harmful microorganisms. Treatments combine various physical processes with the action of beneficial microbes. Large solids such as paper, wood, glass, gravel, and plastic are removed from sewage; left behind are liquid and organic materials that bacteria convert into such by-products as carbon dioxide, nitrates, phosphates, sulfates, ammonia, hydrogen sulfide, and methane.

Bioremediation: Using Microbes to Clean Up Pollutants

In 1988, scientists began using microbes to clean up pollutants and toxic wastes produced by various industrial processes. For example, some bacteria can actually use pollutants as energy sources; others produce enzymes that break down toxins into less harmful substances. By using bacteria in these ways—a process known as **bioremediation**—toxins can be removed from underground wells, chemical spills, toxic waste sites, and oil spills, such as the massive oil spill from an offshore drilling rig in the Gulf of Mexico on April 20, 2010. In addition, bacterial enzymes are used in drain cleaners to remove clogs without adding harmful chemicals to the environment. In some cases, microorganisms indigenous to the environment are used; in others, genetically modified microbes are used. Among the most commonly used microbes are certain species of bacteria of the genera *Pseudomonas* (sū-dō-mō′nas) and *Bacillus* (bä-sil′lus). *Bacillus* enzymes are also used in household detergents to remove spots from clothing.

Insect Pest Control by Microorganisms

Besides spreading diseases, insects can cause devastating crop damage. Insect pest control is therefore important for both agriculture and the prevention of human disease.

The bacterium *Bacillus thuringiensis* (thur-in-jē-en′sis) has been used extensively in the United States to control such pests as alfalfa caterpillars, bollworms, corn borers, cabbageworms, tobacco budworms, and fruit tree leaf rollers. It is incorporated into a dusting powder that is applied to the crops these insects eat. The bacteria produce protein crystals that are toxic to the digestive systems of the insects. The toxin gene also has been inserted into some plants to make them insect resistant.

By using microbial rather than chemical insect control, farmers can avoid harming the environment. Many chemical insecticides, such as DDT, remain in the soil as toxic pollutants and are eventually incorporated into the food chain.

Modern Biotechnology and Recombinant DNA Technology

Earlier, we touched on the commercial use of microorganisms to produce some common foods and chemicals. Such practical applications of microbiology are called **biotechnology.** Although biotechnology has been used in some form for centuries, techniques have become much more sophisticated in the past few decades. In the last several years, biotechnology has undergone a revolution through the advent of recombinant DNA technology to expand the potential of bacteria, viruses, and yeast cells and other fungi as miniature biochemical factories. Cultured plant and animal cells, as well as intact plants and animals, are also used as recombinant cells and organisms.

The applications of recombinant DNA technology are increasing with each passing year. Recombinant DNA techniques have been used thus far to produce a number of natural proteins, vaccines, and enzymes. Such substances have great potential for medical use.

A very exciting and important outcome of recombinant DNA techniques is **gene therapy**—inserting a missing gene or replacing a defective one in human cells. This technique uses a harmless virus to carry the missing or new gene into certain host cells, where the gene is picked up and inserted into the appropriate chromosome. Since 1990, gene therapy has been used to treat patients with adenosine deaminase (ADA) deficiency, a cause of severe combined immunodeficiency disease (SCID), in which cells of the immune system are inactive or missing; Duchenne's muscular dystrophy, a muscle-destroying disease; cystic fibrosis, a disease of the secreting portions of the respiratory passages, pancreas, salivary glands, and sweat glands; and LDL-receptor deficiency, a condition in which low-density lipoprotein (LDL) receptors are defective and LDL cannot enter cells. The LDL remains in the blood in high concentrations and increases the risk of atherosclerosis and coronary artery disease because it leads to fatty plaque formation in blood vessels. Results are still being evaluated. Other genetic diseases may also be treatable by gene therapy in the future, including hemophilia, an inability of the blood to clot normally; diabetes, elevated blood sugar levels; sickle cell disease, an abnormal kind of hemoglobin; and one type of hypercholesterolemia, high blood cholesterol.

Beyond medical applications, recombinant DNA techniques have also been applied to agriculture. For example, genetically altered strains of bacteria have been developed to protect fruit against frost damage, and bacteria are being modified to control insects that damage crops. Recombinant DNA has also been used to improve the appearance, flavor, and shelf life of fruits and vegetables. Potential agricultural uses of recombinant DNA include drought resistance, resistance to insects and microbial diseases, and increased temperature tolerance in crops.

CHECK YOUR UNDERSTANDING

✔ Name two beneficial uses of bacteria. 14

✔ Differentiate biotechnology from recombinant DNA technology. 15

Microbes and Human Disease

LEARNING OBJECTIVES

16   Define *normal microbiota* and *resistance*.

17   Define *biofilm*.

18   Define *emerging infectious disease*.

Normal Microbiota

We all live from birth until death in a world filled with microbes, and we all have a variety of microorganisms on and inside our bodies. These microorganisms make up our **normal microbiota,** or *flora** (Figure 7). The normal microbiota not only do us no harm, but also in some cases can actually benefit us. For example, some normal microbiota protect us against disease by preventing the overgrowth of harmful microbes, and others produce useful substances such as vitamin K and some B vitamins. Unfortunately, under some circumstances normal microbiota can make us sick or infect people we contact. For instance, when some normal microbiota leave their habitat, they can cause disease.

When is a microbe a welcome part of a healthy human, and when is it a harbinger of disease? The distinction between health and disease is in large part a balance between the natural defenses of the body and the disease-producing properties of microorganisms. Whether our bodies overcome the offensive tactics of a particular microbe depends on our **resistance**—the ability to ward off diseases. Important resistance is provided by the barrier of the skin, mucous membranes, cilia, stomach acid, and antimicrobial chemicals such as interferons. Microbes can be destroyed by white blood cells, by the inflammatory response, by fever, and by specific responses of our immune system. Sometimes, when our natural defenses are not strong enough to overcome an invader, they have to be supplemented by antibiotics or other drugs.

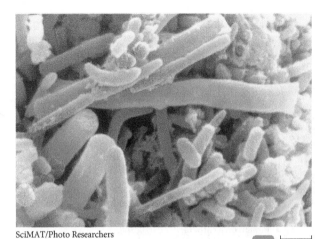

SciMAT/Photo Researchers

SEM | 2 μm

Figure 7 Several types of bacteria found as part of the normal microbiota on the surface of the human tongue.

Q How do we benefit from the production of vitamin K by microbes?

Clinical Case

Staph is the common name for *Staphylococcus aureus* bacteria, which are carried on the skin of about 30% of the human population. Although Andrea is diligent about taking her antibiotic as prescribed, she doesn't seem to be improving. After 3 days, the lesion on her wrist is even larger than before and is now draining yellow pus. Andrea also develops a fever. Her mother insists that she call her doctor to tell him about the latest developments.

Why does Andrea's infection persist after treatment?

Biofilms

In nature, microorganisms may exist as single cells that float or swim independently in a liquid, or they may attach to each other and/or some usually solid surface. This latter mode of behavior is called a **biofilm,** a complex aggregation of microbes. The slime covering a rock in a lake is a biofilm. Use your tongue to feel the biofilm on your teeth. Biofilms can be beneficial. They protect your mucous membranes from harmful microbes, and biofilms in lakes are an important food for aquatic animals. Biofilms can also be harmful. They can clog water pipes, and on medical implants

---
* At one time, bacteria and fungi were thought to be plants, and thus the term *flora* was used.

such as joint prostheses and catheters (Figure 8), they can cause such infections as endocarditis (inflammation of the heart). Bacteria in biofilms are often resistant to antibiotics because the biofilm offers a protective barrier.

Infectious Diseases

An **infectious disease** is a disease in which pathogens invade a susceptible host, such as a human or an animal. In the process, the pathogen carries out at least part of its life cycle inside the host, and disease frequently results. By the end of World War II, many people believed that infectious diseases were under control. They thought malaria would be eradicated through the use of the insecticide DDT to kill mosquitoes, that a vaccine would prevent diphtheria, and that improved sanitation measures would help prevent cholera transmission. Malaria is far from eliminated. Since 1986, local outbreaks have been identified in New Jersey, California, Florida, New York, and Texas, and the disease infects 300 million people worldwide. In 1994, diphtheria appeared in the United States, brought by travelers from the newly independent states of the former Soviet Union, which were experiencing a massive diphtheria epidemic. The epidemic was brought under control in 1998. Cholera outbreaks still occur in less-developed parts of the world.

Emerging Infectious Diseases

These recent outbreaks point to the fact that infectious diseases are not disappearing, but rather seem to be reemerging and increasing. In addition, a number of new diseases—**emerging infectious diseases (EIDs)**—have cropped up in recent years. These are diseases that are new or changing and are increasing or

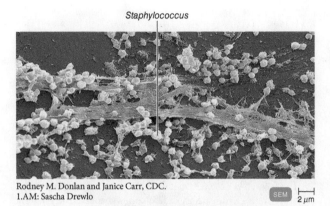

Staphylococcus

Rodney M. Donlan and Janice Carr, CDC.
1.AM: Sascha Drewlo

SEM 2 µm

Figure 8 Biofilm on a catheter. *Staphylococcus* bacteria stick to solid surfaces, forming a slimy layer. Bacteria that break away from this biofilm can cause infections.

Q How does a biofilm's protective barrier make it resistant to antibiotics?

have the potential to increase in incidence in the near future. Some of the factors that have contributed to the development of EIDs are evolutionary changes in existing organisms (e.g., *Vibrio cholerae;* vib′rē-ō kol′-er-ī); the spread of known diseases to new geographic regions or populations by modern transportation (e.g., West Nile virus); and increased human exposure to new, unusual infectious agents in areas that are undergoing ecologic changes such as deforestation and construction (e.g., Venezuelan hemorrhagic virus). EIDs also develop as a result of antimicrobial resistance (e.g., vancomycin-resistant *S. aureus*). An increasing number of incidents in recent years highlights the extent of the problem.

H1N1 influenza (flu), also known as *swine flu,* is a type of influenza caused by a new virus called *influenza H1N1.* H1N1 was first detected in the United States in april 2009. In June 2009, the World Health Organization declared H1N1 flu to be a *global pandemic disease* (a disease that affects large numbers of individuals in a short period of time and occurs worldwide).

Avian influenza A (H5N1), or **bird flu,** caught the attention of the public in 2003, when it killed millions of poultry and 24 people in eight countries in southeast Asia. Avian influenza viruses occur in birds worldwide. Certain wild birds, particularly waterfowl, do not get sick but carry the virus in their intestines and shed it in saliva, nasal secretions, and feces. Most often, the wild birds spread influenza to domesticated birds, in which the virus causes death.

Influenza A viruses are found in many different animals, including ducks, chickens, pigs, whales, horses, and seals. Normally, each subtype of influenza A virus is specific to certain species. However, influenza A viruses normally seen in one species sometimes can cross over and cause illness in another species, and all subtypes of influenza A virus can infect pigs. Although

it is unusual for people to get influenza infections directly from animals, sporadic human infections and outbreaks caused by certain avian influenza A viruses and pig influenza viruses have been reported. As of 2008, avian influenza had sickened 242 people, and about half of them died. Fortunately, the virus has not yet evolved to be transmitted successfully among humans.

Human infections with avian influenza viruses detected since 1997 have not resulted in sustained human-to-human transmission. However, because influenza viruses have the potential to change and gain the ability to spread easily between people, monitoring for human infection and person-to-person transmission is important. The U.S. Food and Drug Administration (FDA) approved a human vaccine against the avian influenza virus in April 2007.

Antibiotics are critical in treating bacterial infections. However, years of overuse and misuse of these drugs have created environments in which antibiotic-resistant bacteria thrive. Random mutations in bacterial genes can make a bacterium resistant to an antibiotic. In the presence of that antibiotic, this bacterium has an advantage over other, susceptible bacteria and is able to proliferate. Antibiotic-resistant bacteria have become a global health crisis.

Staphylococcus aureus causes a wide range of human infections from pimples and boils to pneumonia, food poisoning, and surgical wound infections, and it is a significant cause of hospital-associated infections. After penicillin's initial success in treating *S. aureus* infection, penicillin-resistant *S. aureus* became a major threat in hospitals in the 1950s, requiring the use of methicillin. In the 1980s, **methicillin-resistant *S. aureus,*** called **MRSA,** emerged and became endemic in many hospitals, leading to increasing use of vancomycin. In the late 1990s, *S. aureus* infections that were less sensitive to vancomycin (**vancomycin-intermediate *S. aureus,*** or **VISA**) were reported. In 2002, an infection caused by **vancomycin-resistant *S. aureus* (VRSA)** in a patient in the United States was reported.

In March 2010, the World Health Organization (WHO) reported that in some parts of the world (such as northwestern Russia) about 28% of all individuals with tuberculosis (TB) had the multidrug-resistant form of the disease (MDR-TB). Multidrug-resistant TB is caused by bacteria that are resistant to at least the antibiotics isoniazid and rifampicin, the most effective drugs against tuberculosis.

The antibacterial substances added to various household cleaning products are similar to antibiotics in many ways. When used correctly, they inhibit bacterial growth. However, wiping every household surface with these antibacterial agents creates an environment in which the resistant bacteria survive. Unfortunately, when you really need to disinfect your homes and hands—for example, when a family member comes home from a hospital and is still vulnerable to infection—you may encounter mainly resistant bacteria.

Routine housecleaning and handwashing are necessary, but standard soaps and detergents (without added antibacterials) are fine for these tasks. In addition, quickly evaporating chemicals, such as chlorine bleach, alcohol, ammonia, and hydrogen peroxide, remove potentially pathogenic bacteria but do not leave residues that encourage the growth of resistant bacteria.

Clinical Case

The *S. aureus* bacterium responsible for Andrea's infection is resistant to the β-lactam antibiotic prescribed by Andrea's doctor. Concerned about what his patient is telling him, Andrea's doctor calls the local hospital to let them know he is sending a patient over. In the emergency department, a nurse swabs Andrea's wound and sends it to the hospital lab for culturing. The culture shows that Andrea's infection is caused by methicillin-resistant *Staphylococcus aureus* (MRSA). MRSA produces β-lactamase, an enzyme that destroys β-lactam antibiotics. The attending physician surgically drains the pus from the sore on Andrea's wrist.

How does antibiotic resistance develop?

West Nile encephalitis (WNE) is inflammation of the brain caused by West Nile virus. WNE was first diagnosed in the West Nile region of Uganda in 1937. In 1999 the virus made its first North American appearance in humans in New York City. In 2007, West Nile virus infected over 3600 people in 43 states. West Nile virus is now established in nonmigratory birds in 48 states. The virus, which is carried by birds, is transmitted between birds—and to horses and humans—by mosquitoes. West Nile virus may have arrived in the United States in an infected traveler or in migratory birds.

In 1996, countries worldwide were refusing to import beef from the United Kingdom, where hundreds of thousands of cattle born after 1988 had to be killed because of an epidemic of **bovine spongiform encephalopathy** (en-sef-a-lop´a-thē), also called **BSE** or **mad cow disease**. BSE first came to the attention of microbiologists in 1986 as one of a handful of diseases caused by an infectious protein called a *prion*. Studies suggest that the source of disease was cattle feed prepared from sheep infected with their own version of the disease. Cattle are herbivores (planteaters), but adding protein to their feed improves their growth and health. **Creutzfeldt-Jakob disease** (kroits´felt yä´kôb), or **CJD,** is a human disease also caused by a prion. The incidence of CJD in the United Kingdom is similar to the incidence in other countries. However, by 2005 the United Kingdom reported 154 human cases of CJD caused by a new variant related to the bovine disease.

Escherichia coli is a normal inhabitant of the large intestine of vertebrates, including humans, and its presence is beneficial because it helps produce certain vitamins and breaks down otherwise undigestible foodstuffs. However, a strain called *E. coli* **O157:H7** causes bloody diarrhea when it grows in the intestines. This strain was first recognized in 1982 and since then has emerged as a public health problem. It is now one of the leading causes of diarrhea worldwide. In 1996, some 9000 people in Japan became ill, and 7 died, as a result of infection by *E. coli* O157:H7. The recent outbreaks of *E. coli* O157:H7 in the United States, associated with contamination of undercooked meat and unpasteurized beverages, have led public health officials to call for the development of new methods of testing for bacteria in food.

In 1995, infections of so-called **flesh-eating bacteria** were reported on the front pages of major newspapers. The bacteria are more correctly named invasive group A *Streptococcus* (strep-tō-kok´kus), or IGAS. Rates of IGAS in the United States, Scandinavia, England, and Wales have been increasing.

In 1995, a hospital laboratory technician in Democratic Republic of Congo (DROC) who had fever and bloody diarrhea underwent surgery for a suspected perforated bowel. Afterward he started hemorrhaging, and his blood began clotting in his blood vessels. A few days later, health care workers in the hospital where he was staying developed similar symptoms. One of them was transferred to a hospital in a different city; personnel in the second hospital who cared for this patient also developed symptoms. By the time the epidemic was over, 315 people had contracted **Ebola hemorrhagic fever** (hem-ôr-raj´ik), or **EHF,** and over 75% of them died. The epidemic was controlled when microbiologists instituted training on the use of protective equipment and educational measures in the community. Close personal contact with infectious blood or other body fluids or tissue leads to human-to-human transmission.

Microbiologists first isolated Ebola viruses from humans during earlier outbreaks in DROC in 1976. (The virus is named after Congo's Ebola River.) In 2008, an Ebola virus outbreak occurred in Uganda with 149 cases. In 1989 and 1996, outbreaks among monkeys imported into the United States from the Philippines were caused by another Ebola virus but were not associated with human disease.

Recorded cases of **Marburg virus,** another hemorrhagic fever virus, are rare. The first cases were laboratory workers in Europe who handled African green monkeys from Uganda. Four outbreaks were identified in Africa between 1975 and 1998, involving 2 to 154 people with 56% mortality. In 2004, an outbreak killed 227 people. Microbiologists have been studying many animals but have not yet discovered the natural reservoir (source) of EHF and Marburg viruses.

In 1993, an outbreak of **cryptosporidiosis** (krip-tō-spô-rid-ē-ō´sis) transmitted through the public water supply in Milwaukee, Wisconsin, resulted in diarrheal illness in an estimated 403,000 persons. The microorganism responsible for this outbreak was the protozoan *Cryptosporidium* (krip-tō-spô-ri´dē-um). First reported as a cause of human disease in 1976, it is responsible for up to 30% of the diarrheal illness in developing countries. In the United States, transmission has occurred via drinking water, swimming pools, and contaminated hospital supplies.

AIDS (acquired immunodeficiency syndrome) first came to public attention in 1981 with reports from Los Angeles that a few young homosexual men had died of a previously rare type of pneumonia known as *Pneumocystis* (nü-mō-sis'tis) pneumonia. These men had experienced a severe weakening of the immune system, which normally fights infectious diseases. Soon these cases were correlated with an unusual number of occurrences of a rare form of cancer, Kaposi's sarcoma, among young homosexual men. Similar increases in such rare diseases were found among hemophiliacs and intravenous drug users.

Researchers quickly discovered that the cause of AIDS was a previously unknown virus (see Figure 1e). The virus, now called **human immunodeficiency virus (HIV),** destroys $CD4^+$ T cells, one type of white blood cell important to immune system defenses. Sickness and death result from microorganisms or cancerous cells that might otherwise have been defeated by the body's natural defenses. So far, the disease has been inevitably fatal once symptoms develop.

By studying disease patterns, medical researchers found that HIV could be spread through sexual intercourse, by contaminated needles, from infected mothers to their newborns via breast milk, and by blood transfusions—in short, by the transmission of body fluids from one person to another. Since

1985, blood used for transfusions has been carefully checked for the presence of HIV, and it is now quite unlikely that the virus can be spread by this means.

By the end of 2010, over 1 million people in the United States are living with AIDS. Over 50,000 Americans become infected and 18,000 die each year. As of 2010, health officials estimated that 1.3 million Americans have HIV infection. In 2009, the World Health Organization (WHO) estimated that over 33 million people worldwide are living with HIV/AIDS and that 7500 new infections occur every day.

Since 1994, new treatments have extended the life span of people with AIDS; however, approximately 40,000 new cases occur annually in the United States. The majority of individuals with AIDS are in the sexually active age group. Because heterosexual partners of AIDS sufferers are at high risk of infection, public health officials are concerned that even more women and minorities will contract AIDS. In 1997, HIV diagnoses began increasing among women and minorities. Among the AIDS cases reported in 2009, 26% were women, and 49% were African American.

In the months and years to come, scientists will continue to apply microbiological techniques to help them learn more about the structure of the deadly HIV, how it is transmitted, how it grows in cells and causes disease, how drugs can be directed against it, and whether an effective vaccine can be developed. Public health officials have also focused on prevention through education.

AIDS poses one of this century's most formidable health threats, but it is not the first serious epidemic of a sexually transmitted disease. Syphilis was also once a fatal epidemic disease. As recently as 1941, syphilis caused an estimated 14,000 deaths per year in the United States. With few drugs available for treatment and no vaccines to prevent it, efforts to control the disease focused mainly on altering sexual behavior and on the use of condoms. The eventual development of drugs to treat syphilis contributed significantly to preventing the spread of the disease. According to the Centers for Disease Control and Prevention (CDC), reported cases of syphilis dropped from a record high of 575,000 in 1943 to an all-time low of 5979 cases in 2004. Since then, however, the number of cases has been increasing.

Just as microbiological techniques helped researchers in the fight against syphilis and smallpox, they will help scientists discover the causes of new emerging infectious diseases in the twenty-first century. Undoubtedly there will be new diseases. Ebola virus and *Influenzavirus* are examples of viruses that may be changing their abilities to infect different host species.

Infectious diseases may reemerge because of antibiotic resistance and through the use of microorganisms as weapons. The breakdown of public health measures for previously controlled infections has resulted in unexpected cases of tuberculosis, whooping cough, and diphtheria.

Clinical Case

Mutations develop randomly in bacteria: some mutations are lethal, some have no effect, and some may be beneficial. Once these mutations develop, the offspring of the mutated parent cells also carry the same mutation. Because they have an advantage in the presence of the antibiotic, bacteria that are resistant to antibiotics soon outnumber those that are susceptible to antibiotic therapy. The widespread use of antibiotics selectively allows the resistant bacteria to grow, whereas the susceptible bacteria are killed. Eventually, almost the entire population of bacteria is resistant to the antibiotic.

The emergency department physician prescribes a different antibiotic, vancomycin, which will kill the MRSA in Andrea's wrist. She also explains to Andrea what MRSA is and why it's important they find out where Andrea acquired the potentially lethal bacteria.

What can the emergency department physician tell Andrea about MRSA?

CHECK YOUR UNDERSTANDING

✔ Differentiate normal microbiota and infectious disease. 16

✔ Why are biofilms important? 17

✔ What factors contribute to the emergence of an infectious disease? 18

* * *

The diseases we have mentioned are caused by viruses, bacteria, protozoa, and prions—types of microorganisms. This text introduces you to the enormous variety of microscopic organisms. It shows you how microbiologists use specific techniques and procedures to study the microbes that cause such diseases as AIDS and diarrhea—and diseases that have yet to be discovered. You will also learn how the body responds to microbial infection and how certain drugs combat microbial diseases. Finally, you will learn about the many beneficial roles that microbes play in the world around us.

Clinical Case Resolved

The first MRSA was health care–associated MRSA (HA-MRSA), transmitted between staff and patients in health care settings. In the 1990s, infections by a genetically different strain, community-associated MRSA (CA-MRSA), emerged as a major cause of skin disease in the United States. CA-MRSA enters skin abrasions from environmental surfaces or other people. Andrea has never been hospitalized before now, so they are able to rule out the hospital as the source of infection. Her college courses are all online, so she didn't contract MRSA at the university, either. The local health department sends someone to her family home to swab for the bacteria there.

MRSA is isolated from Andrea's living room sofa, but how did it get there? After speaking with the family, the representative from the health department, knowing that clusters of CA-MRSA infections have been seen among athletes suggests swabbing the mats used by the gymnasts at the school Andrea's sister attends. The cultures come back positive for MRSA. Andrea's sister, although not infected, transferred the bacteria from her skin to the sofa, where Andrea laid her arm. (A person can carry MRSA on the skin without becoming infected.) The bacteria entered through a scratch on Andrea's wrist.

Study Outline

MasteringMICROBIOLOGY™

Test your understanding with quizzes, microbe review, and a chapter post-test at www.masteringmicrobiology.com.

Microbes in Our Lives

1. Living things too small to be seen with the unaided eye are called microorganisms.
2. Microorganisms are important in maintaining Earth's ecological balance.
3. Some microorganisms live in humans and other animals and are needed to maintain good health.
4. Some microorganisms are used to produce foods and chemicals.
5. Some microorganisms cause disease.

Naming and Classifying Microorganisms

Nomenclature

1. In a nomenclature system designed by Carolus Linnaeus (1735), each living organism is assigned two names.
2. The two names consist of a genus and a specific epithet, both of which are underlined or italicized.

Types of Microorganisms

3. Bacteria are unicellular organisms. Because they have no nucleus, the cells are described as prokaryotic.
4. The three major basic shapes of bacteria are bacillus, coccus, and spiral.
5. Most bacteria have a peptidoglycan cell wall; they divide by binary fission, and they may possess flagella.
6. Bacteria can use a wide range of chemical substances for their nutrition.
7. Archaea consist of prokaryotic cells; they lack peptidoglycan in their cell walls.
8. Archaea include methanogens, extreme halophiles, and extreme thermophiles.
9. Fungi (mushrooms, molds, and yeasts) have eukaryotic cells (cells with a true nucleus). Most fungi are multicellular.
10. Fungi obtain nutrients by absorbing organic material from their environment.
11. Protozoa are unicellular eukaryotes.
12. Protozoa obtain nourishment by absorption or ingestion through specialized structures.
13. Algae are unicellular or multicellular eukaryotes that obtain nourishment by photosynthesis.
14. Algae produce oxygen and carbohydrates that are used by other organisms.
15. Viruses are noncellular entities that are parasites of cells.
16. Viruses consist of a nucleic acid core (DNA or RNA) surrounded by a protein coat. An envelope may surround the coat.
17. The principal groups of multicellular animal parasites are flatworms and roundworms, collectively called helminths.
18. The microscopic stages in the life cycle of helminths are identified by traditional microbiological procedures.

Classification of Microorganisms

19. All organisms are classified into Bacteria, Archaea, and Eukarya. Eukarya include protists, fungi, plants, and animals.

A Brief History of Microbiology

The First Observations

1. Robert Hooke observed that cork was composed of "little boxes"; he introduced the term *cell* (1665).
2. Hooke's observations laid the groundwork for development of the cell theory, the concept that all living things are composed of cells.
3. Anton van Leeuwenhoek, using a simple microscope, was the first to observe microorganisms (1673).

The Debate over Spontaneous Generation

4. Until the mid-1880s, many people believed in spontaneous generation, the idea that living organisms could arise from nonliving matter.
5. Francesco Redi demonstrated that maggots appear on decaying meat only when flies are able to lay eggs on the meat (1668).
6. John Needham claimed that microorganisms could arise spontaneously from heated nutrient broth (1745).
7. Lazzaro Spallanzani repeated Needham's experiments and suggested that Needham's results were due to microorganisms in the air entering his broth (1765).
8. Rudolf Virchow introduced the concept of biogenesis: living cells can arise only from preexisting cells (1858).
9. Louis Pasteur demonstrated that microorganisms are in the air everywhere and offered proof of biogenesis (1861).
10. Pasteur's discoveries led to the development of aseptic techniques used in laboratory and medical procedures to prevent contamination by microorganisms.

The Golden Age of Microbiology

11. The science of microbiology advanced rapidly between 1857 and 1914.
12. Pasteur found that yeasts ferment sugars to alcohol and that bacteria can oxidize the alcohol to acetic acid.
13. A heating process called pasteurization is used to kill bacteria in some alcoholic beverages and milk.
14. Agostino Bassi (1835) and Pasteur (1865) showed a causal relationship between microorganisms and disease.
15. Joseph Lister introduced the use of a disinfectant to clean surgical wounds in order to control infections in humans (1860s).
16. Robert Koch proved that microorganisms cause disease. He used a sequence of procedures, now called Koch's postulates (1876), that are used today to prove that a particular microorganism causes a particular disease.
17. In a vaccination, immunity (resistance to a particular disease) is conferred by inoculation with a vaccine.
18. In 1798, Edward Jenner demonstrated that inoculation with cowpox material provides humans with immunity to smallpox.
19. About 1880, Pasteur discovered that avirulent bacteria could be used as a vaccine for fowl cholera; he coined the word *vaccine*.
20. Modern vaccines are prepared from living avirulent micro-organisms or killed pathogens, from isolated components of pathogens, and by recombinant DNA techniques.

The Birth of Modern Chemotherapy: Dreams of a "Magic Bullet"

21. Chemotherapy is the chemical treatment of a disease.

22. Two types of chemotherapeutic agents are synthetic drugs (chemically prepared in the laboratory) and antibiotics (substances produced naturally by bacteria and fungi to inhibit the growth of other microorganisms).
23. Paul Ehrlich introduced an arsenic-containing chemical called salvarsan to treat syphilis (1910).
24. Alexander Fleming observed that the *Penicillium* fungus inhibited the growth of a bacterial culture. He named the active ingredient penicillin (1928).
25. Penicillin has been used clinically as an antibiotic since the 1940s.
26. Researchers are tackling the problem of drug-resistant microbes.

Modern Developments in Microbiology

27. Bacteriology is the study of bacteria, mycology is the study of fungi, and parasitology is the study of parasitic protozoa and worms.
28. Microbiologists are using genomics, the study of all of an organism's genes, to classify bacteria, fungi, and protozoa.
29. The study of AIDS, analysis of the action of interferons, and the development of new vaccines are among the current research interests in immunology.
30. New techniques in molecular biology and electron microscopy have provided tools for advancing our knowledge of virology.
31. The development of recombinant DNA technology has helped advance all areas of microbiology.

Microbes and Human Welfare

1. Microorganisms degrade dead plants and animals and recycle chemical elements to be used by living plants and animals.
2. Bacteria are used to decompose organic matter in sewage.
3. Bioremediation processes use bacteria to clean up toxic wastes.
4. Bacteria that cause diseases in insects are being used as biological controls of insect pests. Biological controls are specific for the pest and do not harm the environment.
5. Using microbes to make products such as foods and chemicals is called biotechnology.
6. Using recombinant DNA, bacteria can produce important substances such as proteins, vaccines, and enzymes.
7. In gene therapy, viruses are used to carry replacements for defective or missing genes into human cells.
8. Genetically modified bacteria are used in agriculture to protect plants from frost and insects and to improve the shelf life of produce.

Microbes and Human Disease

1. Everyone has microorganisms in and on the body; these make up the normal microbiota, or flora.
2. The disease-producing properties of a species of microbe and the host's resistance are important factors in determining whether a person will contract a disease.
3. Bacterial communities that form slimy layers on surfaces are called biofilms.
4. An infectious disease is one in which pathogens invade a susceptible host.
5. An emerging infectious disease (EID) is a new or changing disease showing an increase in incidence in the recent past or a potential to increase in the near future.

Study Questions

Answers to the Review and Multiple Choice questions can be found at the end of this chapter.

Review

1. How did the idea of spontaneous generation come about?
2. Briefly state the role microorganisms play in each of the following:
   a. biological control of pests
   b. recycling of elements
   c. normal microbiota
   d. sewage treatment
   e. human insulin production
   f. vaccine production
   g. biofilms
3. Into which field of microbiology would the following scientists best fit?

Researcher Who	Field
1,3 **a.** Studies biodegradation of toxic wastes	1. Biotechnology
8 **b.** Studies the causative agent of Ebola hemorrhagic fever	2. Immunology
1,4,5 **c.** Studies the production of human proteins by bacteria	3. Microbial ecology
2 **d.** Studies the symptoms of AIDS	4. Microbial genetics
5 **e.** Studies the production of toxin by *E. coli*	5. Microbial physiology
3 **f.** Studies the life cycle of *Cryptosporidium*	6. Molecular biology
4 **g.** Develops gene therapy for a disease	7. Mycology
7 **h.** Studies the fungus *Candida albicans*	8. Virology

4. Match the microorganisms in column A to their descriptions in column B.

Column A	Column B
7 **a.** Archaea	1. Not composed of cells
4 **b.** Algae	2. Cell wall made of chitin
3 **c.** Bacteria	3. Cell wall made of peptidoglycan
2 **d.** Fungi	4. Cell wall made of cellulose; photosynthetic
6 **e.** Helminths	5. Unicellular, complex cell structure lacking a cell wall
5 **f.** Protozoa	6. Multicellular animals
1 **g.** Viruses	7. Prokaryote without peptidoglycan cell wall

5. Match the people in column A to their contribution toward the advancement of microbiology, in column B.

Column A	Column B
11 **a.** Avery, MacLeod, and McCarty	1. Developed vaccine against smallpox
14 **b.** Beadle and Tatum	2. Discovered how DNA controls protein synthesis in a cell
15 **c.** Berg	3. Discovered penicillin

17 **d.** Ehrlich	4. Discovered that DNA can be transferred from one bacterium to another
3 **e.** Fleming	5. Disproved spontaneous generation
9 **f.** Hooke	6. First to characterize a virus
10 **g.** Iwanowski	7. First to use disinfectants in surgical procedures
2 **h.** Jacob and Monod	8. First to observe bacteria
1 **i.** Jenner	9. First to observe cells in plant material and name them
12 **j.** Koch	10. Observed that viruses are filterable
18 **k.** Lancefield	11. Proved that DNA is the hereditary material
4 **l.** Lederberg and Tatum	12. Proved that microorganisms can cause disease
7 **m.** Lister	13. Said living cells arise from preexisting living cells
5 **n.** Pasteur	14. Showed that genes code for enzymes
6 **o.** Stanley	15. Spliced animal DNA to bacterial DNA
8 **p.** van Leeuwenhoek	16. Used bacteria to produce acetone
13 **q.** Virchow	17. Used the first synthetic chemotherapeutic agent
16 **r.** Weizmann	18. Proposed a classification system for streptococci based on antigens in their cell walls

6. The genus name of a bacterium is "erwinia," and the specific epithet is "amylovora." Write the scientific name of this organism correctly. Using this name as an example, explain how scientific names are chosen.
7. It is possible to purchase the following microorganisms in a retail store. Provide a reason for buying each.
   a. *Bacillus thuringiensis* – biological insecticide
   b. *Saccharomyces* – bread, wine, beer.
8. **DRAW IT** Show where airborne microbes ended up in Pasteur's experiment.

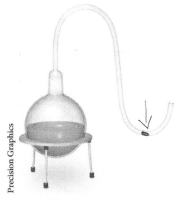

Precision Graphics

9. **NAME IT** What type of microorganism has a peptidoglycan cell wall, has DNA that is not contained in a nucleus, and has flagella?

Bacteria.

Multiple Choice

1. Which of the following is a scientific name?
   a. *Mycobacterium tuberculosis*
   b. Tubercle bacillus
2. Which of the following is *not* a characteristic of bacteria?
   a. are prokaryotic
   b. have peptidoglycan cell walls
   c. have the same shape
   d. grow by binary fission
   e. have the ability to move
3. Which of the following is the most important element of Koch's germ theory of disease? The animal shows disease symptoms when
   a. the animal has been in contact with a sick animal.
   b. the animal has a lowered resistance.
   c. a microorganism is observed in the animal.
   d. a microorganism is inoculated into the animal.
   e. microorganisms can be cultured from the animal.
4. Recombinant DNA is
   a. DNA in bacteria.
   b. the study of how genes work.
   c. the DNA resulting when genes of two different organisms are mixed.
   d. the use of bacteria in the production of foods.
   e. the production of proteins by genes.
5. Which of the following statements is the best definition of *biogenesis*?
   a. Nonliving matter gives rise to living organisms.
   b. Living cells can only arise from preexisting cells.
   c. A vital force is necessary for life.
   d. Air is necessary for living organisms.
   e. Microorganisms can be generated from nonliving matter.
6. Which of the following is a beneficial activity of microorganisms?
   a. Some microorganisms are used as food for humans.
   b. Some microorganisms use carbon dioxide.
   c. Some microorganisms provide nitrogen for plant growth.
   d. Some microorganisms are used in sewage treatment processes.
   e. all of the above
7. It has been said that bacteria are essential for the existence of life on Earth. Which of the following is the essential function performed by bacteria?
   a. control insect populations
   b. directly provide food for humans
   c. decompose organic material and recycle elements
   d. cause disease
   e. produce human hormones such as insulin
8. Which of the following is an example of bioremediation?
   a. application of oil-degrading bacteria to an oil spill
   b. application of bacteria to a crop to prevent frost damage
   c. fixation of gaseous nitrogen into usable nitrogen
   d. production by bacteria of a human protein such as interferon
   e. all of the above

9. Spallanzani's conclusion about spontaneous generation was challenged because Lavoisier had just shown that oxygen was the vital component of air. Which of the following statements is true?
   a. All life requires air.
   b. Only disease-causing organisms require air.
   c. Some microbes do not require air.
   d. Pasteur kept air out of his biogenesis experiments.
   e. Lavoisier was mistaken.
10. Which of the following statements about *E. coli* is *false*?
    a. *E. coli* was the first disease-causing bacterium identified by Koch.
    b. *E. coli* is part of the normal microbiota of humans.
    c. *E. coli* is beneficial in human intestines.
    d. A disease-causing strain of *E. coli* causes bloody diarrhea.
    e. none of the above

Critical Thinking

1. How did the theory of biogenesis lead the way for the germ theory of disease?
2. Even though the germ theory of disease was not demonstrated until 1876, why did Semmelweis (1840) and Lister (1867) argue for the use of aseptic techniques?
3. Find at least three supermarket products made by microorganisms. (*Hint:* The label will state the scientific name of the organism or include the word *culture, fermented,* or *brewed.*)
4. People once believed all microbial diseases would be controlled by the twenty-first century. Name one emerging infectious disease. List three reasons why we are identifying new diseases now.

Clinical Applications

1. The prevalence of arthritis in the United States is 1 in 100,000 children. However, 1 in 10 children in Lyme, Connecticut, developed arthritis between June and September 1973. Allen Steere, a rheumatologist at Yale University, investigated the cases in Lyme and found that 25% of the patients remembered having a skin rash during their arthritic episode and that the disease was treatable with penicillin. Steere concluded that this was a new infectious disease and did not have an environmental, genetic, or immunologic cause.
   a. What was the factor that caused Steere to reach his conclusion?
   b. What is the disease?
   c. Why was the disease more prevalent between June and September?
2. In 1864, Lister observed that patients recovered completely from simple fractures, but that compound fractures had "disastrous consequences." He knew that the application of phenol (carbolic acid) to fields in the town of Carlisle prevented cattle disease. Lister treated compound fractures with phenol, and his patients recovered without complications. How was Lister influenced by Pasteur's work? Why was Koch's work still needed?

Answers to Review and Multiple Choice Study Questions

Review

1. People came to believe that living organisms arise from nonliving matter because they would see flies coming out of manure, maggots coming out of dead animals, and microorganisms appearing in liquids after a day or two.

2. **a.** Certain microorganisms cause diseases in insects. Microorganisms that kill insects can be effective biological control agents because they are specific for the pest and do not persist in the environment.
   b. Carbon, oxygen, nitrogen, sulfur, and phosphorus are required for all living organisms. Microorganisms convert these elements into forms that are useful for other organisms. Many bacteria decompose material and release carbon dioxide into the atmosphere, which plants use. Some bacteria can take nitrogen from the atmosphere and convert it into a form that plants and other microorganisms can use.
   c. Normal microbiota are microorganisms that are found in and on the human body. They do not usually cause disease and can be beneficial.
   d. Organic matter in sewage is decomposed by bacteria into carbon dioxide, nitrates, phosphates, sulfate, and other inorganic compounds in a wastewater treatment plant.
   e. Recombinant DNA techniques have resulted in insertion of the gene for insulin production into bacteria. These bacteria can produce human insulin inexpensively.
   f. Microorganisms can be used as vaccines. Some microbes can be genetically modified to produce components of vaccines.
   g. Biofilms are aggregated bacteria adhering to each other and to a solid surface.

3. **a.** 1, 3   **c.** 1, 4, 5   **e.** 5   **g.** 4
   b. 8   **d.** 2   **f.** 3   **h.** 7

4. **a.** 7   **c.** 3   **e.** 6   **g.** 1
   b. 4   **d.** 2   **f.** 5

5. **a.** 11   **e.** 3   **i.** 1   **m.** 7   **q.** 13
   b. 14   **f.** 9   **j.** 12   **n.** 5   **r.** 16
   c. 15   **g.** 10   **k.** 18   **o.** 6
   d. 17   **h.** 2   **l.** 4   **p.** 8

6. *Erwinia amylovora* is the correct way to write this scientific name. Scientific names can be derived from the names of scientists. In this case, *Erwinia* is derived from Erwin F. Smith, an American plant pathologist. Scientific names also can describe the organism, its habitat, or its niche. *E. amylovora* is a pathogen of plants (*amylo-* = starch; *vora* = eat).

7. **a.** *B. thuringiensis* is sold as a biological insecticide.
   b. *Saccharomyces* is the yeast sold for making bread, wine, and beer.

8.

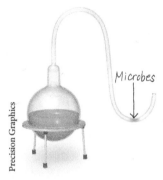

Microbes

Precision Graphics

9. Bacteria

Multiple Choice

1. a   **6.** e
2. c   **7.** c
3. d   **8.** a
4. c   **9.** c
5. b   **10.** a

27

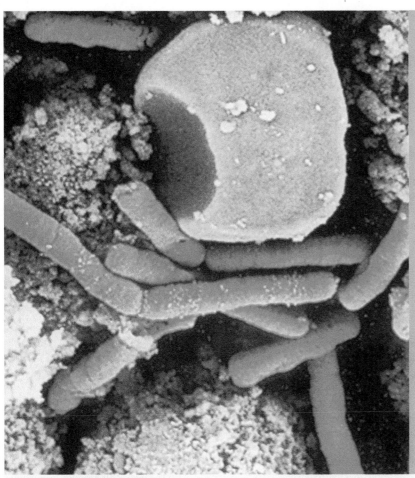

Scott Camazine/Photo Researchers

Chemical Principles

Visualize microbiology and check your
understanding with a pre-test at
www.masteringmicrobiology.com.

We can see a tree rot and smell milk going sour, but we might not realize what is happening on a microscopic level. In both cases, microbes are conducting chemical operations. The tree rots when microorganisms decompose the wood. Milk turns sour from the production of lactic acid by bacteria. Most of the activities of microorganisms are the result of a series of chemical reactions.

Like all organisms, microorganisms use nutrients to make chemical building blocks for growth and other functions essential to life. For most microorganisms, synthesizing these building blocks requires them to break down nutrient substances and use the energy released to assemble the resulting molecular fragments into new substances.

The chemistry of microbes is one of the most important concerns of microbiologists. Knowledge of chemistry is essential to understanding what roles microorganisms play in nature, how they cause disease, how methods for diagnosing disease are developed, how the body's defenses combat infection, and how antibiotics and vaccines are produced to combat the harmful effects of microbes. The *Bacillus anthracis* bacteria in the photograph make a capsule that is not readily digested by animal cells. As discussed in the Clinical Case, these bacteria can grow in mammals by avoiding host defenses. Researchers are investigating ways to identify unique chemicals made by *B. anthracis* and other potential biological weapons in order to detect bioterrorism. To understand the changes that occur in microorganisms and the changes microbes make in the world around us, we need to know how molecules are formed and how they interact.

From Chapter 2 of *Microbiology: An Introduction*, Eleventh Edition. Gerard J. Tortora, Berdell R. Funke, Christine L. Case.

29

The Structure of Atoms

LEARNING OBJECTIVE

1   Describe the structure of an atom and its relation to the physical properties of elements.

All matter—whether air, rock, or a living organism—is made up of small units called atoms. An **atom** is the smallest component of a pure substance that exhibits physical and chemical properties of that substance; an atom cannot be subdivided into smaller substances without losing its properties. Atoms interact with each other in certain combinations to form **molecules.** Living cells are made up of molecules, some of which are very complex. The science of the interaction between atoms and molecules is called **chemistry.**

Atoms are the smallest units of matter that enter into chemical reactions. Every atom has a centrally located **nucleus** and particles called **electrons** that move around the nucleus in regions called electron shells (Figure 1). The nuclei of most atoms are stable—that is, they do not change spontaneously—and nuclei do not participate in chemical reactions. The nucleus is made up of positively ($+$) charged particles called **protons** and uncharged (neutral) particles called **neutrons.** The nucleus, therefore, bears a net positive charge. A **charge** is a property of some subatomic particles that produces an attractive or repulsive force between them; particles of opposite charge attract each other, and particles of the same charge repel each other. Neutrons and protons

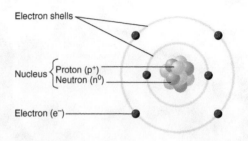

Figure 1 The structure of an atom. In this simplified diagram of a carbon atom, note the central location of the nucleus. The nucleus contains six neutrons and six protons, although not all the protons are visible in this view. The six electrons move about the nucleus in regions called electron shells, shown here as circles.

 What is the atomic number of this atom?

Precision Graphics

have approximately the same weight, which is about 1840 times that of an electron. The charge on electrons is negative ($-$), and in all atoms the number of electrons is equal to the number of protons. Because the total positive charge of the nucleus equals the total negative charge of the electrons, each atom is electrically neutral.

The number of protons in an atomic nucleus ranges from one (in a hydrogen atom) to more than 100 (in the largest atoms known). Atoms are often listed by their **atomic number,** the number of protons in the nucleus. The total number of protons and neutrons in an atom is its approximate **atomic weight.**

Chemical Elements

All atoms with the same number of protons behave the same way chemically and are classified as the same **chemical element.** Each element has its own name and a one- or two-letter symbol, usually derived from the English or Latin name for the element. For example, the symbol for the element hydrogen is H, and the symbol for carbon is C. The symbol for sodium is Na—the first two letters of its Latin name, *natrium*—to distinguish it from nitrogen, N, and from sulfur, S. There are 92 naturally occurring elements. However, only about 26 elements are commonly found in living things. Table 1 lists some of the chemical elements found in living organisms.

Most elements have several **isotopes**—atoms with different numbers of neutrons in their nuclei. All isotopes of an element have the same number of protons in their nuclei, but their atomic weights differ because of the difference in the number of neutrons. For example, in a natural sample of oxygen, all the atoms contain eight protons. However, 99.76% of the atoms have eight neutrons, 0.04% contain nine neutrons, and the remaining 0.2% contain ten neutrons. Therefore, the three isotopes composing a natural sample of oxygen have atomic weights of 16, 17, and 18, although all will have the atomic number 8. Atomic numbers are written as a subscript to the left of an element's chemical

Clinical Case: Drumming Up Dust

Jonathan, a 52-year-old drummer, is doing his best to ignore the cold sweat that is breaking out all over his body. He and his bandmates are performing in a local Philadelphia nightclub, and they are just about finished with the second set of the evening. Jonathan hasn't been feeling well for a while, actually; he has been feeling weak and short of breath for the last 3 days or so. Jonathan makes it to the end of the song, but the noise from the clapping and cheering audience seems to come from far away. He stands up to bow and collapses. Jonathan is admitted to a local emergency department with a mild fever and severe shaking. He is able to tell the admitting nurse that he also has had a dry cough for the last few days. The attending physician orders a chest X-ray exam and sputum culture. Jonathan is diagnosed with bilateral pneumonia caused by *Bacillus anthracis.* The attending physician is astonished by this diagnosis.

How did Jonathan become infected by *B. anthracis?* Read on to find out.

TABLE 1 The Elements of Life*

Element	Symbol	Atomic Number	Approximate Atomic Weight
Hydrogen	H	1	1
Carbon	C	6	12
Nitrogen	N	7	14
Oxygen	O	8	16
Sodium	Na	11	23
Magnesium	Mg	12	24
Phosphorus	P	15	31
Sulfur	S	16	32
Chlorine	Cl	17	35
Potassium	K	19	39
Calcium	Ca	20	40
Iron	Fe	26	56
Iodine	I	53	127

*Hydrogen, carbon, nitrogen, and oxygen are the most abundant chemical elements in living organisms.

symbol. Atomic weights are written as a superscript above the atomic number. Thus, natural oxygen isotopes are represented as $^{16}_{8}O$, $^{17}_{8}O$, and $^{18}_{8}O$. Isotopes of certain elements are extremely useful in biological research, medical diagnosis, the treatment of some disorders, and some forms of sterilization.

Electronic Configurations

In an atom, electrons are arranged in **electron shells,** which are regions corresponding to different **energy levels.** The arrangement is called an **electronic configuration.** Shells are layered outward from the nucleus, and each shell can hold a characteristic maximum number of electrons—two electrons in the innermost shell (lowest energy level), eight electrons in the second shell, and eight electrons in the third shell, if it is the atom's outermost (valence) shell. The fourth, fifth, and sixth electron shells can each accommodate 18 electrons, although there are some exceptions to this generalization. **Table 2** shows the electronic configurations for atoms of some elements found in living organisms.

The outermost shell tends to be filled with the maximum number of electrons. An atom can give up, accept, or share electrons with other atoms to fill this shell. The chemical properties of atoms are largely a function of the number of electrons in the outermost electron shell. When its outer shell is filled, the atom is chemically stable, or inert: it does not tend to react with other atoms. Helium (atomic number 2) and neon (atomic number 10) are examples of atoms of inert gases whose outer shells are filled.

When an atom's outer electron shell is only partially filled, the atom is chemically unstable. Such an atom reacts with other atoms, and this reaction depends, in part, on the degree to which the outer energy levels are filled. Notice the number of electrons in the outer energy levels of the atoms in Table 2. We will see later how the number correlates with the chemical reactivity of the elements.

CHECK YOUR UNDERSTANDING

✔ How does $^{14}_{6}C$ differ from $^{12}_{6}C$? What is the atomic number of each carbon atom? The atomic weight? **1**

How Atoms Form Molecules: Chemical Bonds

LEARNING OBJECTIVES

2 Define *ionic bond, covalent bond, hydrogen bond, molecular weight,* and *mole.*

When the outermost energy level of an atom is not completely filled by electrons, you can think of it as having either unfilled spaces or extra electrons in that energy level, depending on whether it is easier for the atom to gain or lose electrons. For example, an atom of oxygen, with two electrons in the first energy level and six in the second, has two unfilled spaces in the second electron shell; an atom of magnesium has two extra electrons in its outermost shell. The most chemically stable configuration for any atom is to have its outermost shell filled. Therefore, for these two atoms to attain that state, oxygen must gain two electrons, and magnesium must lose two electrons. Because all atoms tend to combine so that the extra electrons in the outermost shell of one atom fill the spaces of the outermost shell of the other atom, oxygen and magnesium combine so that the outermost shell of each atom has the full complement of eight electrons.

The **valence,** or combining capacity, of an atom is the number of extra or missing electrons in its outermost electron shell. For example, hydrogen has a valence of 1 (one unfilled space, or one extra electron), oxygen has a valence of 2 (two unfilled spaces), carbon has a valence of 4 (four unfilled spaces, or four extra electrons), and magnesium has a valence of 2 (two extra electrons).

Basically, atoms achieve the full complement of electrons in their outermost energy shells by combining to form molecules, which are made up of atoms of one or more elements. A molecule that contains at least two different kinds of atoms, such as H_2O (the water molecule), is called a **compound.** In H_2O, the subscript 2 indicates that there are two atoms of hydrogen; the absence of a subscript indicates that there is only one atom of oxygen. Molecules hold together because the valence electrons of the combining atoms form attractive forces, called **chemical bonds,** between the atomic nuclei. Therefore, valence may also be viewed as the bonding capacity of an element. Because energy is required for chemical bond formation, each chemical bond possesses a certain amount of potential chemical energy.

TABLE 2 Electronic Configurations for the Atoms of Some Elements Found in Living Organisms

Element	First Electron Shell (2)*	Second Electron Shell (8)*	Third Electron Shell (8)*	Diagram	Number of Valence (Outermost) Shell Electrons	Number of Unfilled Spaces	Maximum Number of Bonds Formed
Hydrogen	1	—	—		1	1	1
Carbon	2	4	—		4	4	4
Nitrogen	2	5	—		5	3	5
Oxygen	2	6	—		6	2	2
Magnesium	2	8	2		2	6	2
Phosphorus	2	8	5		5	3	5
Sulfur	2	8	6		6	2	6

*Numbers in parentheses indicate the maximum number of electrons in their respective shells.

Precision Graphics

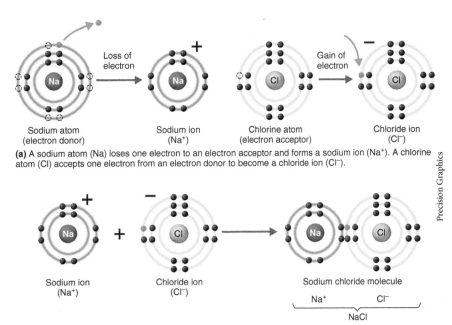

(a) A sodium atom (Na) loses one electron to an electron acceptor and forms a sodium ion (Na⁺). A chlorine atom (Cl) accepts one electron from an electron donor to become a chloride ion (Cl⁻).

Precision Graphics

(b) The sodium and chloride ions are attracted because of their opposite charges and are held together by an ionic bond to form a molecule of sodium chloride.

Figure 2 Ionic bond formation.

 What is an ionic bond?

In general, atoms form bonds in one of two ways: by either gaining or losing electrons from their outer electron shell, or by sharing outer electrons. When atoms have gained or lost outer electrons, the chemical bond is called an *ionic bond*. When outer electrons are shared, the bond is called a *covalent bond*. Although we will discuss ionic and covalent bonds separately, the kinds of bonds actually found in molecules do not belong entirely to either category. Instead, bonds range from the highly ionic to the highly covalent.

Ionic Bonds

Atoms are electrically neutral when the number of positive charges (protons) equals the number of negative charges (electrons). But when an isolated atom gains or loses electrons, this balance is upset. If the atom gains electrons, it acquires an overall negative charge; if the atom loses electrons, it acquires an overall positive charge. Such a negatively or positively charged atom (or group of atoms) is called an **ion.**

Consider the following examples. Sodium (Na) has 11 protons and 11 electrons, with one electron in its outer electron shell. Sodium tends to lose the single outer electron; it is an *electron donor* (Figure 2a). When sodium donates an electron to another atom, it is left with 11 protons and only 10 electrons and so has an overall charge of +1. This positively charged sodium atom is called a sodium

ion and is written as Na⁺. Chlorine (Cl) has a total of 17 electrons, seven of them in the outer electron shell. Because this outer shell can hold eight electrons, chlorine tends to pick up an electron that has been lost by another atom; it is an *electron acceptor* (see Figure 2a). By accepting an electron, chlorine totals 18 electrons. However, it still has only 17 protons in its nucleus. The chloride ion therefore has a charge of −1 and is written as Cl⁻.

The opposite charges of the sodium ion (Na⁺) and chloride ion (Cl⁻) attract each other. The attraction, an ionic bond, holds the two atoms together, and a molecule is formed (Figure 2b). The formation of this molecule, called sodium chloride (NaCl) or table salt, is a common example of ionic bonding. Thus, an **ionic bond** is an attraction between ions of opposite charge that holds them together to form a stable molecule. Put another way, an ionic bond is an attraction between atoms in which one atom loses electrons and another atom gains electrons. Strong ionic bonds, such as those that hold Na⁺ and Cl⁻ together in salt crystals, have limited importance in living cells. But the weaker ionic bonds formed in aqueous (water) solutions are important in biochemical reactions in microbes and other organisms. For example, weaker ionic bonds assume a role in certain antigen–antibody reactions—that is, reactions in which molecules produced by the immune system (antibodies) combine with foreign substances (antigens) to combat infection.

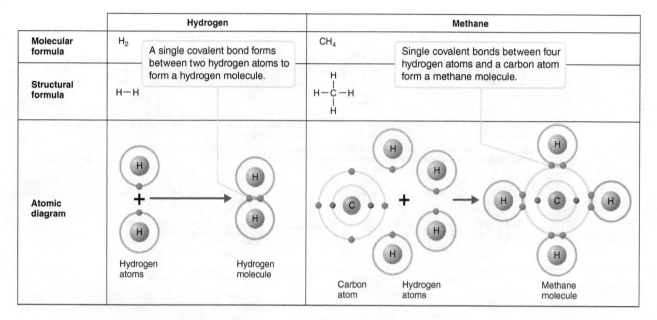

	Hydrogen	Methane
Molecular formula	H_2	CH_4
Structural formula	H—H	H—C—H (with H above and below)
Atomic diagram		

A single covalent bond forms between two hydrogen atoms to form a hydrogen molecule.

Single covalent bonds between four hydrogen atoms and a carbon atom form a methane molecule.

Hydrogen atoms → Hydrogen molecule

Carbon atom   Hydrogen atoms → Methane molecule

Figure 3 Covalent bond formation. On the right are simpler ways to represent molecules. In structural formulas, each covalent bond is written as a straight line between the symbols for two atoms. In molecular formulas, the number of atoms in each molecule is noted by subscripts.

 What is a covalent bond?

Precision Graphics

In general, an atom whose outer electron shell is less than half-filled will lose electrons and form positively charged ions, called **cations.** Examples of cations are the potassium ion (K^+), calcium ion (Ca^{2+}), and sodium ion (Na^+). When an atom's outer electron shell is more than half-filled, the atom will gain electrons and form negatively charged ions, called **anions.** Examples are the iodide ion (I^-), chloride ion (Cl^-), and sulfide ion (S^{2-}).

Covalent Bonds

A **covalent bond** is a chemical bond formed by two atoms sharing one or more pairs of electrons. Covalent bonds are stronger and far more common in organisms than are true ionic bonds. In the hydrogen molecule, H_2, two hydrogen atoms share a pair of electrons. Each hydrogen atom has its own electron plus one electron from the other atom (Figure 3a). The shared pair of electrons actually orbits the nuclei of both atoms. Therefore, the outer electron shells of both atoms are filled. Atoms that share only one pair of electrons form a *single covalent bond*. For simplicity, a single covalent bond is expressed as a single line between the atoms (H—H). Atoms that share two pairs of electrons form a *double covalent bond*, expressed as two single lines (═). A *triple covalent bond*, expressed as three single lines (≡), occurs when atoms share three pairs of electrons.

The principles of covalent bonding that apply to atoms of the same element also apply to atoms of different elements.

Methane (CH_4) is an example of covalent bonding between atoms of different elements (Figure 3b). The outer electron shell of the carbon atom can hold eight electrons but has only four; each hydrogen atom can hold two electrons but has only one. Consequently, in the methane molecule the carbon atom gains four hydrogen electrons to complete its outer shell, and each hydrogen atom completes its pair by sharing one electron from the carbon atom. Each outer electron of the carbon atom orbits both the carbon nucleus and a hydrogen nucleus. Each hydrogen electron orbits both its own nucleus and the carbon nucleus.

Elements such as hydrogen and carbon, whose outer electron shells are half-filled, form covalent bonds quite easily. In fact, in living organisms, carbon almost always forms covalent bonds; it almost never becomes an ion. *Remember:* Covalent bonds are formed by the *sharing* of electrons between atoms. Ionic bonds are formed by *attraction* between atoms that have lost or gained electrons and are therefore positively or negatively charged.

Hydrogen Bonds

Another chemical bond of special importance to all organisms is the **hydrogen bond,** in which a hydrogen atom that is covalently bonded to one oxygen or nitrogen atom is attracted to another oxygen or nitrogen atom. Such bonds are weak and do not bind atoms into molecules. However, they do serve as bridges between different molecules or between various portions of the same molecule.

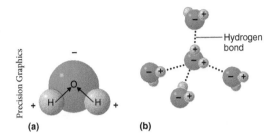

Figure 4 **Hydrogen bond formation in water.** (**a**) In a water molecule, the electrons of the hydrogen atoms are strongly attracted to the oxygen atom. Therefore, the part of the water molecule containing the oxygen atom has a slightly negative charge, and the part containing hydrogen atoms has a slightly positive charge. (**b**) In a hydrogen bond between water molecules, the hydrogen of one water molecule is attracted to the oxygen of another water molecule. Many water molecules may be attracted to each other by hydrogen bonds (black dots).

Q Which chemical elements are usually involved in hydrogen bonding?

When hydrogen combines with atoms of oxygen or nitrogen, the relatively large nucleus of these larger oxygen or nitrogen atoms has more protons and attracts the hydrogen electron more strongly than does the small hydrogen nucleus. Thus, in a molecule of water (H_2O), all the electrons tend to be closer to the oxygen nucleus than to the hydrogen nuclei. As a result, the oxygen portion of the molecule has a slightly negative charge, and the hydrogen portion of the molecule has a slightly positive charge (**Figure 4a**). When the positively charged end of one molecule is attracted to the negatively charged end of another molecule, a hydrogen bond is formed (**Figure 4b**). This attraction can also occur between hydrogen and other atoms of the same molecule, especially in large molecules. Oxygen and nitrogen are the elements most frequently involved in hydrogen bonding.

Hydrogen bonds are considerably weaker than either ionic or covalent bonds; they have only about 5% of the strength of covalent bonds. Consequently, hydrogen bonds are formed and broken relatively easily. This property accounts for the temporary bonding that occurs between certain atoms of large and complex molecules, such as proteins and nucleic acids. Even though hydrogen bonds are relatively weak, large molecules containing several hundred of these bonds have considerable strength and stability. A summary of ionic, covalent and hydrogen bonds is shown in **Table 3**.

Molecular Weight and Moles

You have seen that bond formation results in the creation of molecules. Molecules are often discussed in terms of units of measure called molecular weight and moles. The **molecular weight** of a molecule is the sum of the atomic weights of all its atoms. To relate the molecular level to the laboratory level, we use a unit called the mole. One **mole** of a substance is its molecular weight expressed

	Comparison among Ionic, Covalent, and Hydrogen Bonds
TABLE 3	
Type of Bond	**Definition and Importance**
Ionic	An attraction between ions of opposite charge that holds them together to form a stable molecule. Weaker ionic bonds are important in biochemical reactions such as antigen–antibody reactions.
Covalent	A bond formed by two atoms that share one or more pairs of electrons. Covalent bonds are the most common type of chemical bond in organisms and are responsible for holding together the atoms of most molecules in organisms.
Hydrogen	A relatively weak bond in which a hydrogen atom that is covalently bonded to one oxygen or nitrogen atom is attracted to another oxygen or nitrogen atom. Hydrogen bonds do not bind atoms into molecules, but rather serve as bridges between different molecules or different portions of the same molecule, for example, within proteins and nucleic acids.

in grams. For example, 1 mole of water weighs 18 grams because the molecular weight of H_2O is 18, or $[(2 \times 1) + 16]$.

CHECK YOUR UNDERSTANDING

✔ Differentiate an ionic bond from a covalent bond. 2

Chemical Reactions

LEARNING OBJECTIVE

3 Diagram three basic types of chemical reactions.

As we said earlier, **chemical reactions** involve the making or breaking of bonds between atoms. After a chemical reaction, the total number of atoms remains the same, but there are new molecules with new properties because the atoms have been rearranged.

Energy in Chemical Reactions

Chemical energy occurs whenever bonds between atoms are formed or broken during chemical reactions. All chemical bonds require energy when they are broken and release chemical energy when they are formed. A chemical reaction that absorbs more energy than it releases is called an **endergonic reaction** (*endo* = within), meaning that energy is directed inward. A chemical reaction that releases more energy than it absorbs is called an **exergonic reaction** (*exo* = out), meaning that energy is directed outward.

In this section we will look at three basic types of chemical reactions common to all living cells. By becoming familiar with these reactions, you will be able to understand the specific chemical reactions we will discuss later.

Bioremediation—Bacteria Clean Up Pollution

Although many bacteria have dietary requirements similar to ours—that's why they cause food spoilage—others metabolize (or chemically process) substances that are toxic to most plants and animals: heavy metals, sulfur, petroleum, and mercury.

Oil in the environment can come from natural oil that seeps from petroleum deposits, and it can also come from oil spills. Although there are oil-degrading bacteria in soil and sediments, these bacteria are in such small numbers that they cannot deal with large-scale contamination efficiently. Scientists are now working to improve the efficiency of natural pollution fighters. Using bacteria to degrade pollutants is called *bioremediation*.

One of the most promising successes for bioremediation occurred on an Alaskan beach following the *Exxon Valdez* oil spill in 1989. Several naturally occurring *Pseudomonas* bacteria are able to degrade oil for their carbon and energy requirements. In the presence of air, they remove two carbon atoms at a time from a large petroleum molecule (see the figure).

The bacteria degrade the oil too slowly to clean up an oil spill. However, scientists hit on a very simple way to speed up the process: they simply dumped ordinary nitrogen and phosphorus plant fertilizers (bioenhancers) onto a test beach. The number of oil-degrading bacteria increased compared with that on unfertilized control beaches, and oil was quickly cleared from the test beach.

This technique works on land but has not been studied in open water. A number of questions need to be addressed: Will the fertilizer stay near the oil? Will the fertilizers stimulate toxic algae?

Precision Graphics

Typical saturated hydrocarbon found in petroleum

Two-carbon unit can be metabolized in cell

Synthesis Reactions

When two or more atoms, ions, or molecules combine to form new and larger molecules, the reaction is called a **synthesis reaction.** To synthesize means to put together, and a synthesis reaction *forms new bonds.* Synthesis reactions can be expressed in the following way:

$$
\underset{\substack{\text{Atom, ion,}\\\text{or molecule A}}}{A} \quad + \quad \underset{\substack{\text{Atom, ion,}\\\text{or molecule B}}}{B} \quad \xrightarrow[\text{to form}]{\text{Combine}} \quad \underset{\substack{\text{New molecule}\\AB}}{AB}
$$

The combining substances, A and B, are called the *reactants;* the substance formed by the combination, AB, is the *product.* The arrow indicates the direction in which the reaction proceeds.

Pathways of synthesis reactions in living organisms are collectively called anabolic reactions, or simply **anabolism** (an-ab′ō-lizm). The combining of sugar molecules to form starch and of amino acids to form proteins are two examples of anabolism.

Decomposition Reactions

The reverse of a synthesis reaction is a **decomposition reaction.** To decompose means to break down into smaller parts, and in a decomposition reaction *bonds are broken.* Typically, decomposition reactions split large molecules into smaller molecules, ions, or atoms. A decomposition reaction occurs in the following way:

$$
\underset{\text{Molecule AB}}{AB} \quad \xrightarrow[\text{down into}]{\text{Breaks}} \quad \underset{\substack{\text{Atom, ion,}\\\text{or molecule A}}}{A} \quad + \quad \underset{\substack{\text{Atom, ion,}\\\text{or molecule B}}}{B}
$$

Decomposition reactions that occur in living organisms are collectively called catabolic reactions, or simply **catabolism** (ka-tab′ō-lizm). An example of catabolism is the breakdown of sucrose (table sugar) into simpler sugars, glucose and fructose, during digestion. Bacterial decomposition of petroleum is discussed in the box above.

Exchange Reactions

All chemical reactions are based on synthesis and decomposition. Many reactions, such as **exchange reactions,** are actually part synthesis and part decomposition. An exchange reaction works in the following way:

$$
AB + CD \quad \xrightarrow[\text{to form}]{\text{Recombine}} \quad AD + BC
$$

First, the bonds between A and B and between C and D are broken in a decomposition process. New bonds are then formed between A and D and between B and C in a synthesis process. For example, an exchange reaction occurs when sodium hydroxide (NaOH) and hydrochloric acid (HCl) react to form table salt (NaCl) and water (H_2O), as follows:

$$
NaOH + HCl \longrightarrow NaCl + H_2O
$$

The Reversibility of Chemical Reactions

All chemical reactions are, in theory, reversible; that is, they can occur in either direction. In practice, however, some reactions do this more easily than others. A chemical reaction that is readily reversible (when the end product can revert to the original molecules) is termed a **reversible reaction** and is indicated by two arrows, as shown here:

$$A + B \underset{\text{Breaks down into}}{\overset{\text{Combines to form}}{\rightleftharpoons}} AB$$

Some reversible reactions occur because neither the reactants nor the end products are very stable. Other reactions reverse only under special conditions:

$$A + B \underset{\text{Water}}{\overset{\text{Heat}}{\rightleftharpoons}} AB$$

Whatever is written above or below the arrows indicates the special condition under which the reaction in that direction occurs. In this case, A and B react to produce AB only when heat is applied, and AB breaks down into A and B only in the presence of water. See Figure 8 later in this chapter for another example.

CHECK YOUR UNDERSTANDING

✔ This chemical reaction below is used to remove chlorine from water. What type of reaction is it? **3**

$$HClO + Na_2SO_3 \longrightarrow Na_2SO_4 + HCl$$

Important Biological Molecules

Biologists and chemists divide compounds into two principal classes: inorganic and organic. **Inorganic compounds** are defined as molecules, usually small and structurally simple, which typically lack carbon and in which ionic bonds may play an important role. Inorganic compounds include water, molecular oxygen (O_2), carbon dioxide, and many salts, acids, and bases.

Organic compounds always contain carbon and hydrogen and typically are structurally complex. Carbon is a unique element because it has four electrons in its outer shell and four unfilled spaces. It can combine with a variety of atoms, including other carbon atoms, to form straight or branched chains and rings. Carbon chains form the basis of many organic compounds in living cells, including sugars, amino acids, and vitamins. Organic compounds are held together mostly or entirely by covalent bonds. Some organic molecules, such as polysaccharides, proteins, and nucleic acids, are very large and usually contain thousands of atoms. Such giant molecules are called *macromolecules*. In the following section we will discuss inorganic and organic compounds that are essential for cells.

Inorganic Compounds

LEARNING OBJECTIVES

4   List several properties of water that are important to living systems.

5   Define *acid, base, salt,* and *pH.*

Water

All living organisms require a wide variety of inorganic compounds for growth, repair, maintenance, and reproduction. Water is one of the most important, as well as one of the most abundant, of these compounds, and it is particularly vital to microorganisms. Outside the cell, nutrients are dissolved in water, which facilitates their passage through cell membranes. And inside the cell, water is the medium for most chemical reactions. In fact, water is by far the most abundant component of almost all living cells. Water makes up at least 5–95% of every cell, on average between 65% and 75%. Simply stated, no organism can survive without water.

Water has structural and chemical properties that make it particularly suitable for its role in living cells. As we discussed, the total charge on the water molecule is neutral, but the oxygen region of the molecule has a slightly negative charge, and the hydrogen region has a slightly positive charge (see Figure 4a). Any molecule having such an unequal distribution of charges is called a **polar molecule.** The polar nature of water gives it four characteristics that make it a useful medium for living cells.

First, every water molecule is capable of forming four hydrogen bonds with nearby water molecules (see Figure 4b). This property results in a strong attraction between water molecules. Because of this strong attraction, a great deal of heat is required to separate water molecules from each other to form water vapor; thus, water has a relatively high boiling point (100°C). Because water has such a high boiling point, it exists in the liquid state on most of the Earth's surface. Furthermore, the hydrogen bonding between water molecules affects the density of water, depending on whether it occurs as ice or a liquid. For example, the hydrogen bonds in the crystalline structure of water (ice) make ice take up more space. As a result, ice has fewer molecules than an equal volume of liquid water. This makes its crystalline

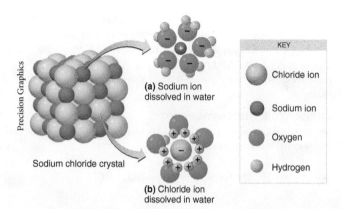

Figure 5 **How water acts as a solvent for sodium chloride (NaCl).** (**a**) The positively charged sodium ion (Na^+) is attracted to the negative part of the water molecule. (**b**) The negatively charged chloride ion (Cl^-) is attracted to the positive part of the water molecule. In the presence of water molecules, the bonds between the Na^+ and Cl^- are disrupted, and the NaCl dissolves in the water.

Q What happens during ionization?

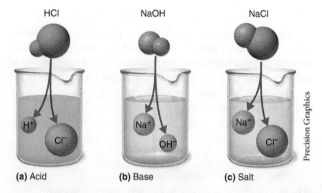

Figure 6 **Acids, bases, and salts.** (**a**) In water, hydrochloric acid (HCl) dissociates into H^+ and Cl^-. (**b**) Sodium hydroxide (NaOH), a base, dissociates into OH^- and Na^+ in water. (**c**) In water, table salt (NaCl) dissociates into positive ions (Na^+) and negative ions (Cl^-), neither of which are H^+ or OH^-.

Q How do acids and bases differ?

structure less dense than liquid water. For this reason, ice floats and can serve as an insulating layer on the surfaces of lakes and streams that harbor living organisms.

Second, the polarity of water makes it an excellent dissolving medium, or **solvent.** Many polar substances undergo **dissociation,** or separation, into individual molecules in water—that is, they dissolve. The negative part of the water molecules is attracted to the positive part of the molecules in the **solute,** or dissolving substance, and the positive part of the water molecules is attracted to the negative part of the solute molecules. Substances (such as salts) that are composed of atoms (or groups of atoms) held together by ionic bonds tend to dissociate into separate cations and anions in water. Thus, the polarity of water allows molecules of many different substances to separate and become surrounded by water molecules (**Figure 5**).

Third, polarity accounts for water's characteristic role as a reactant or product in many chemical reactions. Its polarity facilitates the splitting and rejoining of hydrogen ions (H^+) and hydroxide ions (OH^-). Water is a key reactant in the digestive processes of organisms, whereby larger molecules are broken down into smaller ones. Water molecules are also involved in synthetic reactions; water is an important source of the hydrogen and oxygen that are incorporated into numerous organic compounds in living cells.

Finally, the relatively strong hydrogen bonding between water molecules (see Figure 4b) makes water an excellent temperature buffer. Compared with many other substances, a given quantity of water requires a great gain of heat to increase its temperature and a great loss of heat to decrease its temperature. Normally, heat absorption by molecules increases their kinetic energy and thus increases their rate of motion and their reactivity. In water,

however, heat absorption first breaks hydrogen bonds rather than increasing the rate of motion. Therefore, much more heat must be applied to raise the temperature of water than to raise the temperature of a non–hydrogen-bonded liquid. The reverse is true as water cools. Thus, water more easily maintains a constant temperature than other solvents and tends to protect a cell from fluctuations in environmental temperatures.

Acids, Bases, and Salts

As we saw in Figure 5, when inorganic salts such as sodium chloride (NaCl) are dissolved in water, they undergo **ionization** or *dissociation;* that is, they break apart into ions. Substances called acids and bases show similar behavior.

An **acid** can be defined as a substance that dissociates into one or more hydrogen ions (H^+) and one or more negative ions (anions). Thus, an acid can also be defined as a proton (H^+) donor. A **base** dissociates into one or more positive ions (cations) plus one or more negatively charged hydroxide ions (OH^-) that can accept, or combine with, protons. Thus, sodium hydroxide (NaOH) is a base because it dissociates to release OH^-, which has a strong attraction for protons and is among the most important proton acceptors. A **salt** is a substance that dissociates in water into cations and anions, neither of which is H^+ or OH^-. Figure 6 shows common examples of each type of compound and how they dissociate in water.

Acid–Base Balance: The Concept of pH

An organism must maintain a fairly constant balance of acids and bases to remain healthy. For example, if a particular acid or base concentration is too high or too low, enzymes change in shape and no longer effectively promote chemical reactions in a cell. In the aqueous environment within organisms, acids dissociate into hydrogen ions (H^+) and anions. Bases, in contrast, dissociate into hydroxide ions (OH^-) and cations. The more hydrogen ions that are free in a solution, the more acidic the solution is. Conversely, the more hydroxide ions that are free in a solution, the more basic, or alkaline, it is.

Biochemical reactions—that is, chemical reactions in living systems—are extremely sensitive to even small changes in the acidity or alkalinity of the environments in which they occur. In fact, H^+ and OH^- are involved in almost all biochemical processes, and any deviation from a cell's narrow band of normal H^+ and OH^- concentrations can dramatically modify the cell's functions. For this reason, the acids and bases that are continually formed in an organism must be kept in balance.

It is convenient to express the amount of H^+ in a solution by a logarithmic **pH** scale, which ranges from 0 to 14 (Figure 7). The term *pH* means potential of hydrogen. On a logarithmic scale, a change of one whole number represents a *tenfold* change from the previous concentration. Thus, a solution of pH 1 has ten times more hydrogen ions than a solution of pH 2 and has 100 times more hydrogen ions than a solution of pH 3.

A solution's pH is calculated as $-\log_{10}[H^+]$, the negative logarithm to the base 10 of the hydrogen ion concentration (denoted by brackets), determined in moles per liter $[H^+]$. For example, if the H^+ concentration of a solution is 1.0×10^{-4} moles/liter, or 10^{-4}, its pH equals $-\log_{10}10^{-4} = -(-4) = 4$; this is about the pH value of wine. The pH values of some human body fluids and other common substances are also shown in Figure 7. In the laboratory, you will usually measure the pH of a solution with a pH meter or with chemical test papers.

Acidic solutions contain more H^+ than OH^- and have a pH lower than 7. If a solution has more OH^- than H^+, it is a basic, or alkaline, solution. In pure water, a small percentage of the molecules are dissociated into H^+ and OH^-, so it has a pH of 7. Because the concentrations of H^+ and OH^- are equal, this pH is said to be the pH of a neutral solution.

Keep in mind that the pH of a solution can be changed. We can increase its acidity by adding substances that will increase the concentration of hydrogen ions. As a living organism takes up nutrients, carries out chemical reactions, and excretes wastes, its balance of acids and bases tends to change, and the pH fluctuates. Fortunately, organisms possess natural pH **buffers,** compounds that help keep the pH from changing drastically. But the pH in our environment's water and soil can be altered by waste products from organisms, pollutants from industry, or fertilizers used in agricultural fields or gardens. When bacteria are grown in a laboratory medium, they excrete waste products such as acids that can alter the pH of the medium. If this effect were to continue, the medium would become acidic enough to inhibit bacterial enzymes and kill the bacteria. To prevent this problem, pH buffers are added to the culture medium. One very effective pH buffer for some culture media uses a mixture of K_2HPO_4 and KH_2PO_4.

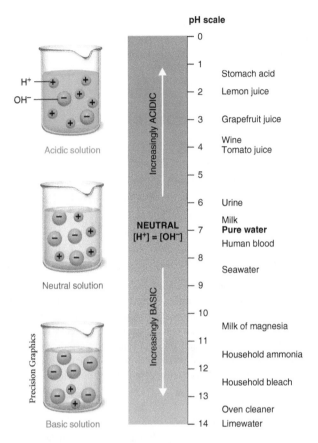

pH scale

Precision Graphics

Acidic solution

Neutral solution

Basic solution

NEUTRAL
$[H^+] = [OH^-]$

Increasingly ACIDIC

Increasingly BASIC

pH	
0	
1	Stomach acid
2	Lemon juice
3	Grapefruit juice
4	Wine / Tomato juice
5	
6	Urine
7	Milk / Pure water / Human blood
8	Seawater
9	
10	Milk of magnesia
11	Household ammonia
12	Household bleach
13	Oven cleaner
14	Limewater

Figure 7 The pH scale.
As pH values decrease from 14 to 0, the H^+ concentration increases. Thus, the lower the pH, the more acidic the solution; the higher the pH, the more basic the solution. If the pH value of a solution is below 7, the solution is acidic; if the pH is above 7, the solution is basic (alkaline). The approximate pH values of some human body fluids and common substances are shown next to the pH scale.

Q At what pH are the concentrations of H^+ and OH^- equal?

Different microbes function best within different pH ranges, but most organisms grow best in environments with a pH value between 6.5 and 8.5. Among microbes, fungi are best able to tolerate acidic conditions, whereas the prokaryotes called cyanobacteria tend to do well in alkaline habitats. *Propionibacterium acnes* (prō-pē-on-ē-bak-ti′rē-um ak′nēz), a bacterium that causes acne, has as its natural environment human skin, which tends to be slightly acidic, with a pH of about 4. *Thiobacillus ferrooxidans* (thī-ō-bä-sil′lus fer-rō-oks′i-danz) is a bacterium that metabolizes elemental sulfur and produces sulfuric acid (H_2SO_4). Its pH range for optimum growth is from 1 to 3.5. The sulfuric acid produced by this bacterium in mine water is important in dissolving uranium and copper from low-grade ore.

CHECK YOUR UNDERSTANDING

✔ Why is the polarity of a water molecule important? 4

✔ Antacids neutralize acid by the following reaction.
  $Mg(OH_2) + 2HCl \rightarrow Mgcl_2 + H_2o$
  Identify the acid, base, and salt. 5

Organic Compounds

LEARNING OBJECTIVES

6   Distinguish organic and inorganic compounds.

7   Define *functional group*.

8   Identify the building blocks of carbohydrates.

9   Differentiate simple lipids, complex lipids, and steroids.

10   Identify the building blocks and structure of proteins.

11   Identify the building blocks of nucleic acids.

12   Describe the role of ATP in cellular activities.

Inorganic compounds, excluding water, constitute about 1–1.5% of living cells. These relatively simple components, whose molecules have only a few atoms, cannot be used by cells to perform complex biological functions. Organic molecules, whose carbon atoms can combine in an enormous variety of ways with other carbon atoms and with atoms of other elements, are relatively complex and thus are capable of more complex biological functions.

Structure and Chemistry

In the formation of organic molecules, carbon's four outer electrons can participate in up to four covalent bonds, and carbon atoms can bond to each other to form straight-chain, branched-chain, or ring structures.

In addition to carbon, the most common elements in organic compounds are hydrogen (which can form one bond), oxygen (two bonds), and nitrogen (three bonds). Sulfur (two bonds) and phosphorus (five bonds) appear less often. Other elements are found, but only in relatively few organic compounds. The elements that are most abundant in living organisms are the same as those that are most abundant in organic compounds (see Table 1).

The chain of carbon atoms in an organic molecule is called the **carbon skeleton;** a huge number of combinations is possible for carbon skeletons. Most of these carbons are bonded to hydrogen atoms. The bonding of other elements with carbon and hydrogen forms characteristic **functional groups,** specific groups of atoms that are most commonly involved in chemical reactions and are responsible for most of the characteristic chemical properties and many of the physical properties of a particular organic compound (**Table 4**).

Different functional groups confer different properties on organic molecules. For example, the hydroxyl group of alcohols is hydrophilic (water-loving) and thus attracts water molecules

TABLE 4 Representative Functional Groups and the Compounds in Which They Are Found

Structure	Name of Group	Biological Importance
R—O—H	Alcohol	Lipids, carbohydates
R—C(=O)—H	Aldehyde*	Reducing sugars such as glucose; polysaccharides
R—C(=O)—R	Ketone*	Metabolic intermediates
R—CH₂—H (Methyl)	Methyl	DNA; energy metabolism
R—CH₂—NH₂	Amino	Proteins
R—C(=O)—O—R'	Ester	Bacterial and eukaryotic plasma membranes
R—CH₂—O—CH₂—R'	Ether	Archaeal plasma membranes
R—CH₂—SH	Sulfhydryl	Energy metabolism; protein structure
R—C(=O)—OH	Carboxyl	Organic acids, lipids, proteins
R—O—P(=O)(O⁻)—O⁻	Phosphate	ATP, DNA

*In an aldehyde, a $C = O$ is at the end of a molecule, in contrast to the internal $C = O$ in a ketone.

to it. This attraction helps dissolve organic molecules containing hydroxyl groups. Because the carboxyl group is a source of hydrogen ions, molecules containing it have acidic properties. Amino groups, by contrast, function as bases because they readily accept hydrogen ions. The sulfhydryl group helps stabilize the intricate structure of many proteins.

Functional groups help us classify organic compounds. For example, the —OH group is present in each of the following molecules:

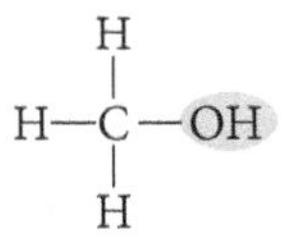

Methanol

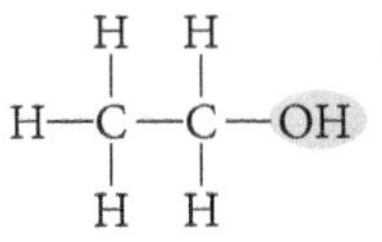

Ethanol

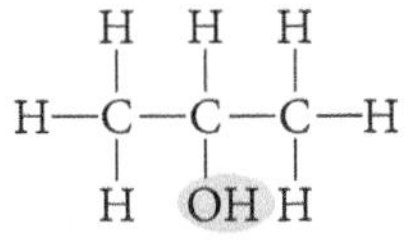

Isopropanol

Because the characteristic reactivity of the molecules is based on the —OH group, they are grouped together in a class called alcohols. The —OH group is called the *hydroxyl group* and is not to be confused with the *hydroxide ion* (OH^-) of bases. The hydroxyl group of alcohols does not ionize at neutral pH; it is covalently bonded to a carbon atom.

When a class of compounds is characterized by a certain functional group, the letter *R* can be used to stand for the remainder of the molecule. For example, alcohols in general may be written R—OH.

Frequently, more than one functional group is found in a single molecule. For example, an amino acid molecule contains both amino and carboxyl groups. The amino acid glycine has the following structure:

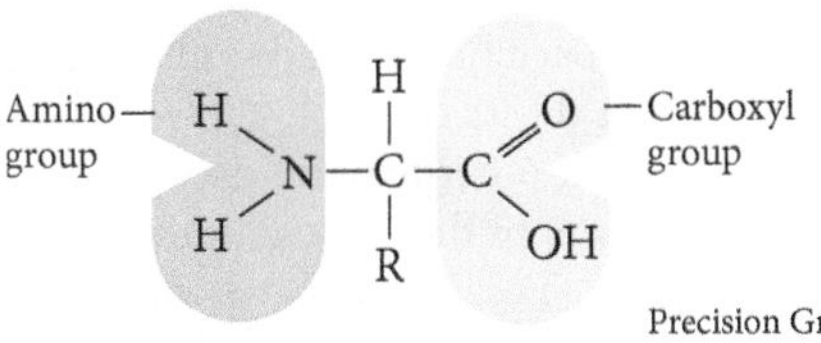

Amino group

Carboxyl group

Precision Graphics

Most of the organic compounds found in living organisms are quite complex; a large number of carbon atoms form the skeleton, and many functional groups are attached. In organic molecules, it is important that each of the four bonds of carbon be satisfied (attached to another atom) and that each of the attaching atoms have its characteristic number of bonds satisfied. Because of this, such molecules are chemically stable.

Small organic molecules can be combined into very large molecules called **macromolecules** (*macro* = large). Macromolecules are usually **polymers** (*poly* = many; *mers* = parts): polymers are formed by covalent bonding of many repeating small molecules called **monomers** (*mono* = one). When two monomers join together, the reaction usually involves the elimination of a hydrogen atom from one monomer and a hydroxyl group from the other; the hydrogen atom and the hydroxyl group combine to produce water:

$$R—OH + OH—R' \longrightarrow R—R' + H_2O$$

This type of exchange reaction is called **dehydration synthesis** (*de* = from; *hydro* = water), or a **condensation reaction,** because a molecule of water is released (Figure 8a). Such macromolecules as carbohydrates, lipids, proteins, and nucleic acids are assembled in the cell, essentially by dehydration synthesis. However, other molecules must also participate to provide energy for bond formation. ATP, the cell's chief energy provider, is discussed at the end of this chapter.

CHECK YOUR UNDERSTANDING

- Define *organic*. 6
- Add the appropriate functional group(s) to the ethyl group below to produce each of the following compounds: ethanol, acetic acid, acetaldehyde, ethanolamine, diethyl ether. 7

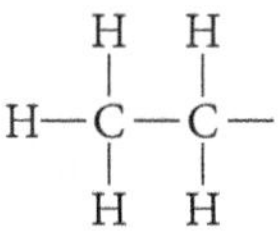

Carbohydrates

The **carbohydrates** are a large and diverse group of organic compounds that includes sugars and starches. Carbohydrates perform a number of major functions in living systems. For instance, one type of sugar (deoxyribose) is a building block of deoxyribonucleic acid (DNA), the molecule that carries hereditary information. Other sugars are needed for the cell walls. Simple carbohydrates are used in the synthesis of amino acids and fats or fatlike substances, which are used to build cell membranes and other structures. Macromolecular carbohydrates function as food reserves. The principal function of carbohydrates, however, is to fuel cell activities with a ready source of energy.

Carbohydrates are made up of carbon, hydrogen, and oxygen atoms. The ratio of hydrogen to oxygen atoms is always 2:1 in simple carbohydrates. This ratio can be seen in the formulas for the carbohydrates ribose ($C_5H_{10}O_5$), glucose ($C_6H_{12}O_6$), and sucrose ($C_{12}H_{22}O_{11}$). Although there are exceptions, the general formula for carbohydrates is $(CH_2O)_n$, where *n* indicates that there are three or more CH_2O units. Carbohydrates can be classified into three major groups on the basis of size: monosaccharides, disaccharides, and polysaccharides.

Monosaccharides

Simple sugars are called **monosaccharides** (*sacchar* = sugar); each molecule contains from three to seven carbon atoms. The number of carbon atoms in the molecule of a simple sugar is indicated by the prefix in its name. For example, simple sugars with three carbons are called trioses. There are also tetroses (four-carbon sugars), pentoses (five-carbon sugars), hexoses (six-carbon sugars), and heptoses (seven-carbon sugars). Pentoses and hexoses are extremely important to living organisms. Deoxyribose is a pentose found in DNA. Glucose, a very common hexose, is the main energy-supplying molecule of living cells.

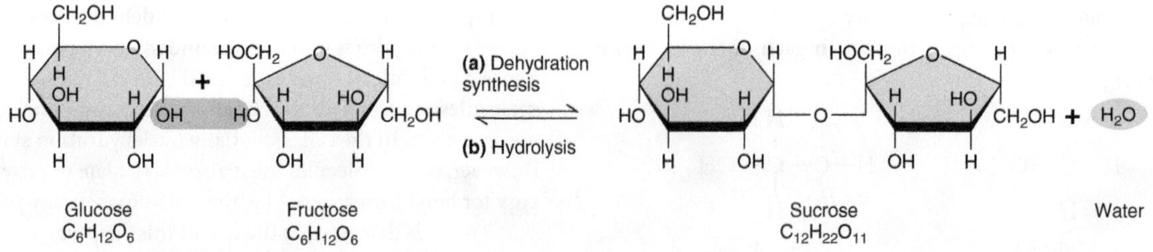

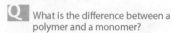

Figure 8 **Dehydration synthesis and hydrolysis.** (**a**) In dehydration synthesis (left to right), the monosaccharides glucose and fructose combine to form a molecule of the disaccharide sucrose. A molecule of water is released in the reaction. (**b**) In hydrolysis (right to left), the sucrose molecule breaks down into the smaller molecules glucose and fructose. For the hydrolysis reaction to proceed, water must be added to the sucrose.

Q What is the difference between a polymer and a monomer?

Disaccharides

Disaccharides (di = two) are formed when two monosaccharides bond in a dehydration synthesis reaction.* For example, molecules of two monosaccharides, glucose and fructose, combine to form a molecule of the disaccharide sucrose (table sugar) and a molecule of water (see Figure 8a). Similarly, the dehydration synthesis of the monosaccharides glucose and galactose forms the disaccharide lactose (milk sugar).

It may seem odd that glucose and fructose have the same chemical formula (see Figure 8), even though they are different monosaccharides. The positions of the oxygens and carbons differ in the two different molecules, and consequently the molecules have different physical and chemical properties. Two molecules with the same chemical formula but different structures and properties are called **isomers** (iso = same).

Disaccharides can be broken down into smaller, simpler molecules when water is added. This chemical reaction, the reverse of dehydration synthesis, is called **hydrolysis** ($hydro$ =water; $lysis$ = to loosen) (**Figure 8b**). A molecule of sucrose, for example, may be hydrolyzed (digested) into its components of glucose and fructose by reacting with the H^+ and OH^- of water.

The cell walls of bacterial cells are composed of disaccharides and proteins (together called peptidoglycan).

Polysaccharides

Carbohydrates in the third major group, the **polysaccharides**, consist of tens or hundreds of monosaccharides joined through dehydration synthesis. Polysaccharides often have side chains branching off the main structure and are classified as macromolecules. Like disaccharides, polysaccharides can be split apart into their constituent sugars through hydrolysis. Unlike monosaccharides and disaccharides, however, they usually lack the characteristic sweetness of sugars such as fructose and sucrose and usually are not soluble in water.

One important polysaccharide is *glycogen,* which is composed of glucose subunits and is synthesized as a storage material by animals and some bacteria. *Cellulose,* another important glucose polymer, is the main component of the cell walls of plants and most algae. Although cellulose is the most abundant carbohydrate on Earth, it can be digested by only a few organisms that have the appropriate enzyme. The polysaccharide *dextran,* which is produced as a sugary slime by certain bacteria, is used in a blood plasma substitute. *Chitin* is a polysaccharide that makes up part of the cell wall of most fungi and the exoskeletons of lobsters, crabs, and insects. *Starch* is a polymer of glucose produced by plants and used as food by humans.

Many animals, including humans, produce enzymes called *amylases* that can break the bonds between the glucose molecules in glycogen. However, this enzyme cannot break the bonds in cellulose. Bacteria and fungi that produce enzymes called *cellulases* can digest cellulose. Cellulases from the fungus *Trichoderma* (trik´ō-dėr-mä) are used for a variety of industrial purposes. One of the more unusual uses is producing stone-washed denim. Because washing the fabric with rocks would damage washing machines, cellulase is used to digest, and therefore soften, the cotton.

CHECK YOUR UNDERSTANDING

✔ Give an example of a monosaccharide, a disaccharide, and a polysaccharide. **8**

Lipids

If lipids were suddenly to disappear from the Earth, all living cells would collapse in a pool of fluid, because lipids are essential to the structure and function of membranes that separate living cells from their environment. **Lipids** (lip = fat) are a second major group of organic compounds found in living matter. Like carbohydrates, they are composed of atoms of carbon, hydrogen, and oxygen, but lipids lack the 2:1 ratio between hydrogen and oxygen atoms. Even though lipids are a very diverse group of compounds, they share one common characteristic: they are *nonpolar* molecules so, unlike water, do not have a positive and a negative end (pole). Therefore,

---

*Carbohydrates composed of 2 to about 20 monosaccharides are called **oligosaccharides** ($oligo$ = few). Disaccharides are the most common oligosaccharides.

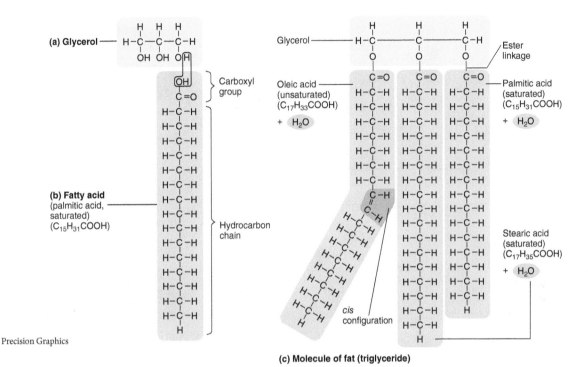

Precision Graphics

(c) **Molecule of fat (triglyceride)**

Figure 9 Structural formulas of simple lipids. (a) Glycerol. **(b)** Palmitic acid, a saturated fatty acid. **(c)** The chemical combination of a molecule of glycerol and three fatty acid molecules (palmitic, stearic, and oleic in this example) forms one molecule of fat (triglyceride) and three molecules of water in a dehydration synthesis reaction. Oleic acid is a *cis* fatty acid. The bond between glycerol and each fatty acid is called an ester linkage. The addition of three water molecules to a fat forms glycerol and three fatty acid molecules in a hydrolysis reaction.

 How do saturated and unsaturated fatty acids differ?

most lipids are insoluble in water but dissolve readily in nonpolar solvents, such as ether and chloroform. Lipids provide the structure of membranes and some cell walls and function in energy storage.

Simple Lipids

Simple lipids, called *fats* or *triglycerides,* contain an alcohol called *glycerol* and a group of compounds known as *fatty acids.* Glycerol molecules have three carbon atoms to which are attached three hydroxyl (—OH) groups (Figure 9a). Fatty acids consist of long hydrocarbon chains (composed only of carbon and hydrogen atoms) ending in a carboxyl (—COOH, organic acid) group (Figure 9b). Most common fatty acids contain an even number of carbon atoms.

A molecule of fat is formed when a molecule of glycerol combines with one to three fatty acid molecules. The number of fatty acid molecules determines whether the fat molecule is a monoglyceride, diglyceride, or triglyceride (Figure 9c). In the reaction, one to three molecules of water are formed (dehydration), depending on the number of fatty acid molecules reacting. The chemical bond formed where the water molecule is removed is called an *ester linkage.* In the reverse reaction, hydrolysis, a fat molecule is broken down into its component fatty acid and glycerol molecules.

Because the fatty acids that form lipids have different structures, there is a wide variety of lipids. For example, three molecules of fatty acid A might combine with a glycerol molecule. Or one molecule each of fatty acids A, B, and C might unite with a glycerol molecule (see Figure 9c).

The primary function of lipids is to form plasma membranes that enclose cells. A plasma membrane supports the cell and allows nutrients and wastes to pass in and out; therefore, the lipids must maintain the same viscosity, regardless of the surrounding temperature. The membrane must be about as viscous as olive oil, without getting too fluid when warmed or too thick when cooled. As everyone who has ever cooked a meal knows, animal fats (such as butter) are usually solid at room temperature, whereas vegetable oils are usually liquid at room temperature. The difference in their respective melting points is due to the degrees of saturation of the fatty acid chains. A fatty acid is said to be *saturated* when it has no double bonds, in which case the carbon skeleton contains the maximum number of hydrogen atoms (see Figure 9c and Figure 10a). Saturated chains become solid more easily because they are relatively straight and are thus able to pack together more closely than unsaturated chains. The double bonds of *unsaturated* chains create kinks in the chain, which keep the chains apart from

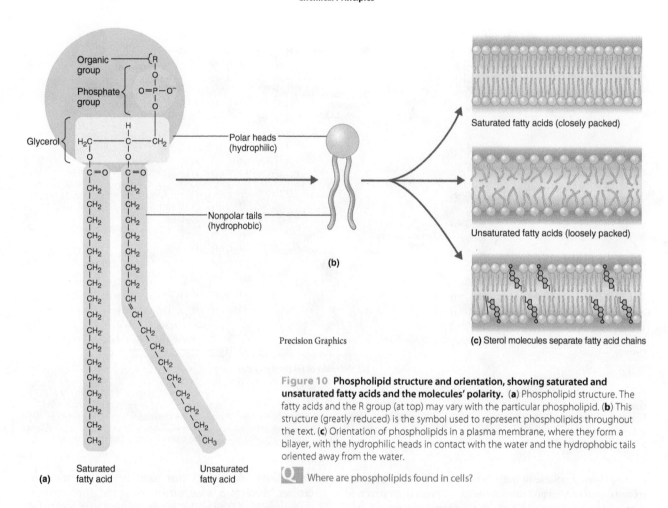

(b)

Precision Graphics

Saturated fatty acids (closely packed)

Unsaturated fatty acids (loosely packed)

(c) Sterol molecules separate fatty acid chains

(a)   Saturated   Unsaturated
        fatty acid   fatty acid

Figure 10 Phospholipid structure and orientation, showing saturated and unsaturated fatty acids and the molecules' polarity. (a) Phospholipid structure. The fatty acids and the R group (at top) may vary with the particular phospholipid. **(b)** This structure (greatly reduced) is the symbol used to represent phospholipids throughout the text. **(c)** Orientation of phospholipids in a plasma membrane, where they form a bilayer, with the hydrophilic heads in contact with the water and the hydrophobic tails oriented away from the water.

Q   Where are phospholipids found in cells?

one another (Figure 10b). Note in Figure 9c that the H atoms on either side of the double bond in oleic acid are on the same side of the unsaturated fatty acid. Such an unsaturated fatty acid is called a *cis* fatty acid. If, instead, the H atoms are on opposite sides of the double bond, the unsaturated acid is called a *trans* fatty acid.

Complex Lipids

Complex lipids contain such elements as phosphorus, nitrogen, and sulfur, in addition to the carbon, hydrogen, and oxygen found in simple lipids. The complex lipids called *phospholipids* are made up of glycerol, two fatty acids, and, in place of a third fatty acid, a phosphate group bonded to one of several organic groups (see Figure 10a). Phospholipids are the lipids that build membranes; they are essential to a cell's survival. Phospholipids have polar as well as nonpolar regions (Figure 10a and b). When placed in water, phospholipid molecules twist themselves in such a way that all polar (hydrophilic) portions orient themselves toward the polar water molecules, with which they then form hydrogen bonds. (Recall that *hydrophilic* means

water-loving.) This forms the basic structure of a plasma membrane (Figure 10c). Polar portions consist of a phosphate group and glycerol. In contrast to the polar regions, all nonpolar (hydrophobic) parts of the phospholipid make contact only with the nonpolar portions of neighboring molecules. (*Hydrophobic* means water-fearing.) Nonpolar portions consist of fatty acids. This characteristic behavior makes phospholipids particularly suitable for their role as a major component of the membranes that enclose cells. Phospholipids enable the membrane to act as a barrier that separates the contents of the cell from the water-based environment in which it lives.

Some complex lipids are useful in identifying certain bacteria. For example, the cell wall of *Mycobacterium tuberculosis* (mī-kō-bak-ti′rē-um tü-bėr-kū-lō′sis), the bacterium that causes tuberculosis, is distinguished by its lipid-rich content. The cell wall contains complex lipids such as waxes and glycolipids (lipids with carbohydrates attached) that give the bacterium distinctive staining characteristics. Cell walls rich in such complex lipids are characteristic of all members of the genus *Mycobacterium*.

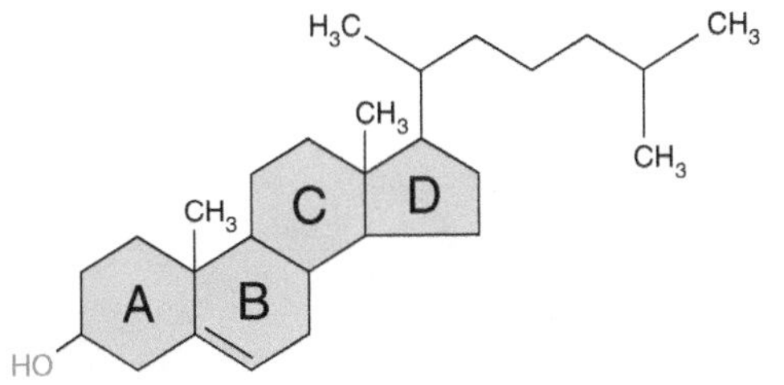

Figure 11 Cholesterol, a steroid. Note the four "fused" carbon rings (labeled A–D), which are characteristic of steroid molecules. The hydrogen atoms attached to the carbons at the corners of the rings have been omitted. The —OH group (colored red) makes this molecule a sterol.

Q Where are sterols found in cells?

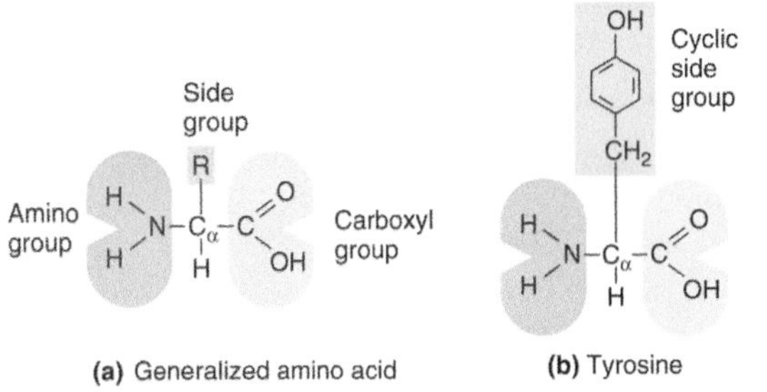

Figure 12 Amino acid structure. (**a**) The general structural formula for an amino acid. The alpha-carbon (C_α) is shown in the center. Different amino acids have different R groups, also called side groups. (**b**) Structural formula for the amino acid tyrosine, which has a cyclic side group.

(**a**) Generalized amino acid   (**b**) Tyrosine

Q What distinguishes one amino acid from another?

Precision Graphics

Steroids

Steroids are structurally very different from lipids. Figure 11 shows the structure of the steroid cholesterol, with the four interconnected carbon rings that are characteristic of steroids. When an —OH group is attached to one of the rings, the steroid is called a *sterol* (an alcohol). Sterols are important constituents of the plasma membranes of animal cells and of one group of bacteria (mycoplasmas), and they are also found in fungi and plants. The sterols separate the fatty acid chains and thus prevent the packing that would harden the plasma membrane at low temperatures (see Figure 10c).

CHECK YOUR UNDERSTANDING

✔ How do simple lipids differ from complex lipids? 9

Proteins

Proteins are organic molecules that contain carbon, hydrogen, oxygen, and nitrogen. Some also contain sulfur. If you were to separate and weigh all the groups of organic compounds in a living cell, the proteins would tip the scale. Hundreds of different proteins can be found in any single cell, and together they make up 50% or more of a cell's dry weight.

Proteins are essential ingredients in all aspects of cell structure and function. *Enzymes* are the proteins that speed up biochemical reactions. But proteins have other functions as well. *Transporter proteins* help transport certain chemicals into and out of cells. Other proteins, such as the *bacteriocins* produced by many bacteria, kill other bacteria. Certain *toxins,* called exotoxins, produced by some disease-causing microorganisms are also proteins. Some proteins play a role in the *contraction* of animal muscle cells and the *movement* of microbial and other types of cells. Other proteins are integral parts of *cell structures* such as walls, membranes, and cytoplasmic components. Still others, such as the *hormones* of certain organisms, have regulatory functions. Proteins called *antibodies* play a role in vertebrate immune systems.

Amino Acids

Just as monosaccharides are the building blocks of larger carbohydrate molecules, and just as fatty acids and glycerol are the building blocks of fats, **amino acids** are the building blocks of proteins. Amino acids contain at least one carboxyl (—COOH) group and one amino (—NH_2) group attached to the same carbon atom, called an alpha-carbon (written C_α) (Figure 12a). Such amino acids are called *alpha-amino acids*. Also attached to the alpha-carbon is a side group (R group), which is the amino acid's distinguishing feature. The side group can be a hydrogen atom, an unbranched or branched chain of atoms, or a ring structure that is cyclic (all carbon) or heterocyclic (when an atom other than carbon is included in the ring). Figure 12b shows the structural formula of tyrosine, an amino acid that has a cyclic side group. The side group can contain functional groups, such as the sulfhydryl group (—SH), the hydroxyl group (—OH), or additional carboxyl or amino groups. These side groups and the carboxyl and alpha-amino groups affect the total structure of a protein, described later. The structures and standard abbreviations of the 20 amino acids found in proteins are shown in Table 5.

Most amino acids exist in either of two configurations called **stereoisomers,** designated by D and L. These configurations are mirror images, corresponding to "right-handed" (D) and "left-handed" (L) three-dimensional shapes (Figure 13). The amino acids found in proteins are always the L-isomers (except for glycine, the simplest amino acid, which does not have stereoisomers). However, D-amino acids occasionally occur in nature—for example, in certain bacterial cell walls and antibiotics. (Many other kinds of organic molecules also can exist in D and L forms. One example is the sugar glucose, which occurs in nature as D-glucose.)

Although only 20 different amino acids occur naturally in proteins, a single protein molecule can contain from 50 to hundreds of amino acid molecules, which can be arranged in an almost infinite number of ways to make proteins of different lengths, compositions, and structures. The number of proteins is practically endless, and every living cell produces many different proteins.

TABLE 5 The 20 Amino Acids Found in Proteins*

Glycine (Gly)

Hydrogen atom

Alanine (Ala)

Unbranched chain

Valine (Val)

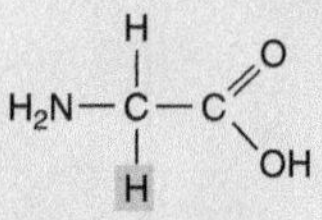

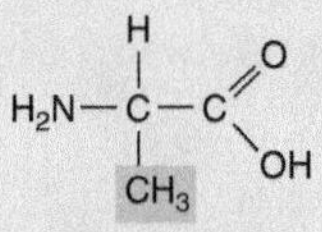

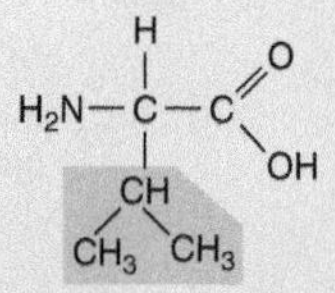

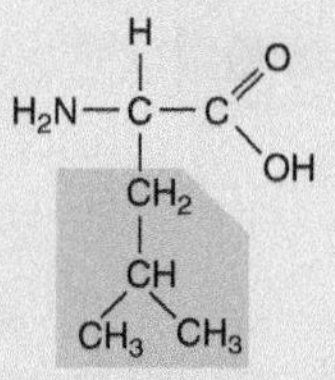

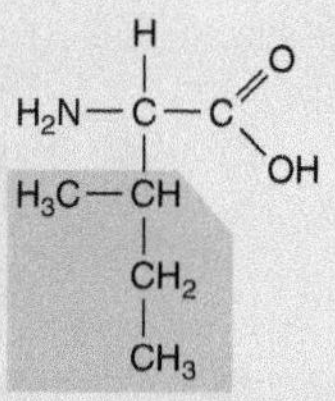

Branched chain

Leucine (Leu)

Branched chain

Isoleucine (Ile)

Branched chain

Serine (Ser)

Hydroxyl (—OH) group

Threonine (Thr)

Hydroxyl (—OH) group

Cysteine (Cys)

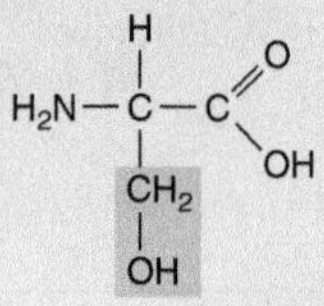

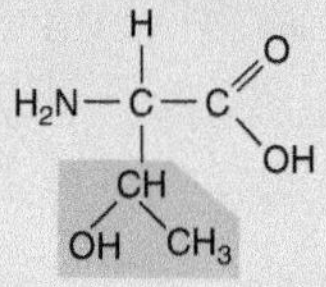

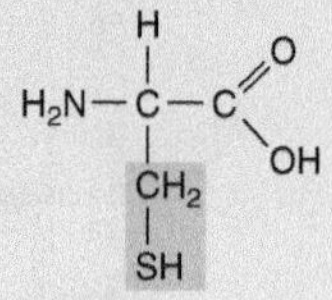

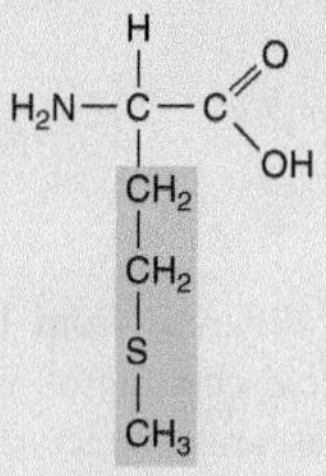

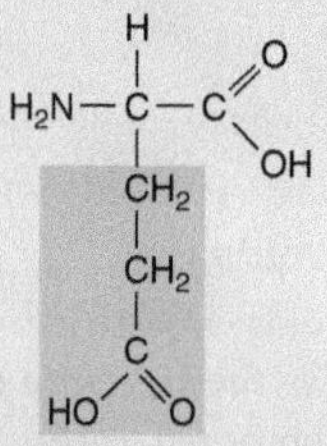

Sulphur-containing (—SH) group

Methionine (Met)

Thioether (SC) group

Glutamic acid (Glu)

Additional carboxyl (—COOH) group, acidic

Aspartic acid (Asp)

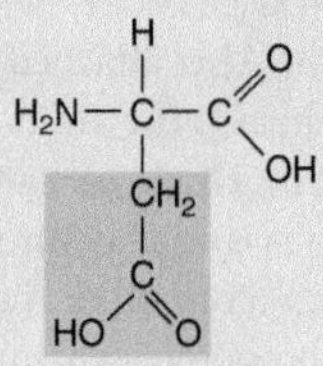

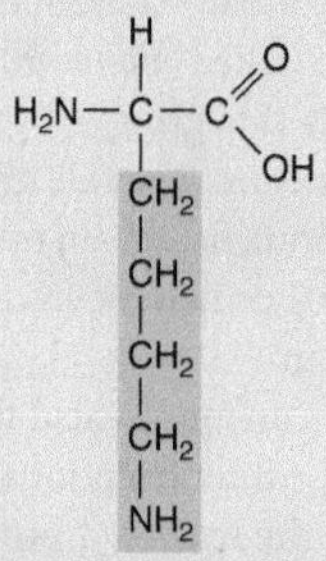

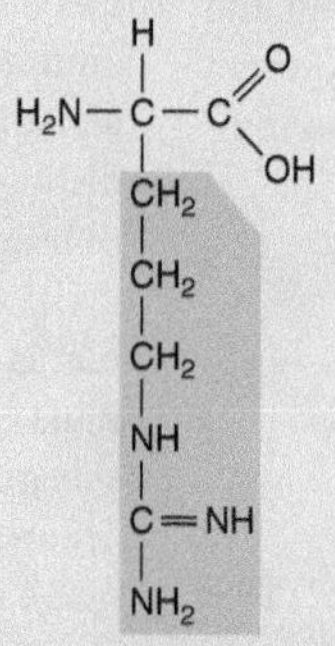

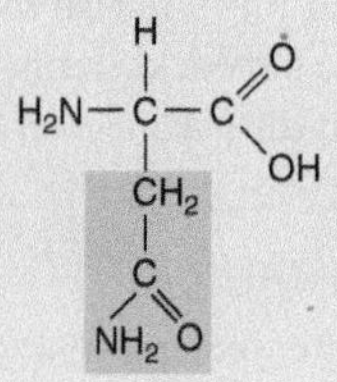

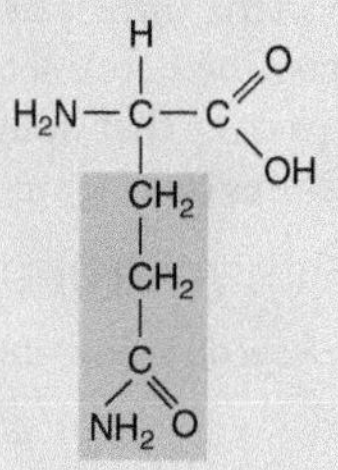

Addtional Carboxyl (—COOH) group, acidic

Lysine (Lys)

Addtional amino (—NH₂) group, basic

Arginine (Arg)

Addtional amino (—NH₂) group, basic

Asparagine (Asn)

Addtional amino (—NH₂) group, basic

Glutamine (Gln)

Addtional amino (—NH₂) group, basic

Phenylalanine (Phe)

Cyclic

Tyrosine (Tyr)

Cyclic

Histidine (His)

Heterocyclic

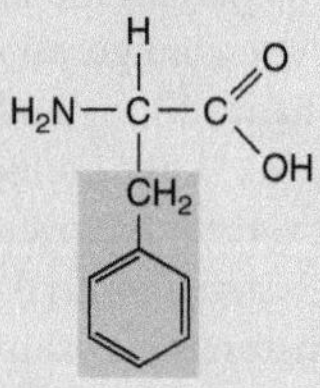

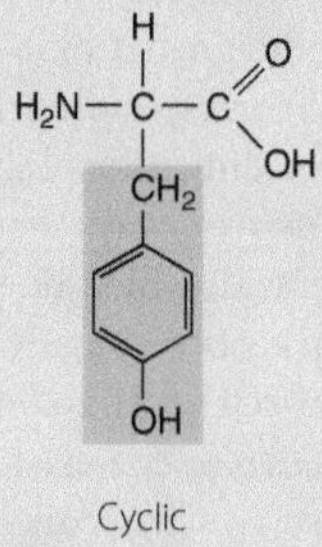

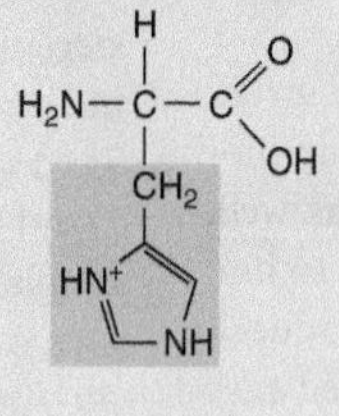

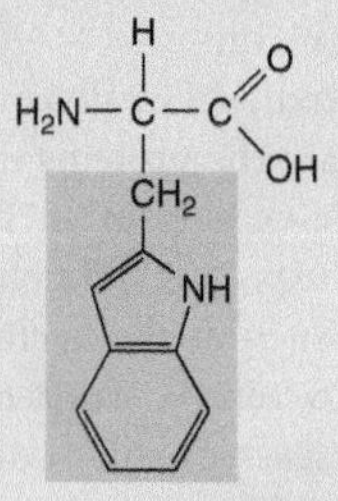

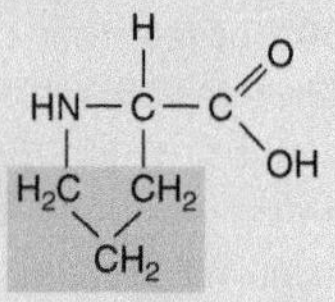

Tryptophan (Trp)

Heterocyclic

Proline (Pro)

Heterocyclic

*Shown are the amino acid names, including the three-letter abbreviation in parentheses (above), their structural formulas (center), and characteristic R group (below). Note that cysteine and methionine are the only amino acids that contain sulfur.

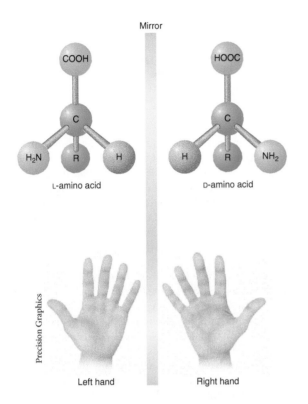

Mirror

L-amino acid

D-amino acid

Left hand

Right hand

Precision Graphics

Figure 13 The L- and D-isomers of an amino acid, shown with ball-and-stick models. The two isomers, like left and right hands, are mirror images of each other and cannot be superimposed on one another. (Try it!)

Q Which isomer is always found in proteins?

Peptide Bonds

Amino acids bond between the carbon atom of the carboxyl (—COOH) group of one amino acid and the nitrogen atom of the amino (—NH$_2$) group of another (Figure 14). The bonds between amino acids are called **peptide bonds.** For every peptide bond formed between two amino acids, one water molecule is released; thus, peptide bonds are formed by dehydration synthesis. The resulting compound in Figure 14 is called a *dipeptide* because it consists of two amino acids joined by a peptide bond. Adding another amino acid to a dipeptide would form a *tripeptide.* Further additions of amino acids would produce a long, chainlike molecule called a *peptide* (4–9 amino acids) or *polypeptide* (10–2000 or more amino acids).

Levels of Protein Structure

Proteins vary tremendously in structure. Different proteins have different architectures and different three-dimensional shapes. This variation in structure is directly related to their diverse functions.

Clinical Case

While Jonathan is in intensive care, his wife, DeeAnn, and adult daughter talk with his physician and an investigator from the Centers for Disease Control and Prevention (CDC) to find the source of Jonathan's *B. anthracis* infection. Environmental investigations uncover *B. anthracis* at Jonathan's home, in his van, and in his workplace, but neither his wife nor children show signs of infection. His bandmates are also tested; they are all negative for *B. anthracis*. The CDC investigator explains to Jonathan's family that *B. anthracis* forms endospores that can survive in soil for up to 60 years. It is rare in humans; however, grazing animals and people who handle their hides or other by-products can become infected. *B. anthracis* cells have capsules that are composed of poly-D-glutamic acid.

Why are the capsules resistant to digestion by phagocytes? (Phagocytes are white blood cells that engulf and destroy bacteria.)

When a cell makes a protein, the polypeptide chain folds spontaneously to assume a certain shape. One reason for folding of the polypeptide is that some parts of a protein are attracted to water and other parts are repelled by it. In practically every case, the function of a protein depends on its ability to recognize and bind to some other molecule. For example, an enzyme binds specifically with its substrate. A hormonal protein binds to a receptor on a cell whose function it will alter. An antibody binds to an antigen (foreign substance) that has invaded the body. The unique shape of each protein permits it to interact with specific other molecules in order to carry out specific functions.

Proteins are described in terms of four levels of organization: primary, secondary, tertiary, and quaternary. The *primary structure* is the unique sequence in which the amino acids are linked together to form a polypeptide chain (Figure 15a). This sequence is genetically determined. Alterations in sequence can have profound metabolic effects. For example, a single incorrect amino acid in a blood protein can produce the deformed hemoglobin molecule characteristic of sickle cell disease. But proteins do not exist as long, straight chains. Each polypeptide chain folds and coils in specific ways into a relatively compact structure with a characteristic three-dimensional shape.

A protein's *secondary structure* is the localized, repetitious twisting or folding of the polypeptide chain. This aspect of a protein's shape results from hydrogen bonds joining the atoms of peptide bonds at different locations along the polypeptide chain.

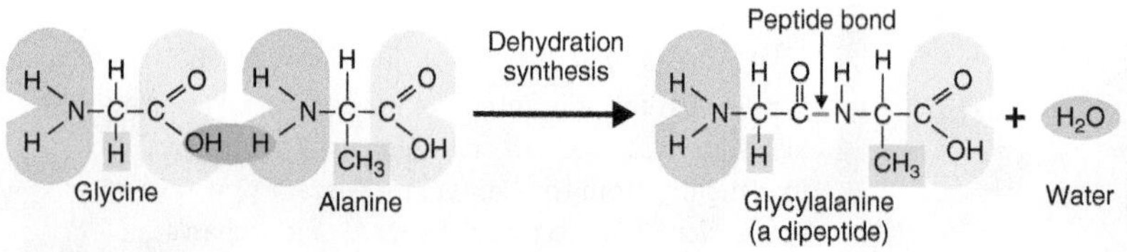

Figure 14 **Peptide bond formation by dehydration synthesis.** The amino acids glycine and alanine combine to form a dipeptide. The newly formed bond between the carbon atom of glycine and the nitrogen atom of alanine is called a peptide bond.

Q How are amino acids related to proteins?

Precision Graphics

The two types of secondary protein structures are clockwise spirals called *helices* (singular: *helix*) and pleated sheets, which form from roughly parallel portions of the chain (Figure 15b). Both structures are held together by hydrogen bonds between oxygen or nitrogen atoms that are part of the polypeptide's backbone.

Tertiary structure refers to the overall three-dimensional structure of a polypeptide chain (Figure 15c). The folding is not repetitive or predictable, as in secondary structure. Whereas secondary structure involves hydrogen bonding between atoms of the amino and carboxyl groups involved in the peptide bonds, tertiary structure involves several interactions between various amino acid side groups in the polypeptide chain. For example, amino acids with nonpolar (hydrophobic) side groups usually interact at the core of the protein, out of contact with water. This *hydrophobic interaction* helps contribute to tertiary structure. Hydrogen bonds between side groups, and ionic

bonds between oppositely charged side groups, also contribute to tertiary structure. Proteins that contain the amino acid cysteine form strong covalent bonds called *disulfide bridges*. These bridges form when two cysteine molecules are brought close together by the folding of the protein. Cysteine molecules contain sulfhydryl groups ($-SH$), and the sulfur of one cysteine molecule bonds to the sulfur on another, forming (by the removal of hydrogen atoms) a disulfide bridge ($S-S$) that holds parts of the protein together.

Some proteins have a *quaternary structure,* which consists of an aggregation of two or more individual polypeptide chains (subunits) that operate as a single functional unit. Figure 15d shows a hypothetical protein consisting of two polypeptide chains. More commonly, proteins have two or more kinds of polypeptide subunits. The bonds that hold a quaternary structure together are basically the same as those that maintain tertiary structure. The overall shape of a protein may be globular (compact and roughly spherical) or fibrous (threadlike).

If a protein encounters a hostile environment in terms of temperature, pH, or salt concentrations, it may unravel and lose its characteristic shape. This process is called **denaturation**. As a result of denaturation, the protein is no longer functional.

The proteins we have been discussing are *simple proteins,* which contain only amino acids. *Conjugated proteins* are combinations of amino acids with other organic or inorganic components. Conjugated proteins are named by their non–amino acid component. Thus, glycoproteins contain sugars, nucleoproteins contain nucleic acids, metalloproteins contain metal atoms, lipoproteins contain lipids, and phosphoproteins contain phosphate groups. Phosphoproteins are important regulators of activity in eukaryotic cells. Bacterial synthesis of phosphoproteins may be important for the survival of bacteria such as *Legionella pneumophila* that grow inside host cells.

CHECK YOUR UNDERSTANDING

✔ What two functional groups are in all amino acids? 10

Nucleic Acids

In 1944, three American microbiologists—Oswald Avery, Colin MacLeod, and Maclyn McCarty—discovered that a substance called **deoxyribonucleic acid (DNA)** is the substance of which genes are made. Nine years later, James Watson and Francis Crick,

Clinical Case

The host's phagocytes cannot easily digest D-forms of amino acids, such as D-glutamic acid found in the capsules of *B. anthracis*. Therefore, infection can develop. The CDC investigator's mention of animal hides gives DeeAnn an idea. Jonathan plays West African drums called *djembe;* the drum skins are made from dried imported goat hides from West Africa. Although most of these hides are legally imported, some slip through the cracks. It's possible that the hides on Jonathan's drums have been illegally imported and therefore have not been inspected by the U.S. Department of Agriculture. To create *djembe* drums, the hides are soaked in water, stretched over the drum body, and then scraped and sanded. The scraping and sanding generates a large amount of aerosolized dust as the hides dry. Sometimes this dust contains *B. anthracis* endospores, which contain dipicolinic acid.

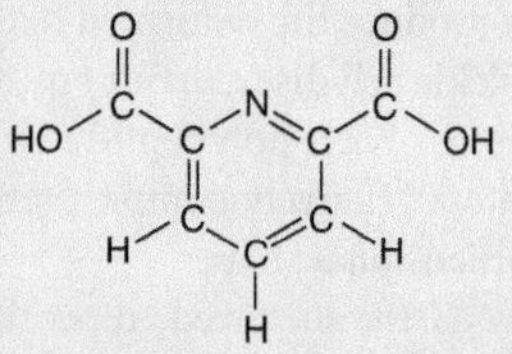

What is the functional group in dipicolinic acid? See the figure above.

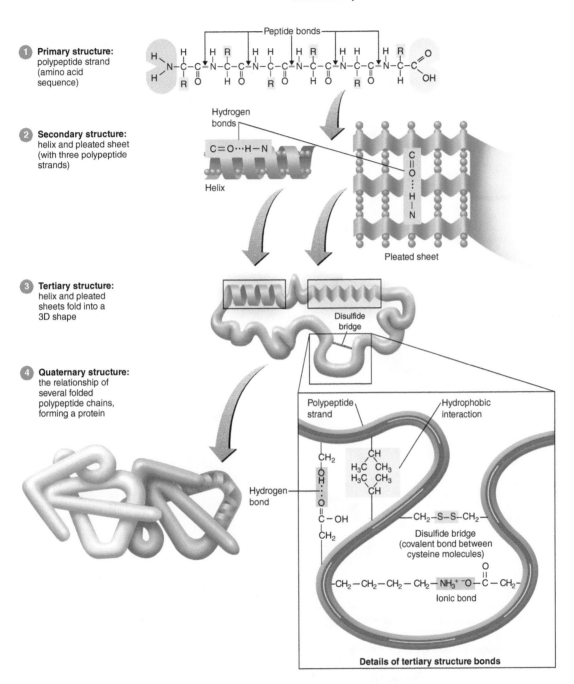

1 **Primary structure:** polypeptide strand (amino acid sequence)

2 **Secondary structure:** helix and pleated sheet (with three polypeptide strands)

3 **Tertiary structure:** helix and pleated sheets fold into a 3D shape

4 **Quaternary structure:** the relationship of several folded polypeptide chains, forming a protein

Peptide bonds

Hydrogen bonds

C=O···H—N

Helix

Pleated sheet

Disulfide bridge

Details of tertiary structure bonds

Polypeptide strand

Hydrophobic interaction

Hydrogen bond

CH₂—S—S—CH₂

Disulfide bridge (covalent bond between cysteine molecules)

—CH₂—CH₂—CH₂—CH₂—NH₃⁺ ⁻O—C—CH₂—

Ionic bond

Figure 15 Protein structure. 1 Primary structure, the amino acid sequence. 2 Secondary structures: helix and pleated sheet. 3 Tertiary structure, the overall three-dimensional folding of a polypeptide chain. 4 Quaternary structure, the relationship between several polypeptide chains that make up a protein. Shown here is the quaternary structure of a hypothetical protein composed of two polypeptide chains.

Q What property of a protein enables it to carry out specific functions?

Precision Graphics

49

The Structure of DNA

Adenine and Thymine (as well as Cytosine and Guanine, not shown here) are nitrogenous bases or nucleobases.

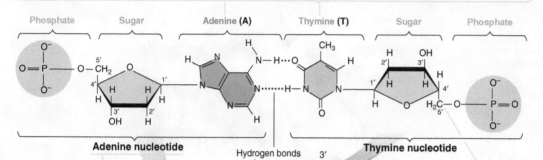

| Phosphate | Sugar | Adenine (A) | Thymine (T) | Sugar | Phosphate |

Adenine nucleotide

Hydrogen bonds

Thymine nucleotide

Individual DNA nucleotides are composed of a deoxyribose sugar molecule covalently bonded to a phosphate group at the 5′ carbon, and to a nitrogen-containing base at the 1′ carbon. The two nucleotides shown here are held together by hydrogen bonds.

Sugar-phosphate backbone

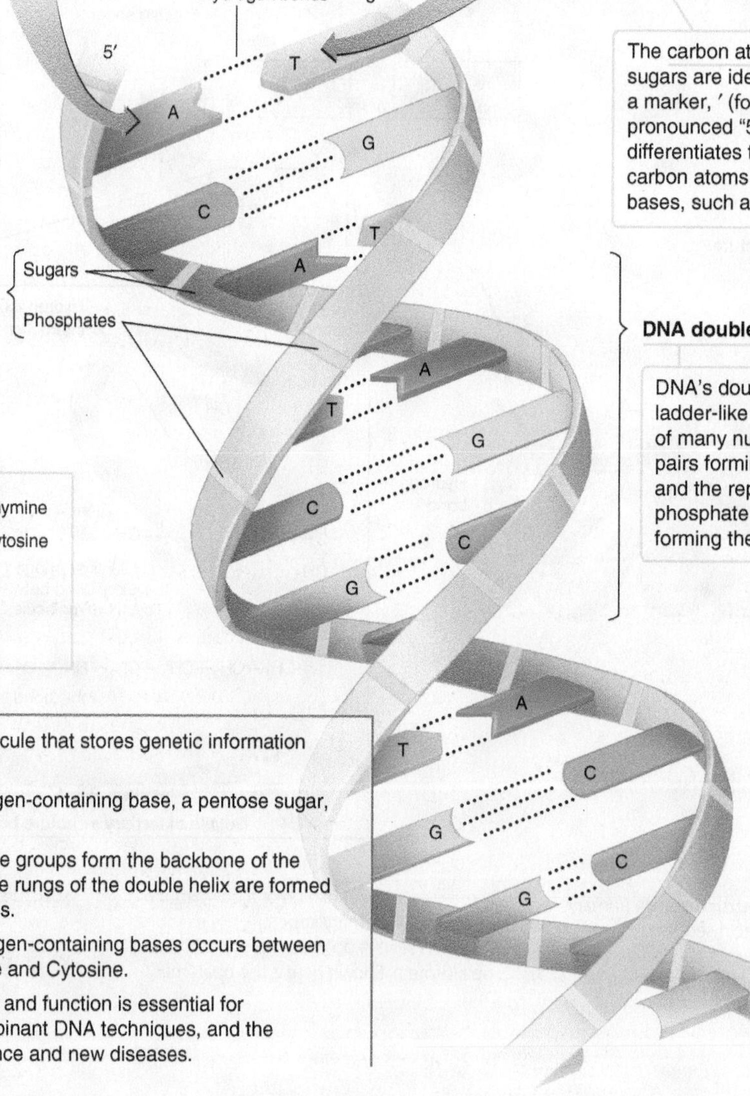

The sugar-phosphate backbone of one strand is upside down, or antiparallel, relative to the backbone of the other strand.

The carbon atoms in the sugars are identified by adding a marker, ′ (for example, 5′, pronounced "5-prime"). This differentiates them from the carbon atoms in the nucleobases, such as Thymine.

DNA double helix

DNA's double-helical, ladder-like form is made up of many nucleotides base pairs forming the rungs, and the repeating sugar-phosphate combination, forming the backbone.

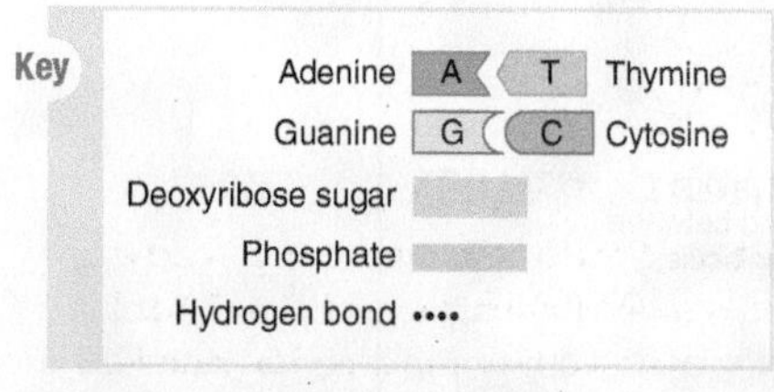

Sugars

Phosphates

Key

Adenine	A ◄ T	Thymine
Guanine	G ◄ C	Cytosine
Deoxyribose sugar		
Phosphate		
Hydrogen bond	••••	

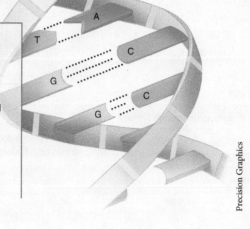

KEYCONCEPTS

- DNA is a double-stranded molecule that stores genetic information in all cells.

- A nucleotide consists of a nitrogen-containing base, a pentose sugar, and a phosphate group.

- Alternating sugar and phosphate groups form the backbone of the double helix (twisted ladder); the rungs of the double helix are formed by the nitrogen-containing bases.

- Complementary pairing of nitrogen-containing bases occurs between Adenine and Thymine; Guanine and Cytosine.

- Familiarity with DNA's structure and function is essential for understanding genetics, recombinant DNA techniques, and the emergence of antibiotic resistance and new diseases.

Precision Graphics

working with molecular models and X-ray information supplied by Maurice Wilkins and Rosalind Franklin, identified the physical structure of DNA. In addition, Crick suggested a mechanism for DNA replication and how it works as the hereditary material. DNA and another substance called **ribonucleic acid (RNA)** are together referred to as **nucleic acids** because they were first discovered in the nuclei of cells. Just as amino acids are the structural units of proteins, nucleotides are the structural units of nucleic acids.

Each **nucleotide** has three parts: a nitrogen-containing base, a pentose (five-carbon) sugar (either **deoxyribose** or **ribose**), and a phosphate group (phosphoric acid). The nitrogen-containing bases are cyclic compounds made up of carbon, hydrogen, oxygen, and nitrogen atoms. The bases are named adenine (A), thymine (T), cytosine (C), guanine (G), and uracil (U). A and G are double-ring structures called **purines,** whereas T, C, and U are single-ring structures referred to as **pyrimidines.**

Nucleotides are named according to their nitrogen-containing base. Thus, a nucleotide containing thymine is a *thymine nucleotide,* one containing adenine is an *adenine nucleotide,* and so on. The term **nucleoside** refers to the combination of a purine or pyrimidine plus a pentose sugar; it does not contain a phosphate group.

DNA

According to the model proposed by Watson and Crick, a DNA molecule consists of two long strands wrapped around each other to form a **double helix** (Figure 16). The double helix looks like a twisted ladder, and each strand is composed of many nucleotides.

Every strand of DNA composing the double helix has a "backbone" consisting of alternating deoxyribose sugar and phosphate groups. The deoxyribose of one nucleotide is joined to the phosphate group of the next. The nitrogen-containing bases make up the rungs of the ladder. Note that the purine A is always paired with the pyrimidine T and that the purine G is always paired with the pyrimidine C. The bases are held together by hydrogen bonds; A and T are held by two hydrogen bonds, and G and C by three. DNA does not contain uracil (U).

The order in which the nitrogen base pairs occur along the backbone is extremely specific and in fact contains the genetic instructions for the organism. Nucleotides form genes, and a single DNA molecule may contain thousands of genes. Genes determine all hereditary traits, and they control all the activities that take place within cells.

One very important consequence of nitrogen-containing base pairing is that if the sequence of bases of one strand is known, then the sequence of the other strand is also known. For example, if one strand has the sequence . . . ATGC . . . , then the other strand has the sequence . . . TACG . . . . Because the sequence of bases of one strand is determined by the sequence of bases of the other, the bases are said to be *complementary.* The actual transfer of information becomes possible because of DNA's unique structure.

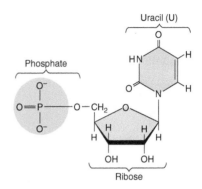

Figure 17 A uracil nucleotide of RNA.

[Q] How are DNA and RNA similar in structure?

RNA

RNA, the second principal kind of nucleic acid, differs from DNA in several respects. Whereas DNA is double-stranded, RNA is usually single-stranded. The five-carbon sugar in the RNA nucleotide is ribose, which has one more oxygen atom than deoxyribose. Also, one of RNA's bases is uracil (U) instead of thymine (Figure 17). The other three bases (A, G, C) are the same as DNA. Three major kinds of RNA have been identified in cells. They are **messenger RNA (mRNA), ribosomal RNA (rRNA),** and **transfer RNA (tRNA).** Each type of RNA has a specific role in protein synthesis.

A comparison between DNA and RNA is presented in Table 6

CHECK YOUR UNDERSTANDING

✔ How do DNA and RNA differ? 11

Adenosine Triphosphate (ATP)

Adenosine triphosphate (ATP) is the principal energy-carrying molecule of all cells and is indispensable to the life of the cell. It stores the chemical energy released by some chemical reactions, and it provides the energy for reactions that require energy. ATP consists of an adenosine unit, composed of adenine and ribose, with three phosphate groups (Ⓟ) attached (Figure 18). In other words, it is an adenine nucleotide (also called adenosine monophosphate, or AMP) with two extra phosphate groups. ATP is called a high-energy molecule because it releases a large amount of usable energy when the third phosphate group is hydrolyzed to become **adenosine diphosphate (ADP).** This reaction can be represented as follows:

Adenosine — Ⓟ — Ⓟ — Ⓟ + H_2O ⇌
Adenosine   Water
triphosphate

Adenosine — Ⓟ — Ⓟ + Ⓟ$_i$ + Energy
Adenosine   Inorganic
diphosphate   phosphate

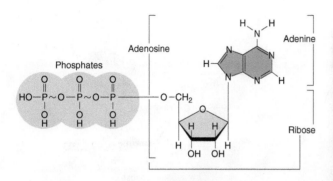

Figure 18 The structure of ATP. High-energy phosphate bonds are indicated by wavy lines. When ATP breaks down to ADP and inorganic phosphate, a large amount of chemical energy is released for use in other chemical reactions.

Q How is ATP similar to a nucleotide in RNA? In DNA?

A cell's supply of ATP at any particular time is limited. Whenever the supply needs replenishing, the reaction goes in the reverse direction; the addition of a phosphate group to ADP and the input of energy produces more ATP. The energy required to attach the terminal phosphate group to ADP is

Clinical Case Resolved

The functional group in dipicolinic acid is carboxyl. *B. anthracis* infection is contracted by contact, ingestion, or inhalation of the endospores. In Jonathan's case, the process of stretching, scraping, and sanding the goat hides had created dust that settled on the drum skin and any surrounding crevices. *B. anthracis* endospores became airborne, or aerosolized, whenever Jonathan beat on the drum. He makes a full recovery, and from now on he makes certain that all parts of any drum he purchases have been legally imported .

supplied by the cell's various oxidation reactions, particularly the oxidation of glucose. ATP can be stored in every cell, where its potential energy is not released until needed.

CHECK YOUR UNDERSTANDING

✔ Which can provide more energy for a cell and why: ATP or ADP? **1224**

TABLE 6 Comparison between DNA and RNA

Backbone	DNA	RNA
Strands	Double-stranded in cells and most DNA viruses to form a double helix; single-stranded in some viruses (parvoviruses).	Single-stranded in cells and most RNA viruses; double-stranded in some viruses (reoviruses).
Composition	The sugar is deoxyribose.	The sugar is ribose.
	The nitrogen-containing bases are adenine (A), thymine (T), cytosine (C), and guanine (G).	The nitrogen-containing bases are adenine (A), uracil (U), cytosine (C), and guanine (G).
Function	Determines all hereditary traits.	Protein synthesis.

Study Outline

Test your understanding with quizzes, microbe review, and a chapter post-test at www.masteringmicrobiology.com.

Introduction

1. The science of the interaction between atoms and molecules is called chemistry.
2. The metabolic activities of microorganisms involve complex chemical reactions.

3. Microbes break down nutrients to obtain energy and to make new cells.

The Structure of Atoms

1. An atom is the smallest unit of a chemical element that exhibits the properties of that element.
2. Atoms consist of a nucleus, which contains protons and neutrons, and electrons, which move around the nucleus.
3. The atomic number is the number of protons in the nucleus; the total number of protons and neutrons is the atomic weight.

Chemical Elements

4. Atoms with the same number of protons and the same chemical behavior are classified as the same chemical element.
5. Chemical elements are designated by abbreviations called chemical symbols.
6. About 26 elements are commonly found in living cells.
7. Atoms that have the same atomic number (are of the same element) but different atomic weights are called isotopes.

Electronic Configurations

8. In an atom, electrons are arranged around the nucleus in electron shells.
9. Each shell can hold a characteristic maximum number of electrons.
10. The chemical properties of an atom are due largely to the number of electrons in its outermost shell.

How Atoms Form Molecules: Chemical Bonds

1. Molecules are made up of two or more atoms; molecules consisting of at least two different kinds of atoms are called compounds.
2. Atoms form molecules in order to fill their outermost electron shells.
3. Attractive forces that bind two atoms together are called chemical bonds.
4. The combining capacity of an atom—the number of chemical bonds the atom can form with other atoms—is its valence.

Ionic Bonds

5. A positively or negatively charged atom or group of atoms is called an ion.
6. A chemical attraction between ions of opposite charge is called an ionic bond.
7. To form an ionic bond, one ion is an electron donor, and the other ion is an electron acceptor.

Covalent Bonds

8. In a covalent bond, atoms share pairs of electrons.
9. Covalent bonds are stronger than ionic bonds and are far more common in organic molecules.

Hydrogen Bonds

10. A hydrogen bond exists when a hydrogen atom covalently bonded to one oxygen or nitrogen atom is attracted to another oxygen or nitrogen atom.
11. Hydrogen bonds form weak links between different molecules or between parts of the same large molecule.

Molecular Weight and Moles)

12. The molecular weight is the sum of the atomic weights of all the atoms in a molecule.
13. A mole of an atom, ion, or molecule is equal to its atomic or molecular weight expressed in grams.

Chemical Reactions

1. Chemical reactions are the making or breaking of chemical bonds between atoms.
2. A change of energy occurs during chemical reactions.
3. Endergonic reactions require more energy than they release; exergonic reactions release more energy.

4. In a synthesis reaction, atoms, ions, or molecules are combined to form a larger molecule.
5. In a decomposition reaction, a larger molecule is broken down into its component molecules, ions, or atoms.
6. In an exchange reaction, two molecules are decomposed, and their subunits are used to synthesize two new molecules.
7. The products of reversible reactions can readily revert to form the original reactants.

■ Important Biological Molecules

Inorganic Compounds

1. Inorganic compounds are usually small, ionically bonded molecules.
2. Water and many common acids, bases, and salts are examples of inorganic compounds.

Water

3. Water is the most abundant substance in cells.
4. Because water is a polar molecule, it is an excellent solvent.
5. Water is a reactant in many of the decomposition reactions of digestion.
6. Water is an excellent temperature buffer.

Acids, Bases, and Salts

7. An acid dissociates into H^+ and anions.
8. A base dissociates into OH^- and cations.
9. A salt dissociates into negative and positive ions, neither of which is H^+ or OH^-.

Acid–Base Balance: The Concept of pH

10. The term *pH* refers to the concentration of H^+ in a solution.
11. A solution of pH 7 is neutral; a pH value below 7 indicates acidity; pH above 7 indicates alkalinity.
12. The pH inside a cell and in culture media is stabilized with pH buffers.

Organic Compounds

1. Organic compounds always contain carbon and hydrogen.
2. Carbon atoms form up to four bonds with other atoms.
3. Organic compounds are mostly or entirely covalently bonded, and many of them are large molecules.

Structure and Chemistry

4. A chain of carbon atoms forms a carbon skeleton.
5. Functional groups of atoms are responsible for most of the properties of organic molecules.
6. The letter *R* may be used to denote the remainder of an organic molecule.
7. Frequently encountered classes of molecules are R—OH (alcohols) and R—COOH (organic acids).
8. Small organic molecules may combine into very large molecules called macromolecules.
9. Monomers usually bond together by dehydration synthesis, or condensation reactions, that form water and a polymer.
10. Organic molecules may be broken down by hydrolysis, a reaction involving the splitting of water molecules.

Carbohydrates

11. Carbohydrates are compounds consisting of atoms of carbon, hydrogen, and oxygen, with hydrogen and oxygen in a 2:1 ratio.

12. Carbohydrates include sugars and starches.

13. Carbohydrates can be classified as monosaccharides, disaccharides, and polysaccharides.

14. Monosaccharides contain from three to seven carbon atoms.

15. Isomers are two molecules with the same chemical formula but different structures and properties—for example, glucose ($C_6H_{12}O_6$) and fructose ($C_6H_{12}O_6$).

16. Monosaccharides may form disaccharides and polysaccharides by dehydration synthesis.

Lipids

17. Lipids are a diverse group of compounds distinguished by their insolubility in water.

18. Simple lipids (fats) consist of a molecule of glycerol and three molecules of fatty acids.

19. A saturated lipid has no double bonds between carbon atoms in the fatty acids; an unsaturated lipid has one or more double bonds. Saturated lipids have higher melting points than unsaturated lipids.

20. Phospholipids are complex lipids consisting of glycerol, two fatty acids, and a phosphate group.

21. Steroids have carbon ring structures; sterols have a functional hydroxyl group.

Proteins

22. Amino acids are the building blocks of proteins.

23. Amino acids consist of carbon, hydrogen, oxygen, nitrogen, and sometimes sulfur.

24. Twenty amino acids occur naturally in proteins.

25. By linking amino acids, peptide bonds (formed by dehydration synthesis) allow the formation of polypeptide chains.

26. Proteins have four levels of structure: primary (sequence of amino acids), secondary (helices or pleats), tertiary (overall three-dimensional structure of a polypeptide), and quaternary (two or more polypeptide chains).

27. Conjugated proteins consist of amino acids combined with inorganic or other organic compounds.

Nucleic Acids

28. Nucleic acids—DNA and RNA—are macromolecules consisting of repeating nucleotides.

29. A nucleotide is composed of a pentose, a phosphate group, and a nitrogen-containing base. A nucleoside is composed of a pentose and a nitrogen-containing base.

30. A DNA nucleotide consists of deoxyribose (a pentose) and one of the following nitrogen-containing bases: thymine or cytosine (pyrimidines) or adenine or guanine (purines).

31. DNA consists of two strands of nucleotides wound in a double helix. The strands are held together by hydrogen bonds between purine and pyrimidine nucleotides: AT and GC.

32. Genes consist of sequences of nucleotides.

33. An RNA nucleotide consists of ribose (a pentose) and one of the following nitrogen-containing bases: cytosine, guanine, adenine, or uracil.

Adenosine Triphosphate (ATP)

34. ATP stores chemical energy for various cellular activities.

35. When the bond to ATP's terminal phosphate group is hydrolyzed, energy is released.

36. The energy from oxidation reactions is used to regenerate ATP from ADP and inorganic phosphate.

Study Questions

Answers to the Review and Multiple Choice questions can be found at the end of this chapter.

Review

1. What is a chemical element?
2. DRAW IT Diagram the electronic configuration of a carbon atom.
3. What type of bond holds the following atoms together?
   a. Li^+ and Cl^- in LiCl
   b. carbon and oxygen atoms in methanol
   c. oxygen atoms in O_2
   d. a hydrogen atom of one nucleotide to a nitrogen or oxygen atom of another nucleotide in:

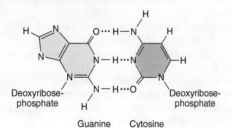

Guanine   Cytosine

4. Classify the following types of chemical reactions.
   a. glucose + fructose → sucrose + H_2O
   b. lactose → glucose + galactose
   c. $NH_4Cl + H_2O → NH_4OH + HCl$
   d. ATP ⇌ ADP + P_i

5. Bacteria use the enzyme urease to obtain nitrogen in a form they can use from urea in the following reaction:

$$CO(NH_2)_2 \quad + \quad H_2O \quad → \quad 2NH_3 \quad + \quad CO_2$$
$$\text{Urea} \qquad\qquad\qquad\qquad \text{Ammonia} \quad \text{Carbon dioxide}$$

What purpose does the enzyme serve in this reaction? What type of reaction is this?

6. Classify the following as subunits of either a carbohydrate, lipid, protein, or nucleic acid.
   a. $CH_3—(CH_2)_7—CH=CH—(CH_2)_7—COOH$
      Oleic acid

b.

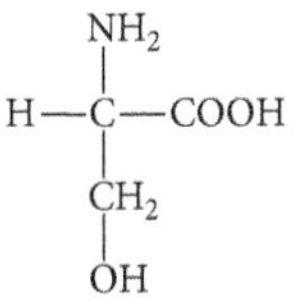

      NH_2

H—C—COOH

     CH_2

     OH

Serine

c. $C_6H_{12}O_6$

d. Thymine nucleotide

7. DRAW IT The artificial sweetener aspartame, or NutraSweet, is made by joining aspartic acid to methylated phenylalanine, as shown below.

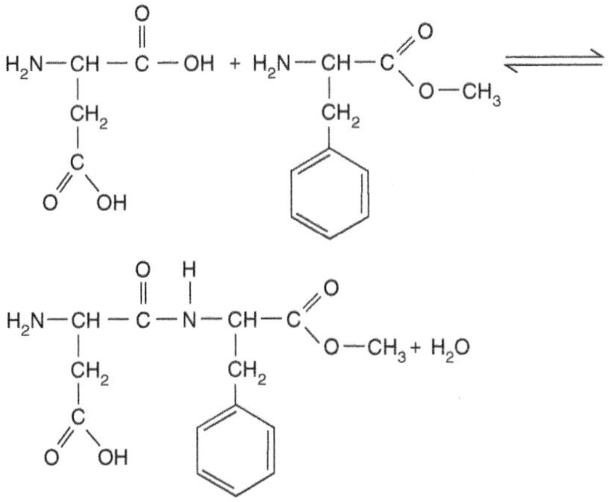

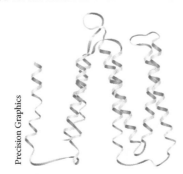

a. What types of molecules are aspartic acid and phenylalanine?
b. What direction is the hydrolysis reaction (left to right or right to left)?
c. What direction is the dehydration synthesis reaction?
d. Circle the atoms involved in the formation of water.
e. Identify the peptide bond.

8. DRAW IT The following diagram shows the bacteriorhodopsin protein. Indicate the regions of primary, secondary, and tertiary structure. Does this protein have quaternary structure?

Precision Graphics

9. DRAW IT Draw a simple lipid, and show how it could be modified to a phospholipid.

10. NAME IT What type of microorganism has a chitin cell wall, has DNA that is contained in a nucleus, and has ergosterol in its plasma membrane?

Multiple Choice

Radioisotopes are frequently used to label molecules in a cell. The fate of atoms and molecules in a cell can then be followed. This process is the basis for questions 1–3.

1. Assume *E. coli* bacteria are grown in a nutrient medium containing the radioisotope ^{16}N. After a 48-hour incubation period, the ^{16}N would most likely be found in the *E. coli*'s
  a. carbohydrates.
  b. lipids.
  c. proteins.
  d. water.
  e. none of the above

2. If *Pseudomonas* bacteria are supplied with radioactively labeled cytosine, after a 24-hour incubation period this cytosine would most likely be found in the cells'
  a. carbohydrates.
  b. DNA.
  c. lipids.
  d. water.
  e. proteins.

3. If *E. coli* were grown in a medium containing the radioactive isotope ^{32}P, the ^{32}P would be found in all of the following molecules of the cell *except*
  a. ATP.
  b. carbohydrates.
  c. DNA.
  d. plasma membrane.
  e. none of the above

4. The optimum pH of *Thiobacillus* bacteria (pH 3,) is _____ times more acid than blood (pH 7).
  a. 4
  b. 10
  c. 100
  d. 1000
  e. 10,000

5. The best definition of ATP is that it is
  a. a molecule stored for food use.
  b. a molecule that supplies energy to do work.
  c. a molecule stored for an energy reserve.
  d. a molecule used as a source of phosphate.

6. Which of the following is an organic molecule?
  a. H_2O (water)
  b. O_2 (oxygen)
  c. $C_{18}H_{29}SO_3$ (Styrofoam)
  d. FeO (iron oxide)
  e. $F_2C{=}CF_2$ (Teflon)

Classify each of the molecules on the left as an acid, base, or salt. The dissociation products of the molecules are shown to help you.

7. $HNO_3 \rightarrow H^+ + NO_3^-$ **a.** acid
8. $H_2SO_4 \rightarrow 2H^+ + SO_4^{2-}$ **b.** base
9. $NaOH \rightarrow Na^+ + OH^-$ **c.** salt
10. $MgSO_4 \rightarrow Mg^{2+} + SO_4^{2-}$

Critical Thinking

1. When you blow bubbles into a glass of water, the following reactions take place:

$$H_2O + CO_2 \xrightarrow{A} H_2CO_3 \xrightarrow{B} H^+ + HCO_3^-$$

   a. What type of reaction is A?
   b. What does reaction B tell you about the type of molecule H_2CO_3 is?

2. What are the common structural characteristics of ATP and DNA molecules?

3. What happens to the relative amount of unsaturated lipids in the plasma membrane when E. coli bacteria grown at 25°C are then grown at 37°C?

4. Giraffes, termites, and koalas eat only plant matter. Because animals cannot digest cellulose, how do you suppose these animals get nutrition from the leaves and wood they eat?

Clinical Applications

1. Ralstonia bacteria make poly-β-hydroxybutyrate (PHB), which is used to make a biodegradable plastic. PHB consists of many of the monomers shown below. What type of molecule is PHB? What is the most likely reason a cell would store this molecule?

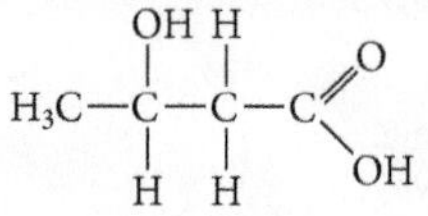

$$H_3C-\underset{\underset{H}{|}}{\overset{\overset{OH}{|}}{C}}-\underset{\underset{H}{|}}{\overset{\overset{H}{|}}{C}}-C\overset{\overset{O}{\diagup\!\!\!\!}}{\underset{\diagdown\!\!\!\!}{OH}}$$

2. Thiobacillus ferrooxidans was responsible for destroying buildings in the Midwest by causing changes in the earth. The original rock, which contained lime ($CaCO_3$) and pyrite (FeS_2), expanded as bacterial metabolism caused gypsum ($CaSO_4$) crystals to form. How did T. ferrooxidans bring about the change from lime to gypsum?

3. Newborn babies are tested for phenylketonuria (PKU), an inherited disease. Individuals with this disease are missing an enzyme to convert phenylalanine (phe) to tyrosine; the resulting accumulation of phe can cause mental retardation, brain damage, and seizures. The Guthrie test for PKU involves culturing Bacillus subtilis, which requires phe to grow. The bacteria are grown on media with a drop of the baby's blood.
   a. What type of chemical is phenylalanine?
   b. What does "no growth" in the Guthrie test mean?
   c. Why must individuals with PKU avoid the sweetener aspartame?

4. The antibiotic amphotericin B causes leaks in cells by combining with sterols in the plasma membrane. Would you expect to use amphotericin B against a bacterial infection? A fungal infection? Offer a reason why amphotericin B has severe side effects in humans.

5. You can smell sulfur when boiling eggs. What amino acids do you expect in the egg?

Answers to Review and Multiple Choice Study Questions

Review

1. Atoms with the same atomic number and chemical behavior are classified as chemical elements.

2.

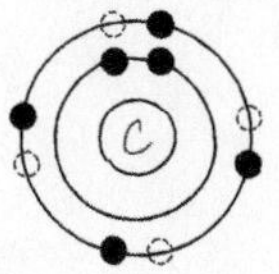

3. a. Ionic
   b. Single covalent bond
   c. Double covalent bonds
   d. Hydrogen bond

4. a. Synthesis reaction, condensation, or dehydration
   b. Decomposition reaction, digestion, or hydrolysis
   c. Exchange reaction
   d. Reversible reaction

5. The enzyme lowers the activation energy required for the reaction and therefore speeds up this decomposition reaction.

6. a. Lipid
   b. Protein
   c. Carbohydrate
   d. Nucleic acid

7. a. Amino acids
   b. Right to left
   c. Left to right

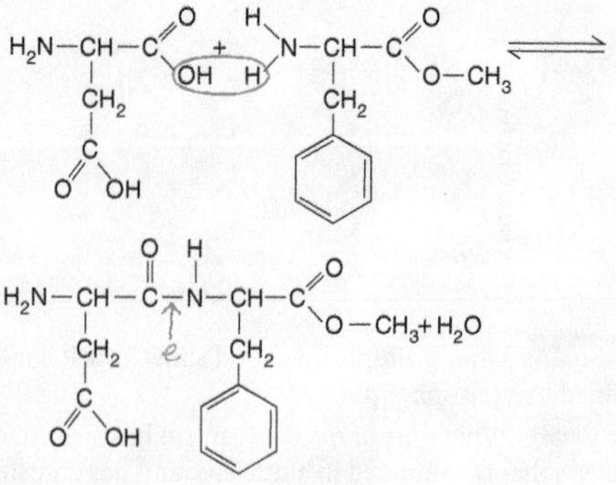

The entire protein shows tertiary structure, held by disulfide bonds. No quaternary structure.

8.

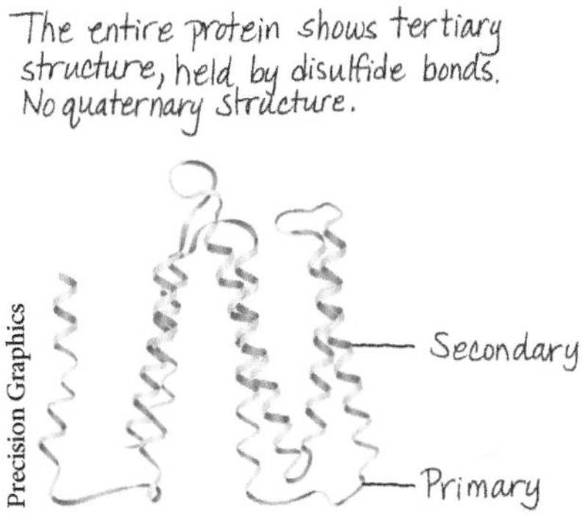
The entire protein shows tertiary structure, held by disulfide bonds. No quaternary structure.
Secondary
Primary
Precision Graphics

9.

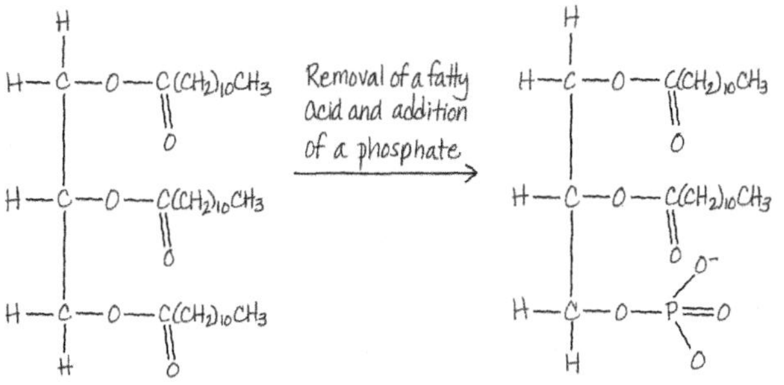
Removal of a fatty acid and addition of a phosphate

10. Fungus

Multiple Choice

1. c **2.** b **3.** b **4.** e **5.** b **6.** c **7.** a **8.** a **9.** b **10.** c

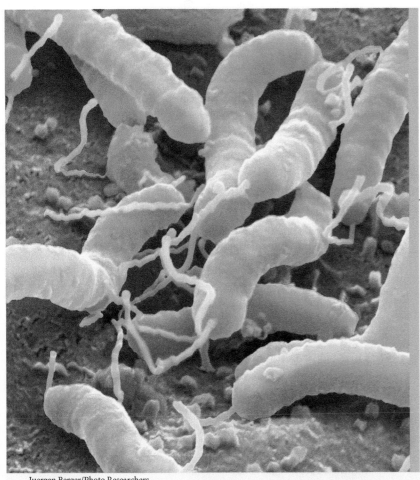

Juergen Berger/Photo Researchers

Observing Microorganisms Through a Microscope

Visualize microbiology and check your understanding with a pre-test at www.masteringmicrobiology.com.

Microorganisms are much too small to be seen with the unaided eye; they must be observed with a microscope. The word *microscope* is derived from the Latin word *micro* (small) and the Greek word *skopos* (to look at). Modern microbiologists use microscopes that produce, with great clarity, magnifications that range from ten to thousands of times greater than those of van Leeuwenhoek's single lens. This chapter describes how different types of microscopes function and why one type might be used in preference to another. *Helicobacter pylori*, shown in the photograph, is a spiral-shaped bacterium that was first seen in cadaver stomachs in 1886. The bacterium was largely ignored until the resolving ability of microscopes was improved. Microscopic examination of these bacteria is described in the Clinical Case.

Some microbes are more readily visible than others because of their larger size or more easily observable features. Many microbes, however, must undergo several staining procedures before their cell walls, capsules, and other structures lose their colorless natural state. The last part of this chapter explains some of the more commonly used methods of preparing specimens for examination through a light microscope.

You may wonder how we are going to sort, count, and measure the specimens we will study. To answer these questions, this chapter opens with a discussion of how to use the metric system for measuring microbes.

From Chapter 3 of *Microbiology: An Introduction*, Eleventh Edition. Gerard J. Tortora, Berdell R. Funke, Christine L. Case.

Units of Measurement

LEARNING OBJECTIVES

1 List the metric units of measurement that are used for microorganisms.

Because microorganisms and their component parts are so very small, they are measured in units that are unfamiliar to many of us in everyday life. When measuring microorganisms, we use the metric system. The standard unit of length in the metric system is the meter (m). A major advantage of the metric system is that the units are related to each other by factors of 10. Thus, 1 m equals

From: "Discovery by Jaworski of Helicobacter pylori and its pathogenetic role in peptic ulcer, gastritis and gastric cancer." JW Konturek. *J Physiol Pharmacol.* 2003 Dec;54 Suppl 3:23–41

Clinical Case: Microscopic Mayhem

Maryanne, a 42-year-old marketing executive and mother of three occasionally works from home, but she always feels that she isn't getting as much done at home as she does in the office. She has been experiencing recurrent stomach pain, which seems to be getting worse. She jokes with her husband that he should buy stock in Pepto-Bismol, because she buys so much of it. At her husband's urging, she finally makes an appointment to see her primary care physician. After hearing that Maryanne feels better immediately after taking Pepto-Bismol, the doctor suspects Maryanne may have a peptic ulcer associated with *Helicobacter pylori*.

5 μm

What is *Helicobacter pylori*? Read on to find out.

10 decimeters (dm) or 100 centimeters (cm) or 1000 millimeters (mm). Units in the U.S. system of measure do not have the advantage of easy conversion by a single factor of 10. For example, we use 3 feet or 36 inches to equal 1 yard.

Microorganisms and their structural components are measured in even smaller units, such as micrometers and nanometers. A **micrometer (μm)** is equal to 0.000001 m (10^{-6} m). The prefix *micro* indicates that the unit following it should be divided by 1 million, or 10^6 (see the "Exponential Notation" section in Appendix). A **nanometer (nm)** is equal to 0.000000001 m (10^{-9} m). Angstrom (Å) was previously used for 10^{-10} m, or 0.1 nm.

Table 1 presents the basic metric units of length and some of their U.S. equivalents. In Table 1, you can compare the microscopic units of measurement with the commonly known macroscopic units of measurement, such as centimeters, meters, and kilometers. If you look ahead to Figure 2, you will see the relative sizes of various organisms on the metric scale.

CHECK YOUR UNDERSTANDING

✔ If a microbe measures 10 μm in length, how long is it in nanometers? 1

Microscopy: The Instruments

LEARNING OBJECTIVES

2 Diagram the path of light through a compound microscope.

3 Define *total magnification* and *resolution*.

4 Identify a use for darkfield, phase-contrast, differential interference contrast, fluorescence, confocal, two-photon, and scanning acoustic microscopy, and compare each with brightfield illumination.

5 Explain how electron microscopy differs from light microscopy.

6 Identify one use for the TEM, SEM, and scanned-probe microscopes.

The simple microscope used by van Leeuwenhoek in the seventeenth century had only one lens and was similar to a magnifying

TABLE **1** Metric Units of Length and U.S. Equivalents

Metric Unit	Meaning of Prefix	Metric Equivalent	U.S. Equivalent
1 kilometer (km)	*kilo* = 1000	1000 m = 10^3 m	3280.84 ft or 0.62 mi; 1 mi = 1.61 km
1 meter (m)		Standard unit of length	39.37 in or 3.28 ft or 1.09 yd
1 decimeter (dm)	*deci* = 1/10	0.1 m = 10^{-1} m	3.94 in
1 centimeter (cm)	*centi* = 1/100	0.01 m = 10^{-2} m	0.394 in; 1 in = 2.54 cm
1 millimeter (mm)	*milli* = 1/1000	0.001 m = 10^{-3} m	
1 micrometer (μm)	*micro* = 1/1,000,000	0.000001 m = 10^{-6} m	
1 nanometer (nm)	*nano* = 1/1,000,000,000	0.000000001 m = 10^{-9} m	
1 picometer (pm)	*pico* = 1/1,000,000,000,000	0.000000000001 m = 10^{-12} m	

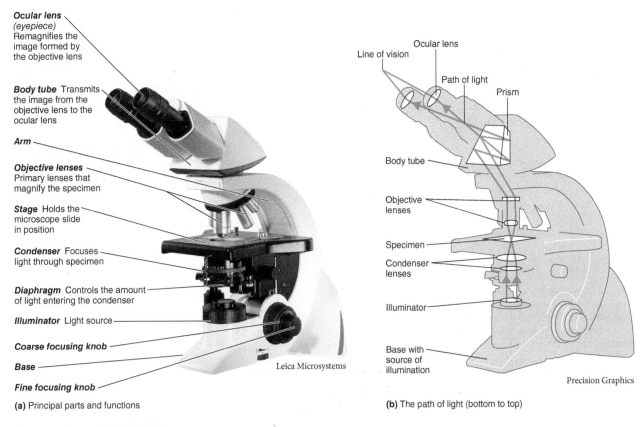

Ocular lens (eyepiece) Remagnifies the image formed by the objective lens

Body tube Transmits the image from the objective lens to the ocular lens

Arm

Objective lenses Primary lenses that magnify the specimen

Stage Holds the microscope slide in position

Condenser Focuses light through specimen

Diaphragm Controls the amount of light entering the condenser

Illuminator Light source

Coarse focusing knob

Base

Fine focusing knob

Leica Microsystems

(a) Principal parts and functions

Ocular lens

Line of vision

Path of light

Prism

Body tube

Objective lenses

Specimen

Condenser lenses

Illuminator

Base with source of illumination

Precision Graphics

(b) The path of light (bottom to top)

Figure 1 **The compound light microscope.**

 What is the total magnification of a compound light microscope with objective lens magnification of 40× and ocular lens of 10×?

glass. However, van Leeuwenhoek was the best lens grinder in the world in his day. His lenses were ground with such precision that a single lens could magnify a microbe 300×. His simple microscopes enabled him to be the first person to see bacteria.

Contemporaries of van Leeuwenhoek, such as Robert Hooke, built compound microscopes, which have multiple lenses. In fact, a Dutch spectacle maker, Zaccharias Janssen, is credited with making the first compound microscope around 1600. However, these early compound microscopes were of poor quality and could not be used to see bacteria. It was not until about 1830 that a significantly better microscope was developed by Joseph Jackson Lister (the father of Joseph Lister). Various improvements to Lister's microscope resulted in the development of the modern compound microscope, the kind used in microbiology laboratories today. Microscopic studies of live specimens have revealed dramatic interactions between microbes (see the Applications of Microbiology box on the next page.)

Animation Microscopy and Staining: Overview

Light Microscopy

Light microscopy refers to the use of any kind of microscope that uses visible light to observe specimens. Here we examine several types of light microscopy.

Compound Light Microscopy

A modern **compound light microscope** has a series of lenses and uses visible light as its source of illumination (Figure 1a). With a compound light microscope, we can examine very small specimens as well as some of their fine detail. A series of finely ground lenses (Figure 1b) forms a clearly focused image that is many times larger than the specimen itself. This magnification is achieved when light rays from an **illuminator,** the light source, pass through a **condenser,** which has lenses that direct the light rays through the specimen. From here, light rays pass into the **objective lenses,** the lenses closest to the specimen. The image of the specimen is magnified again by the **ocular lens,** or *eyepiece.*

We can calculate the **total magnification** of a specimen by multiplying the objective lens magnification (power) by the ocular

61

What Is That Slime?

When bacteria grow, they often stay together in packs called biofilms. This can result in a slimy film on rocks, on food, inside pipes, and on implanted medical devices. Bacterial cells interact and exhibit multicellular organization (**Figure A**).

   Pseudomonas aeruginosa can grow within a human without causing disease until the bacteria form a biofilm that overcomes the host's immune system. Biofilm-forming *P. aeruginosa* bacteria colonize the lungs of cystic fibrosis patients and are a leading cause of death in these patients (**Figure B**). Perhaps biofilms that lead to disease can be prevented by new drugs that destroy the inducer (discussed shortly).

Figure A *Paenibacillus.* **As one small colony moves away from the parent colony, other groups of cells follow the first colony. Soon, all of the other bacteria join the relocation to form this spiraling colony.**

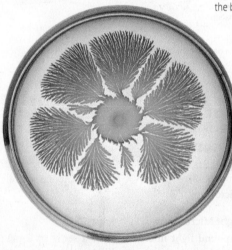

Eshel Ben-Jacob, School of Physics and Astronomy, Tel Aviv U., Israel

Myxobacteria

Myxobacteria are found in decaying organic material and freshwater throughout the world. Although they are bacteria, many myxobacteria never exist as individual cells. *Myxococcus xanthus* cells appear to hunt in packs. In their natural aqueous habitat, *M. xanthus* cells form spherical colonies that surround prey bacteria, where they can secrete digestive enzymes and absorb the nutrients. On solid substrates, other myxobacterial cells glide over a solid surface, leaving slime trails that are followed by other cells. When food is scarce, the cells aggregate to form a mass. Cells within the mass differentiate into a fruiting body that consists of a slime stalk and clusters of spores, as shown in **Figure C**.

Vibrio

Aliivibrio fischeri is a bioluminescent bacterium that lives as a symbiont in the light-producing organ of squid and certain fish. When free-living, the bacteria are at a low concentration and do not give off light. However, when they grow in their host, they are highly concentrated, and each cell is induced to produce the enzyme luciferase, which is used in the chemical pathway of bioluminescence.

How Bacterial Group Behavior Works

Cell density alters gene expression in bacterial cells in a process called quorum sensing. In law, a quorum is the minimum number of members necessary to conduct business. *Quorum sensing* is the ability of bacteria to communicate and coordinate behavior. Bacteria that use quorum sensing produce and secrete a signaling chemical called

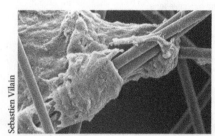

Sebastien Vilain

Figure B *Pseudomonas aeruginosa* **biofilm.**

5 µm
SEM

an *inducer*. As the inducer diffuses into the surrounding medium, other bacterial cells move toward the source and begin producing inducer. The concentration of inducer increases with increasing cell numbers. This, in turn, attracts more cells and initiates synthesis of more inducer.

Figure C **A fruiting body of a myxobacterium.**

Heinrich Lünsdorf, Helmholtz Center for Infection Research, Germany

10 µm

SEM

lens magnification (power). Most microscopes used in microbiology have several objective lenses, including 10× (low power), 40× (high power), and 100× (oil immersion, which is described later in this chapter). Most ocular lenses magnify specimens by a factor of 10. Multiplying the magnification of a specific objective lens with that of the ocular, we see that the total magnifications would be 100× for low power, 400× for high power, and 1000× for oil immersion. Some compound light microscopes can achieve a total magnification of 2000× with the oil immersion lens.

   Resolution (also called *resolving power*) is the ability of the lenses to distinguish fine detail and structure. Specifically, it refers to the ability of the lenses to distinguish two points a specified distance apart. For example, if a microscope has a resolving power of 0.4 nm, it can distinguish two points if they are at least 0.4 nm apart. A general principle of microscopy is that the shorter the wavelength of light used in the instrument, the greater the resolution. The white light used in a compound light microscope has a relatively long wavelength and cannot resolve structures smaller than about 0.2 μm. This fact and other practical considerations limit the magnification achieved by even the best compound light microscopes to about 2000×. By comparison, van Leeuwenhoek's microscopes had a resolution of 1 μm.

Figure 2 shows various specimens that can be resolved by the human eye, light microscope, and electron microscope.

To obtain a clear, finely detailed image under a compound light microscope, specimens must be made to contrast sharply with their *medium* (substance in which they are suspended). To attain such contrast, we must change the refractive index of specimens from that of their medium. The **refractive index** is a measure of the light-bending ability of a medium. We change the refractive index of specimens by staining them, a procedure we will discuss shortly. Light rays move in a straight line through a single medium. After the specimen is stained, when light rays pass through the two materials (the specimen and its medium) with different refractive indexes, the rays change direction (refract) from a straight path by bending or changing angle at the boundary between the materials and increase the image's contrast between the specimen and the medium. As the light rays travel away from the specimen, they spread out and enter the objective lens, and the image is thereby magnified.

To achieve high magnification (1000×) with good resolution, the objective lens must be small. Although we want light traveling through the specimen and medium to refract differently, we do not want to lose light rays after they have passed through the stained specimen. To preserve the direction of light rays at the highest magnification, immersion oil is placed between the glass slide and the oil immersion objective lens (Figure 3). The immersion oil has the same refractive index as glass, so the oil becomes part of the optics of the glass of the microscope. Unless immersion oil is used, light rays are refracted as they enter the air from the slide, and the objective lens would have to be increased in diameter to capture most of them. The oil has the same effect as increasing the objective lens diameter; therefore, it improves the resolving power of the lenses. If oil is not used with an oil immersion objective lens, the image becomes fuzzy, with poor resolution.

Under usual operating conditions, the field of vision in a compound light microscope is brightly illuminated. By focusing the light, the condenser produces a **brightfield illumination** (Figure 4a).

It is not always desirable to stain a specimen. However, an unstained cell has little contrast with its surroundings and is therefore difficult to see. Unstained cells are more easily observed with the modified compound microscopes described in the next section.

Darkfield Microscopy

A **darkfield microscope** is used to examine live microorganisms that either are invisible in the ordinary light microscope, cannot be stained by standard methods, or are so distorted by staining that their characteristics then cannot be identified. Instead of the normal condenser, a darkfield microscope uses a darkfield condenser that contains an opaque disk. The disk blocks light that would enter the objective lens directly. Only light that is reflected off (turned away from) the specimen enters the objective lens. Because there is no direct background light, the specimen appears light against a black background—the dark field (Figure 4b). This technique is frequently used to examine unstained microorganisms suspended in liquid. One use for darkfield microscopy is the examination of very thin spirochetes, such as *Treponema pallidum* (tre-pō-nē′mä pal′li-dum), the causative agent of syphilis.

Phase-Contrast Microscopy

Another way to observe microorganisms is with a **phase-contrast microscope**. Phase-contrast microscopy is especially useful because it permits detailed examination of internal structures in *living* microorganisms. In addition, it is not necessary to fix (attach the microbes to the microscope slide) or stain the specimen—procedures that could distort or kill the microorganisms.

The principle of phase-contrast microscopy is based on the wave nature of light rays and the fact that light rays can be *in phase* (their peaks and valleys match) or *out of phase*. If the wave peak of light rays from one source coincides with the wave peak of light rays from another source, the rays interact to produce *reinforcement* (relative brightness). However, if the wave peak from one light source coincides with the wave trough from another light source, the rays interact to produce *interference* (relative darkness). In a phase-contrast microscope, one set of light rays comes directly from the light source. The other set comes from light that is reflected or diffracted from a particular structure in the specimen. (*Diffraction* is the scattering of light rays as they "touch" a specimen's edge. The diffracted rays are bent away from the parallel light rays that pass farther from the specimen.) When the two sets of light rays—direct rays and reflected or diffracted rays—are brought together, they form an image of the specimen on the ocular lens, containing areas that are relatively light (in phase), through shades of gray, to black (out of phase; Figure 4c). In phase-contrast microscopy, the internal structures of a cell become more sharply defined.

Microscopes and Magnification

KEYCONCEPTS

- Microscopes are used to magnify small objects.
- Because different microscopes have different resolution ranges, the size of a specimen determines which microscopes can be used to view the specimen effectively.
- Most micrographs shown in this text (like the ones below) have size bars and symbols to help you identify the actual size of the specimen and the type of microscope used for that image.
- A red icon indicates that a micrograph has been artificially colorized.

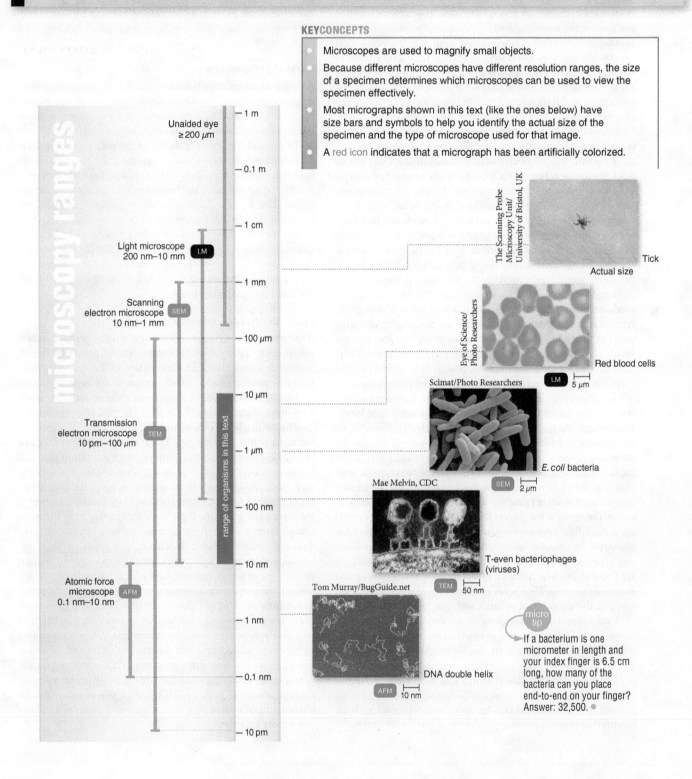

microscopy ranges

— 1 m
Unaided eye
≥ 200 μm

— 0.1 m

— 1 cm
Light microscope
200 nm–10 mm · LM

— 1 mm
Scanning
electron microscope
10 nm–1 mm · SEM

— 100 μm

— 10 μm

Transmission
electron microscope
10 pm–100 μm · TEM

— 1 μm

range of organisms in this text

— 100 nm

— 10 nm
Atomic force
microscope
0.1 nm–10 nm · AFM

— 1 nm

— 0.1 nm

— 10 pm

The Scanning Probe Microscopy Unit/ University of Bristol, UK

Tick
Actual size

Eye of Science/ Photo Researchers

Red blood cells · LM · 5 μm

Scimat/Photo Researchers

E. coli bacteria · SEM · 2 μm

Mae Melvin, CDC

T-even bacteriophages
(viruses) · TEM · 50 nm

Tom Murray/BugGuide.net

DNA double helix · AFM · 10 nm

micro tip
If a bacterium is one micrometer in length and your index finger is 6.5 cm long, how many of the bacteria can you place end-to-end on your finger? Answer: 32,500.

Differential Interference Contrast (DIC) Microscopy

Differential interference contrast (DIC) microscopy is similar to phase-contrast microscopy in that it uses differences in refractive indexes. However, a DIC microscope uses two beams of light instead of one. In addition, prisms split each light beam, adding contrasting colors to the specimen. Therefore, the resolution of a DIC microscope is higher than that of a standard phase-contrast microscope. Also, the image is brightly colored and appears nearly three-dimensional (Figure 5).

Fluorescence Microscopy

Fluorescence microscopy takes advantage of **fluorescence,** the ability of substances to absorb short wavelengths of light (ultraviolet) and give off light at a longer wavelength (visible). Some organisms fluoresce naturally under ultraviolet light; if the specimen to be viewed does not naturally fluoresce, it is stained with one of a group of fluorescent dyes called *fluorochromes*. When microorganisms stained with a fluorochrome are examined under a fluorescence microscope with an ultraviolet or near-ultraviolet light source, they appear as luminescent, bright objects against a dark background.

Fluorochromes have special attractions for different microorganisms. For example, the fluorochrome auramine O, which glows yellow when exposed to ultraviolet light, is strongly absorbed by *Mycobacterium tuberculosis,* the bacterium that causes tuberculosis. When the dye is applied to a sample of material suspected of containing the bacterium, the bacterium can be detected by the appearance of bright yellow organisms against a dark background. *Bacillus anthracis,* the causative agent of anthrax, appears apple green when stained with another fluorochrome, fluorescein isothiocyanate (FITC).

The principal use of fluorescence microscopy is a diagnostic technique called the **fluorescent-antibody (FA) technique,** or **immunofluorescence. Antibodies** are natural defense molecules that are produced by humans and many animals in reaction to a foreign substance, or **antigen.** Fluorescent antibodies for a particular antigen are obtained as follows: an animal is injected with a specific antigen, such as a bacterium, and the animal then begins to produce antibodies against that antigen. After a sufficient time, the antibodies are removed from the serum of the animal. Next, as shown in Figure 6a, a fluorochrome is chemically combined with the antibodies. These fluorescent antibodies are then added to a microscope slide containing an unknown bacterium. If this unknown bacterium is the same bacterium that was injected into the animal, the fluorescent antibodies bind to antigens on the surface of the bacterium, causing it to fluoresce.

This technique can detect bacteria or other pathogenic microorganisms, even within cells, tissues, or other clinical specimens (Figure 6b). Of paramount importance, it can be used to identify a microbe in minutes. Immunofluorescence is especially useful in diagnosing syphilis and rabies.

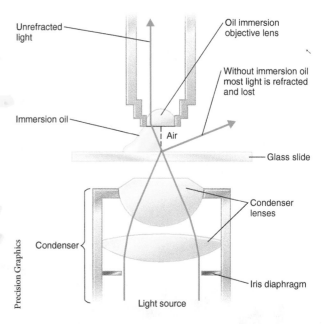

Figure 3 Refraction in the compound microscope using an oil immersion objective lens. Because the refractive indexes of the glass microscope slide and immersion oil are the same, the light rays do not refract when passing from one to the other when an oil immersion objective lens is used. Use of immersion oil is necessary at magnifications greater than 900×.

Q Why is immersion oil necessary at 1000× but not with the lower power objective?

Confocal Microscopy

Confocal microscopy is a technique in light microscopy used to reconstruct three-dimensional images. Like fluorescent microscopy, specimens are stained with fluorochromes so they will emit, or return, light. But instead of illuminating the entire field, in confocal microscopy, one plane of a small region of a specimen is illuminated with a short-wavelength (blue) light which passes the returned light through an aperture aligned with the illuminated region. Each plane corresponds to an image of a fine slice that has been physically cut from a specimen. Successive planes and regions are illuminated until the entire specimen has been scanned. Because confocal microscopy uses a pinhole aperture, it eliminates the blurring that occurs with other microscopes. As a result, exceptionally clear two-dimensional images can be obtained, with improved resolution of up to 40% over that of other microscopes.

Most confocal microscopes are used in conjunction with computers to construct three-dimensional images. The scanned planes of a specimen, which resemble a stack of images, are converted to a digital form that can be used by a computer to construct a three-dimensional representation. The reconstructed images

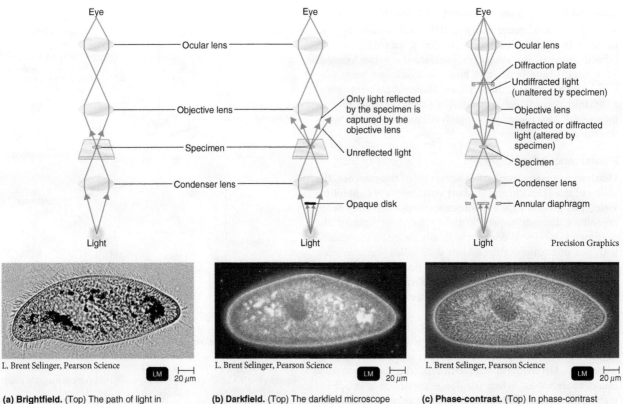

L. Brent Selinger, Pearson Science   LM   20 μm

L. Brent Selinger, Pearson Science   LM   20 μm

L. Brent Selinger, Pearson Science   LM   20 μm

Precision Graphics

(a) Brightfield. (Top) The path of light in brightfield microscopy, the type of illumination produced by regular compound light microscopes. (Bottom) Brightfield illumination shows internal structures and the outline of the transparent pellicle (external covering).

(b) Darkfield. (Top) The darkfield microscope uses a special condenser with an opaque disk that eliminates all light in the center of the beam. The only light that reaches the specimen comes in at an angle; thus, only light reflected by the specimen (blue rays) reaches the objective lens. (Bottom) Against the black background seen with darkfield microscopy, edges of the cell are bright, some internal structures seem to sparkle, and the pellicle is almost visible.

(c) Phase-contrast. (Top) In phase-contrast microscopy, the specimen is illuminated by light passing through an annular (ring-shaped) diaphragm. Direct light rays (unaltered by the specimen) travel a different path from light rays that are reflected or diffracted as they pass through the specimen. These two sets of rays are combined at the eye. Reflected or diffracted light rays are indicated in blue; direct rays are red. (Bottom) Phase-contrast microscopy shows greater differentiation of internal structures and clearly shows the pellicle.

Figure 4 Brightfield, darkfield, and phase-contrast microscopy. The illustrations show the contrasting light pathways of each of these types of microscopy. The photographs compare the protozoan *Paramecium* using these three different microscopy techniques.

Q What are the advantages of brightfield, darkfield, and phase-contrast microscopy?

can be rotated and viewed in any orientation. This technique has been used to obtain three-dimensional images of entire cells and cellular components (Figure 7). In addition, confocal microscopy can be used to evaluate cellular physiology by monitoring the distributions and concentrations of substances such as ATP and calcium ions. **Animation** Light Microscopy

Two-Photon Microscopy

As in confocal microscopy, specimens are stained with a fluorochrome for **two-photon microscopy (TPM)**. Two-photon microscopy uses long-wavelength (red) light, and therefore two photons, instead of one, are needed to excite the fluorochrome to emit light. The longer wavelength allows imaging of living cells in tissues up to 1 mm (1000 μm) deep (Figure 8). Confocal microscopy can image cells in detail only to a depth of less than 100 μm. Additionally, the longer wavelength is less likely to generate singlet oxygen, which damages cells. Another advantage of TPM is that it can track the activity of cells in real time. For example, cells of the immune system have been observed responding to an antigen.

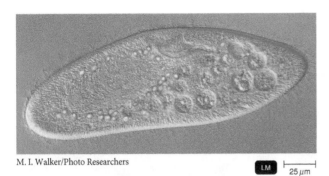

M. I. Walker/Photo Researchers

LM | 25 μm

Figure 5 Differential interference contrast (DIC) microscopy. Like phase-contrast, DIC uses differences in refractive indexes to produce an image, in this case a *Paramecium*. The colors in the image are produced by prisms that split the two light beams used in this process.

Q Why does the image from a DIC microscope appear brightly colored?

Scanning Acoustic Microscopy

Scanning acoustic microscopy (SAM) basically consists of interpreting the action of a sound wave sent through a specimen. A sound wave of a specific frequency travels through the specimen, and a portion of it is reflected back every time it hits an interface within the material. The resolution is about 1 μm. SAM is used to study living cells attached to another surface, such as cancer cells, artery plaque, and bacterial biofilms that foul equipment (Figure 9).

CHECK YOUR UNDERSTANDING

✔ How are brightfield, darkfield, phase-contrast, and fluorescence microscopy similar? **4**

Electron Microscopy

Objects smaller than about 0.2 μm, such as viruses or the internal structures of cells, must be examined with an **electron microscope.** In electron microscopy, a beam of electrons is used instead of light. Like light, free electrons travel in waves. The resolving power of the electron microscope is far greater than that of the other microscopes described here so far. The better resolution of electron microscopes is due to the shorter wavelengths of electrons; the wavelengths of electrons are about 100,000 times smaller than the wavelengths of visible light. Thus, electron microscopes are used to examine structures too small to be resolved with light microscopes. Images produced by electron microscopes are always black and white, but they may be colored artificially to accentuate certain details.

Instead of using glass lenses, an electron microscope uses electromagnetic lenses to focus a beam of electrons onto a specimen. There are two types of electron microscopes: the transmission electron microscope and the scanning electron microscope.

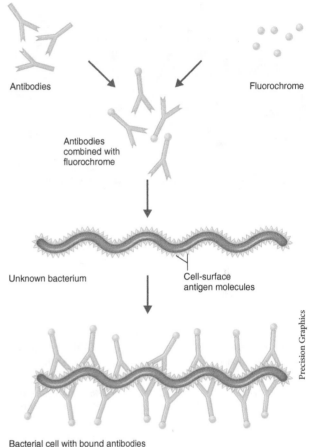

Antibodies

Fluorochrome

Antibodies combined with fluorochrome

Unknown bacterium

Cell-surface antigen molecules

Bacterial cell with bound antibodies combined with fluorochrome

(a)

Precision Graphics

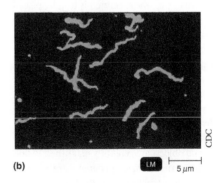

(b)

LM | 5 μm

CDC

Figure 6 The principle of immunofluorescence. (a) A type of fluorochrome is combined with antibodies against a specific type of bacterium. When the preparation is added to bacterial cells on a microscope slide, the antibodies attach to the bacterial cells, and the cells fluoresce when illuminated with ultraviolet light. **(b)** In the fluorescent treponemal antibody absorption (FTA-ABS) test for syphilis shown here, *Treponema pallidum* shows up as green cells against a darker background.

Q Why won't other bacteria fluoresce in the FTA-ABS test?

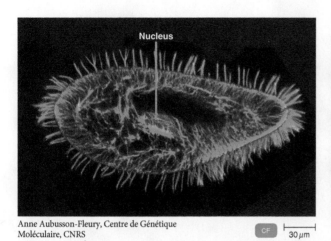

Nucleus

Anne Aubusson-Fleury, Centre de Génétique
Moléculaire, CNRS

CF   ⊢——⊣ 30 μm

Figure 7 Confocal microscopy. Confocal microscopy produces three-dimensional images and can be used to look inside cells. Shown here is the nucleus in *Paramecium multimicronucleatum*.

 What are the advantages of confocal microscopy?

Transmission Electron Microscopy

In the **transmission electron microscope (TEM)**, a finely focused beam of electrons from an electron gun passes through a specially prepared, ultrathin section of the specimen (**Figure 10a**). The beam is focused on a small area of the specimen by an electromagnetic condenser lens that performs roughly the same function as the condenser of a light microscope—directing the beam of electrons in a straight line to illuminate the specimen.

Electron microscopes use electromagnetic lenses to control illumination, focus, and magnification. Instead of being placed on a glass slide, as in light microscopes, the specimen is usually placed on a copper mesh grid. The beam of electrons passes through the specimen and then through an electromagnetic objective lens, which magnifies the image. Finally, the electrons are focused by an electromagnetic projector lens (rather than by an ocular lens as in a light microscope) onto a fluorescent screen or photographic plate. The final image, called a *transmission electron micrograph,* appears as many light and dark areas, depending on the number of electrons absorbed by different areas of the specimen.

The transmission electron microscope can resolve objects as close together as 10 pm, and objects are generally magnified 10,000 to 100,000×. Because most microscopic specimens are so thin, the contrast between their ultrastructures and the background is weak. Contrast can be greatly enhanced by using a "stain" that absorbs electrons and produces a darker image in the stained region. Salts of various heavy metals, such as lead, osmium, tungsten, and uranium, are commonly used as stains. These metals can be fixed onto the specimen (*positive staining*) or used to increase the electron opacity of the surrounding field (*negative staining*). Negative staining is useful for the study of the very smallest specimens, such as virus particles, bacterial flagella, and protein molecules.

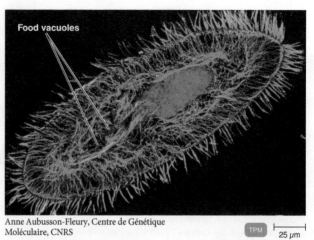

Food vacuoles

Anne Aubusson-Fleury, Centre de Génétique
Moléculaire, CNRS

TPM   ⊢——⊣ 25 μm

Figure 8 Two-photon microscopy (TPM). This procedure makes it possible to image living cells up to 1 mm deep in detail. This image shows food vacuoles in a living *Paramecium*.

 What are the differences between TPM and confocal microscopy?

In addition to positive and negative staining, a microbe can be viewed by a technique called *shadow casting*. In this procedure, a heavy metal such as platinum or gold is sprayed at an angle of about 45° so that it strikes the microbe from only one side. The metal piles up on one side of the specimen, and the uncoated area on the opposite side of the specimen leaves a clear area behind it as a shadow. This gives a three-dimensional

Good, MS; Wend, CF; Bond, LJ; McLean, JS; Panetta, PD; Ahmed, S; Crawford, SL; Daly, DS. "An estimate of biofilm properties using an acoustic microscope." *Ultrasonics, Ferroelectrics and Frequency Control, IEEE Transactions,* Volume 53, Issue 9, Sept. 2006 Page(s):1637–1648. Figure 5B, page 1642. © 2006 IEEE

SAM   ⊢——⊣ 170 μm

Figure 9 Scanning acoustic microscopy (SAM) of a bacterial biofilm on glass. Scanning acoustic microscopy essentially consists of interpreting the action of sound waves through a specimen. © 2006 IEEE.

 What is the principal use of SAM?

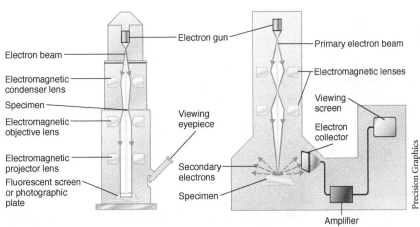

Precision Graphics

Figure 10 Transmission and scanning electron microscopy. The illustrations show the pathways of electron beams used to create images of the specimens. The photographs show a *Paramecium* viewed with both of these types of electron microscopes. Although electron micrographs are normally black and white, these and other electron micrographs in this text have been artificially colorized for emphasis.

Q How do TEM and SEM images of the same organism differ?

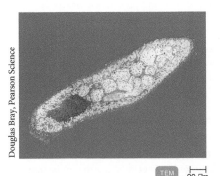

Douglas Bray, Pearson Science

TEM · 20 ☐m

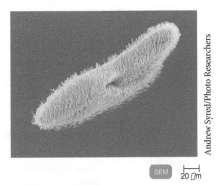

Andrew Syred/Photo Researchers

SEM · 20 ☐m

(a) Transmission. (Top) In a transmission electron microscope, electrons pass through the specimen and are scattered. Magnetic lenses focus the image onto a fluorescent screen or photographic plate. (Bottom) This colorized transmission electron micrograph (TEM) shows a thin slice of *Paramecium*. In this type of microscopy, the internal structures present in the slice can be seen.

(b) Scanning. (Top) In a scanning electron microscope, primary electrons sweep across the specimen and knock electrons from its surface. These secondary electrons are picked up by a collector, amplified, and transmitted onto a viewing screen or photographic plate. (Bottom) In this colorized scanning electron micrograph (SEM), the surface structures of *Paramecium* can be seen. Note the three-dimensional appearance of this cell, in contrast to the two-dimensional appearance of the transmission electron micrograph in part (a).

effect to the specimen and provides a general idea of the size and shape of the specimen.

Transmission electron microscopy has high resolution and is extremely valuable for examining different layers of specimens. However, it does have certain disadvantages. Because electrons have limited penetrating power, only a very thin section of a specimen (about 100 nm) can be studied effectively. Thus, the specimen has no three-dimensional aspect. In addition, specimens must be fixed, dehydrated, and viewed under a high vacuum to prevent electron scattering. These treatments not only kill the specimen, but also cause some shrinkage and distortion, sometimes to the extent that there may appear to be additional structures in a prepared cell. Structures that appear as a result of the method of preparation are called *artifacts*.

Scanning Electron Microscopy

The **scanning electron microscope (SEM)** overcomes the problem of sectioning associated with a transmission electron microscope. A scanning electron microscope provides striking three-dimensional views of specimens (Figure 10b). In scanning electron microscopy, an electron gun produces a finely focused beam of electrons called the primary electron beam. These electrons pass through electromagnetic lenses and are directed over the surface of the specimen. The primary electron beam knocks electrons out of the surface of the specimen, and the secondary electrons thus produced are transmitted to an electron collector, amplified, and used to produce an image on a viewing screen or photographic plate. The image is called a *scanning electron micrograph*. This microscope is especially

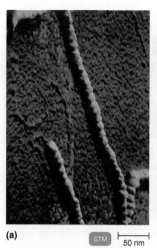 

(a) STM 50 nm   (b) AFM 12 nm

Figure 11 Scanned-probe microscopy. (**a**) Scanning tunneling microscopy (STM) image of RecA protein from *E. coli*. This protein is involved in repair of DNA. (**b**) Atomic force microscopy (AFM) image of perfringolysin O toxin from *Clostridium perfringens*. This protein makes holes in human plasma membranes.

Q What is the principle employed in scanned-probe microscopy?

(a) M. Amrein et al., "Scanning Tunneling Microscopy of recA-DNA Complexes Coated with a Conducting Film," *Science*, 1988 Apr 22; 240(4851):514-6. Reprinted with permission. ©1988 AAAS; (b) Reprinted by permission from Macmillan Publishers, Ltd. D. M. Czajkowsky, et al., "Vertical Collapse of a Cytolysin Prepore Moves its Transmembrane Beta-hairpins to the Membrane," *EMBO*, 2004 Aug 18; 23(16):3206

useful in studying the surface structures of intact cells and viruses. In practice, it can resolve objects as close together as 10 nm, and objects are generally magnified 1000 to 10,000×.

(MM) **Animation** Electron Microscopy

CHECK YOUR UNDERSTANDING

✔ Why do electron microscopes have greater resolution than light microscopes? **5**

Scanned-Probe Microscopy

Since the early 1980s, several new types of microscopes, called **scanned-probe microscopes,** have been developed. They use various kinds of probes to examine the surface of a specimen using electric current, which does not modify the specimen or expose it to damaging, high-energy radiation. Such microscopes can be used to map atomic and molecular shapes, to characterize magnetic and chemical properties, and to determine temperature variations inside cells. Among the new scanned-probe microscopes are the scanning tunneling microscope and the atomic force microscope, discussed next.

Scanning Tunneling Microscopy

Scanning tunneling microscopy (STM) uses a thin metal (tungsten) probe that scans a specimen and produces an image revealing the bumps and depressions of the atoms on the surface of the specimen (Figure 11a). The resolving power of an STM is much greater than that of an electron microscope; it can resolve features that are only about 1/100 the size of an atom. Moreover, special preparation of the specimen for observation is not needed. STMs are used to provide incredibly detailed views of molecules such as DNA.

Atomic Force Microscopy

In **atomic force microscopy (AFM),** a metal-and-diamond probe is gently forced down onto a specimen. As the probe moves along the surface of the specimen, its movements are recorded, and a three-dimensional image is produced (Figure 11b). As with STM, AFM does not require special specimen preparation. AFM is used to image both biological substances (in nearly atomic detail) and molecular processes (such as the assembly of fibrin, a component of a blood clot).

The various types of microscopy just described are summarized in **Table 2.**

CHECK YOUR UNDERSTANDING

✔ For what is TEM used? SEM? Scanned-probe microscopy? **6**

Preparation of Specimens for Light Microscopy

LEARNING OBJECTIVES

7 Differentiate an acidic dye from a basic dye.

8 Explain the purpose of simple staining.

9 List the steps in preparing a Gram stain, and describe the appearance of gram-positive and gram-negative cells after each step.

10 Compare and contrast the Gram stain and the acid-fast stain.

11 Explain why each of the following is used: capsule stain, endospore stain, flagella stain.

From: Helicobacter–The Ease and Difficulty of a New Discovery, Nobel Lecture by J. Robin Warren, December 8, 2005. © The Nobel Foundation 2005

Clinical Case

Helicobacter pylori is a spiral-shaped, gram-negative bacterium with multiple flagella. It is the most common cause of peptic ulcers in humans and can also cause stomach cancer. The first electron micrograph of *H. pylori* was viewed in the 1980s, when Australian physician Robin Warren used an electron microscope to see *H. pylori* in stomach tissue.

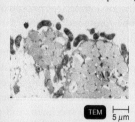

TEM 5 μm

Why was an electron microscope necessary to see the *H. pylori* bacteria?

TABLE **2** **A Summary of Various Types of Microscopes**

Microscope Type	Distinguishing Features	Typical Image	Principal Uses
Light			
Brightfield	Uses visible light as a source of illumination; cannot resolve structures smaller than about 0.2 μm; specimen appears against a bright background. Inexpensive and easy to use.	 L. Brent Selinger, Pearson Science *Paramecium* LM ⊢ 25 μm	To observe various stained specimens and to count microbes; does not resolve very small specimens, such as viruses.
Darkfield	Uses a special condenser with an opaque disk that blocks light from entering the objective lens directly; light reflected by specimen enters the objective lens, and the specimen appears light against a black background.	 L. Brent Selinger, Pearson Science *Paramecium* LM ⊢ 25 μm	To examine living microorganisms that are invisible in brightfield microscopy, do not stain easily, or are distorted by staining; frequently used to detect *Treponema pallidum* in the diagnosis of syphilis.
Phase-contrast	Uses a special condenser containing an annular (ring-shaped) diaphragm. The diaphragm allows direct light to pass through the condenser, focusing light on the specimen and a diffraction plate in the objective lens. Direct and reflected or diffracted light rays are brought together to produce the image. No staining required.	 L. Brent Selinger, Pearson Science *Paramecium* LM ⊢ 25 μm	To facilitate detailed examination of the internal structures of living specimens.
Differential interference contrast (DIC)	Like phase-contrast, uses differences in refractive indexes to produce images. Uses two beams of light separated by prisms; the specimen appears colored as a result of the prism effect. No staining required.	 M. I. Walker/Photo Researchers *Paramecium* LM ⊢ 23 μm	To provide three-dimensional images.
Fluorescence	Uses an ultraviolet or near-ultraviolet source of illumination that causes fluorescent compounds (green-colored) in a specimen to emit light.	 CDC *Treponema pallidum* LM ⊢ 2 μm	For fluorescent-antibody techniques (immunofluorescence) to rapidly detect and identify microbes in tissues or clinical specimens.

(continued)

TABLE 2 A Summary of Various Types of Microscopes (continued)

Microscope Type	Distinguishing Features	Typical Image	Principal Uses
Confocal	Uses a single photon to illuminate one plane of a specimen at a time.	Anne Aubusson-Fleury, Centre de Génétique Moléculaire, CNRS *Paramecium* CF ⊢25 μm⊣	To obtain two- and three-dimensional images of cells for biomedical applications.
Two-Photon	Uses two photons to illuminate a specimen.	Anne Aubusson-Fleury, Centre de Génétique Moléculaire, CNRS *Paramecium* TPM ⊢22 μm⊣	To image living cells, up to depth of 1 mm, reduce phototoxicity, and observe cell activity in real time.
Scanning Acoustic	Uses a sound wave of specific frequency that travels through the specimen with a portion being reflected when it hits an interface within the material. Good, MS; Wend, CF; Bond, LJ; McLean, JS; Panetta, PD; Ahmed, S; Crawford, SL; Daly, DS. "An estimate of biofilm properties using an acoustic microscope." *Ultrasonics, Ferroelectrics and Frequency Control, IEEE Transactions*, Volume 53, Issue 9, Sept. 2006 Page(s):1637–1648. Figure 5B, page 1642. © 2006 IEEE	*Biofilm* SAM ⊢180 μm⊣	To examine living cells attached to another surface, such as cancer cells, artery plaque, and biofilms.
Electron			
Transmission	Uses a beam of electrons instead of light; electrons pass through the specimen; because of the shorter wavelength of electrons, structures smaller than 0.2 μm can be resolved. The image produced is two-dimensional.	Douglas Bray, Pearson Science *Paramecium* TEM ⊢25 μm⊣	To examine viruses or the internal ultrastructure in thin sections of cells (usually magnified 10,000–100,000×).
Scanning	Uses a beam of electrons instead of light; electrons are reflected from the specimen; because of the shorter wavelength of electrons, structures smaller than 0.2 μm can be resolved. The image produced appears three-dimensional.	Andrew Syred/Photo Researchers *Paramecium* SEM ⊢25 μm⊣	To study the surface features of cells and viruses (usually magnified 1000–10,000×).

TABLE 2 *(continued)*

Microscope Type	Distinguishing Features	Typical Image	Principal Uses
Scanned-Probe			
Scanning tunneling	Uses a thin metal probe that scans a specimen and produces an image revealing the bumps and depressions of the atoms on the surface of the specimen. Resolving power is much greater than that of an electron microscope. No special preparation required.	RecA protein from *E. coli* STM 45 nm	Provides very detailed views of molecules inside cells. M. Amrein et al., "Scanning Tunneling Microscopy of recA-DNA Complexes Coated with a Conducting Film," *Science*, 1988 Apr 22; 240(4851):514-6. Reprinted with permission. ©1988 AAAS
Atomic force	Uses a metal-and-diamond probe gently forced down along the surface of the specimen. Produces a three-dimensional image. No special preparation required.	Perfringolysin O toxin from *Clostridium perfringens* AFM 9 nm	Provides three-dimensional images of biological specimens at high resolution in nearly atomic detail and can measure physical properties of biological specimens and molecular processes. Reprinted by permission from Macmillan Publishers, Ltd. D. M. Czajkowsky, et al., "Vertical Collapse of a Cytolysin Prepore Moves its Transmembrane Beta-hairpins to the Membrane," *EMBO*, 2004 Aug 18; 23(16):3206

Because most microorganisms appear almost colorless when viewed through a standard light microscope, we often must prepare them for observation. One way to do this is to stain (color) the specimen. Next we will discuss several different staining procedures.

Preparing Smears for Staining

Most initial observations of microorganisms are made with stained preparations. **Staining** simply means coloring the microorganisms with a dye that emphasizes certain structures. Before the microorganisms can be stained, however, they must be **fixed** (attached) to the microscope slide. Fixing simultaneously kills the microorganisms and fixes them to the slide. It also preserves various parts of microbes in their natural state with only minimal distortion.

When a specimen is to be fixed, a thin film of material containing the microorganisms is spread over the surface of the slide. This film, called a **smear,** is allowed to air dry. In most staining procedures the slide is then fixed by passing it through the flame of a Bunsen burner several times, smear side up, or by covering the slide with methyl alcohol for 1 minute. Stain is applied and then washed off with water; then the slide is blotted with absorbent paper. Without fixing, the stain might wash the microbes off the slide. The stained microorganisms are now ready for microscopic examination.

Stains are salts composed of a positive and a negative ion, one of which is colored and is known as the *chromophore*. The color of so-called **basic dyes** is in the positive ion; in **acidic dyes,** it is in the negative ion. Bacteria are slightly negatively charged at pH 7. Thus, the colored positive ion in a basic dye is attracted to the negatively charged bacterial cell. Basic dyes, which include crystal violet, methylene blue, malachite green, and safranin, are more commonly used than acidic dyes. Acidic dyes are not attracted to most types of bacteria because the dye's negative ions are repelled by the negatively charged bacterial surface, so the stain colors the background instead. Preparing colorless bacteria against a colored background is called **negative staining.** It is valuable for observing overall cell shapes, sizes, and capsules because the cells are made highly visible against a contrasting dark background (see Figure 14a). Distortions of cell size and shape are minimized because fixing is not necessary and the cells do not pick up the stain. Examples of acidic dyes are eosin, acid fuchsin, and nigrosin.

To apply acidic or basic dyes, microbiologists use three kinds of staining techniques: simple, differential, and special.

Simple Stains

A **simple stain** is an aqueous or alcohol solution of a single basic dye. Although different dyes bind specifically to different parts of cells, the primary purpose of a simple stain is to highlight the entire microorganism so that cellular shapes and basic structures are visible. The stain is applied to the fixed smear for a certain length of time and then washed off, and the slide is dried and

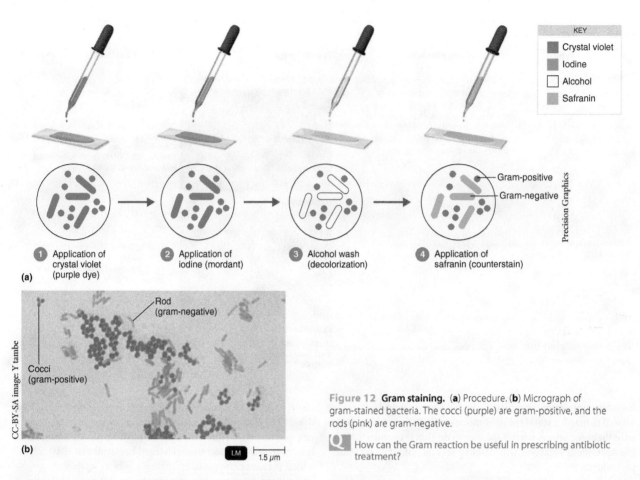

KEY
- Crystal violet
- Iodine
- Alcohol
- Safranin

1 Application of crystal violet (purple dye)

2 Application of iodine (mordant)

3 Alcohol wash (decolorization)

4 Application of safranin (counterstain)

Gram-positive
Gram-negative

Precision Graphics

(a)

CC-BY-SA image: Y tambe

Rod (gram-negative)

Cocci (gram-positive)

(b)

LM 1.5 μm

Figure 12 **Gram staining.** (**a**) Procedure. (**b**) Micrograph of gram-stained bacteria. The cocci (purple) are gram-positive, and the rods (pink) are gram-negative.

Q How can the Gram reaction be useful in prescribing antibiotic treatment?

examined. Occasionally, a chemical is added to the solution to intensify the stain; such an additive is called a **mordant.** One function of a mordant is to increase the affinity of a stain for a biological specimen; another is to coat a structure (such as a flagellum) to make it thicker and easier to see after it is stained with a dye. Some of the simple stains commonly used in the laboratory are methylene blue, carbolfuchsin, crystal violet, and safranin.

CHECK YOUR UNDERSTANDING

✔ Why doesn't a negative stain color a cell? 7

✔ Why is fixing necessary for most staining procedures? 8

Differential Stains

Unlike simple stains, **differential stains** react differently with different kinds of bacteria and thus can be used to distinguish them. The differential stains most frequently used for bacteria are the Gram stain and the acid-fast stain.

Gram Stain

The **Gram stain** was developed in 1884 by the Danish bacteriologist Hans Christian Gram. It is one of the most useful staining

procedures because it classifies bacteria into two large groups: gram-positive and gram-negative.

In this procedure (**Figure 12a**),

1 A heat-fixed smear is covered with a basic purple dye, usually crystal violet. Because the purple stain imparts its color to all cells, it is referred to as a **primary stain.**

2 After a short time, the purple dye is washed off, and the smear is covered with iodine, a mordant. When the iodine is washed off, both gram-positive and gram-negative bacteria appear dark violet or purple.

3 Next, the slide is washed with alcohol or an alcohol-acetone solution. This solution is a **decolorizing agent,** which removes the purple from the cells of some species but not from others.

4 The alcohol is rinsed off, and the slide is then stained with safranin, a basic red dye. The smear is washed again, blotted dry, and examined microscopically.

The purple dye and the iodine combine in the cytoplasm of each bacterium and color it dark violet or purple. Bacteria that retain this color after the alcohol has attempted to decolorize them are classified as **gram-positive;** bacteria that lose the dark violet or purple color after decolorization are classified as **gram-negative** (Figure 12b). Because gram-negative bacteria are colorless after the alcohol wash, they are no longer visible. This is why the basic dye safranin is applied; it turns the gram-negative bacteria pink. Stains such as safranin that have a contrasting color to the primary stain are called **counterstains.** Because gram-positive bacteria retain the original purple stain, they are not affected by the safranin counterstain.

Different kinds of bacteria react differently to the Gram stain because structural differences in their cell walls affect the retention or escape of a combination of crystal violet and iodine, called the crystal violet–iodine (CV–I) complex. Among other differences, gram-positive bacteria have a thicker peptidoglycan (disaccharides and amino acids) cell wall than gram-negative bacteria. In addition, gram-negative bacteria contain a layer of lipopolysaccharide (lipids and polysaccharides) as part of their cell wall. When applied to both gram-positive and gram-negative cells, crystal violet and then iodine readily enter the cells. Inside the cells, the crystal violet and iodine combine to form CV–I. This complex is larger than the crystal violet molecule that entered the cells, and, because of its size, it cannot be washed out of the intact peptidoglycan layer of gram-positive cells by alcohol. Consequently, gram-positive cells retain the color of the crystal violet dye. In gram-negative cells, however, the alcohol wash disrupts the outer lipopolysaccharide layer, and the CV–I complex is washed out through the thin layer of peptidoglycan. As a result, gram-negative cells are colorless until counterstained with safranin, after which they are pink.

In summary, gram-positive cells retain the dye and remain purple. Gram-negative cells do not retain the dye; they are colorless until counterstained with a red dye.

The Gram method is one of the most important staining techniques in medical microbiology. But Gram staining results are not universally applicable, because some bacterial cells stain poorly or not at all. The Gram reaction is most consistent when it is used on young, growing bacteria.

The Gram reaction of a bacterium can provide valuable information for the treatment of disease. Gram-positive bacteria tend to be killed easily by penicillins and cephalosporins. Gram-negative bacteria are generally more resistant because the antibiotics cannot penetrate the lipopolysaccharide layer. Some resistance to these antibiotics among both gram-positive and gram-negative bacteria is due to bacterial inactivation of the antibiotics.

Acid-Fast Stain

Another important differential stain (one that differentiates bacteria into distinctive groups) is the **acid-fast stain,** which binds strongly only to bacteria that have a waxy material in their cell walls. Microbiologists use this stain to identify all bacteria in the genus *Mycobacterium,* including the two important pathogens *Mycobacterium tuberculosis,* the causative agent of tuberculosis,

and *Mycobacterium leprae* (lep'rī), the causative agent of leprosy. This stain is also used to identify the pathogenic strains of the genus *Nocardia* (nō-kär'dē-ä). Bacteria in the genera *Mycobacterium* and *Nocardia* are acid-fast.

In the acid-fast staining procedure, the red dye carbolfuchsin is applied to a fixed smear, and the slide is gently heated for several minutes. (Heating enhances penetration and retention of the dye.) Then the slide is cooled and washed with water. The smear is next treated with acid-alcohol, a decolorizer, which removes the red stain from bacteria that are not acid-fast. The acid-fast microorganisms retain the pink or red color because the carbolfuchsin is more soluble in the cell wall lipids than in the acid-alcohol (Figure 13). In non–acid-fast bacteria, whose cell walls lack the lipid components, the carbolfuchsin is rapidly removed during decolorization, leaving the cells colorless. The smear is then stained with a methylene blue counterstain. Non–acid-fast cells appear blue after the counterstain is applied.

CHECK YOUR UNDERSTANDING

- Why is the Gram stain so useful? 9
- Which stain would be used to identify microbes in the genera *Mycobacterium* and *Nocardia*? 10

Special Stains

Special stains are used to color and isolate specific parts of microorganisms, such as endospores and flagella, and to reveal the presence of capsules.

Clinical Case

The resolving power of the electron microscope is much greater than that of a light microscope. The higher resolution provided unequivocal proof of the presence of spiral bacteria.

Barry Marshall and Alfred Tay, The University of Western Australia

LM. ⊢—⊣ 3 µm

Although bismuth (the key ingredient in Pepto-Bismol) kills *H. pylori,* it is not a cure. Maryanne's physician prescribes the antibiotic clarithromycin. However, one week after finishing treatment, Maryanne's symptoms continue. To see whether *H. pylori* is still present, her physician orders a stomach biopsy to obtain a sample of the mucous lining of Maryanne's stomach. The lab uses light microscoy and a Gram stain to view the sample.

What does the gram stain above show?

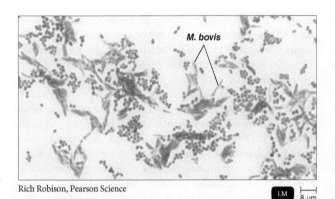

Rich Robison, Pearson Science

LM ⊢ 8 μm

Figure 13 Acid-fast bacteria. The *Mycobacterium bovis* bacteria that have infected this tissue have been stained pink or red with an acid-fast stain. Non–acid-fast cells (*Staphylococcus*) are stained with the methylene blue counterstain.

🅠 Why is *Mycobacterium tuberculosis* easily identified by the acid-fast stain ?

Negative Staining for Capsules

Many microorganisms contain a gelatinous covering called a **capsule**. In medical microbiology, demonstrating the presence of a

capsule is a means of determining the organism's **virulence,** the degree to which a pathogen can cause disease.

Capsule staining is more difficult than other types of staining procedures because capsular materials are soluble in water and may be dislodged or removed during rigorous washing. To demonstrate the presence of capsules, a microbiologist can mix the bacteria in a solution containing a fine colloidal suspension of colored particles (usually India ink or nigrosin) to provide a contrasting background and then stain the bacteria with a simple stain, such as safranin (Figure 14a). Because of their chemical composition, capsules do not accept most biological dyes, such as safranin, and thus appear as halos surrounding each stained bacterial cell.

Endospore (Spore) Staining

An **endospore** is a special resistant, dormant structure formed within a cell that protects a bacterium from adverse environmental conditions. Although endospores are relatively uncommon in bacterial cells, they can be formed by a few genera of bacteria. Endospores cannot be stained by ordinary methods, such as simple staining and Gram staining, because the dyes do not penetrate the wall of the endospore.

The most commonly used endospore stain is the *Schaeffer-Fulton endospore stain* (Figure 14b). Malachite green, the

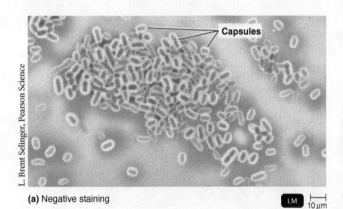

L. Brent Selinger, Pearson Science

(a) Negative staining

LM ⊢ 10 μm

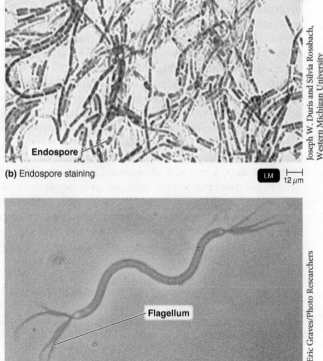

Joseph W. Duris and Silvia Rossbach, Western Michigan University

(b) Endospore staining

LM ⊢ 12 μm

Eric Graves/Photo Researchers

(c) Flagella staining

LM ⊢ 4 μm

Figure 14 Special staining. (**a**) Capsule staining provides a contrasting background, so the capsules of these bacteria, *Klebsiella pneumoniae,* show up as light areas surrounding the stained cells. (**b**) Endospores are seen as green ovals in these rod-shaped cells of the bacterium *Bacillus cereus,* using the Schaeffer-Fulton endospore stain. (**c**) Flagella appear as wavy extensions from the ends of these cells of the bacterium *Spirillum volutans.* In relation to the body of the cell, the flagella are much thicker than normal because layers of the stain have accumulated from treatment of the specimen with a mordant.

🅠 Of what value are capsules, endospores, and flagella to bacteria?

TABLE **3** **A Summary of Various Stains and Their Uses**

Stain	Principal Uses
Simple (methylene blue, carbolfuchsin, crystal violet, safranin)	Used to highlight microorganisms to determine cellular shapes and arrangements. Aqueous or alcohol solution of a single basic dye stains cells. (Sometimes a mordant is added to intensify the stain.)
Differential Gram	Used to distinguish different kinds of bacteria. Classifies bacteria into two large groups: gram-positive and gram-negative. Gram-positive bacteria retain the crystal violet stain and appear purple. Gram-negative bacteria do not retain the crystal violet stain; they remain colorless until counterstained with safranin and then appear pink.
Acid-fast	Used to distinguish *Mycobacterium* species and some species of *Nocardia.* Acid-fast bacteria, once stained with carbolfuchsin and treated with acid-alcohol, remain pink or red because they retain the carbolfuchsin stain. Non–acid-fast bacteria, when stained and treated the same way and then stained with methylene blue, appear blue because they lose the carbolfuchsin stain and are then able to accept the methylene blue stain.
Special	Used to color and isolate various structures, such as capsules, endospores, and flagella; sometimes used as a diagnostic aid.
Negative	Used to demonstrate the presence of capsules. Because capsules do not accept most stains, the capsules appear as unstained halos around bacterial cells and stand out against a contrasting background.
Endospore	Used to detect the presence of endospores in bacteria. When malachite green is applied to a heat-fixed smear of bacterial cells, the stain penetrates the endospores and stains them green. When safranin (red) is then applied, it stains the remainder of the cells red or pink.
Flagella	Used to demonstrate the presence of flagella. A mordant is used to build up the diameters of flagella until they become visible microscopically when stained with carbolfuchsin.

primary stain, is applied to a heat-fixed smear and heated to steaming for about 5 minutes. The heat helps the stain penetrate the endospore wall. Then the preparation is washed for about 30 seconds with water to remove the malachite green from all of the cells' parts except the endospores. Next, safranin, a counterstain, is applied to the smear to stain portions of the cell other than endospores. In a properly prepared smear, the endospores appear green within red or pink cells. Because endospores are highly refractive, they can be detected under the light microscope when unstained, but without a special stain they cannot be differentiated from inclusions of stored material.

Flagella Staining

Bacterial **flagella** (singular: **flagellum**) are structures of locomotion too small to be seen with a light microscope without staining. A tedious and delicate staining procedure uses a mordant and the stain carbolfuchsin to build up the diameters of the flagella until they become visible under the light microscope (**Figure 14c**). Microbiologists use the number and arrangement of flagella as diagnostic aids. (MM) **Animation** Staining

CHECK YOUR UNDERSTANDING

✔ How do unstained endospores appear? Stained endospores? **11**

A summary of stains is presented in **Table 3**.

Clinical Case Resolved

Because it is gram-negative, *H. pylori* stains pink after the counterstain is applied. The results from the lab indicate that the *H. pylori* is still present in Maryanne's stomach lining. Suspecting that the bacteria are resistant to clarithromycin, Maryanne's physician now prescribes two other antibiotics: tetracycline and metronidazole. This time, Maryanne's symptoms do not return. Soon, she is feeling like her old self again and is back in the office full time.

Study Outline

Test your understanding with quizzes, microbe review, and a chapter post-test at www.masteringmicrobiology.com.

Units of Measurement

1. The standard unit of length is the meter (m).
2. Microorganisms are measured in micrometers, μm (10^{-6} m), and in nanometers, nm (10^{-9} m).

Microscopy: The Instruments

1. A simple microscope consists of one lens; a compound microscope has multiple lenses.

Light Microscopy

2. The most common microscope used in microbiology is the compound light microscope (LM).

3. The total magnification of an object is calculated by multiplying the magnification of the objective lens by the magnification of the ocular lens.

4. The compound light microscope uses visible light.

5. The maximum resolution, or resolving power (the ability to distinguish two points) of a compound light microscope is 0.2 µm; maximum magnification is 2000×.

6. Specimens are stained to increase the difference between the refractive indexes of the specimen and the medium.

7. Immersion oil is used with the oil immersion lens to reduce light loss between the slide and the lens.

8. Brightfield illumination is used for stained smears.

9. Unstained cells are more productively observed using darkfield, phase-contrast, or DIC microscopy.

10. The darkfield microscope shows a light silhouette of an organism against a dark background.

11. It is most useful for detecting the presence of extremely small organisms.

12. A phase-contrast microscope brings direct and reflected or diffracted light rays together (in phase) to form an image of the specimen on the ocular lens.

13. It allows the detailed observation of living organisms.

14. The DIC microscope provides a colored, three-dimensional image of the object being observed.

15. It allows detailed observations of living cells.

16. In fluorescence microscopy, specimens are first stained with fluorochromes and then viewed through a compound microscope by using an ultraviolet light source.

17. The microorganisms appear as bright objects against a dark background.

18. Fluorescence microscopy is used primarily in a diagnostic procedure called fluorescent-antibody (FA) technique, or immunofluorescence.

19. In confocal microscopy, a specimen is stained with a fluorescent dye and illuminated with short-wavelength light.

20. Using a computer to process the images, two-dimensional and three-dimensional images of cells can be produced.

Two-Photon Microscopy

21. In TPM, a live specimen is stained with a fluorescent dye and illuminated with long-wavelength light.

Scanning Acoustic Microscopy

22. Scanning acoustic microscopy (SAM) is based on the interpretation of sound waves through a specimen.

23. It is used to study living cells attached to surfaces such as cancer cells, artery plaque, and biofilms.

Electron Microscopy

24. Instead of light, a beam of electrons is used with an electron microscope.

25. Instead of glass lenses, electromagnets control focus, illumination, and magnification.

26. Thin sections of organisms can be seen in an electron micrograph produced using a transmission electron microscope (TEM). Magnification: 10,000–100,000×. Resolving power: 10 pm.

27. Three-dimensional views of the surfaces of whole microorganisms can be obtained with a scanning electron microscope (SEM). Magnification: 1000–10,000×. Resolution: 10 nm.

Scanned-Probe Microscopy

28. Scanning tunneling microscopy (STM) and atomic force microscopy (AFM) produce three-dimensional images of the surface of a molecule.

Preparation of Specimens for Light Microscopy

Preparing Smears for Staining

1. Staining means coloring a microorganism with a dye to make some structures more visible.

2. Fixing uses heat or alcohol to kill and attach microorganisms to a slide.

3. A smear is a thin film of material used for microscopic examination.

4. Bacteria are negatively charged, and the colored positive ion of a basic dye will stain bacterial cells.

5. The colored negative ion of an acidic dye will stain the background of a bacterial smear; a negative stain is produced.

Simple Stains

6. A simple stain is an aqueous or alcohol solution of a single basic dye.

7. It is used to make cellular shapes and arrangements visible.

8. A mordant may be used to improve bonding between the stain and the specimen.

Differential Stains

9. Differential stains, such as the Gram stain and acid-fast stain, differentiate bacteria according to their reactions to the stains.

10. The Gram stain procedure uses a purple stain (crystal violet), iodine as a mordant, an alcohol decolorizer, and a red counterstain.

11. Gram-positive bacteria retain the purple stain after the decolorization step; gram-negative bacteria do not and thus appear pink from the counterstain.

12. Acid-fast microbes, such as members of the genera *Mycobacterium* and *Nocardia,* retain carbolfuchsin after acid-alcohol decolorization and appear red; non–acid-fast microbes take up the methylene blue counterstain and appear blue.

Special Stains

13. Negative staining is used to make microbial capsules visible.

14. The endospore stain and flagella stain are special stains that are used to visualize specific structures in bacterial cells.

Study Questions

Answers to the Review and Multiple Choice questions can be found at the end of this chapter.

Review

1. Fill in the following blanks.
   a. 1 μm = __10__ m
   b. 1 __nm__ = 10^{-9} m
   c. 1 μm = __10^3__ nm

2. Which type of microscope would be best to use to observe each of the following?
   a. a stained bacterial smear _Compound light microscope_
   b. unstained bacterial cells: the cells are small, and no detail is needed _darkfield microscope_
   c. unstained live tissue when it is desirable to see some intracellular detail _Phase-contrast microscope_
   d. a sample that emits light when illuminated with ultraviolet light _Flourescent_
   e. intracellular detail of a cell that is 1 μm long _electron microscope_
   f. unstained live cells in which intracellular structures are shown in color _(DIC) microscope_

3. **DRAW IT** Label the parts of the compound light microscope in the figure below, and then draw the path of light from the illuminator to your eye.

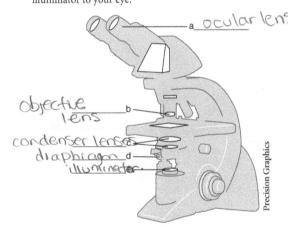

a _ocular lens_
b _objective lens_
condenser lenses
diaphragm d
illuminator

Precision Graphics

4. Calculate the total magnification of the nucleus of a cell being observed through a compound light microscope with a 10× ocular lens and an oil immersion lens. _100 0X_

5. The maximum magnification of a compound microscope is (a) _2,000_; that of an electron microscope, (b) _100,000_. The maximum resolution of a compound microscope is (c) _0.2nm_; that of an electron microscope, (d) _0-0025 nm_. One advantage of a scanning electron microscope over a transmission electron microscope is (e) _seeing 3 dimensional detail._

6. Why is a mordant used in the Gram stain? In the flagella stain?

7. What is the purpose of a counterstain in the acid-fast stain?

8. What is the purpose of a decolorizer in the Gram stain? In the acid-fast stain?

9. Fill in the following table regarding the Gram stain:

Steps	Appearance After This Step of Gram-Positive Cells	Gram-Negative Cells
Crystal violet	a. purple	e. purple
Iodine	b. purple	f. purple
Alcohol-acetone	c. purple	g. colorless
Safranin	d. purple	h. Red

10. **NAME IT** A sputum sample from Calle, a 30-year-old Asian elephant, was smeared onto a slide and air dried. The smear was fixed, covered with carbolfuchsin, and heated for 5 minutes. After washing with water, acid-alcohol was placed on the smear for 30 seconds. Finally, the smear was stained with methylene blue for 30 seconds, washed with water, and dried. On examination at 1000×, the zoo veterinarian saw red rods on the slide. (Calle was treated and recovered.) What microbe do these results suggest?

Multiple Choice

1. Assume you stain *Bacillus* by applying malachite green with heat and then counterstain with safranin. Through the microscope, the green structures are
   a. cell walls.
   b. capsules.
   c. endospores.
   d. flagella.
   e. impossible to identify.

2. Three-dimensional images of live cells can be produced with
   a. darkfield microscopy.
   b. fluorescence microscopy.
   c. transmission electron microscopy.
   d. confocal microscopy.
   e. phase-contrast microscopy.

3. Carbolfuchsin can be used as a simple stain and a negative stain. As a simple stain, the pH is
   a. 2.
   b. higher than the negative stain.
   c. lower than the negative stain.
   d. the same as the negative stain.

4. Looking at the cell of a photosynthetic microorganism, you observe that the chloroplasts are green in brightfield microscopy and red in fluorescence microscopy. You conclude that
   a. chlorophyll is fluorescent.
   b. the magnification has distorted the image.
   c. you're not looking at the same structure in both microscopes.
   d. the stain masked the green color.
   e. none of the above

5. Which of the following is *not* a functionally analogous pair of stains?
   a. nigrosin and malachite green
   b. crystal violet and carbolfuchsin
   c. safranin and methylene blue
   d. ethanol-acetone and acid-alcohol
   e. none of the above

6. Which of the following pairs is *mismatched*?
   a. capsule—negative stain
   b. cell arrangement—simple stain
   c. cell size—negative stain
   d. Gram stain—bacterial identification
   e. none of the above

7. Assume you stain *Clostridium* by applying a basic stain, carbolfuchsin, with heat, decolorizing with acid-alcohol, and counterstaining with an acidic stain, nigrosin. Through the microscope, the endospores are _____1_____, and the cells are stained _____2_____.
   a. 1—red; 2—black
   b. 1—black; 2—colorless
   c. 1—colorless; 2—black
   d. 1—red; 2—colorless
   e. 1—black; 2—red

8. Assume that you are viewing a Gram-stained field of red cocci and blue bacilli through the microscope. You can safely conclude that you have
   a. made a mistake in staining.
   b. two different species.
   c. old bacterial cells.
   d. young bacterial cells.
   e. none of the above

9. In 1996, scientists described a new tapeworm parasite that had killed at least one person. The initial examination of the patient's abdominal mass was most likely made using
   a. brightfield microscopy.
   b. darkfield microscopy.
   c. electron microscopy.
   d. phase-contrast microscopy.
   e. fluorescence microscopy.

10. Which of the following is *not* a modification of a compound light microscope?
    a. brightfield microscopy
    b. darkfield microscopy
    c. electron microscopy
    d. phase-contrast microscopy
    e. fluorescence microscopy

Critical Thinking

1. In a Gram stain, one step could be omitted and still allow differentiation between gram-positive and gram-negative cells. What is that one step?

2. Using a good compound light microscope with a resolving power of 0.3 μm, a 10× ocular lens, and a 100× oil immersion lens, would you be able to discern two objects separated by 3 μm? 0.3 μm? 300 nm?

3. Why isn't the Gram stain used on acid-fast bacteria? If you did Gram stain acid-fast bacteria, what would their Gram reaction be? What is the Gram reaction of non–acid-fast bacteria?

4. Endospores can be seen as refractile structures in unstained cells and as colorless areas in Gram-stained cells. Why is it necessary to do an endospore stain to verify the presence of endospores?

Clinical Applications

1. In 1882, German bacteriologist Paul Erhlich described a method for staining *Mycobacterium* and noted, "It may be that all disinfecting agents which are acidic will be without effect on this [tubercle] bacillus, and one will have to be limited to alkaline agents." How did he reach this conclusion without testing disinfectants?

2. Laboratory diagnosis of *Neisseria gonorrhoeae* infection is based on microscopic examination of Gram-stained pus. Locate the bacteria in this light micrograph. What is the disease?

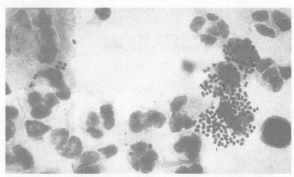

Biophoto Associates/Science Source/Photo Researchers   LM   5 μm

3. Assume that you are viewing a Gram-stained sample of vaginal discharge. Large (10 μm) nucleated red cells are coated with small (0.5 μm wide by 1.5 μm long) blue cells on their surfaces. What is the most likely explanation for the red and blue cells?

Answers to Review and Multiple Choice Study Questions

Review

1. a. 10^{-6} m;   **b.** 1nm;   **c.** 10^3 nm

2. a. Compound light microscope
   b. Darkfield microscope
   c. Phase-contrast microscope
   d. Fluorescence microscope
   e. Electron microscope
   f. Differential interference contrast microscope

3.

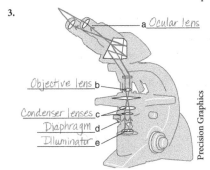

a *Ocular lens*

Objective lens b

Condenser lenses c
Diaphragm d
Illuminator e

Precision Graphics

4.

Ocular Lens Magnification	×	Oil Immersion Lens Magnification	=	Total Magnification of Specimen
10×		100×		1000×

5. a. 2,000×
   b. 100,000×
   c. 0.2 μm
   d. 0.0025 μm
   e. Seeing three-dimensional detail.

6. In a Gram stain, the mordant combines with the basic dye to form a complex that will not wash out of gram-positive cells. In a flagella stain, the mordant accumulates on the flagella so that they can be seen with a light microscope.

7. A counterstain stains the colorless non–acid-fast cells so that they are easily seen through a microscope.

8. In the Gram stain, the decolorizer removes the color from gram-negative cells. In the acid-fast stain, the decolorizer removes the color from non–acid-fast cells.

9. a. Purple   **e.** Purple
   b. Purple   **f.** Purple
   c. Purple   **g.** Colorless
   d. Purple   **h.** Red.

10. An acid-fast bacterium *(Mycobacterium)*.

Multiple Choice

1. c   **3.** b   **5.** a   **7.** d   **9.** a
2. d   **4.** a   **6.** e   **8.** b   **10.** c

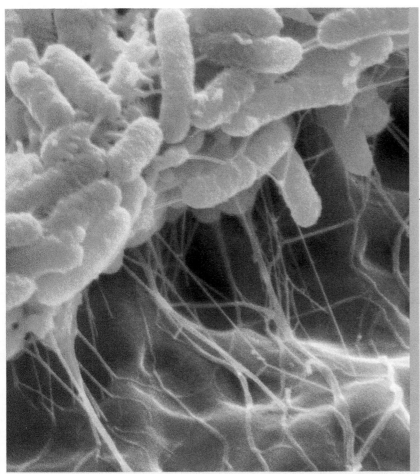

Scimat/Photo Researchers

Functional Anatomy of Prokaryotic and Eukaryotic Cells

Visualize microbiology and check your understanding a with a pre-test at www.masteringmicrobiology.com.

Despite their complexity and variety, all living cells can be classified into two groups, prokaryotes and eukaryotes, based on certain structural and functional characteristics. In general, prokaryotes are structurally simpler and smaller than eukaryotes. The DNA (genetic material) of prokaryotes is usually a single, circularly arranged chromosome and is not surrounded by a membrane; the DNA of eukaryotes is found in multiple chromosomes in a membrane-enclosed nucleus. Prokaryotes lack membrane-enclosed organelles, specialized structures that carry on various activities.

Plants and animals are entirely composed of eukaryotic cells. In the microbial world, bacteria and archaea are prokaryotes. Other cellular microbes—fungi (yeasts and molds), protozoa, and algae—are eukaryotes. Both eukaryotic and prokaryotic cells can have a sticky glycocalyx surrounding them. In nature, most bacteria are found sticking to solid surfaces including other cells rather than free-floating. The glycocalyx is the glue that holds the cells in place. The *Serratia* bacteria in the photograph are attached to plastic; the sticky glycocalyx dried into filaments during microscopic examination. An example of the problem posed by biofilms in hospital water supplies is described in the Clinical Case.

From Chapter 4 of *Microbiology: An Introduction*, Eleventh Edition. Gerard J. Tortora, Berdell R. Funke, Christine L. Case.

Comparing Prokaryotic and Eukaryotic Cells: An Overview

LEARNING OBJECTIVE

1   Compare and contrast the overall cell structure of prokaryotes and eukaryotes.

Prokaryotes and eukaryotes are chemically similar, in the sense that they both contain nucleic acids, proteins, lipids, and carbohydrates. They use the same kinds of chemical reactions to metabolize food, build proteins, and store energy. It is primarily the structure of cell walls and membranes, and the absence of *organelles* (specialized cellular structures that have specific functions), that distinguish prokaryotes from eukaryotes.

The chief distinguishing characteristics of **prokaryotes** (from the Greek words meaning prenucleus) are as follows:

Clinical Case: Infection Detection

Irene Matthews, an infection control nurse in a hospital in Atlanta, Georgia, is in a quandary. Three patients in her hospital have all contracted postprocedure bacterial septicemia. All three have a fever and dangerously low blood pressure. These three patients are in separate areas of the hospital, in different units, and they have all undergone different procedures. The first patient, Joe, a 32-year-old construction worker, is recovering from rotator cuff surgery. He is in relatively good health, otherwise. The second patient, Jessie, a 16-year-old student in intensive care, is in critical condition following an automobile accident. She is on a ventilator and cannot breathe on her own. The third patient, Maureen, a 57-year-old grandmother, is recovering from coronary artery bypass surgery. As far as Irene can tell, the only thing these patients have in common is the infectious agent—*Klebsiella pneumoniae.*

How can three patients in different parts of a hospital contract *Klebsiella pneumoniae?* Read on to find out.

1. Their DNA is not enclosed within a membrane and is usually a singular circularly arranged chromosome. (Some bacteria, such as *Vibrio cholerae,* have two chromosomes, and some bacteria have a linearly arranged chromosome.)

2. Their DNA is not associated with histones (special chromosomal proteins found in eukaryotes); other proteins are associated with the DNA.

3. They lack membrane-enclosed organelles.

4. Their cell walls almost always contain the complex polysaccharide peptidoglycan.

5. They usually divide by **binary fission.** During this process, the DNA is copied, and the cell splits into two cells. Binary fission involves fewer structures and processes than eukaryotic cell division.

Eukaryotes (from the Greek words meaning true nucleus) have the following distinguishing characteristics:

1. Their DNA is found in the cell's nucleus, which is separated from the cytoplasm by a nuclear membrane, and the DNA is found in multiple chromosomes.

2. Their DNA is consistently associated with chromosomal proteins called histones and with nonhistones.

3. They have a number of membrane-enclosed organelles, including mitochondria, endoplasmic reticulum, Golgi complex, lysosomes, and sometimes chloroplasts.

4. Their cell walls, when present, are chemically simple.

5. Cell division usually involves mitosis, in which chromosomes replicate and an identical set is distributed into each of two nuclei. This process is guided by the mitotic spindle, a football-shaped assembly of microtubules. Division of the cytoplasm and other organelles follows so that the two cells produced are identical to each other.

Additional differences between prokaryotic and eukaryotic cells are listed in Table 2, later in this chapter. Next we describe, in detail, the parts of the prokaryotic cell.

CHECK YOUR UNDERSTANDING

✔ What is the main feature that distinguishes prokaryotes from eukaryotes? 1

The Prokaryotic Cell

The members of the prokaryotic world make up a vast heterogeneous group of very small unicellular organisms. Prokaryotes include bacteria and archaea. The majority of prokaryotes, including the photosynthesizing cyanobacteria, are bacteria. Although bacteria and archaea look similar, their chemical composition is different, as will be described later. The thousands of species of bacteria are differentiated by many factors, including morphology (shape), chemical composition (often detected by staining reactions), nutritional requirements, biochemical activities, and sources of energy (sunlight or chemicals). It is estimated that 99% of the bacteria in nature exist in biofilms.

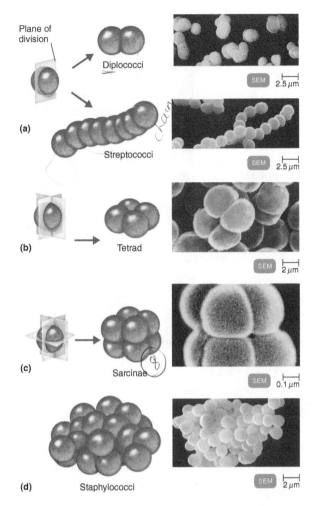

Figure 1 Arrangements of cocci. (**a**) Division in one plane produces diplococci and streptococci. (**b**) Division in two planes produces tetrads. (**c**) Division in three planes produces sarcinae, and (**d**) division in multiple planes produces staphylococci.

How do the planes of division determine the arrangement of cells?

(a)1. Oliver Meckes and Nicole Ottawa/Photo Researchers; 2. Eye of Science/Photo Researchers; (b) Gopal Murti/Photo Researchers; (c) From: "Staphylococcal cell wall: morphogenesis and fatal variations in the presence of penicillin." P. Giesbrecht, T. Kersten, H. Maidhof, and J. Wecke. *Microbiol Mol Biol* Rev. 1998 Dec;62(4):1371–414; Figure 2a; (d) David McCarthy/Photo Researchers

The Size, Shape, and Arrangement of Bacterial Cells

LEARNING OBJECTIVE

2   Identify the three basic shapes of bacteria.

Bacteria come in a great many sizes and several shapes. Most bacteria range from 0.2 to 2.0 μm in diameter and from 2 to 8 μm in length. They have a few basic shapes: spherical **coccus** (plural: cocci, meaning berries), rod-shaped **bacillus** (plural: **bacilli,** meaning little staffs), and **spiral.**

Cocci are usually round but can be oval, elongated, or flattened on one side. When cocci divide to reproduce, the cells can remain attached to one another. Cocci that remain in pairs after dividing are called **diplococci;** those that divide and remain attached in chainlike patterns are called **streptococci** (Figure 1a). Those that divide in two planes and remain in groups of four are known as **tetrads** (Figure 1b). Those that divide in three planes and remain attached in cubelike groups of eight are called **sarcinae** (Figure 1c). Those that divide in multiple planes and form grapelike clusters or broad sheets are called **staphylococci** (Figure 1d). These group characteristics are frequently helpful in identifying certain cocci.

Bacilli divide only across their short axis, so there are fewer groupings of bacilli than of cocci. Most bacilli appear as single rods, called **single bacilli.** (Figure 2a). **Diplobacilli** appear in pairs after division (Figure 2b), and **streptobacilli** occur in chains (Figure 2c). Some bacilli look like straws. Others have tapered ends, like cigars. Still others are oval and look so much like cocci that they are called **coccobacilli** (Figure 2d).

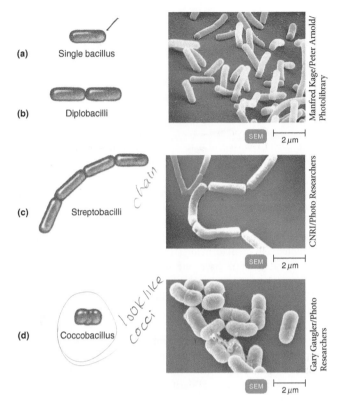

Figure 2 Bacilli. (**a**) Single bacilli. (**b**) Diplobacilli. In the top micrograph, a few joined pairs of bacilli could serve as examples of diplobacilli. (**c**) Streptobacilli. (**d**) Coccobacilli.

Why don't bacilli form tetrads or clusters?

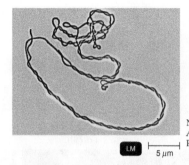

Figure 3 A double-stranded helix formed by *Bacillus subtilis.*

Q What is the difference between the term bacillus and *Bacillus*?

N.H. Mendelson and J.J. Thwaites, *ASM News* 59: 25, 1993. F2 Reprinted by permission

LM 5 μm

"Bacillus" has two meanings in microbiology. As we have just used it, bacillus refers to a bacterial shape. When capitalized and italicized, it refers to a specific genus. For example, the bacterium *Bacillus anthracis* is the causative agent of anthrax. Bacillus cells often form long, twisted chains of cells (Figure 3).

Spiral bacteria have one or more twists; they are never straight. Bacteria that look like curved rods are called **vibrios** (Figure 4a). Others, called **spirilla,** have a helical shape, like a corkscrew, and fairly rigid bodies (Figure 4b). Yet another group of spirals are helical and flexible; they are called **spirochetes** (Figure 4c). Unlike the spirilla, which use propeller-like external appendages called flagella to move, spirochetes move by means of axial filaments, which resemble flagella but are contained within a flexible external sheath.

In addition to the three basic shapes, there are star-shaped cells (genus *Stella*; Figure 5a); rectangular, flat cells (halophilic archaea) of the genus *Haloarcula* (Figure 5b); and triangular cells.

The shape of a bacterium is determined by heredity. Genetically, most bacteria are **monomorphic;** that is, they maintain a single shape. However, a number of environmental conditions can alter that shape. If the shape is altered, identification becomes difficult. Moreover, some bacteria, such as *Rhizobium* (rī-zō'bē-um) and *Corynebacterium* (kô-rī-nē-bak-ti'rē-um), are genetically **pleomorphic,** which means they can have many shapes, not just one.

The structure of a typical prokaryotic cell is shown in Figure 6. We will discuss its components according to the following organization: (1) structures external to the cell wall, (2) the cell wall itself, and (3) structures internal to the cell wall.

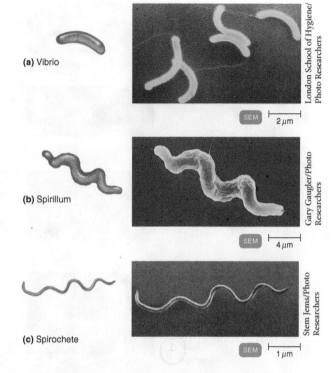

(a) Vibrio

(b) Spirillum

(c) Spirochete

London School of Hygiene/ Photo Researchers

Gary Gaugler/Photo Researchers

Stem Jems/Photo Researchers

SEM 2 μm

SEM 4 μm

SEM 1 μm

Figure 4 Spiral bacteria. (a) Vibrios. **(b)** Spirillum. **(c)** Spirochete.

Q What is the distinguishing feature of spirochete bacteria?

CHECK YOUR UNDERSTANDING

✔ How would you be able to identify streptococci through a microscope? 2

Structures External to the Cell Wall

LEARNING OBJECTIVES

3 Describe the structure and function of the glycocalyx

4 Differentiate flagella, axial filaments, fimbriae, and pili.

Among the possible structures external to the prokaryotic cell wall are the glycocalyx, flagella, axial filaments, fimbriae, and pili.

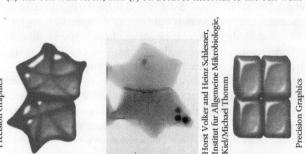

(a) Star-shaped bacteria

TEM 0.5 μm

(b) Rectangular bacteria

TEM 0.5 μm

Precision Graphics

Horst Volker and Heinz Schlesner, Institut fur Allgemeine Mikrobiologie, Kiel/Michael Thomm

Precision Graphics

H. W. Jannasch, Woods Hole Oceanographic Institution

Figure 5 Star-shaped and rectangular prokaryotes. (a) *Stella* (star-shaped). **(b)** *Haloarcula,* a genus of halophilic archaea (rectangular cells).

Q What are the common bacterial shapes?

The Structure of a Prokaryotic Cell

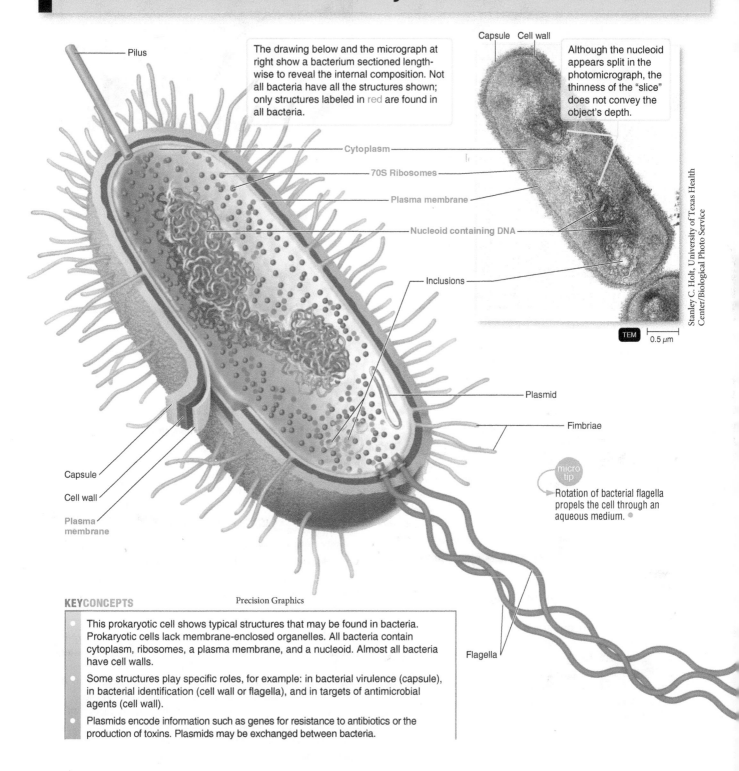

Pilus

The drawing below and the micrograph at right show a bacterium sectioned length-wise to reveal the internal composition. Not all bacteria have all the structures shown; only structures labeled in red are found in all bacteria.

Capsule   Cell wall

Although the nucleoid appears split in the photomicrograph, the thinness of the "slice" does not convey the object's depth.

Cytoplasm

70S Ribosomes

Plasma membrane

Nucleoid containing DNA

Inclusions

Stanley C. Holt, University of Texas Health Center/Biological Photo Service

TEM   0.5 µm

Plasmid

Fimbriae

micro tip

Rotation of bacterial flagella propels the cell through an aqueous medium.

Capsule

Cell wall

Plasma membrane

Flagella

Precision Graphics

KEYCONCEPTS

- This prokaryotic cell shows typical structures that may be found in bacteria. Prokaryotic cells lack membrane-enclosed organelles. All bacteria contain cytoplasm, ribosomes, a plasma membrane, and a nucleoid. Almost all bacteria have cell walls.

- Some structures play specific roles, for example: in bacterial virulence (capsule), in bacterial identification (cell wall or flagella), and in targets of antimicrobial agents (cell wall).

- Plasmids encode information such as genes for resistance to antibiotics or the production of toxins. Plasmids may be exchanged between bacteria.

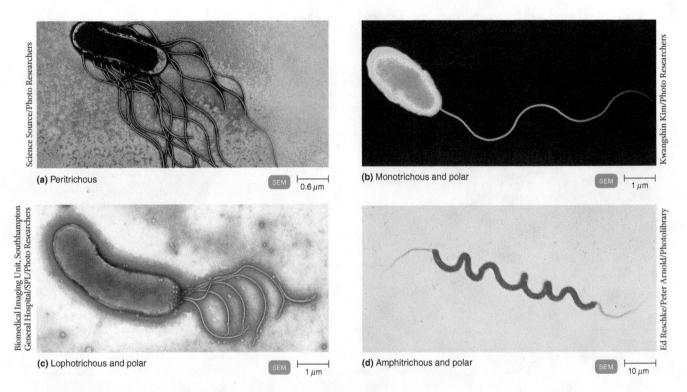

(a) Peritrichous   SEM   0.6 μm

(b) Monotrichous and polar   SEM   1 μm

(c) Lophotrichous and polar   SEM   1 μm

(d) Amphitrichous and polar   SEM   10 μm

Figure 7 Arrangements of bacterial flagella. (**a**) Peritrichous. (**b**)–(**d**) Polar.

Q Not all prokaryotic cells have flagella. What are bacteria without flagella called?

Glycocalyx

Many prokaryotes secrete on their surface a substance called glycocalyx. **Glycocalyx** (meaning sugar coat) is the general term used for substances that surround cells. The bacterial glycocalyx is a viscous (sticky), gelatinous polymer that is external to the cell wall and composed of polysaccharide, polypeptide, or both. Its chemical composition varies widely with the species. For the most part, it is made inside the cell and secreted to the cell surface. If the substance is organized and is firmly attached to the cell wall, the glycocalyx is described as a **capsule.** The presence of a capsule can be determined by using negative staining. If the substance is unorganized and only loosely attached to the cell wall, the glycocalyx is described as **a slime layer.**

In certain species, capsules are important in contributing to bacterial virulence (the degree to which a pathogen causes disease). Capsules often protect pathogenic bacteria from phagocytosis by the cells of the host. (As you will see later, phagocytosis is the ingestion and digestion of microorganisms and other solid particles.) For example, *Bacillus anthracis* produces a capsule of D-glutamic acid. (Recall that the D forms of amino acids are unusual.) Because only encapsulated *B. anthracis* causes anthrax, it is speculated that the capsule may prevent its being destroyed by phagocytosis.

Another example involves *Streptococcus pneumoniae* (strep-tō-kok′kus nü-mō′nē-ī), which causes pneumonia only when the cells are protected by a polysaccharide capsule. Unencapsulated *S. pneumoniae* cells cannot cause pneumonia and are readily phagocytized. The polysaccharide capsule of *Klebsiella* (kleb-sē-el′lä) also prevents phagocytosis and allows the bacterium to adhere to and colonize the respiratory tract.

The glycocalyx is a very important component of biofilms. A glycocalyx that helps cells in a biofilm attach to their target environment and to each other is called an **extracellular polymeric substance (EPS).** The EPS protects the cells within it, facilitates communication among them, and enables the cells to survive by attaching to various surfaces in their natural environment.

Through attachment, bacteria can grow on diverse surfaces such as rocks in fast-moving streams, plant roots, human teeth, medical implants, water pipes, and even other bacteria. *Streptococcus mutans* (mū′tans), an important cause of dental caries, attaches itself to the surface of teeth by a glycocalyx. *S. mutans* may use its capsule as a source of nutrition by breaking it down and utilizing the sugars when energy stores are low. *Vibrio cholerae* (vib′-rē-o kol′-er-ī), the cause of cholera, produces a glycocalyx that helps it attach to the cells of the small intestine. A glycocalyx also can protect a cell against dehydration, and its viscosity may inhibit the movement of nutrients out of the cell.

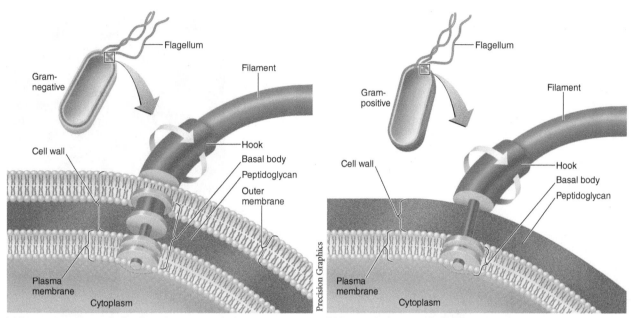

(a) Parts and attachment of a flagellum of a gram-negative bacterium

(b) Parts and attachment of a flagellum of a gram-positive bacterium

Precision Graphics

Figure 8 The structure of a prokaryotic flagellum. The parts and attachment of a flagellum of a gram-negative bacterium and gram-positive bacterium are shown in these highly schematic diagrams.

 How do the basal bodies of gram-negative and gram-positive bacteria differ?

Flagella

Some prokaryotic cells have **flagella** (singular: **flagellum**), which are long filamentous appendages that propel bacteria. Bacteria that lack flagella are referred to as **atrichous** (without projections). Flagella may be **peritrichous** (distributed over the entire cell; Figure 7a) or **polar** (at one or both poles or ends of the cell). If polar, flagella may be **monotrichous** (a single flagellum at one pole; Figure 7b), **lophotrichous** (a tuft of flagella coming from one pole; Figure 7c), or **amphitrichous** (flagella at both poles of the cell; Figure 7d).

A flagellum has three basic parts (Figure 8). The long outermost region, the *filament,* is constant in diameter and contains the globular (roughly spherical) protein *flagellin* arranged in several chains that intertwine and form a helix around a hollow core. In most bacteria, filaments are not covered by a membrane or sheath, as in eukaryotic cells. The filament is attached to a slightly wider *hook,* consisting of a different protein. The third portion of a flagellum is the *basal body,* which anchors the flagellum to the cell wall and plasma membrane.

The basal body is composed of a small central rod inserted into a series of rings. Gram-negative bacteria contain two pairs of rings; the outer pair of rings is anchored to various portions of the cell wall, and the inner pair of rings is anchored to the plasma membrane. In gram-positive bacteria, only the inner pair is present. As you will see later, the flagella (and cilia) of eukaryotic cells are more complex than those of prokaryotic cells.

Each prokaryotic flagellum is a semirigid, helical structure that moves the cell by rotating from the basal body. The rotation of a flagellum is either clockwise or counterclockwise around its long axis. (Eukaryotic flagella, by contrast, undulate in a wavelike motion.) The movement of a prokaryotic flagellum results from rotation of its basal body and is similar to the movement of the shaft of an electric motor. As the flagella rotate, they form a bundle that pushes against the surrounding liquid and propels the bacterium. Flagellar rotation depends on the cell's continuous generation of energy.

Bacterial cells can alter the speed and direction of rotation of flagella and thus are capable of various patterns of **motility,** the ability of an organism to move by itself. When a bacterium moves in one direction for a length of time, the movement is called a "run" or "swim." "Runs" are interrupted by periodic, abrupt, random changes in direction called "tumbles." Then, a "run" resumes. "Tumbles" are caused by a reversal of flagellar rotation (Figure 9a). Some species of bacteria endowed with many flagella—*Proteus* (prō'tē-us), for example (Figure 9b)—can "swarm," or show rapid wavelike movement across a solid culture medium.

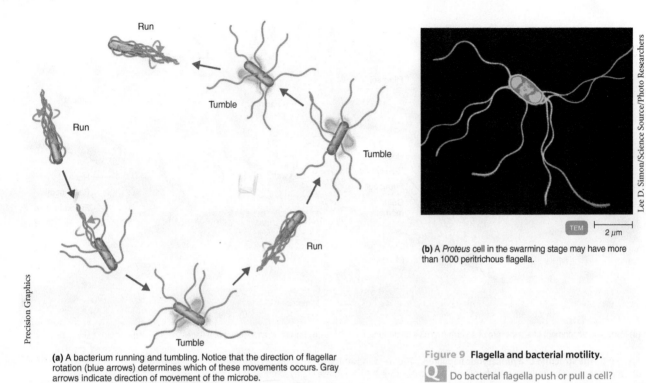

Precision Graphics

(a) A bacterium running and tumbling. Notice that the direction of flagellar rotation (blue arrows) determines which of these movements occurs. Gray arrows indicate direction of movement of the microbe.

Run
Tumble
Run
Tumble
Run
Tumble

TEM 2 µm

Lee D. Simon/Science Source/Photo Researchers

(b) A *Proteus* cell in the swarming stage may have more than 1000 peritrichous flagella.

Figure 9 **Flagella and bacterial motility.**

Q Do bacterial flagella push or pull a cell?

One advantage of motility is that it enables a bacterium to move toward a favorable environment or away from an adverse one. The movement of a bacterium toward or away from a particular stimulus is called **taxis.** Such stimuli include chemicals (**chemotaxis**) and light (**phototaxis**). Motile bacteria contain receptors in various locations, such as in or just under the cell wall. These receptors pick up chemical stimuli, such as oxygen, ribose, and galactose. In response to the stimuli, information is passed to the flagella. If the chemotactic signal is positive, called an *attractant,* the bacteria move toward the stimulus with many runs and few tumbles. If the chemotactic signal is negative, called a *repellent,* the frequency of tumbles increases as the bacteria move away from the stimulus.

The flagellar protein called **H antigen** is useful for distinguishing among **serovars,** or variations within a species, of gram-negative bacteria. For example, there are at least 50 different H antigens for *E. coli.* Those serovars identified as *E. coli* O157:H7 are associated with foodborne epidemics. MM Animations Motility; Flagella: Structure, Movement, Arrangement

Axial Filaments

Spirochetes are a group of bacteria that have unique structure and motility. One of the best-known spirochetes is *Treponema pallidum* (tre-pō-nē′ mä pal′li-dum), the causative agent of syphilis. Another spirochete is *Borrelia burgdorferi* (bôr′-rel-ē-a

burg-dor′ fer-ē), the causative agent of Lyme disease. Spirochetes move by means of **axial filaments,** or **endoflagella,** bundles of fibrils that arise at the ends of the cell beneath an outer sheath and spiral around the cell (Figure 10).

Axial filaments, which are anchored at one end of the spirochete, have a structure similar to that of flagella. The rotation of the filaments produces a movement of the outer sheath that propels the spirochetes in a spiral motion. This type of movement is similar to the way a corkscrew moves through a cork. This corkscrew motion probably enables a bacterium such as *T. pallidum* to move effectively through body fluids. MM Animation Spirochetes

Fimbriae and Pili

Many gram-negative bacteria contain hairlike appendages that are shorter, straighter, and thinner than flagella and are used for attachment and transfer of DNA rather than for motility. These structures, which consist of a protein called *pilin* arranged helically around a central core, are divided into two types, fimbriae and pili, having very different functions. (Some microbiologists use the two terms interchangeably to refer to all such structures, but we distinguish between them.)

Fimbriae (singular: **fimbria**) can occur at the poles of the bacterial cell or can be evenly distributed over the entire surface of the cell. They can number anywhere from a few to several

Figure 10 Axial filaments.

Q How are endoflagella different from flagella?

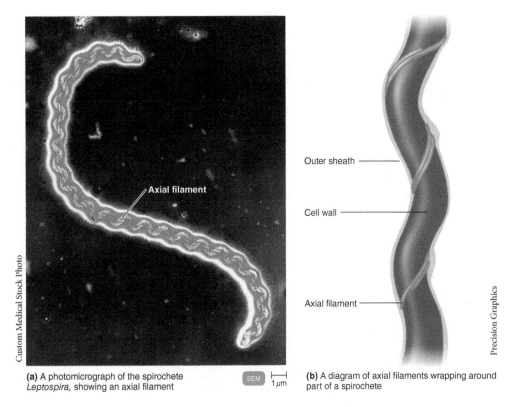

(a) A photomicrograph of the spirochete *Leptospira*, showing an axial filament

SEM | 1 μm

Outer sheath

Cell wall

Axial filament

(b) A diagram of axial filaments wrapping around part of a spirochete

Custom Medical Stock Photo

Precision Graphics

hundred per cell (**Figure 11**). Fimbriae have a tendency to adhere to each other and to surfaces. As a result, they are involved in forming biofilms and other aggregations on the surfaces of liquids, glass, and rocks. Fimbriae can also help bacteria adhere to epithelial surfaces in the body. For example, fimbriae on the bacterium *Neisseria gonorrhoeae* (nī-se′rē-ä go-nôr-rē′ī), the causative agent of gonorrhea, help the microbe colonize mucous membranes. Once colonization occurs, the bacteria can cause disease. The fimbriae of *E. coli* O157 enable this bacterium to adhere to the lining of the small intestine, where it causes a severe watery diarrhea. When fimbriae are absent (because of genetic mutation), colonization cannot happen, and no disease ensues.

Pili (singular: **pilus**) are usually longer than fimbriae and number only one or two per cell. Pili are involved in motility and DNA transfer. In one type of motility, called **twitching motility,** a pilus extends by the addition of subunits of pilin, makes contact with a surface or another cell, and then retracts (powerstroke) as the pilin subunits are disassembled. This is called the *grappling hook model* of twitching motility and results in short, jerky, intermittent movements. Twitching motility has been observed in *Pseudomonas aeruginosa*, *Neisseria gonorrhoeae*, and some strains of *E. coli*. The other type of motility associated with pili is **gliding motility,** the smooth gliding movement of

myxobacteria. Although the exact mechanism is unknown for most myxobacteria, some utilize pilus retraction. Gliding motility provides a means for microbes to travel in environments with a low water content, such as biofilms and soil.

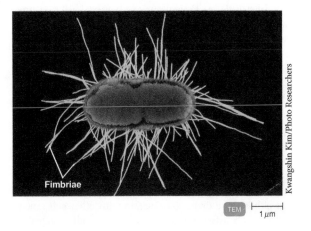

Fimbriae

TEM | 1 μm

Kwangshin Kim/Photo Researchers

Figure 11 Fimbriae. The fimbriae seem to bristle from this *E. coli* cell, which is beginning to divide.

Q Why are fimbriae necessary for colonization?

Some pili are used to bring bacteria together allowing the transfer of DNA from one cell to another, a process called conjugation. Such pili are called **conjugation (sex) pili**. In this process, the conjugation pilus of one bacterium called an F^+ cell connects to receptors on the surface of another bacterium of its own species or a different species. The two cells make physical contact, and DNA from the F^+ cell is transferred to the other cell. The exchanged DNA can add a new function to the recipient cell, such as antibiotic resistance or the ability to digest its medium more efficiently.

CHECK YOUR UNDERSTANDING

✔ Why are bacterial capsules medically important? 3

✔ How do bacteria move? 4

The Cell Wall

LEARNING OBJECTIVES

5   Compare and contrast the cell walls of gram-positive bacteria, gram-negative bacteria, acid-fast bacteria, archaea, and mycoplasmas.

6   Compare and contrast archaea and mycoplasmas.

7   Differentiate *protoplast, spheroplast,* and *L form.*

The **cell wall** of the bacterial cell is a complex, semirigid structure responsible for the shape of the cell. The cell wall surrounds the underlying, fragile plasma (cytoplasmic) membrane and protects it and the interior of the cell from adverse changes in the outside environment (see Figure 6). Almost all prokaryotes have cell walls.

The major function of the cell wall is to prevent bacterial cells from rupturing when the water pressure inside the cell is greater than that outside the cell (see Figure 18d). It also helps maintain the shape of a bacterium and serves as a point of anchorage for flagella. As the volume of a bacterial cell increases, its plasma membrane and cell wall extend as needed. Clinically, the cell wall is important because it contributes to the ability of some species to cause disease and is the site of action of some antibiotics. In addition, the chemical composition of the cell wall is used to differentiate major types of bacteria.

Although the cells of some eukaryotes, including plants, algae, and fungi, have cell walls, their walls differ chemically from those of prokaryotes, are simpler in structure, and are less rigid.

Composition and Characteristics

The bacterial cell wall is composed of a macromolecular network called **peptidoglycan** (also known as *murein*), which is present either alone or in combination with other substances. Peptidoglycan consists of a repeating disaccharide attached by polypeptides to form a lattice that surrounds and protects the entire cell. The disaccharide portion is made up of monosaccharides called N-acetylglucosamine (NAG) and N-acetylmuramic acid (NAM) (from *murus,* meaning wall), which are related to

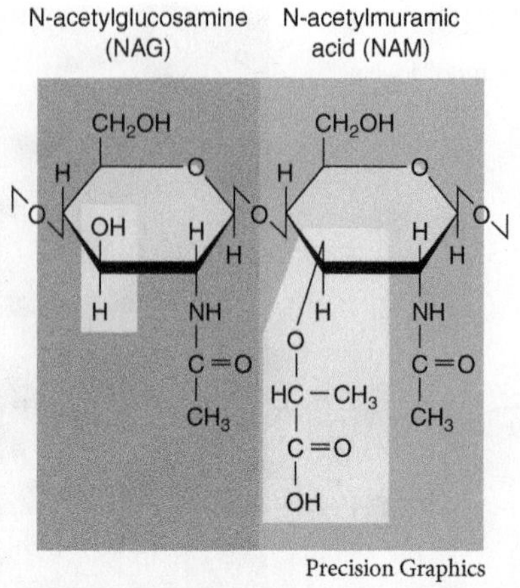

Figure 12 **N-acetylglucosamine (NAG) and N-acetylmuramic acid (NAM) joined as in a peptidoglycan.** The gold areas show the differences between the two molecules. The linkage between them is called a β-1,4 linkage.

Q What kind of molecules are these: carbohydrates, lipids, or proteins?

glucose. The structural formulas for NAG and NAM are shown in Figure 12.

The various components of peptidoglycan are assembled in the cell wall (Figure 13a). Alternating NAM and NAG molecules are linked in rows of 10 to 65 sugars to form a carbohydrate "backbone" (the glycan portion of peptidoglycan). Adjacent rows are linked by **polypeptides** (the peptide portion of peptidoglycan). Although the structure of the polypeptide link varies, it always includes *tetrapeptide side chains,* which consist of four amino acids attached to NAMs in the backbone. The amino acids occur in an alternating pattern of D and L forms. This is unique because the amino acids found in other proteins are L forms. Parallel tetrapeptide side chains may be directly bonded to each other or linked by a *peptide cross-bridge,* consisting of a short chain of amino acids.

Penicillin interferes with the final linking of the peptidoglycan rows by peptide cross-bridges (see Figure 13a). As a result, the cell wall is greatly weakened and the cell undergoes **lysis,** destruction caused by rupture of the plasma membrane and the loss of cytoplasm.

Gram-Positive Cell Walls

In most gram-positive bacteria, the cell wall consists of many layers of peptidoglycan, forming a thick, rigid structure (Figure 13b). By contrast, gram-negative cell walls contain only a thin layer of peptidoglycan (Figure 13c).

In addition, the cell walls of gram-positive bacteria contain *teichoic acids,* which consist primarily of an alcohol (such as glycerol or ribitol) and phosphate. There are two classes of teichoic acids: *lipoteichoic acid,* which spans the peptidoglycan layer and is linked

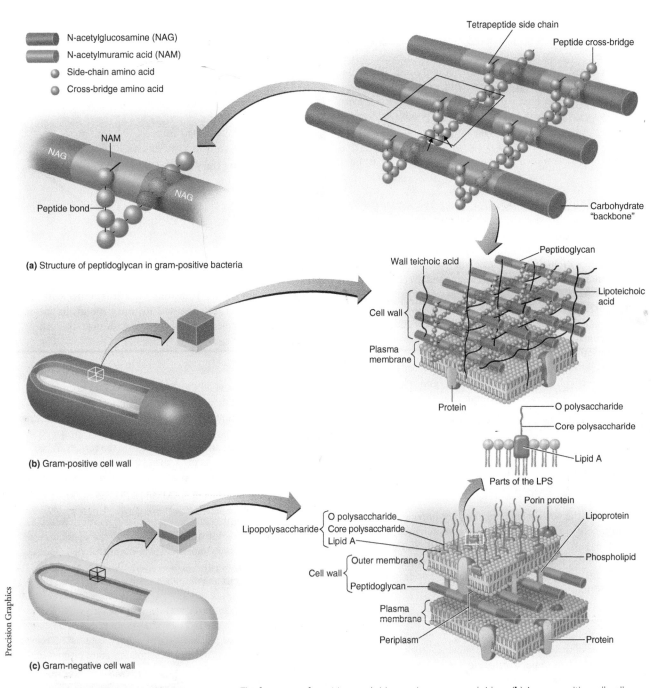

N-acetylglucosamine (NAG)
N-acetylmuramic acid (NAM)
Side-chain amino acid
Cross-bridge amino acid

Tetrapeptide side chain
Peptide cross-bridge

NAM
NAG
NAG
Peptide bond

Carbohydrate "backbone"

(a) Structure of peptidoglycan in gram-positive bacteria

Peptidoglycan
Wall teichoic acid
Lipoteichoic acid
Cell wall
Plasma membrane
Protein

(b) Gram-positive cell wall

O polysaccharide
Core polysaccharide
Lipid A
Parts of the LPS

Lipopolysaccharide
O polysaccharide
Core polysaccharide
Lipid A
Cell wall
Outer membrane
Peptidoglycan
Plasma membrane
Periplasm

Porin protein
Lipoprotein
Phospholipid
Protein

(c) Gram-negative cell wall

Precision Graphics

Figure 13 Bacterial cell walls. (a) The structure of peptidoglycan in gram-positive bacteria. Together the carbohydrate backbone (glycan portion) and tetrapeptide side chains (peptide portion) make up peptidoglycan. The frequency of peptide cross-bridges and the number of amino acids in these bridges · vary with species of bacteria. The small arrows indicate where penicillin interferes with the linkage of peptidoglycan rows by peptide cross-bridges. **(b)** A gram-positive cell wall. **(c)** A gram-negative cell wall.

Q What are the major structural differences between gram-positive and gram-negative cell walls?

to the plasma membrane, and *wall teichoic acid,* which is linked to the peptidoglycan layer. Because of their negative charge (from the phosphate groups), teichoic acids may bind and regulate the movement of cations (positive ions) into and out of the cell. They may also assume a role in cell growth, preventing extensive wall breakdown and possible cell lysis. Finally, teichoic acids provide much of the wall's antigenic specificity and thus make it possible to identify gram-positive bacteria by certain laboratory tests. Similarly, the cell walls of gram-positive streptococci are covered with various polysaccharides that allow them to be grouped into medically significant types.

Gram-Negative Cell Walls

The cell walls of gram-negative bacteria consist of one or a very few layers of peptidoglycan and an outer membrane (see Figure 13c). The peptidoglycan is bonded to lipoproteins (lipids covalently linked to proteins) in the outer membrane and is in the *periplasm,* a gel-like fluid between the outer membrane and the plasma membrane. The periplasm contains a high concentration of degradative enzymes and transport proteins. Gram-negative cell walls do not contain teichoic acids. Because the cell walls of gram-negative bacteria contain only a small amount of peptidoglycan, they are more susceptible to mechanical breakage.

The *outer membrane* of the gram-negative cell consists of lipopolysaccharides (LPS), lipoproteins, and phospholipids (see Figure 13c). The outer membrane has several specialized functions. Its strong negative charge is an important factor in evading phagocytosis and the actions of complement (lyses cells and promotes phagocytosis), two components of the defenses of the host. The outer membrane also provides a barrier to certain antibiotics (for example, penicillin), digestive enzymes such as lysozyme, detergents, heavy metals, bile salts, and certain dyes.

However, the outer membrane does not provide a barrier to all substances in the environment because nutrients must pass through to sustain the metabolism of the cell. Part of the permeability of the outer membrane is due to proteins in the membrane, called **porins,** that form channels. Porins permit the passage of molecules such as nucleotides, disaccharides, peptides, amino acids, vitamin B_{12}, and iron.

The **lipopolysaccharide (LPS)** of the outer membrane is a large complex molecule that contains lipids and carbohydrates and consists of three components: (1) lipid A, (2) a core polysaccharide, and (3) an O polysaccharide. **Lipid A** is the lipid portion of the LPS and is embedded in the top layer of the outer membrane. When gram-negative bacteria die, they release lipid A, which functions as an endotoxin. Lipid A is responsible for the symptoms associated with infections by gram-negative bacteria such as fever, dilation of blood vessels, shock, and blood clotting. The **core polysaccharide** is attached to lipid A and contains unusual sugars. Its role is structural—to provide stability. The **O polysaccharide** extends outward from the core polysaccharide and is composed of sugar molecules. The O polysaccharide

functions as an antigen and is useful for distinguishing species of gram-negative bacteria. For example, the foodborne pathogen *E. coli* O157:H7 is distinguished from other serovars by certain laboratory tests that test for these specific antigens. This role is comparable to that of teichoic acids in gram-positive cells.

Cell Walls and the Gram Stain Mechanism

Now that you have studied the Gram stain and the chemistry of the bacterial cell wall (in the previous section), it is easier to understand the mechanism of the Gram stain. The mechanism is based on differences in the structure of the cell walls of gram-positive and gram-negative bacteria and how each reacts to the various reagents (substances used for producing a chemical reaction). Crystal violet, the primary stain, stains both gram-positive and gram-negative cells purple because the dye enters the cytoplasm of both types of cells. When iodine (the mordant) is applied, it forms large crystals with the dye that are too large to escape through the cell wall. The application of alcohol dehydrates the peptidoglycan of gram-positive cells to make it more impermeable to the crystal violet-iodine. The effect on gram-negative cells is quite different; alcohol dissolves the outer membrane of gram-negative cells and even leaves small holes in the thin peptidoglycan layer through which crystal violet-iodine diffuse. Because gram-negative bacteria are colorless after the alcohol wash, the addition of safranin (the counterstain) turns the cells pink or red. Safranin provides a contrasting color to the primary stain (crystal violet). Although gram-positive and gram-negative cells both absorb safranin, the pink or red color of safranin is masked by the darker purple dye previously absorbed by gram-positive cells.

In any population of cells, some gram-positive cells will give a gram-negative response. These cells are usually dead. However, there are a few gram-positive genera that show an increasing number of gram-negative cells as the culture ages. *Bacillus* and *Clostridium* are examples and are often described as *gram-variable.*

A comparison of some of the characteristics of gram-positive and gram-negative bacteria is presented in **Table 1**.

TABLE 1 Some Comparative Characteristics of Gram-Positive and Gram-Negative Bacteria

Characteristic	Gram-Positive	Gram-Negative
	L. Brent Selinger, Pearson Science LM ⊢ 6 µm	L. Brent Selinger, Pearson Science LM ⊢ 15 µm
Gram Reaction	Retain crystal violet dye and stain blue or purple	Can be decolorized to accept counterstain (safranin) and stain pink or red
Peptidoglycan Layer	Thick (multilayered)	Thin (single-layered)
Teichoic Acids	Present in many	Absent
Periplasmic Space	Absent	Present
Outer Membrane	Absent	Present
Lipopolysaccharide (LPS) Content	Virtually none	High
Lipid and Lipoprotein Content	Low (acid-fast bacteria have lipids linked to peptidoglycan)	High (because of presence of outer membrane)
Flagellar Structure	2 rings in basal body	4 rings in basal body
Toxins Produced	Exotoxins	Endotoxins and exotoxins
Resistance to Physical Disruption	High	Low
Cell Wall Disruption by Lysozyme	High	Low (requires pretreatment to destabilize outer membrane)
Susceptibility to Penicillin and Sulfonamide	High	Low
Susceptibility to Streptomycin, Chloramphenicol, and Tetracycline	Low	High
Inhibition by Basic Dyes	High	Low
Susceptibility to Anionic Detergents	High	Low
Resistance to Sodium Azide	High	Low
Resistance to Drying	High	Low

Atypical Cell Walls

Among prokaryotes, certain types of cells have no walls or have very little wall material. These include members of the genus *Mycoplasma* (mī-kō-plaz′mä) and related organisms. Mycoplasmas are the smallest known bacteria that can grow and reproduce outside living host cells. Because of their size and because they have no cell walls, they pass through most bacterial filters and were first mistaken for viruses. Their plasma membranes are unique among bacteria in having lipids called *sterols*, which are thought to help protect them from lysis (rupture).

Archaea may lack walls or may have unusual walls composed of polysaccharides and proteins but not peptidoglycan. These walls do, however, contain a substance similar to peptidoglycan called *pseudomurein*. Pseudomurein contains N-acetyltalosaminuronic acid instead of NAM and lacks the D-amino acids found in bacterial cell walls. Archaea generally cannot be Gram-stained but appear gram-negative because they do not contain peptidoglycan.

Acid-Fast Cell Walls

Recall that the acid-fast stain is used to identify all bacteria of the genus *Mycobacterium* and pathogenic species of *Nocardia*. These bacteria contain high concentrations (60%) of a hydrophobic waxy lipid (**mycolic acid**) in their cell wall that prevents the uptake of dyes, including those used in the Gram stain. The mycolic acid forms a layer outside of a thin layer of peptidoglycan. The mycolic acid and peptidoglycan are held together by a polysaccharide. The hydrophobic waxy cell wall causes both cultures of *Mycobacterium* to clump and to stick to the walls of the flask. Acid-fast bacteria can be stained with carbolfuchsin; heating enhances penetration of the stain. The carbolfuchsin penetrates the cell wall, binds to cytoplasm, and resists removal by washing with acid-alcohol. Acid-fast bacteria retain the red color of carbolfuchsin because it is more soluble in the cell wall mycolic acid than in the acid-alcohol. If the mycolic acid layer is removed from the cell wall of acid-fast bacteria, they will stain gram-positive with the Gram stain.

Damage to the Cell Wall

Chemicals that damage bacterial cell walls, or interfere with their synthesis, often do not harm the cells of an animal host because the bacterial cell wall is made of chemicals unlike those in eukaryotic cells. Thus, cell wall synthesis is the target for some antimicrobial drugs. One way the cell wall can be damaged is by exposure to the digestive enzyme *lysozyme*. This enzyme occurs naturally in some eukaryotic cells and is a constituent of perspiration, tears, mucus, and saliva. Lysozyme is particularly active on the major cell wall components of most gram-positive bacteria, making them vulnerable to lysis. Lysozyme catalyzes hydrolysis of the bonds between the sugars in the repeating disaccharide "backbone" of peptidoglycan. This act is analogous to cutting the steel supports of a bridge with a cutting torch: the gram-positive cell wall is almost completely destroyed by lysozyme. The cellular contents that remain surrounded by the plasma membrane may remain intact if lysis does not occur; this wall-less cell is termed a **protoplast.** Typically, a protoplast is spherical and is still capable of carrying on metabolism.

Some members of the genus *Proteus,* as well as other genera, can lose their cell walls and swell into irregularly shaped cells called **L forms,** named for the Lister Institute, where they were discovered. They may form spontaneously or develop in response to penicillin (which inhibits cell wall formation) or lysozyme (which removes the cell wall). L forms can live and divide repeatedly or return to the walled state.

When lysozyme is applied to gram-negative cells, usually the wall is not destroyed to the same extent as in gram-positive cells; some of the outer membrane also remains. In this case, the cellular contents, plasma membrane, and remaining outer wall layer are called a **spheroplast,** also a spherical structure. For lysozyme to exert its effect on gram-negative cells, the cells are first treated with EDTA (ethylenediaminetetraacetic acid). EDTA weakens ionic bonds in the outer membrane and thereby damages it, giving the lysozyme access to the peptidoglycan layer.

Protoplasts and spheroplasts burst in pure water or very dilute salt or sugar solutions because the water molecules from the

Clinical Case

The outer membrane of *K. pneumoniae*'s gram-negative cell wall contains the endotoxin, lipid A, which causes fever and capillary dilation.

Irene works with Joe's, Jessie's , and Maureen's physicians to combat this potentially deadly infection. Irene is particularly concerned about Jessie because of her already weakened respiratory condition. All three patients are treated with a β-lactam antibiotic, imipenem. *Klebsiella* bacteria are resistant to many antibiotics, but imipenem seems to be working for Joe and Maureen. Jessie, however, is getting worse.

Why are Jessie's symptoms worsening if the bacteria are being killed?

surrounding fluid rapidly move into and enlarge the cell, which has a much lower internal concentration of water. This rupturing, called **osmotic lysis,** will be discussed in detail shortly.

As noted earlier, certain antibiotics, such as penicillin, destroy bacteria by interfering with the formation of the peptide cross-bridges of peptidoglycan, thus preventing the formation of a functional cell wall. Most gram-negative bacteria are not as susceptible to penicillin as gram-positive bacteria are because the outer membrane of gram-negative bacteria forms a barrier that inhibits the entry of this and other substances, and gram-negative bacteria have fewer peptide cross-bridges. However, gram-negative bacteria are quite susceptible to some β-lactam antibiotics that penetrate the outer membrane better than penicillin.

CHECK YOUR UNDERSTANDING

- Why are drugs that target cell wall synthesis useful? 5
- Why are mycoplasmas resistant to antibiotics that interfere with cell wall synthesis? 6
- How do protoplasts differ from L forms? 7

Structures Internal to the Cell Wall

LEARNING OBJECTIVES

8   Describe the structure, chemistry, and functions of the prokaryotic plasma membrane.

9   Define *simple diffusion, facilitated diffusion, osmosis, active transport,* and *group translocation.*

10   Identify the functions of the nucleoid and ribosomes.

11   Identify the functions of four inclusions.

12   Describe the functions of endospores, sporulation, and endospore germination.

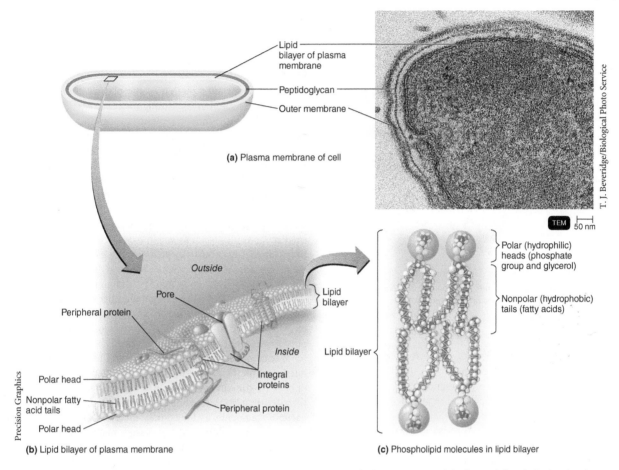

(a) Plasma membrane of cell

T. J. Beveridge/Biological Photo Service

Outside

Pore

Peripheral protein

Inside

Lipid bilayer

Integral proteins

Peripheral protein

Polar head

Nonpolar fatty acid tails

Polar head

Precision Graphics

(b) Lipid bilayer of plasma membrane

Polar (hydrophilic) heads (phosphate group and glycerol)

Nonpolar (hydrophobic) tails (fatty acids)

Lipid bilayer

(c) Phospholipid molecules in lipid bilayer

Figure 14 Plasma membrane. (a) A diagram and micrograph showing the lipid bilayer forming the inner plasma membrane of the gram-negative bacterium *Aquaspirillum serpens*. Layers of the cell wall, including the outer membrane, can be seen outside the inner membrane. **(b)** A portion of the inner membrane showing the lipid bilayer and proteins. The outer membrane of gram-negative bacteria is also a lipid bilayer. **(c)** Space-filling models of several phospholipid molecules as they are arranged in the lipid bilayer.

Q What is the difference between a peripheral and an integral protein?

Thus far, we have discussed the prokaryotic cell wall and structures external to it. We will now look inside the prokaryotic cell and discuss the structures and functions of the plasma membrane and components within the cytoplasm of the cell.

The Plasma (Cytoplasmic) Membrane

The **plasma (cytoplasmic) membrane** (or *inner membrane*) is a thin structure lying inside the cell wall and enclosing the cytoplasm of the cell (see Figure 6). The plasma membrane of prokaryotes consists primarily of phospholipids, which are the most abundant chemicals in the membrane, and proteins. Eukaryotic plasma membranes also contain carbohydrates and sterols, such as cholesterol. Because they lack sterols, prokaryotic plasma membranes are less rigid than eukaryotic membranes. One exception is the wall-less prokaryote *Mycoplasma*, which contains membrane sterols.

Structure

In electron micrographs, prokaryotic and eukaryotic plasma membranes (and the outer membranes of gram-negative bacteria) look like two-layered structures; there are two dark lines with a light space between the lines (Figure 14a). The phospholipid molecules are arranged in two parallel rows, called a *lipid bilayer* (Figure 14b). Each phospholipid molecule contains a polar head, composed of a phosphate group and glycerol that is hydrophilic (water-loving) and soluble in water, and nonpolar tails, composed of fatty acids that are hydrophobic (water-fearing) and insoluble in water (Figure 14c). The polar heads are on the two surfaces of the lipid bilayer, and the nonpolar tails are in the interior of the bilayer.

The protein molecules in the membrane can be arranged in a variety of ways. Some, called *peripheral proteins,* are easily removed from the membrane by mild treatments and lie at

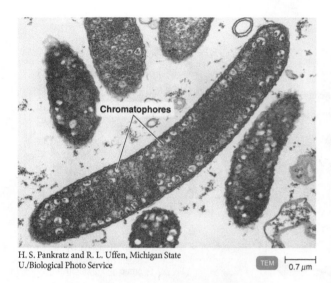

Chromatophores

H. S. Pankratz and R. L. Uffen, Michigan State
U./Biological Photo Service

TEM   0.7 μm

Figure 15 Chromatophores. In this micrograph of *Rhodospirillum rubrum,* a purple (nonsulfur) bacterium, the chromatophores are clearly visible.

Q What is the function of chromatophores?

the inner or outer surface of the membrane. They may function as enzymes that catalyze chemical reactions, as a "scaffold" for support, and as mediators of changes in membrane shape during movement. Other proteins, called *integral proteins,* can be removed from the membrane only after disrupting the lipid bilayer (by using detergents, for example). Most integral proteins penetrate the membrane completely and are called *transmembrane proteins.* Some integral proteins are channels that have a pore, or hole, through which substances enter and exit the cell.

Many of the proteins and some of the lipids on the outer surface of the plasma membrane have carbohydrates attached to them. Proteins attached to carbohydrates are called **glycoproteins;** lipids attached to carbohydrates are called **glycolipids.** Both glycoproteins and glycolipids help protect and lubricate the cell and are involved in cell-to-cell interactions. For example, glycoproteins play a role in certain infectious diseases. The influenza virus and the toxins that cause cholera and botulism enter their target cells by first binding to glycoproteins on their plasma membranes.

Studies have demonstrated that the phospholipid and protein molecules in membranes are not static but move quite freely within the membrane surface. This movement is most probably associated with the many functions performed by the plasma membrane. Because the fatty acid tails cling together, phospholipids in the presence of water form a self-sealing bilayer; as a result, breaks and tears in the membrane heal themselves. The membrane must be about as viscous as olive oil, which allows membrane proteins to move freely enough to perform their

functions without destroying the structure of the membrane. This dynamic arrangement of phospholipids and proteins is referred to as the **fluid mosaic model.**

Functions

The most important function of the plasma membrane is to serve as a selective barrier through which materials enter and exit the cell. In this function, plasma membranes have **selective permeability** (sometimes called *semipermeability*). This term indicates that certain molecules and ions pass through the membrane, but that others are prevented from passing through it. The permeability of the membrane depends on several factors. Large molecules (such as proteins) cannot pass through the plasma membrane, possibly because these molecules are larger than the pores in integral proteins that function as channels. But smaller molecules (such as water, oxygen, carbon dioxide, and some simple sugars) usually pass through easily. Ions penetrate the membrane very slowly. Substances that dissolve easily in lipids (such as oxygen, carbon dioxide, and nonpolar organic molecules) enter and exit more easily than other substances because the membrane consists mostly of phospholipids. The movement of materials across plasma membranes also depends on transporter molecules, which will be described shortly.

Plasma membranes are also important to the breakdown of nutrients and the production of energy. The plasma membranes of bacteria contain enzymes capable of catalyzing the chemical reactions that break down nutrients and produce ATP. In some bacteria, pigments and enzymes involved in photosynthesis are found in infoldings of the plasma membrane that extend into the cytoplasm. These membranous structures are called **chromatophores** or **thylakoids** (Figure 15).

When viewed with an electron microscope, bacterial plasma membranes often appear to contain one or more large, irregular folds called **mesosomes.** Many functions have been proposed for mesosomes. However, it is now known that they are artifacts, not true cell structures. Mesosomes are believed to be folds in the plasma membrane that develop by the process used for preparing specimens for electron microscopy. (MM) Animations
Membrane Structure; Membrane Permeability

Destruction of the Plasma Membrane by Antimicrobial Agents

Because the plasma membrane is vital to the bacterial cell, it is not surprising that several antimicrobial agents exert their effects at this site. In addition to the chemicals that damage the cell wall and thereby indirectly expose the membrane to injury, many compounds specifically damage plasma membranes. These compounds include certain alcohols and quaternary ammonium compounds, which are used as disinfectants. By disrupting the membrane's phospholipids, a group of antibiotics known as the *polymyxins* cause leakage of intracellular contents and subsequent cell death.

The Movement of Materials across Membranes

Materials move across plasma membranes of both prokaryotic and eukaryotic cells by two kinds of processes: passive and active. In *passive processes,* substances cross the membrane from an area of high concentration to an area of low concentration (move with the concentration gradient, or difference), without any expenditure of energy (ATP) by the cell. In *active processes,* the cell must use energy (ATP) to move substances from areas of low concentration to areas of high concentration (against the concentration gradient).

Passive Processes

Passive processes include simple diffusion, facilitated diffusion, and osmosis.

Simple diffusion is the net (overall) movement of molecules or ions from an area of high concentration to an area of low concentration (Figure 16 and Figure 17a). The movement continues until the molecules or ions are evenly distributed. The point of even distribution is called *equilibrium.* Cells rely on simple diffusion to transport certain small molecules, such as oxygen and carbon dioxide, across their cell membranes.

In **facilitated diffusion,** integral membrane proteins function as channels or carriers that facilitate the movement of ions or large molecules across the plasma membrane. Such integral proteins are called *transporters* or *permeases.* Facilitated diffusion is similar to simple diffusion in that the cell *does not* expend energy, because the substance moves from a high to a low concentration. The process differs from simple diffusion in its use of transporters. Some transporters permit the passage of mostly small, inorganic ions that are too hydrophilic to penetrate the nonpolar interior of the lipid bilayer (Figure 17b). These transporters, which are common in pro-

Precision Graphics

(a)

Christine Case

(b)

Figure 16 The principle of simple diffusion. (**a**) After a dye pellet is put into a beaker of water, the molecules of dye in the pellet diffuse into the water from an area of high dye concentration to areas of low dye concentration. (**b**) The dye potassium permanganate in the process of diffusing.

Q Why are passive processes important to a cell?

karyotes, are nonspecific and allow the passage of a wide variety of ions (or even small molecules). Other transporters, which are common in eukaryotes, are specific and transport only specific, usually larger, molecules, such as simple sugars (glucose, fructose, and galactose) and vitamins. In this process, the transported substance binds to a specific transporter on the outer surface of the plasma membrane, which undergoes a change of shape; then the transporter releases the substance on the other side of the membrane (Figure 17c).

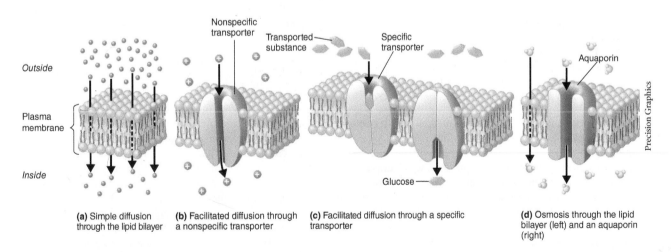

Precision Graphics

Outside

Plasma membrane

Inside

Nonspecific transporter

Transported substance

Specific transporter

Aquaporin

Glucose

(a) Simple diffusion through the lipid bilayer

(b) Facilitated diffusion through a nonspecific transporter

(c) Facilitated diffusion through a specific transporter

(d) Osmosis through the lipid bilayer (left) and an aquaporin (right)

Figure 17 Passive processes.

Q How does simple diffusion differ from facilitated diffusion?

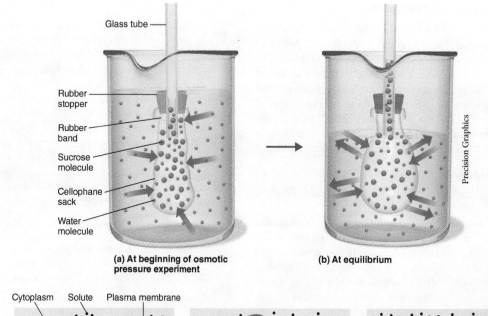

Glass tube

Rubber stopper

Rubber band

Sucrose molecule

Cellophane sack

Water molecule

Precision Graphics

(a) At beginning of osmotic pressure experiment

(b) At equilibrium

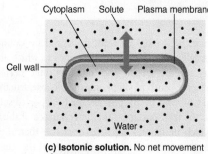

Cytoplasm   Solute   Plasma membrane

Cell wall

Water

(c) Isotonic solution. No net movement of water occurs.

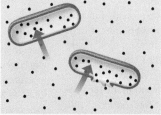

(d) Hypotonic solution. Water moves into the cell. If the cell wall is strong, it contains the swelling. If the cell wall is weak or damaged, the cell bursts (osmotic lysis).

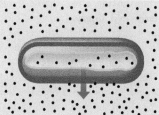

(e) Hypertonic solution. Water moves out of the cell, causing its cytoplasm to shrink (plasmolysis).

Figure 18   The principle of osmosis.
(**a**) Setup at the beginning of an osmotic pressure experiment. Water molecules start to move from the beaker into the sack along the concentration gradient. (**b**) Setup at equilibrium. The osmotic pressure exerted by the solution in the sack pushes water molecules from the sack back into the beaker to balance the rate of water entry into the sack. The height of the solution in the glass tube at equilibrium is a measure of the osmotic pressure. (**c**)–(**e**) The effects of various solutions on bacterial cells.

 Why is osmosis important?

In some cases, molecules that bacteria need are too large to be transported into the cells by these methods. Most bacteria, however, produce enzymes that can break down large molecules into simpler ones (such as proteins into amino acids, or polysaccharides into simple sugars). Such enzymes, which are released by the bacteria into the surrounding medium, are appropriately called *extracellular enzymes*. Once the enzymes degrade the large molecules, the subunits move into the cell with the help of transporters. For example, specific carriers retrieve DNA bases, such as the purine guanine, from extracellular media and bring them into the cell's cytoplasm.

Osmosis is the net movement of solvent molecules across a selectively permeable membrane from an area with a high concentration of solvent molecules (low concentration of solute molecules) to an area of low concentration of solvent molecules (high concentration of solute molecules). In living systems, the chief solvent is water. Water molecules may pass through plasma membranes by moving through the lipid bilayer by simple diffusion or through integral membrane proteins, called *aquaporins*, that function as water channels (**Figure 17d**).

Osmosis may be demonstrated with the apparatus shown in **Figure 18a**. A sack constructed from cellophane, which is a selectively permeable membrane, is filled with a solution of 20% sucrose (table sugar). The cellophane sack is placed into a beaker containing distilled water. Initially, the concentrations of water on either side of the membrane are different. Because of the sucrose molecules, the concentration of water is lower inside the cellophane sack. Therefore, water moves from the beaker (where its concentration is higher) into the cellophane sack (where its concentration is lower).

There is no movement of sugar out of the cellophane sack into the beaker, however, because the cellophane is impermeable to molecules of sugar—the sugar molecules are too large to go through the pores of the membrane. As water moves into the cellophane sack, the sugar solution becomes increasingly dilute, and, because the cellophane sack has expanded to its limit as a result of an increased volume of water, water begins to move up the glass tube. In time, the water that has accumulated in the cellophane sack and the glass tube exerts a downward pressure that forces water molecules out of the cellophane sack and back into the beaker. This movement of water through a selectively permeable membrane produces osmotic pressure. **Osmotic pressure** is the pressure required to prevent the movement of pure water (water with no solutes) into a solution containing some solutes. In other words, osmotic pressure is the pressure needed to stop the flow of water across the selectively permeable membrane (cellophane). When water molecules leave and enter the cellophane sack at the same rate, equilibrium is reached (Figure 18b).

A bacterial cell may be subjected to any of three kinds of osmotic solutions: isotonic, hypotonic, or hypertonic. An **isotonic solution** is a medium in which the overall concentration of solutes equals that found inside a cell (*iso* means equal). Water leaves and enters the cell at the same rate (no net change); the cell's contents are in equilibrium with the solution outside the cell wall (Figure 18c).

Earlier we mentioned that lysozyme and certain antibiotics (such as penicillin) damage bacterial cell walls, causing the cells to rupture, or lyse. Such rupturing occurs because bacterial cytoplasm usually contains such a high concentration of solutes that, when the wall is weakened or removed, additional water enters the cell by osmosis. The damaged (or removed) cell wall cannot constrain the swelling of the cytoplasmic membrane, and the membrane bursts. This is an example of osmotic lysis caused by immersion in a hypotonic solution. A **hypotonic solution** outside the cell is a medium whose concentration of solutes is lower than that inside the cell (*hypo* means under or less). Most bacteria live in hypotonic solutions, and the cell wall resists further osmosis and protects cells from lysis. Cells with weak cell walls, such as gram-negative bacteria, may burst or undergo osmotic lysis as a result of excessive water intake (Figure 18d).

A **hypertonic solution** is a medium having a higher concentration of solutes than inside the cell has (*hyper* means above or more). Most bacterial cells placed in a hypertonic solution shrink and collapse or *plasmolyze* because water leaves the cells by osmosis (Figure 18e). Keep in mind that the terms *isotonic, hypotonic,* and *hypertonic* describe the concentration of solutions outside the cell *relative to* the concentration inside the cell. Animations Passive Transport: Principles of Diffusion, Special Types of Diffusion

Active Processes

Simple diffusion and facilitated diffusion are useful mechanisms for transporting substances into cells when the concentrations of the substances are greater outside the cell. However, when a bacterial cell is in an environment in which nutrients are in low concentration, the cell must use active processes, such as active transport and group translocation, to accumulate the needed substances.

In performing **active transport,** the cell *uses energy* in the form of ATP to move substances across the plasma membrane. Among the substances actively transported are ions (for example Na^+, K^+, H^+, Ca^{2+}, and Cl^-), amino acids, and simple sugars. Although these substances can also be moved into cells by passive processes, their movement by active processes can go against the concentration gradient, allowing a cell to accumulate needed materials. The movement of a substance in active transport is usually from outside to inside, even though the concentration might be much higher inside the cell. Like facilitated diffusion, active transport depends on transporter proteins in the plasma membrane (see Figure 17b, c). There appears to be a different transporter for each transported substance or group of closely related transported substances. Active transport enables microbes to move substances across the plasma membrane at a constant rate, even if they are in short supply.

In active transport, the substance that crosses the membrane is not altered by transport across the membrane. In **group translocation,** a special form of active transport that occurs exclusively in prokaryotes, the substance is chemically altered during transport across the membrane. Once the substance is altered and inside the cell, the plasma membrane is impermeable to it, so it remains inside the cell. This important mechanism enables a cell to accumulate various substances even though they may be in low concentrations outside the cell. Group translocation requires energy supplied by high-energy phosphate compounds, such as phosphoenolpyruvic acid (PEP).

One example of group translocation is the transport of the sugar glucose, which is often used in growth media for bacteria. While a specific carrier protein is transporting the glucose molecule across the membrane, a phosphate group is added to the sugar. This phosphorylated form of glucose, which cannot be transported out, can then be used in the cell's metabolic pathways.

Some eukaryotic cells (those without cell walls) can use two additional active transport processes called phagocytosis and pinocytosis. These processes, which do not occur in bacteria, are explained later in this chapter. Animations Active Transport: Types, Overview

CHECK YOUR UNDERSTANDING

✓ Which agents can cause injury to the bacterial plasma membrane? 8

✓ How are simple diffusion and facilitated diffusion similar? How are they different? 9

Cytoplasm

For a prokaryotic cell, the term **cytoplasm** refers to the substance of the cell inside the plasma membrane (see Figure 6). Cytoplasm is about 80% water and contains primarily proteins (enzymes), carbohydrates, lipids, inorganic ions, and many low-molecular-weight compounds. Inorganic ions are present in much higher concentrations in cytoplasm than in most media. Cytoplasm is thick, aqueous, semitransparent, and elastic. The major structures in the cytoplasm of prokaryotes are a nucleoid (containing DNA), particles called ribosomes, and reserve deposits called inclusions. Protein filaments in the cytoplasm are most likely responsible for the rod and helical cell shapes of bacteria.

Prokaryotic cytoplasm lacks certain features of eukaryotic cytoplasm, such as a cytoskeleton and cytoplasmic streaming. These features will be described later.

The Nucleoid

The **nucleoid** of a bacterial cell (see Figure 6) usually contains a single long, continuous, and frequently circularly arranged thread of double-stranded DNA called the **bacterial chromosome.** This is the cell's genetic information, which carries all the information required for the cell's structures and functions. Unlike the chromosomes of eukaryotic cells, bacterial chromosomes are not surrounded by a nuclear envelope (membrane) and do not include histones. The nucleoid can be spherical, elongated, or dumbbell-shaped. In actively growing bacteria, as much as 20% of the cell volume is occupied by DNA because such cells presynthesize nuclear material for future cells. The chromosome is attached to the plasma membrane. Proteins in the plasma membrane are believed to be responsible for replication of the DNA and segregation of the new chromosomes to daughter cells during cell division.

In addition to the bacterial chromosome, bacteria often contain small usually circular, double-stranded DNA molecules called **plasmids.** These molecules are extrachromosomal genetic elements; that is, they are not connected to the main bacterial chromosome, and they replicate independently of chromosomal DNA. Research indicates that plasmids are associated with plasma membrane proteins. Plasmids usually contain from 5 to 100 genes that are generally not crucial for the survival of the bacterium under normal environmental conditions; plasmids may be gained or lost without harming the cell. Under certain conditions, however, plasmids are an advantage to cells. Plasmids may carry genes for such activities as antibiotic resistance, tolerance to toxic metals, the production of toxins, and the synthesis of enzymes. Plasmids can be transferred from one bacterium to another. In fact, plasmid DNA is used for gene manipulation in biotechnology.

Ribosomes

All eukaryotic and prokaryotic cells contain **ribosomes,** which function as the sites of protein synthesis. Cells that have high

Precision Graphics

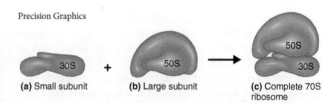

(a) Small subunit **(b)** Large subunit **(c)** Complete 70S ribosome

Figure 19 The prokaryotic ribosome. (**a**) A small 30S subunit and (**b**) a large 50S subunit make up (**c**) the complete 70S prokaryotic ribosome.

Q What is the importance of the differences between prokaryotic and eukaryotic ribosomes with regard to antibiotic therapy?

rates of protein synthesis, such as those that are actively growing, have a large number of ribosomes. The cytoplasm of a prokaryotic cell contains tens of thousands of these very small structures, which give the cytoplasm a granular appearance (see Figure 6).

Ribosomes are composed of two subunits, each of which consists of protein and a type of RNA called *ribosomal RNA (rRNA).* Prokaryotic ribosomes differ from eukaryotic ribosomes in the number of proteins and rRNA molecules they contain; they are also somewhat smaller and less dense than ribosomes of eukaryotic cells. Accordingly, prokaryotic ribosomes are called 70S ribosomes (Figure 19), and those of eukaryotic cells are known as 80S ribosomes. The letter S refers to Svedberg units, which indicate the relative rate of sedimentation during ultra-high-speed centrifugation. Sedimentation rate is a function of the size, weight, and shape of a particle. The subunits of a 70S ribosome are a small 30S subunit containing one molecule of rRNA and a larger 50S subunit containing two molecules of rRNA.

Several antibiotics work by inhibiting protein synthesis on prokaryotic ribosomes. Antibiotics such as streptomycin and gentamicin attach to the 30S subunit and interfere with protein synthesis. Other antibiotics, such as erythromycin and chloramphenicol, interfere with protein synthesis by attaching to the 50S subunit. Because of differences in prokaryotic and eukaryotic ribosomes, the microbial cell can be killed by the antibiotic while the eukaryotic host cell remains unaffected.

Inclusions

Within the cytoplasm of prokaryotic cells are several kinds of reserve deposits, known as **inclusions.** Cells may accumulate certain nutrients when they are plentiful and use them when the environment is deficient. Evidence suggests that macromolecules concentrated in inclusions avoid the increase in osmotic pressure that would result if the molecules were dispersed in the cytoplasm. Some inclusions are common to a wide variety of bacteria, whereas others are limited to a small number of species and therefore serve as a basis for identification.

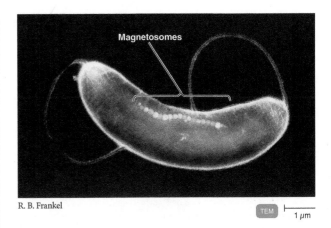

R. B. Frankel

TEM |— 1 µm

Figure 20 Magnetosomes. This micrograph of *Magnetospirillum magnetotacticum* shows a chain of magnetosomes. This bacterium is usually found in shallow freshwater mud.

 How do magnetosomes behave like magnets?

Metachromatic Granules

Metachromatic granules are large inclusions that take their name from the fact that they sometimes stain red with certain blue dyes such as methylene blue. Collectively they are known as **volutin**. Volutin represents a reserve of inorganic phosphate (polyphosphate) that can be used in the synthesis of ATP. It is generally formed by cells that grow in phosphate-rich environments. Metachromatic granules are found in algae, fungi, and protozoa, as well as in bacteria. These granules are characteristic of *Corynebacterium diphtheriae* (kô-rī-nē-bak-ti′ rē-um dif-thi′ rē-ĭ), the causative agent of diphtheria; thus, they have diagnostic significance.

Polysaccharide Granules

Inclusions known as **polysaccharide granules** typically consist of glycogen and starch, and their presence can be demonstrated when iodine is applied to the cells. In the presence of iodine, glycogen granules appear reddish brown and starch granules appear blue.

Lipid Inclusions

Lipid inclusions appear in various species of *Mycobacterium, Bacillus, Azotobacter* (ä-zō-tō-bak′ tér), *Spirillum* (spī-ril′ lum), and other genera. A common lipid-storage material, one unique to bacteria, is the polymer *poly-β-hydroxybutyric acid.* Lipid inclusions are revealed by staining cells with fat-soluble dyes, such as Sudan dyes.

Sulfur Granules

Certain bacteria—for example, the "sulfur bacteria" that belong to the genus *Thiobacillus*—derive energy by oxidizing sulfur and sulfur-containing compounds. These bacteria may deposit **sulfur granules** in the cell, where they serve as an energy reserve.

Carboxysomes

Carboxysomes are inclusions that contain the enzyme ribulose 1,5-diphosphate carboxylase. Photosynthetic bacteria use carbon dioxide as their sole source of carbon and require this enzyme for carbon dioxide fixation. Among the bacteria containing carboxysomes are nitrifying bacteria, cyanobacteria, and thiobacilli.

Gas Vacuoles

Hollow cavities found in many aquatic prokaryotes, including cyanobacteria, anoxygenic photosynthetic bacteria, and halobacteria are called **gas vacuoles.** Each vacuole consists of rows of several individual *gas vesicles,* which are hollow cylinders covered by protein. Gas vacuoles maintain buoyancy so that the cells can remain at the depth in the water appropriate for them to receive sufficient amounts of oxygen, light, and nutrients.

Magnetosomes

Magnetosomes are inclusions of iron oxide (Fe_3O_4) surrounded by invaginations of the plasma membrane. Magnetosomes are formed by several gram-negative bacteria such as *Magnetospirillum magnetotacticum* and act like magnets (Figure 20). Bacteria may use magnetosomes to move downward until they reach a suitable attachment site. In vitro, magnetosomes can decompose hydrogen peroxide, which forms in cells in the presence of oxygen. Researchers speculate that magnetosomes may protect the cell against hydrogen peroxide accumulation.

Endospores

When essential nutrients are depleted, certain gram-positive bacteria, such as those of the genera *Clostridium* and *Bacillus*, form specialized "resting" cells called **endospores** (Figure 21). As you

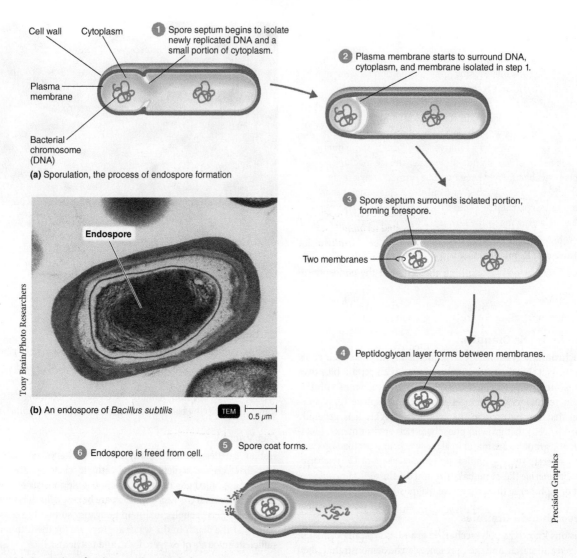

Cell wall   Cytoplasm

1 Spore septum begins to isolate newly replicated DNA and a small portion of cytoplasm.

Plasma membrane

Bacterial chromosome (DNA)

(a) Sporulation, the process of endospore formation

2 Plasma membrane starts to surround DNA, cytoplasm, and membrane isolated in step 1.

Endospore

Tony Brain/Photo Researchers

(b) An endospore of *Bacillus subtilis*   TEM   0.5 μm

3 Spore septum surrounds isolated portion, forming forespore.

Two membranes

4 Peptidoglycan layer forms between membranes.

6 Endospore is freed from cell.   **5** Spore coat forms.

Precision Graphics

Figure 21   Formation of endospores by sporulation.

Q What properties make endospores resistant to processes that normally kill vegetative cells?

will see later, some members of the genus *Clostridium* cause diseases such as gangrene, tetanus, botulism, and food poisoning. Some members of the genus *Bacillus* cause anthrax and food poisoning. Unique to bacteria, endospores are highly durable dehydrated cells with thick walls and additional layers. They are formed internal to the bacterial cell membrane.

When released into the environment, they can survive extreme heat, lack of water, and exposure to many toxic chemicals and radiation. For example, 7500-year-old endospores of *Thermoactinomyces vulgaris* (thér-mō-ak-tin-ō-mĭ′sēs vul-ga′-ris) from the freezing muds of Elk Lake in Minnesota have germinated when rewarmed and placed in a nutrient medium,

and 25- to 40-million-year-old endospores found in the gut of a stingless bee entombed in amber (hardened tree resin) in the Dominican Republic are reported to have germinated when placed in nutrient media. Although true endospores are found in gram-positive bacteria, one gram-negative species, *Coxiella burnetii* (käks-ē-el′lä bėr-ne′tē-ē), the cause of Q fever, forms endosporelike structures that resist heat and chemicals and can be stained with endospore stains.

The process of endospore formation within a vegetative cell takes several hours and is known as **sporulation** or **sporogenesis** (Figure 21a). Vegetative cells of endospore-forming bacteria begin sporulation when a key nutrient, such as the carbon or nitrogen source, becomes scarce or unavailable. In the first observable stage of sporulation, a newly replicated bacterial chromosome and a small portion of cytoplasm are isolated by an ingrowth of the plasma membrane called a *spore septum*. The spore septum becomes a double-layered membrane that surrounds the chromosome and cytoplasm. This structure, entirely enclosed within the original cell, is called a *forespore*. Thick layers of peptidoglycan are laid down between the two membrane layers. Then a thick *spore coat* of protein forms around the outside membrane; this coat is responsible for the resistance of endospores to many harsh chemicals. The original cell is degraded, and the endospore is released.

The diameter of the endospore may be the same as, smaller than, or larger than the diameter of the vegetative cell. Depending on the species, the endospore might be located *terminally* (at one end), *subterminally* (near one end; Figure 21b), or *centrally* inside the vegetative cell. When the endospore matures, the vegetative cell wall ruptures (lyses), killing the cell, and the endospore is freed.

Most of the water present in the forespore cytoplasm is eliminated by the time sporulation is complete, and endospores do not carry out metabolic reactions. The endospore contains a large amount of an organic acid called *dipicolinic acid* (DPA), which is accompanied by a large number of calcium ions. Evidence indicates that DPA protects the endospore DNA against damage. The highly dehydrated endospore core contains only DNA, small amounts of RNA, ribosomes, enzymes, and a few important small molecules. These cellular components are essential for resuming metabolism later.

Endospores can remain dormant for thousands of years. An endospore returns to its vegetative state by a process called **germination.** Germination is triggered by physical or chemical damage to the endospore's coat. The endospore's enzymes then break down the extra layers surrounding the endospore, water enters, and metabolism resumes. Because one vegetative cell forms a single endospore, which, after germination, remains one cell, sporulation in bacteria is *not* a means of reproduction. This process does not increase the number of cells. Bacterial endospores differ from spores formed by (prokaryotic) actinomy-cetes and the eukaryotic fungi and algae, which detach from the parent and develop into another organism and, therefore, represent reproduction.

Endospores are important from a clinical viewpoint and in the food industry because they are resistant to processes that normally kill vegetative cells. Such processes include heating, freezing, desiccation, use of chemicals, and radiation. Whereas most vegetative cells are killed by temperatures above 70°C, endospores can survive in boiling water for several hours or more. Endospores of thermophilic (heat-loving) bacteria can survive in boiling water for 19 hours. Endospore-forming bacteria are a problem in the food industry because they are likely to survive underprocessing, and, if conditions for growth occur, some species produce toxins and disease.

Clinical Case Resolved

It is the glycocalyx that enables bacteria in water to stick inside a pipe. The bacteria grow slowly in the nutrient-poor tap water but do not get washed away by the flowing water. A slimy layer of bacteria can accumulate in a pipe. Irene discovers that the disinfectant in the hospital's water supply was inadequate to prevent bacterial growth. Some bacteria can get dislodged by flowing water, and even normally harmless bacteria can infect a surgical incision or weakened host.

CHECK YOUR UNDERSTANDING

🖊 Where is the DNA located in a prokaryotic cell? 10

🖊 What is the general function of inclusions? 11

🖊 Under what conditions do endospores form? 12

* * *

Having examined the functional anatomy of the prokaryotic cell, we will now look at the functional anatomy of the eukaryotic cell.

The Eukaryotic Cell

As mentioned earlier, eukaryotic organisms include algae, protozoa, fungi, plants, and animals. The eukaryotic cell is typically larger and structurally more complex than the prokaryotic cell (Figure 22). When the structure of the prokaryotic cell in Figure 6 is compared with that of the eukaryotic cell, the differences between the two types of cells become apparent. The principal differences between prokaryotic and eukaryotic cells are summarized in Table 2.

The following discussion of eukaryotic cells will parallel our discussion of prokaryotic cells by starting with structures that extend to the outside of the cell.

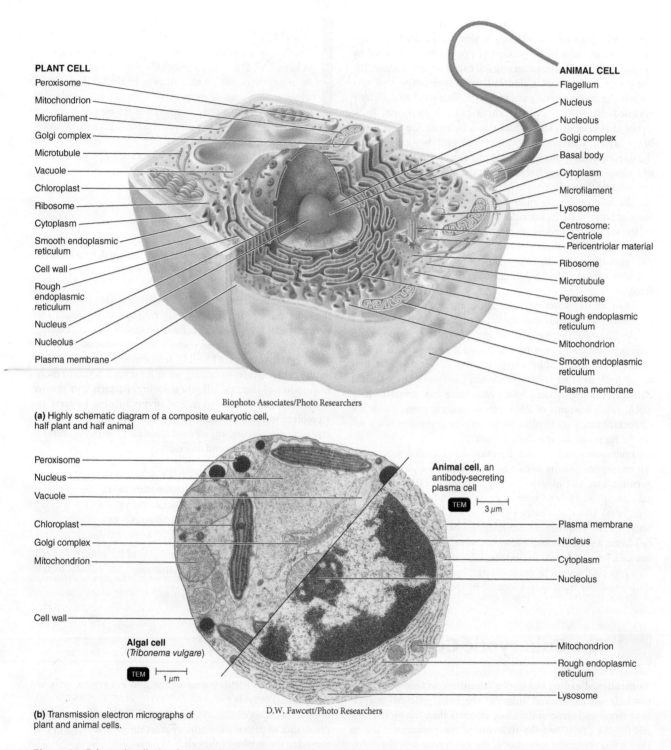

PLANT CELL
- Peroxisome
- Mitochondrion
- Microfilament
- Golgi complex
- Microtubule
- Vacuole
- Chloroplast
- Ribosome
- Cytoplasm
- Smooth endoplasmic reticulum
- Cell wall
- Rough endoplasmic reticulum
- Nucleus
- Nucleolus
- Plasma membrane

ANIMAL CELL
- Flagellum
- Nucleus
- Nucleolus
- Golgi complex
- Basal body
- Cytoplasm
- Microfilament
- Lysosome
- Centrosome:
  - Centriole
  - Pericentriolar material
- Ribosome
- Microtubule
- Peroxisome
- Rough endoplasmic reticulum
- Mitochondrion
- Smooth endoplasmic reticulum
- Plasma membrane

Biophoto Associates/Photo Researchers

(a) Highly schematic diagram of a composite eukaryotic cell, half plant and half animal

- Peroxisome
- Nucleus
- Vacuole
- Chloroplast
- Golgi complex
- Mitochondrion
- Cell wall

Animal cell, an antibody-secreting plasma cell

TEM ⊢ 3 μm

- Plasma membrane
- Nucleus
- Cytoplasm
- Nucleolus
- Mitochondrion
- Rough endoplasmic reticulum
- Lysosome

Algal cell (*Tribonema vulgare*)

TEM ⊢ 1 μm

(b) Transmission electron micrographs of plant and animal cells.

D.W. Fawcett/Photo Researchers

Figure 22 Eukaryotic cells showing typical structures.

Q What kingdoms contain eukaryotic organisms?

Figure 3.1 from *Principles of Anatomy and Physiology*, 9th ed., by Tortora & Grabowski. Copyright © 2000. Reprinted by permission of John Wiley & Sons, Inc.

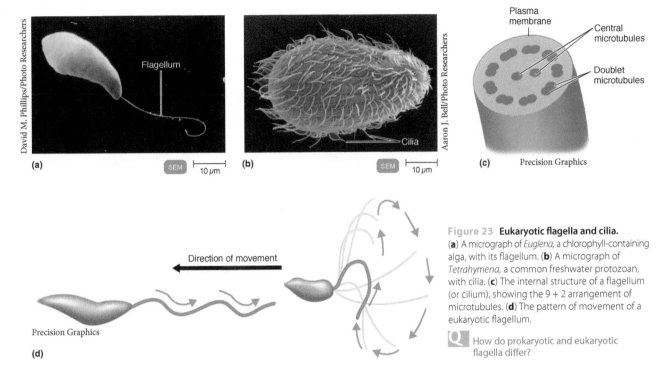

Figure 23 Eukaryotic flagella and cilia.
(**a**) A micrograph of *Euglena,* a chlorophyll-containing alga, with its flagellum. (**b**) A micrograph of *Tetrahymena,* a common freshwater protozoan, with cilia. (**c**) The internal structure of a flagellum (or cilium), showing the 9 + 2 arrangement of microtubules. (**d**) The pattern of movement of a eukaryotic flagellum.

How do prokaryotic and eukaryotic flagella differ?

Flagella and Cilia

LEARNING OBJECTIVE

13 Differentiate prokaryotic and eukaryotic flagella.

Many types of eukaryotic cells have projections that are used for cellular locomotion or for moving substances along the surface of the cell. These projections contain cytoplasm and are enclosed by the plasma membrane. If the projections are few and are long in relation to the size of the cell, they are called **flagella.** If the projections are numerous and short, they are called **cilia** (singular: **cilium**).

Algae of the genus *Euglena* (ū-glē′na) use a flagellum for locomotion, whereas protozoa, such as *Tetrahymena* (tet-rä-hī′ me-nä), use cilia for locomotion (**Figure 23a** and **Figure 23b**). Both flagella and cilia are anchored to the plasma membrane by a basal body, and both consist of nine pairs of microtubules (doublets) arranged in a ring, plus another two microtubules in the center of the ring, an arrangement called a *9 + 2 array* (**Figure 23c**). **Microtubules** are long, hollow tubes made up of a protein called *tubulin.* A prokaryotic flagellum rotates, but a eukaryotic flagellum moves in a wavelike manner (**Figure 23d**). To help keep foreign material out of the lungs, ciliated cells of the human respiratory system move the material along the surface of the cells in the bronchial tubes and trachea toward the throat and mouth.

The Cell Wall and Glycocalyx

LEARNING OBJECTIVE

14 Compare and contrast prokaryotic and eukaryotic cell walls and glycocalyxes.

Most eukaryotic cells have cell walls, although they are generally much simpler than those of prokaryotic cells. Many algae have cell walls consisting of the polysaccharide *cellulose* (as do all plants); other chemicals may be present as well. Cell walls of some fungi also contain cellulose, but in most fungi the principal structural component of the cell wall is the polysaccharide *chitin,* a polymer of N-acetylglucosamine (NAG) units. (Chitin is also the main structural component of the exoskeleton of crustaceans and insects.) The cell walls of yeasts contain the polysaccharides *glucan* and *mannan.* In eukaryotes that lack a cell wall, the plasma membrane may be the outer covering; however, cells that have direct contact with the environment may have coatings outside the plasma membrane. Protozoa do not have a typical cell wall; instead, they have a flexible outer protein covering called a *pellicle.*

In other eukaryotic cells, including animal cells, the plasma membrane is covered by a **glycocalyx,** a layer of material containing substantial amounts of sticky carbohydrates. Some of these carbohydrates are covalently bonded to proteins and lipids in the plasma membrane, forming glycoproteins and glycolipids that anchor the glycocalyx to the cell. The glycocalyx strengthens the cell surface, helps attach cells together, and may contribute to cell–cell recognition.

TABLE 2 Principal Differences between Prokaryotic and Eukaryotic Cells

Characteristic	Prokaryotic	Eukaryotic
	Precision Graphics	Precision Graphics / L. Brent Selinger, Pearson Science — Eukaryotes / Prokaryotes / 10 µm / LM
Size of Cell	Typically 0.2–2.0 µm in diameter	Typically 10–100 µm in diameter
Nucleus	No nuclear membrane or nucleoli	True nucleus, consisting of nuclear membrane and nucleoli
Membrane-Enclosed Organelles	Absent	Present; examples include lysosomes, Golgi complex, endoplasmic reticulum, mitochondria, and chloroplasts
Flagella	Consist of two protein building blocks	Complex; consist of multiple microtubules
Glycocalyx	Present as a capsule or slime layer	Present in some cells that lack a cell wall
Cell Wall	Usually present; chemically complex (typical bacterial cell wall includes peptidoglycan)	When present, chemically simple (includes cellulose and chitin)
Plasma Membrane	No carbohydrates and generally lacks sterols	Sterols and carbohydrates that serve as receptors
Cytoplasm	No cytoskeleton or cytoplasmic streaming	Cytoskeleton; cytoplasmic streaming
Ribosomes	Smaller size (70S)	Larger size (80S); smaller size (70S) in organelles
Chromosome (DNA)	Usually single circular chromosome; typically lacks histones	Multiple linear chromosomes with histones
Cell Division	Binary fission	Involves mitosis
Sexual Recombination	None; transfer of DNA only	Involves meiosis

Eukaryotic cells do not contain peptidoglycan, the framework of the prokaryotic cell wall. This is significant medically because antibiotics, such as penicillins and cephalosporins, act against peptidoglycan and therefore do not affect human eukaryotic cells.

The Plasma (Cytoplasmic) Membrane

LEARNING OBJECTIVE

15 Compare and contrast prokaryotic and eukaryotic plasma membranes.

The **plasma (cytoplasmic) membrane** of eukaryotic and prokaryotic cells is very similar in function and basic structure. There are, however, differences in the types of proteins found in the membranes. Eukaryotic membranes also contain carbohydrates, which serve as attachment sites for bacteria and as receptor sites that assume a role in such functions as cell–cell recognition. Eukaryotic plasma membranes also contain *sterols,* complex lipids not found in

prokaryotic plasma membranes (with the exception of *Mycoplasma* cells). Sterols seem to be associated with the ability of the membranes to resist lysis resulting from increased osmotic pressure.

Substances can cross eukaryotic and prokaryotic plasma membranes by simple diffusion, facilitated diffusion, osmosis, or active transport. Group translocation does not occur in eukaryotic cells. However, eukaryotic cells can use a mechanism called **endocytosis.** This occurs when a segment of the plasma membrane surrounds a particle or large molecule, encloses it, and brings it into the cell.

The three types of endocytosis are phagocytosis, pinocytosis, and receptor-mediated endocytosis. During *phagocytosis,* cellular projections called pseudopods engulf particles and bring them into the cell. Phagocytosis is used by white blood cells to destroy bacteria and foreign substances. In *pinocytosis,* the plasma membrane folds inward, bringing extracellular fluid into the cell, along with whatever substances are dissolved in the fluid. In *receptor-mediated endocytosis,* substances (ligands) bind to receptors in the membrane.

When binding occurs, the membrane folds inward. Receptor-mediated endocytosis is one of the ways viruses can enter animal cells.

Cytoplasm

LEARNING OBJECTIVE

16   Compare and contrast prokaryotic and eukaryotic cytoplasms.

The **cytoplasm** of eukaryotic cells encompasses the substance inside the plasma membrane and outside the nucleus (see Figure 22). The cytoplasm is the substance in which various cellular components are found. (The term **cytosol** refers to the fluid portion of cytoplasm.) A major difference between eukaryotic and prokaryotic cytoplasm is that eukaryotic cytoplasm has a complex internal structure, consisting of exceedingly small rods (*microfilaments* and *intermediate filaments*) and cylinders (*microtubules*). Together, they form the **cytoskeleton.** The cytoskeleton provides support and shape and assists in transporting substances through the cell (and even in moving the entire cell, as in phagocytosis). The movement of eukaryotic cytoplasm from one part of the cell to another, which helps distribute nutrients and move the cell over a surface, is called **cytoplasmic streaming.** Another difference between prokaryotic and eukaryotic cytoplasm is that many of the important enzymes found in the cytoplasmic fluid of prokaryotes are sequestered in the organelles of eukaryotes.

Ribosomes

LEARNING OBJECTIVE

17   Compare the structure and function of eukaryotic and prokaryotic ribosomes.

Attached to the outer surface of rough endoplasmic reticulum are **ribosomes** (see Figure 25), which are also found free in the cytoplasm. As in prokaryotes, ribosomes are the sites of protein synthesis in the cell.

The ribosomes of eukaryotic endoplasmic reticulum and cytoplasm are somewhat larger and denser than those of prokaryotic cells. These eukaryotic ribosomes are 80S ribosomes, each of which consists of a large 60S subunit containing three molecules of rRNA and a smaller 40S subunit with one molecule of rRNA. The subunits are made separately in the nucleolus and, once produced, exit the nucleus and join together in the cytosol. Chloroplasts and mitochondria contain 70S ribosomes, which may indicate their evolution from prokaryotes.

Some ribosomes, called *free ribosomes,* are unattached to any structure in the cytoplasm. Primarily, free ribosomes synthesize proteins used *inside* the cell. Other ribosomes, called *membrane-bound ribosomes,* attach to the nuclear membrane and the endoplasmic reticulum. These ribosomes synthesize proteins destined for insertion in the plasma membrane or for export from the cell. Ribosomes located within mitochondria synthesize mitochondrial proteins. Sometimes 10 to 20 ribosomes join together in a stringlike arrangement called a *polyribosome.*

CHECK YOUR UNDERSTANDING

✔ Identify at least one significant difference between eukaryotic and prokaryotic flagella and cilia, cell walls, plasma membranes, and cytoplasm. 13–16

✔ The antibiotic erythromycin binds with the 50S portion of a ribosome. What effect does this have on a prokaryotic cell? On a eukaryotic cell? 17

Organelles

LEARNING OBJECTIVES

18   Define *organelle.*

19   Describe the functions of the nucleus, endoplasmic reticulum, Golgi complex, lysosomes, vacuoles, mitochondria, chloroplasts, peroxisomes, and centrosomes.

Organelles are structures with specific shapes and specialized functions and are characteristic of eukaryotic cells. They include the nucleus, endoplasmic reticulum, Golgi complex, lysosomes, vacuoles, mitochondria, chloroplasts, peroxisomes, and centrosomes. Not all of the organelles described are found in all cells. Certain cells have their own type and distribution of organelles based on specialization, age, and level of activity.

The Nucleus

The most characteristic eukaryotic organelle is the nucleus (see Figure 22). The **nucleus** (Figure 24) is usually spherical or oval, is frequently the largest structure in the cell, and contains almost all of the cell's hereditary information (DNA). Some DNA is also found in mitochondria and in the chloroplasts of photosynthetic organisms.

The nucleus is surrounded by a double membrane called the **nuclear envelope.** Both membranes resemble the plasma membrane in structure. Tiny channels in the membrane called **nuclear pores** allow the nucleus to communicate with the cytoplasm (Figure 24b). Nuclear pores control the movement of substances between the nucleus and cytoplasm. Within the nuclear envelope are one or more spherical bodies called **nucleoli** (singular: **nucleolus**). Nucleoli are actually condensed regions of chromosomes where ribosomal RNA is being synthesized. Ribosomal RNA is an essential component of ribosomes.

The nucleus also contains most of the cell's DNA, which is combined with several proteins, including some basic proteins called **histones** and nonhistones. The combination of about 165 base pairs of DNA and 9 molecules of histones is referred to as a *nucleosome.* When the cell is not reproducing, the DNA

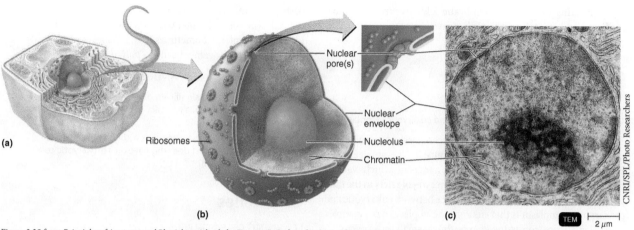

Figure 3.25 from *Principles of Anatomy and Physiology*, 9th ed., by Tortora & Grabowski. Copyright © 2000. Reprinted by permission of John Wiley & Sons, Inc.

Figure 24 **The eukaryotic nucleus.** (**a, b**) Drawings of details of a nucleus. (**c**) A micrograph of a nucleus.

 What keeps the nucleus suspended in the cell?

and its associated proteins appear as a threadlike mass called **chromatin.** During nuclear division, the chromatin coils into shorter and thicker rodlike bodies called **chromosomes.** Prokaryotic chromosomes do not undergo this process, do not have histones, and are not enclosed in a nuclear envelope.

Eukaryotic cells require two elaborate mechanisms: mitosis and meiosis to segregate chromosomes prior to cell division. Neither process occurs in prokaryotic cells.

Endoplasmic Reticulum

Within the cytoplasm of eukaryotic cells is the **endoplasmic reticulum,** or **ER,** an extensive network of flattened membranous sacs or tubules called **cisternae** (Figure 25). The ER network is continuous with the nuclear envelope (see Figure 22a).

Most eukaryotic cells contain two distinct, but interrelated, forms of ER that differ in structure and function. The membrane of **rough ER** is continuous with the nuclear membrane and usually unfolds into a series of flattened sacs. The outer surface of rough ER is studded with ribosomes, the sites of protein synthesis. Proteins synthesized by ribosomes that are attached to rough ER enter cisternae within the ER for processing and sorting. In some cases, enzymes within the cisternae attach the proteins to carbohydrates to form glycoproteins. In other cases, enzymes attach the proteins to phospholipids, also synthesized by rough ER. These molecules may be incorporated into organelle membranes or the plasma membrane. Thus, rough ER is a factory for synthesizing secretory proteins and membrane molecules.

Smooth ER extends from the rough ER to form a network of membrane tubules (see Figure 25). Unlike rough ER, smooth ER does not have ribosomes on the outer surface of its membrane. However, smooth ER contains unique enzymes that make

it functionally more diverse than rough ER. Although it does not synthesize proteins, smooth ER does synthesize phospholipids, as does rough ER. Smooth ER also synthesizes fats and steroids, such as estrogens and testosterone. In liver cells, enzymes of the smooth ER help release glucose into the bloodstream and inactivate or detoxify drugs and other potentially harmful substances (for example, alcohol). In muscle cells, calcium ions released from the sarcoplasmic reticulum, a form of smooth ER, trigger the contraction process.

Golgi Complex

Most of the proteins synthesized by ribosomes attached to rough ER are ultimately transported to other regions of the cell. The first step in the transport pathway is through an organelle called the **Golgi complex.** It consists of 3 to 20 cisternae that resemble a stack of pita bread (Figure 26). The cisternae are often curved, giving the Golgi complex a cuplike shape.

Proteins synthesized by ribosomes on the rough ER are surrounded by a portion of the ER membrane, which eventually buds from the membrane surface to form a **transport vesicle.** The transport vesicle fuses with a cistern of the Golgi complex, releasing proteins into the cistern. The proteins are modified and move from one cistern to another via **transfer vesicles** that bud from the edges of the cisternae. Enzymes in the cisternae modify the proteins to form glycoproteins, glycolipids, and lipoproteins. Some of the processed proteins leave the cisternae in **secretory vesicles,** which detach from the cistern and deliver the proteins to the plasma membrane, where they are discharged by exocytosis. Other processed proteins leave the cisternae in vesicles that deliver their contents to the plasma membrane for incorporation into the membrane. Finally, some processed proteins leave the cisternae in vesicles that are called

storage vesicles. The major storage vesicle is a lysosome, whose structure and functions are discussed next.

Lysosomes

Lysosomes are formed from Golgi complexes and look like membrane-enclosed spheres. Unlike mitochondria, lysosomes have only a single membrane and lack internal structure (see Figure 22). But they contain as many as 40 different kinds of powerful digestive enzymes capable of breaking down various molecules. Moreover, these enzymes can also digest bacteria that enter the cell. Human white blood cells, which use phagocytosis to ingest bacteria, contain large numbers of lysosomes.

Vacuoles

A **vacuole** (see Figure 22) is a space or cavity in the cytoplasm of a cell that is enclosed by a membrane called a *tonoplast*. In plant cells, vacuoles may occupy 5–90% of the cell volume, depending on the type of cell. Vacuoles are derived from the Golgi complex and have several diverse functions. Some vacuoles serve as temporary storage organelles for substances such as proteins, sugars, organic acids, and inorganic ions. Other vacuoles form during endocytosis to help bring food into the cell. Many plant cells also store metabolic wastes and poisons that would otherwise be injurious if they accumulated in the cytoplasm. Finally, vacuoles may take up water, enabling plant cells to increase in size and also providing rigidity to leaves and stems.

Mitochondria

Spherical or rod-shaped organelles called **mitochondria** (singular: **mitochondrion**) appear throughout the cytoplasm of most eukaryotic cells (see Figure 22). The number of mitochondria per cell varies greatly among different types of cells. For example, the protozoan *Giardia* has no mitochondria, whereas liver cells contain 1000 to 2000 per cell. A mitochondrion consists of a double membrane similar in structure to the plasma membrane (Figure 27). The outer mitochondrial membrane is smooth, but the inner mitochondrial membrane is arranged in a series of folds called **cristae** (singular: **crista**). The center of the mitochondrion is a semifluid substance called the **matrix**. Because of the nature and arrangement of the cristae, the inner membrane provides an enormous surface area on which chemical reactions can occur. Some proteins that function in cellular respiration, including the enzyme that makes ATP, are located on the cristae of the inner mitochondrial membrane, and many of the metabolic steps involved in cellular respiration are concentrated in the matrix. Mitochondria are often called the "powerhouses of the cell" because of their central role in ATP production.

Mitochondria contain 70S ribosomes and some DNA of their own, as well as the machinery necessary to replicate, transcribe, and translate the information encoded by their DNA. In addition, mitochondria can reproduce more or less on their own by growing and dividing in two.

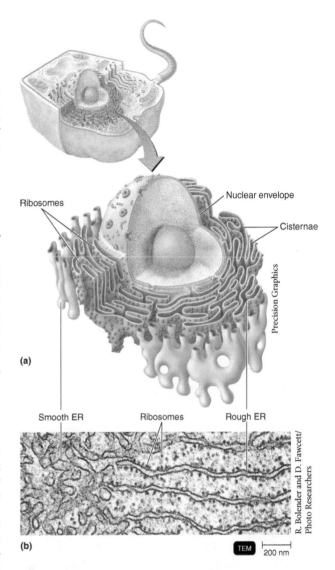

(a)

Ribosomes

Nuclear envelope

Cisternae

Precision Graphics

Smooth ER   Ribosomes   Rough ER

(b)   TEM   200 nm

R. Bolender and D. Fawcett/ Photo Researchers

Figure 25 Rough endoplasmic reticulum and ribosomes. (**a**) A drawing of details of the endoplasmic reticulum. (**b**) A micrograph of the endoplasmic reticulum and ribosomes.

Q   What functions of the smooth ER and rough ER are similar?

Figure 3.20 from *Principles of Anatomy and Physiology*, 9th ed., by Tortora & Grabowski. Copyright © 2000. Reprinted by permission of John Wiley & Sons, Inc.

Chloroplasts

Algae and green plants contain a unique organelle called a **chloroplast** (Figure 28), a membrane-enclosed structure that contains both the pigment chlorophyll and the enzymes required for the light-gathering phases of photosynthesis. The chlorophyll is contained in flattened membrane sacs called **thylakoids;** stacks of thylakoids are called *grana* (singular: **granum**) (see Figure 28).

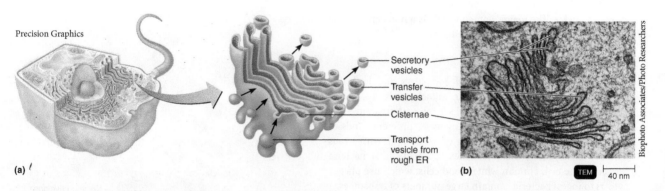

Figure 26 Golgi complex. (**a**) A drawing of details of a Golgi complex. (**b**) A micrograph of a Golgi complex.

[Q] What is the function of the Golgi complex?

Figure 3.21 from *Principles of Anatomy and Physiology*, 9th ed., by Tortora & Grabowski. Copyright © 2000. Reprinted by permission of John Wiley & Sons, Inc.

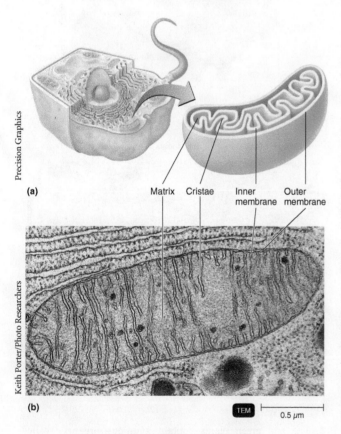

Figure 27 Mitochondria. (**a**) A drawing of details of a mitochondrion. (**b**) A micrograph of a mitochondrion from a rat pancreas cell.

[Q] How are mitochondria similar to prokaryotic cells?

Like mitochondria, chloroplasts contain 70S ribosomes, DNA, and enzymes involved in protein synthesis. They are capable of multiplying on their own within the cell. The way both chloroplasts and mitochondria multiply—by increasing in size and then dividing in two—is strikingly reminiscent of bacterial multiplication.

Peroxisomes

Organelles similar in structure to lysosomes, but smaller, are called **peroxisomes** (see Figure 22). Although peroxisomes were once thought to form by budding off the ER, it is now generally agreed that they form by the division of preexisting peroxisomes.

Peroxisomes contain one or more enzymes that can oxidize various organic substances. For example, substances such as amino acids and fatty acids are oxidized in peroxisomes as part of normal metabolism. In addition, enzymes in peroxisomes oxidize toxic substances, such as alcohol. A by-product of the oxidation reactions is hydrogen peroxide (H_2O_2), a potentially toxic compound. However, peroxisomes also contain the enzyme *catalase,* which decomposes H_2O_2. Because the generation and degradation of H_2O_2 occurs within the same organelle, peroxisomes protect other parts of the cell from the toxic effects of H_2O_2.

Centrosome

The **centrosome,** located near the nucleus, consists of two components: the pericentriolar area and centrioles (see Figure 22). The *pericentriolar material* is a region of the cytosol composed of a dense network of small protein fibers. This area is the organizing center for the mitotic spindle, which plays a critical role in cell division, and for microtubule formation in nondividing cells. Within the pericentriolar material is a pair of cylindrical structures called *centrioles,* each of which is composed of nine clusters of three microtubules (triplets) arranged in a circular

The Evolution of Eukaryotes

LEARNING OBJECTIVE

20   Discuss evidence that supports the endosymbiotic theory of eukaryotic evolution.

Biologists generally believe that life arose on Earth in the form of very simple organisms, similar to prokaryotic cells, about 3.5 to 4 billion years ago. About 2.5 billion years ago, the first eukaryotic cells evolved from prokaryotic cells. Recall that prokaryotes and eukaryotes differ mainly in that eukaryotes contain highly specialized organelles. The theory explaining the origin of eukaryotes from prokaryotes, pioneered by Lynn Margulis, is the **endosymbiotic theory.** According to this theory, larger bacterial cells lost their cell walls and engulfed smaller bacterial cells. This relationship, in which one organism lives within another, is called *endosymbiosis* (*symbiosis* = living together).

According to the endosymbiotic theory, the ancestral eukaryote developed a rudimentary nucleus when the plasma membrane folded around the chromosome. This cell, called a nucleoplasm, may have ingested aerobic bacteria. Some ingested bacteria lived inside the host nucleoplasm. This arrangement evolved into a symbiotic relationship in which the host nucleoplasm supplied nutrients and the endosymbiotic bacterium produced energy that could be used by the nucleoplasm. Similarly, chloroplasts may be descendants of photosynthetic prokaryotes ingested by this early nucleoplasm. Eukaryotic flagella and cilia are believed to have originated from symbiotic associations between the plasma membrane of early eukaryotes and motile spiral bacteria called spirochetes. A living example that suggests how flagella developed is described in the box on the next page.

Studies comparing prokaryotic and eukaryotic cells provide evidence for the endosymbiotic theory. For example, both mitochondria and chloroplasts resemble bacteria in size and shape. Further, these organelles contain circular DNA, which is typical of prokaryotes, and the organelles can reproduce independently of their host cell. Moreover, mitochondrial and chloroplast ribosomes resemble those of prokaryotes, and their mechanism of protein synthesis is more similar to that found in bacteria than eukaryotes. Also, the same antibiotics that inhibit protein synthesis on ribosomes in bacteria also inhibit protein synthesis on ribosomes in mitochondria and chloroplasts.

CHECK YOUR UNDERSTANDING

✔ Which three organelles are not associated with the Golgi complex? What does this suggest about their origin? 20

* * *

Our next concern is to examine microbial metabolism.

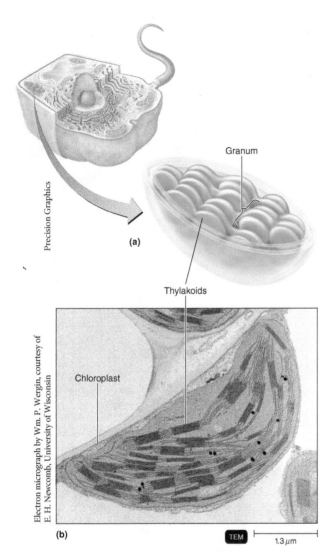

Granum

Thylakoids

Precision Graphics

(a)

Electron micrograph by Wm. P. Wergin, courtesy of E. H. Newcomb, University of Wisconsin

Chloroplast

(b)   TEM |———| 1.3 µm

Figure 28 Chloroplasts. Photosynthesis occurs in chloroplasts; the light-trapping pigments are located on the thylakoids. (**a**) A drawing of details of a chloroplast, showing grana. (**b**) A micrograph of chloroplasts in a plant cell.

Q What are the similarities between chloroplasts and prokaryotic cells?

pattern, an arrangement called a *9 + 0 array*. The 9 refers to the nine clusters of microtubules, and the 0 refers to the absence of microtubules in the center. The long axis of one centriole is at a right angle to the long axis of the other.

CHECK YOUR UNDERSTANDING

✔ Compare the structure of the nucleus of a eukaryote and the nucleoid of a prokaryote. 18

✔ How do rough and smooth ER compare structurally and functionally? 19

Why Microbiologists Study Termites

Dean Soulia and Lynn Margulis/
University of Massachusetts

Although termites are famous for their ability to eat wood, causing damage to wooden structures and recycling cellulose in the soil, they are unable to digest the wood that they eat. To break down the cellulose, termites enlist the help of a variety of microorganisms. Some termites, for example, dig tunnels in the wood, then inoculate the tunnels with fungi that grow on the wood. These termites then eat the fungi, not the wood itself.

What microbiologists find more interesting are the termites that contain, within their digestive tracts, symbiotic microorganisms that digest the cellulose that the termites chew and swallow. In fact, these symbiotic microorganisms can survive only because of even smaller symbionts that live on and within them, without which they would not even be able to move. By studying how a single termite survives, microbiologists have begun to gain an entirely new understanding of symbiosis.

The termite's dependence on nitrogen-fixing bacteria to supply its nitrogen and on protozoans such as *Trichonympha sphaerica* to digest cellulose are examples of endosymbiosis, a symbiotic relationship with an organism that lives inside the body of the host organism (in this case, within the hindgut of the termite).

The picture is more complicated than this, however, for *T. sphaerica* is unable to digest cellulose without the aid of bacteria that live within its body: in other words, the protozoan has its own endosymbionts.

Certain hindgut flagellates such as *T. sphaerica* also demonstrate another form of symbiosis—ectosymbiosis, a symbiotic relationship with organisms that live

outside its body. Advances in microscopy have shown that these flagellates are covered by precise rows consisting of thousands of bacteria, either rods or spirochetes. If these bacteria are killed, the protozoan is unable to move. Instead of using its own flagella, the protozoan relies on the rows of bacteria to row it about like oarsmen in a boat.

The protozoan *Mixotricha*, for example, has rows of spirochetes on its surface (see photo, upper right). The end of each spirochete abuts against a swelling known as a bracket; see part a of the figure. The spirochetes undulate in unison, thereby creating waves of motion along *Mixotricha's* surface.

Rod-shaped bacteria align in grooves that cover the surface of devescovinids, another group of termite-hindgut protozoans. Each rod has 12 flagella that overlap the flagella of the adjacent bacteria to form a continuous filament along the groove (see part b). The bacteria rotate their flagella, thus creating

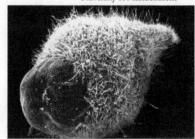

Mixotricha, a protozoan that lives in the termite gut. SEM | 100 μm

coordinated waves along all these rows of filaments, which propel the protozoan.

Sid Tamm and his colleagues at Boston University have found that the protozoa cannot control motility of the ectosymbiotics. *Mixotricha* uses its flagella to steer, and the bacteria push the protozoa forward—shoving and being shoved by its neighbors, much like bumper cars.

Arrangements of bacteria on the surfaces of two protozoans.

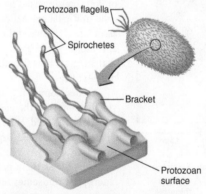
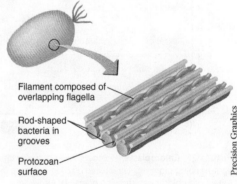

Precision Graphics

(a) Spirochetes attached to brackets over the surface of a *Mixotricha* protozoan align themselves and move in unison.

(b) On this devescovinid protozoan, the flagella from one rod-shaped bacterium overlap the next to form a continuous filament.

Study Outline

Test your understanding with quizzes, microbe review, and a chapter post-test at www.masteringmicrobiology.com.

Comparing Prokaryotic and Eukaryotic Cells: An Overview

1. Prokaryotic and eukaryotic cells are similar in their chemical composition and chemical reactions.

2. Prokaryotic cells lack membrane-enclosed organelles (including a nucleus).
3. Peptidoglycan is found in prokaryotic cell walls but not in eukaryotic cell walls.
4. Eukaryotic cells have a membrane-bound nucleus and other organelles.

■ The Prokaryotic Cell

1. Bacteria are unicellular, and most of them multiply by binary fission.
2. Bacterial species are differentiated by morphology, chemical composition, nutritional requirements, biochemical activities, and source of energy.

The Size, Shape, and Arrangement of Bacterial Cells

1. Most bacteria are 0.2 to 2.0 μm in diameter and 2 to 8 μm in length.
2. The three basic bacterial shapes are coccus (spherical), bacillus (rod-shaped), and spiral (twisted).
3. Pleomorphic bacteria can assume several shapes.

Structures External to the Cell Wall

Glycocalyx

1. The glycocalyx (capsule, slime layer, or extracellular polysaccharide) is a gelatinous polysaccharide and/or polypeptide covering.
2. Capsules may protect pathogens from phagocytosis.
3. Capsules enable adherence to surfaces, prevent desiccation, and may provide nutrients.

Flagella

4. Flagella are relatively long filamentous appendages consisting of a filament, hook, and basal body.
5. Prokaryotic flagella rotate to push the cell.
6. Motile bacteria exhibit taxis; positive taxis is movement toward an attractant, and negative taxis is movement away from a repellent.
7. Flagellar (H) protein is an antigen.

Axial Filaments

8. Spiral cells that move by means of an axial filament (endoflagellum) are called spirochetes.
9. Axial filaments are similar to flagella, except that they wrap around the cell.

Fimbriae and Pili

10. Fimbriae help cells adhere to surfaces.
11. Pili are involved in twitching motility and DNA transfer.

The Cell Wall

Composition and Characteristics

1. The cell wall surrounds the plasma membrane and protects the cell from changes in water pressure.
2. The bacterial cell wall consists of peptidoglycan, a polymer consisting of NAG and NAM and short chains of amino acids.
3. Penicillin interferes with peptidoglycan synthesis.
4. Gram-positive cell walls consist of many layers of peptidoglycan and also contain teichoic acids.

5. Gram-negative bacteria have a lipopolysaccharide-lipoprotein-phospholipid outer membrane surrounding a thin peptidoglycan layer.
6. The outer membrane protects the cell from phagocytosis and from penicillin, lysozyme, and other chemicals.
7. Porins are proteins that permit small molecules to pass through the outer membrane; specific channel proteins allow other molecules to move through the outer membrane.
8. The lipopolysaccharide component of the outer membrane consists of sugars (O polysaccharides), which function as antigens, and lipid A, which is an endotoxin.

Cell Walls and the Gram Stain Mechanism

9. The crystal violet–iodine complex combines with peptidoglycan.
10. The decolorizer removes the lipid outer membrane of gram-negative bacteria and washes out the crystal violet.

Atypical Cell Walls

11. *Mycoplasma* is a bacterial genus that naturally lacks cell walls.
12. Archaea have pseudomurein; they lack peptidoglycan.
13. Acid-fast cell walls have a layer of mycolic acid outside a thin peptidoglycan layer.

Damage to the Cell Wall

14. In the presence of lysozyme, gram-positive cell walls are destroyed, and the remaining cellular contents are referred to as a protoplast.
15. In the presence of lysozyme, gram-negative cell walls are not completely destroyed, and the remaining cellular contents are referred to as a spheroplast.
16. L forms are gram-positive or gram-negative bacteria that do not make a cell wall.
17. Antibiotics such as penicillin interfere with cell wall synthesis.

Structures Internal to the Cell Wall

The Plasma (Cytoplasmic) Membrane

1. The plasma membrane encloses the cytoplasm and is a lipid bilayer with peripheral and integral proteins (the fluid mosaic model).
2. The plasma membrane is selectively permeable.
3. Plasma membranes contain enzymes for metabolic reactions, such as nutrient breakdown, energy production, and photosynthesis.
4. Mesosomes, irregular infoldings of the plasma membrane, are artifacts, not true cell structures.
5. Plasma membranes can be destroyed by alcohols and polymyxins.

The Movement of Materials across Membranes

6. Movement across the membrane may be by passive processes, in which materials move from areas of higher to lower concentration and no energy is expended by the cell.
7. In simple diffusion, molecules and ions move until equilibrium is reached.
8. In facilitated diffusion, substances are transported by transporter proteins across membranes from areas of high to low concentration.
9. Osmosis is the movement of water from areas of high to low concentration across a selectively permeable membrane until equilibrium is reached.

10. In active transport, materials move from areas of low to high concentration by transporter proteins, and the cell must expend energy.

11. In group translocation, energy is expended to modify chemicals and transport them across the membrane.

Cytoplasm

12. Cytoplasm is the fluid component inside the plasma membrane.

13. The cytoplasm is mostly water, with inorganic and organic molecules, DNA, ribosomes, and inclusions.

The Nucleoid

14. The nucleoid contains the DNA of the bacterial chromosome.

15. Bacteria can also contain plasmids, which are circular, extrachromosomal DNA molecules.

Ribosomes)

16. The cytoplasm of a prokaryote contains numerous 70S ribosomes; ribosomes consist of rRNA and protein.

17. Protein synthesis occurs at ribosomes; it can be inhibited by certain antibiotics.

Inclusions

18. Inclusions are reserve deposits found in prokaryotic and eukaryotic cells.

19. Among the inclusions found in bacteria are metachromatic granules (inorganic phosphate), polysaccharide granules (usually glycogen or starch), lipid inclusions, sulfur granules, carboxysomes (ribulose 1,5-diphosphate carboxylase), magnetosomes (Fe_3O_4), and gas vacuoles.

Endospores

20. Endospores are resting structures formed by some bacteria; they allow survival during adverse environmental conditions.

21. The process of endospore formation is called sporulation; the return of an endospore to its vegetative state is called germination.

■ The Eukaryotic Cell

Flagella and Cilia

1. Flagella are few and long in relation to cell size; cilia are numerous and short.

2. Flagella and cilia are used for motility, and cilia also move substances along the surface of the cells.

3. Both flagella and cilia consist of an arrangement of nine pairs and two single microtubules.

The Cell Wall and Glycocalyx

1. The cell walls of many algae and some fungi contain cellulose.

2. The main material of fungal cell walls is chitin.

3. Yeast cell walls consist of glucan and mannan.

4. Animal cells are surrounded by a glycocalyx, which strengthens the cell and provides a means of attachment to other cells.

The Plasma (Cytoplasmic) Membrane

1. Like the prokaryotic plasma membrane, the eukaryotic plasma membrane is a phospholipid bilayer containing proteins.

2. Eukaryotic plasma membranes contain carbohydrates attached to the proteins and sterols not found in prokaryotic cells (except *Mycoplasma* bacteria).

3. Eukaryotic cells can move materials across the plasma membrane by the passive processes used by prokaryotes and by active transport and endocytosis (phagocytosis, pinocytosis, and receptor-mediated endocytosis).

Cytoplasm

1. The cytoplasm of eukaryotic cells includes everything inside the plasma membrane and external to the nucleus.

2. The chemical characteristics of the cytoplasm of eukaryotic cells resemble those of the cytoplasm of prokaryotic cells.

3. Eukaryotic cytoplasm has a cytoskeleton and exhibits cytoplasmic streaming.

Ribosomes

1. 80S ribosomes are found in the cytoplasm or attached to the rough endoplasmic reticulum.

Organelles

1. Organelles are specialized membrane-enclosed structures in the cytoplasm of eukaryotic cells.

2. The nucleus, which contains DNA in the form of chromosomes, is the most characteristic eukaryotic organelle.

3. The nuclear envelope is connected to a system of membranes in the cytoplasm called the endoplasmic reticulum (ER).

4. The ER provides a surface for chemical reactions and serves as a transport network. Protein synthesis and transport occur on the rough ER; lipid synthesis occurs on the smooth ER.

5. The Golgi complex consists of flattened sacs called cisterns. It functions in membrane formation and protein secretion.

6. Lysosomes are formed from Golgi complexes. They store digestive enzymes.

7. Vacuoles are membrane-enclosed cavities derived from the Golgi complex or endocytosis. They are usually found in plant cells that store various substances and provide rigidity to leaves and stems.

8. Mitochondria are the primary sites of ATP production. They contain 70S ribosomes and DNA, and they multiply by binary fission.

9. Chloroplasts contain chlorophyll and enzymes for photosynthesis. Like mitochondria, they contain 70S ribosomes and DNA and multiply by binary fission.

10. A variety of organic compounds are oxidized in peroxisomes. Catalase in peroxisomes destroys H_2O_2.

11. The centrosome consists of the pericentriolar material and centrioles. Centrioles are 9 triplet microtubules involved in formation of the mitotic spindle and microtubules.

The Evolution of Eukaryotes

1. According to the endosymbiotic theory, eukaryotic cells evolved from symbiotic prokaryotes living inside other prokaryotic cells.

Study Questions

Answers to the Review and Multiple Choice questions can be found at the end of this chapter.

Review

1. **DRAW IT** Diagram each of the following flagellar arrangements:
    a. lophotrichous   d. amphitrichous
    b. monotrichous   e. polar
    c. peritrichous

2. Endospore formation is called (a) _____. It is initiated by (b) _____. Formation of a new cell from an endospore is called (c) _____. This process is triggered by (d) _____.

3. **DRAW IT** Draw the bacterial shapes listed in (a), (b), and (c). Then draw the shapes in (d), (e), and (f), showing how they are special conditions of a, b, and c, respectively.
    a. spiral   d. spirochetes
    b. bacillus   e. streptobacilli
    c. coccus   f. staphylococci

4. Match the structures in column A to their functions in column B.

Column A	Column B
_4_ a. Cell wall	1. Attachment to surfaces
_6_ b. Endospore	2. Cell wall formation
_1_ c. Fimbriae	3. Motility
_3_ d. Flagella	4. Protection from osmotic lysis
_1,5_ e. Glycocalyx	5. Protection from phagocytes
_3,9_ f. Pili	6. Resting
_2,8_ g. Plasma membrane	7. Protein synthesis
_7_ h. Ribosomes	8. Selective permeability
	9. Transfer of genetic material

5. Why is an endospore called a resting structure? Of what advantage is an endospore to a bacterial cell?

6. Compare and contrast the following:
    a. simple diffusion and facilitated diffusion
    b. active transport and facilitated diffusion
    c. active transport and group translocation

7. Answer the following questions using the diagrams provided, which represent cross sections of bacterial cell walls.
    a. Which diagram represents a gram-positive bacterium? How can you tell?

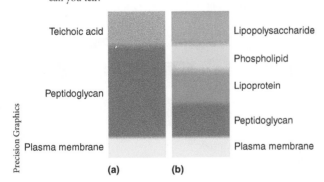

(a)   (b)

b. Explain how the Gram stain works to distinguish these two types of cell walls.
c. Why does penicillin have no effect on most gram-negative cells?
d. How do essential molecules enter cells through each wall?
e. Which cell wall is toxic to humans?

8. Starch is readily metabolized by many cells, but a starch molecule is too large to cross the plasma membrane. How does a cell obtain the glucose molecules from a starch polymer? How does the cell transport these glucose molecules across the plasma membrane?

9. Match the characteristics of eukaryotic cells in column A with their functions in column B.

Column A	Column B
_3_ a. Pericentriolar material	1. Digestive enzyme storage
_4_ b. Chloroplasts	2. Oxidation of fatty acids
_7_ c. Golgi complex	3. Microtubule formation
_1_ d. Lysosomes	4. Photosynthesis
_6_ e. Mitochondria	5. Protein synthesis
_2_ f. Peroxisomes	6. Respiration
_5_ g. Rough ER	7. Secretion

10. **NAME IT** What group of microbes is characterized by cells that form filaments, reproduce by spores, and have peptidoglycan in their cell walls?

Multiple Choice

1. Which of the following is *not* a distinguishing characteristic of prokaryotic cells?
    a. They usually have a single, circular chromosome.
    b. They lack membrane-enclosed organelles.
    c. They have cell walls containing peptidoglycan.
    d. Their DNA is not associated with histones.
    e. They lack a plasma membrane.

Use the following choices to answer questions 2–4.
    a. No change will result; the solution is isotonic.
    b. Water will move into the cell.
    c. Water will move out of the cell.
    d. The cell will undergo osmotic lysis.
    e. Sucrose will move into the cell from an area of higher concentration to one of lower concentration.

2. Which statement best describes what happens when a gram-positive bacterium is placed in distilled water and penicillin?

3. Which statement best describes what happens when a gram-negative bacterium is placed in distilled water and penicillin?

4. Which statement best describes what happens when a gram-positive bacterium is placed in an aqueous solution of lysozyme and 10% sucrose?

5. Which of the following statements best describes what happens to a cell exposed to polymyxins that destroy phospholipids?
    a. In an isotonic solution, nothing will happen.
    b. In a hypotonic solution, the cell will lyse.
    c. Water will move into the cell.
    d. Intracellular contents will leak from the cell.
    e. Any of the above might happen.

Precision Graphics

6. Which of the following is *false* about fimbriae?
   a. They are composed of protein.
   b. They may be used for attachment.
   c. They are found on gram-negative cells.
   d. They are composed of pilin.
   e. They may be used for motility.

7. Which of the following pairs is *mismatched*?
   a. glycocalyx—adherence
   b. pili—reproduction
   c. cell wall—toxin
   d. cell wall—protection
   e. plasma membrane—transport

8. Which of the following pairs is *mismatched*?
   a. metachromatic granules—stored phosphates
   b. polysaccharide granules—stored starch
   c. lipid inclusions—poly-β-hydroxybutyric acid
   d. sulfur granules—energy reserve
   e. ribosomes—protein storage

9. You have isolated a motile, gram-positive cell with no visible nucleus. You can assume this cell has
   a. ribosomes.
   b. mitochondria.
   c. an endoplasmic reticulum.
   d. a Golgi complex.
   e. all of the above

10. The antibiotic amphothericin B disrupts plasma membranes by combining with sterols; it will affect all of the following cells *except*
    a. animal cells.
    b. gram-negative bacterial cells.
    c. fungal cells.
    d. *Mycoplasma* cells.
    e. plant cells.

Critical Thinking

1. How can prokaryotic cells be smaller than eukaryotic cells and still carry on all the functions of life?

2. The smallest eukaryotic cell is the motile alga *Micromonas.* What is the minimum number of organelles this alga must have?

3. Two types of prokaryotic cells have been distinguished: bacteria and archaea. How do these cells differ from each other? How are they similar?

4. In 1985, a 0.5-mm cell was discovered in surgeonfish and named *Epulopiscium fishelsoni.* It was presumed to be a protozoan. In 1993, researchers determined that *Epulopiscium* was actually a gram-positive bacterium. Why do you suppose this organism was initially identified as a protozoan? What evidence would change the classification to bacterium?

5. When *E. coli* cells are exposed to a hypertonic solution, the bacteria produce a transporter protein that can move K⁺ (potassium ions) into the cell. Of what value is the active transport of K⁺, which requires ATP?

Clinical Applications

1. *Clostridium botulinum* is a strict anaerobe; that is, it is killed by the molecular oxygen (O_2) present in air. Humans can die of botulism from eating foods in which *C. botulinum* is growing. How does this bacterium survive on plants picked for human consumption? Why are home-canned foods most often the source of botulism?

2. A South San Francisco child enjoyed bath time at his home because of the colorful orange and red water. The water did not have this rusty color at its source, and the water department could not culture the *Thiobacillus* bacteria responsible for the rusty color from the source. How were the bacteria getting into the household water? What bacterial structures make this possible?

3. Live cultures of *Bacillus thuringiensis* (Dipel) and *B. subtilis* (Kodiak) are sold as pesticides. What bacterial structures make it possible to package and sell these bacteria? For what purpose is each product used?

Answers to Review and Multiple Choice Study Questions

Review

1. a. and e.   b. and e.
   c.
   d. and e.

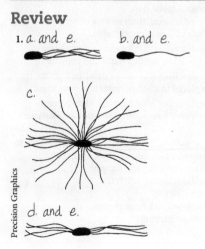

Precision Graphics

2. a. sporogenesis
   b. certain adverse environmental conditions
   c. germination
   d. favorable growth conditions

3.
   a.   d.
   b.   e.
   c.   f.

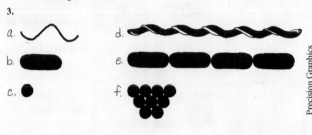

Precision Graphics

4. a. 4
   b. 6
   c. 1

118

d. 3
e. 1, 5
f. 3, 9
g. 2, 8
h. 7

5. An endospore is called a resting structure because it provides a method for one cell to "rest," or survive, as opposed to grow and reproduce. The protective endospore wall allows a bacterium to withstand adverse conditions in the environment.

6. **a.** Both allow materials to cross the plasma membrane from a high concentration to a low concentration without expending energy. Facilitated diffusion requires carrier proteins.
   b. Both require enzymes to move materials across the plasma membrane. In active transport, energy is expended.
   c. Both move materials across the plasma membrane with an expenditure of energy. In group translocation, the substrate is changed after it crosses the membrane.

7. **a.** Diagram (a) refers to a gram-positive bacterium because the lipopolysaccharide–phospholipid–lipoprotein layer is absent.
   b. The gram-negative bacterium initially retains the violet stain, but it is released when the outer membrane is dissolved by the decolorizing agent. After the dye–iodine complex enters, it becomes trapped by the peptidoglycan of gram-positive cells.

   c. The outer layer of the gram-negative cells prevents penicillin from entering the cells.
   d. Essential molecules diffuse through the gram-positive wall. Porins and specific channel proteins in the gram-negative outer membrane allow passage of small water-soluble molecules.
   e. Gram-negative.

8. An extracellular enzyme (amylase) hydrolyzes starch into disaccharides (maltose) and monosaccharides (glucose). A carrier enzyme (maltase) hydrolyzes maltose and moves one glucose into the cell. Glucose can be transported by group translocation as glucose-6-phosphate.

9. **a.** 3
   b. 4
   c. 7
   d. 1
   e. 6
   f. 2
   g. 5

10. Actinomycete

Multiple Choice

1. e	**3.** b	**5.** d	**7.** b	**9.** a
2. d	**4.** a	**6.** e	**8.** e	**10.** b

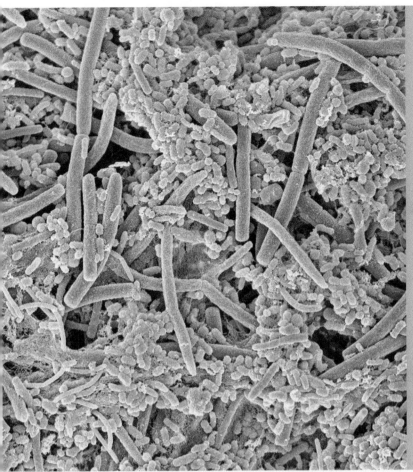

SPL/Photolibrary

Microbial Metabolism

Now that you are familiar with the structure of prokaryotic cells, we can discuss the activities that enable these microbes to thrive. The life-support processes of even the most structurally simple organism involve a large number of complex biochemical reactions. Most, although not all, of the biochemical processes of bacteria also occur in eukaryotic microbes and in the cells of multicellular organisms, including humans. However, the reactions that are unique to bacteria are fascinating because they allow microorganisms to do things we cannot do. For example, some bacteria can live on cellulose, whereas others can live on petroleum. Through their metabolism, bacteria recycle elements after other organisms have used them. Still other bacteria can live on diets of such inorganic substances as carbon dioxide, iron, sulfur, hydrogen gas, and ammonia. Microbial metabolism allows some microorganisms to grow in or on the human body as shown in dental plaque in the photograph. An example of the bacterial metabolism that contributes to dental caries is discussed in the Clinical Case.

This chapter examines some representative chemical reactions that either produce energy (the catabolic reactions) or use energy (the anabolic reactions) in microorganisms. We will also look at how these various reactions are integrated within the cell.

From Chapter 5 of *Microbiology: An Introduction*, Eleventh Edition. Gerard J. Tortora, Berdell R. Funke, Christine L. Case.

Catabolic and Anabolic Reactions

LEARNING OBJECTIVES

1 Define *metabolism*, and describe the fundamental differences between anabolism and catabolism.

2 Identify the role of ATP as an intermediate between catabolism and anabolism.

We use the term **metabolism** to refer to the sum of all chemical reactions within a living organism. Because chemical reactions either release or require energy, metabolism can be viewed as an energy-balancing act. Accordingly, metabolism can be divided into two classes of chemical reactions: those that release energy and those that require energy.

In living cells, the enzyme-regulated chemical reactions that release energy are generally the ones involved in **catabolism,** the breakdown of complex organic compounds into simpler ones. These reactions are called *catabolic,* or *degradative,* reactions. Catabolic reactions are generally *hydrolytic reactions* (reactions which use water and in which chemical bonds are broken), and they are *exergonic* (produce more energy than they consume). An example of catabolism occurs when cells break down sugars into carbon dioxide and water.

The enzyme-regulated energy-requiring reactions are mostly involved in **anabolism,** the building of complex organic molecules from simpler ones. These reactions are called *anabolic,* or *biosynthetic,* reactions. Anabolic processes often involve *dehydration synthesis* reactions (reactions that release water), and they are *endergonic* (consume more energy than they produce). Examples of anabolic processes are the formation of proteins from amino acids, nucleic acids from nucleotides, and polysaccharides from simple sugars. These biosynthetic reactions generate the materials for cell growth.

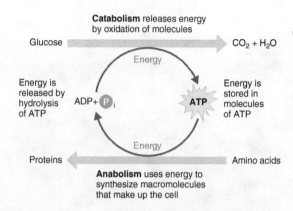

Figure 1 **The role of ATP in coupling anabolic and catabolic reactions.** When complex molecules are split apart (catabolism), some of the energy is transferred to and trapped in ATP, and the rest is given off as heat. When simple molecules are combined to form complex molecules (anabolism), ATP provides the energy for synthesis, and again some energy is given off as heat.

Q How does ATP provide the energy for synthesis?

Precision Graphics

Catabolic reactions provide building blocks for anabolic reactions and furnish the energy needed to drive anabolic reactions. This coupling of energy-requiring and energy-releasing reactions is made possible through the molecule adenosine triphosphate (ATP). ATP stores energy derived from catabolic reactions and releases it later to drive anabolic reactions and perform other cellular work. Recall that a molecule of ATP consists of an adenine, a ribose, and three phosphate groups. When the terminal phosphate group is split from ATP, adenosine diphosphate (ADP) is formed, and energy is released to drive anabolic reactions. Using $\textcircled{P}$ to represent a phosphate group ($\textcircled{P}_i$ represents inorganic phosphate, which is not bound to any other molecule), we write this reaction as follows:

$$ATP \rightarrow ADP + \textcircled{P}_i + energy$$

Then, the energy from catabolic reactions is used to combine ADP and a $\textcircled{P}_i$ to resynthesize ATP:

$$ADP + \textcircled{P}_i + energy \rightarrow ATP$$

Thus, anabolic reactions are coupled to ATP breakdown, and catabolic reactions are coupled to ATP synthesis. This concept of coupled reactions is very important; you will see why by the end of this chapter. For now, you should know that the chemical composition of a living cell is constantly changing: some molecules are broken down while others are being synthesized. This balanced flow of chemicals and energy maintains the life of a cell.

The role of ATP in coupling anabolic and catabolic reactions is shown in Figure 1. Only part of the energy released in catabolism is actually available for cellular functions because part

Clinical Case: More Than a Sweet Tooth

Dr. Antonia Rivera is a pediatric dentist in St. Louis, Missouri. Her latest patient, 7-year-old Micah Thompson, has just left the office with strict instructions about brushing and flossing regularly. What most worries Dr. Rivera, however, is that Micah is her seventh patient this week to present with multiple dental caries, or cavities. Dr. Rivera is used to seeing some increase in tooth decay after Halloween and Easter, but why are all these children getting cavities in the middle of the summer? When possible, she has been speaking to each of the patient's parents or grandparents, but no one has noticed anything out of the ordinary in the children's diets.

Why do so many of Dr. Rivera's patients have multiple dental caries? Read on to find out.

of the energy is lost to the environment as heat. Because the cell must use energy to maintain life, it has a continuous need for new external sources of energy.

Before we discuss how cells produce energy, let's first consider the principal properties of a group of proteins involved in almost all biologically important chemical reactions: enzymes. A cell's **metabolic pathways** (sequences of chemical reactions) are determined by its enzymes, which are in turn determined by the cell's genetic makeup. (MMJ) **Animation** Metabolism: Overview

CHECK YOUR UNDERSTANDING

✔ Distinguish catabolism from anabolism. 1

✔ How is ATP an intermediate between catabolism and anabolism? 2

Enzymes

LEARNING OBJECTIVES

3   Identify the components of an enzyme.

4   Describe the mechanism of enzymatic action.

5   List the factors that influence enzymatic activity.

6   Distinguish competitive and noncompetitive inhibition.

7   Define *ribozyme*.

Collision Theory

Chemical reactions occur when chemical bonds are formed or broken. For reactions to take place, atoms, ions, or molecules must collide. The **collision theory** explains how chemical reactions occur and how certain factors affect the rates of those reactions. The basis of the collision theory is that all atoms, ions, and molecules are continuously moving and are thus continuously colliding with one another. The energy transferred by the particles in the collision can disrupt their electron structures enough to break chemical bonds or form new bonds.

Several factors determine whether a collision will cause a chemical reaction: the velocities of the colliding particles, their energy, and their specific chemical configurations. Up to a point, the higher the particles' velocities, the more probable that their collision will cause a reaction. Also, each chemical reaction requires a specific level of energy. But even if colliding particles possess the minimum energy needed for reaction, no reaction will take place unless the particles are properly oriented toward each other.

Let's assume that molecules of substance AB (the reactant) are to be converted to molecules of substances A and B (the products). In a given population of molecules of substance AB, at a specific temperature, some molecules possess relatively little energy; the majority of the population possesses an average amount of energy; and a small portion of the population has high energy. If only the high-energy AB molecules are able to react and be converted to A and B molecules, then only relatively few molecules at any one time possess enough energy to

react in a collision. The collision energy required for a chemical reaction is its **activation energy,** which is the amount of energy needed to disrupt the stable electronic configuration of any specific molecule so that the electrons can be rearranged.

The **reaction rate**—the frequency of collisions containing sufficient energy to bring about a reaction—depends on the number of reactant molecules at or above the activation energy level. One way to increase the reaction rate of a substance is to raise its temperature. By causing the molecules to move faster, heat increases both the frequency of collisions and the number of molecules that attain activation energy. The number of collisions also increases when pressure is increased or when the reactants are more concentrated (because the distance between molecules is thereby decreased). In living systems, enzymes increase the reaction rate without raising the temperature.

Enzymes and Chemical Reactions

Substances that can speed up a chemical reaction without being permanently altered themselves are called **catalysts.** In living cells, **enzymes** serve as biological catalysts. As catalysts, enzymes are specific. Each acts on a specific substance, called the enzyme's **substrate** (or substrates, when there are two or more reactants), and each catalyzes only one reaction. For example, sucrose (table sugar) is the substrate of the enzyme sucrase, which catalyzes the hydrolysis of sucrose to glucose and fructose.

As catalysts, enzymes typically accelerate chemical reactions. The three-dimensional enzyme molecule has an *active site*, a region that interacts with a specific chemical substance (see Figure 4).

The enzyme orients the substrate into a position that increases the probability of a reaction. The **enzyme–substrate complex** formed by the temporary binding of enzyme and reactants enables the collisions to be more effective and lowers the activation energy of the reaction (**Figure 2**). The enzyme therefore speeds up the reaction by increasing the number of AB molecules that attain sufficient activation energy to react.

An enzyme's ability to accelerate a reaction without the need for an increase in temperature is crucial to living systems because a significant temperature increase would destroy cellular proteins. The crucial function of enzymes, therefore, is to speed up biochemical reactions at a temperature that is compatible with the normal functioning of the cell.

Enzyme Specificity and Efficiency

The specificity of enzymes is made possible by their structures. Enzymes are generally large globular proteins that range in molecular weight from about 10,000 to several million. Each of the thousands of known enzymes has a characteristic three-dimensional shape with a specific surface configuration as a result of its primary, secondary, and tertiary structures. The unique configuration of each enzyme enables it to "find" the correct substrate from among the large number of diverse molecules in the cell.

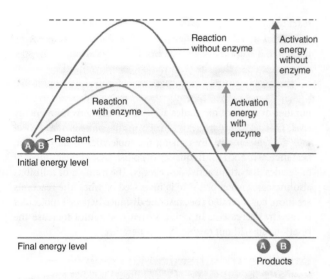

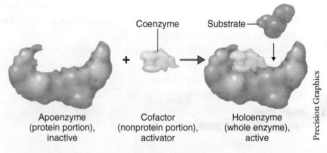

Figure 3 Components of a holoenzyme. Many enzymes require both an apoenzyme (protein portion) and a cofactor (nonprotein portion) to become active. The cofactor can be a metal ion, or if it is an organic molecule, it is called a coenzyme (as shown here). The apoenzyme and cofactor together make up the holoenzyme, or whole enzyme. The substrate is the reactant acted upon by the enzyme.

Q How does the enzyme–substrate complex lower the activation energy of the reaction?

Figure 2 Energy requirements of a chemical reaction. This graph shows the progress of the reaction AB → A + B both without (blue line) and with (red line) an enzyme. The presence of an enzyme lowers the activation energy of the reaction (see arrows). Thus, more molecules of reactant AB are converted to products A and B because more molecules of reactant AB possess the activation energy needed for the reaction.

Q Why does a chemical reaction require increased activation energy without an enzyme as a biological catalyst?

Enzymes are extremely efficient. Under optimum conditions, they can catalyze reactions at rates 10^8 to 10^{10} times (up to 10 billion times) higher than those of comparable reactions without enzymes. The **turnover number** (maximum number of substrate molecules an enzyme molecule converts to product each second) is generally between 1 and 10,000 and can be as high as 500,000. For example, the enzyme DNA polymerase I, which participates in the synthesis of DNA, has a turnover number of 15, whereas the enzyme lactate dehydrogenase, which removes hydrogen atoms from lactic acid, has a turnover number of 1000.

Many enzymes exist in the cell in both active and inactive forms. The rate at which enzymes switch between these two forms is determined by the cellular environment.

Naming Enzymes

The names of enzymes usually end in *-ase*. All enzymes can be grouped into six classes, according to the type of chemical reaction they catalyze (**Table 1**). Enzymes within each of the major classes are named according to the more specific types of reactions they assist. For example, the class called *oxidoreductases* is involved with oxidation-reduction reactions (described shortly). Enzymes in the oxidoreductase class that remove hydrogen from a substrate are called *dehydrogenases;* those that add molecular oxygen (O_2) are called *oxidases*. As you will see later,

dehydrogenase and oxidase enzymes have even more specific names, such as lactate dehydrogenase and cytochrome oxidase, depending on the specific substrates on which they act.

Enzyme Components

Although some enzymes consist entirely of proteins, most consist of both a protein portion, called an **apoenzyme,** and a nonprotein component, called a **cofactor.** Ions of iron, zinc, magnesium, or calcium are examples of cofactors. If the cofactor is an organic molecule, it is called a **coenzyme.** Apoenzymes are inactive by themselves; they must be activated by cofactors. Together, the apoenzyme and cofactor form a **holoenzyme,** or whole, active enzyme (**Figure 3**). If the cofactor is removed, the apoenzyme will not function.

Coenzymes may assist the enzyme by accepting atoms removed from the substrate or by donating atoms required by the substrate. Some coenzymes act as electron carriers, removing electrons from the substrate and donating them to other molecules in subsequent reactions. Many coenzymes are derived from vitamins (**Table 2**). Two of the most important coenzymes in cellular metabolism are **nicotinamide adenine dinucleotide (NAD^+)** and **nicotinamide adenine dinucleotide phosphate ($NADP^+$).** Both compounds contain derivatives of the B vitamin niacin (nicotinic acid), and both function as electron carriers. Whereas NAD^+ is primarily involved in catabolic (energy-yielding) reactions, $NADP^+$ is primarily involved in anabolic (energy-requiring) reactions. The flavin coenzymes, such as **flavin mononucleotide (FMN)** and **flavin adenine dinucleotide (FAD),** contain derivatives of the B vitamin riboflavin and are also electron carriers. Another important coenzyme, **coenzyme A (CoA),** contains a derivative of pantothenic acid, another B vitamin. This coenzyme plays an important role in the synthesis and breakdown of fats and in a series of oxidizing reactions called the Krebs cycle.

TABLE 1 Enzyme Classification Based on Type of Chemical Reaction Catalyzed

Class	Type of Chemical Reaction Catalyzed	Examples
Oxidoreductase	Oxidation-reduction, in which oxygen and hydrogen are gained or lost	Cytochrome oxidase, lactate dehydrogenase
Transferase	Transfer of functional groups, such as an amino group, acetyl group, or phosphate group	Acetate kinase, alanine deaminase
Hydrolase	Hydrolysis (addition of water)	Lipase, sucrase
Lyase	Removal of groups of atoms without hydrolysis	Oxalate decarboxylase, isocitrate lyase
Isomerase	Rearrangement of atoms within a molecule	Glucose-phosphate isomerase, alanine racemase
Ligase	Joining of two molecules (using energy usually derived from the breakdown of ATP)	Acetyl-CoA synthetase, DNA ligase

We will come across all of these coenzymes in our discussion of metabolism later in the chapter.

As noted earlier, some cofactors are metal ions, including iron, copper, magnesium, manganese, zinc, calcium, and cobalt. Such cofactors may help catalyze a reaction by forming a bridge between the enzyme and a substrate. For example, magnesium (Mg^{2+}) is required by many phosphorylating enzymes (enzymes that transfer a phosphate group from ATP to another substrate). The Mg^{2+} can form a link between the enzyme and the ATP molecule. Most trace elements required by living cells are probably used in some such way to activate cellular enzymes.

The Mechanism of Enzymatic Action

Enzymes lower the activation energy of chemical reactions. The general sequence of events in enzyme action is as follows (Figure 4a):

1 The surface of the substrate contacts a specific region of the surface of the enzyme molecule, called the **active site.**

2 A temporary intermediate compound forms, called an **enzyme–substrate complex.**

3 The substrate molecule is transformed by the rearrangement of existing atoms, the breakdown of the substrate molecule, or in combination with another substrate molecule.

4 The transformed substrate molecules—the products of the reaction—are released from the enzyme molecule because they no longer fit in the active site of the enzyme.

5 The unchanged enzyme is now free to react with other substrate molecules.

As a result of these events, an enzyme speeds up a chemical reaction.

TABLE 2 Selected Vitamins and Their Coenzymatic Functions

Vitamin	Function
Vitamin B_1 (Thiamine)	Part of coenzyme cocarboxylase; has many functions, including the metabolism of pyruvic acid
Vitamin B_2 (Riboflavin)	Coenzyme in flavoproteins; active in electron transfers
Niacin (Nicotinic Acid)	Part of NAD molecule*; active in electron transfers
Vitamin B_6 (Pyridoxine)	Coenzyme in amino acid metabolism
Vitamin B_{12} (Cyanocobalamin)	Coenzyme (methyl cyanocobalamide) involved in the transfer of methyl groups; active in amino acid metabolism
Pantothenic Acid	Part of coenzyme A molecule; involved in the metabolism of pyruvic acid and lipids
Biotin	Involved in carbon dioxide fixation reactions and fatty acid synthesis
Folic Acid	Coenzyme used in the synthesis of purines and pyrimidines
Vitamin E	Needed for cellular and macromolecular syntheses
Vitamin K	Coenzyme used in electron transport (naphthoquinones and quinones)

*NAD = nicotinamide adenine dinucleotide

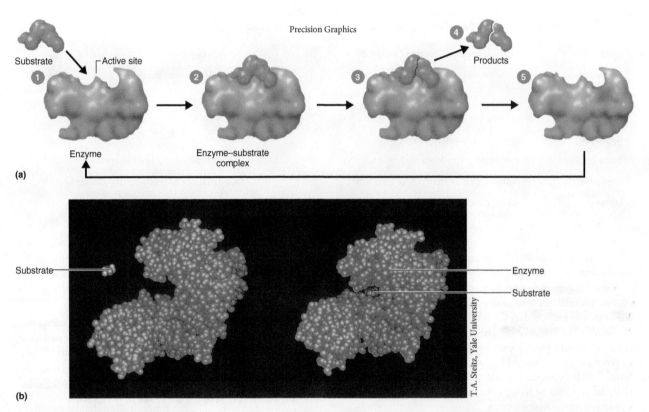

Precision Graphics

(a)

(b)

T.A. Steitz, Yale University

Figure 4 **The mechanism of enzymatic action.** (**a**) ➊ The substrate contacts the active site on the enzyme to form ➋ an enzyme–substrate complex. ➌ The substrate is then transformed into products, ➍ the products are released, and ➎ the enzyme is recovered unchanged. In the example shown, the transformation into products involves a breakdown of the substrate into two products. Other transformations, however, may occur. (**b**) Left: A molecular model of the enzyme in step ➊ of part (a). The active site of the enzyme can be seen here as a groove on the surface of the protein. Right: As the enzyme and substrate meet in step ➋ of part (a), the enzyme changes shape slightly to fit together more tightly with the substrate.

Q Give an example of enzymatic specifity.

As mentioned earlier, enzymes have *specificity* for particular substrates. For example, a specific enzyme may be able to hydrolyze a peptide bond only between two specific amino acids. Other enzymes can hydrolyze starch but not cellulose; even though both starch and cellulose are polysaccharides composed of glucose subunits, the orientations of the subunits in the two polysaccharides differ. Enzymes have this specificity because the three-dimensional shape of the active site fits the substrate somewhat as a lock fits with its key (Figure 4b). However, the active site and substrate are flexible, and they change shape somewhat as they meet to fit together more tightly. The substrate is usually much smaller than the enzyme, and relatively few of the enzyme's amino acids make up the active site.

A certain compound can be a substrate for several different enzymes that catalyze different reactions, so the fate of a compound depends on the enzyme that acts on it. At least four different enzymes can act on glucose 6-phosphate, a molecule important in cell metabolism, and each reaction will yield a different product. (MM) **Animations** Enzymes: Overview, Steps in a Reaction

Factors Influencing Enzymatic Activity

Enzymes are subject to various cellular controls. Two primary types are the control of enzyme *synthesis* and the control of enzyme *activity* (how much enzyme is present versus how active it is).

Several factors influence the activity of an enzyme. Among the more important are temperature, pH, substrate concentration, and the presence or absence of inhibitors.

Temperature

The rate of most chemical reactions increases as the temperature increases. Molecules move more slowly at lower temperatures than at higher temperatures and so may not have enough energy

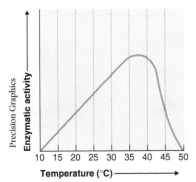

(a) Temperature. The enzymatic activity (rate of reaction catalyzed by the enzyme) increases with increasing temperature until the enzyme, a protein, is denatured by heat and inactivated. At this point, the reaction rate falls steeply.

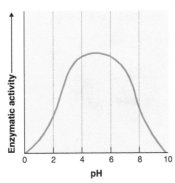

(b) pH. The enzyme illustrated is most active at about pH 5.0.

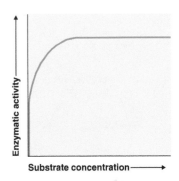

(c) Substrate concentration. With increasing concentration of substrate molecules, the rate of reaction increases until the active sites on all the enzyme molecules are filled, at which point the maximum rate of reaction is reached.

Figure 5 Factors that influence enzymatic activity, plotted for a hypothetical enzyme.

 How will this enzyme act at 25°C? At 45°C? At pH 7?

to cause a chemical reaction. For enzymatic reactions, however, elevation beyond a certain temperature (the optimal temperature) drastically reduces the rate of reaction (Figure 5a). The optimal temperature for most disease-producing bacteria in the human body is between 35°C and 40°C. The rate of reaction declines beyond the optimal temperature because of the enzyme's **denaturation,** the loss of its characteristic three-dimensional structure (tertiary configuration) (Figure 6). Denaturation of a protein involves the breakage of hydrogen bonds and other noncovalent bonds; a common example is the transformation of uncooked egg white (a protein called albumin) to a hardened state by heat.

Denaturation of an enzyme changes the arrangement of the amino acids in the active site, altering its shape and causing the enzyme to lose its catalytic ability. In some cases, denaturation is partially or fully reversible. However, if denaturation continues until the enzyme has lost its solubility and coagulates, the enzyme cannot regain its original properties. Enzymes can also be denatured by concentrated acids, bases, heavy-metal ions (such as lead, arsenic, or mercury), alcohol, and ultraviolet radiation.

pH

Most enzymes have an optimum pH at which their activity is characteristically maximal. Above or below this pH value, enzyme activity, and therefore the reaction rate, decline (Figure 5b). When the H^+ concentration (pH) in the medium is changed drastically, the protein's three-dimensional structure is altered. Extreme changes in pH can cause denaturation. Acids (and bases) alter a protein's three-dimensional structure because the H^+ (and OH^-) compete

with hydrogen and ionic bonds in an enzyme, resulting in the enzyme's denaturation.

Substrate Concentration

There is a maximum rate at which a certain amount of enzyme can catalyze a specific reaction. Only when the concentration of substrate(s) is extremely high can this maximum rate be attained. Under conditions of high substrate concentration, the enzyme is said to be in **saturation;** that is, its active site is always occupied by substrate or product molecules. In this condition, a further increase in substrate concentration will not affect the reaction rate because all active sites are already in use (Figure 5c). Under normal cellular conditions, enzymes are not saturated with substrate(s). At any given time, many of the enzyme molecules are inactive for lack of substrate; thus, the substrate concentration is likely to influence the rate of reaction.

Precision Graphics

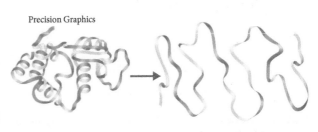

Active (functional) protein   Denatured protein

Figure 6 Denaturation of a protein. Breakage of the noncovalent bonds (such as hydrogen bonds) that hold the active protein in its three-dimensional shape renders the denatured protein nonfunctional.

 When is denaturation irreversible?

Figure 7 Enzyme inhibitors. (**a**) An uninhibited enzyme and its normal substrate. (**b**) A competitive inhibitor. (**c**) One type of noncompetitive inhibitor, causing allosteric inhibition.

How do competitive inhibitors operate in comparison to noncompetitive inhibitors?

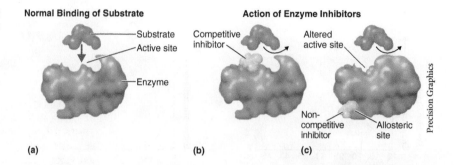

Normal Binding of Substrate

Substrate
Active site
Enzyme

(a)

Action of Enzyme Inhibitors

Competitive inhibitor
Altered active site
Noncompetitive inhibitor
Allosteric site

(b)   (c)

Precision Graphics

Inhibitors

An effective way to control the growth of bacteria is to control their enzymes. Certain poisons, such as cyanide, arsenic, and mercury, combine with enzymes and prevent them from functioning. As a result, the cells stop functioning and die.

Enzyme inhibitors are classified as either competitive or noncompetitive inhibitors (**Figure 7**). **Competitive inhibitors** fill the active site of an enzyme and compete with the normal substrate for the active site. A competitive inhibitor can do this because its shape and chemical structure are similar to those of the normal substrate (**Figure 7b**). However, unlike the substrate, it does not undergo any reaction to form products. Some competitive inhibitors bind irreversibly to amino acids in the active site, preventing any further interactions with the substrate. Others bind reversibly, alternately occupying and leaving the active site; these slow the enzyme's interaction with the substrate. Increasing the substrate concentration can overcome reversible competitive inhibition. As active sites become available, more substrate molecules than competitive inhibitor molecules are available to attach to the active sites of enzymes.

One good example of a competitive inhibitor is sulfanilamide (a sulfa drug), which inhibits the enzyme whose normal substrate is *para*-aminobenzoic acid (PABA):

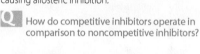

Sulfanilamide   PABA

PABA is an essential nutrient used by many bacteria in the synthesis of folic acid, a vitamin that functions as a coenzyme. When sulfanilamide is administered to bacteria, the enzyme that normally converts PABA to folic acid combines instead with the sulfanilamide. Folic acid is not synthesized, and the bacteria cannot grow. Because human cells do not use PABA to make their folic acid, sulfanilamide can kill bacteria but does not harm human cells.

Noncompetitive inhibitors do not compete with the substrate for the enzyme's active site; instead, they interact with another part of the enzyme (**Figure 7c**). In this process, called **allosteric** ("other space") **inhibition,** the inhibitor binds to a site on the enzyme other than the substrate's binding site, called the **allosteric site.** This binding causes the active site to change its shape, making it nonfunctional. As a result, the enzyme's activity is reduced. This effect can be either reversible or irreversible, depending on whether the active site can return to its original shape. In some cases, allosteric interactions can activate an enzyme rather than inhibit it. Another type of noncompetitive inhibition can operate on enzymes that require metal ions for their activity. Certain chemicals can bind or tie up the metal ion activators and thus prevent an enzymatic reaction. Cyanide can bind the iron in iron-containing enzymes, and fluoride can bind calcium or magnesium. Substances such as cyanide and fluoride are sometimes called *enzyme poisons* because they permanently inactivate enzymes. **Animations** Enzymes: Competitive Inhibition, Noncompetitive Inhibition

Feedback Inhibition

Allosteric inhibitors play a role in a kind of biochemical control called **feedback inhibition,** or **end-product inhibition.** This control mechanism stops the cell from making more of a substance than it needs and thereby wasting chemical resources. In some metabolic reactions, several steps are required for the synthesis of a particular chemical compound, called the *end-product.* The process is similar to an assembly line, with each step catalyzed by a separate enzyme (**Figure 8**). In many anabolic pathways, the final product can allosterically inhibit the activity of one of the enzymes earlier in the pathway. This phenomenon is feedback inhibition.

Feedback inhibition generally acts on the first enzyme in a metabolic pathway (similar to shutting down an assembly line by stopping the first worker). Because the enzyme is inhibited, the product of the first enzymatic reaction in the pathway is not synthesized. Because that unsynthesized product would

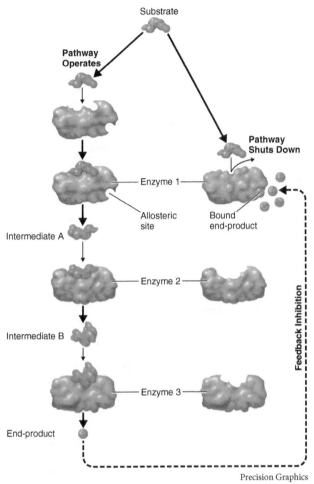

Figure 8 Feedback inhibition.

Q Explain the differences between competitive inhibition and feedback inhibition.

Precision Graphics

normally be the substrate for the second enzyme in the pathway, the second reaction stops immediately as well. Thus, even though only the first enzyme in the pathway is inhibited, the entire pathway shuts down, and no new end-product is formed. By inhibiting the first enzyme in the pathway, the cell also keeps metabolic intermediates from accumulating. As the cell uses up the existing end-product, the first enzyme's allosteric site more often remains unbound, and the pathway resumes activity.

The bacterium *E. coli* can be used to demonstrate feedback inhibition in the synthesis of the amino acid isoleucine, which is required for the cell's growth. In this metabolic pathway, the amino acid threonine is enzymatically converted to isoleucine in five steps. If isoleucine is added to the growth medium for *E. coli,* it inhibits the first enzyme in the pathway,

and the bacteria stop synthesizing isoleucine. This condition is maintained until the supply of isoleucine is depleted. This type of feedback inhibition is also involved in regulating the cells' production of other amino acids, as well as vitamins, purines, and pyrimidines.

Ribozymes

Prior to 1982, it was believed that only protein molecules had enzymatic activity. Researchers working on microbes discovered a unique type of RNA called a **ribozyme.** Like protein enzymes, ribozymes function as catalysts, have active sites that bind to substrates, and are not used up in a chemical reaction. Ribozymes specifically act on strands of RNA by removing sections and splicing together the remaining pieces. In this respect, ribozymes are more restricted than protein enzymes in terms of the diversity of substrates with which they interact.

CHECK YOUR UNDERSTANDING

✔ What is a coenzyme? 3

✔ Why is enzyme specificity important? 4

✔ What happens to an enzyme below its optimal temperature? Above its optimal temperature? 5

✔ Why is feedback inhibition noncompetitive inhibition? 6

✔ What is a ribozyme? 7

Energy Production

LEARNING OBJECTIVES

8 Explain the term *oxidation-reduction*.

9 List and provide examples of three types of phosphorylation reactions that generate ATP.

10 Explain the overall function of metabolic pathways.

Nutrient molecules, like all molecules, have energy associated with the electrons that form bonds between their atoms. When it is spread throughout the molecule, this energy is difficult for the cell to use. Various reactions in catabolic pathways, however, concentrate the energy into the bonds of ATP, which serves as a convenient energy carrier. ATP is generally referred to as having "high-energy" bonds. Actually, a better term is probably *unstable bonds.* Although the amount of energy in these bonds is not exceptionally large, it can be released quickly and easily. In a sense, ATP is similar to a highly flammable liquid such as kerosene. Although a large log might eventually burn to produce more heat than a cup of kerosene, the kerosene is easier to ignite and provides heat more quickly and conveniently. In a similar way, the "high-energy" unstable bonds of ATP provide the cell with readily available energy for anabolic reactions.

Before discussing the catabolic pathways, we will consider two general aspects of energy production: the concept of oxidation-reduction and the mechanisms of ATP generation.

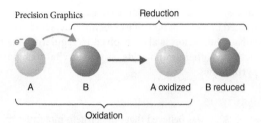

Figure 9 **Oxidation-reduction.** An electron is transferred from molecule A to molecule B. In the process, molecule A is oxidized, and molecule B is reduced.

 How do oxidation and reduction differ?

Oxidation-Reduction Reactions

Oxidation is the removal of electrons (e^-) from an atom or molecule, a reaction that often produces energy. Figure 9 shows an example of an oxidation in which molecule A loses an electron to molecule B. Molecule A has undergone oxidation (meaning that it has lost one or more electrons), whereas molecule B has undergone **reduction** (meaning that it has gained one or more electrons).* Oxidation and reduction reactions are always coupled; in other words, each time one substance is oxidized, another is simultaneously reduced. The pairing of these reactions is called **oxidation-reduction** or a **redox reaction.**

In many cellular oxidations, electrons and protons (hydrogen ions, H^+) are removed at the same time; this is equivalent to the removal of hydrogen atoms, because a hydrogen atom is made up of one proton and one electron. Because most biological oxidations involve the loss of hydrogen atoms, they are also called **dehydrogenation** reactions. Figure 10 shows an example of a biological oxidation. An organic molecule is oxidized by the loss of two hydrogen atoms, and a molecule of NAD^+ is reduced. Recall from our earlier discussion of coenzymes that NAD^+ assists enzymes by accepting hydrogen atoms removed from the substrate, in this case the organic molecule. As shown in Figure 10, NAD^+ accepts two electrons and one proton. One proton (H^+) is left over and is released into the surrounding medium. The reduced coenzyme, NADH, contains more energy than NAD^+. This energy can be used to generate ATP in later reactions.

An important point to remember about biological oxidation-reduction reactions is that cells use them in catabolism to extract energy from nutrient molecules. Cells take nutrients, some of which serve as energy sources, and degrade them from highly reduced compounds (with many hydrogen atoms) to highly oxidized compounds. For example, when a cell oxidizes a molecule of glucose ($C_6H_{12}O_6$) to CO_2 and H_2O, the energy in the glucose molecule is removed in a stepwise manner and ultimately is trapped by ATP, which can then serve as an energy source for energy-requiring reactions. Compounds such as glucose that have many hydrogen atoms are highly reduced compounds, containing a large amount of potential energy. Thus, glucose is a valuable nutrient for organisms. (MM) **Animation** Oxidation-Reduction Reactions

CHECK YOUR UNDERSTANDING

✔ Why is glucose such an important molecule for organisms? **8**

The Generation of ATP

Much of the energy released during oxidation-reduction reactions is trapped within the cell by the formation of ATP. Specifically, an inorganic phosphate group, $℗_i$, is added to ADP with the input of energy to form ATP:

$$\overbrace{\text{Adenosine}\,—\,℗\,\sim\,℗}^{\text{ADP}} + \text{Energy} + ℗_i \longrightarrow$$
$$\underbrace{\text{Adenosine}\,—\,℗\,\sim\,℗\,\sim\,℗}_{\text{ATP}}$$

The symbol $\sim$ designates a "high-energy" bond—that is, one that can readily be broken to release usable energy. The high-energy bond that attaches the third ℗ in a sense contains the energy stored in this reaction. When this ℗ is removed, usable energy is released. The addition of ℗ to a chemical compound is called **phosphorylation**. Organisms use three mechanisms of phosphorylation to generate ATP from ADP.

Substrate-Level Phosphorylation

In **substrate-level phosphorylation,** ATP is usually generated when a high-energy ℗ is directly transferred from a phosphorylated compound (a substrate) to ADP. Generally, the ℗ has acquired its energy during an earlier reaction in which the substrate itself was oxidized. The following example shows only the carbon skeleton and the ℗ of a typical substrate:

$$\text{C—C—C} \sim ℗ + \text{ADP} \rightarrow \text{C—C—C} + \text{ATP}$$

Oxidative Phosphorylation

In **oxidative phosphorylation,** electrons are transferred from organic compounds to one group of electron carriers (usually to NAD^+ and FAD). Then, the electrons are passed through

---

*The terms do not seem logical until one considers the history of the discovery of these reactions. When mercury is heated, it gains weight as mercuric oxide is formed; this was called *oxidation*. Later it was determined that the mercury actually *lost* electrons, and the observed *gain* in oxygen was a direct result of this. Oxidation, therefore, is a *loss* of electrons, and reduction is a *gain* of electrons, but the gain and loss of electrons is not usually apparent as chemical-reaction equations are usually written. For example, in the equations for aerobic respiration later in this chapter, notice that each carbon in glucose had only one oxygen originally, and later, as carbon dioxide, each carbon now has two oxygens. However, the gain or loss of electrons actually responsible for this is not apparent.

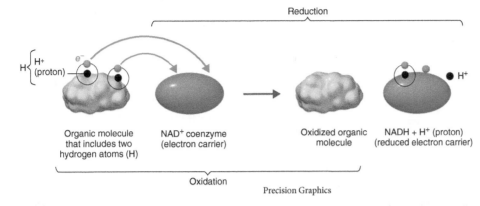

Reduction

Organic molecule that includes two hydrogen atoms (H) | NAD⁺ coenzyme (electron carrier) | Oxidized organic molecule | NADH + H⁺ (proton) (reduced electron carrier)

Oxidation

Precision Graphics

Figure 10 Representative biological oxidation. Two electrons and two protons (altogether equivalent to two hydrogen atoms) are transferred from an organic substrate molecule to a coenzyme, NAD^+. NAD^+ actually receives one hydrogen atom and one electron, and one proton is released into the medium. NAD^+ is reduced to NADH, which is a more energy-rich molecule.

How do organisms use oxidation-reduction reactions?

a series of different electron carriers to molecules of oxygen (O_2) or other oxidized inorganic and organic molecules. This process occurs in the plasma membrane of prokaryotes and in the inner mitochondrial membrane of eukaryotes. The sequence of electron carriers used in oxidative phosphorylation is called an **electron transport chain (system)** (see Figure 14). The transfer of electrons from one electron carrier to the next releases energy, some of which is used to generate ATP from ADP through a process called *chemiosmosis*, to be described later in this chapter.

Photophosphorylation

The third mechanism of phosphorylation, **photophosphorylation,** occurs only in photosynthetic cells, which contain light-trapping pigments such as chlorophylls. In photosynthesis, organic molecules, especially sugars, are synthesized with the energy of light from the energy-poor building blocks carbon dioxide and water. Photophosphorylation starts this process by converting light energy to the chemical energy of ATP and NADPH, which, in turn, are used to synthesize organic molecules. As in oxidative phosphorylation, an electron transport chain is involved.

CHECK YOUR UNDERSTANDING

✔ Outline the three ways that ATP is generated. 9

Metabolic Pathways of Energy Production

Organisms release and store energy from organic molecules by a series of controlled reactions rather than in a single burst. If the energy were released all at once, as a large amount of heat, it could not be readily used to drive chemical reactions and would, in fact, damage the cell. To extract energy from organic compounds and store it in chemical form, organisms pass electrons from one compound to another through a series of oxidation-reduction reactions.

As noted earlier, a sequence of enzymatically catalyzed chemical reactions occurring in a cell is called a metabolic pathway. Below is a hypothetical metabolic pathway that converts starting material A to end-product F in a series of five steps:

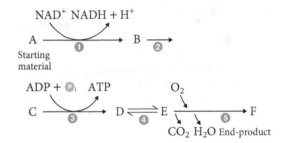

The first step is the conversion of molecule A to molecule B. The curved arrow indicates that the reduction of coenzyme NAD^+ to NADH is coupled to that reaction; the electrons and protons come from molecule A. Similarly, the two arrows in ❸ show a coupling of two reactions. As C is converted to D, ADP is converted to ATP; the energy needed comes from C as it transforms into D. The reaction converting D to E is readily reversible, as indicated by the double arrow. In the fifth step, the curved arrow leading from O_2 indicates that O_2 is a reactant. The curved arrows leading to CO_2 and H_2O indicate that these substances are secondary products produced in the reaction, in addition to F, the end-product that (presumably) interests us the most. Secondary products such as CO_2 and H_2O shown here are sometimes called *by-products* or *waste products*. Keep in mind that almost every reaction in a metabolic pathway is catalyzed by a specific enzyme; sometimes the name of the enzyme is printed near the arrow.

CHECK YOUR UNDERSTANDING

✔ What is the purpose of metabolic pathways? 10

Carbohydrate Catabolism

LEARNING OBJECTIVES

11   Describe the chemical reactions of glycolysis.

12   Identify the functions of the pentose phosphate and Entner-Doudoroff pathways.

13   Explain the products of the Krebs cycle.

14   Describe the chemiosmotic model for ATP generation.

15   Compare and contrast aerobic and anaerobic respiration.

16   Describe the chemical reactions of, and list some products of, fermentation.

Most microorganisms oxidize carbohydrates as their primary source of cellular energy. **Carbohydrate catabolism,** the breakdown of carbohydrate molecules to produce energy, is therefore of great importance in cell metabolism. Glucose is the most common carbohydrate energy source used by cells. Microorganisms can also catabolize various lipids and proteins for energy production.

To produce energy from glucose, microorganisms use two general processes: *cellular respiration* and *fermentation*. (In discussing cellular respiration, we frequently refer to the process simply as respiration, but it should not be confused with breathing.) Both cellular respiration and fermentation usually start with the same first step, glycolysis, but follow different subsequent pathways (Figure 11). Before examining the details of glycolysis, respiration, and fermentation, we will first look at a general overview of the processes.

As shown in Figure 11, the respiration of glucose typically occurs in three principal stages: glycolysis, the Krebs cycle, and the electron transport chain (system).

❶ Glycolysis is the oxidation of glucose to pyruvic acid with the production of some ATP and energy-containing NADH.

❷ The Krebs cycle is the oxidation of acetyl CoA (a derivative of pyruvic acid) to carbon dioxide, with the production of some ATP, energy-containing NADH, and another reduced electron carrier, FADH$_2$ (the reduced form of flavin adenine dinucleotide).

❸ In the electron transport chain (system), NADH and FADH$_2$ are oxidized, contributing the electrons they have carried from the substrates to a "cascade" of oxidation-reduction reactions involving a series of additional electron carriers. Energy from these reactions is used to generate a considerable amount of ATP. In respiration, most of the ATP is generated in the third step.

Because respiration involves a long series of oxidation-reduction reactions, the entire process can be thought of as involving a flow of electrons from the energy-rich glucose molecule to the relatively energy-poor CO$_2$ and H$_2$O molecules. The coupling of ATP production to this flow is somewhat analogous to producing electrical power by using energy from a flowing stream. Carrying the analogy further, you could imagine a stream flowing down a gentle slope during glycolysis and the Krebs cycle, supplying energy to turn two old-fashioned waterwheels. Then the stream rushes down a steep slope in the electron transport chain, supplying energy for a large modern power plant. In a similar way, glycolysis and the Krebs cycle generate a small amount of ATP and also supply the electrons that generate a great deal of ATP at the electron transport chain stage.

Typically, the initial stage of fermentation is also glycolysis (Figure 11). However, once glycolysis has taken place, the pyruvic acid is converted into one or more different products, depending on the type of cell. These products might include alcohol (ethanol) and lactic acid. Unlike respiration, there is no Krebs cycle or electron transport chain in fermentation. Accordingly, the ATP yield, which comes only from glycolysis, is much lower.

Glycolysis

Glycolysis, the oxidation of glucose to pyruvic acid, is usually the first stage in carbohydrate catabolism. Most microorganisms use this pathway; in fact, it occurs in most living cells.

Glycolysis is also called the *Embden-Meyerhof pathway*. The word *glycolysis* means splitting of sugar, and this is exactly what happens. The enzymes of glycolysis catalyze the splitting of glucose, a six-carbon sugar, into two three-carbon sugars. These sugars are then oxidized, releasing energy, and their atoms are rearranged to form two molecules of pyruvic acid. During glycolysis NAD$^+$ is reduced to NADH, and there is a net production of two ATP molecules by substrate-level phosphorylation. Glycolysis does not require oxygen; it can occur whether oxygen is present or not. This pathway is a series of ten chemical reactions, each catalyzed by a different enzyme. The steps are outlined in Figure 12.

To summarize the process, glycolysis consists of two basic stages, a preparatory stage and an energy-conserving stage:

1. First, in the preparatory stage (steps ❶–❹ in Figure 12), two molecules of ATP are used as a six-carbon glucose molecule is phosphorylated, restructured, and split into two three-carbon compounds: glyceraldehyde 3-phosphate (GP) and dihydroxyacetone phosphate (DHAP). ❺ DHAP is readily converted to GP. (The reverse reaction may also occur.) The conversion of DHAP into GP means that from this point on in glycolysis, two molecules of GP are fed into the remaining chemical reactions.

2. In the energy-conserving stage (steps ❻–❿), the two three-carbon molecules are oxidized in several steps to two molecules of pyruvic acid. In these reactions, two molecules of NAD$^+$ are reduced to NADH, and four molecules of ATP are formed by substrate-level phosphorylation.

An Overview of Respiration and Fermentation

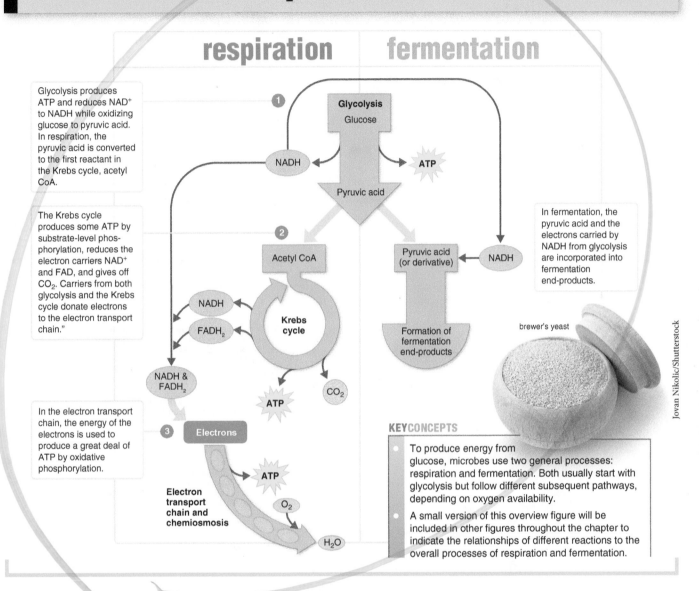

respiration   fermentation

Glycolysis produces ATP and reduces NAD$^+$ to NADH while oxidizing glucose to pyruvic acid. In respiration, the pyruvic acid is converted to the first reactant in the Krebs cycle, acetyl CoA.

The Krebs cycle produces some ATP by substrate-level phosphorylation, reduces the electron carriers NAD$^+$ and FAD, and gives off CO$_2$. Carriers from both glycolysis and the Krebs cycle donate electrons to the electron transport chain."

In the electron transport chain, the energy of the electrons is used to produce a great deal of ATP by oxidative phosphorylation.

In fermentation, the pyruvic acid and the electrons carried by NADH from glycolysis are incorporated into fermentation end-products.

brewer's yeast

Jovan Nikolic/Shutterstock

① Glycolysis — Glucose — NADH — ATP — Pyruvic acid

② Acetyl CoA — NADH — FADH$_2$ — Krebs cycle — ATP — CO$_2$

Pyruvic acid (or derivative) — NADH — Formation of fermentation end-products

NADH & FADH$_2$

③ Electrons — ATP — Electron transport chain and chemiosmosis — O$_2$ — H$_2$O

KEYCONCEPTS

- To produce energy from glucose, microbes use two general processes: respiration and fermentation. Both usually start with glycolysis but follow different subsequent pathways, depending on oxygen availability.
- A small version of this overview figure will be included in other figures throughout the chapter to indicate the relationships of different reactions to the overall processes of respiration and fermentation.

Because two molecules of ATP were needed to get glycolysis started and four molecules of ATP are generated by the process, *there is a net gain of two molecules of ATP for each molecule of glucose that is oxidized.* (MM) **Animations** Glycolysis: Overview, Steps

Alternatives to Glycolysis

Many bacteria have another pathway in addition to glycolysis for the oxidation of glucose. The most common alternative is the pentose phosphate pathway; another alternative is the Entner-Doudoroff pathway.

The Pentose Phosphate Pathway

The **pentose phosphate pathway** (or *hexose monophosphate shunt*) operates simultaneously with glycolysis and provides a means for the breakdown of five-carbon sugars (pentoses) as well as glucose. A key feature of this pathway is that it produces

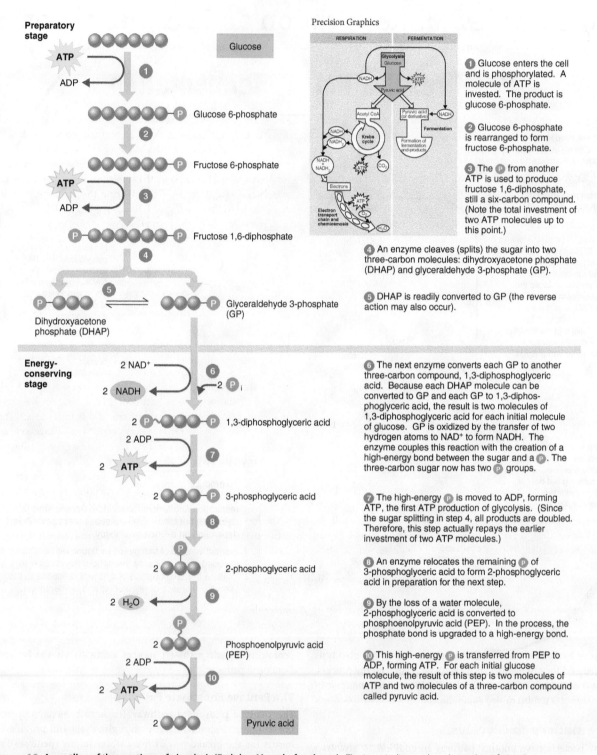

Preparatory stage

Glucose

ATP

ADP

1

Glucose 6-phosphate

2

Fructose 6-phosphate

ATP

ADP

3

Fructose 1,6-diphosphate

4

5

Dihydroxyacetone phosphate (DHAP)

Glyceraldehyde 3-phosphate (GP)

Energy-conserving stage

2 NAD+

6

2 NADH

2 Pi

2

1,3-diphosphoglyceric acid

2 ADP

2 **ATP**

7

2

3-phosphoglyceric acid

8

2

2-phosphoglyceric acid

2 H₂O

9

2

Phosphoenolpyruvic acid (PEP)

2 ADP

2 **ATP**

10

2

Pyruvic acid

Precision Graphics

1 Glucose enters the cell and is phosphorylated. A molecule of ATP is invested. The product is glucose 6-phosphate.

2 Glucose 6-phosphate is rearranged to form fructose 6-phosphate.

3 The P from another ATP is used to produce fructose 1,6-diphosphate, still a six-carbon compound. (Note the total investment of two ATP molecules up to this point.)

4 An enzyme cleaves (splits) the sugar into two three-carbon molecules: dihydroxyacetone phosphate (DHAP) and glyceraldehyde 3-phosphate (GP).

5 DHAP is readily converted to GP (the reverse action may also occur).

6 The next enzyme converts each GP to another three-carbon compound, 1,3-diphosphoglyceric acid. Because each DHAP molecule can be converted to GP and each GP to 1,3-diphosphoglyceric acid, the result is two molecules of 1,3-diphosphoglyceric acid for each initial molecule of glucose. GP is oxidized by the transfer of two hydrogen atoms to NAD+ to form NADH. The enzyme couples this reaction with the creation of a high-energy bond between the sugar and a P. The three-carbon sugar now has two P groups.

7 The high-energy P is moved to ADP, forming ATP, the first ATP production of glycolysis. (Since the sugar splitting in step 4, all products are doubled. Therefore, this step actually repays the earlier investment of two ATP molecules.)

8 An enzyme relocates the remaining P of 3-phosphoglyceric acid to form 2-phosphoglyceric acid in preparation for the next step.

9 By the loss of a water molecule, 2-phosphoglyceric acid is converted to phosphoenolpyruvic acid (PEP). In the process, the phosphate bond is upgraded to a high-energy bond.

10 This high-energy P is transferred from PEP to ADP, forming ATP. For each initial glucose molecule, the result of this step is two molecules of ATP and two molecules of a three-carbon compound called pyruvic acid.

Figure 12 An outline of the reactions of glycolysis (Embden-Meyerhof pathway). The inset indicates the relationship of glycolysis to the overall processes of respiration and fermentation.

Q What is glycolysis?

important intermediate pentoses used in the synthesis of (1) nucleic acids, (2) glucose from carbon dioxide in photosynthesis, and (3) certain amino acids. The pathway is an important producer of the reduced coenzyme NADPH from NADP$^+$. The pentose phosphate pathway yields a net gain of only one molecule of ATP for each molecule of glucose oxidized. Bacteria that use the pentose phosphate pathway include *Bacillus subtilis* (sub′til-us), *E. coli*, *Leuconostoc mesenteroides* (lü-kō-nos′tok mes-en-ter-oi′dēz), and *Enterococcus faecalis* (fē-kāl′is).

The Entner-Doudoroff Pathway

From each molecule of glucose, the **Entner-Doudoroff pathway** produces two molecules of NADPH and one molecule of ATP for use in cellular biosynthetic reactions. Bacteria that have the enzymes for the Entner-Doudoroff pathway can metabolize glucose without either glycolysis or the pentose phosphate pathway. The Entner-Doudoroff pathway is found in some gram-negative bacteria, including *Rhizobium, Pseudomonas* (sū-dō-mō′nas), and *Agrobacterium* (ag-rō-bak-ti′rē-um); it is generally not found among gram-positive bacteria. Tests for the ability to oxidize glucose by this pathway are sometimes used to identify *Pseudomonas* in the clinical laboratory.

CHECK YOUR UNDERSTANDING

🖋 What happens during the preparatory and energy-conserving stages of glycolysis? **11**

🖋 What is the value of the pentose phosphate and Entner-Doudoroff pathways if they produce only one ATP molecule? **12**

Cellular Respiration

After glucose has been broken down to pyruvic acid, the pyruvic acid can be channeled into the next step of either fermentation or cellular respiration (see Figure 11). **Cellular respiration,** or simply **respiration,** is defined as an ATP-generating process in which molecules are oxidized and the final electron acceptor is (almost always) an inorganic molecule. An essential feature of respiration is the operation of an electron transport chain.

There are two types of respiration, depending on whether an organism is an **aerobe,** which uses oxygen, or an **anaerobe,** which does not use oxygen and may even be killed by it. In **aerobic respiration,** the final electron acceptor is O_2; in **anaerobic respiration,** the final electron acceptor is an inorganic molecule other than O_2 or, rarely, an organic molecule. First we will describe respiration as it typically occurs in an aerobic cell.

Aerobic Respiration

The Krebs Cycle The **Krebs cycle,** also called the *tricarboxylic acid (TCA) cycle* or *citric acid cycle,* is a series of biochemical reactions in which the large amount of potential chemical energy

stored in acetyl CoA is released step by step (see Figure 11). In this cycle, a series of oxidations and reductions transfer that potential energy, in the form of electrons, to electron carrier coenzymes, chiefly NAD$^+$. The pyruvic acid derivatives are oxidized; the coenzymes are reduced.

Pyruvic acid, the product of glycolysis, cannot enter the Krebs cycle directly. In a preparatory step, it must lose one molecule of CO_2 and become a two-carbon compound (**Figure 13**, at top). This process is called **decarboxylation.** The two-carbon compound, called an *acetyl group,* attaches to coenzyme A through a high-energy bond; the resulting complex is known as *acetyl coenzyme A (acetyl CoA).* During this reaction, pyruvic acid is also oxidized, and NAD$^+$ is reduced to NADH.

Remember that the oxidation of one glucose molecule produces two molecules of pyruvic acid, so for each molecule of glucose, two molecules of CO_2 are released in this preparatory step, two molecules of NADH are produced, and two molecules of acetyl CoA are formed. Once the pyruvic acid has undergone decarboxylation and its derivative (the acetyl group) has attached to CoA, the resulting acetyl CoA is ready to enter the Krebs cycle.

As acetyl CoA enters the Krebs cycle, CoA detaches from the acetyl group. The two-carbon acetyl group combines with a four-carbon compound called oxaloacetic acid to form the six-carbon citric acid. This synthesis reaction requires energy, which is provided by the cleavage of the high-energy bond between the acetyl group and CoA. The formation of citric acid is thus the first step in the Krebs cycle. The major chemical reactions of this cycle are outlined in Figure 13. Keep in mind that each reaction is catalyzed by a specific enzyme.

The chemical reactions of the Krebs cycle fall into several general categories; one of these is decarboxylation. For example, in step ❸ isocitric acid, a six-carbon compound, is decarboxylated to the five-carbon compound called α-ketoglutaric acid. Another decarboxylation takes place in step ❹. Because one decarboxylation has taken place in the preparatory step and two in the Krebs cycle, all three carbon atoms in pyruvic acid are eventually released as CO_2 by the Krebs cycle. This represents the conversion to CO_2 of all six carbon atoms contained in the original glucose molecule.

Another general category of Krebs cycle chemical reactions is oxidation-reduction. For example, in step ❸, two hydrogen atoms are lost during the conversion of the six-carbon isocitric acid to a five-carbon compound. In other words, the six-carbon compound is oxidized. Hydrogen atoms are also released in the Krebs cycle in steps ❹, ❻, and ❽ and are picked up by the coenzymes NAD$^+$ and FAD. Because NAD$^+$ picks up two electrons but only one additional proton, its reduced form is represented as NADH; however, FAD picks up two complete hydrogen atoms and is reduced to FADH$_2$.

Precision Graphics

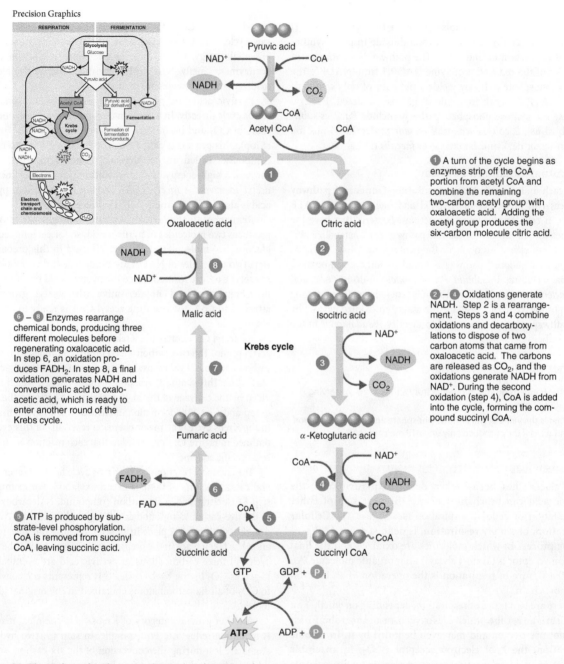

Figure 13 The Krebs cycle. The inset indicates the relationship of the Krebs cycle to the overall process of respiration.

Q What are the products of the Krebs cycle?

If we look at the Krebs cycle as a whole, we see that for every two molecules of acetyl CoA that enter the cycle, four molecules of CO_2 are liberated by decarboxylation, six molecules of NADH and two molecules of $FADH_2$ are produced by oxidation-reduction reactions, and two molecules of ATP are generated by substrate-level

phosphorylation. A molecule of guanosine triphosphate (GTP), formed from guanosine diphosphate (GDP + P_i), is similar to ATP and serves as an intermediary at this point in the cycle. Many of the intermediates in the Krebs cycle also play a role in other pathways, especially in amino acid biosynthesis.

Precision Graphics

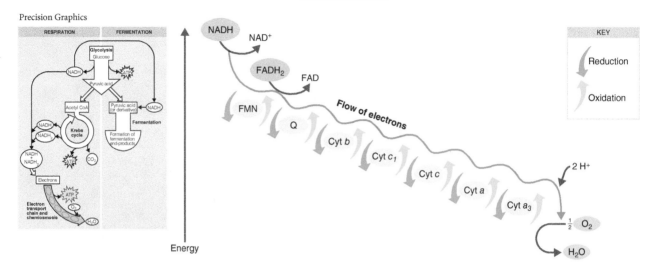

Figure 14 An electron transport chain (system). The inset indicates the relationship of the electron transport chain to the overall process of respiration. In the mitochondrial electron transport chain shown, the electrons pass along the chain in a gradual and stepwise fashion, so energy is released in manageable quantities. To learn where ATP is formed, see Figure 16.

Q What are the functions of the electron transport chain?

The CO_2 produced in the Krebs cycle is ultimately liberated into the atmosphere as a gaseous by-product of aerobic respiration. (Humans produce CO_2 from the Krebs cycle in most cells of the body and discharge it through the lungs during exhalation.) The reduced coenzymes NADH and $FADH_2$ are the most important products of the Krebs cycle because they contain most of the energy originally stored in glucose. During the next phase of respiration, a series of reductions indirectly transfers the energy stored in those coenzymes to ATP. These reactions are collectively called the electron transport chain. **(MM)** Animations Krebs Cycle: Overview, Steps

The Electron Transport Chain (System) An **electron transport chain (system)** consists of a sequence of carrier molecules that are capable of oxidation and reduction. As electrons are passed through the chain, there occurs a stepwise release of energy, which is used to drive the chemiosmotic generation of ATP, to be described shortly. The final oxidation is irreversible. In eukaryotic cells, the electron transport chain is contained in the inner membrane of mitochondria; in prokaryotic cells, it is found in the plasma membrane.

There are three classes of carrier molecules in electron transport chains. The first are **flavoproteins.** These proteins contain flavin, a coenzyme derived from riboflavin (vitamin B_2), and are capable of performing alternating oxidations and reductions. One important flavin coenzyme is flavin mononucleotide (FMN). The second class of carrier molecules are **cytochromes,** proteins with an iron-containing group (heme) capable of existing alternately as a reduced form (Fe^{2+}) and an oxidized form (Fe^{3+}).

The cytochromes involved in electron transport chains include cytochrome b (cyt b), cytochrome c_1 (cyt c_1), cytochrome c (cyt c), cytochrome a (cyt a), and cytochrome a_3 (cyt a_3). The third class is known as **ubiquinones,** or **coenzyme Q,** symbolized Q; these are small nonprotein carriers.

The electron transport chains of bacteria are somewhat diverse, in that the particular carriers used by a bacterium and the order in which they function may differ from those of other bacteria and from those of eukaryotic mitochondrial systems. Even a single bacterium may have several types of electron transport chains. However, keep in mind that all electron transport chains achieve the same basic goal: to release energy as electrons are transferred from higher-energy compounds to lower-energy compounds. Much is known about the electron transport chain in the mitochondria of eukaryotic cells, so this is the chain we will describe.

The first step in the mitochondrial electron transport chain involves the transfer of high-energy electrons from NADH to FMN, the first carrier in the chain (**Figure 14**). This transfer actually involves the passage of a hydrogen atom with two electrons to FMN, which then picks up an additional H^+ from the surrounding aqueous medium. As a result of the first transfer, NADH is oxidized to NAD^+, and FMN is reduced to $FMNH_2$. In the second step in the electron transport chain, $FMNH_2$ passes $2H^+$ to the other side of the mitochondrial membrane (see Figure 16) and passes two electrons to Q. As a result, $FMNH_2$ is oxidized to FMN. Q also picks up an additional $2H^+$ from the surrounding aqueous medium and releases it on the other side of the membrane.

Figure 15 Chemiosmosis. An overview of the mechanism of chemiosmosis. The membrane shown could be a prokaryotic plasma membrane, a eukaryotic mitochondrial membrane, or a photosynthetic thylakoid. The numbered steps are described in the text.

Q What is the proton motive force?

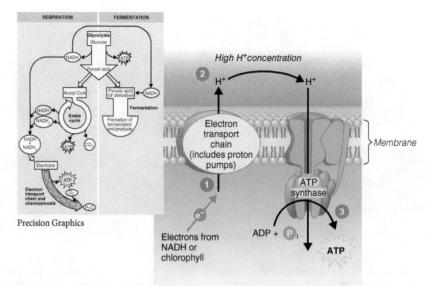

Precision Graphics

The next part of the electron transport chain involves the cytochromes. Electrons are passed successively from Q to cyt *b*, cyt c_1, cyt *c*, cyt *a*, and cyt a_3. Each cytochrome in the chain is reduced as it picks up electrons and is oxidized as it gives up electrons. The last cytochrome, cyt a_3, passes its electrons to molecular oxygen (O_2), which becomes negatively charged and then picks up protons from the surrounding medium to form H_2O.

Notice that Figure 14 shows $FADH_2$, which is derived from the Krebs cycle, as another source of electrons. However, $FADH_2$ adds its electrons to the electron transport chain at a lower level than NADH. Because of this, the electron transport chain produces about one-third less energy for ATP generation when $FADH_2$ donates electrons than when NADH is involved.

An important feature of the electron transport chain is the presence of some carriers, such as FMN and Q, that accept and release protons as well as electrons, and other carriers, such as cytochromes, that transfer electrons only. Electron flow down the chain is accompanied at several points by the active transport (pumping) of protons from the matrix side of the inner mitochondrial membrane to the opposite side of the membrane. The result is a buildup of protons on one side of the membrane. Just as water behind a dam stores energy that can be used to generate electricity, this buildup of protons provides energy for the generation of ATP by the chemiosmotic mechanism.

The Chemiosmotic Mechanism of ATP Generation The mechanism of ATP synthesis using the electron transport chain is called **chemiosmosis.** Substances diffuse passively across membranes from areas of high concentration to areas of

low concentration; this diffusion yields energy. Recall also that the movement of substances *against* such a concentration gradient *requires* energy and that, in such an active transport of molecules or ions across biological membranes, the required energy is usually provided by ATP. In chemiosmosis, the energy released when a substance moves along a gradient is used to *synthesize* ATP. The "substance" in this case refers to protons. In respiration, chemiosmosis is responsible for most of the ATP that is generated. The steps of chemiosmosis are as follows (**Figure 15** and **Figure 16**):

1. As energetic electrons from NADH (or chlorophyll) pass down the electron transport chain, some of the carriers in the chain pump—actively transport—protons across the membrane. Such carrier molecules are called *proton pumps.*

2. The phospholipid membrane is normally impermeable to protons, so this one-directional pumping establishes a proton gradient (a difference in the concentrations of protons on the two sides of the membrane). In addition to a concentration gradient, there is an electrical charge gradient. The excess H^+ on one side of the membrane makes that side positively charged compared with the other side. The resulting electrochemical gradient has potential energy, called the *proton motive force.*

3. The protons on the side of the membrane with the higher proton concentration can diffuse across the membrane only through special protein channels that contain an enzyme called *ATP synthase.* When this flow occurs, energy is released and is used by the enzyme to synthesize ATP from ADP and P_i.

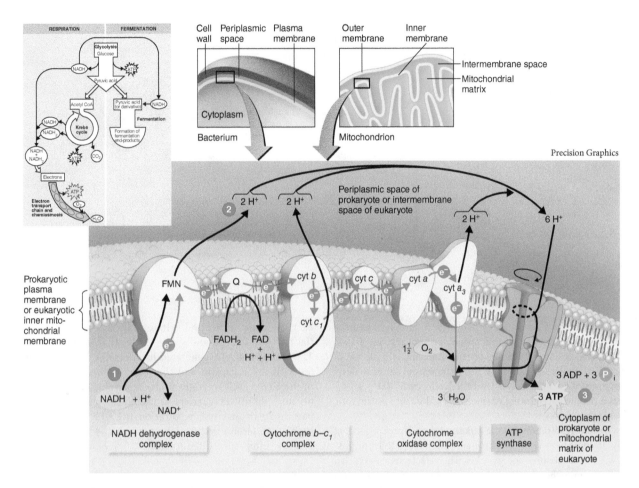

Figure 16 Electron transport and the chemiosmotic generation of ATP. Electron carriers are organized into three complexes, and protons (H^+) are pumped across the membrane at three points. In a prokaryotic cell, protons are pumped across the plasma membrane from the cytoplasmic side. In a eukaryotic cell, they are pumped from the matrix side of the mitochondrial membrane to the opposite side. The flow of electrons is indicated with red arrows.

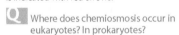 Where does chemiosmosis occur in eukaryotes? In prokaryotes?

Figure 16 shows in detail how the electron transport chain operates in eukaryotes to drive the chemiosmotic mechanism.

❶ Energetic electrons from NADH pass down the electron transport chains. Within the inner mitochondrial membrane, the carriers of the electron transport chain are organized into three complexes, with Q transporting electrons between the first and second complexes, and cyt *c* transporting them between the second and third complexes. ❷ Three components of the system pump protons: the first and third complexes and Q. At the end of the chain, electrons join with protons and oxygen (O_2) in the matrix fluid to form water (H_2O). Thus, O_2 is the final electron acceptor.

Both prokaryotic and eukaryotic cells use the chemiosmotic mechanism to generate energy for ATP production. However, in eukaryotic cells, ❸ the inner mitochondrial membrane contains the electron transport carriers and ATP synthase, whereas in most prokaryotic cells, the plasma membrane does so. An electron transport chain also operates in photophosphorylation and is located in the thylakoid membrane of cyanobacteria and eukaryotic chloroplasts.

A Summary of Aerobic Respiration The electron transport chain regenerates NAD^+ and FAD, which can be used again in glycolysis and the Krebs cycle. The various electron transfers in the electron transport chain generate about 34 molecules of ATP from each molecule of glucose oxidized: approximately three from each of the ten molecules of NADH (a total of 30), and approximately two from each of the two molecules of $FADH_2$ (a total of four). To arrive at the total number of ATP molecules generated for each molecule of glucose, the 34 from chemiosmosis

TABLE 3 ATP Yield during Prokaryotic Aerobic Respiration of One Glucose Molecule

Source	ATP Yield (Method)
Glycolysis	
1. Oxidation of glucose to pyruvic acid	2 ATP (substrate-level phosphorylation)
2. Production of 2 NADH	6 ATP (oxidative phosphorylation in electron transport chain)
Preparatory Step	
1. Formation of acetyl CoA produces 2 NADH	6 ATP (oxidative phosphorylation in electron transport chain)
Krebs Cycle	
1. Oxidation of succinyl CoA to succinic acid	2 GTP (equivalent of ATP; substrate-level phosphorylation)
2. Production of 6 NADH	18 ATP (oxidative phosphorylation in electron transport chain)
3. Production of 2 FADH	4 ATP (oxidative phosphorylation in electron transport chain)
	Total: 38 ATP

are added to those generated by oxidation in glycolysis and the Krebs cycle. In aerobic respiration among prokaryotes, a total of 38 molecules of ATP can be generated from one molecule of glucose. Note that four of those ATPs come from substrate-level phosphorylation in glycolysis and the Krebs cycle. Table 3 provides a detailed accounting of the ATP yield during prokaryotic aerobic respiration.

Aerobic respiration among eukaryotes produces a total of only 36 molecules of ATP. There are fewer ATPs than in prokaryotes because some energy is lost when electrons are shuttled across the mitochondrial membranes that separate glycolysis (in the cytoplasm) from the electron transport chain. No such separation exists in prokaryotes. We can now summarize the overall reaction for aerobic respiration in prokaryotes as follows:

$$C_6H_{12}O_6 + 6\,O_2 + 38\,ADP + 38\,P_i \longrightarrow$$

Glucose   Oxygen

$$6\,CO_2 + 6\,H_2O + 38\,ATP$$

Carbon   Water
dioxide

A summary of the various stages of aerobic respiration in prokaryotes is presented in Figure 17.

Anaerobic Respiration

In anaerobic respiration, the final electron acceptor is an inorganic substance other than oxygen (O_2). Some bacteria, such as *Pseudomonas* and *Bacillus,* can use a nitrate ion (NO_3^-) as a final electron acceptor; the nitrate ion is reduced to a nitrite ion (NO_2^-), nitrous oxide (N_2O), or nitrogen gas (N_2). Other bacteria, such as *Desulfovibrio* (dē-sul-fō-vib′ rē-ō), use sulfate (SO_4^{2-}) as the final electron acceptor to form hydrogen sulfide (H_2S). Still other bacteria use carbonate (CO_3^{2-}) to form methane (CH_4). Anaerobic respiration by

bacteria using nitrate and sulfate as final acceptors is essential for the nitrogen and sulfur cycles that occur in nature. The amount of ATP generated in anaerobic respiration varies with the organism and the pathway. Because only part of the Krebs cycle operates under anaerobic conditions, and because not all the carriers in the electron transport chain participate in anaerobic respiration, the ATP yield is never as high as in aerobic respiration. Accordingly, anaerobes tend to grow more slowly than aerobes. (MMJ) **Animations** Electron Transport Chain: Overview, The Process, Factors Affecting ATP Yield

CHECK YOUR UNDERSTANDING

✔ What are the principal products of the Krebs cycle? **13**

✔ How do carrier molecules function in the electron transport chain? **14**

✔ Compare the energy yield (ATP) of aerobic and anaerobic respiration. **15**

Fermentation

After glucose has been broken down into pyruvic acid, the pyruvic acid can be completely broken down in respiration, as previously described, or it can be converted to an organic product in fermentation, whereupon NAD^+ and $NADP^+$ are regenerated and can enter another round of glycolysis (see Figure 11). **Fermentation** can be defined in several ways, but we define it here as a process that

1. releases energy from sugars or other organic molecules, such as amino acids, organic acids, purines, and pyrimidines;

2. does not require oxygen (but sometimes can occur in its presence);

3. does not require the use of the Krebs cycle or an electron transport chain;

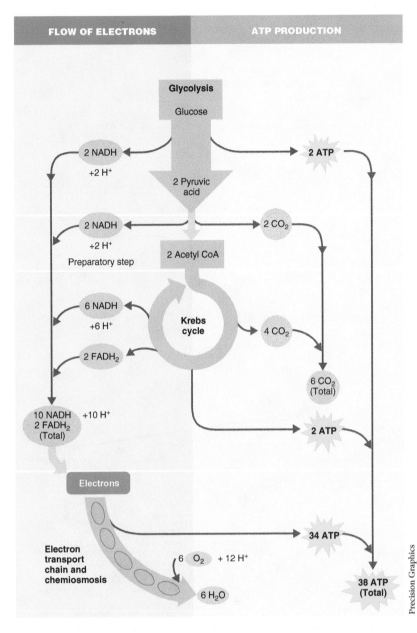

FLOW OF ELECTRONS

ATP PRODUCTION

Glycolysis

Glucose

2 NADH
+2 H⁺

2 ATP

2 Pyruvic
acid

2 NADH
+2 H⁺

Preparatory step

2 CO₂

2 Acetyl CoA

6 NADH
+6 H⁺

**Krebs
cycle**

4 CO₂

2 FADH₂

6 CO₂
(Total)

10 NADH
2 FADH₂
(Total)   +10 H⁺

2 ATP

Electrons

34 ATP

**Electron
transport
chain and
chemiosmosis**

6 O₂ + 12 H⁺

6 H₂O

38 ATP
(Total)

Precision Graphics

Figure 17 A summary of aerobic respiration in prokaryotes. Glucose is broken down completely to carbon dioxide and water, and ATP is generated. This process has three major phases: glycolysis, the Krebs cycle, and the electron transport chain. The preparatory step is between glycolysis and the Krebs cycle. The key event in aerobic respiration is that electrons are picked up from intermediates of glycolysis and the Krebs cycle by NAD⁺ or FAD and are carried by NADH or FADH₂ to the electron transport chain. NADH is also produced during the conversion of pyruvic acid to acetyl CoA. Most of the ATP generated by aerobic respiration is made by the chemiosmotic mechanism during the electron transport chain phase; this is called oxidative phosphorylation.

Q How do aerobic and anaerobic respiration differ?

4. uses an organic molecule as the final electron acceptor;
5. produces only small amounts of ATP (only one or two ATP molecules for each molecule of starting material) because much of the original energy in glucose remains in the chemical bonds of the organic end-products, such as lactic acid or ethanol.

During fermentation, electrons are transferred (along with protons) from reduced coenzymes (NADH, NADPH) to pyruvic acid or its derivatives (Figure 18a). Those final electron acceptors are reduced to the end-products shown in Figure 18b. An essential function of the second stage of fermentation is to ensure a steady supply of NAD⁺ and NADP⁺ so that glycolysis can continue. In fermentation, ATP is generated only during glycolysis.

Microorganisms can ferment various substrates; the end-products depend on the particular microorganism, the substrate, and the enzymes that are present and active. Chemical analyses of these end-products are useful in identifying microorganisms.

141

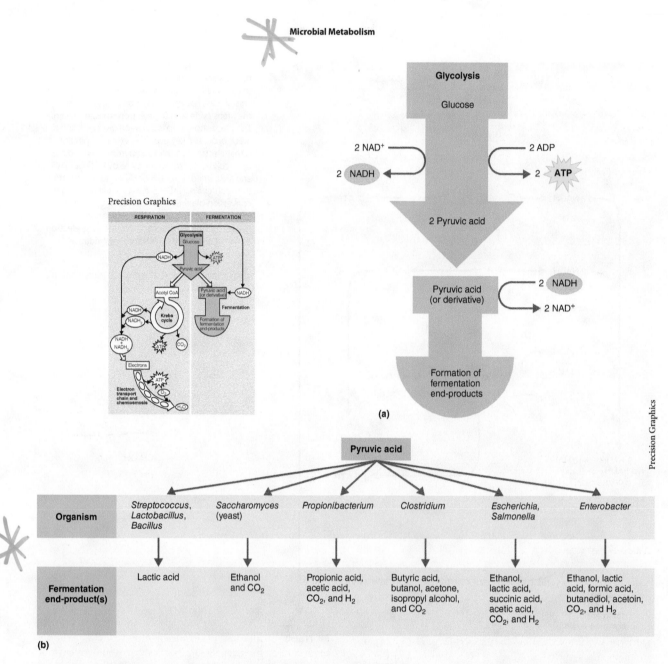

(a)

(b)

Figure 18 Fermentation. The inset indicates the relationship of fermentation to the overall energy-producing processes. (**a**) An overview of fermentation. The first step is glycolysis, the conversion of glucose to pyruvic acid. In the second step, the reduced coenzymes from glycolysis or its alternatives (NADH, NADPH) donate their electrons and hydrogen ions to pyruvic acid or a derivative to form a fermentation end-product.

(**b**) End-products of various microbial fermentations.

Q During which phase of fermentation is ATP generated?

We next consider two of the more important processes: lactic acid fermentation and alcohol fermentation.

Lactic Acid Fermentation

During glycolysis, which is the first phase of **lactic acid fermentation**, a molecule of glucose is oxidized to two molecules of pyruvic acid (Figure 19; see also Figure 10). This oxidation generates the energy that is used to form the two molecules of ATP. In the next step, the two molecules of pyruvic acid are reduced by two molecules of NADH to form two molecules of lactic acid (Figure 19a). Because lactic acid is the end-product of the reaction, it undergoes no further oxidation, and most of the energy produced by the reaction remains stored in the lactic acid. Thus, this fermentation yields only a small amount of energy.

Two important genera of lactic acid bacteria are *Streptococcus* and *Lactobacillus* (lak-tō-bä-sil′lus). Because these microbes produce only lactic acid, they are referred to as **homolactic** (or *homofermentative*). Lactic acid fermentation can result in food spoilage. However, the process can also produce yogurt from milk, sauerkraut from fresh cabbage, and pickles from cucumbers.

Clinical Case

Feeling certain that there must be some connection between the increase in dental caries and the activities of her patients, Dr. Rivera starts to ask more questions about the children's activities. She finds out that they all attend a summer program at the same church in a nearby neighborhood. She also discovers that the culprit isn't candy, but bubblegum. The camp counselors have been giving out bubblegum as an incentive for attendance and good behavior. Although Dr. Rivera is pleased to hear that her patients have all been behaving themselves, she is concerned about the amount of bubblegum they have been chewing on a daily basis. The sucrose in gum causes a decrease in the pH of saliva, and the acid erodes the tooth enamel, thus exposing the tooth to bacterial decay.

If the pH of gum and sucrose is 7, what lowers the salivary pH?

Alcohol Fermentation

Alcohol fermentation also begins with the glycolysis of a molecule of glucose to yield two molecules of pyruvic acid and two molecules of ATP. In the next reaction, the two molecules of pyruvic acid are converted to two molecules of acetaldehyde and two molecules of CO_2 (**Figure 19b**). The two molecules of acetaldehyde are next reduced by two molecules of NADH to form two molecules of ethanol. Again, alcohol fermentation is a low-energy-yield process because most of the energy contained in the initial glucose molecule remains in the ethanol, the end-product.

Alcohol fermentation is carried out by a number of bacteria and yeasts. The ethanol and carbon dioxide produced by the yeast *Saccharomyces* (sak-ä-rō-mī′sēs) are waste products for yeast cells but are useful to humans. Ethanol made by yeasts is the alcohol in alcoholic beverages, and carbon dioxide made by yeasts causes bread dough to rise.

Organisms that produce lactic acid as well as other acids or alcohols are known as **heterolactic** (or *heterofermentative*) and often use the pentose phosphate pathway.

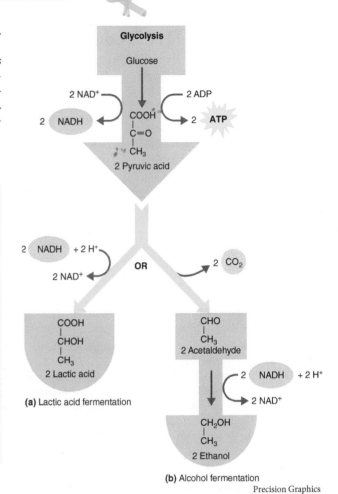

(a) Lactic acid fermentation

(b) Alcohol fermentation

Precision Graphics

Figure 19 Types of fermentation.

What is the difference between homolactic and heterolactic fermentation?

Table 4 lists some of the various microbial fermentations used by industry to convert inexpensive raw materials into useful end-products. **Table 5** provides a summary comparison of aerobic respiration, anaerobic respiration, and fermentation.

(MM) **Animation** Fermentation

CHECK YOUR UNDERSTANDING

✓ List four compounds that can be made from pyruvic acid by an organism that uses fermentation. **16**

Lipid and Protein Catabolism

LEARNING OBJECTIVE

17 Describe how lipids and proteins undergo catabolism.

Our discussion of energy production has emphasized the oxidation of glucose, the main energy-supplying carbohydrate.

143

What Is Fermentation?

To many people, *fermentation* simply means the production of alcohol: grains and fruits are fermented to produce beer and wine. If a food soured, you might say it was "off," or fermented. Here are some definitions of *fermentation*. They range from informal, general usage to more scientific definitions.

1. Any spoilage of food by microorganisms (general use)

2. Any process that produces alcoholic beverages or acidic dairy products (general use)

3. Any large-scale microbial process occurring with or without air (common definition used in industry)

4. Any energy-releasing metabolic process that takes place only under anaerobic conditions (becoming more scientific)

5. Any metabolic process that releases energy from a sugar or other organic molecule, does not require oxygen or an electron transport system, and uses an organic molecule as the final electron acceptor (the definition we use in this text).

moodboard/Fotolia

However, microbes also oxidize lipids and proteins, and the oxidations of all these nutrients are related.

Recall that fats are lipids consisting of fatty acids and glycerol. Microbes produce extracellular enzymes called *lipases* that break fats down into their fatty acid and glycerol components. Each component is then metabolized separately (**Figure 20**). The Krebs cycle functions in the oxidation of glycerol and fatty acids. Many bacteria that hydrolyze fatty acids can use the same enzymes to degrade petroleum products. Although these bacteria are a nuisance when they grow in a fuel storage tank, they are beneficial when they grow in oil spills. Beta-oxidation (is the oxidation of fatty acids) of petroleum.

Proteins are too large to pass unaided through plasma membranes. Microbes produce extracellular *proteases* and *peptidases*,

TABLE 4 Some Industrial Uses for Different Types of Fermentations*

Fermentation End-Product(s)	Industrial or Commercial Use	Starting Material	Microorganism
Ethanol	Beer, wine	Starch, sugar	*Saccharomyces cerevisiae* (yeast, a fungus)
	Fuel	Agricultural wastes	*Saccharomyces cerevisiae* (yeast)
Acetic Acid	Vinegar	Ethanol	*Acetobacter*
Lactic Acid	Cheese, yogurt	Milk	*Lactobacillus, Streptococcus*
	Rye bread	Grain, sugar	*Lactobacillus delbrueckii*
	Sauerkraut	Cabbage	*Lactobacillus plantarum*
	Summer sausage	Meat	*Pediococcus*
Propionic Acid and Carbon Dioxide	Swiss cheese	Lactic acid	*Propionibacterium freudenreichii*
Acetone and Butanol	Pharmaceutical, industrial uses	Molasses	*Clostridium acetobutylicum*
Citric Acid	Flavoring	Molasses	*Aspergillus* (fungus)
Methane	Fuel	Acetic acid	*Methanosarcina*
Sorbose	Vitamin C (ascorbic acid)	Sorbitol	*Gluconobacter*

*Unless otherwise noted, the microorganisms listed are bacteria.

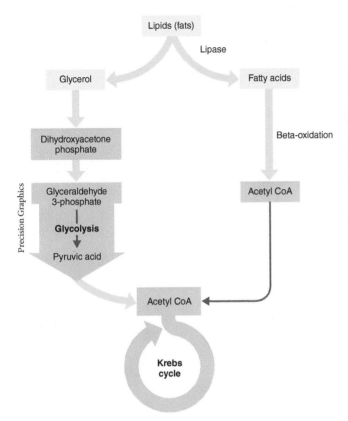

Figure 20 Lipid catabolism. Glycerol is converted into dihydroxyacetone phosphate (DHAP) and catabolized via glycolysis and the Krebs cycle. Fatty acids undergo beta-oxidation, in which carbon fragments are split off two at a time to form acetyl CoA, which is catabolized via the Krebs cycle.

Q What is the role of lipases?

enzymes that break down proteins into their component amino acids, which can cross the membranes. However, before amino acids can be catabolized, they must be enzymatically converted to other substances that can enter the Krebs cycle. In one such

Clinical Case

Dental caries are caused by oral streptococci, including *S. mutans*, *S. salivarius*, and *S. sobrinus*, that attach to tooth surfaces. Oral streptococci ferment sucrose and produce lactic acid, which lowers the salivary pH. Dr. Rivera decides to ask the camp counselors to substitute the bubblegum with a sugarless gum made with xylitol. A study has shown that chewing gum sweetened with xylitol, a naturally occuring sugar alcohol, can significantly lower the number of dental caries in children because it lowers the number of *S. mutans* in the mouth.

Why might xylitol reduce the number of *S. mutans*?

conversion, called **deamination,** the amino group of an amino acid is removed and converted to an ammonium ion (NH_4^+), which can be excreted from the cell. The remaining organic acid can enter the Krebs cycle. Other conversions involve **decarboxylation** (the removal of —COOH) and **dehydrogenation.**

A summary of the interrelationships of carbohydrate, lipid, and protein catabolism is shown in **Figure 21**.

CHECK YOUR UNDERSTANDING

✔ What are the end-products of lipid and protein catabolism? **17**

Biochemical Tests and Bacterial Identification

LEARNING OBJECTIVE

18 Provide two examples of the use of biochemical tests to identify bacteria in the laboratory.

Biochemical testing is frequently used to identify bacteria and yeasts because different species produce different enzymes. Such biochemical tests are designed to detect the presence of enzymes.

TABLE 5 Aerobic Respiration, Anaerobic Respiration, and Fermentation

Energy-Producing Process	Growth Conditions	Final Hydrogen (Electron) Acceptor	Type of Phosphorylation Used to Generate ATP	ATP Molecules Produced per Glucose Molecule
Aerobic Respiration	Aerobic	Molecular oxygen (O_2)	Substrate-level and oxidative	36 (eukaryotes) 38 (prokaryotes)
Anaerobic Respiration	Anaerobic	Usually an inorganic substance (such as NO_3^-, SO_4^{2-}, or CO_3^{2-}) but not molecular oxygen (O_2)	Substrate-level and oxidative	Variable (fewer than 38 but more than 2)
Fermentation	Aerobic or anaerobic	An organic molecule	Substrate-level	2

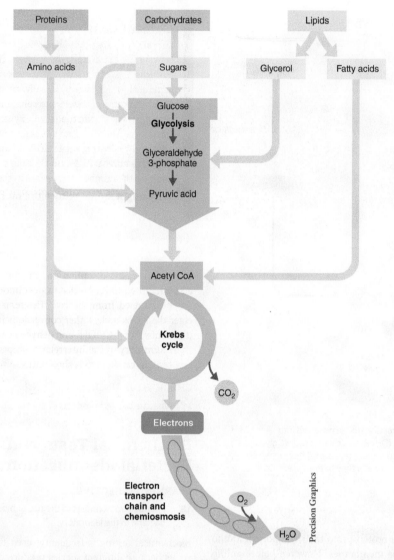

Figure 21 Catabolism of various organic food molecules. Proteins, carbohydrates, and lipids can all be sources of electrons and protons for respiration. These food molecules enter glycolysis or the Krebs cycle at various points.

Q What are the catabolic pathways through which high-energy electrons from all kinds of organic molecules flow on their energy-releasing pathways?

One type of biochemical test is the detection of amino acid catabolizing enzymes involved in decarboxylation and dehydrogenation (Figure 22).

Another biochemical test is a **fermentation test.** The test medium contains protein, a single carbohydrate, a pH indicator, and an inverted Durham tube, which is used to capture gas (Figure 23a). Bacteria inoculated into the tube can use the protein or carbohydrate as a carbon and energy source. If they catabolize the carbohydrate and produce acid, the pH indicator

changes color. Some organisms produce gas as well as acid from carbohydrate catabolism. The presence of a bubble in the Durham tube indicates gas formation (Figure 23b–d).

E. coli ferments the carbohydrate sorbitol. The pathogenic *E. coli* O157 strain, however, does not ferment sorbitol, a characteristic that differentiates it from nonpathogenic, commensal *E. coli*.

In some instances, the waste products of one microorganism can be used as a carbon and energy source by another species. *Acetobacter* (ä-sē-tō-bak′tėr) bacteria oxidize ethanol

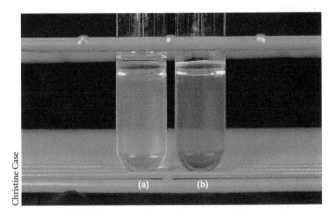

Christine Case

Figure 22 Detecting amino acid catabolizing enzymes in the lab. Bacteria are inoculated in tubes containing glucose, a pH indicator, and a specific amino acid. (**a**) The pH indicator turns to yellow when bacteria produce acid from glucose. (**b**) Alkaline products from decarboxylation turn the indicator to purple.

Q What is decarboxylation?

made by yeast. *Propionibacterium* (prō-pē-on-ē-bak-ti′ re-um) can use lactic acid produced by other bacteria. Propionibacteria convert lactic acid to pyruvic acid in preparation for the Krebs cycle. During the Krebs cycle, propionic acid and CO_2 are made. The holes in Swiss cheese are formed by the accumulation of the CO_2 gas.

Biochemical tests are used to identify bacteria that cause disease. All aerobic bacteria use the electron transport chain (ETC), but not all their ETCs are identical. Some bacteria have cytochrome *c*, but others do not. In the former, *cytochrome c oxidase* is

Christine Case

Figure 24 Use of peptone iron agar to detect the production of H_2S. H_2S produced in the tube precipitates with iron in the medium as ferrous sulfide.

Q What chemical reaction causes the release of H_2S?

the last enzyme, which transfers electrons to oxygen. The oxidase test is routinely used to quickly identify *Neisseria gonorrhoeae*. *Neisseria* is positive for cytochrome oxidase. The oxidase test can also be used to distinguish some gram-negative rods: *Pseudomonas* is oxidase-positive, and *Escherichia* is oxidase-negative.

Shigella causes dysentery. *Shigella* is differentiated from *E. coli* by biochemical tests. Unlike *E. coli*, *Shigella* does not produce gas from lactose and does not produce the enzyme lactate dehydrogenase.

Salmonella bacteria are readily distinguishable from *E. coli* by the production of hydrogen sulfide (H_2S). Hydrogen sulfide is released when the bacteria remove sulfur from amino acids (**Figure 24**). The H_2S combines with iron to form a black precipitate in a culture medium.

The Clinical Focus later in this chapter describes how biochemical tests were used to determine the cause of disease in a young child in Dallas, Texas.

Christine Case

Figure 23 A fermentation test. (**a**) An uninoculated fermentation tube containing the carbohydrate mannitol. (**b**) *Staphylococcus epidermidis* grew on the protein but did not use the carbohydrate. This organism is described as mannitol −. (**c**) *Staphylococcus aureus* produced acid but not gas. This species is mannitol +. (**d**) *Escherichia coli* is also mannitol + and produced acid and gas from mannitol. The gas is trapped in the inverted Durham tube.

Q On what is the *S. epidermidis* growing?

Clinical Case Resolved

S. mutans cannot ferment xylitol; consequently, it doesn't grow and can't produce acid in the mouth. The camp counselors agree to switch to sugarless gum made with xylitol, and Dr. Rivera is pleased. She understands that there will be other sources of sucrose in the children's diets, but at least her patients are no longer going to be adversely affected by the camp's well-intentioned incentives. Researchers are still investigating ways that antimicrobials and vaccines can be used to reduce bacterial colonization. However, reducing consumption of sucrose-containing gum and candy may be an effective preventive measure.

✔ On what biochemical basis are *Pseudomonas* and *Escherichia* differentiated? 18

Photosynthesis

LEARNING OBJECTIVES

19   Compare and contrast cyclic and noncyclic photophosphorylation.

20   Compare and contrast the light-dependent and light-independent reactions of photosynthesis.

21   Compare and contrast oxidative phosphorylation and photophosphorylation.

In all of the metabolic pathways just discussed, organisms obtain energy for cellular work by oxidizing organic compounds. But where do organisms obtain these organic compounds? Some, including animals and many microbes, feed on matter produced by other organisms. For example, bacteria may catabolize compounds from dead plants and animals, or they may obtain nourishment from a living host.

Other organisms synthesize complex organic compounds from simple inorganic substances. The major mechanism for such synthesis is a process called **photosynthesis,** which is carried out by plants and many microbes. Essentially, photosynthesis is the conversion of light energy from the sun into chemical energy. The chemical energy is then used to convert CO_2 from the atmosphere to more reduced carbon compounds, primarily sugars. The word *photosynthesis* summarizes the process: *photo* means light, and *synthesis* refers to the assembly of organic compounds. This synthesis of sugars by using carbon atoms from CO_2 gas is also called **carbon fixation.** Continuation of life as we know it on Earth depends on the recycling of carbon in this way. Cyanobacteria, algae, and green plants all contribute to this vital recycling with photosynthesis.

Photosynthesis can be summarized with the following equations:

1. Plants, algae, and cyanobacteria use water as a hydrogen donor, releasing O_2.

$$6\ CO_2 + 12\ H_2O + \text{Light energy} \longrightarrow$$
$$C_6H_{12}O_6 + 6\ H_2O + 6\ O_2$$

2. Purple sulfur and green sulfur bacteria use H_2S as a hydrogen donor, producing sulfur granules.

$$6\ CO_2 + 12\ H_2S + \text{Light energy} \longrightarrow$$
$$C_6H_{12}O_6 + 6\ H_2O + 12\ S$$

In the course of photosynthesis, electrons are taken from hydrogen atoms, an energy-poor molecule, and incorporated into sugar, an energy-rich molecule. The energy boost is supplied by light energy, although indirectly.

Photosynthesis takes place in two stages. In the first stage, called the **light-dependent (light) reactions,** light energy is used to convert ADP and ⓟ to ATP. In addition, in the predominant form of the light-dependent reactions, the electron carrier $NADP^+$ is reduced to NADPH. The coenzyme NADPH, like NADH, is an energy-rich carrier of electrons. In the second stage, the **light-independent (dark) reactions,** these electrons are used along with energy from ATP to reduce CO_2 to sugar.
(ᴍᴍ) **Animation** Photosynthesis: Overview

The Light-Dependent Reactions: Photophosphorylation

Photophosphorylation is one of the three ways ATP is formed, and it occurs only in photosynthetic cells. In this mechanism, light energy is absorbed by chlorophyll molecules in the photosynthetic cell, exciting some of the molecules' electrons. The chlorophyll principally used by green plants, algae, and cyanobacteria is *chlorophyll a*. It is located in the membranous thylakoids of chloroplasts in algae and green plants and in the thylakoids found in the photosynthetic structures of cyanobacteria. Other bacteria use *bacteriochlorophylls*.

The excited electrons jump from the chlorophyll to the first of a series of carrier molecules, an electron transport chain similar to that used in respiration. As electrons are passed along the series of carriers, protons are pumped across the membrane, and ADP is converted to ATP by chemiosmosis. Chlorophyll and other pigments are packed into thylakoids of chloroplasts and are called **photosystems.** *Photosystem II* is so numbered because even though it was most likely the first photosystem to evolve, it was the second one discovered. It contains chlorophyll that is sensitive to wavelengths of light of 680 nm. *Photosystem I* contains chlorophyll that is sensitive to wavelengths of light of 700 nm. In **cyclic photophosphorylation,** the electrons released from chlorophyll in photosystem I eventually return to chlorophyll (Figure 25a). In **noncyclic photophosphorylation,** which is used in oxygenic organisms, the electrons released from the chlorophyll in photosystem II and photosystem I do not return to chlorophyll but become incorporated into NADPH (Figure 25b). The electrons lost from chlorophyll are replaced by electrons from H_2O. To summarize: the products of noncyclic photophosphorylation are ATP (formed by chemiosmosis using energy released in an electron transport chain), O_2 (from water molecules), and NADPH (in which the hydrogen electrons and protons were derived ultimately from water). (ᴍᴍ) **Animations** Light Reaction: Cyclic Photophosphorylation; Light Reaction: Noncyclic Photophosphorylation

The Light-Independent Reactions: The Calvin-Benson Cycle

The light-independent (dark) reactions are so named because they require no light directly. They include a complex cyclic pathway called the **Calvin-Benson cycle,** in which CO_2 is "fixed"—that is,

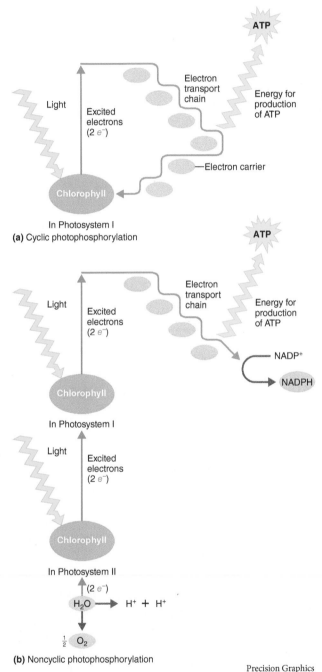

(a) Cyclic photophosphorylation

In Photosystem I

(b) Noncyclic photophosphorylation

Precision Graphics

Figure 25 Photophosphorylation. **(a)** In cyclic photophosphorylation, electrons released from chlorophyll by light return to chlorophyll after passage along the electron transport chain. The energy from electron transfer is converted to ATP. **(b)** In noncyclic photophosphorylation, electrons released from chlorophyll in photosystem II are replaced by electrons from the hydrogen atoms in water. This process also releases hydrogen ions. Electrons from chlorophyll in photosystem I are passed along the electron transport chain to the electron acceptor $NADP^+$. $NADP^+$ combines with electrons and with hydrogen ions from water, forming NADPH.

Q How are oxidative phosphorylation and photophosphorylation similar?

used to synthesize sugars (Figure 26). (MM) **Animation** Light Independent Reactions

CHECK YOUR UNDERSTANDING

✔ How is photosynthesis important to catabolism? 19

✔ What is made during the light-dependent reactions? 20

✔ How are oxidative phosphorylation and photophosphorylation similar? 21

A Summary of Energy Production Mechanisms

LEARNING OBJECTIVE

22 Write a sentence to summarize energy production in cells.

In the living world, energy passes from one organism to another in the form of the potential energy contained in the bonds of chemical compounds. Organisms obtain the energy from oxidation reactions. To obtain energy in a usable form, a cell must have an electron (or hydrogen) donor, which serves as an initial energy source within the cell. Electron donors are diverse and can include photosynthetic pigments, glucose or other organic compounds, elemental sulfur, ammonia, or hydrogen gas (Figure 27). Next, electrons removed from the chemical energy sources are transferred to electron carriers, such as the coenzymes NAD^+, $NADP^+$, and FAD. This transfer is an oxidation-reduction reaction; the initial energy source is oxidized as this first electron carrier is reduced. During this phase, some ATP is produced. In the third stage, electrons are transferred from electron carriers to their final electron acceptors in further oxidation-reduction reactions, producing more ATP.

In aerobic respiration, oxygen (O_2) serves as the final electron acceptor. In anaerobic respiration, inorganic substances other than oxygen, such as nitrate ions (NO_3^-) or sulfate ions (SO_4^{2-}), serve as the final electron acceptors. In fermentation, organic compounds serve as the final electron acceptors. In aerobic and anaerobic respiration, a series of electron carriers called an electron transport chain releases energy that is used by the mechanism of chemiosmosis to synthesize ATP. Regardless of their energy sources, all organisms use similar oxidation-reduction

Figure 26 A simplified version of the Calvin-Benson cycle. This diagram shows three turns of the cycle, in which three molecules of CO_2 are fixed and one molecule of glyceraldehyde 3-phosphate is produced and leaves the cycle. Two molecules of glyceraldehyde 3-phosphate are needed to make one molecule of glucose. Therefore, the cycle must turn six times for each glucose molecule produced, requiring a total investment of 6 molecules of CO_2, 18 molecules of ATP, and 12 molecules of NADPH.

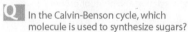 In the Calvin-Benson cycle, which molecule is used to synthesize sugars?

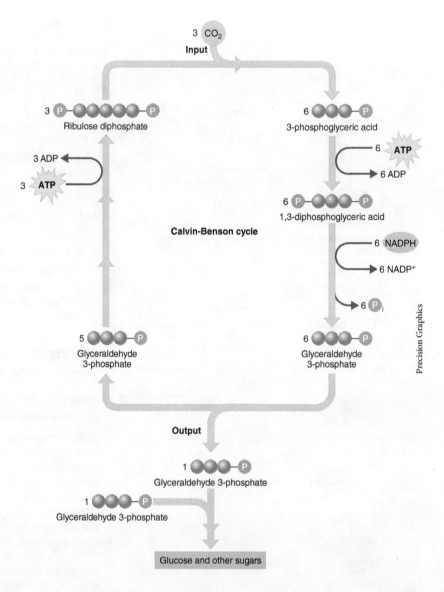

reactions to transfer electrons and similar mechanisms to use the energy released to produce ATP.

CHECK YOUR UNDERSTANDING

✔ Summarize how oxidation enables organisms to get energy from glucose, sulfur, or sunlight. 22

Metabolic Diversity among Organisms

LEARNING OBJECTIVE

23 Categorize the various nutritional patterns among organisms according to carbon source and mechanisms of carbohydrate catabolism and ATP generation.

We have looked in detail at some of the energy-generating metabolic pathways that are used by animals and plants, as well as by many microbes. Microbes are distinguished by their great metabolic diversity, however, and some can sustain themselves on inorganic substances by using pathways that are unavailable to either plants or animals. All organisms, including microbes, can be classified metabolically according to their *nutritional pattern*—their source of energy and their source of carbon.

First considering the energy source, we can generally classify organisms as phototrophs or chemotrophs. **Phototrophs** use light as their primary energy source, whereas **chemotrophs** depend on oxidation-reduction reactions of inorganic or organic compounds for energy. For their principal carbon source, **autotrophs** (self-feeders) use carbon dioxide, and **heterotrophs**

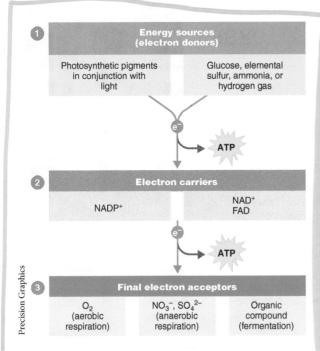

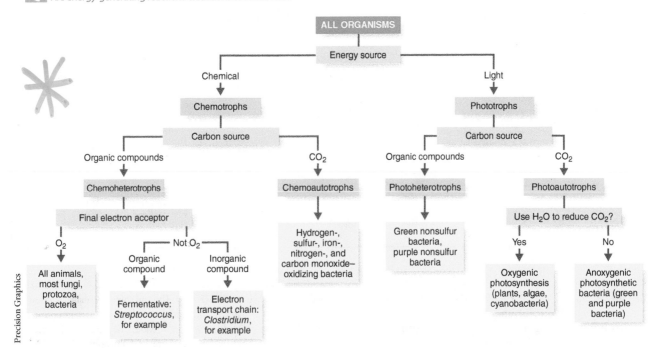

Figure 27 Requirements of ATP production. The production of ATP requires ❶ an energy source (electron donor), ❷ the transfer of electrons to an electron carrier during an oxidation-reduction reaction, and ❸ the transfer of electrons to a final electron acceptor.

Q Are energy-generating reactions oxidations or reductions?

(feeders on others) require an organic carbon source. Auto-trophs are also referred to as *lithotrophs* (rock eating), and het-erotrophs are also referred to as *organotrophs.*

If we combine the energy and carbon sources, we derive the following nutritional classifications for organisms: *photo-autotrophs, photoheterotrophs, chemoautotrophs,* and *chemo-heterotrophs* (Figure 28). Almost all of the medically important microorganisms discussed in this text are chemoheterotrophs. Typically, infectious organisms catabolize substances obtained from the host.

Photoautotrophs

Photoautotrophs use light as a source of energy and carbon dioxide as their chief source of carbon. They include photo-synthetic bacteria (green and purple bacteria and cyanobac-teria), algae, and green plants. In the photosynthetic reactions of cyanobacteria, algae, and green plants, the hydrogen atoms of water are used to reduce carbon dioxide, and oxygen gas is given off. Because this photosynthetic process produces O_2, it is sometimes called **oxygenic.**

In addition to the cyanobacteria, there are several other families of photosynthetic prokaryotes. Each is classified according to the way it reduces CO_2. These bacteria cannot use H_2O to reduce CO_2 and cannot carry on photosynthesis when oxygen is present (they must have an anaerobic environment). Consequently, their photosynthetic process does not produce

Figure 28 A nutritional classification of organisms.

Q What is the basic difference between chemotrophs and phototrophs?

Human Tuberculosis–Dallas, Texas

As you read through this box, you will encounter a series of questions that laboratory technicians ask themselves as they identify bacteria. Try to answer each question before going on to the next one.

1. Daria, a 12-month-old African American girl, is brought by her parents to the emergency department of a Dallas, Texas, hospital. She has a fever of 39°C, a distended abdomen, some abdominal pain, and watery diarrhea. Daria is admitted to the pediatric wing of the hospital, pending results of laboratory and radiologic tests. Test results suggest peritonal tuberculosis. Caused by one of several closely related species in the *Mycobacterium tuberculosis* complex, TB is a reportable condition in the United States. Peritoneal TB is a disease of the intestines and abdominal cavity.

   What organ is usually associated with tuberculosis? How might someone get peritoneal TB?

2. Pulmonary TB is contracted by inhaling the bacteria; ingesting the bacteria can result in peritoneal TB. A laparoscopy reveals that nodules are present in Daria's abdominal cavity. A portion of a nodule is removed for biopsy so that it can be observed for the presence of acid-fast bacteria. Based on the presence of the abdominal nodules, Daria's physician begins conventional antituberculosis treatment. This long-term treatment can last up to 12 months.

   What is the next step?

3. The lab results confirm that acid-fast bacteria are indeed present in Daria's abdominal cavity. The laboratory now needs to identify the *Mycobacterium*

species. Speciation of the *M. tuberculosis* complex is done by biochemical testing in reference laboratories (**Figure A**). The bacteria need to be grown in culture media. Slow-growing mycobacteria may take up to 6 weeks to form colonies.

   After colonies have been isolated, what is the next step?

4. Two weeks later, the laboratory results show that the bacteria are slow-growing. According to the identification scheme, the urease test should be performed.

   What is the result shown in Figure B?

5. Because the urease test is positive, the nitrate reduction test is performed. It shows that the bacteria do not produce the enzyme nitrate reductase. Daria's physician lets her parents know that they are very close to identifying the pathogen that is causing Daria's illness.

   What is the bacterium?

6. *M. bovis* is a pathogen that primarily infects cattle. However, humans can become infected by consuming unpasteurized dairy products or inhaling infectious

Christine Case

Test   Control

Figure B **The urease test. In a positive test, bacterial urease hydrolyzes urea, producing ammonia. The ammonia raises the pH, and the indicator in the medium turns to fuchsia.**

droplets from cattle. Human-to-human transmission occurs only rarely. The clinical and pathologic characteristics of *M. bovis* TB are indistinguishable from *M. tuberculosis* TB, but identification of the bacterium is important for prevention and treatment. Children may be at higher risk. In one study, almost half of the culture-positive pediatric TB cases were caused by *M. bovis*.

Unfortunately, Daria does not recover from her illness. Her cadiovascular system collapses, and she dies. The official cause of death is peritoneal tuberculosis caused by *M. bovis*. Everyone should avoid consuming products from unpasteurized cow's milk, which carry the risk of transmitting *M. bovis* if imported from countries where the bacterium is common in cattle.

Source: Adapted from Rodwell T.C., Moore M., Moser K.S., Brodine S.K., Strathdee S.A, "Mycobacterium bovis Tuberculosis in Binational Communities," Emerging Infectious Diseases, June 2008, Volume 14 (6), pp. 909–916. Available from http://www.cdc.gov/eid/content/14/6/909.htm.

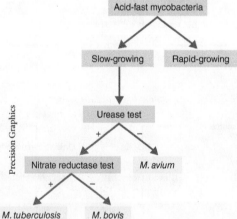
Precision Graphics

Figure A **An identification scheme for selected species of slow-growing mycobacteria.**

O₂ and is called **anoxygenic.** The anoxygenic photoautotrophs are the green and purple bacteria. The **green bacteria,** such as *Chlorobium* (klô-rō′bē-um), use sulfur (S), sulfur compounds (such as hydrogen sulfide, H_2S), or hydrogen gas (H_2) to reduce carbon dioxide and form organic compounds. Applying the energy from light and the appropriate enzymes, these bacteria oxidize sulfide (S^{2-}) or sulfur (S) to sulfate (SO_4^{2-}) or oxidize hydrogen gas to water (H_2O). The **purple bacteria,** such as *Chromatium* (krō-mā′tē-um), also use sulfur, sulfur compounds, or hydrogen gas to reduce carbon dioxide. They are distinguished from the green bacteria by their type of chlorophyll, location of stored sulfur, and ribosomal RNA.

TABLE 6 Photosynthesis Compared in Selected Eukaryotes and Prokaryotes

Characteristic	Eukaryotes		Prokaryotes	
	Algae, Plants	Cyanobacteria	Green Bacteria	Purple Bacteria
Substance That Reduces CO_2	H atoms of H_2O	H atoms of H_2O	Sulfur, sulfur compounds, H_2 gas	Sulfur, sulfur compounds, H_2 gas
Oxygen Production	Oxygenic	Oxygenic (and anoxygenic)	Anoxygenic	Anoxygenic
Type of Chlorophyll	Chlorophyll *a*	Chlorophyll *a*	Bacteriochlorophyll *a*	Bacteriochlorophyll *a* or *b*
Site of Photosynthesis	Chloroplasts with thylakoids	Thylakoids	Chlorosomes	Chromatophores
Environment	Aerobic	Aerobic (and anaerobic)	Anaerobic	Anaerobic

The chlorophylls used by these photosynthetic bacteria are called *bacteriochlorophylls,* and they absorb light at longer wavelengths than that absorbed by chlorophyll *a*. Bacteriochlorophylls of green sulfur bacteria are found in vesicles called *chlorosomes* (or *chlorobium vesicles*) underlying and attached to the plasma membrane. In the purple sulfur bacteria, the bacteriochlorophylls are located in invaginations of the plasma membrane (*chromatophores*).

Table 6 summarizes several characteristics that distinguish eukaryotic photosynthesis from prokaryotic photosynthesis.

(MM) **Animation** Comparing Prokaryotes and Eukaryotes

Photoheterotrophs

Photoheterotrophs use light as a source of energy but cannot convert carbon dioxide to sugar; rather, they use as sources of carbon organic compounds, such as alcohols, fatty acids, other organic acids, and carbohydrates. Photoheterotrophs are anoxygenic. The **green nonsulfur bacteria,** such as *Chloroflexus* (klô-rō-flex′us), and **purple nonsulfur bacteria,** such as *Rhodopseudomonas* (rō-dō-sū-dō-mō′nas), are photoheterotrophs.

Chemoautotrophs

Chemoautotrophs use the electrons from reduced inorganic compounds as a source of energy, and they use CO_2 as their principal source of carbon. They fix CO_2 in the Calvin-Benson Cycle (see Figure 26). Inorganic sources of energy for these organisms include hydrogen sulfide (H_2S) for *Beggiatoa* (bej-jē-ä-tō′ä); elemental sulfur (S) for *Thiobacillus thiooxidans*; ammonia (NH_3) for *Nitrosomonas* (nī-trō-sō-mō′näs); nitrite ions (NO_2^-) for *Nitrobacter* (nī-trō-bak′tėr); hydrogen gas (H_2) for *Cupriavidus* (kü′prē-ä-vid-us); ferrous iron (Fe^{2+}) for *Thiobacillus ferrooxidans;* and carbon monoxide (CO) for *Pseudomonas carboxydohydrogena* (kär′boks-i-dō-hi-drō-je-nä). The energy derived from the oxidation of these inorganic compounds is eventually stored in ATP, which is produced by oxidative phosphorylation.

Chemoheterotrophs

When we discuss photoautotrophs, photoheterotrophs, and chemoautotrophs, it is easy to categorize the energy source and carbon source because they occur as separate entities. However, in chemoheterotrophs, the distinction is not as clear because the energy source and carbon source are usually the same organic compound—glucose, for example. **Chemoheterotrophs** specifically use the electrons from hydrogen atoms in organic compounds as their energy source.

Heterotrophs are further classified according to their source of organic molecules. **Saprophytes** live on dead organic matter, and **parasites** derive nutrients from a living host. Most bacteria, and all fungi, protozoa, and animals, are chemoheterotrophs.

Bacteria and fungi can use a wide variety of organic compounds for carbon and energy sources. This is why they can live in diverse environments. Understanding microbial diversity is scientifically interesting and economically important. In some situations microbial growth is undesirable, such as when rubber-degrading bacteria destroy a gasket or shoe sole. However, these same bacteria might be beneficial if they decomposed discarded rubber products, such as used tires. *Rhodococcus erythropolis* (rō-dō-kok′kus er-i-throp′ō-lis) is widely distributed in soil and can cause disease in humans and other animals. However, this same species is able to replace sulfur atoms in petroleum with atoms of oxygen. A Texas company is currently using *R. erythropolis* to produce desulfurized oil.

CHECK YOUR UNDERSTANDING

✔ Almost all medically important microbes belong to which of the four aforementioned groups? 23

* * *

We will next consider how cells use ATP pathways for the synthesis of organic compounds such as carbohydrates, lipids, proteins, and nucleic acids.

Metabolic Pathways of Energy Use

LEARNING OBJECTIVE

24   Describe the major types of anabolism and their relationship to catabolism.

Up to now we have been considering energy production. Through the oxidation of organic molecules, organisms produce energy by aerobic respiration, anaerobic respiration, and fermentation. Much of this energy is given off as heat. The complete metabolic oxidation of glucose to carbon dioxide and water is considered a very efficient process, but about 45% of the energy of glucose is lost as heat. Cells use the remaining energy, which is trapped in the bonds of ATP, in a variety of ways. Microbes use ATP to provide energy for the transport of substances across plasma membranes—the process called active transport. Microbes also use some of their energy for flagellar motion. Most of the ATP, however, is used in the production of new cellular components. This production is a continuous process in cells and, in general, is faster in prokaryotic cells than in eukaryotic cells.

Autotrophs build their organic compounds by fixing carbon dioxide in the Calvin-Benson cycle (see Figure 26). This requires both energy (ATP) and electrons (from the oxidation of NADPH). Heterotrophs, by contrast, must have a ready source of organic compounds for biosynthesis—the production of needed cellular components, usually from simpler molecules. The cells use these compounds as both the carbon source and the energy source. We will next consider the biosynthesis of a few representative classes of biological molecules: carbohydrates, lipids, amino acids, purines, and pyrimidines. As we do so, keep in mind that synthesis reactions require a net input of energy.

Polysaccharide Biosynthesis

Microorganisms synthesize sugars and polysaccharides. The carbon atoms required to synthesize glucose are derived from the intermediates produced during processes such as glycolysis and the Krebs cycle and from lipids or amino acids. After synthesizing glucose (or other simple sugars), bacteria may assemble it into more complex polysaccharides, such as glycogen. For bacteria to build glucose into glycogen, glucose units must be phosphorylated and linked. The product of glucose phosphorylation is glucose 6-phosphate. Such a process involves the expenditure of energy, usually in the form of ATP. In order for bacteria to synthesize glycogen, a molecule of ATP is added to glucose 6-phosphate to form *adenosine diphosphoglucose (ADPG)* (Figure 29). Once ADPG is synthesized, it is linked with similar units to form glycogen.

Using a nucleotide called uridine triphosphate (UTP) as a source of energy and glucose 6-phosphate, animals synthesize glycogen (and many other carbohydrates) from *uridine diphosphoglucose, UDPG* (see Figure 29). A compound related to UDPG, called *UDP-N-acetylglucosamine (UDPNAc),* is a key starting material in the biosynthesis of peptidoglycan, the

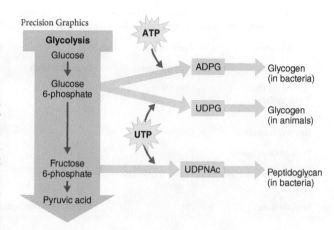

Figure 29   The biosynthesis of polysaccharides.

Q   How are polysaccharides used in cells?

substance that forms bacterial cell walls. UDPNAc is formed from fructose 6-phosphate, and the reaction also uses UTP.

Lipid Biosynthesis

Because lipids vary considerably in chemical composition, they are synthesized by a variety of routes. Cells synthesize fats by joining glycerol and fatty acids. The glycerol portion of the fat is derived from dihydroxyacetone phosphate, an intermediate formed during glycolysis. Fatty acids, which are long-chain hydrocarbons (hydrogen linked to carbon), are built up when two-carbon fragments of acetyl CoA are successively added to each other (Figure 30). As with polysaccharide synthesis, the building units of fats and other lipids are linked via dehydration synthesis reactions that require energy, not always in the form of ATP.

The most important role of lipids is to serve as structural components of biological membranes, and most membrane lipids are phospholipids. A lipid of a very different structure, cholesterol, is also found in plasma membranes of eukaryotic cells. Waxes are lipids that are important components of the cell wall of acid-fast bacteria. Other lipids, such as carotenoids, provide the red, orange, and yellow pigments of some microorganisms. Some lipids form portions of chlorophyll molecules. Lipids also function in energy storage. Recall that the breakdown products of lipids after biological oxidation feed into the Krebs cycle.

Amino Acid and Protein Biosynthesis

Amino acids are required for protein biosynthesis. Some microbes, such as *E. coli,* contain the enzymes necessary to use starting materials, such as glucose and inorganic salts, for the synthesis of all the amino acids they need. Organisms with the necessary enzymes can synthesize all amino acids directly or indirectly from intermediates of carbohydrate metabolism (Figure 31a). Other microbes require that the environment provide some preformed amino acids.

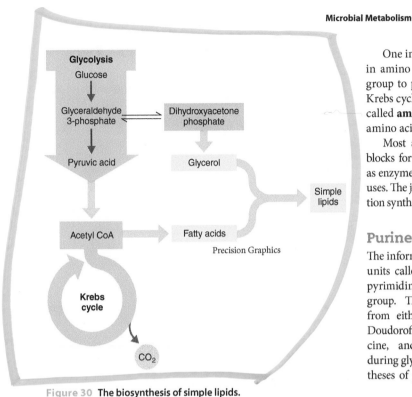

Figure 30 **The biosynthesis of simple lipids.**

Q What is the primary use of lipids in cells?

One important source of the *precursors* (intermediates) used in amino acid synthesis is the Krebs cycle. Adding an amine group to pyruvic acid or to an appropriate organic acid of the Krebs cycle converts the acid into an amino acid. This process is called **amination.** If the amine group comes from a preexisting amino acid, the process is called **transamination** (Figure 31b).

Most amino acids within cells are destined to be building blocks for protein synthesis. Proteins play major roles in the cell as enzymes, structural components, and toxins, to name just a few uses. The joining of amino acids to form proteins involves dehydration synthesis and requires energy in the form of ATP.

Purine and Pyrimidine Biosynthesis

The informational molecules DNA and RNA consist of repeating units called *nucleotides,* each of which consists of a purine or pyrimidine, a pentose (five-carbon sugar), and a phosphate group. The five-carbon sugars of nucleotides are derived from either the pentose phosphate pathway or the Entner-Doudoroff pathway. Certain amino acids—aspartic acid, glycine, and glutamine—made from intermediates produced during glycolysis and in the Krebs cycle participate in the biosyntheses of purines and pyrimidines (Figure 32). The carbon and

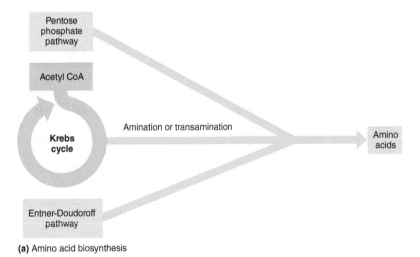

(a) Amino acid biosynthesis

Figure 31 **The biosynthesis of amino acids.**
(a) Pathways of amino acid biosynthesis through amination or transamination of intermediates of carbohydrate metabolism from the Krebs cycle, pentose phosphate pathway, and Entner-Doudoroff pathway. **(b)** Transamination, a process by which new amino acids are made with the amine groups from old amino acids. Glutamic acid and aspartic acid are both amino acids; the other two compounds are intermediates in the Krebs cycle.

Q What is the function of amino acids in cells?

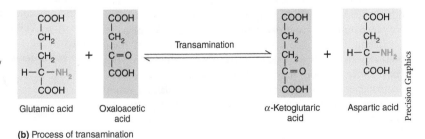

(b) Process of transamination

155

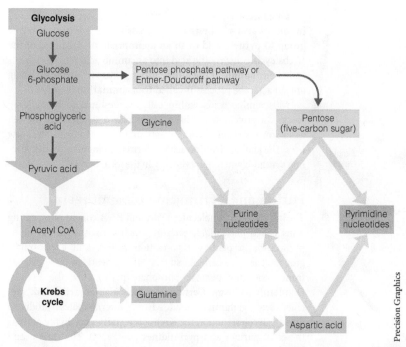

Figure 32 **The biosynthesis of purine and pyrimidine nucleotides.**

Q What are the functions of nucleotides in a cell?

Precision Graphics

nitrogen atoms derived from these amino acids form the purine and pyrimidine rings, and the energy for synthesis is provided by ATP. DNA contains all the information necessary to determine the specific structures and functions of cells. Both RNA and DNA are required for protein synthesis. In addition, such nucleotides as ATP, NAD^+, and $NADP^+$ assume roles in stimulating and inhibiting the rate of cellular metabolism.

CHECK YOUR UNDERSTANDING

✔ Where do amino acids required for protein synthesis come from? **24**

The Integration of Metabolism

LEARNING OBJECTIVE

25 Define *amphibolic pathways*.

We have seen thus far that the metabolic processes of microbes produce energy from light, inorganic compounds, and organic compounds. Reactions also occur in which energy is used for biosynthesis. With such a variety of activity, you might imagine that anabolic and catabolic reactions occur independently of each other in space and time. Actually, anabolic and catabolic reactions are joined through a group of common intermediates (identified as key intermediates in **Figure 33**). Both anabolic and catabolic reactions also share some metabolic pathways, such as the Krebs cycle. For example, reactions in the Krebs cycle not only participate in the oxidation of glucose but also produce intermediates that can be converted to amino acids. Metabolic pathways that function in

both anabolism and catabolism are called **amphibolic pathways,** meaning that they are dual-purpose.

Amphibolic pathways bridge the reactions that lead to the breakdown and synthesis of carbohydrates, lipids, proteins, and nucleotides. Such pathways enable simultaneous reactions to occur in which the breakdown product formed in one reaction is used in another reaction to synthesize a different compound, and vice versa. Because various intermediates are common to both anabolic and catabolic reactions, mechanisms exist that regulate synthesis and breakdown pathways and allow these reactions to occur simultaneously. One such mechanism involves the use of different coenzymes for opposite pathways. For example, NAD^+ is involved in catabolic reactions, whereas $NADP^+$ is involved in anabolic reactions. Enzymes can also coordinate anabolic and catabolic reactions by accelerating or inhibiting the rates of biochemical reactions.

The energy stores of a cell can also affect the rates of biochemical reactions. For example, if ATP begins to accumulate, an enzyme shuts down glycolysis; this control helps to synchronize the rates of glycolysis and the Krebs cycle. Thus, if citric acid consumption increases, either because of a demand for more ATP or because anabolic pathways are draining off intermediates of the citric acid cycle, glycolysis accelerates and meets the demand. **MM** **Animation** Metabolism: The Big picture

CHECK YOUR UNDERSTANDING

✔ Summarize the integration of metabolic pathways using peptidoglycan synthesis as an example. **25**

Microbial Metabolism

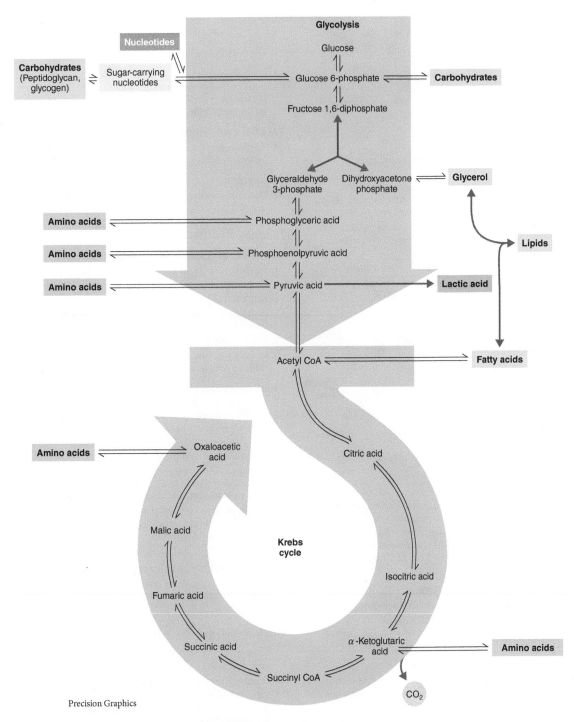

Precision Graphics

Figure 33 The integration of metabolism. Key intermediates are shown. Although not indicated in the figure, amino acids and ribose are used in the synthesis of purine and pyrimidine nucleotides (see Figure 32). The double arrows indicate amphibolic pathways.

Q What is the purpose of an amphibolic pathway?

Study Outline

Test your understanding with quizzes, microbe review, and a chapter post-test at www.masteringmicrobiology.com.

Catabolic and Anabolic Reactions

1. The sum of all chemical reactions within a living organism is known as metabolism.
2. Catabolism refers to chemical reactions that result in the breakdown of more complex organic molecules into simpler substances. Catabolic reactions usually release energy.
3. Anabolism refers to chemical reactions in which simpler substances are combined to form more complex molecules. Anabolic reactions usually require energy.
4. The energy of catabolic reactions is used to drive anabolic reactions.
5. The energy for chemical reactions is stored in ATP.

Enzymes

1. Enzymes are proteins, produced by living cells, that catalyze chemical reactions by lowering the activation energy.
2. Enzymes are generally globular proteins with characteristic three-dimensional shapes.
3. Enzymes are efficient, can operate at relatively low temperatures, and are subject to various cellular controls.

Naming Enzymes

4. Enzyme names usually end in -ase.
5. The six classes of enzymes are defined on the basis of the types of reactions they catalyze.

Enzyme Components

6. Most enzymes are holoenzymes, consisting of a protein portion (apoenzyme) and a nonprotein portion (cofactor).
7. The cofactor can be a metal ion (iron, copper, magnesium, manganese, zinc, calcium, or cobalt) or a complex organic molecule known as a coenzyme (NAD^+, $NADP^+$, FMN, FAD, or coenzyme A).

The Mechanism of Enzymatic Action

8. When an enzyme and substrate combine, the substrate is transformed, and the enzyme is recovered.
9. Enzymes are characterized by specificity, which is a function of their active sites.

Factors Influencing Enzymatic Activity

10. At high temperatures, enzymes undergo denaturation and lose their catalytic properties; at low temperatures, the reaction rate decreases.
11. The pH at which enzymatic activity is maximal is known as the optimum pH.
12. Enzymatic activity increases as substrate concentration increases until the enzymes are saturated.

13. Competitive inhibitors compete with the normal substrate for the active site of the enzyme. Noncompetitive inhibitors act on other parts of the apoenzyme or on the cofactor and decrease the enzyme's ability to combine with the normal substrate.

Feedback Inhibition

14. Feedback inhibition occurs when the end-product of a metabolic pathway inhibits an enzyme's activity near the start of the pathway.

Ribozymes

15. Ribozymes are enzymatic RNA molecules that cut and splice RNA in eukaryotic cells.

Energy Production

Oxidation-Reduction Reactions

1. Oxidation is the removal of one or more electrons from a substrate. Protons (H^+) are often removed with the electrons.
2. Reduction of a substrate refers to its gain of one or more electrons.
3. Each time a substance is oxidized, another is simultaneously reduced.
4. NAD^+ is the oxidized form; NADH is the reduced form.
5. Glucose is a reduced molecule; energy is released during a cell's oxidation of glucose.

The Generation of ATP

6. Energy released during certain metabolic reactions can be trapped to form ATP from ADP and P_i (phosphate). Addition of a P_i to a molecule is called phosphorylation.
7. During substrate-level phosphorylation, a high-energy P from an intermediate in catabolism is added to ADP.
8. During oxidative phosphorylation, energy is released as electrons are passed to a series of electron acceptors (an electron transport chain) and finally to O_2 or another inorganic compound.
9. During photophosphorylation, energy from light is trapped by chlorophyll, and electrons are passed through a series of electron acceptors. The electron transfer releases energy used for the synthesis of ATP.

Metabolic Pathways of Energy Production

10. A series of enzymatically catalyzed chemical reactions called metabolic pathways store energy in and release energy from organic molecules.

Carbohydrate Catabolism

1. Most of a cell's energy is produced from the oxidation of carbohydrates.
2. Glucose is the most commonly used carbohydrate.
3. The two major types of glucose catabolism are respiration, in which glucose is completely broken down, and fermentation, in which it is partially broken down.

Glycolysis

4. The most common pathway for the oxidation of glucose is glycolysis. Pyruvic acid is the end-product.

5. Two ATP and two NADH molecules are produced from one glucose molecule.

Alternatives to Glycolysis

6. The pentose phosphate pathway is used to metabolize five-carbon sugars; one ATP and 12 NADPH molecules are produced from one glucose molecule.

7. The Entner-Doudoroff pathway yields one ATP and two NADPH molecules from one glucose molecule.

Cellular Respiration

8. During respiration, organic molecules are oxidized. Energy is generated from the electron transport chain.

9. In aerobic respiration, O_2 functions as the final electron acceptor.

10. In anaerobic respiration, the final electron acceptor is usually an inorganic molecule other than O_2.

11. Decarboxylation of pyruvic acid produces one CO_2 molecule and one acetyl group.

12. Two-carbon acetyl groups are oxidized in the Krebs cycle. Electrons are picked up by NAD^+ and FAD for the electron transport chain.

13. From one molecule of glucose, oxidation produces six molecules of NADH, two molecules of $FADH_2$, and two molecules of ATP.

14. Decarboxylation produces six molecules of CO_2.

15. Electrons are brought to the electron transport chain by NADH.

16. The electron transport chain consists of carriers, including flavoproteins, cytochromes, and ubiquinones.

17. Protons being pumped across the membrane generate a proton motive force as electrons move through a series of acceptors or carriers.

18. Energy produced from movement of the protons back across the membrane is used by ATP synthase to make ATP from ADP and Ⓟ$_i$.

19. In eukaryotes, electron carriers are located in the inner mitochondrial membrane; in prokaryotes, electron carriers are in the plasma membrane.

20. In aerobic prokaryotes, 38 ATP molecules can be produced from complete oxidation of a glucose molecule in glycolysis, the Krebs cycle, and the electron transport chain.

21. In eukaryotes, 36 ATP molecules are produced from complete oxidation of a glucose molecule.

22. The final electron acceptors in anaerobic respiration include NO_3^-, SO_4^{2-}, and CO_3^{2-}.

23. The total ATP yield is less than in aerobic respiration because only part of the Krebs cycle operates under anaerobic conditions.

Fermentation

24. Fermentation releases energy from sugars or other organic molecules by oxidation.

25. O_2 is not required in fermentation.

26. Two ATP molecules are produced by substrate-level phosphorylation.

27. Electrons removed from the substrate reduce NAD^+.

28. The final electron acceptor is an organic molecule.

29. In lactic acid fermentation, pyruvic acid is reduced by NADH to lactic acid.

30. In alcohol fermentation, acetaldehyde is reduced by NADH to produce ethanol.

31. Heterolactic fermenters can use the pentose phosphate pathway to produce lactic acid and ethanol.

Lipid and Protein Catabolism

1. Lipases hydrolyze lipids into glycerol and fatty acids.

2. Fatty acids and other hydrocarbons are catabolized by beta-oxidation.

3. Catabolic products can be further broken down in glycolysis and the Krebs cycle.

4. Before amino acids can be catabolized, they must be converted to various substances that enter the Krebs cycle.

5. Transamination, decarboxylation, and dehydrogenation reactions convert the amino acids to be catabolized.

Biochemical Tests and Bacterial Identification

1. Bacteria and yeast can be identified by detecting action of their enzymes.

2. Fermentation tests are used to determine whether an organism can ferment a carbohydrate to produce acid and gas.

Photosynthesis

1. Photosynthesis is the conversion of light energy from the sun into chemical energy; the chemical energy is used for carbon fixation.

The Light-Dependent Reactions: Photophosphorylation

2. Chlorophyll *a* is used by green plants, algae, and cyanobacteria; it is found in thylakoid membranes.

3. Electrons from chlorophyll pass through an electron transport chain, from which ATP is produced by chemiosmosis.

4. Photosystems are made up of chlorophyll and other pigments packed into thylakoid membranes.

5. In cyclic photophosphorylation, the electrons return to the chlorophyll.

6. In noncyclic photophosphorylation, the electrons are used to reduce $NADP^+$. The electrons from H2O or H_2S replace those lost from chlorophyll.

7. When H2O is oxidized by green plants, algae, and cyanobacteria, O2 is produced; when H_2S is oxidized by the sulfur bacteria, S^0 granules are produced.

The Light-Independent Reactions: The Calvin-Benson Cycle

8. CO_2 is used to synthesize sugars in the Calvin-Benson cycle.

A Summary of Energy Production Mechanisms

1. Sunlight is converted to chemical energy in oxidation-reduction reactions carried on by phototrophs. Chemotrophs can use this chemical energy.

2. In oxidation-reduction reactions, energy is derived from the transfer of electrons.

3. To produce energy, a cell needs an electron donor (organic or inorganic), a system of electron carriers, and a final electron acceptor (organic or inorganic).

Metabolic Diversity among Organisms

1. Photoautotrophs obtain energy by photophosphorylation and fix carbon from CO_2 via the Calvin-Benson cycle to synthesize organic compounds.
2. Cyanobacteria are oxygenic phototrophs. Green bacteria and purple bacteria are anoxygenic phototrophs.
3. Photoheterotrophs use light as an energy source and an organic compound for their carbon source and electron donor.
4. Chemoautotrophs use inorganic compounds as their energy source and carbon dioxide as their carbon source.
5. Chemoheterotrophs use complex organic molecules as their carbon and energy sources.

Metabolic Pathways of Energy Use

Polysaccharide Biosynthesis

1. Glycogen is formed from ADPG.
2. UDPNAc is the starting material for the biosynthesis of peptidoglycan.

Lipid Biosynthesis

3. Lipids are synthesized from fatty acids and glycerol.
4. Glycerol is derived from dihydroxyacetone phosphate, and fatty acids are built from acetyl CoA.

Amino Acid and Protein Biosynthesis

5. Amino acids are required for protein biosynthesis.
6. All amino acids can be synthesized either directly or indirectly from intermediates of carbohydrate metabolism, particularly from the Krebs cycle.

Purine and Pyrimidine Biosynthesis

7. The sugars composing nucleotides are derived from either the pentose phosphate pathway or the Entner-Doudoroff pathway.
8. Carbon and nitrogen atoms from certain amino acids form the backbones of the purines and pyrimidines.

The Integration of Metabolism

1. Anabolic and catabolic reactions are integrated through a group of common intermediates.
2. Such integrated metabolic pathways are referred to as amphibolic pathways.

Study Questions

Answers to the Review and Multiple Choice questions can be found at the end of this chapter.

Review

Use the following diagrams (a), (b), and (c) for question 1.

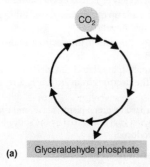

(a) Glyceraldehyde phosphate

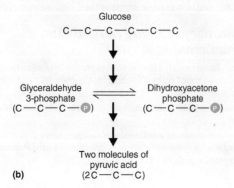

(b)

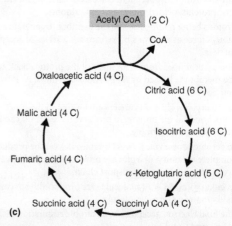

(c)

1. Name pathways diagrammed in parts (a), (b), and (c) of the figure.
   a. Show where glycerol is catabolized and where fatty acids are catabolized.
   b. Show where glutamic acid (an amino acid) is catabolized:

$$HOOC - CH_2 - CH_2 - \overset{\overset{\textstyle H}{|}}{\underset{\underset{\textstyle NH_2}{|}}{C}} - COOH$$

   c. Show how these pathways are related.
   d. Where is ATP required in pathways (a) and (b)?
   e. Where is CO_2 released in pathways (b) and (c)?

f. Show where a long-chain hydrocarbon such as petroleum is catabolized.

g. Where is NADH (or FADH₂ or NADPH) used and produced in these pathways?

h. Identify four places where anabolic and catabolic pathways are integrated.

2. DRAW IT Using the diagrams below, show each of the following:
a. where the substrate will bind
b. where the competitive inhibitor will bind
c. where the noncompetitive inhibitor will bind
d. which of the four elements could be the inhibitor in feedback inhibition
e. What effect will the reactions in (a), (b), and (c) have?

Precision Graphics

3. DRAW IT An enzyme and substrate are combined. The rate of reaction begins as shown in the following graph. To complete the graph, show the effect of increasing substrate concentration on a constant enzyme concentration. Show the effect of increasing temperature.

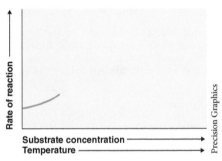

Precision Graphics

4. Define *oxidation-reduction*, and differentiate the following terms:
a. aerobic and anaerobic respiration
b. respiration and fermentation
c. cyclic and noncyclic photophosphorylation

5. There are three mechanisms for the phosphorylation of ADP to produce ATP. Write the name of the mechanism that describes each of the reactions in the following table.

ATP Generated by	Reaction
a. _____	An electron, liberated from chlorophyll by light, is passed down an electron transport chain.
b. _____	Cytochrome *c* passes two electrons to cytochrome *a*.
c. _____	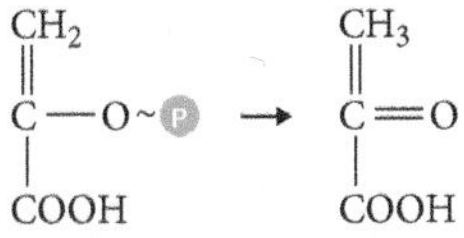 $CH_2 \parallel C{-}O{\sim}\text{℗} \rightarrow C{=}O$ COOH → COOH Phosphoenolpyruvic acid → Pyruvic acid

6. All of the energy-producing biochemical reactions that occur in cells, such as photophosphorylation and glycolysis, are _____ reactions.

7. Fill in the following table with the carbon source and energy source of each type of organism.

Organism	Carbon Source	Energy Source
Photoautotroph	a. _____	b. _____
Photoheterotroph	c. _____	d. _____
Chemoautotroph	e. _____	f. _____
Chemoheterotroph	g. _____	h. _____

8. Write your own definition of the chemiosmotic mechanism of ATP generation. On Figure 16, mark the following using the appropriate letter:
a. the acidic side of the membrane
b. the side with a positive electrical charge
c. potential energy
d. kinetic energy

9. Why must NADH be reoxidized? How does this happen in an organism that uses respiration? Fermentation?

10. NAME IT What nutritional type is a colorless microbe that uses the Calvin cycle, uses H_2 as the electron donor to its ETC, and uses elemental S as the final electron acceptor in the ETC?

Multiple Choice

1. Which substance in the following reaction is being reduced?

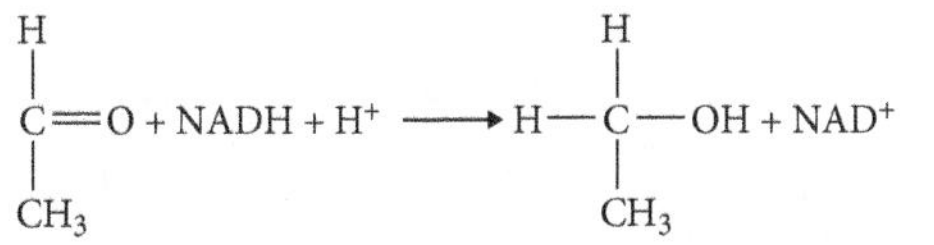

$$\begin{array}{c} H \\ | \\ C{=}O + NADH + H^+ \longrightarrow H{-}C{-}OH + NAD^+ \\ | \\ CH_3 \qquad\qquad\qquad CH_3 \end{array}$$
Acetaldehyde   Ethanol

a. acetaldehyde   c. ethanol
b. NADH   d. NAD^+

2. Which of the following reactions produces the most molecules of ATP during aerobic metabolism?
a. glucose → glucose 6-phosphate
b. phosphoenolpyruvic acid → pyruvic acid
c. glucose → pyruvic acid
d. acetyl CoA → $CO_2 + H_2O$
e. succinic acid → fumaric acid

3. Which of the following processes does *not* generate ATP?
a. photophosphorylation
b. the Calvin-Benson cycle
c. oxidative phosphorylation
d. substrate-level phosphorylation
e. none of the above

4. Which of the following compounds has the greatest amount of energy for a cell?
a. CO_2
b. ATP
c. glucose
d. O_2
e. lactic acid

5. Which of the following is the best definition of the Krebs cycle?
   a. the oxidation of pyruvic acid
   b. the way cells produce CO_2
   c. a series of chemical reactions in which NADH is produced from the oxidation of pyruvic acid
   d. a method of producing ATP by phosphorylating ADP
   e. a series of chemical reactions in which ATP is produced from the oxidation of pyruvic acid

6. Which of the following is the best definition of *respiration*?
   a. a sequence of carrier molecules with O_2 as the final electron acceptor
   b. a sequence of carrier molecules with an inorganic molecule as the final electron acceptor
   c. a method of generating ATP
   d. the complete oxidation of glucose to CO_2 and H_2O
   e. a series of reactions in which pyruvic acid is oxidized to CO_2 and H_2O

Use the following choices to answer questions 7–10.
   a. *E. coli* growing in glucose broth at 35°C with O_2 for 5 days
   b. *E. coli* growing in glucose broth at 35°C without O_2 for 5 days
   c. both a and b
   d. neither a nor b

7. Which culture produces the most lactic acid?
8. Which culture produces the most ATP?
9. Which culture uses NAD^+?
10. Which culture uses the most glucose?

Critical Thinking

1. Explain why, even under ideal conditions, *Streptococcus* grows slowly.
2. The following graph shows the normal rate of reaction of an enzyme and its substrate (blue) and the rate when an excess of competitive inhibitor is present (red). Explain why the graph appears as it does.

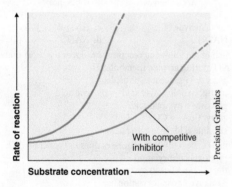

3. Compare and contrast carbohydrate catabolism and energy production in the following bacteria:
   a. *Pseudomonas,* an aerobic chemoheterotroph
   b. *Spirulina,* an oxygenic photoautotroph
   c. *Ectothiorhodospira,* an anoxygenic photoautotroph

4. How much ATP could be obtained from the complete oxidation of one molecule of glucose? From one molecule of butterfat containing one glycerol and three 12-carbon chains?

5. The chemoautotroph *Thiobacillus* can obtain energy from the oxidation of arsenic ($As^{3+} \rightarrow As^{5+}$). How does this reaction provide energy? How can humans put this bacterium to use?

Clinical Applications

1. *Haemophilus influenzae* requires hemin (X factor) to synthesize cytochromes and NAD^+ (V factor) from other cells. For what does it use these two growth factors? What diseases does *H. influenzae* cause?

2. The drug Hivid, also called ddC, inhibits DNA synthesis. It is used to treat HIV infection and AIDS. How does this drug work?

3. The bacterial enzyme streptokinase is used to digest fibrin (blood clots) in patients with atherosclerosis. Why doesn't injection of streptokinase cause a streptococcal infection? How do we know the streptokinase will digest fibrin only and not good tissues?

Answers to Review and Multiple Choice Study Questions

Review

1. **(a)** is the Calvin-Benson cycle, **(b)** is glycolysis, and **(c)** is the Krebs cycle.
   a. Glycerol is catabolized by pathway (b) as dihydroxyacetone phosphate. Fatty acids by pathway (c) as acetyl groups.
   b. In pathway (c) at α-ketoglutaric acid.
   c. Glyceraldehyde-3-phosphate from the Calvin-Benson cycle enters glycolysis. Pyruvic acid from glycolysis is decarboxylated to produce acetyl for the Krebs cycle.
   d. In (a), between glucose and glyceraldehyde-3-phosphate.
   e. The conversion of pyruvic acid to acetyl, isocitric acid to α-ketoglutaric acid, and α-ketoglutaric acid to succinyl~CoA.
   f. By pathway (c) as acetyl groups.
   g.

	Uses	Produces
Calvin-Benson cycle	6 NADPH	
Glycolysis		2 NADH
Pyruvic acid → acetyl		1 NADH
Isocitric acid → α-ketoglutaric acid		1 NADH
α-ketoglutaric acid → Succinyl~CoA		1 NADH
Succinic acid → Fumaric acid		1 FADH$_2$
Malic acid → Oxaloacetic acid		1 NADH

   h. Dihydroxyacetone phosphate; acetyl; oxaloacetic acid; α-ketoglutaric acid.

2.

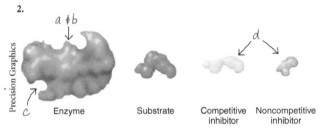

Enzyme   Substrate   Competitive inhibitor   Noncompetitive inhibitor

e. When the enzyme and substrate combine, the substrate molecule will be transformed.

When the competitive inhibitor binds to the enzyme, the enzyme will not be able to bind with the substrate.

When the noncompetitive inhibitor binds to the enzyme, the active site of the enzyme will be changed so the enzyme cannot bind with the substrate.

3.

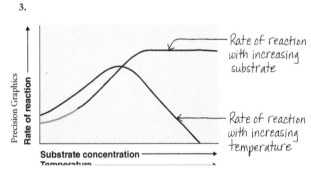

Rate of reaction with increasing substrate

Rate of reaction with increasing temperature

Substrate concentration

Temperature

4. Oxidation-reduction: A coupled reaction in which one substance loses electrons and another gains electrons.
   a. The final electron acceptor in aerobic respiration is molecular oxygen; in anaerobic respiration, it is another inorganic molecule.
   b. An electron transport chain is used in respiration but not in fermentation. The final electron acceptor in respiration is usually inorganic; in fermentation it is usually organic.
   c. In cyclic photophosphorylation, electrons are returned to chlorophyll. In noncyclic photophosphorylation, chlorophyll receives electrons from hydrogen atoms.

5. **a.** Photophosphorylation
   b. Oxidative phosphorylation
   c. Substrate-level phosphorylation

6. oxidation

7. **a.** CO_2 **e.** CO_2
   b. Light **f.** Inorganic molecules
   c. Organic molecules **g.** Organic molecules
   d. Light **h.** Organic molecules

8. Protons are pumped from one side of the membrane to the other; transfer of protons back across the membrane generates ATP.
   a and b. Outer portion is acidic, and has a positive electrical charge.
   c. Energy-conserving sites are the three loci where protons are pumped out. **d.** Kinetic energy is realized at ATP synthase

9. NAD$^+$ is needed to pick up more electrons. NADH is usually reoxidized in respiration. NADH can be reoxidized in fermentation.

10. Chemoautotroph

Multiple Choice

1. a	**3.** b	**5.** c	**7.** b	**9.** c
2. d	**4.** c	**6.** b	**8.** a	**10.** b

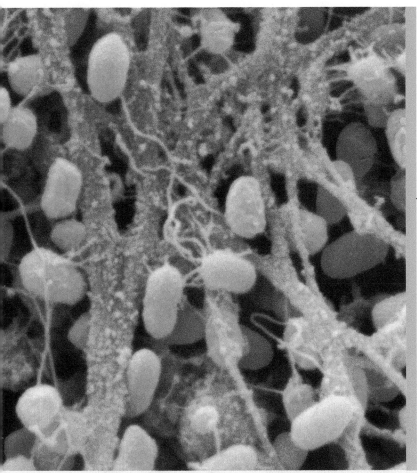

Scimat/Photo Researchers

Microbial Growth

Visualize microbiology and check your
understanding with a pre-test at
www.masteringmicrobiology.com.

When we talk about microbial growth, we are really referring to the *number* of cells, not the *size* of the cells. Microbes that are "growing" are increasing in number, accumulating into *colonies* (groups of cells large enough to be seen without a microscope) of hundreds of thousands of cells or *populations* of billions of cells. Although individual cells approximately double in size during their lifetime, this change is not very significant compared with the size increases observed during the lifetime of plants and animals.

Many bacteria survive and grow slowly in nutrient-poor environments by forming biofilms. The *Serratia marcescens* bacteria in the photo have formed a biofilm on a piece of plastic. Biofilms are frequently sources of health care associated infections such as the one described in the Clinical Case.

Microbial populations can become incredibly large in a very short time. By understanding the conditions necessary for microbial growth, we can determine how to control the growth of microbes that cause diseases and food spoilage. We can also learn how to encourage the growth of helpful microbes and those we wish to study.

In this chapter we will examine the physical and chemical requirements for microbial growth, the various kinds of culture media, bacterial cell division, the phases of microbial growth, and the methods of measuring microbial growth.

From Chapter 6 of *Microbiology: An Introduction*, Eleventh Edition. Gerard J. Tortora, Berdell R. Funke, Christine L. Case.

The Requirements for Growth

LEARNING OBJECTIVES

1   Classify microbes into five groups on the basis of preferred temperature range.

2   Identify how and why the pH of culture media is controlled.

3   Explain the importance of osmotic pressure to microbial growth.

4   Name a use for each of the four elements (carbon, nitrogen, sulfur, and phosphorus) needed in large amounts for microbial growth.

5   Explain how microbes are classified on the basis of oxygen requirements.

6   Identify ways in which aerobes avoid damage by toxic forms of oxygen.

The requirements for microbial growth can be divided into two main categories: physical and chemical. Physical aspects include temperature, pH, and osmotic pressure. Chemical requirements include sources of carbon, nitrogen, sulfur, phosphorus, oxygen, trace elements, and organic growth factors.

Physical Requirements

Temperature

Most microorganisms grow well at the temperatures that humans favor. However, certain bacteria are capable of growing at extremes of temperature that would certainly hinder the survival of almost all eukaryotic organisms.

Microorganisms are classified into three primary groups on the basis of their preferred range of temperature: **psychrophiles** (cold-loving microbes), **mesophiles** (moderate-temperature–loving microbes), and **thermophiles** (heat-loving microbes). Most bacteria grow only within a limited range of temperatures, and their maximum and minimum growth temperatures are only

Clinical Case: Glowing in the Dark

Reginald MacGruder, an investigator at the Centers for Disease Control and Prevention (CDC) in Atlanta, Georgia, has a mystery on his hands. Earlier this year, he was involved in the recall of an intravenous heparin solution that was blamed for causing *Pseudomonas fluorescens* bloodstream infections in patients in four different states. It seemed that everything was under control, but now, three months after the recall, 19 patients in two other states develop the same *P. fluorescens* bloodstream infections. It makes no sense to Dr. MacGruder; how could this infection be popping up again so soon after the recall? Could another heparin batch be tainted?

What is *P. fluorescens*? Read on to find out.

about 30°C apart. They grow poorly at the high and low temperature extremes within their range.

Each bacterial species grows at particular minimum, optimum, and maximum temperatures. The **minimum growth temperature** is the lowest temperature at which the species will grow. The **optimum growth temperature** is the temperature at which the species grows best. The **maximum growth temperature** is the highest temperature at which growth is possible. By graphing the growth response over a temperature range, we can see that the optimum growth temperature is usually near the top of the range; above that temperature the rate of growth drops off rapidly (**Figure 1**). This happens presumably because the high temperature has inactivated necessary enzymatic systems of the cell.

Figure 1 Typical growth rates of different types of microorganisms in response to temperature. The peak of the curve represents optimum growth (fastest reproduction). Notice that the reproductive rate drops off very quickly at temperatures only a little above the optimum. At either extreme of the temperature range, the reproductive rate is much lower than the rate at the optimum temperature.

 Why is it difficult to define *psychrophile*, *mesophile*, and *thermophile*?

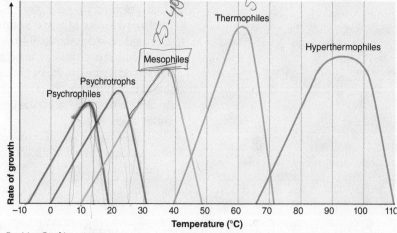

Precision Graphics

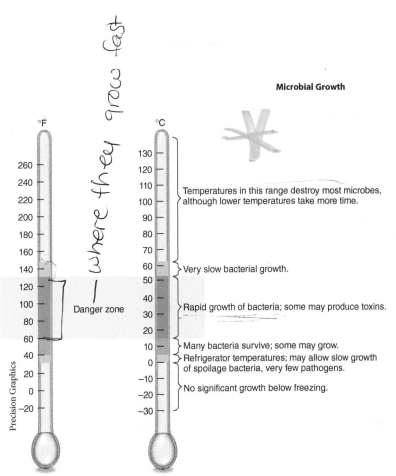

Microbial Growth

where they grow fast

Temperatures in this range destroy most microbes, although lower temperatures take more time.

Very slow bacterial growth.

Danger zone

Rapid growth of bacteria; some may produce toxins.

Many bacteria survive; some may grow.

Refrigerator temperatures; may allow slow growth of spoilage bacteria, very few pathogens.

No significant growth below freezing.

Precision Graphics

Figure 2 Food preservation temperatures. Low temperatures decrease microbial reproduction rates, which is the basic principle of refrigeration. There are always some exceptions to the temperature responses shown here; for example, certain bacteria grow well at temperatures that would kill most bacteria, and a few bacteria can actually grow at temperatures well below freezing.

Q Which bacterium would theoretically be more likely to grow at refrigerator temperatures: a human intestinal pathogen or a soilborne plant pathogen?

The ranges and maximum growth temperatures that define bacteria as psychrophiles, mesophiles, or thermophiles are not rigidly defined. Psychrophiles, for example, were originally considered simply to be organisms capable of growing at 0°C. However, there seem to be two fairly distinct groups capable of growth at that temperature. One group, composed of psychrophiles in the strictest sense, can grow at 0°C but has an optimum growth temperature of about 15°C. Most of these organisms are so sensitive to higher temperatures that they will not even grow in a reasonably warm room (25°C). Found mostly in the oceans' depths or in certain polar regions, such organisms seldom cause problems in food preservation. The other group that can grow at 0°C has higher optimum temperatures, usually 20–30°C and cannot grow above about 40°C. Organisms of this type are much more common than psychrophiles and are the most likely to be encountered in low-temperature food spoilage because they grow fairly well at refrigerator temperatures. We will use the term **psychrotrophs,** which food microbiologists favor, for this group of spoilage microorganisms.

Refrigeration is the most common method of preserving household food supplies. It is based on the principle that microbial reproductive rates decrease at low temperatures. Although microbes usually survive even subfreezing temperatures (they might become entirely dormant), they gradually decline in number. Some species decline faster than others. Psychrotrophs

actually do not grow well at low temperatures, except in comparison with other organisms; given time, however, they are able to slowly degrade food. Such spoilage might take the form of mold mycelium, slime on food surfaces, or off-tastes or off-colors in foods. The temperature inside a properly set refrigerator will greatly slow the growth of most spoilage organisms and will entirely prevent the growth of all but a few pathogenic bacteria. **Figure 2** illustrates the importance of low temperatures for preventing the growth of spoilage and disease organisms. When large amounts of food must be refrigerated, it is important to keep in mind the slow cooling rate of a large quantity of warm food (**Figure 3**).

Mesophiles, with an optimum growth temperature of 25–40°C, are the most common type of microbe. Organisms that have adapted to live in the bodies of animals usually have an optimum temperature close to that of their hosts. The optimum temperature for many pathogenic bacteria is about 37°C, and incubators for clinical cultures are usually set at about this temperature. The mesophiles include most of the common spoilage and disease organisms.

Thermophiles are microorganisms capable of growth at high temperatures. Many of these organisms have an optimum growth temperature of 50–60°C, about the temperature of water from a hot water tap. Such temperatures can also be reached in sunlit soil and in thermal waters such as hot springs. Remarkably, many thermophiles cannot grow at temperatures below

Figure 3 **The effect of the amount of food on its cooling rate in a refrigerator and its chance of spoilage.** Notice that in this example, the pan of rice with a depth of 5 cm (2 in) cooled through the incubation temperature range of the *Bacillus cereus* in about 1 hour, whereas the pan of rice with a depth of 15 cm (6 in) remained in this temperature range for about 5 hours.

Q Given a shallow pan and a deep pot with the same volume, which would cool faster? Why?

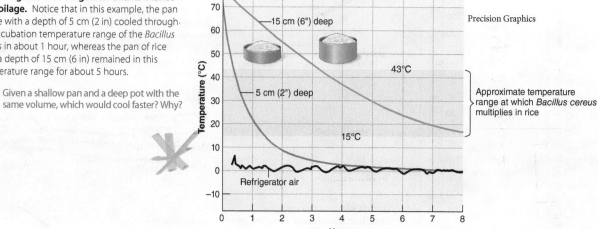

about 45°C. Endospores formed by thermophilic bacteria are unusually heat resistant and may survive the usual heat treatment given canned goods. Although elevated storage temperatures may cause surviving endospores to germinate and grow, thereby spoiling the food, these thermophilic bacteria are not considered a public health problem. Thermophiles are important in organic compost piles, in which the temperature can rise rapidly to 50–60°C.

Some microbes, members of the Archaea, have an optimum growth temperature of 80°C or higher. These organisms are called **hyperthermophiles,** or sometimes **extreme thermophiles.** Most of these organisms live in hot springs associated with volcanic activity; sulfur is usually important in their metabolic activity. The known record for bacterial growth and replication at high temperatures is about 121°C near deep-sea hydrothermal vents. See the box on the facing page. The immense pressure in the ocean depths prevents water from boiling even at temperatures well above 100°C.

pH

pH refers to the acidity or alkalinity of a solution. Most bacteria grow best in a narrow pH range near neutrality, between pH 6.5 and 7.5. Very few bacteria grow at an acidic pH below about pH 4. This is why a number of foods, such as sauerkraut, pickles, and many cheeses, are preserved from spoilage by acids produced by bacterial fermentation. Nonetheless, some bacteria, called **acidophiles,** are remarkably tolerant of acidity. One type of chemoautotrophic bacteria, which is found in the drainage water from coal mines and oxidizes sulfur to form sulfuric acid, can survive at a pH value of 1. Molds and yeasts will grow over a greater pH range than bacteria will, but the optimum pH of molds and yeasts is gener-

ally below that of bacteria, usually about pH 5 to 6. Alkalinity also inhibits microbial growth but is rarely used to preserve foods.

When bacteria are cultured in the laboratory, they often produce acids that eventually interfere with their own growth. To neutralize the acids and maintain the proper pH, chemical buffers are included in the growth medium. The peptones and amino acids in some media act as buffers, and many media also contain phosphate salts. Phosphate salts have the advantage of exhibiting their buffering effect in the pH growth range of most bacteria. They are also nontoxic; in fact, they provide phosphorus, an essential nutrient.

Osmotic Pressure

Microorganisms obtain almost all their nutrients in solution from the surrounding water. Thus, they require water for growth, and their composition is 80–90% water. High osmotic pressures have the effect of removing necessary water from a cell. When a microbial cell is in a solution whose concentration of solutes is higher than in the cell (the environment is *hypertonic* to the cell), the cellular water passes out through the plasma membrane to the high solute concentration. This osmotic loss of water causes **plasmolysis,** or shrinkage of the cell's cytoplasm (Figure 4).

The importance of this phenomenon is that the growth of the cell is inhibited as the plasma membrane pulls away from the cell wall. Thus, the addition of salts (or other solutes) to a solution, and the resulting increase in osmotic pressure, can be used to preserve foods. Salted fish, honey, and sweetened condensed milk are preserved largely by this mechanism; the high salt or sugar concentrations draw water out of any microbial cells that are present

Life in the Extreme

Until humans explored the deep-ocean floor, scientists believed that only a few forms of life could survive in that high-pressure, completely dark, oxygen-poor environment. Then, in 1977, *Alvin*, the deep-sea submersible carried two scientists 2600 meters below the surface at the Galápagos Rift (about 350 km northeast of the Galápagos Islands). There, amid the vast expanse of barren basalt rocks, the scientists found unexpectedly rich oases of life. Superheated water from beneath the seafloor rises through fractures in the Earth's crust called vents. Mats of bacteria grow along the sides of the vents, where temperatures exceed 100°C (see the figure).

Ecosystem of the Hydrothermal Vents

Life at the surface of the world's oceans depends on photosynthetic organisms, such as plants and algae, which harness the sun's energy to fix carbon dioxide (CO_2) to make carbohydrates. At the deep-ocean floor, where no light penetrates, photosynthesis is not possible. The scientists found that the primary producers at the ocean floor are chemoautotrophic bacteria. Using chemical energy from hydrogen sulfide (H_2S) as a source of energy to fix CO_2, the chemoautotrophs create an environment that supports higher life forms. Hydrothermal vents in the seafloor supply the H_2S and CO_2.

New Products from Hydrothermal Vents

Terrestrial fungi and bacteria have had a major impact on the development of antimicrobial and antitumor compounds since the 1930s. Hydrothermal vents are the next frontier in the hunt for new drugs. In 2010 a peptide produced by *Thermovibrio ammonificans* was shown to induce apoptosis (cell death) and thus potential anticancer activity. Currently, researchers are growing *Pyrococcus furiosus* because it produces alternative fuels, hydrogen gas, and butanol. DNA polymerases (enzymes that synthesize DNA) isolated from two archaea living near deep-sea vents are being used in the polymerase chain reaction (PCR), a technique for making many copies of DNA. In PCR, single-stranded DNA is made by heating a chromosome fragment to 98°C and cooling it so that DNA polymerase can copy each strand. DNA polymerase from *Thermococcus litoralis*, called Vent$_R$, and from *Pyrococcus*, called Deep Vent$_R$, are not denatured at 98°C. These enzymes can be used in automatic thermalcyclers to repeat the heating and cooling cycles, allowing many copies of DNA to be made easily and quickly.

Al Giddings/Al Giddings Images

|— 1 m

A white microbial biofilm is visible on this deep-sea hydrothermal vent. Water is being emitted through the ocean floor at temperatures above 100°C.

Precision Graphics

(a) Cell in isotonic solution. Under these conditions, the solute concentration in the cell is equivalent to a solute concentration of 0.85% sodium chloride (NaCl).

(b) Plasmolyzed cell in hypertonic solution. If the concentration of solutes such as NaCl is higher in the surrounding medium than in the cell (the environment is hypertonic), water tends to leave the cell. Growth of the cell is inhibited.

Figure 4 Plasmolysis.

Q Why is osmotic pressure an important factor in microbial growth?

and thus prevent their growth. These effects of osmotic pressure are roughly related to the *number* of dissolved molecules and ions in a volume of solution.

Some organisms, called **extreme halophiles**, have adapted so well to high salt concentrations that they actually require them for growth. In this case, they may be termed **obligate halophiles.** Organisms from such saline waters as the Dead Sea often require nearly 30% salt, and the inoculating loop (a device for handling bacteria in the laboratory) used to transfer them must first be dipped into a saturated salt solution. More common are **facultative halophiles,** which do not require high salt concentrations but are able to grow at salt concentrations up to 2%, a concentration that inhibits the growth of many other organisms. A few species of facultative halophiles can tolerate even 15% salt.

Most microorganisms, however, must be grown in a medium that is nearly all water. For example, the concentration of agar (a complex polysaccharide isolated from marine algae) used to solidify microbial growth media is usually about 1.5%. If markedly higher concentrations are used, the increased osmotic pressure can inhibit the growth of some bacteria.

If the osmotic pressure is unusually low (the environment is *hypotonic*)—such as in distilled water, for example—water tends to enter the cell rather than leave it. Some microbes that have a relatively weak cell wall may be lysed by such treatment.

CHECK YOUR UNDERSTANDING

- Why are hyperthermophiles that grow at temperatures above 100°C seemingly limited to oceanic depths? **1**
- Other than controlling acidity, what is an advantage of using phosphate salts as buffers in growth media? **2**
- Why might primitive civilizations have used food preservation techniques that rely on osmotic pressure? **3**

Chemical Requirements

Carbon

Besides water, one of the most important requirements for microbial growth is carbon. Carbon is the structural backbone of living matter; it is needed for all the organic compounds that make up a living cell. Half the dry weight of a typical bacterial cell is carbon. Chemoheterotrophs get most of their carbon from the source of their energy—organic materials such as proteins, carbohydrates, and lipids. Chemoautotrophs and photoautotrophs derive their carbon from carbon dioxide.

Nitrogen, Sulfur, and Phosphorus

In addition to carbon, microorganisms need other elements to synthesize cellular material. For example, protein synthesis requires considerable amounts of nitrogen as well as some sulfur. The syntheses of DNA and RNA also require nitrogen and some phosphorus, as does the synthesis of ATP, the molecule so important for the storage and transfer of chemical energy within the cell. Nitrogen makes up about 14% of the dry weight

of a bacterial cell, and sulfur and phosphorus together constitute about another 4%.

Organisms use nitrogen primarily to form the amino group of the amino acids of proteins. Many bacteria meet this requirement by decomposing protein-containing material and reincorporating the amino acids into newly synthesized proteins and other nitrogen-containing compounds. Other bacteria use nitrogen from ammonium ions (NH_4^+), which are already in the reduced form and are usually found in organic cellular material. Still other bacteria are able to derive nitrogen from nitrates (compounds that dissociate to give the nitrate ion, NO_3^-, in solution).

Some important bacteria, including many of the photosynthesizing cyanobacteria, use gaseous nitrogen (N_2) directly from the atmosphere. This process is called **nitrogen fixation.** Some organisms that can use this method are free-living, mostly in the soil, but others live cooperatively in symbiosis with the roots of legumes such as clover, soybeans, alfalfa, beans, and peas. The nitrogen fixed in the symbiosis is used by both the plant and the bacterium.

Sulfur is used to synthesize sulfur-containing amino acids and vitamins such as thiamine and biotin. Important natural sources of sulfur include the sulfate ion (SO_4^{2-}), hydrogen sulfide, and the sulfur-containing amino acids.

Phosphorus is essential for the synthesis of nucleic acids and the phospholipids of cell membranes. Among other places, it is also found in the energy bonds of ATP. A source of phosphorus is the phosphate ion (PO_4^{3-}). Potassium, magnesium, and calcium are also elements that microorganisms require, often as cofactors for enzymes.

Trace Elements

Microbes require very small amounts of other mineral elements, such as iron, copper, molybdenum, and zinc; these are referred to as **trace elements.** Most are essential for the functions of certain enzymes, usually as cofactors. Although these elements are sometimes added to a laboratory medium, they are usually assumed to be naturally present in tap water and other components of media. Even most distilled waters contain adequate amounts, but tap water is sometimes specified to ensure that these trace minerals will be present in culture media.

Oxygen

We are accustomed to thinking of molecular oxygen (O_2) as a necessity of life, but it is actually in a sense a poisonous gas. Very little molecular oxygen existed in the atmosphere during most of Earth's history—in fact, it is possible that life could not have arisen had oxygen been present. However, many current forms of life have metabolic systems that require oxygen for aerobic respiration. As we have seen, hydrogen atoms that have been stripped from organic compounds combine with oxygen to form water. This process yields a great deal of energy while neutralizing a potentially toxic gas—a very neat solution, all in all.

TABLE 1 The Effect of Oxygen on the Growth of Various Types of Bacteria

	a. Obligate Aerobes	b. Facultative Anaerobes	c. Obligate Anaerobes	d. Aerotolerant Anaerobes	e. Microaerophiles
Effect of Oxygen on Growth	Only aerobic growth; oxygen required.	Both aerobic and anaerobic growth; greater growth in presence of oxygen.	Only anaerobic growth; ceases in presence of oxygen.	Only anaerobic growth; but continues in presence of oxygen.	Only aerobic growth; oxygen required in low concentration.
Bacterial Growth in Tube of Solid Growth Medium					
Explanation of Growth Patterns	Growth occurs only where high concentrations of oxygen have diffused into the medium.	Growth is best where most oxygen is present, but occurs throughout tube.	Growth occurs only where there is no oxygen.	Growth occurs evenly; oxygen has no effect.	Growth occurs only where a low concentration of oxygen has diffused into medium.
Explanation of Oxygen's Effects	Presence of enzymes catalase and superoxide dismutase (SOD) allows toxic forms of oxygen to be neutralized; can use oxygen.	Presence of enzymes catalase and SOD allows toxic forms of oxygen to be neutralized; can use oxygen.	Lacks enzymes to neutralize harmful forms of oxygen; cannot tolerate oxygen.	Presence of one enzyme, SOD, allows harmful forms of oxygen to be partially neutralized; tolerates oxygen.	Produce lethal amounts of toxic forms of oxygen if exposed to normal atmospheric oxygen.

Microbes that use molecular oxygen (aerobes) extract more energy from nutrients than microbes that do not use oxygen (anaerobes). Organisms that require oxygen to live are called **obligate aerobes** (Table 1a).

Obligate aerobes are at a disadvantage because oxygen is poorly soluble in the water of their environment. Therefore, many of the aerobic bacteria have developed, or retained, the ability to continue growing in the absence of oxygen. Such organisms are called **facultative anaerobes** (Table 1b). In other words, facultative anaerobes can use oxygen when it is present but are able to continue growth by using fermentation or anaerobic respiration when oxygen is not available. However, their efficiency in producing energy decreases in the absence of oxygen. Examples of facultative anaerobes are the familiar *Escherichia coli* that are found in the human intestinal tract. Many yeasts are also facultative anaerobes. Many microbes are able to substitute other electron acceptors, such as nitrate ions, for oxygen, which is something humans are unable to do.

Obligate anaerobes (Table 1c) are bacteria that are unable to use molecular oxygen for energy-yielding reactions. In fact, most are harmed by it. The genus *Clostridium* (klôs-tri′ dē-um), which contains the species that cause tetanus and botulism, is the most familiar example. These bacteria do use oxygen atoms present in cellular materials; the atoms are usually obtained from water.

Understanding how organisms can be harmed by oxygen requires a brief discussion of the toxic forms of oxygen:

1. **Singlet oxygen** ($^1O_2^-$) is normal molecular oxygen (O_2) that has been boosted into a higher-energy state and is extremely reactive.

2. **Superoxide radicals** (O_2^-), or **superoxide anions,** are formed in small amounts during the normal respiration of organisms that use oxygen as a final electron acceptor, forming water. In the presence of oxygen, obligate anaerobes also appear to form some superoxide radicals, which are so toxic to cellular components that all organisms attempting to grow in atmospheric oxygen must produce an enzyme, **superoxide dismutase (SOD),** to neutralize them. Their toxicity is caused by their great instability, which leads them to steal an electron from a neighboring molecule, which in turn becomes a radical and steals an electron, and so on. Aerobic bacteria, facultative anaerobes growing aerobically, and aerotolerant anaerobes (discussed shortly) produce SOD, with which they convert the superoxide radical into molecular oxygen (O_2) and hydrogen peroxide (H_2O_2):

$$O_2^- + O_2^- + 2\,H^+ \longrightarrow H_2O_2 + O_2$$

3. The hydrogen peroxide produced in this reaction contains the **peroxide anion** O_2^{2-} and is also toxic. Later, you may encounter it as the active principle in the antimicrobial agents hydrogen peroxide and benzoyl peroxide. Because the hydrogen peroxide produced during normal aerobic respiration is toxic, microbes have developed enzymes to neutralize it. The most familiar of these is **catalase,** which converts it into water and oxygen:

$$2\,H_2O_2 \longrightarrow 2\,H_2O + O_2$$

Catalase is easily detected by its action on hydrogen peroxide. When a drop of hydrogen peroxide is added to a colony of bacterial cells producing catalase, oxygen bubbles are released. Anyone who has put hydrogen peroxide on a wound will recognize that cells in human tissue also contain catalase. The other enzyme that breaks down hydrogen peroxide is **peroxidase,** which differs from catalase in that its reaction does not produce oxygen:

$$H_2O_2 + 2\,H^+ \longrightarrow 2\,H_2O$$

Another important form of reactive oxygen, **ozone (O_3),** is also discussed.

4. The **hydroxyl radical** (OH·) is another intermediate form of oxygen and probably the most reactive. It is formed in the cellular cytoplasm by ionizing radiation. Most aerobic respiration produces traces of hydroxyl radicals, but they are transient.

These toxic forms of oxygen are an essential component of one of the body's most important defenses against pathogens, phagocytosis. In the phagolysosome of the phagocytic cell, ingested pathogens are killed by exposure to singlet oxygen, superoxide radicals, peroxide anions of hydrogen peroxide, and hydroxyl radicals and other oxidative compounds.

Obligate anaerobes usually produce neither superoxide dismutase nor catalase. Because aerobic conditions probably lead to an accumulation of superoxide radicals in their cytoplasm, obligate anaerobes are extremely sensitive to oxygen.

Aerotolerant anaerobes (Table 1d) cannot use oxygen for growth, but they tolerate it fairly well. On the surface of a solid medium, they will grow without the use of special techniques (discussed later) required for obligate anaerobes. Many of the aerotolerant bacteria characteristically ferment carbohydrates to lactic acid. As lactic acid accumulates, it inhibits the growth of aerobic competitors and establishes a favorable ecological niche for lactic acid producers. A common example of lactic acid–producing aerotolerant anaerobes is the lactobacilli used in the production of many acidic fermented foods, such as pickles and cheese. In the laboratory, they are handled and grown much like any other bacteria, but they make no use of the oxygen in the air. These bacteria can tolerate oxygen because they possess SOD or an equivalent system that neutralizes the toxic forms of oxygen previously discussed.

A few bacteria are **microaerophiles** (Table 1e). They are aerobic; they do require oxygen. However, they grow only in oxygen concentrations lower than those in air. In a test tube of solid nutrient medium, they grow only at a depth where small amounts of oxygen have diffused into the medium; they do not grow near the oxygen-rich surface or below the narrow zone of adequate oxygen. This limited tolerance is probably due to their sensitivity to superoxide radicals and peroxides, which they produce in lethal concentrations under oxygen-rich conditions.

Organic Growth Factors

Essential organic compounds an organism is unable to synthesize are known as **organic growth factors;** they must be directly obtained from the environment. One group of organic growth factors for humans is vitamins. Most vitamins function as coenzymes, the organic cofactors required by certain enzymes in order to function. Many bacteria can synthesize all their own vitamins and do not depend on outside sources. However, some bacteria lack the enzymes needed for the synthesis of certain vitamins, and for them those vitamins are organic growth factors. Other organic growth factors required by some bacteria are amino acids, purines, and pyrimidines.

CHECK YOUR UNDERSTANDING

✓ If bacterial cells were given a sulfur source containing radioactive sulfur (^{35}S) in their culture media, in what molecules would the ^{35}S be found in the cells? 4

✓ How would one determine whether a microbe is a strict anaerobe? 5

✓ Oxygen is so pervasive in the environment that it would be very difficult for a microbe to always avoid physical contact with it. What, therefore, is the most obvious way for a microbe to avoid damage? 6

Biofilms

LEARNING OBJECTIVE

7 Describe the formation of biofilms and their potential for causing infection.

In nature, microorganisms seldom live in the isolated single-species colonies that we see on laboratory plates. They more typically live in communities called **biofilms.** This fact was not well appreciated until the development of confocal microscopy made the three-dimensional structure of biofilms more visible. Biofilms reside in a matrix made up primarily of polysaccharides, but also containing DNA and proteins, that is often informally called *slime*. A biofilm also can be considered a *hydrogel*, which is a complex polymer containing many times its dry weight in water. Cell-to-cell chemical communication, or *quorum sensing*, allows bacteria to coordinate their activity and group together into communities that provide benefits not unlike those of multicellular organisms. Therefore, biofilms are not just bacterial slime layers but biological systems; the bacteria are organized into a coordinated, functional community. Biofilms are usually attached to a surface, such as a rock in a pond, a human tooth (plaque), or a mucous membrane. This community might be of a single species or of a diverse group of microorganisms. Biofilms also might take other, more varied forms. The floc that forms in certain types of sewage treatment is an example. In fast-flowing streams, the biofilm might be in the form of filamentous streamers. Within a biofilm community, the bacteria are able to share nutrients and are sheltered from harmful factors in the environment, such as desiccation, antibiotics, and the body's immune system. The close proximity of microorganisms within a biofilm might also have the advantage of facilitating the transfer of genetic information by, for example, conjugation.

A biofilm usually begins to form when a free-swimming (*planktonic*) bacterium attaches to a surface. If these bacteria grew in a uniformly thick monolayer, they would become overcrowded, nutrients would not be available in lower depths, and toxic wastes could accumulate. Microorganisms in biofilm communities sometimes avoid these problems by forming pillar-like structures (**Figure 5**) with channels between them, through which water can carry incoming nutrients and outgoing wastes. This constitutes a primitive circulatory system. Individual microbes and clumps of slime occasionally leave the established biofilm and move to a new location where the biofilm becomes extended. Such a biofilm is generally composed of a surface layer about 10 μm thick, with pillars that extend up to 200 μm above it.

The microorganisms in biofilms can work cooperatively to carry out complex tasks. For example, the digestive systems of ruminant animals, such as cattle, require many different microbial species to break down cellulose. The microbes in a ruminant's digestive system are located mostly within biofilm communities. Biofilms are also essential elements in the proper functioning of sewage treatment systems. They can also, however, be a problem in pipes and tubing, where their accumulations impede circulation.

Biofilms are an important factor in human health. For example, microbes in biofilms are probably 1000 times more resistant to microbicides. Experts at the Centers for Disease Control and Prevention (CDC) estimate that 70% of human bacterial infections involve biofilms. Most nosocomial infections (infections acquired in health care facilities) are probably related to biofilms on medical catheters. In fact, biofilms form on almost all indwelling medical devices, including mechanical heart valves. Biofilms, which also can include those formed by fungi such as *Candida*, are encountered in many disease conditions, such as infections related to the use of contact lenses, dental caries, and infections by pseudomonad bacteria.

One approach to preventing biofilm formation is to incorporate antimicrobials into surfaces on which biofilms might form. Because the chemical signals that allow quorum sensing are

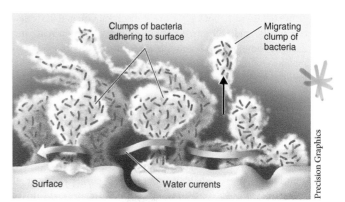

Water currents move, as shown by the blue arrow, among pillars of slime formed by the growth of bacteria attached to solid surfaces. This allows efficient access to nutrients and removal of bacterial waste products. Individual slime-forming bacteria or bacteria in clumps of slime detach and move to new locations.

Figure 5 Biofilms.

Q Why is the prevention of biofilms important in a health care environment?

essential to biofilm formation, research is underway to determine the makeup of these chemical signals and perhaps block them. Another approach involves the discovery that lactoferrin, which is abundant in many human secretions, can inhibit biofilm formation. Lactoferrin binds iron, especially among the pseudomonads that are responsible for cystic fibrosis biofilms, the cause of the pathology of this hereditary disease. The lack of iron inhibits the surface motility essential for the aggregation of the bacteria into biofilms.

Most laboratory methods in microbiology today use organisms being cultured in their planktonic mode. However, microbiologists now predict that there will be an increasing focus on how microorganisms actually live in relation with one another and that this will be considered in industrial and medical research.

CHECK YOUR UNDERSTANDING

✔ Identify a way in which pathogens find it advantageous to form biofilms. 7

Culture Media

LEARNING OBJECTIVES

8   Distinguish chemically defined and complex media.

9   Justify the use of each of the following: anaerobic techniques, living host cells, candle jars, selective and differential media, enrichment medium.

10   Differentiate biosafety levels 1, 2, 3, and 4.

A nutrient material prepared for the growth of microorganisms in a laboratory is called a **culture medium.** Some bacteria can grow well on just about any culture medium; others require special media, and still others cannot grow on any nonliving medium yet developed. Microbes that are introduced into a culture medium to initiate growth are called an **inoculum.** The microbes that grow and multiply in or on a culture medium are referred to as a **culture.**

Suppose we want to grow a culture of a certain microorganism, perhaps the microbes from a particular clinical specimen. What criteria must the culture medium meet? First, it must contain the right nutrients for the specific microorganism we want to grow. It should also contain sufficient moisture, a properly adjusted pH, and a suitable level of oxygen, perhaps none at all. The medium must initially be **sterile**—that is, it must initially contain no living microorganisms—so that the culture will contain only the microbes (and their offspring) we add to the medium. Finally, the growing culture should be incubated at the proper temperature.

A wide variety of media are available for the growth of microorganisms in the laboratory. Most of these media, which are available from commercial sources, have premixed components and require only the addition of water and then sterilization. Media are constantly being developed or revised for use in the isolation and identification of bacteria that are of interest to researchers in such fields as food, water, and clinical microbiology.

When it is desirable to grow bacteria on a solid medium, a solidifying agent such as agar is added to the medium. A complex polysaccharide derived from a marine alga, **agar** has long been used as a thickener in foods such as jellies and ice cream.

Agar has some very important properties that make it valuable to microbiology, and no satisfactory substitute has ever been found. Few microbes can degrade agar, so it remains solid. Also, agar liquefies at about 100°C (the boiling point of water) and at sea level remains liquid until the temperature drops to about 40°C. For laboratory use, agar is held in water baths at about 50°C. At this temperature, it does not injure most bacteria when it is poured over them. Once the agar has solidified, it can be incubated at temperatures approaching 100°C before it again liquefies; this property is particularly useful when thermophilic bacteria are being grown.

Agar media are usually contained in test tubes or *Petri dishes.* The test tubes are called *slants* when their contents are allowed to solidify with the tube held at an angle so that a large surface area for growth is available. When the agar solidifies in a vertical tube, it is called a *deep.* Petri dishes, named for their inventor, are shallow dishes with a lid that nests over the bottom to prevent contamination; when filled, they are called *Petri* (or culture) *plates.*

Chemically Defined Media

To support microbial growth, a medium must provide an energy source, as well as sources of carbon, nitrogen, sulfur,

TABLE 2	A Chemically Defined Medium for Growing a Typical Chemoheterotroph, Such as *Escherichia coli*
Constituent	**Amount**
Glucose	5.0 g
Ammonium phosphate, monobasic ($NH_4H_2PO_4$)	1.0 g
Sodium chloride (NaCl)	5.0 g
Magnesium sulfate ($MgSO_4 \cdot 7H_2O$)	0.2 g
Potassium phosphate, dibasic (K_2HPO_4)	1.0 g
Water	1 liter

phosphorus, and any organic growth factors the organism is unable to synthesize. A **chemically defined medium** is one whose exact chemical composition is known. For a chemoheterotroph, the chemically defined medium must contain organic growth factors that serve as a source of carbon and energy. For example, as shown in **Table 2**, glucose is included in the medium for growing the chemoheterotroph *E. coli.*

As **Table 3** shows, many organic growth factors must be provided in the chemically defined medium used to cultivate a species of *Leuconostoc.* Organisms that require many growth factors are described as *fastidious.* Organisms of this type, such as *Lactobacillus,* are sometimes used in tests that determine the concentration of a particular vitamin in a substance. To perform such a *microbiological assay,* a growth medium is prepared that contains all the growth requirements of the bacterium except the vitamin being assayed. Then the medium, test substance, and bacterium are combined, and the growth of bacteria is measured. This bacterial growth, which is reflected by the amount of lactic acid produced, will be proportional to the amount of vitamin in the test substance. The more lactic acid, the more the *Lactobacillus* cells have been able to grow, so the more vitamin is present.

Complex Media

Chemically defined media are usually reserved for laboratory experimental work or for the growth of autotrophic bacteria. Most heterotrophic bacteria and fungi, such as you would work with in an introductory lab course, are routinely grown on **complex media** made up of nutrients including extracts from yeasts, meat, or plants, or digests of proteins from these and other sources. The exact chemical composition varies slightly from batch to batch. **Table 4** shows one widely used recipe.

In complex media, the energy, carbon, nitrogen, and sulfur requirements of the growing microorganisms are provided primarily by protein. Protein is a large, relatively insoluble molecule that a minority of microorganisms can

TABLE 3 Defined Culture Medium for *Leuconostoc mesenteroides*

Carbon and Energy

Glucose, 25 g

Salts

NH_4Cl, 3.0 g
K_2HPO_4*, 0.6 g
KH_2PO_4*, 0.6 g
$MgSO_4$, 0.1 g

Amino Acids, 100–200 µg each

Alanine, arginine, asparagine, aspartate, cysteine, glutamate, glutamine, glycine, histidine, isoleucine, leucine, lysine, methionine, phenylalanine, proline, serine, threonine, tryptophan, tyrosine, valine

Purines and Pyrimidines, 10 mg of each

Adenine, guanine, uracil, xanthine

Vitamins, 0.01–1 mg each

Biotin, folate, nicotinic acid, pyridoxal, pyridoxamine, pyridoxine, riboflavin, thiamine, pantothenate, *p*-aminobenzoic acid

Trace Elements, 2–10 µg each

Fe, Co, Mn, Zn, Cu, Ni, Mo

Buffer, pH 7

Sodium acetate, 25 g

Distilled Water, 1,000 ml

*Also serves as buffer.

Table 4.2, p. 89 from *Biology of Microorganisms* 13th ed., by Michael T. Madigan, John M. Martinko, David A. Stahl and David P. Clark. Copyright © 2012. Printed and electronically reproduced by permission of Pearson Education, Inc., Upper Saddle River, New Jersey.

TABLE 4 Composition of Nutrient Agar, a Complex Medium for the Growth of Heterotrophic Bacteria

Constituent	Amount
Peptone (partially digested protein)	5.0 g
Beef extract	3.0 g
Sodium chloride	8.0 g
Agar	15.0 g
Water	1 liter

utilize directly, but a partial digestion by acids or enzymes reduces protein to shorter chains of amino acids called *peptones*. These small, soluble fragments can be digested by most bacteria.

Vitamins and other organic growth factors are provided by meat extracts or yeast extracts. The soluble vitamins and minerals from the meats or yeasts are dissolved in the extracting water, which is then evaporated so that these factors are concentrated. (These extracts also supplement the organic nitrogen and carbon compounds.) Yeast extracts are particularly rich in the B vitamins. If a complex medium is in liquid form, it is called **nutrient broth.** When agar is added, it is called **nutrient agar.** (This terminology can be confusing; just remember that agar itself is not a nutrient.)

Anaerobic Growth Media and Methods

The cultivation of anaerobic bacteria poses a special problem. Because anaerobes might be killed by exposure to oxygen, special media called **reducing media** must be used. These media contain ingredients, such as sodium thioglycolate, that chemically combine with dissolved oxygen and deplete the oxygen in the culture medium. To routinely grow and maintain pure cultures of obligate anaerobes, microbiologists use reducing media stored in ordinary, tightly capped test tubes. These media are heated shortly before use to drive off absorbed oxygen.

When the culture must be grown in Petri plates to observe individual colonies, several methods are available. Laboratories that work with relatively few culture plates at a time can use systems that can incubate the microorganisms in sealed boxes and jars in which the oxygen is chemically removed after the culture plates have been introduced and the container sealed. Some systems require that water be added to an envelope of chemicals before the container is closed, as shown in Figure 6, and require a catalyst. The chemicals produce hydrogen and carbon dioxide (about 4–10%) and remove the oxygen in the container by combining it, in the presence of the catalyst, with hydrogen to form water. In another commercially available system, the envelope of chemicals (the active ingredient is ascorbic acid) is simply opened to expose it to oxygen in the container's atmosphere. No water or catalyst is needed. The atmosphere in such containers usually has less than 5% oxygen, about 18% CO_2, and no hydrogen. In a recently introduced system, each individual Petri plate (OxyPlate) becomes an anaerobic chamber. The medium in the plate contains an enzyme, oxyrase, which combines oxygen with hydrogen, removing oxygen as water is formed.

Laboratories that have a large volume of work with anaerobes often use an anaerobic chamber, such as that shown in Figure 7. The chamber is filled with inert gases (typically about 85% N_2, 10% H_2, and 5% CO_2) and is equipped with air locks to introduce cultures and materials.

Special Culture Techniques

Many bacteria have never been successfully grown on artificial laboratory media. *Mycobacterium leprae*, the leprosy bacillus, is now usually grown in armadillos, which have a relatively low body temperature that matches the requirements of the microbe.

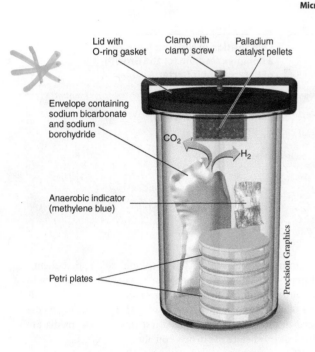

Figure 6 **A jar for cultivating anaerobic bacteria on Petri plates.** When water is mixed with the chemical packet containing sodium bicarbonate and sodium borohydride, hydrogen and carbon dioxide are generated. Reacting on the surface of a palladium catalyst in a screened reaction chamber, which may also be incorporated into the chemical packet, the hydrogen and atmospheric oxygen in the jar combine to form water. The oxygen is thus removed. Also in the jar is an anaerobic indicator containing methylene blue, which is blue when oxidized and turns colorless when the oxygen is removed (as shown here).

Q What is the technical name for bacteria that require a higher-than-atmospheric-concentration of CO_2 for growth?

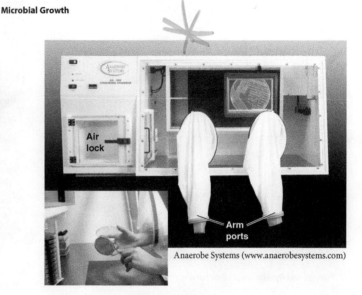

Anaerobe Systems (www.anaerobesystems.com)

Figure 7 **An anaerobic chamber.** Materials are introduced through the small doors in the air-lock chamber at the left. The operator works through arm ports in airtight sleeves. The airtight sleeves extend into the cabinet when it is in use. This unit also features an internal camera and monitor.

Q In what way would an anaerobic chamber resemble the Space Laboratory orbiting in the vacuum of space?

Another example is the syphilis spirochete, although certain nonpathogenic strains of this microbe have been grown on laboratory media. With few exceptions, the obligate intracellular bacteria, such as the rickettsias and the chlamydias, do not grow on artificial media. Like viruses, they can reproduce only in a living host cell.

Many clinical laboratories have special *carbon dioxide incubators* in which to grow aerobic bacteria that require concentrations of CO_2 higher or lower than that found in the atmosphere. Desired CO_2 levels are maintained by electronic controls. High CO_2 levels are also obtained with simple *candle jars*. Cultures are placed in a large sealed jar containing a lighted candle, which consumes oxygen. The candle stops burning when the air in the jar has a lowered concentration of oxygen (at about 17% O_2, still adequate for the growth of aerobic bacteria). An elevated concentration of CO_2 (about 3%) is also present. Microbes that grow better at high CO_2 concentrations are called **capnophiles.** The low-oxygen, high-CO_2 conditions resemble those found in the intestinal tract, respiratory tract, and other body tissues where pathogenic bacteria grow.

Candle jars are still used occasionally, but more often commercially available chemical packets are used to generate carbon dioxide atmospheres in containers. When only one or two Petri plates of cultures are to be incubated, clinical laboratory investigators often use small plastic bags with self-contained chemical gas generators that are activated by crushing the packet or moistening it with a few milliliters of water. These packets are sometimes specially designed to provide precise concentrations of carbon dioxide (usually higher than can be obtained in candle jars) and oxygen for culturing organisms such as the microaerophilic *Campylobacter* bacteria.

Some microorganisms are so dangerous that they can be handled only under extraordinary systems of containment called *biosafety level 4 (BSL-4)*. Level 4 labs are popularly known as "the hot zone." Only a handful of such labs exists in the United States. The lab is a sealed environment within a larger building and has an atmosphere under negative pressure, so that aerosols containing pathogens will not escape. Both intake and exhaust air is filtered through high-efficiency particulate air filters; the exhaust air is filtered twice. All waste materials leaving the lab are rendered noninfectious. The personnel wear "space suits" that are connected to an air supply (**Figure 8**).

Jim Gathany, CDC

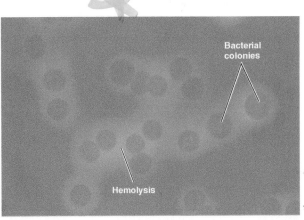

Christine Case

2 mm

Figure 8 Technicians in a biosafety level 4 (BSL-4) laboratory. Personnel working in a BSL-4 facility wear a "space suit" that is connected to an outside air supply.

[Q] If a technician were working with pathogenic prions, how would material leaving the lab be rendered noninfectious?

Figure 9 Blood agar, a differential medium containing red blood cells. The bacteria have lysed the red blood cells (beta-hemolysis), causing the clear areas around the colonies.

[Q] Of what value are hemolysins to pathogens?

Less dangerous organisms are handled at lower levels of biosafety. For example, a basic microbiology teaching laboratory would be BSL-1. Organisms that present a moderate risk of infection can be handled at BSL-2 levels, that is, on open laboratory benchtops with appropriate gloves, lab coats, or possibly face and eye protection. BSL-3 labs are intended for highly infectious airborne pathogens such as the tuberculosis agent. Biological safety cabinets similar in appearance to the anaerobic chamber shown in Figure 7 are used. The laboratory itself should be negatively pressurized and equipped with air filters to prevent release of the pathogen from the laboratory.

Selective and Differential Media

In clinical and public health microbiology, it is frequently necessary to detect the presence of specific microorganisms associated with disease or poor sanitation. For this task, selective and differential media are used. **Selective media** are designed to suppress the growth of unwanted bacteria and encourage the growth of the desired microbes. For example, bismuth sulfite agar is one medium used to isolate the typhoid bacterium, the gram-negative *Salmonella typhi* (tī′fē), from feces. Bismuth sulfite inhibits gram-positive bacteria and most gram-negative intestinal bacteria (other than *S. typhi*), as well. Sabouraud's dextrose agar, which has a pH of 5.6, is used to isolate fungi that outgrow most bacteria at this pH.

Differential media make it easier to distinguish colonies of the desired organism from other colonies growing on the same plate. Similarly, pure cultures of microorganisms have identifiable reactions with differential media in tubes or plates. Blood agar (which contains red blood cells) is a medium that microbiologists often use to identify bacterial species that destroy red blood cells. These species, such as *Streptococcus pyogenes* (pī-äj′ en-ēz), the bacterium that causes strep throat, show a clear ring around their colonies (beta-hemolysis) where they have lysed the surrounding blood cells (Figure 9).

Sometimes, selective and differential characteristics are combined in a single medium. Suppose we want to isolate the common bacterium *Staphylococcus aureus,* found in the nasal passages. This organism has a tolerance for high concentrations of sodium chloride; it can also ferment the carbohydrate mannitol to form acid. Mannitol salt agar contains 7.5% sodium chloride, which will discourage the growth of competing organisms and thus *select for* (favor the growth of) *S. aureus.* This salty medium also contains a pH indicator that changes color if the mannitol in the medium is fermented to acid; the mannitol-fermenting colonies of *S. aureus* are thus *differentiated from* colonies of bacteria that do not ferment mannitol. Bacteria that grow at the high salt concentration *and* ferment mannitol to acid can be readily identified by the color change (Figure 10). These are probably colonies of *S. aureus,* and their identification can be confirmed by additional tests.

Enrichment Culture

Because bacteria present in small numbers can be missed, especially if other bacteria are present in much larger numbers, it is sometimes necessary to use an **enrichment culture.**

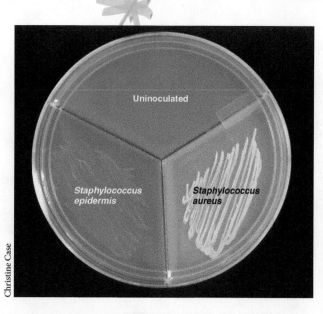

Figure 10 Differential medium. This medium is mannitol salt agar, and bacteria capable of fermenting the mannitol in the medium to acid (*Staphylococcus aureus*) cause the medium to change color to yellow. This **differentiates** between bacteria that can ferment mannitol and those that cannot. Actually, this medium is also *selective* because the high salt concentration prevents the growth of most bacteria but not *Staphlylococcus* spp.

 Are bacteria capable of growing at a high osmotic pressure likely to be capable of growing in the mucus found in nostrils?

This is often the case for soil or fecal samples. The medium (enrichment medium) for an enrichment culture is usually liquid and provides nutrients and environmental conditions that favor the growth of a particular microbe but not others. In this sense, it is also a selective medium, but it is designed to increase very small numbers of the desired type of organism to detectable levels.

Suppose we want to isolate from a soil sample a microbe that can grow on phenol and is present in much smaller numbers than other species. If the soil sample is placed in a liquid enrichment medium in which phenol is the only source of carbon and energy, microbes unable to metabolize phenol will not grow. The culture medium is allowed to incubate for a few days, and then a small amount of it is transferred into another flask of the same medium. After a series of such transfers, the surviving population will consist of bacteria capable of metabolizing phenol. The bacteria are given time to grow in the medium between transfers; this is the enrichment stage. Any nutrients in the original inoculum are rapidly diluted out with the successive transfers. When the last dilution is streaked onto a solid medium of the same composition, only those colonies of organisms capable of

using phenol should grow. A remarkable aspect of this particular technique is that phenol is normally lethal to most bacteria.

Table 5 summarizes the purposes of the main types of culture media.

Clinical Case

P. fluorescens is an aerobic, gram-negative rod that grows best between 25°C and 30°C and grows poorly at the standard hospital microbiology incubation temperatures (35°C to 37°C). The bacteria are so named because they produce a pigment that fluoresces under ultraviolet light. While reviewing the facts of the latest outbreak, Dr. MacGruder learns that the most recent patients were last exposed to the contaminated heparin 84 to 421 days before onset of their infections. On-site investigations confirmed that the patients' clinics are no longer using the recalled heparin and had, in fact, returned all unused inventory. Concluding that these patients did not develop infections during the previous outbreak, Dr. MacGruder must look for a new source of infection. The patients all have indwelling venous catheters: tubes that are inserted into a vein for long-term delivery of concentrated solutions, such as anticancer drugs. Dr. MacGruder orders cultures of the new heparin being used, but the results do not recover any organisms. He then orders blood and catheter cultures from each of the patients.

Illuminated with white light | Illuminated with ultraviolet light

The organism cultured from both the patients' blood and their catheters is shown in the figure. What organism is it?

CHECK YOUR UNDERSTANDING

- Could humans exist on chemically defined media, at least under laboratory conditions? **8**
- Could Louis Pasteur, in the 1800s, have grown rabies viruses in cell culture instead of in living animals? **9**
- What BSL is your laboratory? **10**

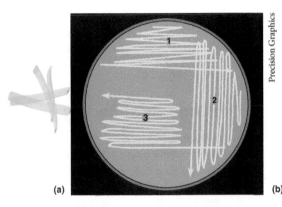
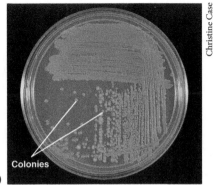

(a)   Precision Graphics

(b)   Christine Case

Colonies

Figure 11 The streak plate method for isolating pure bacterial cultures. (a) Arrows indicate the direction of streaking. Streak series 1 is made from the original bacterial culture. The inoculating loop is sterilized following each streak series. In series 2 and 3, the loop picks up bacteria from the previous series, diluting the number of cells each time. There are numerous variants of such patterns. **(b)** In series 3 of this example, notice that well-isolated colonies of bacteria of two different types, red and yellow, have been obtained.

Q Is a colony formed as a result of streaking a plate always derived from a single bacterium? Why or why not?

Obtaining Pure Cultures

LEARNING OBJECTIVES

11 Define *colony*.

12 Describe how pure cultures can be isolated by using the streak plate method.

Most infectious materials, such as pus, sputum, and urine, contain several different kinds of bacteria; so do samples of soil, water, or food. If these materials are plated out onto the surface of a solid medium, colonies will form that are exact copies of the original organism. A visible **colony** theoretically arises from a single spore or vegetative cell or from a group of the same microorganisms attached to one another in clumps or chains. Estimates are that only about 1% of bacteria in ecosystems produce colonies by conventional culture methods. Microbial colonies often have a distinctive appearance that distinguishes one microbe from another (see Figure 10). The bacteria must be distributed widely enough so that the colonies are visibly separated from each other.

Most bacteriological work requires pure cultures, or clones, of bacteria. The isolation method most commonly used to get pure cultures is the **streak plate method** (Figure 11). A sterile inoculating loop is dipped into a mixed culture that contains more than one type of microbe and is streaked in a pattern over the surface of the nutrient medium. As the pattern is traced, bacteria are rubbed off the loop onto the medium. The last cells to be rubbed off the loop are far enough apart to grow into isolated colonies. These colonies can be picked up with an inoculating loop and transferred to a test tube of nutrient medium to form a pure culture containing only one type of bacterium.

The streak plate method works well when the organism to be isolated is present in large numbers relative to the total population. However, when the microbe to be isolated is present only in very small numbers, its numbers must be greatly increased by selective enrichment before it can be isolated with the streak plate method.

CHECK YOUR UNDERSTANDING

✓ Can you think of any reason why a colony does not grow to an infinite size, or at least fill the confines of the Petri plate? 11

✓ Could a pure culture of bacteria be obtained by the streak plate method if there were only one desired microbe in a bacterial suspension of billions? 12

Preserving Bacterial Cultures

LEARNING OBJECTIVE

13 Explain how microorganisms are preserved by deep-freezing and lyophilization (freeze-drying).

Refrigeration can be used for the short-term storage of bacterial cultures. Two common methods of preserving microbial cultures

TABLE 5 Culture Media

Type	Purpose
Chemically Defined	Growth of chemoautotrophs and photoautotrophs; microbiological assays
Complex	Growth of most chemoheterotrophic organisms
Reducing	Growth of obligate anaerobes
Selective	Suppression of unwanted microbes; encouraging desired microbes
Differential	Differentiation of colonies of desired microbes from others
Enrichment	Similar to selective media but designed to increase numbers of desired microbes to detectable levels

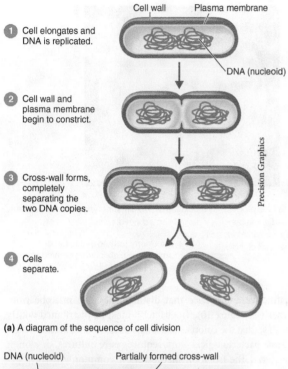

① Cell elongates and DNA is replicated.

② Cell wall and plasma membrane begin to constrict.

③ Cross-wall forms, completely separating the two DNA copies.

④ Cells separate.

Cell wall   Plasma membrane

DNA (nucleoid)

Precision Graphics

(a) A diagram of the sequence of cell division

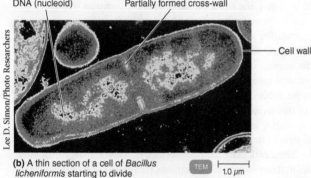

DNA (nucleoid)   Partially formed cross-wall

Cell wall

Lee D. Simon/Photo Researchers

(b) A thin section of a cell of *Bacillus licheniformis* starting to divide

TEM   1.0 μm

Figure 12 Binary fission in bacteria.

Q In what way is budding different from binary fission?

for long periods are deep-freezing and lyophilization. **Deep-freezing** is a process in which a pure culture of microbes is placed in a suspending liquid and quick-frozen at temperatures ranging from –50°C to –95°C. The culture can usually be thawed and cultured even several years later. During **lyophilization (freeze-drying)**, a suspension of microbes is quickly frozen at temperatures ranging from –54°C to –72°C, and the water is removed by a high vacuum (sublimation). While under vacuum, the container is sealed by melting the glass with a high-temperature torch. The remaining powderlike residue that contains the surviving microbes can be stored for years. The organisms can be revived at any time by hydration with a suitable liquid nutrient medium.

CHECK YOUR UNDERSTANDING

✔ If the Space Station in Earth orbit suddenly ruptured, the humans on board would die instantly from cold and the vacuum of space. Would all the bacteria in the capsule also be killed? **13**

The Growth of Bacterial Cultures

LEARNING OBJECTIVES

14 Define *bacterial growth*, including *binary fission*.

15 Compare the phases of microbial growth, and describe their relation to generation time.

16 Explain four direct methods of measuring cell growth.

17 Differentiate direct and indirect methods of measuring cell growth.

18 Explain three indirect methods of measuring cell growth.

Being able to represent graphically the enormous populations resulting from the growth of bacterial cultures is an essential part of microbiology. It is also necessary to be able to determine microbial numbers, either directly, by counting, or indirectly, by measuring their metabolic activity.

Bacterial Division

As we mentioned at the beginning of the chapter, bacterial growth refers to an increase in bacterial numbers, not an increase in the size of the individual cells. Bacteria normally reproduce by **binary fission** (Figure 12).

A few bacterial species reproduce by **budding**; they form a small initial outgrowth (a bud) that enlarges until its size approaches that of the parent cell, and then it separates. Some filamentous bacteria (certain actinomycetes) reproduce by producing chains of conidiospores carried externally at the tips of the filaments. A few filamentous species simply fragment, and the fragments initiate the growth of new cells. (MM) **Animations** Binary Fission; Bacterial Growth: Overview

Generation Time

For purposes of calculating the generation time of bacteria, we will consider only reproduction by binary fission, which is by far the most common method. As you can see in Figure 13, one cell's division produces two cells, two cells' divisions produce four cells, and so on. When the number of cells in each generation is expressed as a power of 2, the exponent tells the number of doublings (generations) that have occurred.

The time required for a cell to divide (and its population to double) is called the **generation time.** It varies considerably among organisms and with environmental conditions, such as temperature. Most bacteria have a generation time of 1 to 3 hours; others require more than 24 hours per generation.

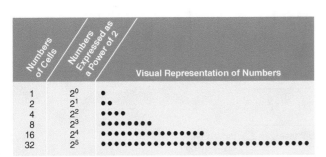

Numbers of Cells	Numbers Expressed as a Power of 2	Visual Representation of Numbers
1	2^0	
2	2^1	
4	2^2	
8	2^3	
16	2^4	
32	2^5	

(a) Visual representation of increase in bacterial number over five generations. The number of bacteria doubles in each generation. The superscript indicates the generation; that is, $2^5 = 5$ generations.

Precision Graphics

Generation Number	Number of Cells		Log$_{10}$ of Number of Cells
0	$2^0 =$	1	0
5	$2^5 =$	32	1.51
10	$2^{10} =$	1,024	3.01
15	$2^{15} =$	32,768	4.52
16	$2^{16} =$	65,536	4.82
17	$2^{17} =$	131,072	5.12
18	$2^{18} =$	262,144	5.42
19	$2^{19} =$	524,288	5.72
20	$2^{20} =$	1,048,576	6.02

(b) Conversion of the number of cells in a population into the logarithmic expression of this number. To arrive at the numbers in the center column, use the y^x key on your calculator. Enter 2 on the calculator; press y^x; enter 5; then press the = sign. The calculator will show the number 32. Thus, the fifth-generation population of bacteria will total 32 cells. To arrive at the numbers in the right-hand column, use the log key on your calculator. Enter the number 32; then press the log key. The calculator will show, rounded off, that the log$_{10}$ of 32 is 1.51.

Figure 13 Cell division.

 If a single bacterium reproduced every 30 minutes, how many would there be in 2 hours?

If binary fission continues unchecked, an enormous number of cells will be produced. If a doubling occurred every 20 minutes—which is the case for *E. coli* under favorable conditions—after 20 generations a single initial cell would increase to over 1 million cells. This would require a little less than 7 hours. In 30 generations, or 10 hours, the population would be 1 billion, and in 24 hours it would be a number trailed by 21 zeros. It is difficult to graph population changes of such enormous magnitude by using arithmetic numbers. This is why logarithmic scales are generally used to graph bacterial growth. Understanding logarithmic representations of bacterial populations requires some use of mathematics and is necessary for anyone studying microbiology.

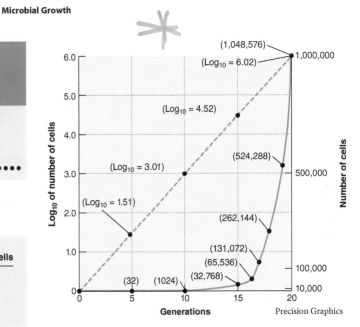

Figure 14 A growth curve for an exponentially increasing population, plotted logarithmically (dashed line) and arithmetically (solid line). For demonstration purposes, this graph has been drawn so that the arithmetic and logarithmic curves intersect at 1 million cells. This figure demonstrates why it is necessary to graph changes in the immense numbers of bacterial populations by logarithmic plots rather than by arithmetic numbers. For example, note that at ten generations the line representing arithmetic numbers has not even perceptibly left the baseline, whereas the logarithmic plot point for the tenth generation (3.01) is halfway up the graph.

 If the arithmetic numbers (solid line) were plotted for two more generations, would the line still be on the page?

Logarithmic Representation of Bacterial Populations

To illustrate the difference between logarithmic and arithmetic graphing of bacterial populations, let's express 20 bacterial generations both logarithmically and arithmetically. In five generations (2^5), there would be 32 cells; in ten generations (2^{10}), there would be 1024 cells, and so on. (If your calculator has a y^x key and a log key, you can duplicate the numbers in the third column of Figure 13.)

In Figure 14, notice that the arithmetically plotted line (solid) does not clearly show the population changes in the early stages of the growth curve at this scale. In fact, the first ten generations do not even appear to leave the baseline. Furthermore, another one or two arithmetic generations graphed to the same scale would greatly increase the height of the graph and take the line off the page.

The dashed line in Figure 14 shows how these plotting problems can be avoided by graphing the log$_{10}$ of the population numbers. The log$_{10}$ of the population is plotted at 5, 10, 15, and 20 generations. Notice that a straight line is formed and that a

Understanding the Bacterial Growth Curve

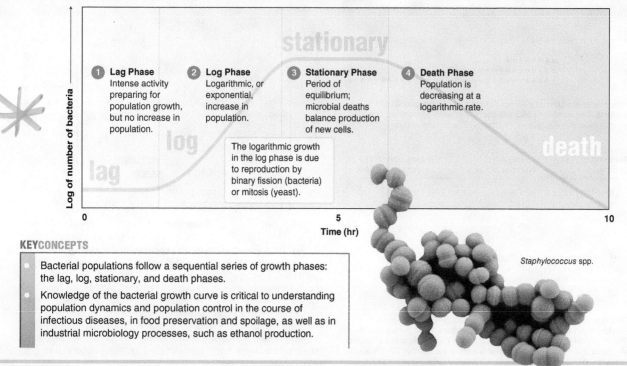

① Lag Phase
Intense activity preparing for population growth, but no increase in population.

② Log Phase
Logarithmic, or exponential, increase in population.

③ Stationary Phase
Period of equilibrium; microbial deaths balance production of new cells.

④ Death Phase
Population is decreasing at a logarithmic rate.

The logarithmic growth in the log phase is due to reproduction by binary fission (bacteria) or mitosis (yeast).

stationary

log

lag

death

Log of number of bacteria

Time (hr)

0 5 10

Staphylococcus spp.

KEYCONCEPTS

- Bacterial populations follow a sequential series of growth phases: the lag, log, stationary, and death phases.

- Knowledge of the bacterial growth curve is critical to understanding population dynamics and population control in the course of infectious diseases, in food preservation and spoilage, as well as in industrial microbiology processes, such as ethanol production.

Patrick Polito, Life Sciences Division, Ethox International, A Moog Company

thousand times this population (1,000,000,000, or $\log_{10}$ 9.0) could be accommodated in relatively little extra space. However, this advantage is obtained at the cost of distorting our "common sense" perception of the actual situation. We are not accustomed to thinking in logarithmic relationships, but it is necessary for a proper understanding of graphs of microbial populations.

CHECK YOUR UNDERSTANDING

☛ Can a complex organism, such as a beetle, divide by binary fission? 14

Phases of Growth

When a few bacteria are inoculated into a liquid growth medium and the population is counted at intervals, it is possible to plot a **bacterial growth curve** that shows the growth of cells over time (Figure 15). There are four basic phases of growth: the lag, log, stationary, and death phases. (MM) **Animation** Bacterial Growth Curve

The Lag Phase

For a while, the number of cells changes very little because the cells do not immediately reproduce in a new medium. This period of little or no cell division is called the **lag phase,** and it

can last for 1 hour or several days. During this time, however, the cells are not dormant. The microbial population is undergoing a period of intense metabolic activity involving, in particular, synthesis of enzymes and various molecules. (The situation is analogous to a factory being equipped to produce automobiles; there is considerable tooling-up activity but no immediate increase in the automobile population.)

The Log Phase

Eventually, the cells begin to divide and enter a period of growth, or logarithmic increase, called the **log phase,** or **exponential growth phase.** Cellular reproduction is most active during this period, and generation time reaches a constant minimum. Because the generation time is constant, a logarithmic plot of growth during the log phase is a straight line. The log phase is the time when cells are most active metabolically and is preferred for industrial purposes where, for example, a product needs to be produced efficiently.

The Stationary Phase

If exponential growth continued unchecked, startlingly large numbers of cells could arise. For example, a single bacterium (at a weight of 9.5×10^{-13} g per cell) dividing every 20 minutes for only 25.5 hours can theoretically produce a population equivalent in weight to that of an 80,000-ton aircraft carrier. In reality, this does not happen. Eventually, the growth rate slows, the number of microbial deaths balances the number of new cells, and the population stabilizes. This period of equilibrium is called the **stationary phase.**

What causes exponential growth to stop is not always clear. The exhaustion of nutrients, accumulation of waste products, and harmful changes in pH may all play a role.

The Death Phase

The number of deaths eventually exceeds the number of new cells formed, and the population enters the **death phase,** or **logarithmic decline phase.** This phase continues until the population is diminished to a tiny fraction of the number of cells in the previous phase or until the population dies out entirely. Some species pass through the entire series of phases in only a few days; others retain some surviving cells almost indefinitely.

CHECK YOUR UNDERSTANDING

✔ If two mice started a family within a fixed enclosure, with a fixed food supply, would the population curve be the same as a bacterial growth curve? 15

Direct Measurement of Microbial Growth

The growth of microbial populations can be measured in a number of ways. Some methods measure cell numbers; other methods measure the population's total mass, which is often directly proportional to cell numbers. Population numbers are usually recorded as the number of cells in a milliliter of liquid or in a gram of solid material. Because bacterial populations are usually very large, most methods of counting them are based on direct or indirect counts of very small samples; calculations then determine the size of the total population. Assume, for example, that a millionth of a milliliter (10^{-6} ml) of sour milk is found to contain 70 bacterial cells. Then there must be 70 times 1 million, or 70 million, cells per milliliter.

However, it is not practical to measure out a millionth of a milliliter of liquid or a millionth of a gram of food. Therefore, the procedure is done indirectly, in a series of dilutions. For example, if we add 1 ml of milk to 99 ml of water, each milliliter of this dilution now has one-hundredth as many bacteria as each milliliter of the original sample had. By making a series of such dilutions, we can readily estimate the number of bacteria in our original sample. To count microbial populations in solid foods (such as hamburger), an homogenate of one part food to nine parts water is finely ground in a food blender. Samples of this initial one-tenth dilution can then be transferred with a pipette for further dilutions or cell counts.

Plate Counts

The most frequently used method of measuring bacterial populations is the **plate count.** An important advantage of this method is that it measures the number of viable cells. One disadvantage may be that it takes some time, usually 24 hours or more, for visible colonies to form. This can be a serious problem in some applications, such as quality control of milk, when it is not possible to hold a particular lot for this length of time.

Plate counts assume that each live bacterium grows and divides to produce a single colony. This is not always true, because bacteria frequently grow linked in chains or as clumps. Therefore, a colony often results, not from a single bacterium, but from short segments of a chain or from a bacterial clump. To reflect this reality, plate counts are often reported as **colony-forming units (CFU).**

When a plate count is performed, it is important that only a limited number of colonies develop in the plate. When too many colonies are present, some cells are overcrowded and do not develop; these conditions cause inaccuracies in the count. The U.S. Food and Drug Administration convention is to count only plates with 25 to 250 colonies, but many microbiologists prefer plates with 30 to 300 colonies. To ensure that some colony counts will be within this range, the original inoculum is diluted several times in a process called **serial dilution** (Figure 16).

Serial Dilutions Let's say, for example, that a milk sample has 10,000 bacteria per milliliter. If 1 ml of this sample were plated out, there would theoretically be 10,000 colonies formed in the Petri plate of medium. Obviously, this would not produce a countable plate. If 1 ml of this sample were transferred to a tube containing 9 ml of sterile water, each milliliter of fluid in this tube would now contain 1000 bacteria. If 1 ml of this sample were inoculated into a Petri plate, there would still be too many potential colonies to count on a plate. Therefore, another serial dilution could be made. One milliliter containing 1000 bacteria would be transferred to a second tube of 9 ml of water. Each milliliter of this tube would now contain only 100 bacteria, and if 1 ml of the contents of this tube were plated out, potentially 100 colonies would be formed—an easily countable number.

Pour Plates and Spread Plates A plate count is done by either the pour plate method or the spread plate method. The **pour plate method** follows the procedure shown in Figure 17a. Either 1.0 ml or 0.1 ml of dilutions of the bacterial suspension is introduced into a Petri dish. The nutrient medium, in which the agar is kept liquid by holding it in a water bath at about 50°C, is poured over the sample, which is then mixed into the medium by gentle agitation of the plate. When the agar solidifies, the plate is incubated. With the pour plate technique, colonies will grow within the nutrient agar (from cells suspended in the nutrient medium as the agar solidifies) as well as on the surface of the agar plate.

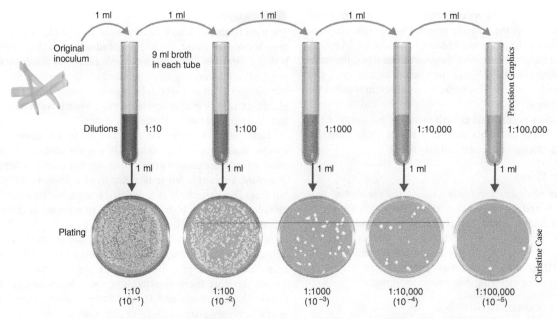

1 ml   1 ml   1 ml   1 ml   1 ml

Original inoculum   9 ml broth in each tube

Precision Graphics

Dilutions   1:10   1:100   1:1000   1:10,000   1:100,000

1 ml   1 ml   1 ml   1 ml   1 ml

Plating

Christine Case

1:10 (10^{-1})   1:100 (10^{-2})   1:1000 (10^{-3})   1:10,000 (10^{-4})   1:100,000 (10^{-5})

Calculation: Number of colonies on plate × reciprocal of dilution of sample = number of bacteria/ml
(For example, if 54 colonies are on a plate of 1:1000 dilution, then the count is 54 × 1000 = 54,000 bacteria/ml in sample.)

Figure 16 Serial dilutions and plate counts. In serial dilutions, the original inoculum is diluted in a series of dilution tubes. In our example, each succeeding dilution tube will have only one-tenth the number of microbial cells as the preceding tube. Then, samples of the dilution are used to inoculate Petri plates, on which colonies grow and can be counted. This count is then used to estimate the number of bacteria in the original sample.

 Why were the dilutions of 1:10,000 and 1:100,000 not counted? Theoretically, how many colonies should appear on the 1:100 plate?

This technique has some drawbacks because some relatively heat-sensitive microorganisms may be damaged by the melted agar and will therefore be unable to form colonies. Also, when certain differential media are used, the distinctive appearance of the colony on the surface is essential for diagnostic purposes. Colonies that form beneath the surface of a pour plate are not satisfactory for such tests. To avoid these problems, the **spread plate method** is frequently used instead (Figure 17b). A 0.1-ml inoculum is added to the surface of a prepoured, solidified agar medium. The inoculum is then spread uniformly over the surface of the medium with a specially shaped, sterilized glass or metal rod. This method positions all the colonies on the surface and avoids contact between the cells and melted agar.

Filtration

When the quantity of bacteria is very small, as in lakes or relatively pure streams, bacteria can be counted by **filtration** methods (Figure 18). In this technique, at least 100 ml of water are passed through a thin membrane filter whose pores are too small to allow bacteria to pass. Thus, the bacteria are filtered out and retained on the surface of the filter. This filter is then transferred to a Petri dish containing a pad soaked in liquid nutrient medium, where colonies arise from the bacteria on the filter's surface. This method is applied frequently to detection and enumeration of coliform bacteria, which are indicators of fecal contamination of food or water. The colonies formed by these bacteria are distinctive when a differential nutrient medium is used. (The colonies shown in Figure 18b are examples of coliforms.)

The Most Probable Number (MPN) Method

Another method for determining the number of bacteria in a sample is the **most probable number (MPN) method,** illustrated in Figure 19. This statistical estimating technique is based on the fact that the greater the number of bacteria in a sample, the more dilution is needed to reduce the density to the point at which no bacteria are left to grow in the tubes in a dilution series. The MPN method is most useful when the

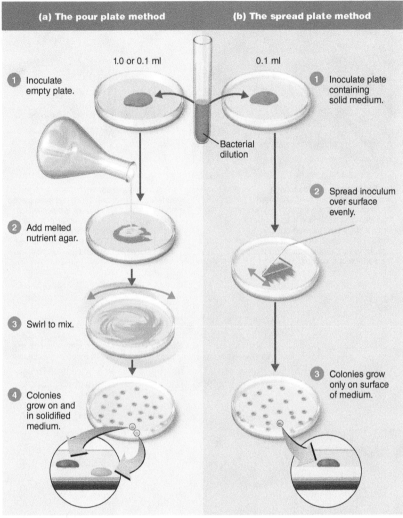

Precision Graphics

Figure 17 Methods of preparing plates for plate counts. (**a**) The pour plate method. (**b**) The spread plate method.

Q In what instances would the pour plate method be more appropriate than the spread plate method?

microbes being counted will not grow on solid media (such as the chemoautotrophic nitrifying bacteria). It is also useful when the growth of bacteria in a liquid differential medium is used to identify the microbes (such as coliform bacteria, which selectively ferment lactose to acid, in water testing). The MPN is only a statement that there is a 95% chance that the bacterial population falls within a certain range and that the MPN is statistically the most probable number.

Direct Microscopic Count

In the method known as the **direct microscopic count,** a measured volume of a bacterial suspension is placed within a defined area on a microscope slide. Because of time considerations, this method is often used to count the number of bacteria in milk. A 0.01-ml sample is spread over a marked square centimeter of slide, stain is added so that the bacteria can be seen, and the sample is viewed under the oil immersion objective lens. The area of the viewing field of this objective can be determined. Once the number of bacteria has been counted in several different fields, the average number of bacteria per viewing field can be calculated. From these data, the number of bacteria in the square centimeter over which the sample was spread can also be calculated. Because this area on the slide contained 0.01 ml of sample, the number of bacteria in each milliliter of the suspension is the number of bacteria in the sample times 100.

A specially designed slide called a *Petroff-Hausser cell counter* is also used in direct microscopic counts (Figure 20).

Motile bacteria are difficult to count by this method, and, as happens with other microscopic methods, dead cells are about

Figure 18 Counting bacteria by filtration.

 Could you make a pour plate in the usual Petri dish with a 10-ml inoculum? Why or why not?

From: "Bismuth dimercaptopropanol (BisBAL) inhibits the expression of extracellular polysaccharides and proteins by Brevundimonas diminuta: implications for membrane microfiltration." A.R. Badireddy, S. Chellam, S. Yanina, P. Gassman, K.M. Rosso. *Biotechnol Bioeng.* 2008 Feb 15;99(3):634–43

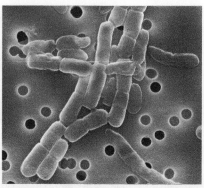

(a) The bacterial populations in bodies of water can be determined by passing a sample through a membrane filter. Here, the bacteria in a 100 ml water sample have been sieved out onto the surface of a membrane filter. These bacteria form visible colonies when placed on the surface of a suitable medium.

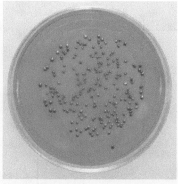

(b) A membrane filter with bacteria on its surface, as described in (a), has been placed on Endo agar. This medium is selective for gram-negative bacteria; lactose fermenters, such as the coliforms, form distinctive colonies. There are 214 colonies visible, so we would record 214 bacteria per 100 ml in the water sample.

Christine Case

Combination of Positives	MPN Index/ 100 ml	95% Confidence Limits	
		Lower	Upper
4-2-0	22	6.8	50
4-2-1	26	9.8	70
4-3-0	27	9.9	70
4-3-1	33	10	70
4-4-0	34	14	100
5-0-0	23	6.8	70
5-0-1	31	10	70
5-0-2	43	14	100
5-1-0	33	10	100
5-1-1	46	14	120
5-1-2	63	22	150
5-2-0	49	15	150
5-2-1	70	22	170
5-2-2	94	34	230
5-3-0	79	22	220
5-3-1	110	34	250
5-3-2	140	52	400

Volume of Inoculum for Each Set of Five Tubes	Tubes of Nutrient Medium (Sets of Five Tubes)	Number of Positive Tubes in Set
10 ml		5
1 ml		3
0.1 ml		1

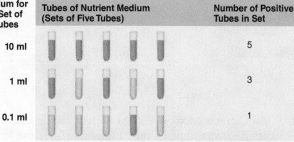

(a) Most probable number (MPN) dilution series. In this example, there are three sets of tubes and five tubes in each set. Each tube in the first set of five tubes receives 10 ml of the inoculum, such as a sample of water. Each tube in the second set of five tubes receives 1 ml of the sample, and the third set, 0.1 ml each. There were enough bacteria in the sample so that all five tubes in the first set showed bacterial growth and were recorded as positive. In the second set, which received only one-tenth as much inoculum, only three tubes were positive. In the third set, which received one-hundredth as much inoculum, only one tube was positive.

(b) MPN table. MPN tables enable us to calculate for a sample the microbial numbers that are statistically likely to lead to such a result. The number of positive tubes is recorded for each set: in the shaded example, 5, 3, and 1. If we look up this combination in an MPN table, we find that the MPN index per 100 ml is 110. Statistically, this means that 95% of the water samples that give this result contain 34–250 bacteria, with 110 being the most probable number.

Precision Graphics

Figure 19 The most probable number (MPN) method.

 Under what circumstances is the MPN method used to determine the number of bacteria in a sample?

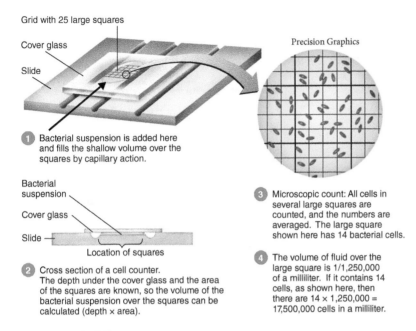

Grid with 25 large squares

Cover glass

Slide

Precision Graphics

1 Bacterial suspension is added here and fills the shallow volume over the squares by capillary action.

Bacterial suspension

Cover glass

Slide

Location of squares

2 Cross section of a cell counter. The depth under the cover glass and the area of the squares are known, so the volume of the bacterial suspension over the squares can be calculated (depth × area).

3 Microscopic count: All cells in several large squares are counted, and the numbers are averaged. The large square shown here has 14 bacterial cells.

4 The volume of fluid over the large square is 1/1,250,000 of a milliliter. If it contains 14 cells, as shown here, then there are 14 × 1,250,000 = 17,500,000 cells in a milliliter.

Figure 20 Direct microscopic count of bacteria with a Petroff-Hausser cell counter. The average number of cells within a large square multiplied by a factor of 1,250,000 gives the number of bacteria per milliliter.

Q This type of counting, despite its obvious disadvantages, is often used in estimating the bacterial population in dairy products. Why?

as likely to be counted as live ones. In addition to these disadvantages, a rather high concentration of cells is required to be countable—about 10 million bacteria per milliliter. The chief advantage of microscopic counts is that no incubation time is required, and they are usually reserved for applications in which time is the primary consideration. This advantage also holds for *electronic cell counters,* sometimes known as *Coulter counters,* which automatically count the number of cells in a measured volume of liquid. These instruments are used in some research laboratories and hospitals.

Clinical Case

The bacteria in the blood and catheter cultures fluoresce under ultraviolet light. The results from the culture show that P. *fluorescens* is present in the blood of 15 patients, in 17 catheters, and in the blood and catheters of four patients. The bacteria survived even after the heparin recall. Dr. MacGruder would like to have some idea how many bacteria are colonizing a patient's catheter. Because the amount of nutrients in a patient's catheter is minimal, he concludes that the bacteria grow slowly. He does some calculations based on the assumption that five *Pseudomonas* cells, with a generation time of 35 hours, may have been originally introduced into the catheters.

Approximately how many cells would there be after a month?

CHECK YOUR UNDERSTANDING

✔ Why is it difficult to measure realistically the growth of a filamentous mold isolate by the plate count method? 16

Estimating Bacterial Numbers by Indirect Methods

It is not always necessary to count microbial cells to estimate their numbers. In science and industry, microbial numbers and activity are determined by some of the following indirect means as well.

Turbidity

For some types of experimental work, estimating **turbidity** is a practical way of monitoring bacterial growth. As bacteria multiply in a liquid medium, the medium becomes turbid, or cloudy with cells.

The instrument used to measure turbidity is a *spectrophotometer* (or colorimeter). In the spectrophotometer, a beam of light is transmitted through a bacterial suspension to a light-sensitive detector (**Figure 21**). As bacterial numbers increase, less light will reach the detector. This change of light will register on the instrument's scale as the *percentage of transmission.* Also printed on the instrument's scale is a logarithmic expression called the *absorbance* (sometimes called *optical density,* or *OD,* which is calculated as Abs = 2 − log of % transmittance). The absorbance is used to plot bacterial growth. When the bacteria are in logarithmic growth or decline, a graph of absorbance versus time will form an approximately straight line. If absorbance readings are matched with plate counts of the same culture, this correlation can be used in future estimations of bacterial numbers obtained by measuring turbidity.

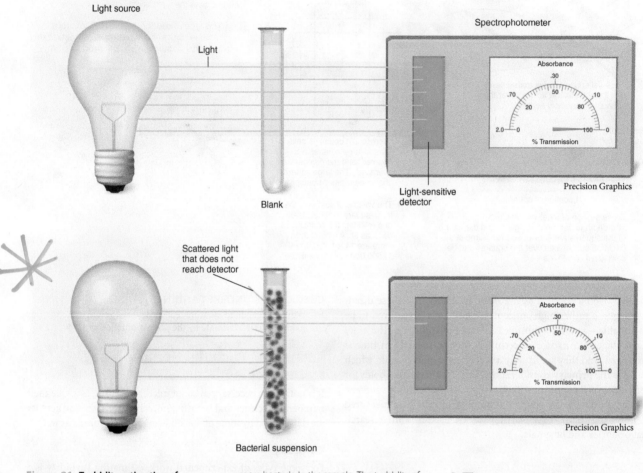

Light source

Light

Blank

Spectrophotometer

Absorbance

.30

.50

.70 .10

20 80

2.0 0 100 0

% Transmission

Light-sensitive
detector

Precision Graphics

Scattered light
that does not
reach detector

Absorbance

.30

.50

.70 .10

20 80

2.0 0 100 0

% Transmission

Precision Graphics

Bacterial suspension

Figure 21 Turbidity estimation of bacterial numbers. The amount of light striking the light-sensitive detector on the spectrophotometer is inversely proportional to the number of bacteria under standardized conditions. The less light transmitted, the more bacteria in the sample. The turbidity of the sample could be reported as either 20% transmittance or 0.7 absorbance. Readings in absorbance are a logarithmic function and are sometimes useful in plotting data.

Q Why is turbidity more useful in measuring contamination of liquids by large numbers, rather than small numbers, of bacteria?

More than a million cells per milliliter must be present for the first traces of turbidity to be visible. About 10 million to 100 million cells per milliliter are needed to make a suspension turbid enough to be read on a spectrophotometer. Therefore, turbidity is not a useful measure of contamination of liquids by relatively small numbers of bacteria.

Metabolic Activity

Another indirect way to estimate bacterial numbers is to measure a population's *metabolic activity*. This method assumes that the amount of a certain metabolic product, such as acid or CO_2, is in direct proportion to the number of bacteria present. An example of a practical application of a metabolic test is the microbiological assay in which acid production is used to determine amounts of vitamins.

Dry Weight

For filamentous bacteria and molds, the usual measuring methods are less satisfactory. A plate count would not measure this increase in filamentous mass. In plate counts of actinomycetes and molds, it is mostly the number of asexual spores that is counted instead. This is not a good measure of growth. One of the better ways to measure the growth of filamentous organisms is by *dry weight*. In this procedure, the fungus is removed from the growth medium, filtered to remove extraneous material, and dried in a desiccator. It is then weighed. For bacteria, the same basic procedure is followed.

CHECK YOUR UNDERSTANDING

✔ Direct methods usually require an incubation time for a colony. Why is this not always feasible for analyzing foods? 17

✔ If there is no good method for analyzing a product for its vitamin content, what is a feasible method of determining the vitamin content? 18

* * *

You now have a basic understanding of the requirements for, and measurements of, microbial growth.

Clinical Case Resolved

Biofilms are dense accumulations of cells. Five cells might go through 20 generations in a month, producing 7.79×10^6 cells. Now Dr. MacGruder knows that the *P. fluorescens* bacteria are present in the patients' indwelling catheters. He orders the catheters to be replaced and has the CDC examine the used catheters with scanning electron microscopy. They discover that the *P. fluorescens* colonized the inside of the catheters by forming biofilms. In his report to the CDC, Dr. MacGruder explains that the *P. fluorescens* bacteria may have entered the bloodstreams of these patients at the same time as the first outbreak, but not in sufficient quantities to cause symptoms at that time. Biofilm formation enabled the bacteria to persist in the patients' catheters. He notes that previous electron microscopy studies indicate that nearly all indwelling vascular catheters become colonized by microorganisms that are embedded in a biofilm layer and that heparin has been reported to stimulate biofilm formation. Dr. MacGruder concludes that the bacteria in the biofilm were dislodged by subsequent uncontaminated intravenous solutions and released into the bloodstream, finally causing infections months after initial colonization.

Study Outline

MasteringMICROBIOLOGY™

Test your understanding with quizzes, microbe review, and a chapter post-test at www.masteringmicrobiology.com.

The Requirements for Growth

1. The growth of a population is an increase in the number of cells.
2. The requirements for microbial growth are both physical and chemical.

Physical Requirements

3. On the basis of preferred temperature ranges, microbes are classified as psychrophiles (cold-loving), mesophiles (moderate-temperature-loving), and thermophiles (heat-loving).
4. The minimum growth temperature is the lowest temperature at which a species will grow, the optimum growth temperature is the temperature at which it grows best, and the maximum growth temperature is the highest temperature at which growth is possible.
5. Most bacteria grow best at a pH value between 6.5 and 7.5.

6. In a hypertonic solution, most microbes undergo plasmolysis; halophiles can tolerate high salt concentrations.

Chemical Requirements

7. All organisms require a carbon source; chemoheterotrophs use an organic molecule, and autotrophs typically use carbon dioxide.
8. Nitrogen is needed for protein and nucleic acid synthesis. Nitrogen can be obtained from the decomposition of proteins or from NH_4^+ or NO_3^-; a few bacteria are capable of nitrogen (N_2) fixation.
9. On the basis of oxygen requirements, organisms are classified as obligate aerobes, facultative anaerobes, obligate anaerobes, aerotolerant anaerobes, and microaerophiles.
10. Aerobes, facultative anaerobes, and aerotolerant anaerobes must have the enzymes superoxide dismutase ($2 \, O_2^- + 2 \, H^+ \longrightarrow O_2 + H_2O_2$) and either catalase ($2 \, H_2O_2 \longrightarrow 2 \, H_2O + O_2$) or peroxidase ($H_2O_2 + 2 \, H^+ \longrightarrow 2 \, H_2O$).
11. Other chemicals required for microbial growth include sulfur, phosphorus, trace elements, and, for some microorganisms, organic growth factors.

Biofilms

1. Microbes adhere to surfaces and accumulate as biofilms on solid surfaces in contact with water.
2. Biofilms form on teeth, contact lenses, and catheters.
3. Microbes in biofilms are more resistant to antibiotics than are free-swimming microbes.

Culture Media

1. A culture medium is any material prepared for the growth of bacteria in a laboratory.
2. Microbes that grow and multiply in or on a culture medium are known as a culture.
3. Agar is a common solidifying agent for a culture medium.

Chemically Defined Media

4. A chemically defined medium is one in which the exact chemical composition is known.

Complex Media

5. A complex medium is one in which the exact chemical composition varies slightly from batch to batch.

Anaerobic Growth Media and Methods

6. Reducing media chemically remove molecular oxygen (O_2) that might interfere with the growth of anaerobes.
7. Petri plates can be incubated in an anaerobic jar, anaerobic chamber, or OxyPlate.

Special Culture Techniques

8. Some parasitic and fastidious bacteria must be cultured in living animals or in cell cultures.
9. CO_2 incubators or candle jars are used to grow bacteria that require an increased CO_2 concentration.
10. Procedures and equipment to minimize exposure to pathogenic microorganisms are designated as biosafety levels 1 through 4.

Selective and Differential Media

11. By inhibiting unwanted organisms with salts, dyes, or other chemicals, selective media allow growth of only the desired microbes.
12. Differential media are used to distinguish different organisms.

Enrichment Culture

13. An enrichment culture is used to encourage the growth of a particular microorganism in a mixed culture.

Obtaining Pure Cultures

1. A colony is a visible mass of microbial cells that theoretically arose from one cell.
2. Pure cultures are usually obtained by the streak plate method.

Preserving Bacterial Cultures

1. Microbes can be preserved for long periods of time by deep-freezing or lyophilization (freeze-drying).

The Growth of Bacterial Cultures

Bacterial Division)

1. The normal reproductive method of bacteria is binary fission, in which a single cell divides into two identical cells.
2. Some bacteria reproduce by budding, aerial spore formation, or fragmentation.

Generation Time

3. The time required for a cell to divide or a population to double is known as the generation time.

Logarithmic Representation of Bacterial Populations

4. Bacterial division occurs according to a logarithmic progression (two cells, four cells, eight cells, and so on).

Phases of Growth

5. During the lag phase, there is little or no change in the number of cells, but metabolic activity is high.
6. During the log phase, the bacteria multiply at the fastest rate possible under the conditions provided.
7. During the stationary phase, there is an equilibrium between cell division and death.
8. During the death phase, the number of deaths exceeds the number of new cells formed.

Direct Measurement of Microbial Growth

9. A heterotrophic plate count reflects the number of viable microbes and assumes that each bacterium grows into a single colony; plate counts are reported as number of colony-forming units (CFU).
10. A plate count may be done by either the pour plate method or the spread plate method.
11. In filtration, bacteria are retained on the surface of a membrane filter and then transferred to a culture medium to grow and subsequently be counted.
12. The most probable number (MPN) method can be used for microbes that will grow in a liquid medium; it is a statistical estimation.
13. In a direct microscopic count, the microbes in a measured volume of a bacterial suspension are counted with the use of a specially designed slide.

Estimating Bacterial Numbers by Indirect Methods

14. A spectrophotometer is used to determine turbidity by measuring the amount of light that passes through a suspension of cells.
15. An indirect way of estimating bacterial numbers is measuring the metabolic activity of the population (for example, acid production or oxygen consumption).
16. For filamentous organisms such as fungi, measuring dry weight is a convenient method of growth measurement.

Study Questions

Answers to the Review and Multiple Choice questions can be found at the end of this chapter.

Review

1. Describe binary fission.
2. Macronutrients (needed in relatively large amounts) are often listed as CHONPS. What does each of these letters indicate, and why are they needed by the cell?
3. Define and explain the importance of each of the following:
   a. catalase
   b. hydrogen peroxide
   c. peroxidase
   d. superoxide radical
   e. superoxide dismutase
4. Seven methods of measuring microbial growth were explained in this chapter. Categorize each as either a direct or an indirect method.
5. By deep-freezing, bacteria can be stored without harm for extended periods. Why do refrigeration and freezing preserve foods?
6. A pastry chef accidentally inoculated a cream pie with six *S. aureus* cells. If *S. aureus* has a generation time of 60 minutes, how many cells would be in the cream pie after 7 hours?
7. Nitrogen and phosphorus added to beaches following an oil spill encourage the growth of natural oil-degrading bacteria. Explain why the bacteria do not grow if nitrogen and phosphorus are not added.
8. Differentiate complex and chemically defined media.
9. **DRAW IT** Draw the following growth curves for *E. coli*, starting with 100 cells with a generation time of 30 minutes at 35°C, 60 minutes at 20°C, and 3 hours at 5°C.
   a. The cells are incubated for 5 hours at 35°C.
   b. After 5 hours, the temperature is changed to 20°C for 2 hours.
   c. After 5 hours at 35°C, the temperature is changed to 5°C for 2 hours followed by 35°C for 5 hours.

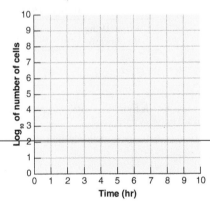

10. **NAME IT** A prokaryotic cell hitched a ride to Earth on a space shuttle from some unknown planet. The organism is a psychrophile, an obligate halophile, and an obligate aerobe. Based on the characteristics of the microbe, describe the planet.

Multiple Choice

Use the following information to answer questions 1 and 2. Two culture media were inoculated with four different bacteria. After incubation, the following results were obtained:

Organism	Medium 1	Medium 2
Escherichia coli	Red colonies	No growth
Staphylococcus aureus	No growth	Growth
Staphylococcus epidermidis	No growth	Growth
Salmonella enterica	Colorless colonies	No growth

1. Medium 1 is
   a. selective.
   b. differential.
   c. both selective and differential.
2. Medium 2 is
   a. selective.
   b. differential.
   c. both selective and differential.

Use the following graph to answer questions 3 and 4.

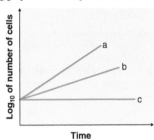

3. Which of the lines best depicts the log phase of a thermophile incubated at room temperature?
4. Which of the lines best depicts the log phase of *Listeria monocytogenes* growing in a human?
5. Assume you inoculated 100 facultatively anaerobic cells onto nutrient agar and incubated the plate aerobically. You then inoculated 100 cells of the same species onto nutrient agar and incubated the second plate anaerobically. After incubation for 24 hours, you should have
   a. more colonies on the aerobic plate.
   b. more colonies on the anaerobic plate.
   c. the same number of colonies on both plates.
6. The term *trace elements* refers to
   a. the elements CHONPS.
   b. vitamins.
   c. nitrogen, phosphorus, and sulfur.
   d. small mineral requirements.
   e. toxic substances.

7. Which one of the following temperatures would most likely kill a mesophile?
   a. −50°C
   b. 0°C
   c. 9°C
   d. 37°C
   e. 60°C

8. Which of the following is *not* a characteristic of biofilms?
   a. antibiotic resistance
   b. hydrogel
   c. iron deficiency
   d. quorum sensing

9. Which of the following types of media would *not* be used to culture aerobes?
   a. selective media
   b. reducing media
   c. enrichment media
   d. differential media
   e. complex media

10. An organism that has peroxidase and superoxide dismutase but lacks catalase is most likely an
    a. aerobe.
    b. aerotolerant anaerobe.
    c. obligate anaerobe.

Critical Thinking

1. *E. coli* was incubated with aeration in a nutrient medium containing two carbon sources, and the following growth curve was made from this culture.
   a. Explain what happened at the time marked *x*.
   b. Which substrate provided "better" growth conditions for the bacteria? How can you tell?

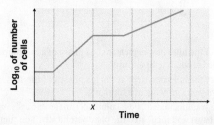

2. *Clostridium* and *Streptococcus* are both catalase-negative. *Streptococcus* grows by fermentation. Why is *Clostridium* killed by oxygen, whereas *Streptococcus* is not?

3. Most laboratory media contain a fermentable carbohydrate and peptone because the majority of bacteria require carbon, nitrogen, and energy sources in these forms. How are these three needs met by glucose–minimal salts medium? (*Hint:* See Table 2.)

4. Flask A contains yeast cells in glucose–minimal salts broth incubated at 30°C with aeration. Flask B contains yeast cells in glucose–minimal salts broth incubated at 30°C in an anaerobic jar. The yeasts are facultative anaerobes.
   a. Which culture produced more ATP?
   b. Which culture produced more alcohol?
   c. Which culture had the shorter generation time?
   d. Which culture had the greater cell mass?
   e. Which culture had the higher absorbance?

Clinical Applications

1. Assume that after washing your hands, you leave ten bacterial cells on a new bar of soap. You then decide to do a plate count of the soap after it was left in the soap dish for 24 hours. You dilute 1 g of the soap 1:10^6 and plate it on heterotrophic plate count agar. After 24 hours of incubation, there are 168 colonies. How many bacteria were on the soap? How did they get there?

2. Heat lamps are commonly used to maintain foods at about 50°C for as long as 12 hours in cafeteria serving lines. The following experiment was conducted to determine whether this practice poses a potential health hazard.

   Beef cubes were surface-inoculated with 500,000 bacterial cells and incubated at 43–53°C to establish temperature limits for bacterial growth. The following results were obtained from heterotrophic plate counts performed on beef cubes at 6 and 12 hours after inoculation:

	Temp. (°C)	Bacteria per Gram of Beef After	
		6 hr	12 hr
Staphylococcus aureus	43	140,000,000	740,000,000
	51	810,000	59,000
	53	650	300
Salmonella typhimurium	43	3,200,000	10,000,000
	51	950,000	83,000
	53	1,200	300
Clostridium perfringens	43	1,200,000	3,600,000
	51	120,000	3,800
	53	300	300

   Draw the growth curves for each organism. What holding temperature would you recommend? Assuming that cooking kills bacteria in foods, how could these bacteria contaminate the cooked foods? What disease does each organism cause?

3. The number of bacteria in saliva samples was determined by collecting the saliva, making serial dilutions, and inoculating nutrient agar by the pour plate method. The plates were incubated aerobically for 48 hours at 37°C.

	Bacteria per ml Saliva	
	Before Using Mouthwash	After Using Mouthwash
Mouthwash 1	13.1×10^6	10.9×10^6
Mouthwash 2	11.7×10^6	14.2×10^5
Mouthwash 3	9.3×10^5	7.7×10^5

What can you conclude from these data? Did all the bacteria present in each saliva sample grow?

Answers to Review and Multiple Choice Study Questions

Review

1. In binary fission, the cell elongates, and the chromosome replicates. Next, the nuclear material is evenly divided. The plasma membrane invaginates toward the center of the cell. The cell wall thickens and grows inward between the membrane invaginations; two new cells result.

2. Carbon: synthesis of molecules that make up a living cell. Hydrogen: source of electrons and component of organic molecules. Oxygen: component of organic molecules; electron acceptor in aerobes. Nitrogen: component of amino acids. Phosphorus: in phospholipids and nucleic acids. Sulfur: In some amino acids.

3. **a.** Catalyzes the breakdown of H_2O_2 to O_2 and H_2O.
   b. H_2O_2; peroxide ion is O_2^{2-}.
   c. Catalyzes the breakdown of H_2O_2;Peroxidase Superoxide dismutase

$$NADH + H^+ + H_2O_2 \longrightarrow NAD^+ + 2H_2O$$

   d. O_2^-; this anion has one unpaired electron.
   e. Converts superoxide to O_2 and H_2O_2;

$$2O_2^- + 2H^+ \longrightarrow O_2 + H_2O_2$$

   The enzymes are important in protecting the cell from the strong oxidizing agents, peroxide and superoxide, that form during respiration.

4. Direct methods are those in which the microorganisms are seen and counted. Direct methods are direct microscopic count, plate count, filtration, and most probable number.

5. The growth rate of bacteria slows down with decreasing temperatures. Mesophilic bacteria will grow slowly at refrigeration temperatures and will remain dormant in a freezer. Bacteria will not spoil food quickly in a refrigerator.

6. Number of cells $\times\ 2^{n\ generations}$ = Total number of cells

6	$\times$	2^7	=	768

7. Petroleum can meet the carbon and energy requirements for an oil-degrading bacterium; however, nitrogen and phosphate are usually not available in large quantities. Nitrogen and phosphate are essential for making proteins, phospholipids, nucleic acids, and ATP.

8. A chemically defined medium is one in which the exact chemical composition is known. A complex medium is one in which the exact chemical composition is not known.

9.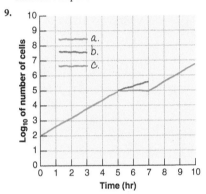

10. Cold, salty, aerobic

Multiple Choice

1. c	3. 3	5. c	7. e	9. b
2. a	4. 1	6. d	8. c	10. b

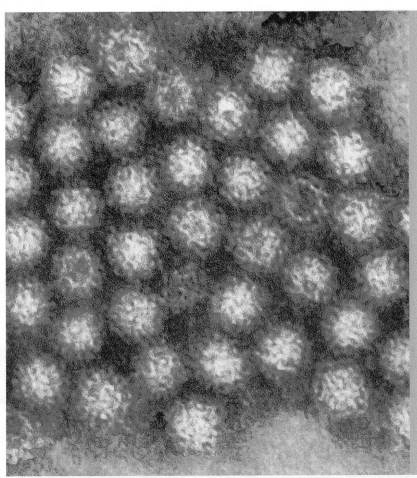

Charles D. Humphrey, CDC

Visualize microbiology and check your understanding with a pre-test at www.masteringmicrobiology.com.

The Control of Microbiology Growth

The scientific control of microbial growth began only about 100 years ago. Pasteur's work on microorganisms led scientists to believe that microbes were a possible cause of disease. In the mid-1800s, the Hungarian physician Ignaz Semmelweis and English physician Joseph Lister used this thinking to develop some of the first microbial control practices for medical procedures. These practices included washing hands with microbe-killing chloride of lime and using the techniques of **aseptic surgery** to prevent microbial contamination of surgical wounds. Until that time, hospital-acquired infections, or *nosocomial infections,* were the cause of death in at least 10% of surgical cases, and as high as 25% in delivering mothers. Ignorance of microbes was such that during the American Civil War, a surgeon might have cleaned his scalpel on his boot sole between incisions. We now know that handwashing is the best way to prevent transmission of pathogens such as the norovirus in the photo. Controlling noroviruses on environmental surfaces is the topic of the Clinical Case.

Over the last century, scientists have continued to develop a variety of physical methods and chemical agents to control microbial growth.

From Chapter 7 of *Microbiology: An Introduction*, Eleventh Edition. Gerard J. Tortora, Berdell R. Funke, Christine L. Case.
Copyright © 2013 by Pearson Education, Inc. All rights reserved.

The Terminology of Microbial Control

LEARNING OBJECTIVE

1 Define the following key terms related to microbial control: *sterilization, disinfection, antisepsis, degerming, sanitization, biocide, germicide, bacteriostasis,* and *asepsis.*

A word frequently used, and misused, in discussing the control of microbial growth is *sterilization.* **Sterilization** is the removal or destruction of *all* living microorganisms. Heating is the most common method used for killing microbes, including the most resistant forms, such as endospores. A sterilizing agent is called a **sterilant.** Liquids or gases can be sterilized by filtration.

One would think that canned food in the supermarket is completely sterile. In reality, the heat treatment required to ensure absolute sterility would unnecessarily degrade the quality of the food. Instead, food is subjected only to enough heat to destroy the endospores of *Clostridium botulinum* (bo-tū-lĭ′ num), which can produce a deadly toxin. This limited heat treatment is termed **commercial sterilization.** The endospores of a number of thermophilic bacteria, capable of causing food spoilage but not human disease, are considerably more resistant to heat than *C. botulinum.* If present, they will survive, but their survival is usually of no practical consequence; they will not grow at normal food storage temperatures. If canned foods in a supermarket were incubated at temperatures in the growth range of these thermophiles (above about 45°C), significant food spoilage would occur.

Complete sterilization is often not required in other settings. For example, the body's normal defenses can cope with a few microbes entering a surgical wound. A drinking glass or a fork in a restaurant requires only enough microbial control to prevent the transmission of possibly pathogenic microbes from one person to another.

Control directed at destroying harmful microorganisms is called **disinfection.** It usually refers to the destruction of vegetative (non–endospore-forming) pathogens, which is not the same thing as complete sterility. Disinfection might make use of chemicals, ultraviolet radiation, boiling water, or steam. In practice, the term is most commonly applied to the use of a chemical (a *disinfectant*) to treat an inert surface or substance. When this treatment is directed at living tissue, it is called **antisepsis,** and the chemical is then called an *antiseptic.* Therefore, in practice the same chemical might be called a disinfectant for one use and an antiseptic for another. Of course, many chemicals suitable for wiping a tabletop would be too harsh to use on living tissue.

There are modifications of disinfection and antisepsis. For example, when someone is about to receive an injection, the skin is swabbed with alcohol—the process of **degerming** (or *degermation*), which mostly results in the mechanical removal, rather than the killing, of most of the microbes in a limited area. Restaurant glassware, china, and tableware are subjected to **sanitization,** which is intended to lower microbial counts to safe public health levels and minimize the chances of disease transmission from one user to another. This is usually accomplished by high-temperature washing or, in the case of glassware in a bar, washing in a sink followed by a dip in a chemical disinfectant.

Table 1 summarizes the terminology relating to the control of microbial growth.

Names of treatments that cause the outright death of microbes have the suffix *-cide,* meaning kill. A **biocide,** or **germicide,** kills microorganisms (usually with certain exceptions, such as endospores); a *fungicide* kills fungi; a *virucide* inactivates viruses; and so on. Other treatments only inhibit the growth and multiplication of bacteria; their names have the suffix *-stat* or *-stasis,* meaning to stop or to steady, as in **bacteriostasis.** Once a bacteriostatic agent is removed, growth might resume.

Sepsis, from the Greek for decay or putrid, indicates bacterial contamination, as in septic tanks for sewage treatment. (The term is also used to describe a disease condition.) *Aseptic* means that an object or area is free of pathogens. A**sepsis** is the absence of significant contamination. Aseptic techniques are important in surgery to minimize contamination from the instruments, operating personnel, and the patient.

CHECK YOUR UNDERSTANDING

✔ The usual definition of *sterilization* is the removal or destruction of all forms of microbial life; how could there be practical exceptions to this simple definition? 1

The Rate of Microbial Death

LEARNING OBJECTIVE

2 Describe the patterns of microbial death caused by treatments with microbial control agents.

Clinical Case: A School Epidemic

It is 9:00 A.M. on a Wednesday morning, and Amy Garza, the school nurse at Westview Elementary School in Rockville, Maryland, has been on the phone since she came in to work at 7:00 A.M. So far this morning, she has received reports of students unable to attend school today because of some sort of gastrointestinal ailment. They all have the same symptoms: nausea and vomiting, diarrhea, and a low-grade fever. As Amy picks up the phone to call the principal to give her an update, she receives her eighth call of the day. Keith Jackson, a first-grade teacher who has been out sick since Monday, calls to tell Amy that his physician sent his stool sample to the laboratory for testing. The results came back positive for norovirus.

What is norovirus? Read on to find out.

TABLE 1 Terminology Relating to the Control of Microbial Growth

	Definition	Comments
Sterilization	Destruction or removal of all forms of microbial life, including endospores but with the possible exception of prions.	Usually done by steam under pressure or a sterilizing gas, such as ethylene oxide.
Commercial Sterilization	Sufficient heat treatment to kill endospores of *Clostridium botulinum* in canned food.	More-resistant endospores of thermophilic bacteria may survive, but they will not germinate and grow under normal storage conditions.
Disinfection	Destruction of vegetative pathogens.	May make use of physical or chemical methods.
Antisepsis	Destruction of vegetative pathogens on living tissue.	Treatment is almost always by chemical antimicrobials.
Degerming	Removal of microbes from a limited area, such as the skin around an injection site.	Mostly a mechanical removal by an alcohol-soaked swab.
Sanitization	Treatment is intended to lower microbial counts on eating and drinking utensils to safe public health levels.	May be done with high-temperature washing or by dipping into a chemical disinfectant.

When bacterial populations are heated or treated with antimicrobial chemicals, they usually die at a constant rate. For example, suppose a population of 1 million microbes has been treated for 1 minute, and 90% of the population has died. We are now left with 100,000 microbes. If the population is treated for another minute, 90% of *those* microbes die, and we are left with 10,000 survivors. In other words, for each minute the treatment is applied, 90% of the remaining population is killed (Table 2). If the death curve is plotted logarithmically, the death rate is constant, as shown by the straight line in Figure 1a.

Several factors influence the effectiveness of antimicrobial treatments:

- *The number of microbes.* The more microbes there are to begin with, the longer it takes to eliminate the entire population (Figure 1b).
- *Environmental influences.* The presence of organic matter often inhibits the action of chemical antimicrobials. In hospitals, the presence of organic matter in blood, vomitus, or feces influences the selection of disinfectants. Microbes in surface biofilms are difficult for biocides to reach effectively. Because their activity is due to temperature-dependent chemical reactions, disinfectants work somewhat better under warm conditions.

The nature of the suspending medium is also a factor in heat treatment. Fats and proteins are especially protective, and a medium rich in these substances protects microbes, which will then have a higher survival rate. Heat is also measurably more effective under acidic conditions.

- *Time of exposure.* Chemical antimicrobials often require extended exposure to affect more-resistant microbes or endospores. See the discussion of equivalent treatments.
- *Microbial characteristics.* The concluding section of this chapter discusses how microbial characteristics affect the choice of chemical and physical control methods.

CHECK YOUR UNDERSTANDING

⊯ How is it possible that a solution containing a million bacteria would take longer to sterilize than one containing a half-million bacteria? 2

Actions of Microbial Control Agents

LEARNING OBJECTIVE

3 Describe the effects of microbial control agents on cellular structures.

In this section, we examine the ways various agents actually kill or inhibit microbes.

Alteration of Membrane Permeability

A microorganism's plasma membrane, located just inside the cell wall, is the target of many microbial control agents. This membrane actively regulates the passage of nutrients into the

TABLE 2 Microbial Exponential Death Rate: An Example

Time (min)	Deaths per Minute	Number of Survivors
0	0	1,000,000
1	900,000	100,000
2	90,000	10,000
3	9000	1000
4	900	100
5	90	10
6	9	1

Understanding the Microbial Death Curve

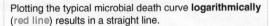

Plotting the typical microbial death curve **logarithmically** (red line) results in a straight line.

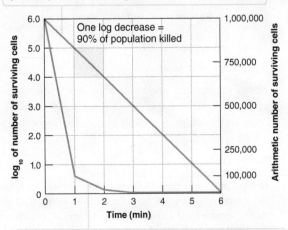

(a) Plotting the typical microbial death curve **arithmetically** (blue line) is impractical: at 3 minutes the population of 1000 cells would only be a hundredth of the graphed distance between 100,000 and the baseline.

sterile surgical equipment

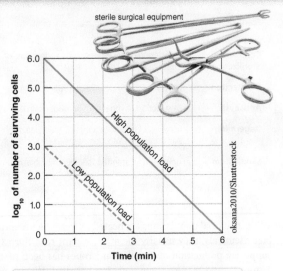

(b) Logarithmic plotting (red) reveals that if the rate of killing is the same, it will take longer to kill all members of a larger population than a smaller one, whether using heat or chemical treatments.

KEY CONCEPTS

- Bacterial populations usually die at a constant rate when heated or when treated with antimicrobial chemicals.
- It is necessary to use logarithmic numbers to graph bacterial populations effectively.
- Understanding logarithmic death curves for microbial populations, including the elements of time and the size of the initial population, is especially useful in food preservation and in the sterilization of media or medical supplies.

preserved food

---

cell and the elimination of wastes from the cell. Damage to the lipids or proteins of the plasma membrane by antimicrobial agents causes cellular contents to leak into the surrounding medium and interferes with the growth of the cell.

Damage to Proteins and Nucleic Acids

Bacteria are sometimes thought of as "little bags of enzymes." Enzymes, which are primarily protein, are vital to all cellular activities. Recall that the functional properties of proteins are the result of their three-dimensional shape. This shape is maintained by chemical bonds that link adjoining portions of the amino acid chain as it folds back and forth upon itself. Some of those bonds are hydrogen bonds, which are susceptible to breakage by heat or certain chemicals; breakage results in denaturation of the protein.

Covalent bonds are stronger but are also subject to attack. For example, disulfide bridges, which play an important role in protein structure by joining amino acids with exposed sulfhydryl (—SH) groups, can be broken by certain chemicals or sufficient heat.

The nucleic acids DNA and RNA are the carriers of the cell's genetic information. Damage to these nucleic acids by heat, radiation, or chemicals is frequently lethal to the cell; the cell can no longer replicate, nor can it carry out normal metabolic functions such as the synthesis of enzymes.

CHECK YOUR UNDERSTANDING

✔ Would a chemical microbial control agent that affects plasma membranes affect humans? **3**

Physical Methods of Microbial Control

LEARNING OBJECTIVES

4 Compare the effectiveness of moist heat (boiling, autoclaving, pasteurization) and dry heat.

5 Describe how filtration, low temperatures, high pressure, desiccation, and osmotic pressure suppress microbial growth.

6 Explain how radiation kills cells.

As early as the Stone Age, humans likely were already using some physical methods of microbial control to preserve foods. Drying (desiccation) and salting (osmotic pressure) were probably among the earliest techniques.

When selecting methods of microbial control, one must consider what else, besides the microbes, a particular method will affect. For example, heat might inactivate certain vitamins or antibiotics in a solution. Repeated heating damages many laboratory and hospital materials, such as rubber and latex tubing. There are also economic considerations; for example, it may be less expensive to use presterilized, disposable plasticware than to repeatedly wash and resterilize glassware.

Heat

A visit to any supermarket will demonstrate that heat-preserved canned goods represent one of the most common methods of food preservation. Heat is also usually used to sterilize laboratory media and glassware and hospital instruments. Heat appears to kill microorganisms by denaturing their enzymes; the resultant changes to the three-dimensional shapes of these proteins inactivate them.

Heat resistance varies among different microbes; these differences can be expressed through the concept of thermal death point. **Thermal death point (TDP)** is the lowest temperature at which all the microorganisms in a particular liquid suspension will be killed in 10 minutes.

Another factor to be considered in sterilization is the length of time required. This is expressed as **thermal death time (TDT),** the minimal length of time for all bacteria in a particular liquid culture to be killed at a given temperature. Both TDP and TDT are useful guidelines that indicate the severity of treatment required to kill a given population of bacteria.

Decimal reduction time (DRT, or *D value*) is a third concept related to bacterial heat resistance. DRT is the time, in minutes, in which 90% of a population of bacteria at a given temperature will be killed (in Table 2 and Figure 1a, DRT is 1 minute).

Moist Heat Sterilization

Moist heat kills microorganisms primarily by coagulating proteins (denaturation), which is caused by breakage of the hydrogen bonds that hold the proteins in their three-dimensional structure. This coagulation process is familiar to anyone who has watched an egg white frying.

One type of moist heat "sterilization" is boiling, which kills vegetative forms of bacterial pathogens, almost all viruses, and fungi and their spores within about 10 minutes, usually much faster. Free-flowing (unpressurized) steam is essentially the same temperature as boiling water. Endospores and some viruses, however, are not destroyed this quickly. Some hepatitis viruses, for example, can survive up to 30 minutes of boiling, and some bacterial endospores can resist boiling for more than 20 hours. Boiling is therefore not always a reliable sterilization procedure. However, brief boiling, even at high altitudes, will kill most pathogens. The use of boiling to sanitize glass baby bottles is a familiar example.

Reliable sterilization with moist heat requires temperatures above that of boiling water. These high temperatures are most commonly achieved by steam under pressure in an **autoclave** (Figure 2). Autoclaving is the preferred method of sterilization, unless the material to be sterilized can be damaged by heat or moisture.

The higher the pressure in the autoclave, the higher the temperature. For example, when free-flowing steam at a temperature of 100°C is placed under a pressure of 1 atmosphere above sea level pressure—that is, about 15 pounds of pressure per square inch (psi)—the temperature rises to 121°C. Increasing the pressure to 20 psi raises the temperature to 126°C. The relationship between temperature and pressure is shown in Table 3.

Sterilization in an autoclave is most effective when the organisms either are contacted by the steam directly or are contained in a small volume of aqueous (primarily water) liquid. Under these conditions, steam at a pressure of about 15 psi (121°C) will kill *all* organisms (but not prions) and their endospores in about 15 minutes.

Autoclaving is used to sterilize culture media, instruments, dressings, intravenous equipment, applicators, solutions, syringes, transfusion equipment, and numerous other items that can withstand high temperatures and pressures. Large industrial autoclaves are called *retorts*, but the same principle applies for the common household pressure cooker used in the home canning of foods.

Heat requires extra time to reach the center of solid materials, such as canned meats, because such materials do not develop the efficient heat-distributing convection currents that occur in liquids. Heating large containers also requires extra time. Table 4 shows the different time requirements for sterilizing liquids in various container sizes.

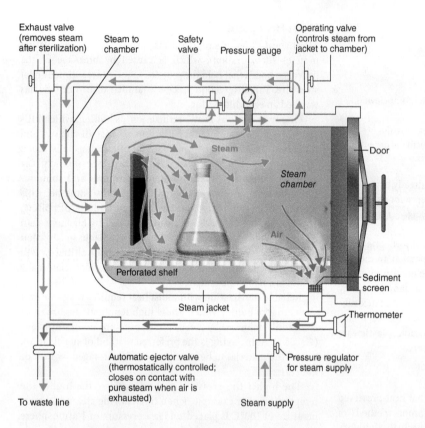

Exhaust valve (removes steam after sterilization)
Steam to chamber
Safety valve
Pressure gauge
Operating valve (controls steam from jacket to chamber)
Steam
Door
Steam chamber
Air
Perforated shelf
Sediment screen
Steam jacket
Thermometer
Automatic ejector valve (thermostatically controlled; closes on contact with pure steam when air is exhausted)
Pressure regulator for steam supply
To waste line
Steam supply

Figure 2 An autoclave. The entering steam forces the air out of the bottom (blue arrows). The automatic ejector valve remains open as long as an air-steam mixture is passing out of the waste line. When all the air has been ejected, the higher temperature of the pure steam closes the valve, and the pressure in the chamber increases.

Q How would an empty, uncapped flask be positioned for sterilization in an autoclave?

Precision Graphics

Unlike sterilizing aqueous solutions, sterilizing the surface of a solid requires that steam actually contact it. To sterilize dry glassware, bandages, and the like, care must be taken to ensure that steam contacts all surfaces. For example, aluminum foil is impervious to steam and should not be used to wrap dry materials that are to be sterilized; paper should be used instead. Care should also be taken to avoid trapping air in the bottom of a dry container: trapped air will not be replaced by steam, because steam is

	TABLE 3 The Relationship between the Pressure and Temperature of Steam at Sea Level*	
Pressure (psi in Excess of Atmospheric Pressure)	**Temperature (°C)**
0	100
5	110
10	116
15	121
20	126
30	135

*At higher altitudes, the atmospheric pressure is less, a phenomenon that must be taken into account in operating an autoclave. For example, to reach sterilizing temperatures (121°C) in Denver, Colorado, whose altitude is 5280 feet (1600 meters), the pressure shown on the autoclave gauge would need to be higher than the 15 psi shown in the table.

TABLE 4 The Effect of Container Size on Autoclave Sterilization Times for Liquid Solutions*		
Container Size	**Liquid Volume**	**Sterilization Time (min)**
Test tube: 18 × 150 mm	10 ml	15
Erlenmeyer flask: 125 ml	95 ml	15
Erlenmeyer flask: 2000 ml	1500 ml	30
Fermentation bottle: 9000 ml	6750 ml	70

*Sterilization times in the autoclave include the time for the contents of the containers to reach sterilization temperatures. For smaller containers, this is only 5 min or less, but for a 9000-ml bottle it might be as much as 70 min. A container is usually not filled past 75% of its capacity.

lighter than air. The trapped air is the equivalent of a small hot-air oven, which, as we will see shortly, requires a higher temperature and longer time to sterilize materials. Containers that can trap air should be placed in a tipped position so that the steam will force out the air. Products that do not permit penetration by moisture, such as mineral oil or petroleum jelly, are not sterilized by the same methods used to sterilize aqueous solutions.

Several commercially available methods can indicate whether heat treatment has achieved sterilization. Some of these are chemical reactions in which an indicator changes color when the proper times and temperatures have been reached (Figure 3). In some designs, the word *sterile* or *autoclaved* appears on wrappings or tapes. A widely used test consists of preparations of specified species of bacterial endospores impregnated into paper strips. After the strips are autoclaved, they can then be aseptically inoculated into culture media. Growth in the culture media indicates survival of the endospores and therefore inadequate processing. Other designs use endospore suspensions that can be released, after heating, into a surrounding culture medium within the same vial.

Steam under pressure fails to sterilize when the air is not completely exhausted. This can happen with the premature closing of the autoclave's automatic ejector valve (see Figure 2). The principles of heat sterilization have a direct bearing on home canning. As anyone familiar with home canning knows, the steam must flow vigorously out of the valve in the lid for several minutes to carry with it all the air before the pressure cooker is sealed. If the air is not completely exhausted, the container will not reach the temperature expected for a given pressure. Because of the possibility of botulism, a kind of food poisoning resulting from improper canning methods, anyone doing home canning should obtain reliable directions and follow them exactly.

Pasteurization

In the early days of microbiology, Louis Pasteur found a practical method of preventing the spoilage of beer and wine. Pasteur used mild heating, which was sufficient to kill the organisms that caused the particular spoilage problem without seriously damaging the taste of the product. The same principle was later applied to milk to produce what we now call pasteurized milk. The intent of **pasteurization** of milk was to eliminate pathogenic microbes. It also lowers microbial numbers, which prolongs milk's good quality under refrigeration. Many relatively heat-resistant (**thermoduric**) bacteria survive pasteurization, but these are unlikely to cause disease or cause refrigerated milk to spoil.

Products other than milk, such as ice cream, yogurt, and beer, all have their own pasteurization times and temperatures, which often differ considerably. There are several reasons for these variations. For example, heating is less efficient in foods that are more viscous, and fats in food can have a protective

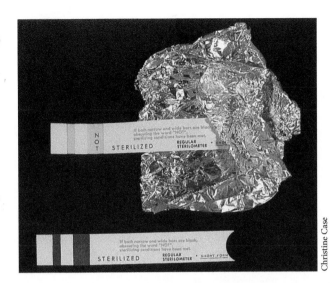

Christine Case

Figure 3 Examples of sterilization indicators. The strips indicate whether the item has been properly sterilized. The word *NOT* appears if heating has been inadequate. In the illustration, the indicator that was wrapped with aluminum foil was not sterilized because steam couldn't penetrate the foil.

Q What should have been used instead of aluminum foil to wrap the items?

effect on microorganisms. The dairy industry routinely uses a test to determine whether products have been pasteurized: the *phosphatase test* (phosphatase is an enzyme naturally present in milk). If the product has been pasteurized, phosphatase will have been inactivated.

Most milk pasteurization today uses temperatures of at least 72°C, but for only 15 seconds. This treatment, known as **high-temperature short-time (HTST) pasteurization,** is applied as the milk flows continuously past a heat exchanger. In addition to killing pathogens, HTST pasteurization lowers total bacterial counts, so the milk keeps well under refrigeration.

Milk can also be sterilized—something quite different from pasteurization—by **ultra-high-temperature (UHT) treatments.** It can then be stored for several months without refrigeration (also see *commercial sterilization*). UHT-treated milk is widely sold in Europe and is especially necessary in less developed parts of the world where refrigeration facilities are not always available. In the United States, UHT is sometimes used on the small containers of coffee creamers found in restaurants. To avoid giving the milk a cooked taste, the process avoids having the milk touch a surface hotter than the milk itself. Usually, the liquid milk (or juice) is sprayed through a nozzle into a chamber filled with high-temperature steam under pressure. A small volume of fluid sprayed into an atmosphere of high-temperature steam exposes a relatively large surface area on the fluid droplets to

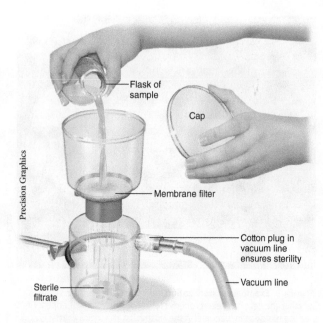

Figure 4 **Filter sterilization with a disposable, presterilized plastic unit.** The sample is placed into the upper chamber and forced through the membrane filter by a vacuum in the lower chamber. Pores in the membrane filter are smaller than the bacteria, so bacteria are retained on the filter. The sterilized sample can then be decanted from the lower chamber. Similar equipment with removable filter disks is used to count bacteria in samples.

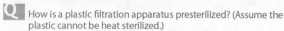 How is a plastic filtration apparatus presterilized? (Assume the plastic cannot be heat sterilized.)

heating by the steam; sterilizing temperatures are reached almost instantaneously. After reaching a temperature of 140°C for 4 seconds, the fluid is rapidly cooled in a vacuum chamber. The milk or juice is then packaged in a presterilized, airtight container.

The heat treatments we have just discussed illustrate the concept of **equivalent treatments:** as the temperature is increased, much less time is needed to kill the same number of microbes. For example, the destruction of highly resistant endospores might take 70 minutes at 115°C, whereas only 7 minutes might be needed at 125°C. Both treatments yield the same result.

Dry Heat Sterilization

Dry heat kills by oxidation effects. A simple analogy is the slow charring of paper in a heated oven, even when the temperature remains below the ignition point of paper. One of the simplest methods of dry heat sterilization is direct **flaming.** You will use this procedure many times in the microbiology laboratory when you sterilize inoculating loops. To effectively sterilize the inoculating loop, you heat the wire to a red glow. A similar principle is used in *incineration,* an effective way to sterilize and dispose of contaminated paper cups, bags, and dressings.

Another form of dry heat sterilization is **hot-air sterilization.** Items to be sterilized by this procedure are placed in an oven. Generally, a temperature of about 170°C maintained for nearly 2 hours ensures sterilization. The longer period and higher temperature (relative to moist heat) are required because the heat in water is more readily transferred to a cool body than is the heat in air. For example, imagine the different effects of immersing your hand in boiling water at 100°C (212°F) and of holding it in a hot-air oven at the same temperature for the same amount of time.

Filtration

Filtration is the passage of a liquid or gas through a screenlike material with pores small enough to retain microorganisms (often the same apparatus used for counting). A vacuum is created in the receiving flask; air pressure then forces the liquid through the filter. Filtration is used to sterilize heat-sensitive materials, such as some culture media, enzymes, vaccines, and antibiotic solutions.

Some operating theaters and rooms occupied by burn patients receive filtered air to lower the numbers of airborne microbes. **High-efficiency particulate air (HEPA) filters** remove almost all microorganisms larger than about 0.3 μm in diameter.

In the early days of microbiology, hollow candle-shaped filters of unglazed porcelain were used to filter liquids. The long and indirect passageways through the walls of the filter adsorbed the bacteria. Unseen pathogens that passed through the filters (causing such diseases as rabies) were called *filterable viruses.*

In recent years, **membrane filters,** composed of such substances as cellulose esters or plastic polymers, have become popular for industrial and laboratory use (Figure 4). These filters are only 0.1 mm thick. The pores of membrane filters include, for example, 0.22-μm and 0.45-μm sizes, which are intended for bacteria. Some very flexible bacteria, such as spirochetes, or the wall-less mycoplasma, will sometimes pass through such filters, however. Filters are available with pores as small as 0.01 μm, a size that will retain viruses and even some large protein molecules.

Low Temperatures

The effect of low temperatures on microorganisms depends on the particular microbe and the intensity of the application. For example, at temperatures of ordinary refrigerators (0–7°C), the metabolic rate of most microbes is so reduced that they cannot reproduce or synthesize toxins. In other words, ordinary refrigeration has a bacteriostatic effect. Yet psychrotrophs do grow slowly at refrigerator temperatures and will alter the appearance and taste of foods after a time. For example, a single microbe reproducing only three times a day would reach a population of more than 2 million within a week. Pathogenic bacteria generally will not grow at refrigerator temperatures.

Surprisingly, some bacteria can grow at temperatures several degrees below freezing. Most foods remain unfrozen until −2°C or lower. Rapidly attained subfreezing temperatures tend to render microbes dormant but do not necessarily kill them. Slow freezing is more harmful to bacteria; the ice crystals that form and grow disrupt the cellular and molecular structure of the bacteria. Thawing, being inherently slower, is actually the more damaging part of a freeze-thaw cycle. Once frozen, one-third of the population of some vegetative bacteria might survive a year, whereas other species might have very few survivors after this time. Many eukaryotic parasites, such as the roundworms that cause human trichinellosis, are killed by several days of freezing temperatures.

High Pressure

High pressure applied to liquid suspensions is transferred instantly and evenly throughout the sample. If the pressure is high enough, it alters the molecular structures of proteins and carbohydrates, resulting in the rapid inactivation of vegetative bacterial cells. Endospores are relatively resistant to high pressure. They can, however, be killed by other techniques, such as combining high pressure with elevated temperatures or by alternating pressure cycles that cause spore germination, followed by pressure-caused death of the resulting vegetative cells. Fruit juices preserved by high-pressure treatments have been marketed in Japan and the United States. An advantage is that these treatments preserve the flavors, colors, and nutrient values of the products.

Desiccation

In the absence of water, known as **desiccation,** microorganisms cannot grow or reproduce but can remain viable for years. Then, when water is made available to them, they can resume their growth and division. This is the principle that underlies lyophilization, or freeze-drying, a laboratory process for preserving microbes. Certain foods are also freeze-dried (for example, coffee and some fruit additives for dry cereals).

The resistance of vegetative cells to desiccation varies with the species and the organism's environment. For example, the gonorrhea bacterium can withstand desiccation for only about an hour, but the tuberculosis bacterium can remain viable for months. Viruses are generally resistant to desiccation, but they are not as resistant as bacterial endospores, some of which have survived for centuries. This ability of certain dried microbes and endospores to remain viable is important in a hospital setting. Dust, clothing, bedding, and dressings might contain infectious microbes in dried mucus, urine, pus, and feces.

Osmotic Pressure

The use of high concentrations of salts and sugars to preserve food is based on the effects of *osmotic pressure.* High concentrations of these substances create a hypertonic environment that causes water to leave the microbial cell. This process resembles preservation by desiccation, in that both methods deny the cell the moisture it needs for growth. The principle of osmotic pressure is used in the preservation of foods. For example, concentrated salt solutions are used to cure meats, and thick sugar solutions are used to preserve fruits.

As a general rule, molds and yeasts are much more capable than bacteria of growing in materials with low moisture or high osmotic pressures. This property of molds, sometimes combined with their ability to grow under acidic conditions, is the reason that molds, rather than bacteria, cause spoilage of fruits and grains. It is also part of the reason molds are able to form mildew on a damp wall or a shower curtain.

Radiation

Radiation has various effects on cells, depending on its wavelength, intensity, and duration. Radiation that kills microorganisms (sterilizing radiation) is of two types: ionizing and nonionizing.

Ionizing radiation—gamma rays, X rays, or high-energy electron beams—has a wavelength shorter than that of nonionizing radiation, less than about 1 nm. Therefore, it carries much more energy (**Figure 5**). *Gamma rays* are emitted by certain radioactive elements such as cobalt, and electron beams are produced by accelerating electrons to high energies in special machines. *X rays,* which are produced by machines in a manner similar to the production of electron beams, are similar to gamma rays. Gamma rays penetrate deeply but may require hours to sterilize large masses; *high-energy electron beams* have much lower penetrating power but usually require only a few seconds of exposure. The principal effect of ionizing radiation is the ionization of water, which forms highly reactive hydroxyl radicals. These radicals react with organic cellular components, especially DNA.

The so-called target theory of damage by radiation supposes that ionizing particles, or packets of energy, pass through or close to vital portions of the cell; these constitute "hits." One, or a few, hits may only cause nonlethal mutations, some of them conceivably useful. More hits are likely to cause sufficient mutations to kill the microbe.

The food industry has recently renewed its interest in the use of radiation for food preservation. Low-level ionizing radiation, used for years in many countries, has been approved in the United States for processing spices and certain meats and vegetables. Ionizing radiation, especially high-energy electron beams, is used to sterilize pharmaceuticals and disposable dental and medical supplies, such as plastic syringes, surgical gloves, suturing materials, and catheters. As a protection against

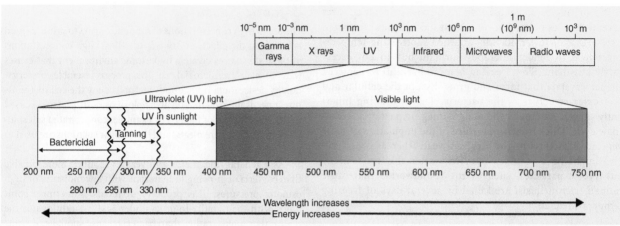

Precision Graphics

Figure 5 The radiant energy spectrum. Visible light and other forms of radiant energy radiate through space as waves of various lengths. Ionizing radiation, such as gamma rays and X rays, has a wavelength shorter than 1 nm. Nonionizing radiation, such as ultraviolet (UV) light, has a wavelength between 1 nm and about 380 nm, where the visible spectrum begins.

 How might increased UV radiation (due to decrease in the ozone layer) affect the Earth's ecosystems?

bioterrorism, the postal service often uses electron beam radiation to sterilize certain classes of mail.

Nonionizing radiation has a wavelength longer than that of ionizing radiation, usually greater than about 1 nm. The best example of nonionizing radiation is ultraviolet (UV) light. UV light damages the DNA of exposed cells by causing bonds to form between adjacent pyrimidine bases, usually thymines, in DNA chains. These *thymine dimers* inhibit correct replication of the DNA during reproduction of the cell. The UV wavelengths most effective for killing microorganisms are about 260 nm; these wavelengths are specifically absorbed by cellular DNA. UV radiation is also used to control microbes in the air. A UV, or "germicidal," lamp is commonly found in hospital rooms, nurseries, operating rooms, and cafeterias. UV light is also used to disinfect vaccines and other medical products. A major disadvantage of UV light as a disinfectant is that the radiation is not very penetrating, so the organisms to be killed must be directly exposed to the rays. Organisms protected by solids and such coverings as paper, glass, and textiles are not affected. Another potential problem is that UV light can damage human eyes, and prolonged exposure can cause burns and skin cancer in humans.

Sunlight contains some UV radiation, but the shorter wavelengths—those most effective against bacteria—are screened out by the ozone layer of the atmosphere. The antimicrobial effect of sunlight is due almost entirely to the formation of singlet oxygen in the cytoplasm. Many pigments produced by bacteria provide protection from sunlight.

Microwaves do not have much direct effect on microorganisms, and bacteria can readily be isolated from the interior of recently operated microwave ovens. Moisture-containing foods are heated by microwave action, and the heat will kill most vegetative pathogens. Solid foods heat unevenly because of the uneven distribution of moisture. For this reason, pork cooked in a microwave oven has been responsible for outbreaks of trichinellosis.

Table 5 summarizes the physical methods of microbial control.

CHECK YOUR UNDERSTANDING

✔ How is microbial growth in canned foods prevented? **4**

✔ Why would a can of pork take longer to sterilize at a given temperature than a can of soup that also contained pieces of pork? **5**

✔ What is the connection between the killing effect of radiation and hydroxyl radical forms of oxygen? **6**

Chemical Methods of Microbial Control

LEARNING OBJECTIVES

7 List the factors related to effective disinfection.

8 Interpret the results of use-dilution tests and the disk-diffusion method.

9 Identify the methods of action and preferred uses of chemical disinfectants.

10 Differentiate halogens used as antiseptics from halogens used as disinfectants.

TABLE 5 Physical Methods Used to Control Microbial Growth

Methods	Mechanism of Action	Comment	Preferred Use
Heat			
1. Moist heat			
a. Boiling or flowing steam	Protein denaturation	Kills vegetative bacterial and fungal pathogens and almost all viruses within 10 min; less effective on endospores.	Dishes, basins, pitchers, various equipment
b. Autoclaving	Protein denaturation	Very effective method of sterilization; at about 15 psi of pressure (121°C), all vegetative cells and their endospores are killed in about 15 min.	Microbiological media, solutions, linens, utensils, dressings, equipment, and other items that can withstand temperature and pressure
2. Pasteurization	Protein denaturation	Heat treatment for milk (72°C for about 15 sec) that kills all pathogens and most nonpathogens.	Milk, cream, and certain alcoholic beverages (beer and wine)
3. Dry heat			
a. Direct flaming	Burning contaminants to ashes	Very effective method of sterilization.	Inoculating loops
b. Incineration	Burning to ashes	Very effective method of sterilization.	Paper cups, contaminated dressings, animal carcasses, bags, and wipes
c. Hot-air sterilization	Oxidation	Very effective method of sterilization but requires temperature of 170°C for about 2 hr.	Empty glassware, instruments, needles, and glass syringes
Filtration	Separation of bacteria from suspending liquid	Removes microbes by passage of a liquid or gas through a screenlike material; most filters in use consist of cellulose acetate or nitrocellulose.	Useful for sterilizing liquids (enzymes, vaccines) that are destroyed by heat
Cold			
1. Refrigeration	Decreased chemical reactions and possible changes in proteins	Has a bacteriostatic effect.	Food, drug, and culture preservation
2. Deep-freezing	Decreased chemical reactions and possible changes in proteins	An effective method for preserving microbial cultures, in which cultures are quick-frozen between − 50° and − 95°C.	Food, drug, and culture preservation
3. Lyophilization	Decreased chemical reactions and possible changes in proteins	Most effective method for long-term preservation of microbial cultures; water removed by high vacuum at low temperature.	Food, drug, and culture preservation
High Pressure	Alteration of molecular structure of proteins and carbohydrates	Preserves of colors, flavors, nutrient values.	Fruit juices
Desiccation	Disruption of metabolism	Involves removing water from microbes; primarily bacteriostatic.	Food preservation
Osmotic Pressure	Plasmolysis	Results in loss of water from microbial cells.	Food preservation
Radiation			
1. Ionizing	Destruction of DNA	Not widespread in routine sterilization.	Sterilizing pharmaceuticals and medical and dental supplies
2. Nonionizing	Damage to DNA	Radiation is not very penetrating.	Control of closed environment with UV (germicidal) lamp

11   Identify the appropriate uses for surface-active agents.

12   List the advantages of glutaraldehyde over other chemical disinfectants.

13   Identify chemical sterilizers.

Chemical agents are used to control the growth of microbes on both living tissue and inanimate objects. Unfortunately, few chemical agents achieve sterility; most of them merely reduce microbial populations to safe levels or remove vegetative forms of pathogens from objects. A common problem in disinfection is the selection of an agent. No single disinfectant is appropriate for all circumstances.

Principles of Effective Disinfection

By reading the label, we can learn a great deal about a disinfectant's properties. Usually the label indicates what groups of organisms the disinfectant is effective against. Remember that the concentration of a disinfectant affects its action, so it should always be diluted exactly as specified by the manufacturer.

Also consider the nature of the material being disinfected. For example, are organic materials present that might interfere with the action of the disinfectant? Similarly, the pH of the medium often has a great effect on a disinfectant's activity.

Another very important consideration is whether the disinfectant will easily make contact with the microbes. An area might need to be scrubbed and rinsed before the disinfectant is applied. In general, disinfection is a gradual process. Thus, to be effective, a disinfectant might need to be left on a surface for several hours.

Evaluating a Disinfectant

Use-Dilution Tests

There is a need to evaluate the effectiveness of disinfectants and antiseptics. The current standard is the American Official Analytical Chemist's **use-dilution test.** Metal or glass cylinders (8 mm × 10 mm) are dipped into standardized cultures of the test bacteria grown in liquid media, removed, and dried at 37°C for a short time. The dried cultures are then placed into a solution of the disinfectant at the concentration recommended by the manufacturer and left there for 10 minutes at 20°C. Following this exposure, the cylinders are transferred to a medium that permits the growth of any surviving bacteria. The effectiveness of the disinfectant can then be determined by the number of cultures that grow.

Variations of this method are used for testing the effectiveness of antimicrobial agents against endospores, mycobacteria that cause tuberculosis, viruses, and fungi, because they are difficult to control with chemicals. Also, tests of antimicrobials intended for special purposes, such as dairy utensil disinfection, may substitute other test bacteria.

The Disk-Diffusion Method

The **disk-diffusion method** is used in teaching laboratories to evaluate the efficacy of a chemical agent. A disk of filter paper is soaked with a chemical and placed on an agar plate that has been previously inoculated and incubated with the test organism. After incubation, if the chemical is effective, a clear zone representing inhibition of growth can be seen around the disk (Figure 6).

Disks containing antibiotics are commercially available and used to determine microbial susceptibility to antibiotics.

Types of Disinfectants

Phenol and Phenolics

Lister was the first to use **phenol** (carbolic acid) to control surgical infections in the operating room. Its use had been suggested by its effectiveness in controlling odor in sewage. It is now rarely used as an antiseptic or disinfectant because it irritates the skin and has a disagreeable odor. It is often used in throat lozenges for its local anesthetic effect but has little antimicrobial effect at the low concentrations used. At concentrations above 1% (such as in some throat sprays), however, phenol has a significant antibacterial effect. The structure of a phenol molecule is shown in Figure 7a.

Derivatives of phenol, called **phenolics,** contain a molecule of phenol that has been chemically altered to reduce its irritating qualities or increase its antibacterial activity in combination with a soap or detergent. Phenolics exert antimicrobial activity by injuring lipid-containing plasma membranes, which results in leakage of cellular contents. The cell wall of mycobacteria, the causes of tuberculosis and leprosy, are rich in lipids, which make them susceptible to phenol derivatives. A useful property of phenolics as disinfectants is that they remain active in the presence of organic compounds, are stable, and persist for long periods after application. For these reasons, phenolics are suitable agents for disinfecting pus, saliva, and feces.

One of the most frequently used phenolics is derived from coal tar, a group of chemicals called *cresols*. A very important cresol is *O-phenylphenol* (see Figure 6 and Figure 7b), the main ingredient in most formulations of Lysol. Cresols are very good surface disinfectants.

Bisphenols

Bisphenols are derivatives of phenol that contain two phenolic groups connected by a bridge (*bis* indicates *two*). One bisphenol, *hexachlorophene* (Figure 6 and Figure 7c), is an ingredient of a prescription lotion, pHisoHex, used for surgical and hospital microbial control procedures. Gram-positive staphylococci and streptococci, which can cause skin infections in newborns, are particularly susceptible to hexachlorophene, so it is often used to control such infections in nurseries. However, excessive use of this bisphenol, such as bathing infants with it several times a day, can lead to neurological damage.

Another widely used bisphenol is *triclosan* (Figure 7d), an ingredient in antibacterial soaps and at least one toothpaste. Triclosan has even been incorporated into kitchen cutting boards and the handles of knives and other plastic kitchenware. Its use is now so widespread that resistant bacteria have been reported, and concerns about its effect on microbes' resistance to certain antibiotics have been raised. Triclosan inhibits an enzyme needed for the biosynthesis of fatty acids (lipids), which mainly affects the integrity of the plasma membrane. It is especially effective against gram-positive bacteria but also

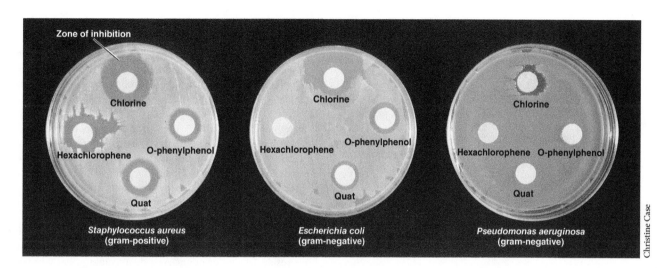

Zone of inhibition

Chlorine

Hexachlorophene   O-phenylphenol

Quat

Staphylococcus aureus
(gram-positive)

Chlorine

Hexachlorophene   O-phenylphenol

Quat

Escherichia coli
(gram-negative)

Chlorine

Hexachlorophene   O-phenylphenol

Quat

Pseudomonas aeruginosa
(gram-negative)

Christine Case

Figure 6 Evaluation of disinfectants by the disk-diffusion method. In this experiment, paper disks are soaked in a solution of disinfectant and placed on the surface of a nutrient medium on which a culture of test bacteria has been spread to produce uniform growth.

At the top of each plate, the tests show that chlorine (as sodium hypochlorite) was effective against all the test bacteria but was more effective against gram-positive bacteria.

At the bottom row of each plate, the tests show that the quaternary ammonium compound ("quat") was also more effective against the gram-positive bacteria, but it did not affect the pseudomonads at all.

At the left side of each plate, the tests show that hexachlorophene was effective against gram-positive bacteria only.

At the right sides, O-phenylphenol was ineffective against pseudomonads but was almost equally effective against the gram-positive bacteria and the gram-negative bacteria.

All four chemicals worked against the gram-positive test bacteria, but only one of the four chemicals affected pseudomonads.

Q Why are the pseudomonads less affected by the four chemicals shown in the figure?

works well against yeasts and gram-negative bacteria. There are certain exceptions, such as *Pseudomonas aeruginosa*, a gram-negative bacterium that is very resistant to triclosan, as well as to many other antibiotics and disinfectants.

Biguanides

Biguanides have a broad spectrum of activity, with a mode of action primarily affecting bacterial cell membranes. They are especially effective against gram-positive bacteria. Biguanides are also effective against gram-negative bacteria, with the significant exception of most pseudomonads. Biguanides are not sporicidal but have some activity against enveloped viruses. The best known biguanide is *chlorhexidine,* which is frequently used for microbial control on skin and mucous membranes. Combined with a detergent or alcohol, chlorhexidine is very often used for surgical hand scrubs and preoperative skin preparation in patients. *Alexidine* is a similar biguanide and is more rapid in its action than chlorhexidine. Eventually, alexidine is expected to replace Betadine in many applications see below.

Halogens

The **halogens,** particularly iodine and chlorine, are effective antimicrobial agents, both alone and as constituents of inorganic or organic compounds. *Iodine* (I₂) is one of the oldest and most effective antiseptics. It is active against all kinds of bacteria, many endospores, various fungi, and some viruses. Iodine impairs protein synthesis and alters cell membranes, apparently by forming complexes with amino acids and unsaturated fatty acids.

Iodine is available as a **tincture**—that is, in solution in aqueous alcohol—and as an iodophor. An **iodophor** is a combination of iodine and an organic molecule, from which the iodine is released slowly. Iodophors have the antimicrobial activity of iodine, but they do not stain and are less irritating. The most common

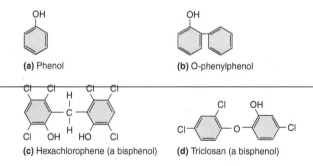

(a) Phenol

(b) O-phenylphenol

(c) Hexachlorophene (a bisphenol)

(d) Triclosan (a bisphenol)

Figure 7 The structure of phenolics and bisphenols.

Q Some lozenges intended to alleviate the symptoms of a sore throat contain phenol. Why include this ingredient?

207

TABLE 6 Biocidal Action of Various Concentrations of Ethanol in Aqueous Solution against *Streptococcus pyogenes*

Concentration of Ethanol (%)	Time of Exposure (sec)				
	10	20	30	40	50
100	G	G	G	G	G
95	NG	NG	NG	NG	NG
90	NG	NG	NG	NG	NG
80	NG	NG	NG	NG	NG
70	NG	NG	NG	NG	NG
60	NG	NG	NG	NG	NG
50	G	G	NG	NG	NG
40	G	G	G	G	G

Note:
G = growth
NG = no growth

commercial preparation is Betadine, which is a *povidone-iodine*. Povidone is a surface-active iodophor that improves the wetting action and serves as a reservoir of free iodine. Iodines are used mainly for skin disinfection and wound treatment. Many campers are familiar with using iodine for water treatment.

Chlorine (Cl_2), as a gas or in combination with other chemicals, is another widely used disinfectant. Its germicidal action is caused by the hypochlorous acid (HOCl) that forms when chlorine is added to water:

(1)

$$Cl_2 + H_2O \rightleftharpoons H^+ + Cl^- + HOCl$$

Chlorine   Water   Hydrogen ion   Chloride ion   Hypochlorous acid

(2)

$$HOCl \rightleftharpoons H^+ + OCl^-$$

Hypochlorous acid   Hydrogen ion   Hypochlorite ion

Hypochlorous acid is a strong oxidizing agent that prevents much of the cellular enzyme system from functioning. Hypochlorous acid is the most effective form of chlorine because it is neutral in electrical charge and diffuses as rapidly as water through the cell wall. Because of its negative charge, the hypochlorite ion (OCl^-) cannot enter the cell freely.

A liquid form of compressed chlorine gas is used extensively for disinfecting municipal drinking water, water in swimming pools, and sewage. Several compounds of chlorine are also effective disinfectants. For example, solutions of *calcium hypochlorite* [$Ca(OCl)_2$] are used to disinfect dairy equipment and

restaurant eating utensils. This compound, once called chloride of lime, was used as early as 1825, long before the concept of a germ theory for disease, to soak hospital dressings in Paris hospitals. It was also the disinfectant used in the 1840s by Semmelweis to control hospital infections during childbirth. Another chlorine compound, *sodium hypochlorite* (NaOCl; see Figure 6), is used as a household disinfectant and bleach (Clorox) and as a disinfectant in dairies, food-processing establishments, and hemodialysis systems. When the quality of drinking water is in question, household bleach can provide a rough equivalent of municipal chlorination. After two drops of bleach are added to a liter of water (four drops if the water is cloudy) and the mixture has sat for 30 minutes, the water is considered safe for drinking under emergency conditions.

The food-processing industry makes wide use of chlorine dioxide solution as a surface disinfectant because it does not leave residual tastes or odors. As a disinfectant, it has a broad spectrum of activity against bacteria and viruses and at high concentrations is even effective against cysts and endospores. At low concentrations, chlorine dioxide can be used as an antiseptic.

An important group of chlorine compounds are the *chloramines,* combinations of chlorine and ammonia. Most municipal water-treatment systems mix ammonia with chlorine to form chloramines. (Chloramines are toxic to aquarium fish, but pet shops sell chemicals to neutralize them.) U.S. military forces in the field are issued tablets (Chlor-Floc) that contain *sodium dichloroisocyanurate,* a chloramine combined with an agent that flocculates (coagulates) suspended materials in a water sample, causing them to settle out, clarifying the water. Chloramines are also used to sanitize glassware and eating utensils and to treat dairy and food-manufacturing equipment. They are relatively stable compounds that release chlorine over long periods. Chloramines are relatively effective in organic matter but have the disadvantages of acting more slowly and being less effective than hypochlorite.

Alcohols

Alcohols effectively kill bacteria and fungi but not endospores and nonenveloped viruses. The mechanism of action of alcohol is usually protein denaturation, but alcohol can also disrupt membranes and dissolve many lipids, including the lipid component of enveloped viruses. Alcohols have the advantage of acting and then evaporating rapidly and leaving no residue. When the skin is swabbed (degermed) before an injection, most of the microbial control activity comes from simply wiping away dirt and microorganisms, along with skin oils. However, alcohols are unsatisfactory antiseptics when applied to wounds. They cause coagulation of a layer of protein under which bacteria continue to grow.

Two of the most commonly used alcohols are ethanol and isopropanol. The recommended optimum concentration of *ethanol* is 70%, but concentrations between 60% and 95% seem to kill as well (Table 6). Pure ethanol is less effective than aqueous solutions (ethanol mixed with water) because denaturation requires water. *Isopropanol,* often sold as rubbing alcohol, is slightly superior to ethanol as an antiseptic and disinfectant. Moreover, it is less volatile, less expensive, and more easily obtained than ethanol.

Washing hands with soap and water is an effective sanitation method. Use soap and *warm* water (if possible), and rub hands together for 20 seconds (imagine singing "Happy Birthday" twice through). Then rinse, dry with a paper towel or air dryer, and try to use a paper towel to turn off the faucet. Alcohol-based (about 62% alcohol) hand sanitizers such as Purell and Germ-X are very popular for use when hands are not visibly soiled. Rub the product over the surfaces of the hands and fingers until they are dry. Claims that products will kill 99.9% of germs should be viewed with caution; such effectiveness is seldom reached under typical user's conditions. Also, certain pathogens, such as the spore-forming *Clostridium difficile* and viruses that lack a lipid envelope, are comparatively resistant to alcohol-based hand sanitizers.

Ethanol and isopropanol are often used to enhance the effectiveness of other chemical agents. For example, an aqueous solution of Zephiran kills about 40% of the population of a test organism in 2 minutes, whereas a tincture of Zephiran kills about 85% in the same period. To compare the effectiveness of tinctures and aqueous solutions, see Figure 10.

Heavy Metals and Their Compounds

Several heavy metals can be biocidal or antiseptic, including silver, mercury, and copper. The ability of very small amounts of heavy metals, especially silver and copper, to exert antimicrobial activity is referred to as **oligodynamic action** (*oligo* means few). Centuries ago, Egyptians found that putting silver coins in water barrels served to keep the water clean of unwanted organic growths. This action can be seen when we place a coin or other clean piece of metal containing silver or copper on a culture on an inoculated Petri plate. Extremely small amounts of metal diffuse from the coin and inhibit the growth of bacteria for some distance around the coin (Figure 8). This effect is produced by the action of heavy metal ions on microbes. When the metal ions combine with the sulfhydryl groups on cellular proteins, denaturation results.

Silver is used as an antiseptic in a 1% *silver nitrate* solution. At one time, many states required that the eyes of newborns be treated with a few drops of silver nitrate to guard against an infection of the eyes called ophthalmia neonatorum, which the infants might have contracted as they passed through the birth canal. In recent years, antibiotics have replaced silver nitrate for this purpose.

Recently, there has been renewed interest in the use of silver as an antimicrobial agent. Silver-impregnated dressings that slowly release silver ions have proven especially useful against antibiotic-resistant bacteria. The enthusiasm for incorporating silver in all manner of consumer products is increasing. Among the newer products being sold are plastic food containers

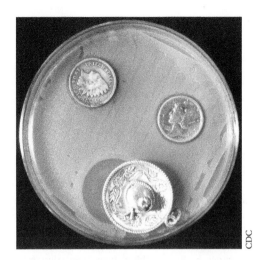

CDC

Figure 8 Oligodynamic action of heavy metals. Clear zones where bacterial growth has been inhibited are seen around the sombrero charm (pushed aside), the dime, and the penny. The charm and the dime contain silver; the penny contains copper.

Q The coins used in this demonstration were minted many years ago; why were more contemporary coins not used?

infused with silver nanoparticles, which are intended to keep food fresher, and silver-infused athletic shirts and socks, which are claimed to minimize odors.

A combination of silver and the drug sulfadiazine, *silver-sulfadiazine,* is the most common formulation. It is available as a topical cream for use on burns. Silver can also be incorporated into indwelling catheters, which are a common source of hospital infections, and in wound dressings. *Surfacine* is a relatively new antimicrobial for application to surfaces, either animate or inanimate. It contains water-insoluble silver iodide in a polymer carrier and is very persistent, lasting at least 13 days. When a bacterium contacts the surface, the cell's outer membrane is recognized, and a lethal amount of silver ions is released.

Inorganic mercury compounds, such as *mercuric chloride,* have a long history of use as disinfectants. They have a very broad spectrum of activity; their effect is primarily bacteriostatic. However, their use is now limited because of their toxicity, corrosiveness, and ineffectiveness in organic matter. At present, the primary use of mercurials is to control mildew in paints.

Copper in the form of *copper sulfate* or other copper-containing additives is used chiefly to destroy green algae (algicide) that grow in reservoirs, stock ponds, swimming pools, and fish tanks. If the water does not contain excessive organic matter, copper compounds are effective in concentrations of one part per million of water. To prevent mildew, copper compounds such as *copper 8-hydroxyquinoline* are sometimes included in paint. In the nineteenth century, the wine regions of Europe were plagued by fungal diseases that affected the grapevines.

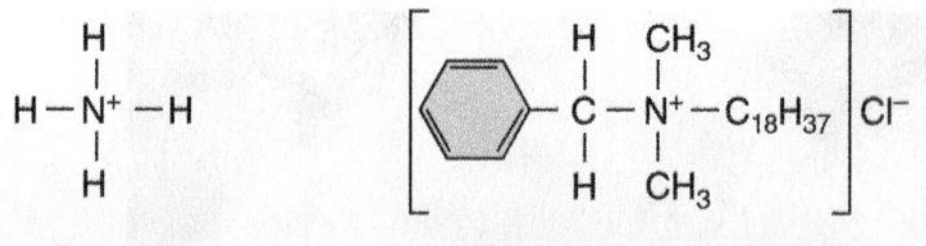

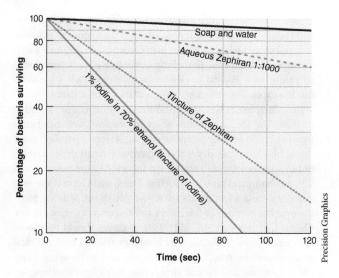

Figure 9 **The ammonium ion and a quaternary ammonium compound, benzalkonium chloride (Zephiran).** Notice how other groups replace the hydrogens of the ammonium ion.

Q Are quats most effective against gram-positive or gram-negative bacteria?

It was observed that vines near the road were less affected than those further afield. The reason was that these roadside vines had been sprayed with a mixture of copper sulfate and lime (both visible and bitter to the taste) to deter passers-by on the road from eating the grapes. Because of this chance observation, mixtures based on copper ions (known as Bordeaux mixture) have long been used to control fungal diseases of plants.

Long term use of alcohol-based hand sanitizers often causes problems with skin dryness. A relatively new hand sanitizer, Xgel, does not contain alcohol but uses copper contained in a skin lotion formulation. Xgel may be more effective as an antimicrobial than alcohol-based hand sanitizers.

Another metal used as an antimicrobial is zinc. The effect of trace amounts of zinc can be seen on weathered roofs of buildings down-slope from galvanized (zinc-coated) fittings. The roof is lighter-colored where biological growth, mostly algae, is impeded. Copper- and zinc-treated shingles are available. *Zinc chloride* is a common ingredient in mouthwashes, and *zinc pyrithione* is an ingredient in antidandruff shampoos.

Surface-Active Agents

Surface-active agents, or **surfactants,** can decrease surface tension among molecules of a liquid. Such agents include soaps and detergents.

Soaps and Detergents Soap has little value as an antiseptic, but it does have an important function in the mechanical removal of microbes through scrubbing. The skin normally contains dead cells, dust, dried sweat, microbes, and oily secretions from oil glands. Soap breaks the oily film into tiny droplets, a process called *emulsification,* and the water and soap together lift up the emulsified oil and debris and float them away as the lather is washed off. In this sense, soaps are good degerming agents.

Acid-Anionic Sanitizers *Acid-anionic* surface-active sanitizers are very important in cleaning dairy utensils and equipment. Their sanitizing ability is related to the negatively charged portion (anion) of the molecule, which reacts with the plasma membrane. These sanitizers, which act on a wide spectrum of microbes, including troublesome thermoduric bacteria, are nontoxic, noncorrosive, and fast acting.

Figure 10 **A comparison of the effectiveness of various antiseptics.** The steeper the downward slope of the killing curve, the more effective the antiseptic is. A 1% iodine in 70% ethanol solution is the most effective; soap and water are the least effective. Notice that a tincture of Zephiran is more effective than an aqueous solution of the same antiseptic.

Q Why is the tincture of Zephiran more effective than the aqueous solution?

Quaternary Ammonium Compounds (Quats) The most widely used surface-active agents are the cationic detergents, especially the **quaternary ammonium compounds (quats).** Their cleansing ability is related to the positively charged portion—the cation—of the molecule. Their name is derived from the fact that they are modifications of the four-valence ammonium ion, NH_4^+ (Figure 9). Quaternary ammonium compounds are strongly bactericidal against gram-positive bacteria and less active against gram-negative bacteria (see Figure 6).

Quats are also fungicidal, amebicidal, and virucidal against enveloped viruses. They do not kill endospores or mycobacteria. (See the Clinical Focus later in this chapter.) Their chemical mode of action is unknown, but they probably affect the plasma membrane. They change the cell's permeability and cause the loss of essential cytoplasmic constituents, such as potassium.

Two popular quats are Zephiran, a brand name of *benzalkonium chloride* (see Figure 9), and Cepacol, a brand name of *cetylpyridinium chloride.* They are strongly antimicrobial, colorless, odorless, tasteless, stable, easily diluted, and nontoxic, except at high concentrations. If your mouthwash bottle fills with foam when shaken, the mouthwash probably contains a quat. However, organic matter interferes with their activity, and they are rapidly neutralized by soaps and anionic detergents.

Anyone involved in medical applications of quats should remember that certain bacteria, such as some species of *Pseudomonas,* not only survive in quaternary ammonium compounds but actively grow in them. These microbes are resistant not only to the disinfectant solution but also to gauze and bandages moistened with it, because the fibers tend to neutralize the quats.

Before we move on to the next group of chemical agents, refer to Figure 10, which compares the effectiveness of some of the antiseptics we have discussed so far.

Chemical Food Preservatives

Chemical preservatives are frequently added to foods to retard spoilage. *Sulfur dioxide* (SO_2) has long been used as a disinfectant, especially in wine-making. Homer's *Odyssey*, written nearly 2800 years ago, mentions its use. Among the more common additives are sodium benzoate, sorbic acid, and calcium propionate. These chemicals are simple organic acids, or salts of organic acids, which the body readily metabolizes and which are generally judged to be safe in foods. *Sorbic acid,* or its more soluble salt *potassium sorbate,* and *sodium benzoate* prevent molds from growing in certain acidic foods, such as cheese and soft drinks. Such foods, usually with a pH of 5.5 or lower, are most susceptible to spoilage by molds. *Calcium propionate,* an effective fungistat used in bread, prevents the growth of surface molds and the *Bacillus* bacterium that causes ropy bread. These organic acids inhibit mold growth, not by affecting the pH but by interfering with the mold's metabolism or the integrity of the plasma membrane.

Sodium nitrate and *sodium nitrite* are added to many meat products, such as ham, bacon, hot dogs, and sausage. The active ingredient is sodium nitrite, which certain bacteria in the meats can also produce from sodium nitrate. These bacteria use nitrate as a substitute for oxygen under anaerobic conditions. The nitrite has two main functions: to preserve the pleasing red color of the meat by reacting with blood components in the meat, and to prevent the germination and growth of any botulism endospores that might be present. Nitrite selectively inhibits certain iron-containing enzymes of *Clostridium botulinum.* There has been some concern that the reaction of nitrites with amino acids can form certain carcinogenic products known as **nitrosamines,** and the amount of nitrites added to foods has generally been reduced recently for this reason. However, the use of nitrites continues because of their established value in preventing botulism. Because nitrosamines are formed in the body from other sources, the added risk posed by a limited use of nitrates and nitrites in meats is lower than was once thought.

Antibiotics

The antimicrobials discussed in this chapter are not useful for ingestion or injection to treat disease. Antibiotics are used for this purpose. The use of antibiotics is highly restricted; however, at least two have considerable use in food preservation. Neither is of value for clinical purposes. *Nisin* is often added to cheese to inhibit the growth of certain endospore-forming spoilage bacteria. It is an example of a bacteriocin, a protein that is produced by one bacterium and inhibits another. Nisin is present naturally in small amounts in many dairy products. It is tasteless, readily digested, and nontoxic. *Natamycin* (pimaricin) is an antifungal antibiotic approved for use in foods, mostly cheese.

Aldehydes

Aldehydes are among the most effective antimicrobials. Two examples are formaldehyde and glutaraldehyde. They inactivate proteins by forming covalent cross-links with several organic functional groups on proteins ($—NH_2$, $—OH$, $—COOH$, and $—SH$). *Formaldehyde gas* is an excellent disinfectant. However, it is more commonly available as *formalin*, a 37% aqueous solution of formaldehyde gas. Formalin was once used extensively to preserve biological specimens and inactivate bacteria and viruses in vaccines.

Glutaraldehyde is a chemical relative of formaldehyde that is less irritating and more effective than formaldehyde. Glutaraldehyde is used to disinfect hospital instruments, including endoscopes and respiratory therapy equipment, but they must be carefully cleaned first. When used in a 2% solution (Cidex), it is bactericidal, tuberculocidal, and virucidal in 10 minutes and sporicidal in 3 to 10 hours. Glutaraldehyde is one of the few liquid chemical disinfectants that can be considered a sterilizing agent. However, 30 minutes is often considered the maximum time allowed for a sporicide to act, which is a criterion glutaraldehyde cannot meet. Both glutaraldehyde and formalin are used by morticians for embalming.

A possible replacement for glutaraldehyde for many uses is *ortho-phthalaldehyde* (OPA), which is more effective against many microbes and has fewer irritating properties.

Clinical Case

Norovirus, a nonenveloped virus, is one cause of acute gastroenteritis. It can be spread by consuming fecally contaminated food or water, coming in direct contact with an infected person, or touching a contaminated surface. Amy is able to rule out foodborne transmission immediately. The small private school does not have a school lunch program; all students and staff bring their lunches from home. After meeting with the principal, Amy speaks to the custodial staff and directs them to use a quat to clean the school. She asks them to pay special attention to areas with high potential for fecal contamination, especially toilet seats, flush handles, toilet stall inner door handles, and restroom door inner handles. Amy is sure she has avoided a major outbreak, but by Friday, 42 students and six more staff members call in to report similar symptoms.

Why didn't the quat work to kill the virus?

Infection Following Steroid Injection

As you read through this box, you will encounter a series of questions that infection control officers ask themselves as they track the source of infection. Try to answer each question before going on to the next one.

1. Dr. Priya Agarwal, an infectious disease physician, called the department of health to report that in the last 3 months, she had seen 12 patients with *Mycobacterium abscessus* joint and soft-tissue infections. Slow-growing mycobacteria, including *M. tuberculosis* and *M. leprae,* are common human pathogens, but Dr. Agarwal was concerned because these infections were caused by rapidly growing mycobacteria (RGM).
   Where are these RGM normally found?

2. RGM are usually found in soil and water. In Dr. Agarwal's report, she noted that all 12 patients received injections for arthritis from the same physician. The injection procedure consisted of cleaning the skin with cotton balls soaked in diluted (1:10) Zephiran, painting the skin with commercially prepared iodine swabs,

anesthetizing the area with 0.5 ml of 1% lidocaine in a sterile 22-gauge needle and syringe, and injecting 0.5–1.0 ml of betamethasone, a cortisone-like steroid, into the joint with a sterile 20-gauge needle and syringe.
   What did Dr. Agarwal need to do to determine the source of the infection?

3. Dr. Agarwal ordered cultures from the inside surface of an open metal container of forceps and the inside surface of a metal container of cotton balls. She also requested cultures of the iodine prep swabs, Zephiran-soaked cotton balls, solutions of lidocaine and betamethasone, diluted and undiluted Zephiran, and a sealed bottle of distilled water used to dilute the Zephiran.
   What type of disinfectant is Zephiran?

4. Zephiran is a quat. Results of cultures from the laboratory showed that only the cotton balls soaked in Zephiran had grown *M. abscessus.* Dr. Agarwal then performed a disk-diffusion assay (see the figure above) of both diluted and undiluted Zephiran.
   What did the assay reveal? What should Dr. Agarwal tell the physician about preventing future infections?

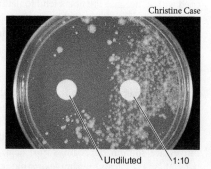
Christine Case

Undiluted   1:10

Disk-diffusion test of Zephiran against *M. abscessus.*

5. Recent research has shown that soaking cotton balls in disinfectant selects for resistant bacteria. Additionally, the disinfecting ability of Zephiran and other quats is reduced by the presence of organic material, such as cotton balls. Dr. Agarwal informed the physician that cotton balls should not be stored in the disinfectant; doing so can cause patients to be inoculated with bacteria.

Source: Adapted from *Clinical Infectious Diseases* 43:823–830 (2006).

Chemical Sterilization

Sterilization with liquid chemicals is possible, but even sporicidal chemicals such as glutaraldehyde are usually not considered to be practical sterilants. However, the gaseous chemosterilants are frequently used as substitutes for physical sterilization processes. Their application requires a closed chamber similar to a steam autoclave. Probably the most familiar example is *ethylene oxide:*

$$\begin{array}{c} H_2C{-}CH_2 \\ \diagdown\diagup \\ O \end{array}$$

Its activity depends on *alkylation,* that is, replacing the proteins' labile hydrogen atoms in a chemical group (such as —SH, —COOH, or —CH₂CH₂OH) with a chemical radical. This leads to cross-linking of nucleic acids and proteins and inhibits vital cellular functions. Ethylene oxide kills all microbes and endospores but requires a lengthy exposure period of several hours. It is toxic and explosive in its pure form, so it is usually mixed with a nonflammable gas, such as carbon dioxide. Among its advantages is that it carries out sterilization at ambient temperatures and it is highly penetrating.

Larger hospitals often are able to sterilize even mattresses in special ethylene oxide sterilizers.

Chlorine dioxide is a short-lived gas that is usually manufactured at the place of use. Notably, it has been used to fumigate enclosed building areas contaminated with endospores of anthrax. It is much more stable in aqueous solution. Its most common use is in water treatment prior to chlorination, where its purpose is to remove, or reduce the formation of, certain carcinogenic compounds sometimes formed in the chlorination of water.

Plasmas

In addition to the traditional three states of matter—liquid, gas, and solid—there might be considered to exist a fourth state of matter, plasma. **Plasma** is a state of matter in which a gas is excited, in this case by an electromagnetic field, to make a mixture of nuclei with assorted electrical charges and free electrons. Health care facilities are increasingly facing the challenge of sterilizing metal or plastic surgical instruments used for many newer procedures in arthroscopic or laparoscopic surgery. Such devices have long, hollow tubes, many with an interior diameter of only a few millimeters, and are difficult to sterilize. *Plasma sterilization* is a reliable method for this. The instruments are placed in a container in which a combination of a vacuum, electromagnetic field, and chemicals such as hydrogen peroxide (sometimes with peracetic acid, as well) form the plasma. Such plasmas have many free radicals that quickly destroy even endospore-forming microbes. The advantage of plasma sterilization, which has elements of both physical and chemical sterilization, is that it requires only low temperatures, but it is relatively expensive.

Supercritical Fluids

The use of supercritical fluids in sterilization combines chemical and physical methods. When carbon dioxide is compressed into a "supercritical" state, it has properties of both a liquid (with increased solubility) and a gas (with a lowered surface tension). Organisms exposed to *supercritical carbon dioxide* are inactivated, including most vegetative organisms that cause spoilage and foodborne pathogens. Even endospore inactivation requires a temperature of only about 45°C. Used for a number of years in treating certain foods, supercritical carbon dioxide has more recently been used to decontaminate medical implants, such as bone, tendons, or ligaments taken from donor patients.

Peroxygens and Other Forms of Oxygen

Peroxygens are a group of oxidizing agents that includes hydrogen peroxide and peracetic acid.

Hydrogen peroxide is an antiseptic found in many household medicine cabinets and in hospital supply rooms. It is not a good antiseptic for open wounds. It is quickly broken down to water and gaseous oxygen by the action of the enzyme catalase, which is present in human cells. However, hydrogen peroxide does effectively disinfect inanimate objects; in such applications, it is even sporicidal at high concentrations. On a nonliving surface, the normally protective enzymes of aerobic bacteria and facultative anaerobes are overwhelmed by high concentrations of peroxide. Because of these factors, and its rapid degradation into harmless water and oxygen, the food industry is increasing its use of hydrogen peroxide for aseptic packaging. The packaging material passes through a hot solution of the chemical before being assembled into a container. In addition, many wearers of contact lenses are familiar with hydrogen peroxide's use as a disinfectant. After the lens is disinfected, a platinum catalyst in the lens-disinfecting kit destroys residual hydrogen peroxide so that it does not persist on the lens, where it might cause eye irritation.

Heated, gaseous hydrogen peroxide can be used as a sterilant of atmosphere and surfaces. Hospital rooms, for example, can be decontaminated quickly and routinely with equipment available under the brand name Bioquell. The room is sealed with the generating apparatus inside and the controls on the outside. Once the sealed room has undergone a decontamination cycle, the hydrogen peroxide vapor is catalytically converted into water vapor and oxygen.

Peracetic acid (peroxyactic acid, or *PAA)* is one of the most effective liquid chemical sporicides available and can be used as a sterilant. Its mode of action is similar to that of hydrogen peroxide. It is generally effective on endospores and viruses within 30 minutes and kills vegetative bacteria and fungi in less than 5 minutes. PAA has many applications in the disinfection of food-processing and medical equipment, especially endoscopes, because it leaves no toxic residues (only water and small amounts of acetic acid) and is minimally affected by the presence of organic matter. The FDA has approved use of PAA for the washing of fruits and vegetables.

Other oxidizing agents include *benzoyl peroxide*, which is probably most familiar as the main ingredient in over-the-counter medications for acne. *Ozone (O_3)* is a highly reactive form of oxygen that is generated by passing oxygen through high-voltage electrical discharges. It is responsible for the air's rather fresh odor after a lightning storm, in the vicinity of electrical sparking, or around an ultraviolet light. Ozone is often used to supplement chlorine in the disinfection of water because it helps neutralize tastes and odors. Although ozone is a more effective killing agent than chlorine, its residual activity is difficult to maintain in water.

Clinical Case

Quats are virucidal against enveloped viruses. By Monday, a total of 103 out of 266 staff and students call in sick with vomiting and diarrhea. With almost half the school either out sick or returning to school after being sick, Amy decides to call the Maryland State Health Department. After going over her records with a health department statistician, she finds out that the most significant risk factors for infection are contact with an ill person or being in the first grade. All but five first-graders have reported sick with diarrheal illness. Because the school is so small, the first-grade classroom also houses the computer lab for the school. Both students and staff share these computers. The health department sends someone to swab the first-grade classroom, and norovirus is cultured from a computer mouse.

How did the virus get from a computer mouse in the first grade classroom to all of the other grades and staff?

✔ If you wanted to disinfect a surface contaminated by vomit and a surface contaminated by a sneeze, why would your choice of disinfectant make a difference? 7

✔ Which is more likely to be used in a medical clinic laboratory, a use-dilution test or a disk-diffusion test? 8

✔ Why is alcohol effective against some viruses and not others? 9

✔ Is Betadine an antiseptic or a disinfectant when it is used on skin? 10

✔ What characteristics make surface-active agents attractive to the dairy industry? 11

✔ What chemical disinfectants can be considered sporicides? 12

✔ What chemicals are used to sterilize? 13

Microbial Characteristics and Microbial Control

LEARNING OBJECTIVE

14 Explain how the type of microbe affects the control of microbial growth.

Many biocides tend to be more effective against gram-positive bacteria, as a group, than against gram-negative bacteria. This principle is illustrated in **Figure 11**, which presents a simplified hierarchy of relative resistance of major microbial groups to biocides. A principal factor in this relative resistance to biocides is the external lipopolysaccharide layer of gram-negative bacteria. Within gram-negative bacteria, members of the genera *Pseudomonas* and *Burkholderia* are of special interest. These closely related bacteria are unusually resistant to biocides (see Figure 6) and will even grow actively in some disinfectants and antiseptics, most notably the quaternary ammonium compounds. These bacteria are also resistant to many antibiotics. This resistance to chemical antimicrobials is related mostly to the characteristics of their *porins* (structural openings in the wall of gram-negative bacteria). Porins are highly selective of molecules that they permit to enter the cell.

The mycobacteria are another group of non–endospore-forming bacteria that exhibit greater than normal resistance to chemical biocides. (See the Clinical Focus later in this chapter.) This group includes *Mycobacterium tuberculosis*, the pathogen that causes tuberculosis. The cell wall of this organism and other members of this genus have a waxy, lipid-rich component. Instruction labels on disinfectants often state whether they are tuberculocidal, indicating that they are effective against mycobacteria. Special tuberculocidal tests have been developed to evaluate the effectiveness of biocides against this bacterial group.

Bacterial endospores are affected by relatively few biocides. (The activity of the major chemical antimicrobial groups against mycobacteria and endospores is summarized in **Table 7**.) The cysts and oocysts of protozoa are also relatively resistant to chemical disinfection.

The resistance of viruses to biocides largely depends on the presence or absence of an envelope. Antimicrobials that are lipid-soluble

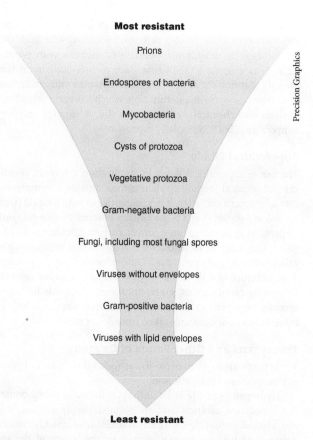

Most resistant

Prions

Endospores of bacteria

Mycobacteria

Cysts of protozoa

Vegetative protozoa

Gram-negative bacteria

Fungi, including most fungal spores

Viruses without envelopes

Gram-positive bacteria

Viruses with lipid envelopes

Least resistant

Precision Graphics

Figure 11 Decreasing order of resistance of microorganisms to chemical biocides.

Q Why are viruses with lipid-containing envelopes relatively susceptible to certain biocides?

are more likely to be effective against enveloped viruses. The label of such an agent will indicate that it is effective against lipophilic viruses. Nonenveloped viruses, which have only a protein coat, are more resistant—fewer biocides are active against them.

A special problem, not yet completely solved, is the reliable killing of prions. Prions are infectious proteins that are the cause of neurological diseases known as spongiform encephalopathies, such as the popularly named mad cow disease. To destroy prions, infected animal carcasses are incinerated. A major problem is the disinfection of surgical instruments exposed to prion contamination. Normal autoclaving has proven to be inadequate. The World Health Organization (WHO) and the Centers for Disease Control and Prevention (CDC) have recommended the combined use of a solution of sodium hydroxide and autoclaving at 134°C. Recent reports indicate that surgical instruments have been successfully treated to inactivate prions, which are proteins, by addition of protease enzymes to the cleaning solution. Surgeons sometimes resort to using disposable instruments.

TABLE 7 The Effectiveness of Chemical Antimicrobials against Endospores and Mycobacteria

Chemical Agent	Endospores	Mycobacteria
Mercury	No activity	No activity
Phenolics	Poor	Good
Bisphenols	No activity	No activity
Quats	No activity	No activity
Chlorines	Fair	Fair
Iodine	Poor	Good
Alcohols	Poor	Good
Glutaraldehyde	Fair	Good
Chlorhexidine	No activity	Fair

In summary, it is important to remember that microbial control methods, especially biocides, are not uniformly effective against all microbes.

Table 8 summarizes chemical agents used to control microbial growth.

CHECK YOUR UNDERSTANDING

✔ The presence or absence of endospores has an obvious effect on microbial control, but why are gram-negative bacteria more resistant to chemical biocides than gram-positive bacteria? 14

Clinical Case Resolved

Norovirus is an extremely contagious virus and can spread quickly from person to person. It is also nonenveloped, so it cannot be easily destroyed by a biocide. Amy asks the principal if, once the school is back to full capacity, she can hold an assembly to discuss the importance of handwashing with the students and staff. Proper washing with soap and water can eliminate the transmission of norovirus to other people or surfaces. Amy also meets again with the custodial staff to discuss the health department's recommendations. According to the health department, when cleaning environmental surfaces that are visibly soiled with feces or vomitus, the staff should wear masks and gloves, use a disposable towel that has been soaked in dilute detergent to wipe the surface for at least 10 seconds, and then apply a 1:10 household bleach solution for at least 1 minute. Although Amy knows this won't be the last time her school is affected by a virus, she is certain she has taken a positive step toward protecting her students and staff from this particular virus.

The compounds discussed in this chapter are not generally useful in the treatment of diseases.

TABLE 8 Chemical Agents Used to Control Microbial Growth

Chemical Agent	Mechanism of Action	Preferred Use	Comment
Phenol and Phenolics			
Phenol	Disruption of plasma membrane, denaturation of enzymes.	Rarely used, except as a standard of comparison.	Seldom used as a disinfectant or antiseptic because of its irritating qualities and disagreeable odor.
Phenolics	Disruption of plasma membrane, denaturation of enzymes.	Environmental surfaces, instruments, skin surfaces, and mucous membranes.	Derivatives of phenol that are reactive even in the presence of organic material; O-phenylphenol is an example.
Bisphenols	Probably disruption of plasma membrane.	Disinfectant hand soaps and skin lotions.	Triclosan is an especially common example of a bisphenol. Broad spectrum, but most effective against gram-positives.
Biguanides (Chlorhexidine)	Disruption of plasma membrane.	Skin disinfection, especially for surgical scrubs.	Bactericidal to gram-positives and gram-negatives; nontoxic, persistent.

(continued)

TABLE 8   Chemical Agents Used to Control Microbial Growth *(continued)*

Chemical Agent	Mechanism of Action	Preferred Use	Comment
Halogens	Iodine inhibits protein function and is a strong oxidizing agent; chlorine forms the strong oxidizing agent hypochlorous acid, which alters cellular components.	Iodine is an effective antiseptic available as a tincture and an iodophor; chlorine gas is used to disinfect water; chlorine compounds are used to disinfect dairy equipment, eating utensils, household items, and glassware.	Iodine and chlorine may act alone or as components of inorganic and organic compounds.
Alcohols	Protein denaturation and lipid dissolution.	Thermometers and other instruments. When the skin is swabbed with alcohol before an injection, most of the disinfecting action probably comes from a simple wiping away (degerming) of dirt and some microbes.	Bactericidal and fungicidal, but not effective against endospores or nonenveloped viruses; commonly used alcohols are ethanol and isopropanol.
Heavy Metals and Their Compounds	Denaturation of enzymes and other essential proteins.	Silver nitrate may be used to prevent ophthalmia neonatorum; silver-sulfadiazine is used as a topical cream on burns; copper sulfate is an algicide.	Heavy metals such as silver and mercury are biocidal.
Surface-Active Agents			
Soaps and detergents	Mechanical removal of microbes through scrubbing.	Skin degerming and removal of debris.	Many antibacterial soaps contain antimicrobials.
Acid-anionic sanitizers	Not certain; may involve enzyme inactivation or disruption.	Sanitizers in dairy and food-processing industries.	Wide spectrum of activity; nontoxic, noncorrosive, fast-acting.
Quaternary ammonium compounds (cationic detergents)	Enzyme inhibition, protein denaturation, and disruption of plasma membranes.	Antiseptic for skin, instruments, utensils, rubber goods.	Bactericidal, bacteriostatic, fungicidal, and virucidal against enveloped viruses. Examples of quats are Zephiran and Cepacol.
Chemical Food Preservatives			
Organic acids	Metabolic inhibition, mostly affecting molds; action not related to their acidity.	Sorbic acid and benzoic acid effective at low pH; parabens much used in cosmetics, shampoos; calcium propionate used in bread.	Widely used to control mold and some bacteria in foods and cosmetics.
Nitrates/nitrites	Active ingredient is nitrite, which is produced by bacterial action on nitrate. Nitrite inhibits certain iron-containing enzymes of anaerobes.	Meat products such as ham, bacon, hot dogs, sausage.	Prevents growth of *Clostridium botulinum* in food; also imparts a red color.
Aldehydes	Protein denaturation.	Glutaraldehyde (Cidex) is less irritating than formaldehyde and is used for disinfecting medical equipment.	Very effective antimicrobials.
Chemical Sterilization			
Ethylene oxide and other gaseous sterilants	Inhibits vital cellular functions.	Mainly for sterilization of materials that would be damaged by heat.	Ethylene oxide is the most commonly used. Heated hydrogen peroxide and chlorine dioxide have special uses.
Plasma sterilization	Inhibits vital cellular functions.	Especially useful for tubular medical instruments.	Usually hydrogen peroxide excited in a vacuum by an electromagnetic field.
Supercritical fluids	Inhibits vital cellular functions.	Especially useful for sterilizing organic medical implants.	Carbon dioxide compressed to a supercritical state.
Peroxygens and Other Forms of Oxygen	Oxidation.	Contaminated surfaces; some deep wounds, in which they are very effective against oxygen-sensitive anaerobes.	Ozone is widely used as a supplement for chlorination; hydrogen peroxide is a poor antiseptic but a good disinfectant. Peracetic acid is especially effective.

Study Outline

The Terminology of Microbial Control

1. The control of microbial growth can prevent infections and food spoilage.
2. Sterilization is the process of removing or destroying all microbial life on an object.
3. Commercial sterilization is heat treatment of canned foods to destroy *C. botulinum* endospores.
4. Disinfection is the process of reducing or inhibiting microbial growth on a nonliving surface.
5. Antisepsis is the process of reducing or inhibiting microorganisms on living tissue.
6. The suffix *-cide* means to kill; the suffix *-stat* means to inhibit.
7. Sepsis is bacterial contamination.

The Rate of Microbial Death

1. Bacterial populations subjected to heat or antimicrobial chemicals usually die at a constant rate.
2. Such a death curve, when plotted logarithmically, shows this constant death rate as a straight line.
3. The time it takes to kill a microbial population is proportional to the number of microbes.
4. Microbial species and life cycle phases (e.g., endospores) have different susceptibilities to physical and chemical controls.
5. Organic matter may interfere with heat treatments and chemical control agents.
6. Longer exposure to lower heat can produce the same effect as shorter time at higher heat.

Actions of Microbial Control Agents

Alteration of Membrane Permeability

1. The susceptibility of the plasma membrane is due to its lipid and protein components.
2. Certain chemical control agents damage the plasma membrane by altering its permeability.

Damage to Proteins and Nucleic Acids

3. Some microbial control agents damage cellular proteins by breaking hydrogen bonds and covalent bonds.
4. Other agents interfere with DNA and RNA and protein synthesis.

Physical Methods of Microbial Control

Heat

1. Heat is frequently used to kill microorganisms.
2. Moist heat kills microbes by denaturing enzymes.

3. Thermal death point (TDP) is the lowest temperature at which all the microbes in a liquid culture will be killed in 10 minutes.
4. Thermal death time (TDT) is the length of time required to kill all bacteria in a liquid culture at a given temperature.
5. Decimal reduction time (DRT) is the length of time in which 90% of a bacterial population will be killed at a given temperature.
6. Boiling (100°C) kills many vegetative cells and viruses within 10 minutes.
7. Autoclaving (steam under pressure) is the most effective method of moist heat sterilization. The steam must directly contact the material to be sterilized.
8. In HTST pasteurization, a high temperature is used for a short time (72°C for 15 seconds) to destroy pathogens without altering the flavor of the food. Ultra-high-temperature (UHT) treatment (140°C for 4 seconds) is used to sterilize dairy products.
9. Methods of dry heat sterilization include direct flaming, incineration, and hot-air sterilization. Dry heat kills by oxidation.
10. Different methods that produce the same effect (reduction in microbial growth) are called equivalent treatments.

Filtration

11. Filtration is the passage of a liquid or gas through a filter with pores small enough to retain microbes.
12. Microbes can be removed from air by high-efficiency particulate air (HEPA) filters.
13. Membrane filters composed of cellulose esters are commonly used to filter out bacteria, viruses, and even large proteins.

Low Temperatures

14. The effectiveness of low temperatures depends on the particular microorganism and the intensity of the application.
15. Most microorganisms do not reproduce at ordinary refrigerator temperatures (0–7°C).
16. Many microbes survive (but do not grow) at the subzero temperatures used to store foods.

High Pressure

17. High pressure denatures proteins in vegetative cells.

Desiccation

18. In the absence of water, microorganisms cannot grow but can remain viable.
19. Viruses and endospores can resist desiccation.

Osmotic Pressure

20. Microorganisms in high concentrations of salts and sugars undergo plasmolysis.
21. Molds and yeasts are more capable than bacteria of growing in materials with low moisture or high osmotic pressure.

Radiation

22. The effects of radiation depend on its wavelength, intensity, and duration.
23. Ionizing radiation (gamma rays, X rays, and high-energy electron beams) has a high degree of penetration and exerts its effect primarily by ionizing water and forming highly reactive hydroxyl radicals.

24. Ultraviolet (UV) radiation, a form of nonionizing radiation, has a low degree of penetration and causes cell damage by making thymine dimers in DNA that interfere with DNA replication; the most effective germicidal wavelength is 260 nm.

25. Microwaves can kill microbes indirectly as materials get hot.

Chemical Methods of Microbial Control

1. Chemical agents are used on living tissue (as antiseptics) and on inanimate objects (as disinfectants).
2. Few chemical agents achieve sterility.

Principles of Effective Disinfection

3. Careful attention should be paid to the properties and concentration of the disinfectant to be used.
4. The presence of organic matter, degree of contact with microorganisms, and temperature should also be considered.

Evaluating a Disinfectant

5. In the use-dilution test, bacterial survival in the manufacturer's recommended dilution of a disinfectant is determined.
6. Viruses, endospore-forming bacteria, mycobacteria, and fungi can also be used in the use-dilution test.
7. In the disk-diffusion method, a disk of filter paper is soaked with a chemical and placed on an inoculated agar plate; a zone of inhibition indicates effectiveness.

Types of Disinfectants

8. Phenolics exert their action by injuring plasma membranes.
9. Bisphenols such as triclosan (over the counter) and hexachlorophene (prescription) are widely used in household products.
10. Biguanides damage plasma membranes of vegetative cells.
11. Some halogens (iodine and chlorine) are used alone or as components of inorganic or organic solutions.
12. Iodine may combine with certain amino acids to inactivate enzymes and other cellular proteins.
13. Iodine is available as a tincture (in solution with alcohol) or as an iodophor (combined with an organic molecule).
14. The germicidal action of chlorine is based on the formation of hypochlorous acid when chlorine is added to water.
15. Alcohols exert their action by denaturing proteins and dissolving lipids.
16. In tinctures, they enhance the effectiveness of other antimicrobial chemicals.

17. Aqueous ethanol (60–95%) and isopropanol are used as disinfectants.
18. Silver, mercury, copper, and zinc are used as germicides.
19. They exert their antimicrobial action through oligodynamic action. When heavy metal ions combine with sulfhydryl (—SH) groups, proteins are denatured.
20. Surface-active agents decrease the surface tension among molecules of a liquid; soaps and detergents are examples.
21. Soaps have limited germicidal action but assist in removing microorganisms.
22. Acid-anionic detergents are used to clean dairy equipment.
23. Quats are cationic detergents attached to NH_4^+.
24. By disrupting plasma membranes, quats allow cytoplasmic constituents to leak out of the cell.
25. Quats are most effective against gram-positive bacteria.
26. SO_2, sorbic acid, benzoic acid, and propionic acid inhibit fungal metabolism and are used as food preservatives.
27. Nitrate and nitrite salts prevent germination of *C. botulinum* endospores in meats.
28. Nisin and natamycin are anibiotics used to preserve foods, especially cheese.
29. Aldehydes such as formaldehyde and glutaraldehyde exert their antimicrobial effect by inactivating proteins.
30. They are among the most effective chemical disinfectants.
31. Ethylene oxide is the gas most frequently used for sterilization.
32. It penetrates most materials and kills all microorganisms by protein denaturation.
33. Free radicals in plasma gases are used to sterilize plastic instruments.
34. Supercritical fluids, which have properties of liquid and gas, can sterilize at low temperatures.
35. Hydrogen peroxide, peracetic acid, benzoyl peroxide, and ozone exert their antimicrobial effect by oxidizing molecules inside cells.

Microbial Characteristics and Microbial Control

1. Gram-negative bacteria are generally more resistant than gram-positive bacteria to disinfectants and antiseptics.
2. Mycobacteria, endospores, and protozoan cysts and oocysts are very resistant to disinfectants and antiseptics.
3. Nonenveloped viruses are generally more resistant than enveloped viruses to disinfectants and antiseptics.
4. Prions are resistant to disinfection and autoclaving.

Study Questions

Answers to the Review and Multiple Choice questions can be found at the end of this chapter.

Review

1. The thermal death time for a suspension of *Bacillus subtilis* endospores is 30 minutes in dry heat and less than 10 minutes in an autoclave. Which type of heat is more effective? Why?

2. If pasteurization does not achieve sterilization, why is pasteurization used to treat food?

3. Thermal death point is not considered an accurate measure of the effectiveness of heat sterilization. List three factors that can alter thermal death point.

4. The antimicrobial effect of gamma radiation is due to (a) _____. The antimicrobial effect of ultraviolet radiation is due to (b) _____.

5. **DRAW IT** A bacterial culture was in log phase in the following figure. At time *x*, an antibacterial compound was added to the culture. Draw the lines indicating addition of a bactericidal compound and a bacteriostatic compound. Explain why the viable count does not immediately drop to zero at *x*.

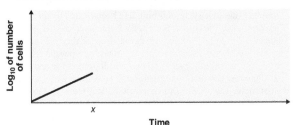

6. How do autoclaving, hot air, and pasteurization illustrate the concept of equivalent treatments?

7. How do salts and sugars preserve foods? Why are these considered physical rather than chemical methods of microbial control? Name one food that is preserved with sugar and one preserved with salt. How do you account for the occasional growth of *Penicillium* mold in jelly, which is 50% sucrose?

8. The use-dilution values for two disinfectants tested under the same conditions are as follows: Disinfectant A—1:2; Disinfectant B—1:10,000. If both disinfectants are designed for the same purpose, which would you select?

9. A large hospital washes burn patients in a stainless steel tub. After each patient, the tub is cleaned with a quat. It was noticed that 14 of 20 burn patients acquired *Pseudomonas* infections after being bathed. Provide an explanation for this high rate of infection.

10. **NAME IT** What bacterium has porins, is resistant to triclosan, and survives and may grow in quats?

Multiple Choice

1. Which of the following does *not* kill endospores?
    a. autoclaving
    b. incineration
    c. hot-air sterilization
    d. pasteurization
    e. All of the above kill endospores.

2. Which of the following is most effective for sterilizing mattresses and plastic Petri dishes?
    a. chlorine
    b. ethylene oxide
    c. glutaraldehyde
    d. autoclaving
    e. nonionizing radiation

3. Which of these disinfectants does *not* act by disrupting the plasma membrane?
    a. phenolics
    b. phenol
    c. quaternary ammonium compounds
    d. halogens
    e. biguanides

4. Which of the following *cannot* be used to sterilize a heat-labile solution stored in a plastic container?
    a. gamma radiation
    b. ethylene oxide
    c. supercritical fluids
    d. autoclaving
    e. short-wavelength radiation

5. Which of the following is *not* a characteristic of quaternary ammonium compounds?
    a. bactericidal against gram-positive bacteria
    b. sporicidal
    c. amoebicidal
    d. fungicidal
    e. kills enveloped viruses

6. A classmate is trying to determine how a disinfectant might kill cells. You observed that when he spilled the disinfectant in your reduced litmus milk, the litmus turned blue again. You suggest to your classmate that
    a. the disinfectant might inhibit cell wall synthesis.
    b. the disinfectant might oxidize molecules.
    c. the disinfectant might inhibit protein synthesis.
    d. the disinfectant might denature proteins.
    e. he take his work away from yours.

7. Which of the following is most likely to be bactericidal?
    a. membrane filtration
    b. ionizing radiation
    c. lyophilization (freeze-drying)
    d. deep-freezing
    e. all of the above

8. Which of the following is used to control microbial growth in foods?
    a. organic acids
    b. alcohols
    c. aldehydes
    d. heavy metals
    e. all of the above

Use the following information to answer questions 9 and 10. The data were obtained from a use-dilution test comparing four disinfectants against *Salmonella choleraesuis*. G = growth, NG = no growth

	Bacterial Growth after Exposure to			
Dilution	Disinfectant A	Disinfectant B	Disinfectant C	Disinfectant D
1:2	NG	G	NG	NG
1:4	NG	G	NG	G
1:8	NG	G	G	G
1:16	G	G	G	G

9. Which disinfectant is the most effective?

10. Which disinfectant(s) is (are) bactericidal?
    a. A, B, C, and D
    b. A, C, and D
    c. A only
    d. B only
    e. none of the above

Critical Thinking

1. The disk-diffusion method was used to evaluate three disinfectants. The results were as follows:

Disinfectant	Zone of Inhibition
X	0 mm
Y	5 mm
Z	10 mm

   a. Which disinfectant was the most effective against the organism?

   b. Can you determine whether compound Y was bactericidal or bacteriostatic?

2. For each of the following bacteria, explain why it is often resistant to disinfectants.
   a. *Mycobacterium*
   b. *Pseudomonas*
   c. *Bacillus*

3. A use-dilution test was used to evaluate two disinfectants against *Salmonella choleraesuis*. The results were as follows:

Time of Exposure (min)	Bacterial Growth after Exposures		
	Disinfectant A	Disinfectant B Diluted with Distilled Water	Disinfectant B Diluted with Tap Water
10	G	NG	G
20	G	NG	NG
30	NG	NG	NG

   a. Which disinfectant was the most effective?

   b. Which disinfectant should be used against *Staphylococcus*?

4. To determine the lethal action of microwave radiation, two 10^5 suspensions of *E. coli* were prepared. One cell suspension was exposed to microwave radiation while wet, whereas the other was lyophilized (freeze-dried) and then exposed to radiation. The results are shown in the following figure. Dashed lines indicate the temperature of the samples. What is the most likely method of lethal action of microwave radiation? How do you suppose these data might differ for *Clostridium*?

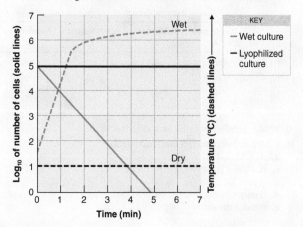

Clinical Applications

1. *Entamoeba histolytica* and *Giardia lamblia* were isolated from the stool sample of a 45-year-old man, and *Shigella sonnei* was isolated from the stool sample of an 18-year-old woman. Both patients experienced diarrhea and severe abdominal cramps, and prior to onset of digestive symptoms both had been treated by the same chiropractor. The chiropractor had administered colonic irrigations (enemas) to these patients. The device used for this treatment was a gravity-dependent apparatus using 12 liters of tap water. There were no check valves to prevent backflow, so all parts of the apparatus could have become contaminated with feces during each colonic treatment. The chiropractor provided colonic treatment to four or five patients per day. Between patients, the adaptor piece that is inserted into the rectum was placed in a "hot-water sterilizer."

   What two errors were made by the chiropractor?

2. Between March 9 and April 12, five chronic peritoneal dialysis patients at one hospital became infected with *Pseudomonas aeruginosa*. Four patients developed peritonitis (inflammation of the abdominal cavity), and one developed a skin infection at the catheter insertion site. All patients with peritonitis had low-grade fever, cloudy peritoneal fluid, and abdominal pain. All patients had permanent indwelling peritoneal catheters, which the nurse wiped with gauze that had been soaked with an iodophor solution each time the catheter was connected to or disconnected from the machine tubing. Aliquots of the iodophor were transferred from stock bottles to small in-use bottles. Cultures from the dialysate concentrate and the internal areas of the dialysis machines were negative; iodophor from a small in-use plastic container yielded a pure culture of *P. aeruginosa*.

   What improper technique led to this infection?

3. You are investigating a national outbreak of *Ralstonia mannitolilytica* associated with use of a contaminated oxygen-delivery device among pediatric patients. The device adds moisture to and warms the oxygen. Each hospital followed the manufacturer's recommendation to use a detergent to clean the reusable components of the device between patients. Tap water is permitted in the device because the device uses a reusable 0.01-μm filter as a biological barrier between the air and water compartments. *Ralstonia* is a gram-negative rod commonly found in water.

   Why did disinfection fail?

   What do you recommend for disinfecting? The device cannot be autoclaved.

Answers to Review and Multiple Choice Study Questions

Review

1. Autoclave. Because of the high specific heat of water, moist heat is readily transferred to cells.

2. Pasteurization destroys most organisms that cause disease or rapid spoilage of food.

3. Variables that affect determination of the thermal death point are
   - The innate heat resistance of the strain of bacteria
   - The past history of the culture, whether it was freeze-dried, wetted, etc.
   - The clumping of the cells during the test
   - The amount of water present
   - The organic matter present
   - Media and incubation temperature used to determine viability of the culture after heating

4. **a.** the ability of ionizing radiation to break DNA directly. However, because of the high water content of cells, free radicals (H· and OH·) that break DNA strands are likely to form.
   b. formation of thymine dimers.

5.

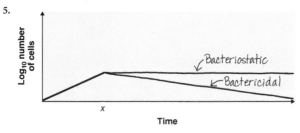

6. All three processes kill microorganisms; however, as moisture and/or temperatures are increased, less time is required to achieve the same result.

7. Salts and sugars create a hypertonic environment. Salts and sugars (as preservatives) do not directly affect cell structures or metabolism; instead, they alter the osmotic pressure. Jams and jellies are preserved with sugar; meats are usually preserved with salt. Molds are more capable of growth in high osmotic pressure than are bacteria.

8. Disinfectant B is preferable because it can be diluted more and still be effective.

9. Quaternary ammonium compounds are most effective against gram-positive bacteria. Gram-negative bacteria that were stuck in cracks or around the drain of the tub would not have been washed away when the tub was cleaned. These gram-negative bacteria could survive the washing procedure. Some pseudomonads can grow on quats that have accumulated.

10. Pseudomonads (*Pseudomonas* and *Burkholderia*)

Multiple Choice

1. d	3. d	5. b	7. b	9. a
2. b	4. d	6. b	8. a	10. b

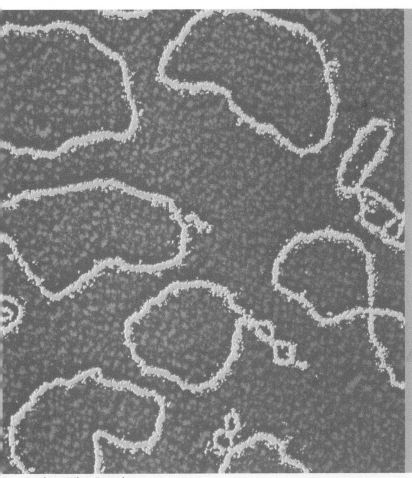

Gopal Murti/Photo Researchers

Microbial Genetics

Visualize microbiology and check your
understanding with a pre-test at
www.masteringmicrobiology.com.

Virtually all the microbial traits you have read about previously are controlled
or influenced by heredity. The inherited traits of microbes include their
shape and structural features, their metabolism, their ability to move or
behave in various ways, and their ability to interact with other organisms—perhaps
causing disease. Individual organisms transmit these characteristics to their
offspring through genes.

The development of antibiotic resistance in microorganisms depends on
genetics. Antibiotic resistance is often carried on plasmids such as those in the
figure. Plasmids are readily transferred between bacterial cells. They are responsible
for the emergence of methicillin-resistant *Staphylococcus aureus* and the recent
emergence of carbapenem-resistant *Klebsiella pneumoniae*. The emergence of
vancomycin-resistant *S. aureus* (VRSA) poses a serious threat to patient care. In this
chapter you will see how VRSA acquired this trait.

Emerging diseases provide another reason why it is important to understand
genetics. New diseases are the results of genetic changes in some existing organism;
for example, *E. coli* O157:H7 acquired the genes for Shiga toxin from *Shigella*.

Currently, microbiologists are using genetics to discover relatedness among
organisms, to explore the origins of organisms such as HIV and H1N1 influenza
virus, and to study how genes are expressed.

From Chapter 8 of *Microbiology: An Introduction*, Eleventh Edition. Gerard J. Tortora, Berdell R. Funke, Christine L. Case.

Structure and Function of the Genetic Material

LEARNING OBJECTIVES

1 Define *genetics, genome, chromosome, gene, genetic code, genotype, phenotype,* and *genomics.*

2 Describe how DNA serves as genetic information.

3 Describe the process of DNA replication.

4 Describe protein synthesis, including transcription, RNA processing, and translation.

5 Compare protein synthesis in prokaryotes and eukaryotes.

Genetics is the science of heredity; it includes the study of what genes are, how they carry information, how they are replicated and passed to subsequent generations of cells or passed between organisms, and how the expression of their information within an organism determines the particular characteristics of that organism. The genetic information in a cell is called the **genome.** A cell's genome includes its chromosomes and plasmids. **Chromosomes** are structures containing DNA that physically carry hereditary information; the chromosomes contain the genes. **Genes** are segments of DNA (except in some viruses, in which they are made of RNA) that code for functional products.

Clinical Case: Where There's Smoke

Marcel DuBois, a 70-year-old grandfather of 12, quietly hangs up the phone. His doctor has just called him with the results of his stool DNA test that he undertook at the Mayo Clinic last week. Marcel's doctor suggested this experimental, noninvasive screening tool for colorectal cancer because Marcel is not comfortable with the colonoscopy procedure and usually tries to postpone getting one. The stool DNA test, however, uses stool samples, which contain cells that have been shed from the colon lining. The DNA from these cells is tested for DNA markers that may indicate the presence of precancerous polyps or cancerous tumors. Marcel makes an appointment to come in to see his doctor the next afternoon.

Once in the office, the doctor explains to Marcel and his wife, Janice, that the stool DNA test detected the presence of serrated colorectal polyps. This type of polyp is usually difficult to see with a colonoscopy because it is not raised and can be the same color as the colon wall.

How can DNA show whether a person has cancer? Read on to find out.

DNA is a macromolecule composed of repeating units called *nucleotides.* Recall that each nucleotide consists of a nucleobase (adenine, thymine, cytosine, or guanine), deoxyribose (a pentose sugar), and a phosphate group. The DNA within a cell exists as long strands of nucleotides twisted together in pairs to form a double helix. Each strand has a string of alternating sugar and phosphate groups (its *sugar-phosphate backbone*), and a nitrogenous base is attached to each sugar in the backbone. The two strands are held together by hydrogen bonds between their nitrogenous bases. The **base pairs** always occur in a specific way: adenine always pairs with thymine, and cytosine always pairs with guanine. Because of this specific base pairing, the base sequence of one DNA strand determines the base sequence of the other strand. The two strands of DNA are thus *complementary.*

The structure of DNA helps explain two primary features of biological information storage. First, the linear sequence of bases provides the actual information. Genetic information is encoded by the sequence of bases along a strand of DNA, in much the same way as our written language uses a linear sequence of letters to form words and sentences. The genetic language, however, uses an alphabet with only four letters—the four kinds of nucleobases in DNA (or RNA). But 1000 of these four bases, the number contained in an average-sized gene, can be arranged in 4^{1000} different ways. This astronomically large number explains how genes can be varied enough to provide all the information a cell needs to grow and perform its functions. The **genetic code,** the set of rules that determines how a nucleotide sequence is converted into the amino acid sequence of a protein, is discussed in more detail later in the chapter.

Second, the complementary structure allows for the precise duplication of DNA during cell division. Each offspring cell receives one of the original strands from the parent; thus ensuring one strand that functions correctly.

Much of cellular metabolism is concerned with translating the genetic message of genes into specific proteins. A gene usually codes for a messenger RNA (mRNA) molecule, which ultimately results in the formation of a protein. Alternatively, the gene product can be a ribosomal RNA (rRNA), transfer RNA (tRNA), or microRNA (miRNA). As we will see, all of these types of RNA are involved in the process of protein synthesis. When the ultimate molecule for which a gene codes (a protein, for example) has been produced, we say that the gene has been *expressed.*

Genotype and Phenotype

The **genotype** of an organism is its genetic makeup, the information that codes for all the particular characteristics of the organism. The genotype represents *potential* properties, but not the properties themselves. **Phenotype** refers to *actual, expressed* properties, such as the organism's ability to perform a particular chemical reaction. Phenotype, then, is the manifestation of genotype.

In molecular terms, an organism's genotype is its collection of genes, its entire DNA. What constitutes the organism's phenotype in molecular terms? In a sense, an organism's phenotype is its collection of proteins. Most of a cell's properties derive from the structures and functions of its proteins. In microbes, most proteins are either *enzymatic* (catalyze particular reactions) or *structural* (participate in large functional complexes such as membranes or flagella). Even phenotypes that depend on structural macromolecules other than proteins (such as lipids or polysaccharides) rely indirectly on proteins. For instance, the structure of a complex lipid or polysaccharide molecule results from the catalytic activities of enzymes that synthesize, process, and degrade those molecules. Thus, although it is not completely accurate to say that phenotypes are due only to proteins, it is a useful simplification.

DNA and Chromosomes

Bacteria typically have a single circular chromosome consisting of a single circular molecule of DNA with associated proteins. The chromosome is looped and folded and attached at one or several points to the plasma membrane. The DNA of *E. coli* has about 4.6 million base pairs and is about 1 mm long—1000 times longer than the entire cell (Figure 1a). However, the chromosome takes up only about 10% of the cell's volume because the DNA is twisted, or *supercoiled.*

Originally, the location of genes on a bacterial chromosome was determined by experiments on the transfer of genes from one cell to another. These processes will be discussed later in this chapter. Therefore, the bacterial chromosome map is marked in minutes corresponding to when the genes are transferred from a donor cell to a recipient cell (Figure 1b). The entire genome does not consist of back-to-back genes. Noncoding regions called **short tandem repeats (STRs)** occur in most genomes, including that of *E. coli.* STRs are repeating sequences of two- to five-base sequences. These are used in DNA fingerprinting.

Now, the complete base sequences of chromosomes can be determined. Computers are used to search for *open-reading frames,* that is, regions of DNA that are likely to encode a protein. As you will see later, these are base sequences between start and stop codons. The sequencing and molecular characterization of genomes is called **genomics.** The use of genomics to track West Nile virus is described in the Clinical Focus later in this chapter.

The Flow of Genetic Information

DNA replication makes possible the flow of genetic information from one generation to the next. As shown in Figure 2, the DNA of a cell replicates before cell division so that each offspring cell receives a chromosome identical to the parent's. Within each metabolizing cell, the genetic information contained in DNA also flows in another way: it is transcribed into mRNA and then translated into protein. We describe the processes of transcription and translation later in this chapter.

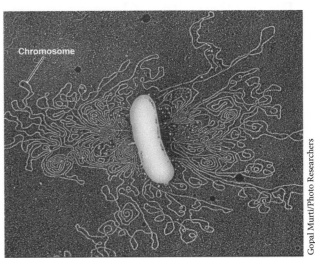

(a) The tangled mass and looping strands of DNA emerging from this disrupted *E. coli* cell are part of its single chromosome.

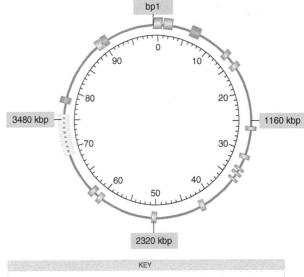

(b) A genetic map of the chromosome of *E. coli.* The numbers inside the circle indicate the number of minutes it takes to transfer the genes during mating between two cells; the numbers in colored boxes indicate the number of base pairs. 1 kbp = 1000 base pairs.

KEY

Amino acid metabolism	Carbohydrate metabolism
DNA replication and repair	Membrane synthesis
Lipid metabolism	

Figure 1 A prokaryotic chromosome.

Q What is a gene? What is an open-reading frame?

The Flow of Genetic Information

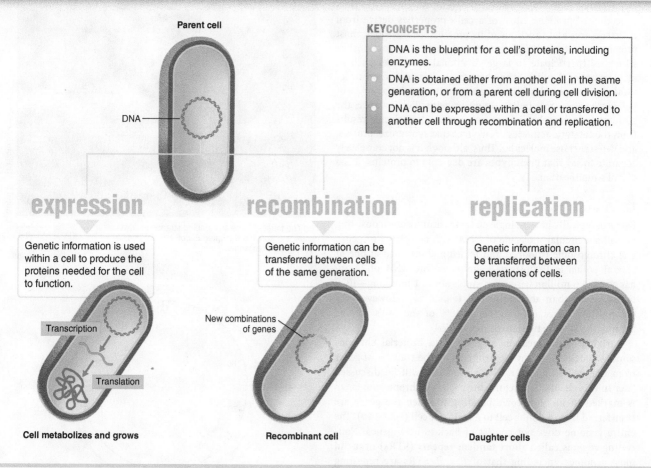

Parent cell

DNA

- DNA is the blueprint for a cell's proteins, including enzymes.
- DNA is obtained either from another cell in the same generation, or from a parent cell during cell division.
- DNA can be expressed within a cell or transferred to another cell through recombination and replication.

expression

Genetic information is used within a cell to produce the proteins needed for the cell to function.

Transcription

Translation

Cell metabolizes and grows

recombination

Genetic information can be transferred between cells of the same generation.

New combinations of genes

Recombinant cell

replication

Genetic information can be transferred between generations of cells.

Daughter cells

Precision Graphics

CHECK YOUR UNDERSTANDING

✔ Give a clinical application of genomics. 1

✔ Why is the base pairing in DNA important? 2

DNA Replication

In DNA replication, one "parental" double-stranded DNA molecule is converted to two identical "daughter" molecules. The complementary structure of the nitrogenous base sequences in the DNA molecule is the key to understanding DNA replication. Because the bases along the two strands of double-helical DNA are complementary, one strand can act as a template for the production of the other strand (**Figure 3a**).

DNA replication requires the presence of several cellular proteins that direct a particular sequence of events. Enzymes involved in DNA replication and other processes are listed in **Table 1.** When replication begins, the supercoiling is relaxed by *topoisomerase*

or *gyrase,* and the two strands of parental DNA are unwound by *helicase* and separated from each other in one small DNA segment after another. Free nucleotides present in the cytoplasm of the cell are matched up to the exposed bases of the single-stranded parental DNA. Where thymine is present on the original strand, only adenine can fit into place on the new strand; where guanine is present on the original strand, only cytosine can fit into place, and so on. Any bases that are improperly base-paired are removed and replaced by replication enzymes. Once aligned, the newly added nucleotide is joined to the growing DNA strand by an enzyme called **DNA polymerase.** Then the parental DNA is unwound a bit further to allow the addition of the next nucleotides. The point at which replication occurs is called the *replication fork.*

As the replication fork moves along the parental DNA, each of the unwound single strands combines with new nucleotides. The original strand and this newly synthesized daughter strand then rewind. Because each new double-stranded DNA molecule contains

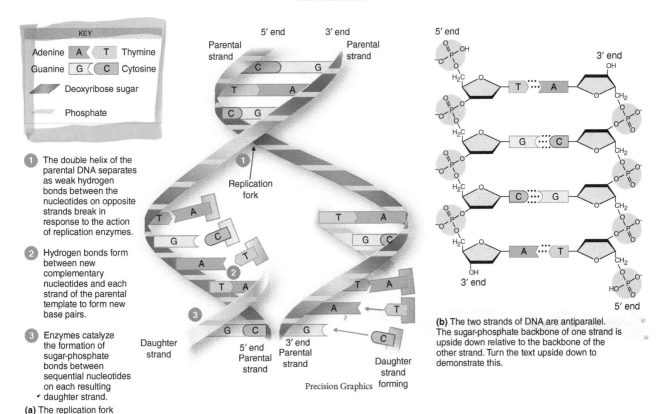

KEY

Adenine	A ⟨ T	Thymine
Guanine	G ⟨ C	Cytosine
Deoxyribose sugar		
Phosphate		

1 The double helix of the parental DNA separates as weak hydrogen bonds between the nucleotides on opposite strands break in response to the action of replication enzymes.

2 Hydrogen bonds form between new complementary nucleotides and each strand of the parental template to form new base pairs.

3 Enzymes catalyze the formation of sugar-phosphate bonds between sequential nucleotides on each resulting daughter strand.

(a) The replication fork

5′ end Parental strand
3′ end Parental strand
Replication fork
Daughter strand
5′ end Parental strand
3′ end Parental strand
Daughter strand forming
Precision Graphics

(b) The two strands of DNA are antiparallel. The sugar-phosphate backbone of one strand is upside down relative to the backbone of the other strand. Turn the text upside down to demonstrate this.

Figure 3 **DNA replication.**

 What is the advantage of semiconservative replication?

TABLE 1 **Important Enzymes in DNA Replication, Expression, and Repair**

DNA Gyrase	Relaxes supercoiling ahead of the replication fork
DNA Ligase	Makes covalent bonds to join DNA strands; joins Okazaki fragments and new segments in excision repair
DNA Polymerase	Synthesizes DNA; proofreads and repairs DNA
Endonucleases	Cut DNA backbone in a strand of DNA; facilitate repair and insertions
Exonucleases	Cut DNA from an exposed end of DNA; facilitate repair
Helicase	Unwinds double-stranded DNA
Methylase	Adds methyl group to selected bases in newly made DNA
Photolyase	Uses visible light energy to separate UV-induced pyrimidine dimers
Ribozyme	RNA enzyme that removes introns and splices exons together
RNA Polymerase	Copies RNA from a DNA template
RNA Primase	An RNA polymerase that makes RNA primers from a DNA template
snRNP	RNA-protein complex that removes introns and splices exons together
Topoisomerase	Relaxes supercoiling ahead of the replication fork; separates DNA circles at the end of DNA replication
Transposase	Cuts DNA backbone, leaving single-stranded "sticky ends"

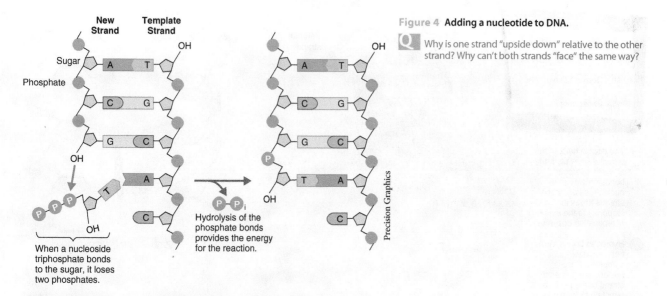

New Strand **Template Strand**

Sugar

Phosphate

When a nucleoside triphosphate bonds to the sugar, it loses two phosphates.

Hydrolysis of the phosphate bonds provides the energy for the reaction.

Precision Graphics

Figure 4 Adding a nucleotide to DNA.

Q Why is one strand "upside down" relative to the other strand? Why can't both strands "face" the same way?

one original (conserved) strand and one new strand, the process of replication is referred to as **semiconservative replication.**

Before looking at DNA replication in more detail, let's take a closer look at the structure of DNA. It is important to understand the concept that the paired DNA strands are oriented in opposite directions relative to each other. Notice that the carbon atoms of the sugar component of each nucleotide are numbered 1′ (pronounced "one prime") to 5′. For the paired bases to be next to each other, the sugar components in one strand are upside down relative to the other. The end with the hydroxyl

Precision Graphics

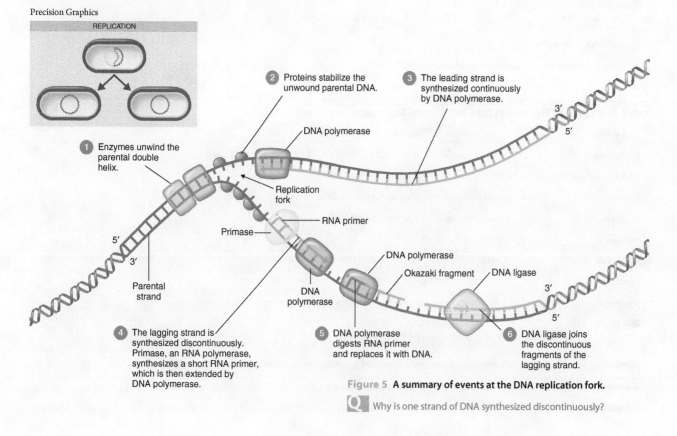

REPLICATION

1 Enzymes unwind the parental double helix.

2 Proteins stabilize the unwound parental DNA.

3 The leading strand is synthesized continuously by DNA polymerase.

DNA polymerase

Replication fork

RNA primer

Primase

5′

3′

Parental strand

DNA polymerase

DNA polymerase

Okazaki fragment

DNA ligase

3′

5′

4 The lagging strand is synthesized discontinuously. Primase, an RNA polymerase, synthesizes a short RNA primer, which is then extended by DNA polymerase.

5 DNA polymerase digests RNA primer and replaces it with DNA.

6 DNA ligase joins the discontinuous fragments of the lagging strand.

Figure 5 A summary of events at the DNA replication fork.

Q Why is one strand of DNA synthesized discontinuously?

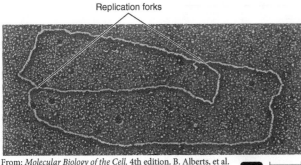

Replication forks

From: *Molecular Biology of the Cell.* 4th edition. B. Alberts, et al.
New York: Garland Science; 2002, Figure 5-6. Copyright © 2002.

SEM |—— 20 nm

(a) An *E. coli* chromosome in the process of replicating

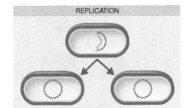

REPLICATION

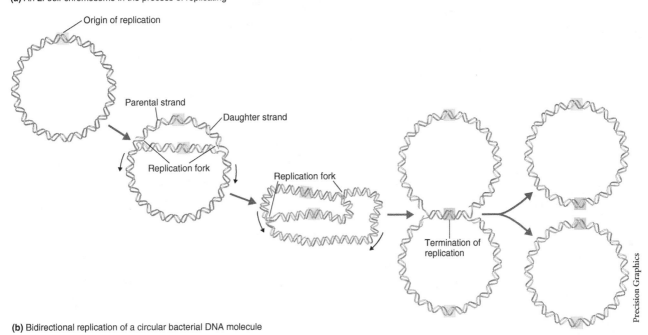

Origin of replication

Parental strand

Daughter strand

Replication fork

Replication fork

Termination of
replication

Precision Graphics

(b) Bidirectional replication of a circular bacterial DNA molecule

Figure 6   Replication of bacterial DNA.

Q   What is the origin of replication?

attached to the 3′ carbon is called the 3′ end of the DNA strand; the end having a phosphate attached to the 5′ carbon is called the 5′ end. The way in which the two strands fit together dictates that the 5′ → 3′ direction of one strand runs counter to the 5′ → 3′ direction of the other strand (Figure 3b). This structure of DNA affects the replication process because DNA polymerases can add new nucleotides to the 3′ end only. Therefore, as the replication fork moves along the parental DNA, the two new strands must grow in different directions.

DNA replication requires a great deal of energy. The energy is supplied from the nucleotides, which are actually nucleoside triphosphates. You already know about ATP; the only difference between ATP and the adenine nucleotide in DNA is the sugar

component. Deoxyribose is the sugar in the nucleosides used to synthesize DNA, and nucleoside triphosphates with ribose are used to synthesize RNA. Two phosphate groups are removed to add the nucleotide to a growing strand of DNA; hydrolysis of the nucleoside is exergonic and provides energy to make the new bonds in the DNA strand (Figure 4).

Figure 5 provides more detail about the many steps that go into this complex process.

DNA replication by some bacteria, such as *E. coli,* goes *bidirectionally* around the chromosome (Figure 6). Two replication forks move in opposite directions away from the origin of replication. Because the bacterial chromosome is a closed loop, the replication forks eventually meet when replication is completed. The two

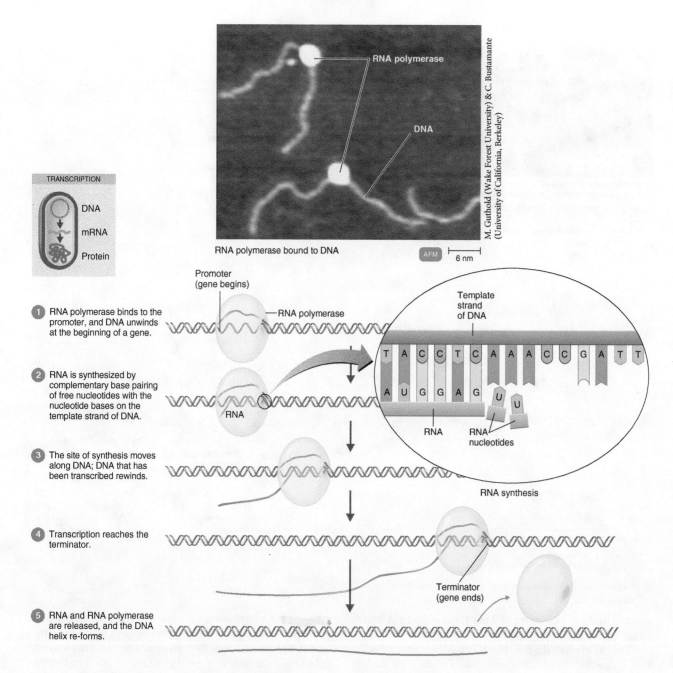

RNA polymerase

DNA

M. Guthold (Wake Forest University) & C. Bustamante (University of California, Berkeley)

RNA polymerase bound to DNA

AFM 6 nm

TRANSCRIPTION

DNA → mRNA → Protein

Promoter (gene begins)

1. RNA polymerase binds to the promoter, and DNA unwinds at the beginning of a gene.

RNA polymerase

2. RNA is synthesized by complementary base pairing of free nucleotides with the nucleotide bases on the template strand of DNA.

RNA

3. The site of synthesis moves along DNA; DNA that has been transcribed rewinds.

4. Transcription reaches the terminator.

Terminator (gene ends)

5. RNA and RNA polymerase are released, and the DNA helix re-forms.

Template strand of DNA

T A C C T C A A A C C G A T T
A U G G A G

RNA   RNA nucleotides

RNA synthesis

Figure 7 The process of transcription. The orienting diagram indicates the relationship of transcription to the overall flow of genetic information within a cell.

Q When does transcription stop?

Figure 3.1 in *Dealing with Genes* by Paul Berg & Maxine Singer. Copyright © 1992. Reprinted by permission of University Science Books.

loops must be separated by a topoisomerase. Much evidence shows an association between the bacterial plasma membrane and the origin of replication. After duplication, if each copy of the origin binds to the membrane at opposite poles, then each daughter cell receives one copy of the DNA molecule—that is, one complete chromosome.

DNA replication is an amazingly accurate process. Typically, mistakes are made at a rate of only 1 in every 10^{10} bases incorporated. Such accuracy is largely due to the *proofreading* capability of DNA polymerase. As each new base is added, the enzyme evaluates whether it forms the proper complementary base-pairing structure. If not, the enzyme excises the improper base and replaces it with the correct one. In this way, DNA can be replicated very accurately, allowing each daughter chromosome to be virtually identical to the parental DNA.

(MM) **Animations** DNA Replication: Overview, Forming the Replication Fork, Replication Proteins, Synthesis

CHECK YOUR UNDERSTANDING

✔ Describe DNA replication, including the functions of DNA gyrase, DNA ligase, and DNA polymerase. 3

RNA and Protein Synthesis

How is the information in DNA used to make the proteins that control cell activities? In the process of *transcription*, genetic information in DNA is copied, or transcribed, into a complementary base sequence of RNA. The cell then uses the information encoded in this RNA to synthesize specific proteins through the process of *translation*. We now take a closer look at these two processes as they occur in a bacterial cell.

Transcription

Transcription is the synthesis of a complementary strand of RNA from a DNA template. We will discuss transcription in pro-karyotic cells here. **Ribosomal RNA (rRNA)** forms an integral part of ribosomes, the cellular machinery for protein synthesis. Transfer RNA is also involved in protein synthesis, as we will see. **Messenger RNA (mRNA)** carries the coded information for making specific proteins from DNA to ribosomes, where proteins are synthesized.

During transcription, a strand of mRNA is synthesized using a specific portion of the cell's DNA as a template. In other words, the genetic information stored in the sequence of nitrogenous bases of DNA is rewritten so that the same information appears in the base sequence of mRNA. As in DNA replication, a G in the DNA template dictates a C in the mRNA being made, a C in the DNA template dictates a G in the mRNA, and a T in the DNA template dictates an A in the mRNA. However, an A in the DNA template dictates a uracil (U) in the mRNA, because RNA contains U instead of T. (U has a chemical structure slightly different from T, but it base-pairs in the same way.) If, for example, the template portion of DNA has the base sequence 3'-ATGCAT, the newly synthesized mRNA strand will have the complementary base sequence 5'-UACGUA.

The process of transcription requires both an enzyme called *RNA polymerase* and a supply of RNA nucleotides (**Figure 7**). Transcription begins when RNA polymerase binds to the DNA at a site called the **promoter.** Only one of the two DNA strands serves as the template for RNA synthesis for a given gene. Like DNA, RNA is synthesized in the 5′ → 3′ direction. RNA synthesis continues until RNA polymerase reaches a site on the DNA called the **terminator.**

The process of transcription allows the cell to produce short-term copies of genes that can be used as the direct source of information for protein synthesis. Messenger RNA acts as an

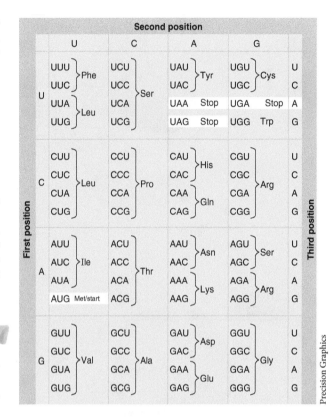

Figure 8 The genetic code. The three nucleotides in an mRNA codon are designated, respectively, as the first position, second position, and third position of the codon on the mRNA. Each set of three nucleotides specifies a particular amino acid, represented by a three-letter abbreviation. The codon AUG, which specifies the amino acid methionine, is also the start of protein synthesis. The word *Stop* identifies the nonsense codons that signal the termination of protein synthesis.

(Q) What is the advantage of the degeneracy of the genetic code?

Precision Graphics

intermediate between the permanent storage form, DNA, and the process that uses the information, translation. (MM) **Animations** Transcription: Overview, Process

Translation

We have seen how the genetic information in DNA is transferred to mRNA during transcription. Now we will see how mRNA serves as the source of information for the synthesis of proteins. Protein synthesis is called **translation** because it involves decoding the "language" of nucleic acids and converting that information into the "language" of proteins.

The language of mRNA is in the form of **codons,** groups of three nucleotides, such as AUG, GGC, or AAA. The sequence of codons on an mRNA molecule determines the sequence of amino acids that will be in the protein being synthesized. Each codon "codes" for a particular amino acid. This is the genetic code (**Figure 8**).

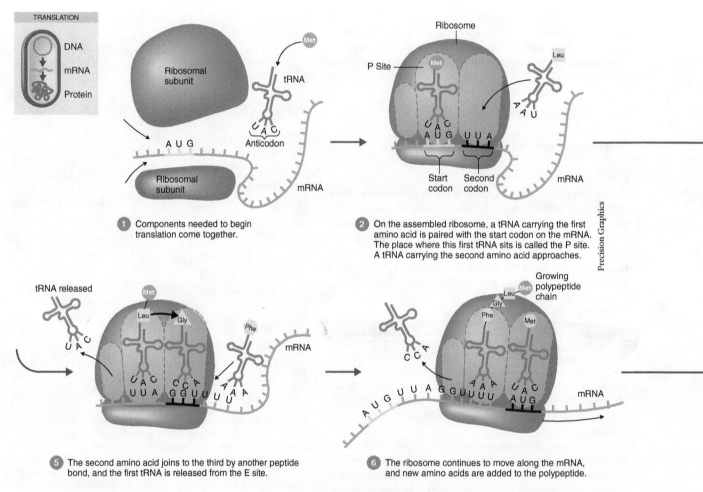

1. Components needed to begin translation come together.

2. On the assembled ribosome, a tRNA carrying the first amino acid is paired with the start codon on the mRNA. The place where this first tRNA sits is called the P site. A tRNA carrying the second amino acid approaches.

5. The second amino acid joins to the third by another peptide bond, and the first tRNA is released from the E site.

6. The ribosome continues to move along the mRNA, and new amino acids are added to the polypeptide.

Precision Graphics

Figure 9 The process of translation. The overall goal of translation is to produce proteins using mRNAs as the source of biological information. The complex cycle of events illustrated here shows the primary role of tRNA and ribosomes in the decoding of this information. The ribosome acts as the site where the mRNA-encoded information is decoded, as well as the site where individual amino acids are connected into polypeptide chains. The tRNA molecules act as the actual "translators"—one end of each tRNA recognizes a specific mRNA codon, while the other end carries the amino acid coded for by that codon.

Q   When does translation stop?

Precision Graphics

Codons are written in terms of their base sequence in mRNA. Notice that there are 64 possible codons but only 20 amino acids. This means that most amino acids are signaled by several alternative codons, a situation referred to as the **degeneracy** of the code. For example, leucine has six codons, and alanine has four codons. Degeneracy allows for a certain amount of change, or mutation, in the DNA without affecting the protein ultimately produced.

Of the 64 codons, 61 are sense codons, and 3 are nonsense codons. **Sense codons** code for amino acids, and **nonsense codons** (also called *stop codons*) do not. Rather, the nonsense codons—UAA, UAG, and UGA—signal the end of the protein molecule's synthesis. The start codon that initiates the synthesis of the protein molecule is AUG, which is also the codon for methionine. In bacteria, the start AUG codes for formylmethionine rather than the methionine found in other parts of the protein. The initiating methionine is often removed later, so not all proteins contain methionine.

The codons of mRNA are converted into protein through the process of translation. The codons of an mRNA are "read" sequentially; and, in response to each codon, the appropriate amino acid is assembled into a growing chain. The site of translation is the ribosome, and **transfer RNA (tRNA)** molecules both recognize the specific codons and transport the required amino acids.

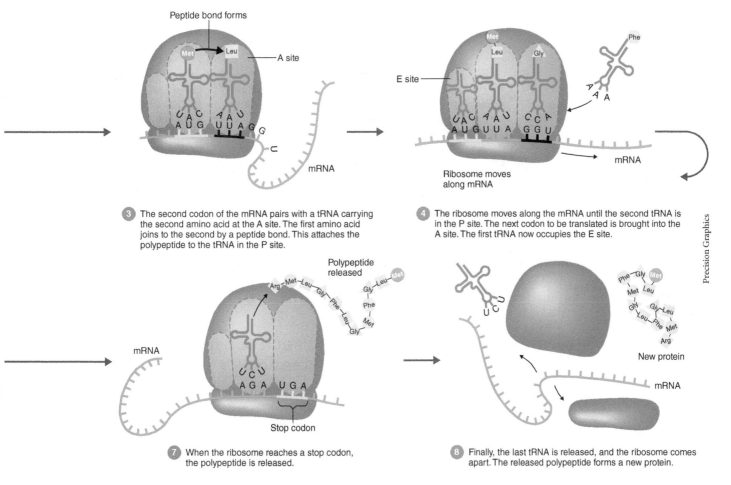

3 The second codon of the mRNA pairs with a tRNA carrying the second amino acid at the A site. The first amino acid joins to the second by a peptide bond. This attaches the polypeptide to the tRNA in the P site.

4 The ribosome moves along the mRNA until the second tRNA is in the P site. The next codon to be translated is brought into the A site. The first tRNA now occupies the E site.

7 When the ribosome reaches a stop codon, the polypeptide is released.

8 Finally, the last tRNA is released, and the ribosome comes apart. The released polypeptide forms a new protein.

Precision Graphics

Figure 9 The process of translation. (continued)

Each tRNA molecule has an **anticodon,** a sequence of three bases that is complementary to a codon. In this way, a tRNA molecule can base-pair with its associated codon. Each tRNA can also carry on its other end the amino acid encoded by the codon that the tRNA recognizes. The functions of the ribosome are to direct the orderly binding of tRNAs to codons and to assemble the amino acids brought there into a chain, ultimately producing a protein.

Figure 9 shows the details of translation. The necessary components assemble: the two ribosomal subunits, a tRNA with the anticodon UAC, and the mRNA molecule to be translated, along with several additional protein factors. This sets up the start codon (AUG) in the proper position to allow translation to begin. After the ribosome joins the first two amino acids with a peptide bond, the first tRNA molecule leaves the ribosome. The ribosome then moves along the mRNA to the next codon. As the proper amino acids are brought into line one by one, peptide bonds are formed between them, and a polypeptide chain results. Translation ends when one of the three nonsense codons in the mRNA is reached. The ribosome then comes apart into its two subunits, and the mRNA and newly synthesized polypeptide chain are released. The ribosome, the mRNA, and the tRNAs are then available to be used again.

The ribosome moves along the mRNA in the $5' \rightarrow 3'$ direction. As a ribosome moves along the mRNA, it will soon allow the start codon to be exposed. Additional ribosomes can then assemble and begin synthesizing protein. In this way, there are usually a number of ribosomes attached to a single mRNA, all at various stages of protein synthesis. In prokaryotic cells, the translation of mRNA into protein can begin even before

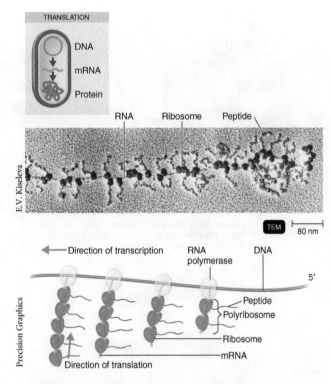

Figure 10 Simultaneous transcription and translation in bacteria. Many molecules of mRNA are being synthesized simultaneously. The longest mRNA molecules were the first to be transcribed at the promoter. Note the ribosomes attached to the newly forming mRNA. The micrograph shows a polyribosome (many ribosomes) in a single bacterial gene.

Q Why can translation begin before transcription is complete in prokaryotes but not in eukaryotes?

transcription is complete (**Figure 10**). Because mRNA is produced in the cytoplasm, the start codons of an mRNA being transcribed are available to ribosomes before the entire mRNA molecule is even made.

In eukaryotic cells, transcription takes place in the nucleus. The mRNA must be completely synthesized and moved through the nuclear membrane to the cytoplasm before translation can begin. In addition, the RNA undergoes processing before it leaves the nucleus. In eukaryotic cells, the regions of genes that code for proteins are often interrupted by noncoding DNA. Thus, eukaryotic genes are composed of **exons,** the regions of DNA *expressed,* and **introns,** the *intervening* regions of DNA that do not encode protein. In the nucleus, RNA polymerase synthesizes a molecule called an RNA transcript that contains copies of the introns. Particles called **small nuclear ribonucleoproteins,** abbreviated **snRNPs** and pronounced "snurps," remove the introns and splice the exons together. In

some organisms, the introns act as ribozymes to catalyze their own removal (**Figure 11**).

* * *

To summarize, genes are the units of biological information encoded by the sequence of nucleotide bases in DNA. A gene is expressed, or turned into a product within the cell, through the processes of transcription and translation. The genetic information carried in DNA is transferred to a temporary mRNA molecule by transcription. Then, during translation, the mRNA directs the assembly of amino acids into a polypeptide chain: a ribosome attaches to mRNA, tRNAs deliver the amino acids to the ribosome as directed by the mRNA codon sequence, and the ribosome assembles the amino acids into the chain that will be the newly synthesized protein. (MM) **Animations** Translation: Overview, Genetic Code, Process

CHECK YOUR UNDERSTANDING

☑ What is the role of the promoter, terminator, and mRNA in transcription? **4**

☑ How does mRNA production in eukaryotes differ from the process in prokaryotes? **5**

The Regulation of Bacterial Gene Expression

LEARNING OBJECTIVES

6 Define *operon.*

7 Explain pre-transcriptional regulation of gene expression in bacteria.

8 Explain post-transcriptional regulation of gene expression.

A cell's genetic machinery and its metabolic machinery are integrated and interdependent. The bacterial cell carries out an enormous number of metabolic reactions. The common feature of all metabolic reactions is that they are catalyzed by enzymes. Feedback inhibition stops a cell from performing unneeded chemical reactions. Feedback inhibition stops enzymes that have already been synthesized. We will now look at mechanisms to prevent synthesis of enzymes that are not needed.

We have seen that genes, through transcription and translation, direct the synthesis of proteins, many of which serve as enzymes—the very enzymes used for cellular metabolism. Because protein synthesis requires a huge amount of energy, regulation of protein synthesis is important to the cell's energy economy. Cells save energy by making only those proteins needed at a particular time. Next we look at how chemical reactions are regulated by controlling the synthesis of the enzymes.

Many genes, perhaps 60–80%, are not regulated but are instead *constitutive,* meaning that their products are constantly

Figure 11 RNA processing in eukaryotic cells.

Q Why can't the RNA transcript be used for translation?

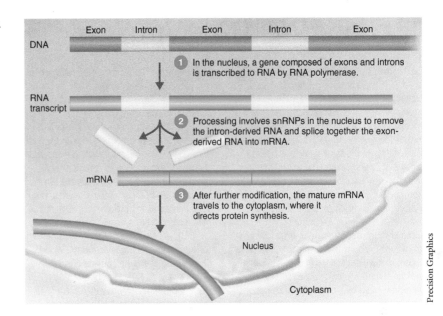

DNA | Exon | Intron | Exon | Intron | Exon

1 In the nucleus, a gene composed of exons and introns is transcribed to RNA by RNA polymerase.

RNA transcript

2 Processing involves snRNPs in the nucleus to remove the intron-derived RNA and splice together the exon-derived RNA into mRNA.

mRNA

3 After further modification, the mature mRNA travels to the cytoplasm, where it directs protein synthesis.

Nucleus

Cytoplasm

Precision Graphics

produced at a fixed rate. Usually these genes, which are effectively turned on all the time, code for enzymes that the cell needs in fairly large amounts for its major life processes; the enzymes of glycolysis are examples. The production of other enzymes is regulated so that they are present only when needed. *Trypanosoma,* the protozoan parasite that causes African sleeping sickness, has hundreds of genes coding for surface glycoproteins. Each protozoan cell turns on only one glycoprotein gene at a time. As the host's immune system kills parasites with one type of surface molecule, parasites expressing a different surface glycoprotein can continue to grow.

Pre-transcriptional Control

Two genetic control mechanisms known as repression and induction regulate the transcription of mRNA and consequently the synthesis of enzymes from them. These mechanisms control the formation and amounts of enzymes in the cell, not the activities of the enzymes.

Repression

The regulatory mechanism that inhibits gene expression and decreases the synthesis of enzymes is called **repression.** Repression is usually a response to the overabundance of an end-product of a metabolic pathway; it causes a decrease in the rate of synthesis of the enzymes leading to the formation of that product. Repression is mediated by regulatory proteins called **repressors,** which block the ability of RNA polymerase to initiate transcription from the repressed genes. The default position of a repressible gene is *on.*

Induction

The process that turns on the transcription of a gene or genes is **induction.** A substance that acts to induce transcription of a gene is called an **inducer,** and enzymes that are synthesized in the presence of inducers are *inducible enzymes.* The genes required for lactose metabolism in *E. coli* are a well-known example of an inducible system. One of these genes codes for the enzyme β-galactosidase, which splits the substrate lactose into two simple sugars, glucose and galactose. (β refers to the type of linkage that joins the glucose and galactose.) If *E. coli* is placed into a medium in which no lactose is present, the organisms contain almost no β-galactosidase; however, when lactose is added to the medium, the bacterial cells produce a large quantity of the enzyme. Lactose is converted in the cell to the related compound allolactose, which is the inducer for these genes; the presence of lactose thus indirectly induces the cells to synthesize more enzyme. The default position of an inducible gene is *off.* (MM) **Animations** Operons: Induction, Repression

The Operon Model of Gene Expression

Details of the control of gene expression by induction and repression are described by the operon model. François Jacob and Jacques Monod formulated this general model in 1961 to account for the regulation of protein synthesis. They based their model on studies of the induction of the enzymes of lactose catabolism in *E. coli.* In addition to β-galactosidase, these enzymes include lac permease, which is involved in the transport of lactose into the cell, and transacetylase, which metabolizes certain disaccharides other than lactose.

Tracking West Nile Virus

On August 23, 1999, an infectious disease physician from a hospital in northern Queens contacted the New York City Department of Health (NYCDOH) to report two patients with encephalitis. On investigation, the NYCDOH initially identified a cluster of six patients with encephalitis. At the same time, local health officials observed increased fatalities among New York City birds. No bacteria were cultured from the patients' blood or cerebrospinal fluid. Viruses transmitted by mosquitoes are a likely cause of aseptic encephalitis during the summer months. These viruses are called arboviruses. Arboviruses, *arthropod-borne*, are viruses that are maintained in nature through biological transmission between susceptible vertebrate hosts by blood-feeding arthropods, such as mosquitoes.

Nucleic acid sequencing of isolates from birds was performed at the CDC on September 23. Comparison of the nucleic acid sequences to databases indicated that the viruses were closely related to West Nile virus (WNV, see the photo), which had never been isolated in the Western Hemisphere.

By 2007, WNV had been found in birds in all states except Alaska and Hawaii. By 2009, the CDC considered West Nile virus endemic in the United States. The recognition of WNV in the Western Hemisphere in the summer of 1999 marked the first introduction in recent history of an Old World flavivirus into the New World.

West Nile virus was first isolated in 1937 in the West Nile district of Uganda. In the early 1950s, scientists recognized WNV encephalitis outbreaks in humans in Egypt and Israel. Initially considered a minor arbovirus, WNV has emerged as a major public health and veterinary concern in southern Europe, the Mediterranean basin, and North America.

Researchers looked at the virus's genome for clues about its path around the world. The flavivirus genome consists of a positive, single-stranded RNA 11,000 to 12,000 nucleotides long. (Positive RNA can act as mRNA and be translated.) The virus has acquired several mutations, and researchers are looking for clues in these mutations to determine the virus's journey.

1. Using the portions of the genomes (shown below) that encode viral proteins, can you determine how similar are these viruses? Can you figure out its movement around the world?
   Determine the amino acids encoded, and group the viruses based on percentage of similarity to the Uganda strain.

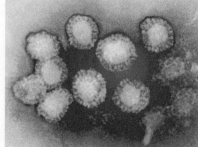

Linda Stannard, UCT/Photo Researchers

West Nile virus TEM ⊢——⊣ 50 nm

2. Based on amino acids, there are two groups called clades.
   Which group is older?

3. The North American and Australian strains have accumulated more mutations, so these should be more recent.
   Calculate the percentage of difference between nucleotides to see how the viruses are related within their clade.

4. Although genetically related groups or clades can be seen, the actual journey of the virus remains elusive.

Source: Adapted from CDC data.

Australia	A	C	C	C	C	G	T	C	C	A	C	C	C	T	T	T	C	A	A	T	T
Egypt	A	A	T	C	G	A	T	C	A	T	C	T	T	C	G	T	C	G	A	T	C
France	A	A	T	C	G	A	T	C	A	T	C	G	T	C	G	T	C	G	A	T	C
Israel	A	T	C	C	A	T	T	C	A	T	C	C	T	C	A	T	C	G	A	T	T
Italy	A	T	C	C	A	C	T	C	A	T	C	C	T	C	G	T	C	G	A	T	T
Kenya	A	T	C	C	A	T	C	A	T	C	C	T	C	G	T	C	G	A	T	T	
Mexico	A	A	C	C	C	T	T	C	C	T	C	C	C	C	T	T	C	G	A	T	T
United States	A	A	C	C	C	T	C	C	T	C	C	C	C	T	T	C	G	A	T	T	
Uganda	A	T	A	C	G	A	T	C	A	T	G	C	T	C	G	T	C	C	A	T	C

The genes for the three enzymes involved in lactose uptake and utilization are next to each other on the bacterial chromosome and are regulated together (**Figure 12**). These genes, which determine the structures of proteins, are called *structural genes* to distinguish them from an adjoining control region on the DNA. When lactose is introduced into the culture medium, the *lac* structural genes are all transcribed and translated rapidly and simultaneously. We will now see how this regulation occurs.

In the control region of the *lac* operon are two relatively short segments of DNA. One, the *promoter*, is the region of DNA where RNA polymerase initiates transcription. The other is the **operator,** which is like a traffic light that acts as a go or stop signal for transcription of the structural genes. A set of operator and promoter sites and the structural genes they control define an **operon;** thus, the combination of the three *lac* structural genes and the adjoining control regions is called the *lac* operon.

A regulatory gene called the *I gene* encodes a **repressor** protein that switches inducible and repressible operons on or off. The *lac* operon is an **inducible operon** (see Figure 12). In the absence of lactose, the repressor binds to the operator site, thus preventing transcription. If lactose is present, the repressor binds to a metabolite of lactose instead of to the operator, and lactose-digesting enzymes are transcribed.

In **repressible operons,** the structural genes are transcribed until they are turned off, or *repressed* (Figure 13). The genes for the enzymes involved in the synthesis of tryptophan are regulated in this manner. The structural genes are transcribed and translated, leading to tryptophan synthesis. When excess tryptophan is present, the tryptophan acts as a **corepressor** binding to the repressor protein. The repressor protein can now bind to the operator, stopping further tryptophan synthesis.

(MM) **Animation** Operons: Overview

CHECK YOUR UNDERSTANDING

✓ Use the following metabolic pathway to answer the questions that follow it. 6

Substrate *A* $\xrightarrow{\text{enzyme } a}$ Intermediate *B* $\xrightarrow{\text{enzyme } b}$ End-product *C*

a. If enzyme *a* is inducible and is not being synthesized at present, a
(1) _____ protein must be bound tightly to the
(2) _____ site. When the inducer is present, it will bind to
the (3) _____ so that (4) _____ can occur.

b. If enzyme *a* is repressible, end-product *C*, called a
(1) _____, causes the (2) _____ to bind to the
(3) _____. What causes derepression?

Positive Regulation

Regulation of the lactose operon also depends on the level of glucose in the medium, which in turn controls the intracellular level of the small molecule **cyclic AMP (cAMP)**, a substance derived from ATP that serves as a cellular alarm signal. Enzymes that metabolize glucose are constitutive, and cells grow at their maximal rate with glucose as their carbon source because they can use it most efficiently (Figure 14). When glucose is no longer available, cAMP accumulates in the cell. The cAMP binds to the allosteric site of *catabolic activator protein (CAP).* CAP then binds to the *lac* promoter, which initiates transcription by making it easier for RNA polymerase to bind to the promoter. Thus transcription of the *lac* operon requires both the presence of lactose and the absence of glucose (Figure 15).

Cyclic AMP is an example of an *alarmone,* a chemical alarm signal that promotes a cell's response to environmental or nutritional stress. (In this case, the stress is the lack of glucose.)

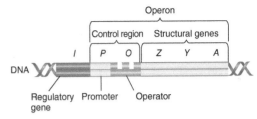

1 **Structure of the operon.** The operon consists of the promoter (*P*) and operator (*O*) sites and structural genes that code for the protein. The operon is regulated by the product of the regulatory gene (*I*).

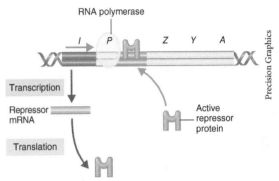

2 **Repressor active, operon off.** The repressor protein binds with the operator, preventing transcription from the operon.

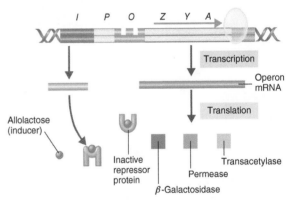

3 **Repressor inactive, operon on.** When the inducer allolactose binds to the repressor protein, the inactivated repressor can no longer block transcription. The structural genes are transcribed, ultimately resulting in the production of the enzymes needed for lactose catabolism.

Figure 12 An inducible operon. Lactose-digesting enzymes are produced in the presence of lactose. In *E. coli,* the genes for the three enzymes are in the *lac* operon. β-galactosidase is encoded by *lacZ*. The *lacY* gene encodes the lac permease, and *lacA* encodes transacetylase, whose function in lactose metabolism is still unclear.

[Q] What causes transcription of an inducible enzyme?

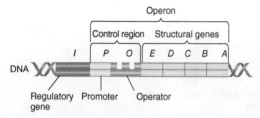

DNA

Regulatory gene   Promoter   Operator

Control region   Structural genes

Operon

1 Structure of the operon. The operon consists of the promoter (*P*) and operator (*O*) sites and structural genes that code for the protein. The operon is regulated by the product of the regulatory gene (*I*).

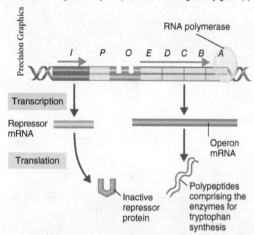

RNA polymerase

Transcription

Repressor mRNA

Translation

Operon mRNA

Inactive repressor protein

Polypeptides comprising the enzymes for tryptophan synthesis

2 Repressor inactive, operon on. The repressor is inactive, and transcription and translation proceed, leading to the synthesis of tryptophan.

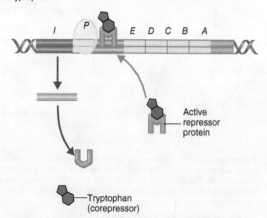

Active repressor protein

Tryptophan (corepressor)

3 Repressor active, operon off. When the corepressor tryptophan binds to the repressor protein, the activated repressor binds with the operator, preventing transcription from the operon.

Figure 13 A repressible operon. Tryptophan, an amino acid, is produced by anabolic enzymes encoded by five structural genes. Accumulation of tryptophan represses transcription of these genes, preventing further synthesis of tryptophan. The *E. coli trp* operon is shown here.

Q What causes transcription of a repressible enzyme?

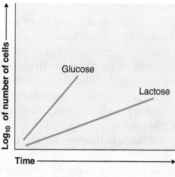

(a) Bacteria growing on glucose as the sole carbon source grow faster than on lactose.

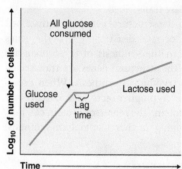

(b) Bacteria growing in a medium containing glucose and lactose first consume the glucose and then, after a short lag time, the lactose. During the lag time, intracellular cAMP increases, the *lac* operon is transcribed, more lactose is transported into the cell, and β-galactosidase is synthesized to break down lactose.

Figure 14 The growth rate of *E. coli* on glucose and lactose.

Q When both glucose and lactose are present, why will cells use glucose first?

The same mechanism involving cAMP allows the cell to grow on other sugars. Inhibition of the metabolism of alternative carbon sources by glucose is termed **catabolite repression** (or the *glucose effect*). When glucose is available, the level of cAMP in the cell is low, and consequently CAP is not bound.

Epigenetic Control

Eukaryotic and bacterial cells can turn genes off by methylating certain nucleotides. The methylated (off) genes are passed to offspring cells. Unlike mutations, this isn't permanent, and the genes can be turned on in a later generation. This is called *epigenetic inheritance* (*epigenetic* = on genes). Epigenetics may explain why bacteria behave differently in a biofilm.

Post-transcriptional Control

Some regulatory mechanisms stop protein synthesis after transcription has occurred. Single-stranded RNA molecules of approximately 22 nucleotides, called **microRNAs (miRNAs),** inhibit protein production in eukaryotic cells. In humans, miRNAs produced during development allow different cells to

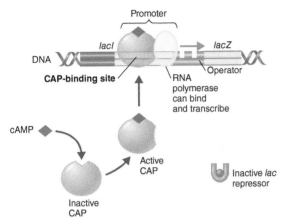

(a) Lactose present, glucose scarce (cAMP level high). If glucose is scarce, the high level of cAMP activates CAP, and the *lac* operon produces large amounts of mRNA for lactose digestion.

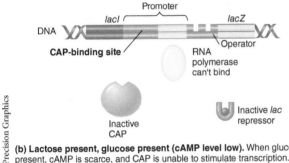

(b) Lactose present, glucose present (cAMP level low). When glucose is present, cAMP is scarce, and CAP is unable to stimulate transcription.

Figure 15 Positive regulation of the *lac* operon.

Q Will transcription of the *lac* operon occur in the presence of lactose and glucose? In the presence of lactose and the absence of glucose? In the presence of glucose and the absence of lactose?

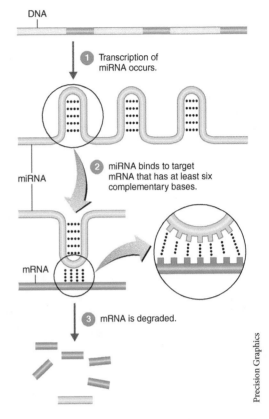

1 Transcription of miRNA occurs.

2 miRNA binds to target mRNA that has at least six complementary bases.

3 mRNA is degraded.

Figure 16 MicroRNAs control a wide range of activities in cells.

Q In mammals, some miRNAs hybridize with viral RNA. What would happen if a mutation occurred in the miRNA gene?

produce different proteins. Heart cells and skin cells have the same genes, but the cells in each organ produce different proteins because of miRNAs produced in each cell type during development. Similar short RNAs in bacteria enable the cell to cope with environmental stresses, such as low temperature or oxidative damage. An miRNA base-pairs with a complementary mRNA, forming a double-standard RNA. This double-standard RNA is enzymatically destroyed so that the mRNA-encoded protein is not made (**Figure 16**). The action of another type of RNA, siRNA, is similar.

CHECK YOUR UNDERSTANDING

✔ What is the role of cAMP in regulating gene expression? 7

✔ How does miRNA stop protein synthesis? 8

Mutation: Change in the Genetic Material

LEARNING OBJECTIVES

9 Classify mutations by type.

10 Describe two ways mutations can be repaired.

11 Describe the effect of mutagens on the mutation rate.

12 Outline the methods of direct and indirect selection of mutants.

13 Identify the purpose of and outline the procedure for the Ames test.

A **mutation** is a permanent change in the base sequence of DNA. Such a change in the base sequence of a gene will sometimes cause a change in the product encoded by that gene. For example, when the gene for an enzyme mutates, the enzyme encoded by the gene may become inactive or less active because its amino acid sequence has changed. Such a change in genotype may be disadvantageous, or even lethal, if the cell loses a

Precision Graphics

239

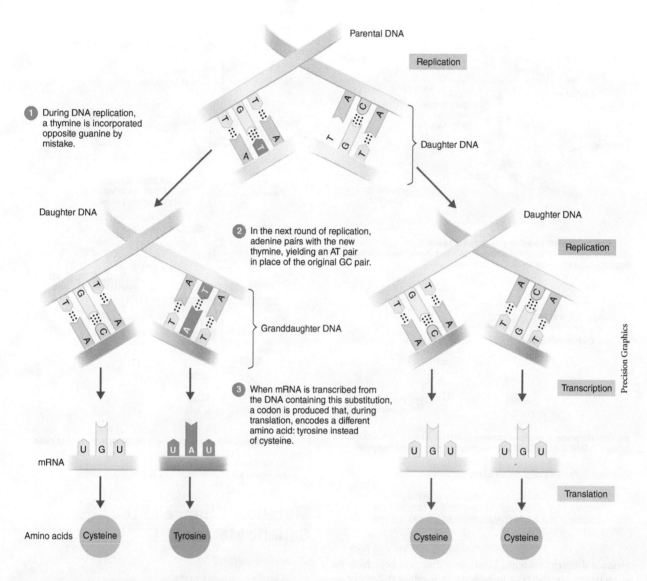

① During DNA replication, a thymine is incorporated opposite guanine by mistake.

② In the next round of replication, adenine pairs with the new thymine, yielding an AT pair in place of the original GC pair.

③ When mRNA is transcribed from the DNA containing this substitution, a codon is produced that, during translation, encodes a different amino acid: tyrosine instead of cysteine.

Parental DNA

Replication

Daughter DNA

Daughter DNA

Daughter DNA

Granddaughter DNA

Replication

Transcription

mRNA

Translation

Amino acids   Cysteine   Tyrosine   Cysteine   Cysteine

Precision Graphics

Figure 17 Base substitutions. This mutation leads to an altered protein in a granddaughter cell.

Q Does a base substitution always result in a different amino acid?

phenotypic trait it needs. However, a mutation can be beneficial if, for instance, the altered enzyme encoded by the mutant gene has a new or enhanced activity that benefits the cell.

Many simple mutations are silent (neutral); the change in DNA base sequence causes no change in the activity of the product encoded by the gene. Silent mutations commonly occur when one nucleotide is substituted for another in the DNA, especially at a location corresponding to the third position of the mRNA codon. Because of the degeneracy of the genetic code, the resulting new codon might still code for the same amino

acid. Even if the amino acid is changed, the function of the protein may not change if the amino acid is in a nonvital portion of the protein, or is chemically very similar to the original amino acid.

Types of Mutations

The most common type of mutation involving single base pairs is **base substitution** (or *point mutation*), in which a single base at one point in the DNA sequence is replaced with a different base. When the DNA replicates, the result is a substituted base pair (Figure 17). For example, AT might be substituted for GC, or CG for GC. If a base substitution occurs within a gene that codes for a protein, the mRNA transcribed from the gene will carry an incorrect base at that position. When the mRNA is translated into protein, the incorrect base may cause the insertion of an incorrect amino acid in the protein. If the base substitution results in an amino acid substitution in the synthesized protein, this change in the DNA is known as a **missense mutation** (Figure 18a and Figure 18b).

The effects of such mutations can be dramatic. For example, sickle cell disease is caused by a single change in the gene for globin, the protein component of hemoglobin. Hemoglobin is primarily responsible for transporting oxygen from the lungs to the tissues. A single missense mutation, a change from an A to a T at a specific site, results in the change from glutamic acid to valine in the protein. The effect of this change is that the shape of the hemoglobin molecule changes under conditions of low oxygen, altering the shape of the red blood cells such that movement of the cells through small capillaries is greatly impeded.

By creating a nonsense (stop) codon in the middle of an mRNA molecule, some base substitutions effectively prevent the synthesis of a complete functional protein; only a fragment is synthesized. A base substitution resulting in a nonsense codon is thus called a **nonsense mutation** (Figure 18c).

Besides base-pair mutations, there are also changes in DNA called **frameshift mutations,** in which one or a few nucleotide pairs are deleted or inserted in the DNA (Figure 18d). This mutation can shift the "translational reading frame"—that is, the three-by-three grouping of nucleotides recognized as codons by the tRNAs during translation. For example, deleting one nucleotide pair in the middle of a gene causes changes in many amino acids downstream from the site of the original mutation. Frameshift mutations almost always result in a long stretch of altered amino acids and the production of an inactive protein from the mutated gene. In most cases, a nonsense codon will eventually be encountered and thereby terminate translation.

Occasionally, mutations occur where significant numbers of bases are added to (inserted into) a gene. Huntington's disease, for example, is a progressive neurological disorder caused by extra bases inserted into a particular gene.

Base substitutions and frameshift mutations may occur spontaneously because of occasional mistakes made during DNA replication. These **spontaneous mutations** apparently occur in the absence of any mutation-causing agents. Agents in the environment, such as certain chemicals and radiation, that directly or indirectly bring about mutations are called **mutagens.** In the microbial world, certain mutations result in resistance to antibiotics.

CHECK YOUR UNDERSTANDING

✔ How can a mutation be beneficial? 9

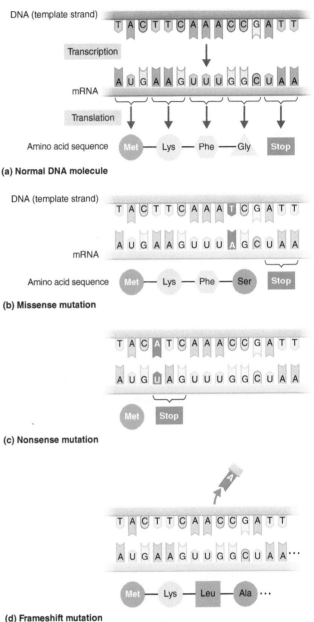

(a) **Normal DNA molecule**

(b) **Missense mutation**

(c) **Nonsense mutation**

(d) **Frameshift mutation**

Precision Graphics

Figure 18 Types of mutations and their effects on the amino acid sequences of proteins.

Q What happens if base 9 in (a) is changed to a C?

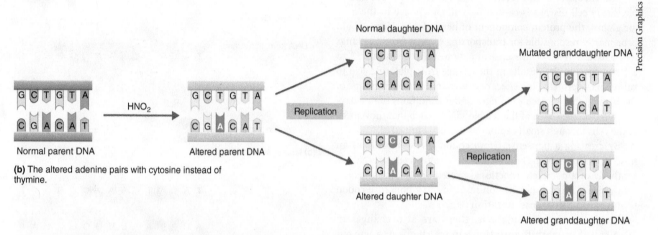

(a) Adenosine nucleoside normally base-pairs by hydrogen bonds with an oxygen and a hydrogen of a thymine or uracil nucleotide.

Altered adenine will hydrogen bond with a hydrogen and a nitrogen of a cytosine nucleotide.

Normal daughter DNA

Mutated granddaughter DNA

Normal parent DNA

Altered parent DNA

Replication

Altered daughter DNA

Replication

Altered granddaughter DNA

(b) The altered adenine pairs with cytosine instead of thymine.

Precision Graphics

Figure 19 Oxidation of nucleotides makes a mutagen. The nitrous acid emitted into the air by burning fossil fuels oxidizes adenine.

 What is a mutagen?

Clinical Case

A person's DNA can undergo mutations. One improper nucleotide in DNA creates a mutation, which could alter the function of the gene. Cancer is abnormal cell growth caused by mutations. These mutations can be inherited.

As Marcel and his wife, Janice, drive home from the doctor's office, they review Marcel's family history. Marcel's brother, Robert, passed away from colon cancer 10 years ago, but Marcel has always been the picture of health. Even at 70, he hasn't given a thought to retiring from his Memphis barbeque restaurant that he once co-owned with his brother until Robert's death.

What factors may have contributed to Marcel's colon cancer?

Mutagens

Chemical Mutagens

One of the many chemicals known to be a mutagen is nitrous acid. Figure 19 shows how exposure of DNA to nitrous acid can convert the base adenine (A) to a form that no longer pairs with thymine (T) but instead pairs with cytosine (C). When DNA containing such modified adenines replicates, one daughter DNA molecule will have a base-pair sequence different from that of the parent DNA. Eventually, some AT base pairs of the parent will have been changed to GC base pairs in a granddaughter cell. Nitrous acid makes a specific base-pair change in DNA. Like all mutagens, it alters DNA at random locations.

Another type of chemical mutagen is the **nucleoside analog.** These molecules are structurally similar to normal nitrogenous bases, but they have slightly altered base-pairing properties. Examples, 2-aminopurine and 5-bromouracil, are shown in Figure 20. When nucleoside analogs are given to growing cells, the analogs are randomly incorporated into cellular DNA in place of the normal bases. Then, during DNA replication, the analogs cause mistakes in base pairing. The incorrectly paired

Figure 20 Nucleoside analogs and the nitrogenous bases they replace. A nucleoside is phosphorylated, and the resulting nucleotide used to synthesize DNA.

Q Why do these drugs kill cells?

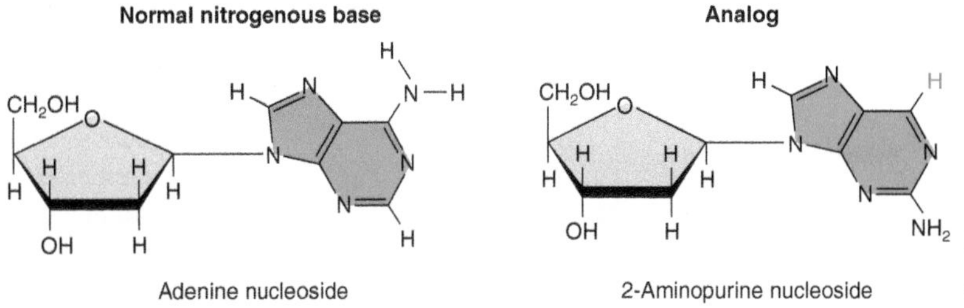

Normal nitrogenous base

Adenine nucleoside

Analog

2-Aminopurine nucleoside

(a) The 2-aminopurine is incorporated into DNA in place of adenine but can pair with cytosine, so an AT pair becomes a CG pair.

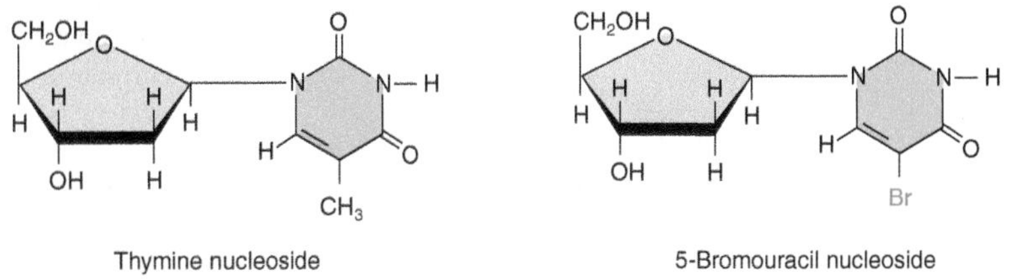

Thymine nucleoside

5-Bromouracil nucleoside

(b) The 5-bromouracil is used as an anticancer drug because it is mistaken for thymine by cellular enzymes but pairs with cytosine. In the next DNA replication, an AT pair becomes a GC pair.

bases will be copied during subsequent replication of the DNA, resulting in base-pair substitutions in the progeny cells. Some antiviral and antitumor drugs are nucleoside analogs, including AZT (azidothymidine), one of the primary drugs used to treat HIV infection.

Still other chemical mutagens cause small deletions or insertions, which can result in frameshifts. For instance, under certain conditions, benzopyrene, which is present in smoke and soot, is an effective *frameshift mutagen*. Aflatoxin—produced by *Aspergillus flavus* (a-spèr-jil′ lus flā′ vus), a mold that grows on peanuts and grain—is a frameshift mutagen, as are the acridine dyes used experimentally against herpesvirus infections. Frameshift mutagens usually have the right size and chemical properties to slip between the stacked base pairs of the DNA double helix. They may work by slightly offsetting the two strands of DNA, leaving a gap or bulge in one strand or the other. When the staggered DNA strands are copied during DNA synthesis, one or more base pairs can be inserted or deleted in the new double-stranded DNA. Interestingly, frameshift mutagens are often potent carcinogens.

Radiation

X rays and gamma rays are forms of radiation that are potent mutagens because of their ability to ionize atoms and molecules. The penetrating rays of ionizing radiation cause electrons to pop out of their usual shells. These electrons bombard other molecules and cause more damage, and many of the resulting ions and free radicals (molecular fragments with unpaired electrons) are very reactive. Some of these ions oxidize bases in DNA, resulting in errors in DNA replication and repair that produce mutations (see Figure 19). An even more serious outcome is the breakage of covalent bonds in the sugar-phosphate backbone of DNA, which causes physical breaks in chromosomes.

Another form of mutagenic radiation is ultraviolet (UV) light, a nonionizing component of ordinary sunlight. However, the most mutagenic component of UV light (wavelength 260 nm) is screened out by the ozone layer of the atmosphere. The most important effect of direct UV light on DNA is the formation of harmful covalent bonds between certain bases. Adjacent thymines in a DNA strand can cross-link to form thymine dimers. Such dimers, unless repaired, may cause serious damage or death to the cell because it cannot properly transcribe or replicate such DNA.

Bacteria and other organisms have enzymes that can repair UV-induced damage. **Photolyases,** also known as *light-repair enzymes,* use visible light energy to separate the dimer back to the original two thymines. **Nucleotide excision repair,** shown in Figure 21, is not restricted to UV-induced damage; it can repair mutations from other causes as well. Enzymes cut out the incorrect base and fill in the gap with newly synthesized DNA that is complementary to the correct strand. For many years biologists questioned how the incorrect base could be distinguished from the correct base if it was not physically distorted like a thymine dimer. In 1970, Hamilton Smith provided the answer with the discovery of **methylases.** These enzymes add a methyl group to selected bases soon after a DNA strand is made. A repair endonuclease then cuts the nonmethylated strand.

Exposure to UV light in humans, such as by excessive suntanning, causes a large number of thymine dimers in skin cells. Unrepaired dimers may result in skin cancers. Humans

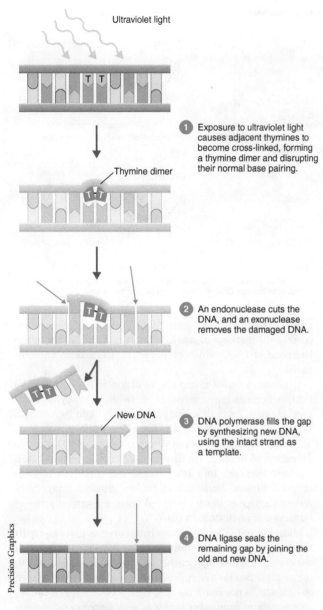

Ultraviolet light

1 Exposure to ultraviolet light causes adjacent thymines to become cross-linked, forming a thymine dimer and disrupting their normal base pairing.

Thymine dimer

2 An endonuclease cuts the DNA, and an exonuclease removes the damaged DNA.

New DNA

3 DNA polymerase fills the gap by synthesizing new DNA, using the intact strand as a template.

4 DNA ligase seals the remaining gap by joining the old and new DNA.

Precision Graphics

Figure 21 The creation and repair of a thymine dimer caused by ultraviolet light. After exposure to UV light, adjacent thymines can become cross-linked, forming a thymine dimer. In the absence of visible light, the nucleotide excision repair mechanism is used in a cell to repair the damage.

Q How do excision repair enzymes "know" which strand is incorrect?

with xeroderma pigmentosum, an inherited condition that results in increased sensitivity to UV light, have a defect in nucleotide excision repair; consequently, they have an increased risk of skin cancer.

The Frequency of Mutation

The **mutation rate** is the probability that a gene will mutate when a cell divides. The rate is usually stated as a power of 10, and because mutations are very rare, the exponent is always a negative number. For example, if there is one chance in 10,000 that a gene will mutate when the cell divides, the mutation rate is 1/10,000, which is expressed as 10^{-4}. Spontaneous mistakes in DNA replication occur at a very low rate, perhaps only once in 10^9 replicated base pairs (a mutation rate of 10^{-9}). Because the average gene has about 10^3 base pairs, the spontaneous rate of mutation is about one in 10^6 (a million) replicated genes.

Mutations usually occur more or less randomly along a chromosome. The occurrence of random mutations at low frequency is an essential aspect of the adaptation of species to their environment, for evolution requires that genetic diversity be generated randomly and at a low rate. For example, in a bacterial population of significant size—say, greater than 10^7 cells—a few new mutant cells will always be produced in every generation. Most mutations either are harmful and likely to be removed from the gene pool when the individual cell dies or are neutral. However, a few mutations may be beneficial. For example, a mutation that confers antibiotic resistance is beneficial to a population of bacteria that is regularly exposed to antibiotics. Once such a trait has appeared through mutation, cells carrying the mutated gene are more likely than other cells to survive and reproduce as long as the environment stays the same. Soon most of the cells in the population will have the gene; an evolutionary change will have occurred, although on a small scale.

A mutagen usually increases the spontaneous rate of mutation, which is about one in 10^6 replicated genes, by a factor of 10 to 1000 times. In other words, in the presence of a mutagen, the normal rate of 10^{-6} mutations per replicated gene becomes a rate of 10^{-5} to 10^{-3} per replicated gene. Mutagens are used experimentally to enhance the production of mutant cells for research on the genetic properties of microorganisms and for commercial purposes. **(MM) Animation** Mutations: Types, Repair

CHECK YOUR UNDERSTANDING

✓ How can mutations be repaired? **10**

✓ How do mutagens affect the mutation rate? **11**

Identifying Mutants

Mutants can be detected by selecting or testing for an altered phenotype. Whether or not a mutagen is used, mutant cells with specific mutations are always rare compared with other cells in the population. The problem is detecting such a rare event.

Experiments are usually performed with bacteria because they reproduce rapidly, so large numbers of organisms (more than 10^9 per milliliter of nutrient broth) can easily be used. Furthermore, because bacteria generally have only one copy of each gene per cell, the effects of a mutated gene are not masked

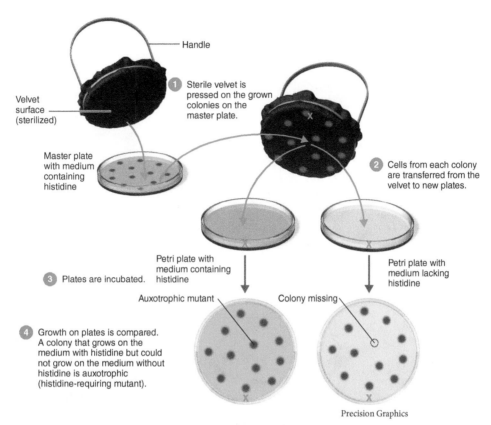

Figure 22 Replica plating. In this example, the auxotrophic mutant cannot synthesize histidine. The plates must be carefully marked (with an X here) to maintain orientation so that colony positions are known in relation to the original master plate.

Q What is an auxotroph?

by the presence of a normal version of the gene, as in many eukaryotic organisms.

Positive (direct) selection involves the detection of mutant cells by rejection of the unmutated parent cells. For example, suppose we were trying to find mutant bacteria that are resistant to penicillin. When the bacterial cells are plated on a medium containing penicillin, the mutant can be identified directly. The few cells in the population that are resistant (mutants) will grow and form colonies, whereas the normal, penicillin-sensitive parental cells cannot grow.

To identify mutations in other kinds of genes, **negative (indirect) selection** can be used. This process selects a cell that cannot perform a certain function, using the technique of **replica plating**. For example, suppose we wanted to use replica plating to identify a bacterial cell that has lost the ability to synthesize the amino acid histidine (Figure 22). First, about 100 bacterial cells are inoculated onto an agar plate. This plate, called the master plate, contains a medium with histidine on which all cells will grow. After

18 to 24 hours of incubation, each cell reproduces to form a colony. Then a pad of sterile material, such as latex, filter paper, or velvet, is pressed over the master plate, and some of the cells from each colony adhere to the velvet. Next, the velvet is pressed down onto two (or more) sterile plates. One plate contains a medium without histidine, and one contains a medium with histidine on which the original, nonmutant bacteria can grow. Any colony that grows on the medium with histidine on the master plate but that cannot synthesize its own histidine will not be able to grow on the medium without histidine. The mutant colony can then be identified on the master plate. Of course, because mutants are so rare (even those induced by mutagens), many plates must be screened with this technique to isolate a specific mutant.

Replica plating is a very effective means of isolating mutants that require one or more new growth factors. Any mutant microorganism having a nutritional requirement that is absent in the parent is known as an **auxotroph.** For example, an auxotroph may lack an enzyme needed to synthesize a particular

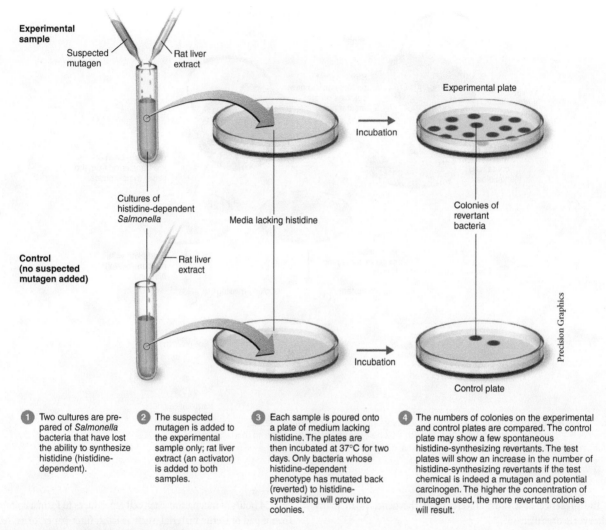

1. Two cultures are pre-pared of *Salmonella* bacteria that have lost the ability to synthesize histidine (histidine-dependent).

2. The suspected mutagen is added to the experimental sample only; rat liver extract (an activator) is added to both samples.

3. Each sample is poured onto a plate of medium lacking histidine. The plates are then incubated at 37°C for two days. Only bacteria whose histidine-dependent phenotype has mutated back (reverted) to histidine-synthesizing will grow into colonies.

4. The numbers of colonies on the experimental and control plates are compared. The control plate may show a few spontaneous histidine-synthesizing revertants. The test plates will show an increase in the number of histidine-synthesizing revertants if the test chemical is indeed a mutagen and potential carcinogen. The higher the concentration of mutagen used, the more revertant colonies will result.

Figure 23 **The Ames reverse gene mutation test.**

Q Do all mutagens cause cancer?

amino acid and will therefore require that amino acid as a growth factor in its nutrient medium.

Identifying Chemical Carcinogens

Many known mutagens have been found to be **carcinogens,** substances that cause cancer in animals, including humans. In recent years, chemicals in the environment, the workplace, and the diet have been implicated as causes of cancer in humans. The usual subjects of tests to determine potential carcinogens are animals, and the testing procedures are time-consuming and expensive. Now there are faster and less expensive procedures for the preliminary screening of potential carcinogens. One of these, called the **Ames test,** uses bacteria as carcinogen indicators.

The Ames test is based on the observation that exposure of mutant bacteria to mutagenic substances may cause new mutations that reverse the effect (the change in phenotype) of the original mutation. These are called *reversions.* Specifically, the test measures the reversion of histidine auxotrophs of *Salmonella* (his⁻ cells, mutants that have lost the ability to synthesize histidine) to histidine-synthesizing cells (his⁺) after treatment with a mutagen (Figure 23). Bacteria are incubated in both the presence and absence of the substance being tested. Because animal enzymes must activate many chemicals into forms that are chemically reactive for mutagenic or carcinogenic activity to appear, the chemical to be tested and the mutant bacteria are incubated together with rat liver extract, a rich source of activation enzymes. If the substance being tested is mutagenic, it will cause the reversion of his⁻ bacteria to his⁺ bacteria at a rate higher than the spontaneous reversion rate. The number of observed revertants indicates the degree to which a substance is mutagenic and therefore possibly carcinogenic.

The test can be used in many ways. Several potential mutagens can be qualitatively tested by spotting the individual chemicals on small paper disks on a single plate inoculated with bacteria. The Ames test is routinely used to evaluate new chemicals and air and water pollutants.

About 90% of the substances found by the Ames test to be mutagenic have also been shown to be carcinogenic in animals. By the same token, the more mutagenic substances have generally been found to be more carcinogenic.

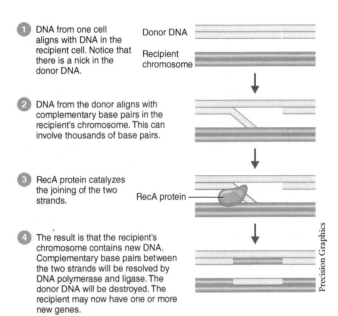

1. DNA from one cell aligns with DNA in the recipient cell. Notice that there is a nick in the donor DNA.

Donor DNA
Recipient chromosome

2. DNA from the donor aligns with complementary base pairs in the recipient's chromosome. This can involve thousands of base pairs.

3. RecA protein catalyzes the joining of the two strands.

RecA protein

4. The result is that the recipient's chromosome contains new DNA. Complementary base pairs between the two strands will be resolved by DNA polymerase and ligase. The donor DNA will be destroyed. The recipient may now have one or more new genes.

Precision Graphics

Figure 24 Genetic recombination by crossing over. Foreign DNA can be inserted into a chromosome by breaking and rejoining the chromosome. This can insert one or more new genes into the chromosome.

Q What type of enzyme breaks the DNA?

Clinical Case

Not all mutations are inherited; some are induced by genotoxins, that is, chemicals that damage a cell's genetic material. Marcel is not overweight, makes sure he spends time with his family, and has never smoked. Researchers have known since the 1970s that people who consume cooked meat and meat products are more likely to develop colon cancer. The suspect cancer-causing chemicals are aromatic amines that form during high-heat cooking.

Marcel has owned his Memphis barbeque restaurant for over 50 years. He is a hands-on type of employer and is always in the kitchen overseeing the cooking process. All of his barbequed meat is seared over high heat and then slow-cooked for hours. Marcel is considered the expert in this technique, but now it seems as if his profession could be a factor in his disease.

What test can be used to determine whether a chemical is genotoxic?

chromosome. Figure 24 shows one mechanism for genetic recombination. If a cell picks up a foreign DNA (called donor DNA in the figure), some of it could insert into the cell's chromosome—a process called **crossing over**—and some of the genes carried by the chromosomes are shuffled. The DNA has recombined, so that the chromosome now carries a portion of the donor's DNA.

If A and B represent DNA from different individuals, how are they brought close enough together to recombine? In eukaryotes, genetic recombination is an ordered process that usually occurs as part of the sexual cycle of the organism. Crossing over generally takes place during the formation of reproductive cells, such that these cells contain recombinant DNA. In bacteria, genetic recombination can happen in a number of ways, which we will discuss in the following sections.

Like mutation, genetic recombination contributes to a population's genetic diversity, which is the source of variation in evolution. In highly evolved organisms such as present-day microbes, recombination is more likely than mutation to be beneficial because recombination will less likely destroy a gene's function and may bring together combinations of genes that enable the organism to carry out a valuable new function.

The major protein that constitutes the flagella of *Salmonella* is also one of the primary proteins that causes our immune systems to respond. However, these bacteria have the capability of producing two different flagellar proteins. As our immune system mounts a response against those cells containing one form

CHECK YOUR UNDERSTANDING

☑ How would you isolate an antibiotic-resistant bacterium? An antibiotic-sensitive bacterium? 12

☑ What is the principle behind the Ames test? 13

Genetic Transfer and Recombination

LEARNING OBJECTIVES

14 Differentiate horizontal and vertical gene transfer.

15 Compare the mechanisms of genetic recombination in bacteria.

16 Describe the functions of plasmids and transposons.

Genetic recombination refers to the exchange of genes between two DNA molecules to form new combinations of genes on a

of the flagellar protein, those organisms producing the second are not affected. Which flagellar protein is produced is determined by a recombination event that apparently occurs somewhat randomly within the chromosomal DNA. Thus, by altering the flagellar protein produced, *Salmonella* can better avoid the defenses of the host.

Vertical gene transfer occurs when genes are passed from an organism to its offspring. Plants and animals transmit their genes by vertical transmission. Bacteria can pass their genes not only to their offspring, but also laterally, to other microbes of the same generation. This is known as **horizontal gene transfer** (see Figure 2). Horizontal gene transfer between bacteria occurs in several ways. In all of the mechanisms, the transfer involves a **donor cell** that gives a portion of its total DNA to a **recipient cell.** Once transferred, part of the donor's DNA is usually incorporated into the recipient's DNA; the remainder is degraded by cellular enzymes. The recipient cell that incorporates donor DNA into its own DNA is called a *recombinant.* The transfer of genetic material between bacteria is by no means a frequent event; it may occur in only 1% or less of an entire population. Let's examine in detail the specific types of genetic transfer. (MM) **Animation** Horizontal Gene Transfer: Overview

Transformation in Bacteria

During the process of **transformation,** genes are transferred from one bacterium to another as "naked" DNA in solution. This process was first demonstrated over 70 years ago, although it was not understood at the time. Not only did transformation show that genetic material could be transferred from one bacterial cell to another, but study of this phenomenon eventually led to the conclusion that DNA is the genetic material. The initial experiment on transformation was performed by Frederick Griffith in England in 1928 while he was working with two strains of *Streptococcus pneumoniae.* One, a virulent (pathogenic) strain, has a polysaccharide capsule that prevents phagocytosis. The bacteria grow and cause pneumonia. The other, an avirulent strain, lacks the capsule and does not cause disease.

Griffith was interested in determining whether injections of heat-killed bacteria of the encapsulated strain could be used to vaccinate mice against pneumonia. As he expected, injections of living encapsulated bacteria killed the mouse (Figure 25a); injections of live nonencapsulated bacteria (Figure 25b) or dead encapsulated bacteria (Figure 25c) did not kill the mouse. However, when the dead encapsulated bacteria were mixed with live nonencapsulated bacteria and injected into the mice, many of the mice died. In the blood of the dead mice, Griffith found living, encapsulated bacteria. Hereditary material (genes) from the dead bacteria had entered the live cells and changed them genetically so that their progeny were encapsulated and therefore virulent (Figure 25d).

Subsequent investigations based on Griffith's research revealed that bacterial transformation could be carried out

without mice. A broth was inoculated with live nonencapsulated bacteria. Dead encapsulated bacteria were then added to the broth. After incubation, the culture was found to contain living bacteria that were encapsulated and virulent. The nonencapsulated bacteria had been transformed; they had acquired a new hereditary trait by incorporating genes from the killed encapsulated bacteria.

The next step was to extract various chemical components from the killed cells to determine which component caused the transformation. These crucial experiments were performed in the United States by Oswald T. Avery and his associates Colin M. MacLeod and Maclyn McCarty. After years of research, they announced in 1944 that the component responsible for transforming harmless *S. pneumoniae* into virulent strains was DNA. Their results provided one of the conclusive indications that DNA was indeed the carrier of genetic information.

Since the time of Griffith's experiment, considerable information has been gathered about transformation. In nature, some bacteria, perhaps after death and cell lysis, release their

---

Clinical Case Resolved

The Ames test allows rapid screening of chemicals for genotoxicity. The his⁻ mutant *Salmonella* bacteria used in the Ames test are spread over glucose–minimal salts agar plates. A paper disk saturated with 2-aminofluorene (2-AF), an aromatic amine, is placed on the culture. The figure, for example, shows that reversion of the his⁻ mutation allowed the *Salmonella* to grow. This indicates that the chemical is mutagenic and is therefore potentially carcinogenic.

L. Brent Selinger, Pearson Science

There are studies indicating that 2-AF activated by enzymes is more damaging than 2-AF alone, suggesting that the interaction between diet and intestinal microbiota is more likely to cause cancer than just diet. Variations in diet produce little change in the kinds of bacteria in the intestine, but they produce dramatic changes in the metabolic activity of the bacteria.

The detection of serrated colorectal polyps from Marcel's stool DNA test led to a diagnosis of an early, rather than late, stage of colorectal cancer. The offending polyps are found and removed, and Marcel undergoes chemotherapy to kill any missed cancer cells in his colon.

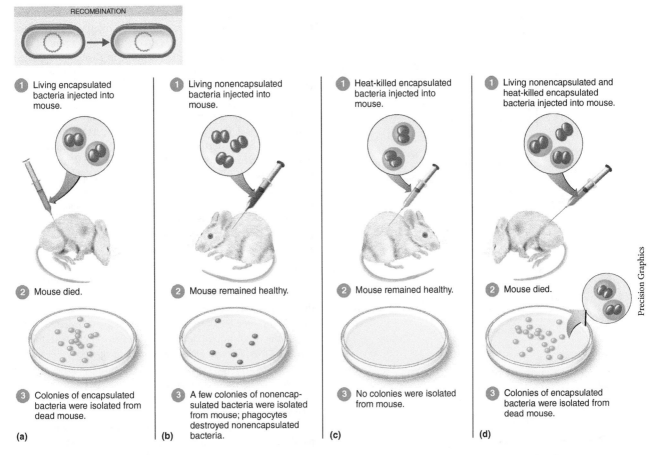

RECOMBINATION

(a)
1. Living encapsulated bacteria injected into mouse.
2. Mouse died.
3. Colonies of encapsulated bacteria were isolated from dead mouse.

(b)
1. Living nonencapsulated bacteria injected into mouse.
2. Mouse remained healthy.
3. A few colonies of nonencapsulated bacteria were isolated from mouse; phagocytes destroyed nonencapsulated bacteria.

(c)
1. Heat-killed encapsulated bacteria injected into mouse.
2. Mouse remained healthy.
3. No colonies were isolated from mouse.

(d)
1. Living nonencapsulated and heat-killed encapsulated bacteria injected into mouse.
2. Mouse died.
3. Colonies of encapsulated bacteria were isolated from dead mouse.

Precision Graphics

Figure 25 Griffith's experiment demonstrating genetic transformation.
(**a**) Living encapsulated bacteria caused disease and death when injected into a mouse. (**b**) Living nonencapsulated bacteria are readily destroyed by the phagocytic defenses of the host, so the mouse remained healthy after injection. (**c**) After being killed by heat, encapsulated bacteria lost the ability to cause disease. (**d**) However, the combination of living nonencapsulated bacteria and heat-killed encapsulated bacteria (neither of which alone causes disease) did cause disease. Somehow, the live nonencapsulated bacteria were transformed by the dead encapsulated bacteria so that they acquired the ability to form a capsule and therefore cause disease. Subsequent experiments proved the transforming factor to be DNA.

[Q] Why did encapsulated bacteria kill the mouse while nonencapsulated bacteria did not? What killed the mouse in (d)?

Precision Graphics

DNA into the environment. Other bacteria can then encounter the DNA and, depending on the particular species and growth conditions, take up fragments of DNA and integrate them into their own chromosomes by recombination. A protein called RecA binds to the cell's DNA and then to donor DNA causing the exchange of strands. A recipient cell with this new combination of genes is a kind of hybrid, or recombinant cell (Figure 26). All the descendants of such a recombinant cell will be identical to it. Transformation occurs naturally among very few genera of bacteria, including *Bacillus, Haemophilus* (hē-mä′ fi-lus), *Neisseria, Acinetobacter* (á sin-ē-tō-bak-tėr), and certain strains of the genera *Streptococcus* and *Staphylococcus.*

Even though only a small portion of a cell's DNA is transferred to the recipient, the molecule that must pass through the recipient cell wall and membrane is still very large. When a recipient cell is in a physiological state in which it can take up the donor DNA, it is said to be competent. **Competence** results from alterations in the cell wall that make it permeable to large DNA molecules. (MM) **Animation** Transformation

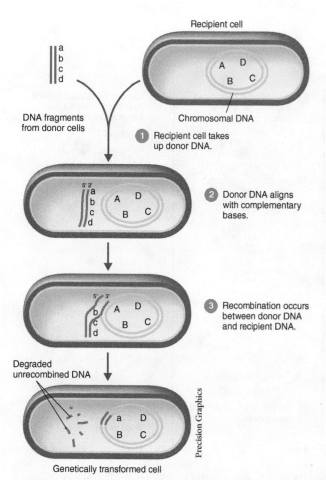

Figure 26 The mechanism of genetic transformation in bacteria. Some similarity is needed for the donor and recipient to align. Genes *a, b, c,* and *d* may be mutations of genes *A, B, C,* and *D*.

Q What type of enzyme cuts the donor DNA?

Conjugation in Bacteria

Another mechanism by which genetic material is transferred from one bacterium to another is known as **conjugation.** Conjugation is mediated by one kind of *plasmid,* a circular piece of DNA that replicates independently from the cell's chromosome. However, plasmids differ from bacterial chromosomes in that the genes they carry are usually not essential for the growth of the cell under normal conditions. The plasmids responsible for conjugation are transmissible between cells during conjugation.

Conjugation differs from transformation in two major ways. First, conjugation requires direct cell-to-cell contact. Second, the conjugating cells must generally be of opposite mating type; donor cells must carry the plasmid, and recipient cells usually do not. In gram-negative bacteria, the plasmid carries genes that code for the synthesis of *sex pili,* projections from the donor's cell surface that contact the recipient and help bring the two cells into direct contact (Figure 27a). Gram-positive bacterial cells produce sticky surface molecules that cause cells to come into direct contact with each other. In the process of conjugation, the plasmid is replicated during the transfer of a single-stranded copy of the plasmid DNA to the recipient, where the complementary strand is synthesized (Figure 27b).

Because most experimental work on conjugation has been done with *E. coli,* we will describe the process in this organism. In *E. coli,* the **F factor (fertility factor)** was the first plasmid observed to be transferred between cells during conjugation. Donors carrying F factors (F$^+$ cells) transfer the plasmid to recipients (F$^-$ cells), which become F$^+$ cells as a result (Figure 28a). In some cells carrying F factors, the factor integrates into the chromosome, converting the F$^+$ cell to an **Hfr cell** (high frequency of recombination) (Figure 28b). When conjugation occurs between an Hfr cell and an F$^-$ cell, the Hfr cell's chromosome (with its integrated F factor) replicates, and a parental strand of the chromosome is transferred to the recipient cell (Figure 28c). Replication of the Hfr chromosome begins in the middle of the integrated F factor, and a small piece of the F factor leads the chromosomal genes into the F$^-$ cell. Usually, the chromosome breaks before it is completely transferred. Once within the recipient cell, donor DNA can recombine with the recipient's DNA. (Donor DNA that is not integrated is degraded.) Therefore, by conjugation with an Hfr cell, an F$^-$ cell may acquire new versions of chromosomal genes (just as in transformation). However, it remains an F$^-$ cell because it did not receive a complete F factor during conjugation.

Conjugation is used to map the location of genes on a bacterial chromosome. The genes for the synthesis of threonine (*thr*) and leucine (*leu*) are first, reading clockwise from 0. Their locations were determined by conjugation experiments. Assume that conjugation is allowed for only 1 minute between an Hfr strain that is his$^+$, pro$^+$, thr$^+$, and leu$^+$, and an F$^-$ strain that is his$^-$, pro$^-$, thr$^-$, and leu$^-$. If the F$^-$ acquired the ability to synthesize threonine, then the *thr* gene is located early in the chromosome, between 0 and 1 minute. If after 2 minutes the F$^-$ cell now becomes thr$^+$ and leu$^+$, the order of these two genes on the chromosome must be *thr, leu.* (MM) **Animation** Conjugation: Overview, F Factor, Hfr Conjugation, Chromosome Mapping

Transduction in Bacteria

A third mechanism of genetic transfer between bacteria is **transduction.** In this process, bacterial DNA is transferred from a donor cell to a recipient cell inside a virus that infects bacteria, called a **bacteriophage,** or **phage.**

To understand how transduction works, we will consider the life cycle of one type of transducing phage of *E. coli;* this phage carries out **generalized transduction** (Figure 29).

During phage reproduction, phage DNA and proteins are synthesized by the host bacterial cell. The phage DNA should

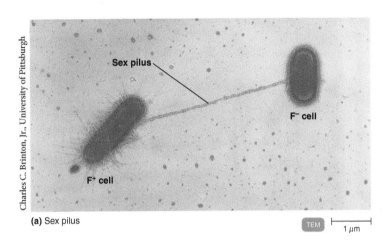

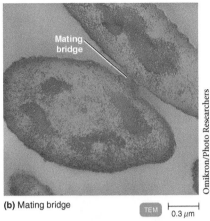

(a) Sex pilus   TEM ⊢——⊣ 1 μm

(b) Mating bridge   TEM ⊢——⊣ 0.3 μm

Charles C. Brinton, Jr., University of Pittsburgh

Omikron/Photo Researchers

Figure 27 Bacterial conjugation.

Q What is an F⁺ cell?

be packaged inside the phage protein coat. However, bacterial DNA, plasmid DNA, or even DNA of another virus may be packaged inside a phage protein coat.

All genes contained within a bacterium infected by a generalized transducing phage are equally likely to be packaged in a phage coat and transferred. In another type of transduction, called **specialized transduction,** only certain bacterial genes are transferred. In one type of specialized transduction, the phage codes for certain toxins produced by their bacterial hosts, such as diphtheria toxin for *Corynebacterium diphtheriae* (kôr′-i-nē-bak-ti-rē-um dif-thi′-rē-ī), erythrogenic toxin for *Streptococcus pyogenes*, and Shiga toxin for *E. coli* O157:H7.

Animation Transduction: Generalized Transduction

CHECK YOUR UNDERSTANDING

✔ Differentiate horizontal and vertical gene transfer. 14

✔ Compare conjugation between the following pairs: F⁺ × F⁻, Hfr × F⁻. 15

Plasmids and Transposons

Plasmids and transposons are genetic elements that provide additional mechanisms for genetic change. They occur in both prokaryotic and eukaryotic organisms, but this discussion focuses on their role in genetic change in prokaryotes.

Plasmids

Plasmids are self-replicating, gene-containing circular pieces of DNA about 1–5% the size of the bacterial chromosome (Figure 30a). They are found mainly in bacteria but also in some eukaryotic microorganisms, such as *Saccharomyces cerevisiae*. The F factor is a **conjugative plasmid** that carries genes for sex pili and for the transfer of the plasmid to another cell. Although plasmids are usually dispensable, under certain conditions genes

carried by plasmids can be crucial to the survival and growth of the cell. For example, **dissimilation plasmids** code for enzymes that trigger the catabolism of certain unusual sugars and hydrocarbons. Some species of *Pseudomonas* can actually use such exotic substances as toluene, camphor, and hydrocarbons of petroleum as primary carbon and energy sources because they have catabolic enzymes encoded by genes carried on plasmids. Such specialized capabilities permit the survival of those microorganisms in very diverse and challenging environments. Because of their ability to degrade and detoxify a variety of unusual compounds, many of them are being investigated for possible use in the cleanup of environmental wastes.

Other plasmids code for proteins that enhance the pathogenicity of a bacterium. The strain of *E. coli* that causes infant diarrhea and traveler's diarrhea carries plasmids that code for toxin production and for bacterial attachment to intestinal cells. Without these plasmids, *E. coli* is a harmless resident of the large intestine; with them, it is pathogenic. Other plasmid-encoded toxins include the exfoliative toxin of *Staphylococcus aureus, Clostridium tetani* neurotoxin, and toxins of *Bacillus anthracis*. Still other plasmids contain genes for the synthesis of **bacteriocins,** toxic proteins that kill other bacteria. These plasmids have been found in many bacterial genera, and they are useful markers for the identification of certain bacteria in clinical laboratories.

Resistance factors (R factors) are plasmids that have significant medical importance. They were first discovered in Japan in the late 1950s after several dysentery epidemics. In some of these epidemics, the infectious agent was resistant to the usual antibiotic. Following isolation, the pathogen was also found to be resistant to a number of different antibiotics. In addition, other normal bacteria from the patients (such as *E. coli*) proved to be resistant as well. Researchers soon discovered that these bacteria acquired

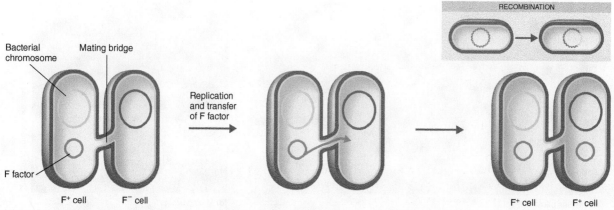

(a) When an F factor (a plasmid) is transferred from a donor (F⁺) to a recipient (F⁻), the F⁻ cell is converted to an F⁺ cell.

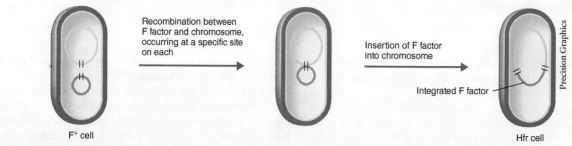

(b) When an F factor becomes integrated into the chromosome of an F⁺ cell, it makes the cell a high frequency of recombination (Hfr) cell.

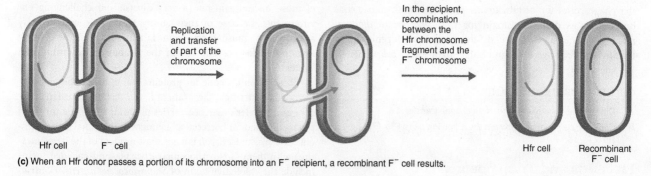

(c) When an Hfr donor passes a portion of its chromosome into an F⁻ recipient, a recombinant F⁻ cell results.

Figure 28 Conjugation in *E. coli*.

Q Do bacteria reproduce during conjugation?

resistance through the spread of genes from one organism to another. The plasmids that mediated this transfer are R factors.

R factors carry genes that confer upon their host cell resistance to antibiotics, heavy metals, or cellular toxins. Many R factors contain two groups of genes. One group is called the **resistance transfer factor (RTF)** and includes genes for plasmid replication and conjugation. The other group, the **r-determinant,** has the resistance genes; it codes for the production of enzymes that inactivate certain drugs or toxic substances (Figure 30b).

Different R factors, when present in the same cell, can recombine to produce R factors with new combinations of genes in their r-determinants.

In some cases, the accumulation of resistance genes within a single plasmid is quite remarkable. For example, Figure 30b shows a genetic map of resistance plasmid R100. Carried on this plasmid are resistance genes for sulfonamides, streptomycin, chloramphenicol, and tetracycline, as well as genes for resistance to mercury. This particular plasmid can be transferred between a number of enteric species, including *Escherichia, Klebsiella,* and *Salmonella.*

R factors present very serious problems for treating infectious diseases with antibiotics. The widespread use of antibiotics in medicine and agriculture has led to the preferential survival (selection) of bacteria that have R factors, so populations of resistant bacteria grow larger and larger. The transfer of resistance between bacterial cells of a population, and even between bacteria of different genera, also contributes to the problem. The ability to reproduce sexually with members of its own species defines a eukaryotic species. However, a bacterial species can conjugate and transfer plasmids to other species. *Neisseria* may have acquired its penicillinase-producing plasmid from *Streptococcus,* and *Agrobacterium* can transfer plasmids to plant cells. Nonconjugative plasmids may be transferred from one cell to another by inserting themselves into a conjugative plasmid or a chromosome or by transformation when released from a dead cell. Insertion is made possible by an insertion sequence, which will be discussed shortly.

Plasmids are an important tool for genetic engineering.

Transposons

Transposons are small segments of DNA that can move (be "transposed") from one region of a DNA molecule to another. These pieces of DNA are 700 to 40,000 base pairs long.

In the 1950s, American geneticist Barbara McClintock discovered transposons in corn, but they occur in all organisms and have been studied most thoroughly in microorganisms. They may move from one site to another site on the same chromosome or to another chromosome or plasmid. As you might imagine, the frequent movement of transposons could wreak havoc inside a cell. For example, as transposons move about on chromosomes, they may insert themselves *within* genes, inactivating them. Fortunately, transposition occurs relatively rarely. The frequency of transposition is comparable to the spontaneous mutation rate that occurs in bacteria—that is, from 10^{-5} to 10^{-7} per generation.

All transposons contain the information for their own transposition. As shown in Figure 31a, the simplest transposons, also called **insertion sequences (IS),** contain only a gene that codes for an enzyme (*transposase,* which catalyzes the cutting and resealing of DNA that occurs in transposition) and recognition sites. *Recognition sites* are short inverted repeat sequences of DNA that the enzyme recognizes as recombination sites between the transposon and the chromosome.

Complex transposons also carry other genes not connected with the transposition process. For example, bacterial transposons may contain genes for enterotoxin or for antibiotic resistance (Figure 31b). Plasmids such as R factors are frequently made up of a collection of transposons (Figure 31c).

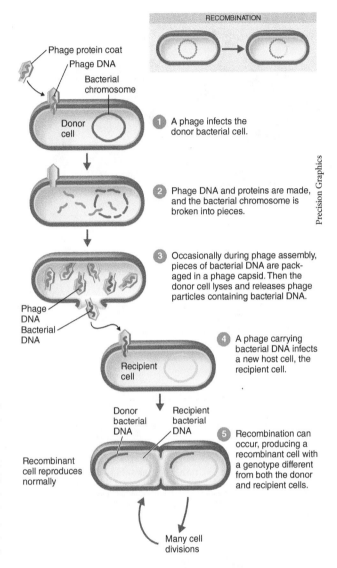

1 A phage infects the donor bacterial cell.

2 Phage DNA and proteins are made, and the bacterial chromosome is broken into pieces.

3 Occasionally during phage assembly, pieces of bacterial DNA are packaged in a phage capsid. Then the donor cell lyses and releases phage particles containing bacterial DNA.

4 A phage carrying bacterial DNA infects a new host cell, the recipient cell.

5 Recombination can occur, producing a recombinant cell with a genotype different from both the donor and recipient cells.

Figure 29 Transduction by a bacteriophage. Shown here is generalized transduction, in which any bacterial DNA can be transferred from one cell to another.

Q How could *E. coli* acquire the Shiga toxin gene?

Transposons with antibiotic resistance genes are of practical interest, but there is no limitation on the kinds of genes that transposons can have. Thus, transposons provide a natural mechanism for the movement of genes from one chromosome to another. Furthermore, because they may be carried between cells on plasmids or viruses, they can also spread from one organism—or even species—to another. For example, vancomycin resistance was transferred from *Enterococcus faecalis* to *Staphylococcus aureus*

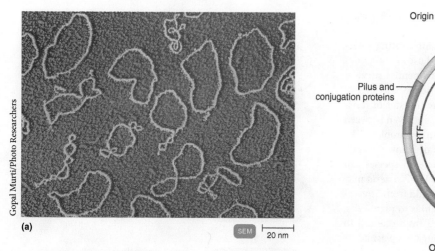

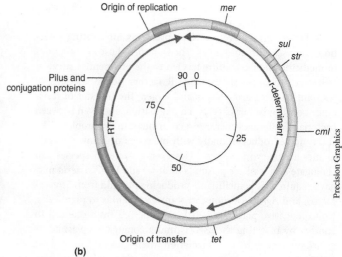

(a)

SEM | 20 nm

(b)

Origin of replication

mer

sul

str

Pilus and conjugation proteins

90 0

75

25

50

RTF

r-determinant

cml

Origin of transfer

tet

Precision Graphics

Figure 30 R factor, a type of plasmid.
(**a**) Plasmids from *E. coli* bacteria. (**b**) A diagram of an R factor, which has two parts: the RTF contains genes needed for plasmid replication and transfer of the plasmid by conjugation, and the r-determinant carries genes for resistance to four different antibiotics and mercury (*sul* = sulfonamide resistance, *str* = streptomycin resistance, *cml* = chloramphenicol resistance, *tet* = tetracycline resistance, *mer* = mercury resistance); numbers are base pairs × 1000.

Q Why are R factors important in the treatment of infectious diseases?

IS1

A C T T A C T G A T   A T C A G T A A G T

Transposase gene

T G A A T G A C T A   T A G T C A T T C A

Inverted repeat   Inverted repeat

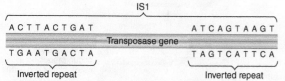

(**a**) An insertion sequence (IS), the simplest transposon, contains a gene for transposase, the enzyme that catalyzes transposition. The tranposase gene is bounded at each end by inverted repeat sequences that function as recognition sites for the transposon. IS1 is one example of an insertion sequence, shown here with simplified IR sequences.

Tn5

Kanamycin resistance

IS1   IS1

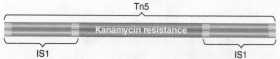

(**b**) Complex transposons carry other genetic material in addition to transposase genes. The example shown here, Tn5, carries the gene for kanamycin resistance and has complete copies of the insertion sequence IS1 at each end.

A C T T A C T G

A T   A T C A G T A A G T

Transposase gene

T G A A T G A C T A   T A

G T C A T T C A

1 Transposase cuts DNA, leaving sticky ends.

IS1

Kanamycin resistance

IS1

Precision Graphics

2 Sticky ends of transposon and target DNA anneal.

(**c**) Insertion of the transposon Tn5 into R100 plasmid

Figure 31 Transposons and insertion.

Q Why are transposons sometimes referred to as "jumping genes"?

via a transposon called Tn1546. Transposons are thus a potentially powerful mediator of evolution in organisms. (MM) Animations
Transposons: Overview, Insertion Sequences, Complex Transposons

CHECK YOUR UNDERSTANDING

✔ What types of genes do plasmids carry? 16

Genes and Evolution

LEARNING OBJECTIVE

17   Discuss how genetic mutation and recombination provide material for natural selection to act upon.

We have now seen how gene activity can be controlled by the cell's internal regulatory mechanisms and how genes themselves can be altered or rearranged by mutation, transposition,

and recombination. All these processes provide diversity in the descendants of cells. Diversity provides the raw material for evolution, and natural selection provides its driving force. Natural selection will act on diverse populations to ensure the survival of those fit for that particular environment. The different kinds of microorganisms that exist today are the result of a long history of evolution. Microorganisms have continually changed by alterations in their genetic properties and acquisition of adaptations to many different habitats.

CHECK YOUR UNDERSTANDING

✔ Natural selection means that the environment favors survival of some genotypes. From where does diversity in genotypes come? 17

Study Outline

Mastering MICROBIOLOGY™

Test your understanding with quizzes, microbe review, and a chapter post-test at www.masteringmicrobiology.com.

Structure and Function of the Genetic Material

1. Genetics is the study of what genes are, how they carry information, how their information is expressed, and how they are replicated and passed to subsequent generations or other organisms.
2. DNA in cells exists as a double-stranded helix; the two strands are held together by hydrogen bonds between specific nitrogenous base pairs: AT and CG.
3. A gene is a segment of DNA, a sequence of nucleotides, that encodes a functional product, usually a protein.
4. The DNA in a cell is duplicated before the cell divides, so each offspring cell receives the same genetic information.

Genotype and Phenotype

5. Genotype is the genetic composition of an organism, its entire complement of DNA.
6. Phenotype is the expression of the genes: the proteins of the cell and the properties they confer on the organism.

DNA and Chromosomes

7. The DNA in a chromosome exists as one long double helix associated with various proteins that regulate genetic activity.
8. Genomics is the molecular characterization of genomes.

The Flow of Genetic Information

9. Information contained in the DNA is transcribed into RNA and translated into proteins.

DNA Replication

10. During DNA replication, the two strands of the double helix separate at the replication fork, and each strand is used as a template by DNA polymerases to synthesize two new strands of DNA according to the rules of nitrogenous base pairing.
11. The result of DNA replication is two new strands of DNA, each having a base sequence complementary to one of the original strands.
12. Because each double-stranded DNA molecule contains one original and one new strand, the replication process is called semiconservative.
13. DNA is synthesized in one direction designated $5' \rightarrow 3'$. At the replication fork, the leading strand is synthesized continuously and the lagging strand discontinuously.
14. DNA polymerase proofreads new molecules of DNA and removes mismatched bases before continuing DNA synthesis.
15. Each daughter bacterium receives a chromosome that is virtually identical to the parent's.

RNA and Protein Synthesis

16. During transcription, the enzyme RNA polymerase synthesizes a strand of RNA from one strand of double-stranded DNA, which serves as a template.
17. RNA is synthesized from nucleotides containing the bases A, C, G, and U, which pair with the bases of the DNA strand being transcribed.
18. RNA polymerase binds the promoter; transcription begins at AUG; the region of DNA that is the end point of transcription is the terminator; RNA is synthesized in the $5' \rightarrow 3'$ direction.
19. Translation is the process in which the information in the nucleotide base sequence of mRNA is used to dictate the amino acid sequence of a protein.

20. The mRNA associates with ribosomes, which consist of rRNA and protein.
21. Three-base segments of mRNA that specify amino acids are called codons.
22. The genetic code refers to the relationship among the nucleotide base sequence of DNA, the corresponding codons of mRNA, and the amino acids for which the codons code.
23. The genetic code is degenerate; that is, most amino acids are coded for by more than one codon.
24. Specific amino acids are attached to molecules of tRNA. Another portion of the tRNA has a base triplet called an anticodon.
25. The base pairing of codon and anticodon at the ribosome results in specific amino acids being brought to the site of protein synthesis.
26. The ribosome moves along the mRNA strand as amino acids are joined to form a growing polypeptide; mRNA is read in the $5' \rightarrow 3'$ direction.
27. Translation ends when the ribosome reaches a stop codon on the mRNA.

The Regulation of Bacterial Gene Expression

1. Regulating protein synthesis at the gene level is energy-efficient because proteins are synthesized only as they are needed.
2. Constitutive enzymes produce products at a fixed rate. Examples are genes for the enzymes in glycolysis.
3. For these gene regulatory mechanisms, the control is aimed at mRNA synthesis.

Pre-transcriptional Control

4. When cells are exposed to a particular end-product, the synthesis of enzymes related to that product is repressed.
5. In the presence of certain chemicals (inducers), cells synthesize more enzymes. This process is called induction.
6. In bacteria, a group of coordinately regulated structural genes with related metabolic functions, plus the promoter and operator sites that control their transcription, are called an operon.
7. In the operon model for an inducible system, a regulatory gene codes for the repressor protein.
8. When the inducer is absent, the repressor binds to the operator, and no mRNA is synthesized.
9. When the inducer is present, it binds to the repressor so that it cannot bind to the operator; thus, mRNA is made, and enzyme synthesis is induced.
10. In repressible systems, the repressor requires a corepressor in order to bind to the operator site; thus, the corepressor controls enzyme synthesis.
11. Transcription of structural genes for catabolic enzymes (such as β-galactosidase) is induced by the absence of glucose. Cyclic AMP and CRP must bind to a promoter in the presence of an alternative carbohydrate.
12. Methylated nucleotides are not transcribed in epigenetic control.

Post-transcriptional Control

13. MicroRNAs combine with mRNA; the resulting double-stranded RNA is destroyed.

Mutation: Change in the Genetic Material

1. A mutation is a change in the nitrogenous base sequence of DNA; that change causes a change in the product coded for by the mutated gene.
2. Many mutations are neutral, some are disadvantageous, and others are beneficial.

Types of Mutations

3. A base substitution occurs when one base pair in DNA is replaced with a different base pair.
4. Alterations in DNA can result in missense mutations (which cause amino acid substitutions) or nonsense mutations (which create stop codons).
5. In a frameshift mutation, one or a few base pairs are deleted or added to DNA.
6. Mutagens are agents in the environment that cause permanent changes in DNA.
7. Spontaneous mutations occur without the presence of any mutagen.

Mutagens

8. Chemical mutagens include base-pair mutagens, nucleoside analogs, and frameshift mutagens.
9. Ionizing radiation causes the formation of ions and free radicals that react with DNA; base substitutions or breakage of the sugar-phosphate backbone results.
10. Ultraviolet (UV) radiation is nonionizing; it causes bonding between adjacent thymines.
11. Damage to DNA caused by UV radiation can be repaired by enzymes that cut out and replace the damaged portion of DNA.
12. Light-repair enzymes repair thymine dimers in the presence of visible light.

The Frequency of Mutation

13. Mutation rate is the probability that a gene will mutate when a cell divides; the rate is expressed as 10 to a negative power.
14. Mutations usually occur randomly along a chromosome.
15. A low rate of spontaneous mutations is beneficial in providing the genetic diversity needed for evolution.

Identifying Mutants

16. Mutants can be detected by selecting or testing for an altered phenotype.
17. Positive selection involves the selection of mutant cells and the rejection of nonmutated cells.
18. Replica plating is used for negative selection—to detect, for example, auxotrophs that have nutritional requirements not possessed by the parent (nonmutated) cell.

Identifying Chemical Carcinogens

19. The Ames test is a relatively inexpensive and rapid test for identifying possible chemical carcinogens.
20. The test assumes that a mutant cell can revert to a normal cell in the presence of a mutagen and that many mutagens are carcinogens.

Genetic Transfer and Recombination

1. Genetic recombination, the rearrangement of genes from separate groups of genes, usually involves DNA from different organisms; it contributes to genetic diversity.

2. In crossing over, genes from two chromosomes are recombined into one chromosome containing some genes from each original chromosome.

3. Vertical gene transfer occurs during reproduction when genes are passed from an organism to its offspring.

4. Horizontal gene transfer in bacteria involves a portion of the cell's DNA being transferred from donor to recipient.

5. When some of the donor's DNA has been integrated into the recipient's DNA, the resultant cell is called a recombinant.

Transformation in Bacteria

6. During this process, genes are transferred from one bacterium to another as "naked" DNA in solution.

7. This process occurs naturally among a few genera of bacteria.

Conjugation in Bacteria

8. This process requires contact between living cells.

9. One type of genetic donor cell is an F$^+$; recipient cells are F$^-$. F cells contain plasmids called F factors; these are transferred to the F$^-$ cells during conjugation.

10. When the plasmid becomes incorporated into the chromosome, the cell is called an Hfr (high frequency of recombination) cell.

11. During conjugation, an Hfr cell can transfer chromosomal DNA to an F$^-$ cell. Usually, the Hfr chromosome breaks before it is fully transferred.

Transduction in Bacteria

12. In this process, DNA is passed from one bacterium to another in a bacteriophage and is then incorporated into the recipient's DNA.

13. In generalized transduction, any bacterial genes can be transferred.

Plasmids and Transposons

14. Plasmids are self-replicating circular molecules of DNA carrying genes that are not usually essential for the cell's survival.

15. There are several types of plasmids, including conjugative plasmids, dissimilation plasmids, plasmids carrying genes for toxins or bacteriocins, and resistance factors.

16. Transposons are small segments of DNA that can move from one region to another region of the same chromosome or to a different chromosome or a plasmid.

17. Transposons are found in chromosomes, in plasmids, and in the genetic material of viruses. They vary from simple (insertion sequences) to complex.

18. Complex transposons can carry any type of gene, including antibiotic-resistance genes, and are thus a natural mechanism for moving genes from one chromosome to another.

Genes and Evolution

1. Diversity is the precondition for evolution.

2. Genetic mutation and recombination provide a diversity of organisms, and the process of natural selection allows the growth of those best adapted to a given environment.

Study Questions

Answers to the Review and Multiple Choice questions can be found at this end of this chapter.

Review

1. Briefly describe the components of DNA, and explain its functional relationship to RNA and protein.

2. DRAW IT Identify and mark each of the following on the portion of DNA undergoing replication: replication fork, DNA polymerase, RNA primer, parent strands, leading strand, lagging strand, the direction of replication on each strand, and the 5′ end of each strand.

5′
3′

3. Match the following examples of mutagens.

Column A	Column B
__2__ a. A mutagen that is incorporated into DNA in place of a normal base	1. Frameshift mutagen
__4__ b. A mutagen that causes the formation of highly reactive ions	2. Nucleoside analog
__3__ c. A mutagen that alters adenine so that it base-pairs with cytosine	3. Base-pair mutagen
__1__ d. A mutagen that causes insertions	4. Ionizing radiation
__5__ e. A mutagen that causes the formation of pyrimidine dimers	5. Nonionizing radiation

4. The following is a code for a strand of DNA.

DNA	3′ A T A T _ _ _ T T T _ _ _ _ _ _ _ _ _
	1 2 3 4 5 6 7 8 9 10 11 12 13 14 15 16 17 18 19
mRNA	C G U U G A
tRNA	U G G
Amino Acid	Met _____ _____ _____ _____

ATAT = Promoter sequence

a. Using the genetic code provided in Figure 8, fill in the blanks to complete the segment of DNA shown.

b. Fill in the blanks to complete the sequence of amino acids coded for by this strand of DNA.

c. Write the code for the complementary strand of DNA completed in part (a).

d. What would be the effect if C were substituted for T at base 10?

e. What would be the effect if A were substituted for G at base 11?

f. What would be the effect if G were substituted for T at base 14?

g. What would be the effect if C were inserted between bases 9 and 10?

h. How would UV radiation affect this strand of DNA?

i. Identify a nonsense sequence in this strand of DNA.

5. When iron is not available, *E. coli* can stop synthesis of all proteins, such as superoxide dismutase and succinate dehydrogenase, that require iron. Describe a mechanism for this regulation.

6. Identify when (before transcription, after transcription but before translation, after translation) each of the following regulatory mechanisms functions.

a. ATP combines with an enzyme, altering its shape.

b. A short RNA is synthesized that is complementary to mRNA.

c. Methylation of DNA occurs.

d. An inducer combines with a repressor.

7. Which sequence is the best target for damage by UV radiation: AGGCAA, CTTTGA, or GUAAAU? Why aren't all bacteria killed when they are exposed to sunlight?

8. You are provided with cultures with the following characteristics:

Culture 1: F+, genotype $A^+ B^+ C^+$

Culture 2: F−, genotype $A^- B^- C^-$

a. Indicate the possible genotypes of a recombinant cell resulting from the conjugation of cultures 1 and 2.

b. Indicate the possible genotypes of a recombinant cell resulting from conjugation of the two cultures after the F+ has become an Hfr cell.

9. Why are mutation and recombination important in the process of natural selection and the evolution of organisms?

10. NAME IT Normally a commensal in the human intestine, this bacterium became pathogenic after acquiring a toxin gene from a *Shigella* bacterium.

Multiple Choice

Match the following terms to the definitions in questions 1and 2.

a. conjugation
b. transcription
c. transduction
d. transformation
e. translation

1. Transfer of DNA from a donor to a recipient cell by a bacteriophage.

2. Transfer of DNA from a donor to a recipient as naked DNA in solution.

3. Feedback inhibition differs from repression because feedback inhibition
a. is less precise.
b. is slower acting.
c. stops the action of preexisting enzymes.
d. stops the synthesis of new enzymes.
e. all of the above

4. Bacteria can acquire antibiotic resistance by all of the following *except*
a. mutation.
b. insertion of transposons.
c. conjugation.
d. snRNPs.
e. transformation.

5. Suppose you inoculate three flasks of minimal salts broth with *E. coli*. Flask A contains glucose. Flask B contains glucose and lactose. Flask C contains lactose. After a few hours of incubation, you test the flasks for the presence of β-galactosidase. Which flask(s) do you predict will have this enzyme?
a. A   d. A and B
b. B   e. B and C
c. C

6. Plasmids differ from transposons in that plasmids
a. become inserted into chromosomes.
b. are self-replicated outside the chromosome.
c. move from chromosome to chromosome.
d. carry genes for antibiotic resistance.
e. none of the above

Use the following choices to answer questions 7 and 8.
a. catabolite repression   d. repression
b. DNA polymerase   e. translation
c. induction

7. Mechanism by which the presence of glucose inhibits the *lac* operon.

8. The mechanism by which lactose controls the *lac* operon.

9. Two offspring cells are most likely to inherit which one of the following from the parent cell?
a. a change in a nucleotide in mRNA
b. a change in a nucleotide in tRNA
c. a change in a nucleotide in rRNA
d. a change in a nucleotide in DNA
e. a change in a protein

10. Which of the following is *not* a method of horizontal gene transfer?
a. binary fission
b. conjugation
c. integration of a transposon
d. transduction
e. transformation

Critical Thinking

1. Nucleoside analogs and ionizing radiation are used in treating cancer. These mutagens can cause cancer, so why do you suppose they are used to treat the disease?

2. Replication of the *E. coli* chromosome takes 40 to 45 minutes, but the organism has a generation time of 26 minutes. How does the cell have time to make complete chromosomes for each offspring cell?

3. *Pseudomonas* has a plasmid containing the *mer* operon, which includes the gene for mercuric reductase. This enzyme catalyzes the reduction of the mercuric ion Hg^{2+} to the uncharged form of mercury, Hg^0. Hg^{2+} is quite toxic to cells; Hg^0 is not.
  a. What do you suppose is the inducer for this operon?
  b. The protein encoded by one of the *mer* genes binds Hg^{2+} in the periplasm and brings it into the cell. Why would a cell bring in a toxin?
  c. What is the value of the *mer* operon to *Pseudomonas*?

Clinical Applications

1. Ciprofloxacin, erythromycin, and acyclovir are used to treat microbial infections. Ciprofloxacin inhibits DNA gyrase. Erythromycin binds in front of the A site on the 50S subunit of a ribosome. Acyclovir is a guanine analog.
  a. What steps in protein synthesis are inhibited by each drug?
  b. Which drug is more effective against bacteria? Why?
  c. Which drugs will have effects on the host's cells? Why?
  d. Use the index to identify the disease for which acyclovir is primarily used. Why is it more effective than erythromycin for treating this disease?

2. HIV, the virus that causes AIDS, was isolated from three individuals, and the amino acid sequences for the viral coat were determined. Of the amino acid sequences shown below, which two of the viruses are most closely related? How can these amino acid sequences be used to identify the source of a virus?

Patient	Viral Amino Acid Sequence											
A	Asn	Gln	Thr	Ala	Ala	Ser	Lys	Asn	Ile	Asp	Ala	Leu
B	Asn	Leu	His	Ser	Asp	Lys	Ile	Asn	Ile	Ile	Leu	Leu
C	Asn	Gln	Thr	Ala	Asp	Ser	Ile	Val	Ile	Asp	Ala	Leu

3. Human herpesvirus-8 (HHV-8) is common in parts of Africa, the Middle East, and the Mediterranean, but is rare elsewhere except in AIDS patients. Genetic analyses indicate that the African strain is not changing, whereas the Western strain is accumulating changes. Using the portions of the HHV-8 genomes (shown below) that encode one of the viral proteins, how similar are these two viruses? What mechanism can account for the changes? What disease does HHV-8 cause?

Western   3′-ATGGAGTTCTTCTGGACAAGA
African   3′-ATAAACTTTTCTTGACAACG

Answers to Review and Multiple Choice Study Questions

Review

1. DNA consists of a strand of alternating sugars (deoxyribose) and phosphate groups with a nitrogenous base attached to each sugar. The bases are adenine, thymine, cytosine, and guanine. DNA exists in a cell as two strands twisted together to form a double helix. The two strands are held together by hydrogen bonds between their nitrogenous bases. The bases are paired in a specific, complementary way: A-T and C-G. The information held in the sequence of nucleotides in DNA is the basis for synthesis of RNA and proteins in a cell.

2.

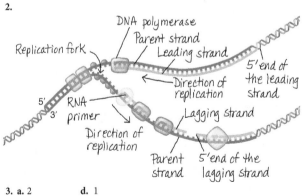

3. a. 2   **d.** 1
  b. 4   **e.** 5
  c. 3

4. a. ATAT<u>TACTTTGCATGGACT</u>.
  b. met-lys-arg-thr-(end).
  c. TATAATGAAACGTTCCTGA.
  d. No change.

  e. Cysteine substituted for arginine.
  f. Proline substituted for threonine (missense mutation).
  g. Frameshift mutation.
  h. Adjacent thymines might polymerize.
  i. ACT.

5. Iron deficiency could stimulate miRNA that is complementary to RNA encoding iron-requiring proteins.

6. a. After translation.
  b. After transcription.
  c. Before transcription.
  d. Before transcription.

7. CTTTGA. Endospores and pigments offer protection against UV radiation. Additionally, repair mechanisms can remove and replace thymine polymers.

8. a. Culture 1 will remain the same. Culture 2 will convert to F^+ but will have its original genotype.
  b. The donor and recipient cells' DNA can recombine to form combinations of $A^+B^+C^+$ and $A^-B^-C^-$. If the F plasmid also is transferred, the recipient cell may become F^+.

9. Mutation and recombination provide genetic diversity. Environmental factors select for the survival of organisms through natural selection. Genetic diversity is necessary for the survival of some organisms through the processes of natural selection. Organisms that survive may undergo further genetic change, resulting in the evolution of the species.

10. *Escherichia coli*

Multiple Choice

1. c	3. c	5. c	7. a	9. d
2. d	4. d	6. b	8. c	10. a

Biotechnology and DNA Technology

From Chapter 9 of *Microbiology: An Introduction*, Eleventh Edition. Gerard J. Tortora, Berdell R. Funke, Christine L. Case.
Copyright © 2013 by Pearson Education, Inc. All rights reserved.

Biotechnology and DNA Technology

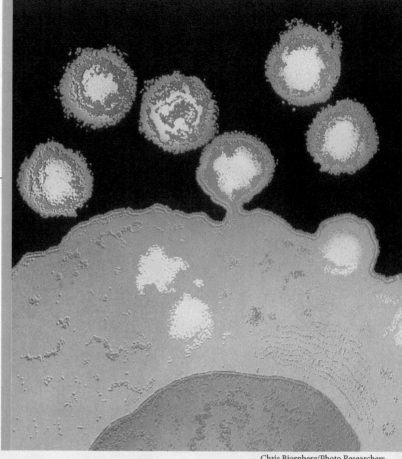

Chris Bjornberg/Photo Researchers

For thousands of years, people have been consuming foods that are produced by the action of microorganisms. Bread, chocolate, and soy sauce are some of the best-known examples. But it was only just over 100 years ago that scientists showed that microorganisms are responsible for these products. This knowledge opened the way for using microorganisms to produce other important products. Since World War I, microbes have been used to produce a variety of chemicals, such as ethanol, acetone, and citric acid. Since World War II, microorganisms have been grown on a large scale to produce antibiotics. More recently, microbes and their enzymes are replacing a variety of chemical processes involved in manufacturing such products as paper, textiles, and fructose. Using microbes or their enzymes instead of chemical syntheses offers several advantages: microbes may use inexpensive, abundant raw materials, such as starch; microbes work at normal temperatures and pressure, thereby avoiding the need for expensive and dangerous pressurized systems; and microbes don't produce toxic, hard-to-treat wastes. In the past 30 years, DNA technology has been added to the tools used to make products.

In this chapter you will learn the tools and techniques that are used to research and develop a product. You will also learn how DNA technology is used to track outbreaks of infectious disease and to provide evidence for courts of law in forensic microbiology. The Clinical Case illustrates the use of DNA technology to track HIV (see the photo).

Visualize microbiology and check your understanding with a pre-test at www.masteringmicrobiology.com.

Introduction to Biotechnology

LEARNING OBJECTIVES

1   Compare and contrast biotechnology, genetic modification, and recombinant DNA technology.

2   Identify the roles of a clone and a vector in making recombinant DNA.

Biotechnology is the use of microorganisms, cells, or cell components to make a product. Microbes have been used in the commercial production of foods, vaccines, antibiotics, and vitamins for years. Bacteria are also used in mining to extract valuable elements from ore. Additionally, animal cells have been used to produce viral vaccines since the 1950s. Until the 1980s, products made by living cells were all made by naturally occurring cells; the role of scientists was to find the appropriate cell and develop a method for large-scale cultivation of the cells.

Now, microorganisms as well as entire plants are being used as "factories" to produce chemicals that the organisms don't naturally make. The latter is made possible by inserting genes into cells by **recombinant DNA (rDNA) technology,** which is sometimes called *genetic engineering*. The development of rDNA technology is expanding the practical applications of biotechnology almost beyond imagination.

Recombinant DNA Technology

Recombination of DNA occurs naturally in microbes. In the 1970s and 1980s, scientists developed artificial techniques for making recombinant DNA.

A gene from a vertebrate animal, including a human, can be inserted into the DNA of a bacterium, or a gene from a virus into a yeast may be used. In many cases, the recipient can then be made to express the gene, which may code for a commercially useful product. Thus, bacteria with genes for human insulin are now being used to produce insulin for treating diabetes, and a vaccine for hepatitis B is being made by yeast carrying a gene for part of the hepatitis virus (the yeast produces a viral coat protein). Scientists hope that such an approach may prove useful in producing vaccines against other infectious agents, thus eliminating the need to use whole organisms, as in conventional vaccines.

The rDNA techniques can also be used to make thousands of copies of the same DNA molecule—to *amplify* DNA, thus generating sufficient DNA for various kinds of experimentation and analysis. This technique has practical application for identifying microbes, such as viruses, that can't be cultured.

An Overview of Recombinant DNA Procedures

Figure 1 presents an overview of some of the procedures typically used for making rDNA, along with some promising applications.

The gene of interest is inserted into the vector DNA in vitro. In this example, the vector is a plasmid. The DNA molecule chosen as a vector must be a self-replicating type, such as a plasmid or a viral genome. This recombinant vector DNA is taken up by a cell such as a bacterium, where it can multiply. The cell containing the recombinant vector is then grown in culture to form a **clone** of many genetically identical cells, each of which carries copies of the vector. This cell clone therefore contains many copies of the gene of interest. This is why DNA vectors are often called *gene-cloning vectors,* or simply *cloning vectors*. (In addition to referring to a culture of identical cells, the word *clone* is also routinely used as a verb, to describe the entire process, as in "to clone a gene.")

The final step varies according to whether the gene itself or the product of the gene is of interest. From the cell clone, the researcher may isolate ("harvest") large quantities of the gene of interest, which may then be used for a variety of purposes. The gene may even be inserted into another vector for introduction into another kind of cell (such as a plant or animal cell). Alternatively, if the gene of interest is expressed (transcribed and translated) in the cell clone, its protein product can be harvested and used for a variety of purposes.

The advantages of using recombinant DNA for obtaining such proteins is illustrated by one of its early successes, human growth hormone (hGH). Some individuals do not produce adequate amounts of hGH, so their growth is stunted. In the past, hGH needed to correct this deficiency had to be obtained

Clinical Case: No Ordinary Checkup

Dr. B. is closing his dental practice after 20 years. Four years ago, he went to his family doctor because of debilitating exhaustion. He thought he had a flu virus that he could not shake, and he was also having night sweats. His doctor ordered a myriad of blood tests, but only one came back positive. Dr. B. had HIV. Although he immediately began an HIV treatment regimen, one year later he was diagnosed with AIDS. Now, two years later, Dr. B. is very ill and can no longer work.

Dr. B. lets his employees know the situation and suggests that they all get tested for HIV. All of Dr. B.'s employees, including the hygienists, test negative. Dr. B. also writes an open letter to his patients informing them of his decision to close his practice and why he is doing so. This letter prompts 400 former patients to be tested for HIV, seven of whom test positive for antibodies against HIV.

What type of test can determine whether these patients have contracted HIV from Dr. B.? Read on to find out.

A Typical Genetic Modification Procedure

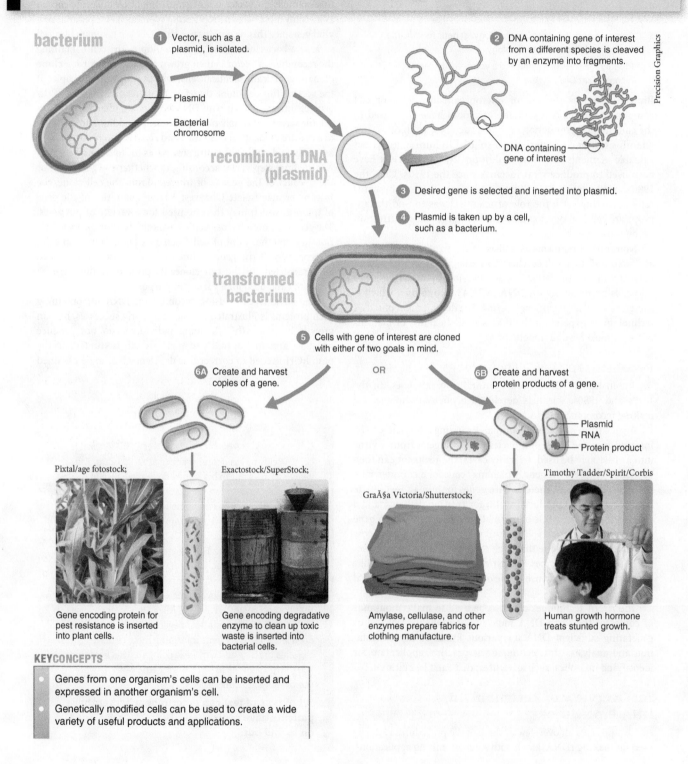

bacterium

① Vector, such as a plasmid, is isolated.

Plasmid

Bacterial chromosome

② DNA containing gene of interest from a different species is cleaved by an enzyme into fragments.

Precision Graphics

recombinant DNA (plasmid)

DNA containing gene of interest

③ Desired gene is selected and inserted into plasmid.

④ Plasmid is taken up by a cell, such as a bacterium.

transformed bacterium

⑤ Cells with gene of interest are cloned with either of two goals in mind.

⑥A Create and harvest copies of a gene.

OR

⑥B Create and harvest protein products of a gene.

Plasmid
RNA
Protein product

Pixtal/age fotostock;

Exactostock/SuperStock;

GraÃ§a Victoria/Shutterstock;

Timothy Tadder/Spirit/Corbis

Gene encoding protein for pest resistance is inserted into plant cells.

Gene encoding degradative enzyme to clean up toxic waste is inserted into bacterial cells.

Amylase, cellulase, and other enzymes prepare fabrics for clothing manufacture.

Human growth hormone treats stunted growth.

KEYCONCEPTS

- Genes from one organism's cells can be inserted and expressed in another organism's cell.
- Genetically modified cells can be used to create a wide variety of useful products and applications.

from human pituitary glands at autopsy. (Human growth hormone from other animals is not effective in humans.) This practice was not only expensive but also dangerous because on several occasions neurological diseases were transmitted with the hormone. Human growth hormone produced by genetically modified *E. coli* is a pure and cost-effective product. Recombinant DNA techniques also result in faster production of the hormone than traditional methods might allow.

CHECK YOUR UNDERSTANDING

✔ Differentiate biotechnology and recombinant DNA technology. 1

✔ In one sentence, describe how a vector and clone are used. 2

Tools of Biotechnology

LEARNING OBJECTIVES

3   Compare selection and mutation.

4   Define *restriction enzymes*, and outline how they are used to make recombinant DNA.

5   List the four properties of vectors.

6   Describe the use of plasmid and viral vectors.

7   Outline the steps in PCR, and provide an example of its use.

Research scientists and technicians isolate bacteria and fungi from natural environments such as soil and water to find, or *select,* the organisms that produce a desired product. The selected organism can be mutated to make more product or to make a better product.

Selection

In nature, organisms with characteristics that enhance survival are more likely to survive and reproduce than are variants that lack the desirable traits. This is called *natural selection.* Humans use **artificial selection** to select desirable breeds of animals or strains of plants to cultivate. As microbiologists learned how to isolate and grow microorganisms in pure culture, they were able to select the ones that could accomplish the desired objective, such as brewing beer more efficiently, for example, or producing a new antibiotic. Over 2000 strains of antibiotic-producing bacteria have been discovered by testing soil bacteria and selecting the strains that produce an antibiotic.

Mutation

Mutations are responsible for much of the diversity of life. A bacterium with a mutation that confers resistance to an antibiotic will survive and reproduce in the presence of that antibiotic. Biologists working with antibiotic-producing microbes discovered that they could create new strains by exposing microbes to mutagens. After random mutations were created in penicillin-producing *Penicillium* by exposing fungal cultures to radiation,

the highest-yielding variant among the survivors was selected for another exposure to a mutagen. Using mutations, biologists increased the amount of penicillin produced by the fungus over 1000 times.

Screening each mutant for penicillin production is a tedious process. **Site-directed mutagenesis** can be used to make a specific change in a gene. Suppose you determine that changing one amino acid will make a laundry enzyme work better in cold water. Using the genetic code, you could, using the techniques described next, produce the sequence of DNA that encodes that amino acid and insert it into the gene for that enzyme.

The science of molecular genetics has advanced to such a degree that many routine cloning procedures are performed using prepackaged materials and procedures that are very much like cookbook recipes. Scientists have a grab bag of methods from which to choose, depending on the ultimate application of their experiments. Next we describe some of the most important tools and techniques, and later we will consider some applications.

Restriction Enzymes

Recombinant DNA technology has its technical roots in the discovery of **restriction enzymes,** a special class of DNA-cutting enzymes that exist in many bacteria. First isolated in 1970, restriction enzymes in nature had actually been observed earlier, when certain bacteriophages were found to have a restricted host range. If these phages were used to infect bacteria other than their usual hosts, restriction enzymes in the new host destroyed almost all the phage DNA. Restriction enzymes protect a bacterial cell by hydrolyzing phage DNA. The bacterial DNA is protected from digestion because the cell **methylates** (adds methyl groups to) some of the cytosines in its DNA. The purified forms of these bacterial enzymes are used in today's laboratories.

What is important for rDNA techniques is that a restriction enzyme recognizes and cuts, or *digests,* only one particular sequence of nucleotide bases in DNA, and it cuts this sequence in the same way each time. Typical restriction enzymes used in cloning experiments recognize four-, six-, or eight-base sequences. Hundreds of restriction enzymes are known, each producing DNA fragments with characteristic ends. A few restriction enzymes are listed in Table 1. You can see they are named for their bacterial source. Some of these enzymes (e.g., *Hae*III) cut both strands of DNA in the same place, producing **blunt ends,** and others make staggered cuts in the two strands—cuts that are not directly opposite each other (Figure 2). These staggered ends, or **sticky ends,** are most useful in rDNA because they can be used to join two different pieces of DNA that were cut by the same restriction

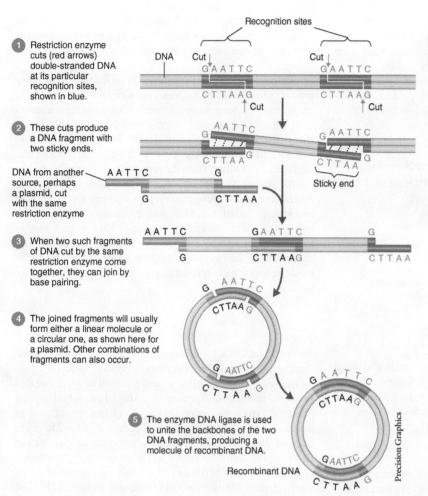

1. Restriction enzyme cuts (red arrows) double-stranded DNA at its particular recognition sites, shown in blue.

2. These cuts produce a DNA fragment with two sticky ends.

DNA from another source, perhaps a plasmid, cut with the same restriction enzyme

3. When two such fragments of DNA cut by the same restriction enzyme come together, they can join by base pairing.

4. The joined fragments will usually form either a linear molecule or a circular one, as shown here for a plasmid. Other combinations of fragments can also occur.

5. The enzyme DNA ligase is used to unite the backbones of the two DNA fragments, producing a molecule of recombinant DNA.

Recombinant DNA

Precision Graphics

Figure 2 The role of a restriction enzyme in making recombinant DNA.

Q Why are restriction enzymes used to make recombinant DNA?

TABLE 1   Selected Restriction Enzymes Used in rDNA Technology

Enzyme	Bacterial Source	Recognition Sequence
BamHI	Bacillus amyloliquefaciens	G↓G A T C C G C T A G↑G
EcoRI	Escherichia coli	G↓A A T T C C T T A A↑G
HaeIII	Haemophilus aegyptius	G G↓C C C C↑G G
HindIII	Haemophilus influenzae	A↓A G C T T T T C G A↑A

enzyme. The sticky ends "stick" to stretches of single-stranded DNA by complementary base pairing.

Notice in Figure 2 that the darker base sequences on the two strands are the same but run in opposite directions. Staggered cuts leave stretches of single-stranded DNA at the ends of the DNA fragments. If two fragments of DNA from different sources have been produced by the action of the same restriction enzyme, the two pieces will have identical sets of sticky ends and can be spliced (recombined) in vitro. The sticky ends join spontaneously by hydrogen bonding (base pairing). The enzyme DNA ligase is used to covalently link the backbones of the DNA pieces, producing an rDNA molecule. (MM) **Animation** Recombinant DNA Technology

Vectors

A great variety of different types of DNA molecules can serve as vectors, provided that they have certain properties. The most important property is self-replication; once in a cell, a vector must be capable of replicating. Any DNA that is inserted in the vector will be replicated in the process. Thus, vectors serve as vehicles for the replication of desired DNA sequences.

Vectors also need to be of a size that allows them to be manipulated outside the cell during recombinant DNA procedures. Smaller vectors are more easily manipulated than larger DNA molecules, which tend to be more fragile. Preservation is another important property of vectors. The circular form of DNA molecules is important in protecting the DNA of the vector from destruction by the recipient of the vector. Notice in Figure 3 that the DNA of a plasmid is circular. Another preservation mechanism occurs when the DNA of a virus inserts itself quickly into the chromosome of the host.

When it is necessary to retrieve cells containing the vector, a marker gene contained within the vector can often help make selection easy. Common selectable marker genes are for antibiotic resistance or for an enzyme that carries out an easily identified reaction.

Plasmids are one of the primary vectors in use, particularly variants of R factor plasmids. Plasmid DNA can be cut with the same restriction enzymes as the DNA to be cloned, so that all pieces of the DNA will have the same sticky ends. When the pieces are mixed, the DNA to be cloned will become inserted into the plasmid (Figure 2). Note that other possible combinations of fragments can occur as well, including the plasmid reforming a circle with no DNA inserted.

Some plasmids are capable of existing in several different species. They are called **shuttle vectors** and can be used to move cloned DNA sequences among organisms, such as among bacterial, yeast, and mammalian cells, or among bacterial, fungal, and plant cells. Shuttle vectors can be very useful in the process of genetically modifying multicellular organisms—for example, by trying to insert herbicide resistance genes into plants.

A different kind of vector is viral DNA. This type of vector can usually accept much larger pieces of foreign DNA than plasmids can. After the DNA has been inserted into the viral vector, it can be cloned in the virus's host cells. The choice of a suitable vector depends on many factors, including the organism that will receive the new gene and the size of the DNA to be cloned. Retroviruses, adenoviruses, and herpesviruses are being used to insert corrective genes into human cells that have defective genes.

CHECK YOUR UNDERSTANDING

✔ How are selection and mutation used in biotechnology? 3

✔ What is the value of restriction enzymes in recombinant DNA technology? 4

✔ What criteria must a vector meet? 5

✔ Why is a vector used in recombinant DNA technology? 6

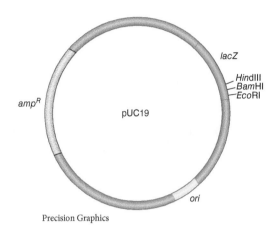

Precision Graphics

Figure 3 A plasmid used for cloning. A plasmid vector used for cloning in the bacterium *E. coli* is pUC19. An origin of replication (*ori*) allows the plasmid to be self-replicating. Two genes, one encoding resistance to the antibiotic ampicillin (*amp^R*) and one encoding the enzyme β-galactosidase (*lacZ*), serve as marker genes. Foreign DNA can be inserted at the restriction enzyme sites.

Q What is a vector in recombinant DNA technology?

Polymerase Chain Reaction

The **polymerase chain reaction (PCR)** is a technique by which small samples of DNA can be quickly amplified, that is, increased to quantities that are large enough for analysis.

Starting with just one gene-sized piece of DNA, PCR can be used to make literally billions of copies in only a few hours. The PCR process is shown in Figure 4.

1 Each strand of the target DNA will serve as a template for DNA synthesis.

2 To this DNA is added a supply of the four nucleotides (for assembly into new DNA) and the enzyme for catalyzing the synthesis, DNA polymerase. Short pieces of nucleic acid called primers are also added to help start the reaction. The primers are complementary to the ends of the target DNA and

3 will hybridize to the fragments to be amplified.

4 Then, the polymerase synthesizes new complementary strands.

5 After each cycle of synthesis, the DNA is heated to convert all the new DNA into single strands. Each newly synthesized DNA strand serves in turn as a template for more new DNA.

As a result, the process proceeds exponentially. All of the necessary reagents are added to a tube, which is placed in a *thermal cycler*. The thermal cycler can be set for the desired temperatures, times, and number of cycles. Use of an automated thermal cycler is made possible by the use of DNA polymerase

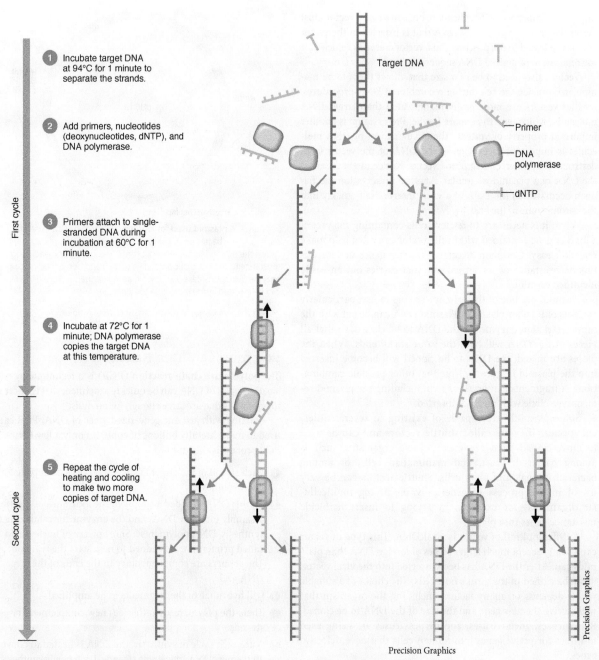

First cycle

1. Incubate target DNA at 94°C for 1 minute to separate the strands.

2. Add primers, nucleotides (deoxynucleotides, dNTP), and DNA polymerase.

3. Primers attach to single-stranded DNA during incubation at 60°C for 1 minute.

4. Incubate at 72°C for 1 minute; DNA polymerase copies the target DNA at this temperature.

Second cycle

5. Repeat the cycle of heating and cooling to make two more copies of target DNA.

Target DNA

Primer

DNA polymerase

dNTP

Precision Graphics

Precision Graphics

Precision Graphics

Figure 4   The polymerase chain reaction. Deoxynucleotides (dNTPs) base-pair with the target DNA: adenine pairs with thymine, and cytosine pairs with guanine.

Q How does *reverse-transcription PCR* differ from this figure?

taken from a thermophilic bacterium such as *Thermus aquaticus*; the enzyme from such organisms can survive the heating phase without being destroyed. Thirty cycles, completed in just a few hours, will increase the amount of target DNA by more than a billion times.

The amplified DNA can be seen by gel electrophoresis. In *real-time PCR*, or *quantitative PCR* (*qPCR*), the newly made DNA is tagged with a fluorescent dye, so that the levels of fluorescence can be measured after every PCR cycle (that's the *real time* aspect). Another PCR procedure called *reverse-transcription PCR* uses viral RNA or a cell's mRNA as the template. The enzyme, reverse transcriptase, makes DNA from the RNA template, and the DNA is then amplified.

Note that PCR can only be used to amplify relatively small, specific sequences of DNA as determined by the choice of primers. It cannot be used to amplify an entire genome.

PCR can be applied to any situation that requires the amplification of DNA. Especially noteworthy are diagnostic tests that use PCR to detect the presence of infectious agents in situations in which they would otherwise be undetectable. A qPCR test provides rapid identification of drug-resistant *Mycobacterium tuberculosis*. This bacterium can take up to 6 weeks to culture, leaving patients untreated. (MM) Animations PCR: Overview, Components, Process

CHECK YOUR UNDERSTANDING

✔ For what is each of the following used in PCR: primer, DNA polymerase, 94°C? 7

Techniques of Genetic Modification

LEARNING OBJECTIVES

8 Describe five ways of getting DNA into a cell.

9 Describe how a genomic library is made.

10 Differentiate cDNA from synthetic DNA.

11 Explain how each of the following is used to locate a clone: antibiotic-resistance genes, DNA probes, gene products.

12 List one advantage of modifying each of the following: *E. coli*, *Saccharomyces cerevisiae*, mammalian cells, plant cells.

Inserting Foreign DNA into Cells

Recombinant DNA procedures require that DNA molecules be manipulated outside the cell and then returned to living cells. There are several ways to introduce DNA into cells. The choice of method is usually determined by the type of vector and host cell being used.

In nature, plasmids are usually transferred between closely related microbes by cell-to-cell contact, such as in conjugation. To modify a cell, a plasmid must be inserted into a cell by **transformation,** a procedure during which cells can take up DNA from the surrounding environment. Many cell types, including *E. coli*, yeast, and mammalian cells, do not naturally transform; however, simple chemical treatments can make all of these cell types *competent*, or able to take up external DNA. For *E. coli*, the procedure for making cells competent is to soak them in a solution of calcium chloride for a brief period. Following this treatment, the now-competent cells are mixed with the cloned DNA and given a mild heat shock. Some of these cells will then take up the DNA.

There are other ways to transfer DNA to cells. A process called **electroporation** uses an electrical current to form microscopic pores in the membranes of cells; the DNA then enters the cells through the pores. Electroporation is generally applicable to all cells; those with cell walls often must be converted to protoplasts first. **Protoplasts** are produced by enzymatically removing the cell wall, thereby allowing more direct access to the plasma membrane.

The process of **protoplast fusion** also takes advantage of the properties of protoplasts. Protoplasts in solution fuse at a low but significant rate; the addition of polyethylene glycol increases the frequency of fusion (Figure 5a). In the new hybrid cell, the DNA derived from the two "parent" cells may undergo natural recombination. This method is especially valuable in the genetic manipulation of plant and algal cells (Figure 5b).

A remarkable way of introducing foreign DNA into plant cells is to literally shoot it directly through the thick cellu-

Clinical Case

Reverse-transcription PCR using a primer for an HIV gene can be used to amplify DNA for analysis. The Centers for Disease Control and Prevention (CDC) interviews the seven former patients to determine whether their histories show any additional risk factors for contracting HIV. Five out of the seven have no identified risk factors for HIV other than having had invasive procedures performed on them by Dr. B. The CDC then performs reverse-transcription PCR on DNA from white blood cells in Dr. B.'s peripheral blood and the seven HIV-positive patients (see the figure).

What can be concluded from the PCR amplification in the figure?

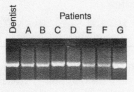

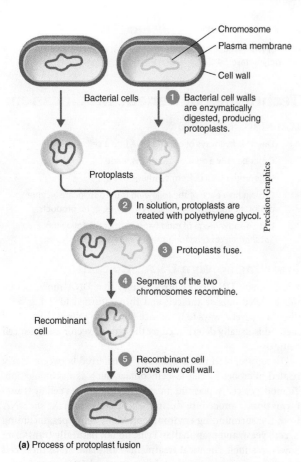

Chromosome

Plasma membrane

Cell wall

Bacterial cells

1 Bacterial cell walls are enzymatically digested, producing protoplasts.

Protoplasts

2 In solution, protoplasts are treated with polyethylene glycol.

3 Protoplasts fuse.

4 Segments of the two chromosomes recombine.

Recombinant cell

5 Recombinant cell grows new cell wall.

(a) Process of protoplast fusion

Precision Graphics

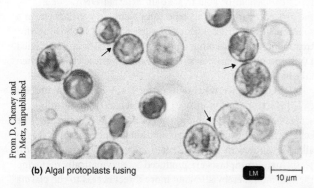

From D. Cheney and B. Metz, unpublished

(b) Algal protoplasts fusing

 LM 10 μm

Figure 5 Protoplast fusion. (a) A diagram of protoplast fusion with bacterial cells. **(b)** Protoplast algal cells are shown fusing at the arrows. Removal of the cell wall left only the delicate plasma membranes, which will fuse together, allowing the exchange of DNA.

Q What is a protoplast?

Reproduced by permission from D'Arcy, C. J., D. M. Eastburn, and G. L. Schumann. 2001. *Illustrated Glossary of Plant Pathology*. *The Plant Health Instructor*. DOI: 10.1094/PHI-1-2001-0219-01

Figure 6 A gene gun, which can be used to insert DNA-coated "bullets" into a cell.

Q Name four other methods of inserting DNA into a cell.

lose walls using a gene gun (Figure 6). Microscopic particles of tungsten or gold are coated with DNA and propelled by a burst of helium through the plant cell walls. Some of the cells express the introduced DNA as though it were their own.

DNA can be introduced directly into an animal cell by **microinjection.** This technique requires the use of a glass micropipette with a diameter that is much smaller than the cell. The micropipette punctures the plasma membrane, and DNA can be injected through it (Figure 7).

Thus, there is a great variety of different restriction enzymes, vectors, and methods of inserting DNA into cells. But foreign DNA will survive only if it is either present on a self-replicating vector or incorporated into one of the cell's chromosomes by recombination.

Obtaining DNA

We have seen how genes can be cloned into vectors by using restriction enzymes and how genes can be transformed or transferred into a variety of cell types. But how do biologists obtain the genes they are interested in? There are two main sources of genes: (1) genomic libraries containing either natural copies of genes or cDNA copies of genes made from mRNA, and (2) synthetic DNA.

Genomic Libraries

Isolating specific genes as individual pieces of DNA is seldom practical. Therefore, researchers interested in genes from a particular organism start by extracting the organism's DNA, which can be obtained from cells of any organism, whether plant, animal, or microbe, by lysing the cells and precipitating the DNA. This process results in a DNA mass that includes the organism's entire

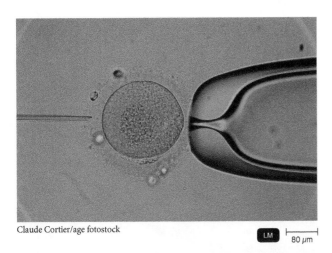

Claude Cortier/age fotostock

LM ├─────┤ 80 μm

Figure 7 The microinjection of foreign DNA into an egg. The egg is first immobilized by applying mild suction to the large, blunt, holding pipette (right). Several hundred copies of the gene of interest are then injected into the nucleus of the cell through the tiny end of the micropipette (left).

Q Why is microinjection impractical for bacterial and fungal cells?

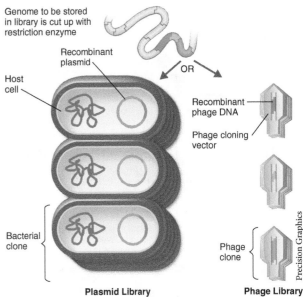

Figure 8 Genomic libraries. Each fragment of DNA, containing about one gene, is carried by a vector, either a plasmid within a bacterial cell or a phage.

Q Differentiate an RFLP from a gene.

genome. After the DNA is digested by restriction enzymes, the restriction fragments are then spliced into plasmid or phage vectors, and the recombinant vectors are introduced into bacterial cells. The goal is to make a collection of clones large enough to ensure that at least one clone exists for every gene in the organism. This collection of clones containing different DNA fragments is called a **genomic library;** each "book" is a bacterial or phage strain that contains a fragment of the genome (Figure 8). Such libraries are essential for maintaining and retrieving DNA clones; they can even be purchased commercially.

Cloning genes from eukaryotic organisms presents a specific problem. Genes of eukaryotic cells generally contain both **exons,** stretches of DNA that code for protein, and **introns,** intervening stretches of DNA that do not code for protein. When the RNA transcript of such a gene is converted to mRNA, the introns are removed. To clone genes of eukaryotic cells, it is desirable to use a version of the gene that lacks introns because a gene that includes introns may be too large to work with easily. In addition, if such a gene is put into a bacterial cell, the bacterium will not usually be able to remove the introns from the RNA transcript, and therefore it will not be able to make the correct protein product. However, an artificial gene that contains only exons can be produced by using an enzyme called **reverse transcriptase** to synthesize **complementary DNA (cDNA)** from an mRNA template (Figure 9). This synthesis is the reverse of the normal DNA-to-RNA transcription process. A DNA copy of mRNA is produced by reverse transcriptase. Following this, the mRNA is enzymatically digested away. DNA

polymerase then synthesizes a complementary strand of DNA, creating a double-stranded piece of DNA containing the information from the mRNA. Molecules of cDNA produced from a mixture of all the mRNAs from a tissue or cell type can then be cloned to form a cDNA library.

The cDNA method is the most common method of obtaining eukaryotic genes. A difficulty with this method is that long molecules of mRNA may not be completely reverse-transcribed into DNA; the reverse transcription often aborts, forming only parts of the desired gene.

Synthetic DNA

Under certain circumstances, genes can be made in vitro with the help of DNA synthesis machines (Figure 10). A keyboard on the machine is used to enter the desired sequence of nucleotides, much as letters are entered into a word processor to compose a sentence. A microprocessor controls the synthesis of the DNA from stored supplies of nucleotides and the other necessary reagents. A chain of about 120 nucleotides can be synthesized by this method. Unless the gene is very small, at least several chains must be synthesized separately and linked together to form an entire gene.

The difficulty of this approach, of course, is that the sequence of the gene must be known before it can be synthesized. If the gene has not already been isolated, then the only way to predict the DNA sequence is by knowing the amino acid sequence of the protein product of the gene. If this amino acid sequence is

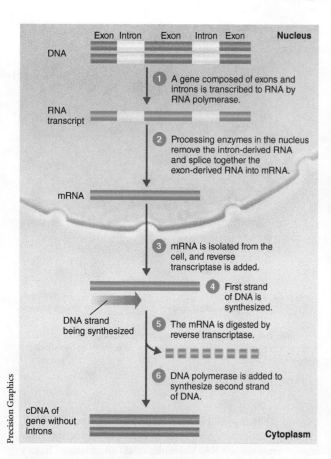

Exon Intron   Exon   Intron Exon   **Nucleus**

DNA

1 A gene composed of exons and introns is transcribed to RNA by RNA polymerase.

RNA transcript

2 Processing enzymes in the nucleus remove the intron-derived RNA and splice together the exon-derived RNA into mRNA.

mRNA

3 mRNA is isolated from the cell, and reverse transcriptase is added.

4 First strand of DNA is synthesized.

DNA strand being synthesized

5 The mRNA is digested by reverse transcriptase.

6 DNA polymerase is added to synthesize second strand of DNA.

cDNA of gene without introns

Cytoplasm

Precision Graphics

Figure 9 Making complementary DNA (cDNA) for a eukaryotic gene. Reverse transcriptase catalyzes the synthesis of double-stranded DNA from an RNA template.

Q How does reverse transcriptase differ from DNA polymerase?

known, in principle one can work backward through the genetic code to obtain the DNA sequence. Unfortunately, the degeneracy of the code prevents an unambiguous determination; thus, if the protein contains a leucine, for example, which of the six codons for leucine is the one in the gene?

For these reasons, it is rare to clone a gene by synthesizing it directly, although some commercial products such as insulin, interferon, and somatostatin are produced from chemically synthesized genes. Desired restriction sites were added to the synthetic genes so that the genes could be inserted into plasmid vectors for cloning in *E. coli*. Synthetic DNA plays a much more useful role in selection procedures, as we will see.

CHECK YOUR UNDERSTANDING

✔ Contrast the five ways of putting DNA into a cell. **8**

✔ What is the purpose of a genomic library? **9**

✔ Why isn't cDNA synthetic? **10**

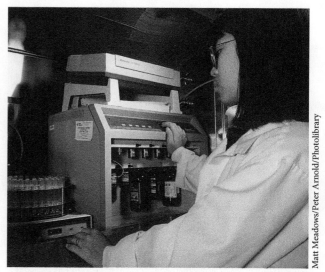

Matt Meadows/Peter Arnold/Photolibrary

Figure 10 A DNA synthesis machine. Short sequences of DNA can be synthesized by instruments such as this one.

Q What are some of the disadvantages of using a DNA synthesis machine?

Clinical Case

The primer amplifies all eight samples and confirms that Dr. B. and seven of his former patients are all infected with HIV. The CDC then sequences the amplified DNA and compares the sequencing to an HIV isolate from Cleveland (local control) and an isolate from Haiti (outlier). A portion of the coding (5′ to 3′) is shown below.

Patient A	GCTTG	GGCTG	GCGCT	GAAGT	GAGA
Patient B	GCTAT	TGCTG	GCGCT	GAATT	GCAC
Patient C	GCCAT	AGCTG	GCGCA	GAAGT	GCAC
Patient D	GCTAT	TGGCG	TGGCT	GACAG	AGAA
Patient E	GCACC	TGCTG	GCGCT	GAAGT	GAAA
Patient F	CAGAT	TGTGT	TGATT	GAACC	TCAC
Patient G	GCTAT	TGCTG	GCGCT	GAAGT	GAAA
Dentist	GCTAT	TGCTG	GCGCT	GAAGT	GCAC
Local control	CAGAC	TACTG	CTAGG	AAAAA	TATT
Outlier	GAAGA	CGAAA	GGACT	GCTAT	TCAG

What is the percent similarity among the viruses?

Selecting a Clone

In cloning, it is necessary to select the particular cell that contains the specific gene of interest. This is difficult because out of millions of cells, only a very few cells might contain the desired gene. Here we will examine a typical screening procedure known as *blue-white screening,* from the color of the bacterial colonies formed at the end of the screening process.

The plasmid vector used contains a gene (amp^R) coding for resistance to the antibiotic ampicillin. The host bacterium will not be able to grow on the test medium, which contains ampicillin, unless the vector has transferred the ampicillin-resistance gene. The plasmid vector also contains a second gene, this one for the enzyme β-galactosidase (*lacZ*). Notice in Figure 3 that there are several sites in *lacZ* that can be cut by restriction enzymes.

The procedure is shown in Figure 11. The two genes, called marker genes, are used so that the insertion of plasmid DNA into the host bacterium can be determined. In the blue-white screening procedure, a library of bacteria is cultured in a medium called X-gal. X-gal contains two essential components other than those necessary to support normal bacterial growth. One is the antibiotic ampicillin, which prevents the growth of any bacterium that has not successfully received the ampicillin-resistance gene from the plasmid. The other, called X-gal, is a substrate for β-galactosidase.

Only bacteria that picked up the plasmid will grow—because they are now ampicillin resistant. Bacteria that picked up the recombinant plasmid—in which the new gene was inserted into the *lacZ* gene—will not hydrolyze lactose and will produce white colonies. If a bacterium received the original plasmid containing the intact *lacZ* gene, the cells will hydrolyze X-gal to produce a blue-colored compound; the colony will be blue.

What remains to be done can still be difficult. The above procedure has isolated white colonies known to contain foreign DNA, but it is still not known whether this is the desired fragment of foreign DNA. A second procedure is needed to identify these bacteria. If the foreign DNA in the plasmid codes for the production of an identifiable product, the bacterial isolate only needs to be grown in culture and tested. However, in some cases the gene itself must be identified in the host bacterium.

Colony hybridization is a common method of identifying cells that carry a specific cloned gene. **DNA probes,** short segments of single-stranded DNA that are complementary to the desired gene, are synthesized. If the DNA probe finds a match, it will adhere to the target gene. The DNA probe is labeled with an enzyme or fluorescent dye so its presence can be detected. A typical colony hybridization experiment is shown in Figure 12. An array of DNA probes arranged in a DNA chip can be used to identify pathogens.

Making a Gene Product

We have just seen how to identify cells carrying a particular gene. The gene products are frequently the objective of genetic modification. Most of the earliest work in genetic modification used

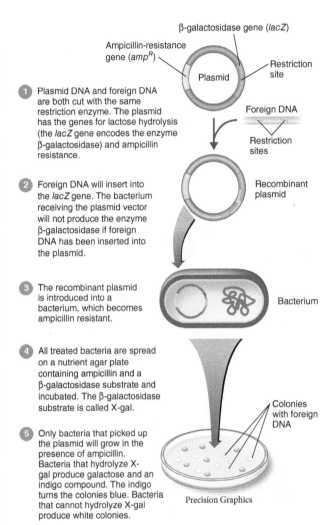

1. Plasmid DNA and foreign DNA are both cut with the same restriction enzyme. The plasmid has the genes for lactose hydrolysis (the *lacZ* gene encodes the enzyme β-galactosidase) and ampicillin resistance.

2. Foreign DNA will insert into the *lacZ* gene. The bacterium receiving the plasmid vector will not produce the enzyme β-galactosidase if foreign DNA has been inserted into the plasmid.

3. The recombinant plasmid is introduced into a bacterium, which becomes ampicillin resistant.

4. All treated bacteria are spread on a nutrient agar plate containing ampicillin and a β-galactosidase substrate and incubated. The β-galactosidase substrate is called X-gal.

5. Only bacteria that picked up the plasmid will grow in the presence of ampicillin. Bacteria that hydrolyze X-gal produce galactose and an indigo compound. The indigo turns the colonies blue. Bacteria that cannot hydrolyze X-gal produce white colonies.

Precision Graphics

Figure 11 **Blue-white screening, one method of selecting recombinant bacteria.**

Q Why are some colonies blue and others white?

E. coli to synthesize the gene products. *E. coli* is easily grown, and researchers are very familiar with this bacterium and its genetics. For example, some inducible promoters, such as that of the *lac* operon, have been cloned, and cloned genes can be attached to such promoters. The synthesis of great amounts of the cloned gene product can then be directed by the addition of an inducer. Such a method has been used to produce gamma interferon in *E. coli* (Figure 13). However, *E. coli* also has several disadvantages. Like other gram-negative bacteria, it produces endotoxins as part of the outer layer of its cell wall. Because endotoxins cause fever and shock in mammals, their accidental presence in products intended for human use would be a serious problem.

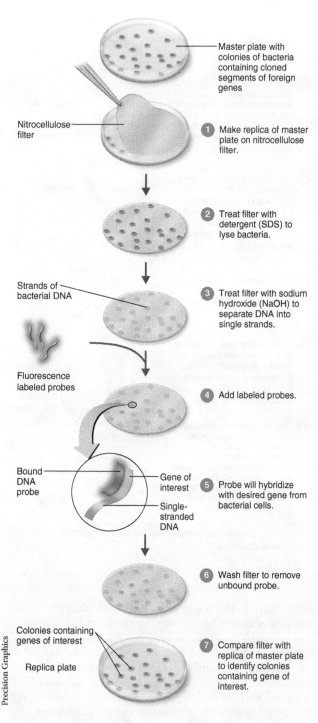

Master plate with colonies of bacteria containing cloned segments of foreign genes

Nitrocellulose filter

1 Make replica of master plate on nitrocellulose filter.

2 Treat filter with detergent (SDS) to lyse bacteria.

Strands of bacterial DNA

3 Treat filter with sodium hydroxide (NaOH) to separate DNA into single strands.

Fluorescence labeled probes

4 Add labeled probes.

Bound DNA probe

Gene of interest

Single-stranded DNA

5 Probe will hybridize with desired gene from bacterial cells.

6 Wash filter to remove unbound probe.

Colonies containing genes of interest

Replica plate

7 Compare filter with replica of master plate to identify colonies containing gene of interest.

Figure 12 Colony hybridization: using a DNA probe to identify a cloned gene of interest.

Q What is a DNA probe?

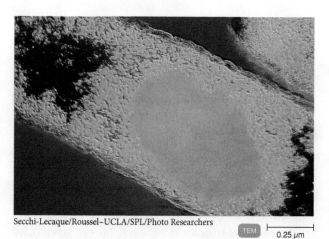

Secchi-Lecaque/Roussel–UCLA/SPL/Photo Researchers

TEM   0.25 μm

Figure 13 *E. coli* genetically modified to produce gamma interferon, a human protein that promotes an immune response. The product, visible here as an orange-colored substance, can be released by lysis of the cell.

Q What is one advantage of using *E. coli* for genetic engineering? One disadvantage?

Another disadvantage of *E. coli* is that it does not usually secrete protein products. To obtain a product, cells must usually be broken open and the product purified from the resulting "soup" of cell components. Recovering the product from such a mixture is expensive when done on an industrial scale. It is more economical to have an organism secrete the product so that it can be recovered continuously from the growth medium. One approach has been to link the product to a natural *E. coli* protein that the bacterium does secrete. However, gram-positive bacteria, such as *Bacillus subtilis,* are more likely to secrete their products and are often preferred industrially for that reason.

Another microbe being used as a vehicle for expressing rDNA is baker's yeast, *Saccharomyces cerevisiae.* Its genome is only about four times larger than that of *E. coli* and is probably the best understood eukaryotic genome. Yeasts may carry plasmids, and the plasmids are easily transferred into yeast cells after their cell walls have been removed. As eukaryotic cells, yeasts may be more successful in expressing foreign eukaryotic genes than bacteria. Furthermore, yeasts are likely to continuously secrete the product. Because of all these factors, yeasts have become the eukaryotic workhorse of biotechnology.

Mammalian cells in culture, even human cells, can be genetically modified much like bacteria to produce various products. Scientists have developed effective methods of growing certain mammalian cells in culture as hosts for growing viruses. Mammalian cells are often the best suited to making protein products for medical use because the cells secrete their products and there is a low risk of toxins or allergens. Using mammalian cells to make foreign gene products on an industrial scale often

Precision Graphics

requires a preliminary step of cloning the gene in bacteria. Consider the example of colony-stimulating factor (CSF). A protein produced naturally in tiny amounts by white blood cells, CSF is valuable because it stimulates the growth of certain cells that protect against infection. To produce huge amounts of CSF industrially, the gene is first inserted into a plasmid, and bacteria are used to make multiple copies of the plasmid (see Figure 1). The recombinant plasmids are inserted into mammalian cells that are grown in bottles.

Plant cells can also be grown in culture, altered by recombinant DNA techniques, and then used to generate genetically modified plants. Such plants may prove useful as sources of valuable products, such as plant alkaloids (the painkiller codeine, for example), the isoprenoids that are the basis of synthetic rubber, and melanin (the animal skin pigment) for use in sunscreens. Genetically modified plants have many advantages for the production of human therapeutic agents, including vaccines and antibodies. The advantages include large-scale, low-cost production using agriculture and low risk of product contamination by mammalian pathogens or cancer-causing genes. Genetically modifying plants often requires use of a bacterium. We will return to the topic of genetically modified plants later in the chapter.

CHECK YOUR UNDERSTANDING

☞ How are recombinant clones identified? **11**

☞ What types of cells are used for cloning rDNA? **12**

Clinical Case

The sequences from Dr. B. and patients A, B, C, E, and G share 87.5% of the nucleotide sequence, which is comparable to reported similarities for known linked infections.

Identify the amino acids encoded by the viral DNA. Did this change the percent similarity?

Applications of DNA Technology

LEARNING OBJECTIVES

13 List at least five applications of DNA technology.

14 Define RNAi.

15 Discuss the value of genome projects.

16 Define the following terms: *random shotgun sequencing, bioinformatics, proteomics.*

17 Diagram the Southern blotting procedure, and provide an example of its use.

18 Diagram DNA fingerprinting, and provide an example of its use.

19 Outline genetic engineering with *Agrobacterium.*

We have now described the entire sequence of events in cloning a gene. As indicated earlier, such cloned genes can be applied in a variety of ways. One is to produce useful substances more efficiently and less expensively. Another is to obtain information from the cloned DNA that is useful for either basic research, medicine, or forensics. A third is to use cloned genes to alter the characteristics of cells or organisms.

Therapeutic Applications

An extremely valuable pharmaceutical product is the hormone insulin, a small protein produced by the pancreas that controls the body's uptake of glucose from blood. For many years, people with insulin-dependent diabetes have controlled their disease by injecting insulin obtained from the pancreases of slaughtered animals. Obtaining this insulin is an expensive process, and the insulin from animals is not as effective as human insulin.

Because of the value of human insulin and the small size of the protein, producing human insulin by recombinant DNA techniques was an early goal for the pharmaceutical industry. To produce the hormone, synthetic genes were first constructed for each of the two short polypeptide chains that make up the insulin molecule. The small size of these chains—only 21 and 30 amino acids long—made it possible to use synthetic genes. Following the procedure described earlier, each of the two synthetic genes was inserted into a plasmid vector and linked to the end of a gene coding for the bacterial enzyme β-galactosidase, so that the insulin polypeptide was coproduced with the enzyme. Two different *E. coli* bacterial cultures were used, one to produce each of the insulin polypeptide chains. The polypeptides were then recovered from the bacteria, separated from the β-galactosidase, and chemically joined to make human insulin. This accomplishment was one of the early commercial successes of DNA technology, and it illustrates a number of the principles and procedures discussed in this chapter.

Another human hormone that is now being produced commercially by genetic modification of *E. coli* is somatostatin. At one time 500,000 sheep brains were needed to produce 5 mg of animal somatostatin for experimental purposes. By contrast, only 8 liters of a genetically modified bacterial culture are now required to obtain the equivalent amount of the human hormone.

Subunit vaccines, consisting only of a protein portion of a pathogen, are being made by genetically modifying yeasts. Subunit vaccines have been produced for a number of diseases, notably hepatitis B. One of the advantages of a subunit vaccine is that there is no chance of becoming infected from the vaccine. The protein is harvested from genetically modified cells and purified for use as a vaccine. Animal viruses such as vaccinia virus can be genetically modified to carry a gene for another microbe's surface protein. When injected, the virus acts as a vaccine against the other microbe.

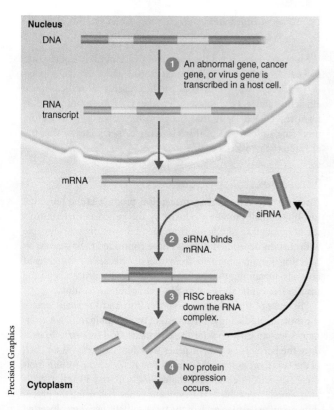

Nucleus

DNA

1 An abnormal gene, cancer gene, or virus gene is transcribed in a host cell.

RNA transcript

mRNA

siRNA

2 siRNA binds mRNA.

3 RISC breaks down the RNA complex.

4 No protein expression occurs.

Cytoplasm

Precision Graphics

Figure 14 Gene silencing could provide treatments for a wide range of diseases.

Q Does RNAi act during or after transcription?

therapy has been used to treat hemophilia B and severe combined immunodeficiency. Adenoviruses and retroviruses are used most often to deliver genes; however, some researchers are working with plasmid vectors. The first gene therapy to treat hemophilia in humans was done in 1990. An attenuated retrovirus was used as the vector. Several gene therapy trials are in progress using genetically modified adenovirus carrying human gene *p53* to treat a variety of cancers. The *p53* gene, which encodes a tumor-suppressing protein, is the most frequently mutated gene in cancer cells.

Thus far, gene therapy results have not been impressive; there have been a few deaths attributed to the viral vectors. There is a great deal of preliminary work to do, and cures may not be possible for all genetic diseases. Antisense DNA introduced into cells is also being explored to treat hepatitis, skin cancer, and high cholesterol.

Gene silencing is a natural process that occurs in a wide variety of eukaryotes and is apparently a defense against viruses and transposons. Gene silencing is similar to miRNA in that a gene encoding a small piece of RNA is transcribed. Following transcription, RNAs called **small interfering RNAs (siRNAs)** are formed after processing by an enzyme called *Dicer*. The siRNA molecules bind to mRNA, causing its enzymatic destruction by proteins called the **RNA-induced silencing complex (RISC)** and thus *silencing* the expression of a gene (**Figure 14**). A new technology called **RNA interference (RNAi)** holds promise for gene therapy and treating cancer and viral infections.

DNA vaccines are usually circular plasmids that include a gene encoding a viral protein under the transcriptional control of a promoter region active in human cells. The plasmids are cloned in bacteria. Several trial vaccines against HIV, SARS, influenza, and malaria are being tested. **Table 2** lists some other important rDNA products used in medical therapy.

The importance of recombinant DNA technology to medical research cannot be emphasized enough. Artificial blood for use in transfusions can now be prepared using human hemoglobin produced in genetically modified pigs. Sheep have also been genetically modified to produce a number of drugs in their milk. This procedure has no apparent effect upon the sheep, and they provide a ready source of raw material for the product that does not require sacrificing animals.

Gene therapy may eventually provide cures for some genetic diseases. It is possible to imagine removing some cells from a person and transforming them with a normal gene to replace a defective or mutated gene. When these cells are returned to the person, they should function normally. For example, gene

Clinical Case Resolved

The amino acid sequence reflects the nucleotide sequence. Analysis of the amino acid signature pattern confirms that the viruses from the dentist and patients are closely related. HIV has a high mutation rate, so HIVs from different individuals are genetically distinct. Dr. B.'s HIV is different from the local control and from the outlier. Dr. B.'s amino acid sequences and those of patients A, B, C, E, and G are distinct from those in the control and in the outlier and from two dental patients with known behavioral risks for HIV infection.

PCR and RFLP analysis has made it possible to track transmission of disease between individuals, communities, and countries. This tracking works best with pathogens that have enough genetic variation to identify different strains. Although Dr. B. finally succumbs to his disease, his five former patients have been on HIV treatment regimens since testing positive, and so far they do not seem to be in danger of progressing to AIDS.

TABLE **2** **Some Pharmaceutical Products of rDNA**

Product	Comments
α-Glucosidase	Produced by genetically modified mammalian cells to treat Pompe disease
Antitrypsin	Assists emphysema patients; produced by genetically modified sheep
Bone Morphogenic Proteins	Induces new bone formation; useful in healing fractures and reconstructive surgery; produced by mammalian cell culture
Cervical Cancer Vaccine	Consists of viral proteins; produced by *S. cerevisiae* or by insect cells
Colony-Stimulating Factor	Counteracts effects of chemotherapy; improves resistance to infectious disease such as AIDS; treatment of leukemia; produced by *E. coli* and *S. cerevisiae*
Epidermal Growth Factor (EGF)	Heals wounds, burns, ulcers; produced by *E. coli*
Erythropoietin (EPO)	Treatment of anemia; produced by mammalian cell culture
Factor VII	Treatment of hemorrhagic strokes; produced by mammalian cell culture
Factor VIII	Treatment of hemophilia; improves clotting; produced by mammalian cell culture
Interferon	
IFN–α	Therapy for leukemia, melanoma, and hepatitis; produced by *E. coli* and *S. cerevisiae* (yeast)
IFN–β	Treatment for multiple sclerosis; produced by mammalian cell culture
IFN–γ	Treatment of chronic granulomatous disease; produced by *E. coli*
Hepatitis B Vaccine	Produced by *S. cerevisiae* that carries hepatitis-virus gene on a plasmid
Human Growth Hormone (hGH)	Corrects growth deficiencies in children; produced by *E. coli*
Human Insulin	Therapy for diabetes; better tolerated than insulin extracted from animals; produced by *E. coli*
Influenza Vaccine	Vaccine made from *E. coli* or *S. cerevisiae* carrying virus genes
Interleukins	Regulate the immune system; possible treatment for cancer; produced by *E. coli*
Monoclonal Antibodies	Possible therapy for cancer and transplant rejection; used in diagnostic tests; produced by mammalian cell culture (from fusion of cancer cell and antibody-producing cell)
Orthoclone OKT3 Muromonab-CD3	Monoclonal antibody used in transplant patients to help suppress the immune system, reducing the chance of tissue rejection; produced by mouse cells
Prourokinase	Anticoagulant; therapy for heart attacks; produced by *E. coli* and yeast
Pulmozyme (rhDNase)	Enzyme used to break down mucous secretions in cystic fibrosis patients; produced by mammalian cell culture
Relaxin	Used to ease childbirth; produced by *E. coli*
Superoxide Dismutase (SOD)	Minimizes damage caused by oxygen free radicals when blood is resupplied to oxygen-deprived tissues; produced by *S. cerevisiae* and *Komagataella pastoris* (yeast)
Taxol	Plant product used for treatment for ovarian cancer; produced in *E. coli*
Tissue Plasminogen Activator	Dissolves the fibrin of blood clots; therapy for heart attacks; produced by mammalian cell culture
Tumor Necrosis Factor (TNF)	Causes disintegration of tumor cells; produced by *E. coli*
Veterinary Use	
Canine Distemper Vaccine	Canarypox virus carrying canine distemper virus genes
Feline Leukemia Vaccine	Canarypox virus carrying feline leukemia virus genes

In mice, RNAi has been shown to inhibit hepatitis B virus. The siRNA can be injected into a cell or introduced in a DNA vector. A small DNA insert encoding siRNA against the gene of interest could be cloned into a DNA vector. When transferred into a cell, the cell would produce the desired siRNA.

CHECK YOUR UNDERSTANDING

✔ Explain how DNA technology can be used to treat disease and to prevent disease. 13

✔ What is gene silencing? 14

Genome Projects

The first genome to be sequenced was the small genome from a bacteriophage. That occurred in 1977. In 1995, the genome of a free-living cell—*Haemophilus influenzae*—was sequenced. Since then, 1000 prokaryotic genomes and over 400 eukaryotic genomes have been sequenced. It was shotgun sequencing that enabled scientists to sequence the genome of a free-living cell. In **shotgun sequencing,** small pieces of a genome are sequenced, and the sequences are then assembled using a computer. Any gaps between the pieces then have to be found and sequenced (**Figure 15**). This technique can be used on environmental samples to study the genomes of microorganisms that have not been cultured. The study of genetic material taken directly from environmental samples is called **metagenomics.**

The Human Genome Project was an international 13-year effort, formally begun in October 1990 and completed in 2003.

The goal of this project was to sequence the entire human genome, approximately 3 billion nucleotide pairs, comprising 20,000 to 25,000 genes. Thousands of people in 18 countries participated in this project. Researchers collected blood (female) or sperm (male) samples from a large number of donors. Only a few samples were processed as DNA resources, and the source names are protected so that neither donors nor scientists know whose samples were used. Development of shotgun sequencing greatly speeded the process, and the genome is nearly complete.

One surprising finding was that less than 2% of the genome encodes a functional product—the other 98% includes miRNA genes, viral remnants, repetitive sequences (called *short tandem repeats*), introns, the chromosome ends (called *telomeres*), and transposons. Currently, researchers are locating specific genes and determining their functions.

The next goal of researchers is the Human Proteome Project, which will map all the proteins expressed in human cells. Even before it is completed, however, it is yielding data that are of immense value to our understanding of biology. It will also eventually be of great medical benefit, especially for the diagnosis and treatment of genetic diseases.

Scientific Applications

Recombinant DNA technology can be used to make products, but this is not its only important application. Because of its ability to produce many copies of DNA, it can serve as a sort of DNA "printing press." Once a large amount of a particular piece of DNA

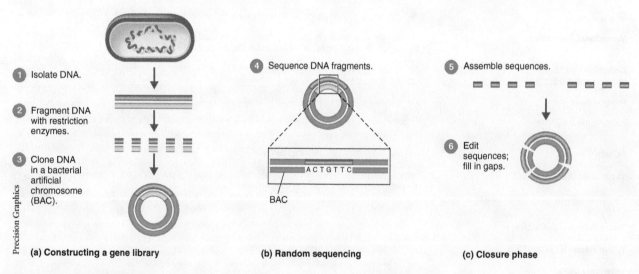

(a) **Constructing a gene library**

1 Isolate DNA.

2 Fragment DNA with restriction enzymes.

3 Clone DNA in a bacterial artificial chromosome (BAC).

(b) **Random sequencing**

4 Sequence DNA fragments.

ACTGTTC

BAC

(c) **Closure phase**

5 Assemble sequences.

6 Edit sequences; fill in gaps.

Precision Graphics

Figure 15 Shotgun sequencing. In this technique, a genome is cut into pieces, and each piece is sequenced. Then the pieces are fit together. There may be gaps if a specific DNA fragment was not sequenced.

Q Does this technique identify genes and their locations?

is available, various analytic techniques, discussed in this section, can be used to "read" the information contained in the DNA.

In 2010, Minimal Genome Project researchers synthesized a copy of the entire *Mycoplasma mycoides* genome and transplanted it into a *M. capricolum* cell that had had its DNA removed. The modified cell produced *M. mycoides* proteins. This experiment showed that large-scale changes to a genome can be made and that an existing cell will accept this DNA.

DNA sequencing has produced an enormous amount of information that has spawned the new field of **bioinformatics,** the science of understanding the function of genes through computer-assisted analysis. DNA sequences are stored in web-based databases referred to as GenBank. Genomic information can be searched with computer programs to find specific sequences or to look for similar patterns in the genomes of different organisms. Microbial genes are now being searched to identify molecules that are the virulence factors of pathogens. By comparing genomes, researchers discovered that *Chlamydia trachomatis* (tra-kō′ mä-tis) produces a toxin similar to that of *Clostridium difficile* (dif′ fī-sē-il).

The next goal is to identify proteins encoded by these genes. **Proteomics** is the science of determining all of the proteins expressed in a cell.

Reverse genetics is an approach to discovering the function of a gene from a genetic sequence. Reverse genetics attempts to connect a given genetic sequence with specific effects on the organism. For example, if you mutate or block a gene (see the discussion of gene silencing earlier in this chapter), you can then look for a characteristic the organism lost.

An example of the use of human DNA sequencing is the identification and cloning of the mutant gene that causes cystic fibrosis (CF). CF is characterized by the oversecretion of mucus, leading to blocked respiratory passageways. The sequence of the mutated gene can be used as a diagnostic tool in a hybridization technique called **Southern blotting** (Figure 16), named for Ed Southern, who developed the technique in 1975.

In this technique,

① human DNA is first digested with a restriction enzyme, yielding thousands of fragments of various sizes. The different fragments are then separated by **gel electrophoresis.**

② The fragments are put in a well at one end of a layer of agarose gel. Then an electrical current is passed through the gel. While the charge is applied, the different-sized pieces of DNA migrate through the gel at different rates. The fragments are called **RFLPs** (pronounced "rif-lip"), for *restriction fragment length polymorphisms.*

③–④ The separated fragments are transferred onto a filter by blotting.

⑤ The fragments on the filter are then exposed to a labeled probe made from the cloned gene of interest, in this case the

CF gene. The probe will hybridize to this mutant gene but not to the normal gene.

⑥ Fragments to which the probe binds are identified by fluorescence or a colored dye. With this method, any person's DNA can be tested for the presence of the mutated gene.

Genetic testing can now be used to screen for several hundred genetic diseases. Such screening procedures can be performed on prospective parents and also on fetal tissue. Two of the more commonly screened genes are those associated with inherited forms of breast cancer and the gene responsible for Huntington's disease. Genetic testing can help a physician prescribe the correct medication for a patient. The drug herceptin, for example, is effective only in breast cancer patients with a specific nucleotide sequence in the HER2 gene.

Forensic Microbiology

For several years, microbiologists have used RFLPs in a method of identification known as **DNA fingerprinting** to identify bacterial or viral pathogens (Figure 17).

DNA chips and *PCR microarrays* that can screen a sample for multiple pathogens at once are now being used. In a PCR microarray, up to 22 primers from different microorganisms can be used to initiate the PCR. A suspect microorganism is identified if DNA is copied from one of the primers. At the Centers for Disease Control and Prevention (CDC), PulseNet uses RFLPs to track outbreaks of foodborne disease. In some cases, PCR using specific primers can be used to track a bacterial strain to locate the source of an outbreak.

The genomics of pathogens has become a mainstay of monitoring, preventing, and controlling infectious disease. The use of genomics to trace a disease outbreak is described in the Clinical Focus later in this chapter. The new field of **forensic microbiology** developed because hospitals, food manufacturers, and individuals can be sued in courts of law and because microorganisms can be used as weapons. Microbial forensics has been used in court a few times. In the 1990s, DNA fingerprints of HIV were used for the first time to obtain a rape conviction. Since then, a physician was convicted of injecting his former lover with HIV from one of his patients, based on the DNA fingerprint of the HIV. In the 2001 anthrax attacks in the United States, DNA fingerprints of *Bacillus anthracis* were used to track the source and then the alleged attacker. Northern Arizona University researchers determined that the *B. anthracis* endospores used in a 1993 attack by a cult in Japan were actually a nonpathogenic vaccine strain. No one was hurt when those endospores were released. Currently, a DNA database is being developed for microorganisms that could be used in biological crimes.

The requirements to prove in a court of law the source of a microbe are stricter than for the medical community. For example, to prove intent to commit harm requires collecting evidence properly and establishing a chain of custody of that evidence.

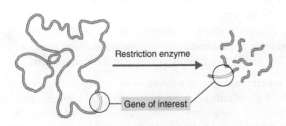

1 DNA containing the gene of interest is extracted from human cells and cut into fragments by restriction enzymes.

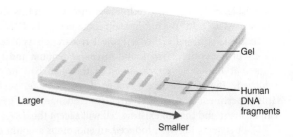

2 The fragments are separated according to size by gel electrophoresis. Each band consists of many copies of a particular DNA fragment. The bands are invisible but can be made visible by staining.

3 The DNA bands are transferred to a nitrocellulose filter by blotting. The solution passes through the gel and filter to the paper towels by capillary action.

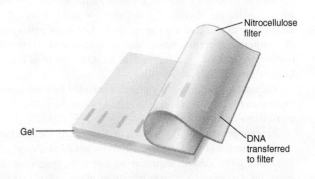

4 This produces a nitrocellulose filter with DNA fragments positioned exactly as on the gel.

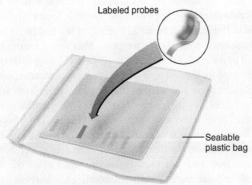

5 The filter is exposed to a labeled probe for a specific gene. The probe will base-pair (hybridize) with a short sequence present on the gene.

6 The fragment containing the gene of interest is identified by a band on the filter.

Figure 16 Southern blotting.

Q What is the purpose of Southern blotting?

Kenneth Rosen

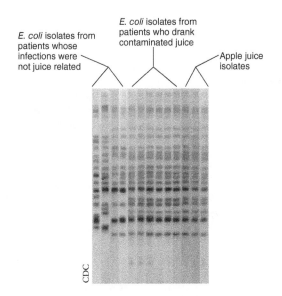

Figure 17 **DNA fingerprints used to track an infectious disease.** This figure shows the RFLP patterns of bacterial isolates from an outbreak of *Escherichia coli* O157:H7. The isolates from apple juice are identical to the patterns of isolates from patients who drank the contaminated juice but different from those from patients whose infections were not juice related.

What is forensic microbiology?

Microbial properties that are unimportant in public health may be important clues in forensic investigations. The American Academy of Microbiology recently proposed professional certification in forensic microbiology.

DNA can often be extracted from preserved and fossilized materials, including mummies and extinct plants and animals. Although such material is very rare, and usually partially degraded, PCR enables researchers to study environments and organisms that no longer exist in their natural form. The study of unusual organisms has also led to advances in basic taxonomy.

Nanotechnology

Nanotechnology deals with the design and manufacture of extremely small electronic circuits and mechanical devices built at the molecular level of matter. Molecule-sized robots or computers can be used to detect contamination in food, diseases in plants, or biological weapons. However, the small machines require small (a nanometer is 10^{-9} meters; 1000 nm fit in 1 μm) wires and components. Bacteria may provide the needed small metals. Researchers at the U.S. Geological Survey have cultured several anaerobic bacteria that reduce toxic selenium, Se^{4+}, to nontoxic elemental Se^0, which forms into nanospheres (Figure 18). Researchers are using bacteria to produce nano-

Figure 18 *Bacillus* cells growing on selenium form chains of elemental selenium.

What might bacteria provide for nanotechnology?

R. S. Oremland et al., "Structural and Spectral Features of Selenium Nanospheres Produced by Se-respiring Bacteria," *Applied Environmental Microbiology*, 2004 Jan; 70(1):52–60, F1A. © 2004, American Society for Microbiology

spheres for potential drug targeting and delivery. Researchers with the U.S. Department of Energy are using bacteria in nanoscale electrical circuits to make hydrogen gas. Swedish researchers are using *Acetobacter xylinum* to build cellulose nanofibers for artificial blood vessels.

CHECK YOUR UNDERSTANDING

✔ How are shotgun sequencing, bioinformatics, and proteomics related to genome projects? **15**, **16**

✔ What is Southern blotting? **17**

✔ Why do RFLPs result in a DNA fingerprint? **18**

Agricultural Applications

The process of selecting for genetically desirable plants has always been a time-consuming one. Performing conventional plant crosses is laborious and involves waiting for the planted seed to germinate and for the plant to mature. Plant breeding has been revolutionized by the use of plant cells grown in culture. Clones of plant cells, including cells that have been genetically altered by recombinant DNA techniques, can be grown in large numbers. These cells can then be induced to regenerate whole plants, from which seeds can be harvested.

Recombinant DNA can be introduced into plant cells in several ways. Previously we mentioned protoplast fusion and the use of DNA-coated "bullets." The most elegant method, however, makes use of a plasmid called the **Ti plasmid** (*Ti* stands for tumor-inducing), which occurs naturally in the bacterium *Agrobacterium tumefaciens* (tu' me-fash-enz). This bacterium infects certain plants, in which the Ti plasmid causes the formation of a tumorlike growth called a crown gall (Figure 19). A part of the Ti plasmid, called T-DNA, integrates into the genome of the infected plant. The T-DNA stimulates local cellular growth (the crown gall) and simultaneously causes the production of certain products used by the bacteria as a source of nutritional carbon and nitrogen.

For plant scientists, the attraction of the Ti plasmid is that it provides a vehicle for introducing rDNA into a plant (Figure 20). A scientist can insert foreign genes into the T-DNA, put the recombinant plasmid back into the *Agrobacterium* cell, and use the bacterium to insert the recombinant Ti plasmid into a plant cell. The plant cell with the foreign gene can then be used to generate a new plant. With luck, the new plant will express the foreign gene. Unfortunately, *Agrobacterium* does not naturally infect grasses, so it cannot be used to improve grains such as wheat, rice, or corn.

Noteworthy accomplishments of this approach are the introduction into plants of resistance to the herbicide glyphosate, and a *Bacillus thuringiensis*–derived insecticidal toxin (Bt). Normally, the herbicide kills both weeds and useful plants by inhibiting an enzyme necessary for making certain essential amino acids. *Salmonella* bacteria happen to have this enzyme, and some salmonellae have a mutant enzyme that is resistant to the herbicide. When the DNA for this enzyme is introduced into a crop plant, the crop becomes resistant to the herbicide, which then kills only the weeds. There is now a variety of plants in which different herbicide and pesticide resistances have been engineered. Resistance to drought, viral infection, and several other environmental stresses has also been engineered

Holt Studios International Ltd./Alamy

Crown gall

Figure 19 Crown gall disease on a rose plant. The tumorlike growth is stimulated by a gene on the Ti plasmid carried by the bacterium *Agrobacterium tumefaciens,* which has infected the plant.

Q What are some of the agricultural applications of recombinant DNA technology?

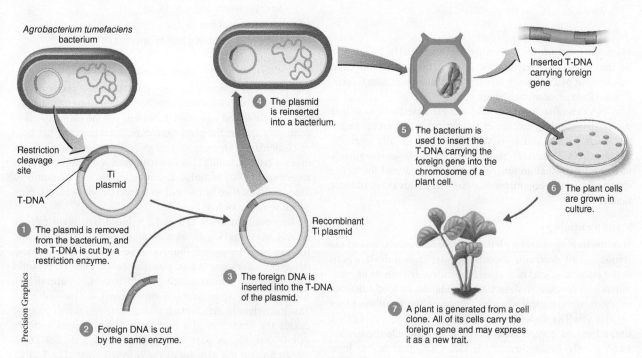

Precision Graphics

Agrobacterium tumefaciens bacterium

Restriction cleavage site

Ti plasmid

T-DNA

1 The plasmid is removed from the bacterium, and the T-DNA is cut by a restriction enzyme.

2 Foreign DNA is cut by the same enzyme.

3 The foreign DNA is inserted into the T-DNA of the plasmid.

Recombinant Ti plasmid

4 The plasmid is reinserted into a bacterium.

5 The bacterium is used to insert the T-DNA carrying the foreign gene into the chromosome of a plant cell.

Inserted T-DNA carrying foreign gene

6 The plant cells are grown in culture.

7 A plant is generated from a cell clone. All of its cells carry the foreign gene and may express it as a new trait.

Figure 20 Using the Ti plasmid as a vector for genetic modification in plants.

Q Why is the Ti plasmid important to biotechnology?

Norovirus—Who Is Responsible for the Outbreak?

As you read through this box, you will encounter a series of questions that microbiologists ask themselves as they trace a disease outbreak. Whether the microbiologist is called as expert witness in court will depend on whether a lawsuit is filed. Try to answer each question before going on to the next one.

1. On May 7, Nadia Koehler, a microbiologist at a county health department, is notified of a gastroenteritis outbreak among 115 people. The case is defined as vomiting and diarrhea and fever, cramps, or nausea.
   What information does Nadia need?

2. Nadia needs to find out where the ill people have been in the past 48 hours. After several interviews, Nadia finds out that the ill people include 23 school employees, 55 publishing company employees, 9 employees of a social service organization, and 28 other people (see **Figure A**).
   Now what does Nadia need to know?

3. Next, Nadia finds out what these 115 people have in common. In her investigation, Nadia discovers that on May 2, the school staff

   had been served a party-sized sandwich catered by a national franchise restaurant. On May 3, the publishing company and social service staff luncheons were catered by the same restaurant. The remaining 28 people ate sandwiches at the same restaurant, at varying times between these two days.
   What does Nadia do next?

4. Nadia analyzes exposures to 16 food items; the results show that eating lettuce is significantly associated with illness.
   What is Nadia's next step?

5. Nadia then requests a reverse-transcription PCR (RT-PCR) using a norovirus primer to be done on stool samples (**Figure B**).
   What did Nadia conclude?

6. RT-PCR confirmed norovirus infection. Nadia's next request is for a sequence analysis to be performed on 21 stool specimens. The results demonstrated 100% sequence homology for the 21 specimens.
   What should Nadia do next?

7. Nadia learns that a food handler employed by the restaurant had experienced vomiting and diarrhea on May 1. The food handler believes he had acquired illness from his child. The child's illness was traced to an ill cousin who had been exposed to norovirus at a child-care center. The food handler's vomiting ended by the early morning of May 2, and he returned to work at the restaurant later that morning.
   What should Nadia look for now?

8. Now Nadia compares the virus strains from the food handler to the ones from the ill customers. She requests a sequence

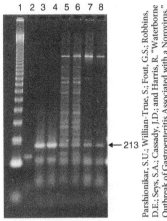

Figure B Results of PCR of patient samples. Lane 1, 123-bp size ladders. Lane 2, negative RT-PCR control; Lanes 3–8, patient samples. Norovirus is identified by the 213-bp band of DNA.

Parshionikar, S.U.; Willian-True, S.; Fout, G.S.; Robbins, D.E.; Seys, S.A.; Cassady, J.D.; and Harris, R. "Waterborne Outbreak of Gastroenteritis Associated with a Norovirus." *Applied and Environmental Microbiology*, September 2003, p. 5263–5268, Vol. 69, No. 9, Fig. 2

analysis on viruses from the food handler and eight ill customers. They are identical to the strains identified in step 6.
Where does Nadia look next?

9. Nadia looks for any areas in the restaurant that still may be contaminated by the norovirus. She finds out that the lettuce was sliced each morning by the food handler who had been sick. Nadia's inspection reveals that the food preparation sink is also used for handwashing. The sink was not sanitized before and after the lettuce was washed. The health department closes the restaurant until it can be cleaned with the proper sanitizers.

Noroviruses are the most common cause of outbreaks of acute gastroenteritis worldwide. During fall 2008, three norovirus outbreaks occurred on college campuses, resulting in a total of approximately 1000 cases of reported illness, including at least 10 hospitalizations, and prompted closure of one of the three campuses.

Source: Adapted from *MMWR* 55(14): 395–397, April 14, 2006; 58(39): 1095–1100, October 9, 2009.

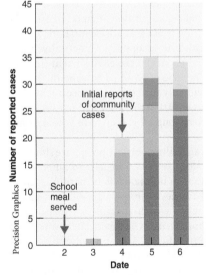

Figure A Number of cases reported.

KEY

- Reported community cases
- Social service group
- School employees
- Publishing company employees

into crop plants. *Bacillus thuringiensis* bacteria are pathogenic to some insects because they produce a protein called Bt toxin that interferes with the insect digestive tract. The Bt gene has been inserted into a variety of crop plants, including cotton and potatoes, so insects that eat the plants will be killed.

Another example involves MacGregor tomatoes, which stay firm after harvest because the gene for polygalacturonase (PG), the enzyme that breaks down pectin, is suppressed. The suppression was accomplished by **antisense DNA technology.** First, a length of DNA complementary to the PG mRNA is synthesized. This antisense DNA is taken up by the cell and binds to the mRNA to inhibit translation. The DNA-RNA hybrid is broken down by the cell's enzymes, freeing the antisense DNA to disable another mRNA.

Perhaps the most exciting potential use of genetically modified plants concerns nitrogen fixation, the ability to convert the nitrogen gas in the air to compounds that living cells can use. The availability of such nitrogen-containing nutrients is usually the main factor limiting crop growth. But in nature, only certain bacteria have genes for carrying out this process. Some plants, such as alfalfa, benefit from a symbiotic relationship with these microbes. Species of the symbiotic bacterium *Rhizobium* have already been genetically modified for enhanced nitrogen fixation. In the future, *Rhizobium* strains may be designed that can colonize such crop plants as corn and wheat, perhaps eliminating their requirement for nitrogen fertilizer. The ultimate goal would be to introduce functioning nitrogen-fixation genes directly into the plants. Although this goal cannot be achieved with our current knowledge, work toward it will continue because of its potential for dramatically increasing the world's food supply.

An example of a genetically modified bacterium now in agricultural use is *Pseudomonas fluorescens* that has been engineered to produce Bt toxin, normally produced by *Bacillus thuringiensis.* This toxin kills certain insects, such as the European corn borer. The genetically altered *Pseudomonas,* which produces much more toxin than *B. thuringiensis,* can be added to plant seeds and in time will enter the vascular system of the growing plant. Its toxin is ingested by the feeding borer larvae and kills them (but is harmless to humans and other warm-blooded animals).

Animal husbandry has also benefited from rDNA technology. We have seen how one of the early commercial products of rDNA was human growth hormone. By similar methods it is possible to manufacture bovine growth hormone (bGH). When bGH is injected into beef cattle, it increases their weight gain; in dairy cows, it also causes a 10% increase in milk production. Such procedures have met with resistance from consumers, especially in Europe, primarily as a result of as-yet unsubstantiated

fears that some of the bGH would be present in the milk or meat of these cattle and might be harmful to humans.

Table 3 lists these and several other rDNA products used in agriculture and animal husbandry.

CHECK YOUR UNDERSTANDING

✔ Of what value is the plant pathogen *Agrobacterium*? 19

Safety Issues and the Ethics of Using DNA Technology

LEARNING OBJECTIVE

20 List the advantages of, and problems associated with, the use of genetic modification techniques.

There will always be concern about the safety of any new technology, and genetic modification and biotechnology are certainly no exceptions. One reason for this concern is that it is nearly impossible to prove that something is entirely safe under all conceivable conditions. People worry that the same techniques that can alter a microbe or plant to make them useful to humans could also inadvertently make them pathogenic to humans or otherwise dangerous to living organisms or could create an ecological nightmare. Therefore, laboratories engaged in rDNA research must meet rigorous standards of control to avoid either accidentally releasing genetically modified organisms into the environment or exposing humans to any risk of infection. To reduce risk further, microbiologists engaged in genetic modification often delete from the microbes' genomes certain genes that are essential for growth in environments outside the laboratory. Genetically modified organisms intended for use in the environment (in agriculture, for example) may be engineered to contain "suicide genes"—genes that eventually turn on to produce a toxin that kills the microbes, thus ensuring that they will not survive in the environment for very long after they have accomplished their task.

The safety issues in agricultural biotechnology are similar to those concerning chemical pesticides: toxicity to humans and to nonpest species. Although not shown to be harmful, genetically modified foods have not been popular with consumers. In 1999, researchers in Ohio noticed that humans may develop allergies to *Bacillus thuringiensis* (Bt) toxin after working in fields sprayed with the insecticide. And an Iowa study showed that the caterpillar stage of Monarch butterflies could be killed by ingesting windblown Bt-carrying pollen that landed on milkweed, the caterpillars' normal food. Crop plants can be genetically modified for herbicide resistance so that fields can be sprayed to eliminate weeds without killing the desired crop. However, if the modified plants pollinate related weed species, weeds could become resistant to herbicides, making it more

TABLE 3 Some Agriculturally Important Products of rDNA Technology

Product	Comments
AGRICULTURAL PRODUCTS	
Bt cotton and Bt corn	Plants have toxin-producing gene from *Bacillus thuringiensis;* toxin kills insects that eat plants.
Genetically modified tomatoes , raspberries	Antisense gene blocks pectin degradation, so fruits have longer shelf life.
Pseudomonas fluorescens bacterium	Has toxin-producing gene from insect pathogen *B. thuringiensis;* toxin kills root-eating insects that ingest bacteria.
Pseudomonas syringae, ice-minus bacterium	Lacks normal protein product that initiates undesirable ice formation on plants.
Rhizobium meliloti bacterium	Modified for enhanced nitrogen fixation.
Round up (glyphosate)-resistant crops	Plants have bacterial gene; allows use of herbicide on weeds without damaging crops.
ANIMAL HUSBANDRY PRODUCTS	
Bovine growth hormone (bGH)	Improves weight gain and milk production in cattle; produced by *E. coli.*
Porcine growth hormone (pGH)	Improves weight gain in swine; produced by *E. coli.*
Transgenic animals	Genetic modification of animals to produce medically useful products in their milk.
OTHER FOOD PRODUCTION PRODUCTS	
Cellulase	Enzyme that degrades cellulose to make animal feedstocks; produced by *E. coli.*
Chymogen	Causes formation of milk curds in cheese-making; produced by *Aspergillus niger.*

difficult to control unwanted plants. An unanswered question is whether releasing genetically modified organisms will alter evolution as genes move to wild species.

These developing technologies also raise a variety of ethical issues. Genetic testing for diseases is becoming routine. Who should have access to this information? Should employers have the right to know the results of such tests? How can we be assured that such information will not be used to discriminate against certain groups? Should individuals be told they will get an incurable disease? If so, when?

Genetic counseling, which provides advice and counseling to prospective parents with family histories of genetic disease, is becoming more important in considerations about whether to have children.

There are probably just as many harmful applications of a new technology as there are helpful ones. It is particularly easy to imagine DNA technology being used to develop new and powerful biological weapons. In addition, because such research efforts are performed under top-secret conditions, it is virtually impossible for the general public to learn of them.

Perhaps more than most new technologies, molecular genetics holds the promise of affecting human life in previously unimaginable ways. It is important that society and individuals be given every opportunity to understand the potential impact of these new developments.

Like the invention of the microscope, the development of DNA techniques is causing profound changes in science, agriculture, and human health care. With this technology only slightly more than 30 years old, it is difficult to predict exactly what changes will occur. However, it is likely that within another 30 years, many of the treatments and diagnostic methods discussed in this text will have been replaced by far more powerful techniques based on the unprecedented ability to manipulate DNA precisely.

CHECK YOUR UNDERSTANDING

✓ Identify two advantages and two problems associated with genetically modified organisms. 20

Study Outline

Test your understanding with quizzes, microbe review, and a chapter post-test at www.masteringmicrobiology.com

Introduction to Biotechnology

1. Biotechnology is the use of micro-organisms, cells, or cell components to make a product.

Recombinant DNA Technology

2. Closely related organisms can ex-change genes in natural recombination.

3. Genes can be transferred among unrelated species via laboratory manipulation, called recombinant DNA technology.

4. Recombinant DNA is DNA that has been artificially manipulated to combine genes from two different sources.

An Overview of Recombinant DNA Procedures

5. A desired gene is inserted into a DNA vector, such as a plasmid or a viral genome.

6. The vector inserts the DNA into a new cell, which is grown to form a clone.

7. Large quantities of the gene product can be harvested from the clone.

Tools of Biotechnology

Selection

1. Microbes with desirable traits are selected for culturing by artificial selection.

Mutation

2. Mutagens are used to cause mutations that might result in a microbe with desirable traits.

3. Site-directed mutagenesis is used to change a specific codon in a gene.

Restriction Enzymes

4. Prepackaged kits are available for rDNA techniques.

5. A restriction enzyme recognizes and cuts only one particular nucleotide sequence in DNA.

6. Some restriction enzymes produce sticky ends, short stretches of single-stranded DNA at the ends of the DNA fragments.

7. Fragments of DNA produced by the same restriction enzyme will spontaneously join by base pairing. DNA ligase can covalently link the DNA backbones.

Vectors

8. Shuttle vectors are plasmids that can exist in several different species.

9. A plasmid containing a new gene can be inserted into a cell by transformation.

10. A virus containing a new gene can insert the gene into a cell.

Polymerase Chain Reaction

11. The polymerase chain reaction (PCR) is used to make multiple copies of a desired piece of DNA enzymatically.

12. PCR can be used to increase the amounts of DNA in samples to detectable levels. This may allow sequencing of genes, the diagnosis of genetic diseases, or the detection of viruses.

Techniques of Genetic Modification

Inserting Foreign DNA into Cells

1. Cells can take up naked DNA by transformation. Chemical treatments are used to make cells that are not naturally competent take up DNA.

2. Pores made in protoplasts and animal cells by electric current in the process of electroporation can provide entrance for new pieces of DNA.

3. Protoplast fusion is the joining of cells whose cell walls have been removed.

4. Foreign DNA can be introduced into plant cells by shooting DNA-coated particles into the cells.

5. Foreign DNA can be injected into animal cells by using a fine glass micropipette.

Obtaining DNA

6. Genomic libraries can be made by cutting up an entire genome with restriction enzymes and inserting the fragments into bacterial plasmids or phages.

7. Complementary DNA (cDNA) made from mRNA by reverse transcription can be cloned in genomic libraries.

8. Synthetic DNA can be made in vitro by a DNA synthesis machine.

Selecting a Clone

9. Antibiotic-resistance markers on plasmid vectors are used to identify cells containing the engineered vector by direct selection.

10. In blue-white screening, the vector contains the genes for amp^R and β-galactosidase.

11. The desired gene is inserted into the β-galactosidase gene site, destroying the gene.

12. Clones containing the recombinant vector will be resistant to ampicillin and unable to hydrolyze X-gal (white colonies). Clones containing the vector without the new gene will be blue. Clones lacking the vector will not grow.

13. Clones containing foreign DNA can be tested for the desired gene product.

14. A short piece of labeled DNA called a DNA probe can be used to identify clones carrying the desired gene.

Making a Gene Product

15. E. coli is used to produce proteins using rDNA because E. coli is easily grown and its genomics are well understood.

16. Efforts must be made to ensure that E. coli's endotoxin does not contaminate a product intended for human use.

17. To recover the product, *E. coli* must be lysed, or the gene must be linked to a gene that produces a naturally secreted protein.
18. Yeasts can be genetically modified and are likely to secrete a gene product continuously.
19. Genetically modified mammalian cells can be grown to produce proteins such as hormones for medical use.
20. Genetically modified plant cells can be grown and used to produce plants with new properties.

Applications of DNA Technology

1. Cloned DNA is used to produce products, study the cloned DNA, and alter the phenotype of an organism.

Therapeutic Applications

2. Synthetic genes linked to the β-galactosidase gene (*lacZ*) in a plasmid vector were inserted into *E. coli*, allowing *E. coli* to produce and secrete the two polypeptides used to make human insulin.
3. Cells and viruses can be modified to produce a pathogen's surface protein, which can be used as a vaccine.
4. DNA vaccines consist of rDNA cloned in bacteria.
5. Gene therapy can be used to cure genetic diseases by replacing the defective or missing gene.
6. RNAi may be useful to prevent expression of abnormal proteins.

Genome Projects

7. Nucleotide sequences of the genomes over 1000 organisms, including humans, have been completed.
8. This leads to determining the proteins produced in a cell.

Scientific Applications

9. DNA can be used to increase understanding of DNA, for genetic fingerprinting, and for gene therapy.
10. DNA sequencing machines are used to determine the nucleotide base sequence of restriction fragments in shotgun sequencing.

11. Bioinformatics is the use of computer applications to study genetic data; proteomics is the study of a cell's proteins.
12. Southern blotting can be used to locate a gene in a cell.
13. DNA probes can be used to quickly identify a pathogen in body tissue or food.
14. Forensic microbiologists use DNA fingerprinting to identify the source of bacterial or viral pathogens.
15. Bacteria may be used to make nano-sized materials for nanotechnology machines.

Agricultural Applications

16. Cells from plants with desirable characteristics can be cloned to produce many identical cells. These cells can then be used to produce whole plants from which seeds can be harvested.
17. Plant cells can be modified by using the Ti plasmid vector. The tumor-producing T genes are replaced with desired genes, and the recombinant DNA is inserted into *Agrobacterium*. The bacterium naturally transforms its plant hosts.
18. Antisense DNA can prevent expression of unwanted proteins.

Safety Issues and the Ethics of Using DNA Technology

1. Strict safety standards are used to avoid the accidental release of genetically modified microorganisms.
2. Some microbes used in rDNA cloning have been altered so that they cannot survive outside the laboratory.
3. Microorganisms intended for use in the environment may be modified to contain suicide genes so that the organisms do not persist in the environment.
4. Genetic testing raises a number of ethical questions: Should employers and insurance companies have access to a person's genetic records? Will some people be targeted for either breeding or sterilization? Will genetic counseling be available to everyone?
5. Genetically modified crops must be safe for consumption and for release in the environment.

Study Questions

Answers to the Review and Multiple Choice questions can be found at the end of this chapter.

Review

1. Compare and contrast the following terms:
   a. *cDNA* and *gene*
   b. *restriction fragment* and *gene*
   c. *DNA probe* and *gene*
   d. *DNA polymerase* and *DNA ligase*
   e. *rDNA* and *cDNA*
   f. *genome* and *proteome*
2. Differentiate the following terms. Which one is "hit and miss"— that is, does *not* add a specific gene to a cell?
   a. protoplast fusion
   b. gene gun
   c. microinjection
   d. electroporation

3. Some commonly used restriction enzymes are listed in Table 1.
   a. Indicate which enzymes produce sticky ends.
   b. Of what value are sticky ends in making recombinant DNA?
4. Suppose you want multiple copies of a gene you have synthesized. How would you obtain the necessary copies by cloning? By PCR?

5. **DRAW IT** Using the following map of plasmid pMICRO, diagram the locations of the restriction fragments that result from digesting pMICRO with *Eco*RI, *Hin*dIII, and both enzymes together following electrophoresis. Which enzyme makes the smallest fragment containing the tetracycline resistance gene?

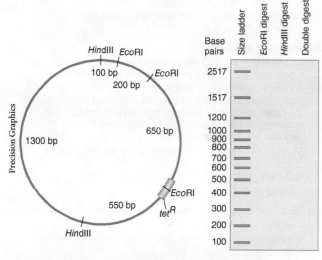

6. Describe a recombinant DNA experiment in two or three sentences. Use the following terms: intron, exon, DNA, mRNA, cDNA, RNA polymerase, reverse transcriptase.

7. List at least two examples of the use of rDNA in medicine and in agriculture.

8. You are attempting to insert a gene for saltwater tolerance into a plant by using the Ti plasmid. In addition to the desired gene, you add a gene for tetracycline resistance (*tet*^R) to the plasmid. What is the purpose of the *tet*^R gene?

9. How does RNAi "silence" a gene?

10. **NAME IT** This virus family, normally associated with AIDS, may be useful for gene therapy.

Multiple Choice

1. Restriction enzymes were first discovered with the observation that
   a. DNA is restricted to the nucleus.
   b. phage DNA is destroyed in a host cell.
   c. foreign DNA is kept out of a cell.
   d. foreign DNA is restricted to the cytoplasm.
   e. all of the above

2. The DNA probe, 3'-GGCTTA, will hybridize with which of the following?
   a. 5'-CCGUUA
   b. 5'-CCGAAT
   c. 5'-GGCTTA
   d. 3'-CCGAAT
   e. 3'-GGCAAU

3. Which of the following is the fourth basic step to genetically modify a cell?
   a. transformation
   b. ligation
   c. plasmid cleavage
   d. restriction-enzyme digestion of gene
   e. isolation of gene

4. The following enzymes are used to make cDNA. What is the second enzyme used to make cDNA?
   a. reverse transcriptase
   b. ribozyme
   c. RNA polymerase
   d. DNA polymerase

5. If you put a gene in a virus, the next step in genetic modification would be
   a. insertion of a plasmid.
   b. transformation.
   c. transduction.
   d. PCR.
   e. Southern blotting.

6. You have a small gene that you want replicated by PCR. You add radioactively labeled nucleotides to the PCR thermal cycler. After three replication cycles, what percentage of the DNA single strands are radioactively labeled?
   a. 0%
   b. 12.5%
   c. 50%
   d. 87.5%
   e. 100%

Match the following choices to the statements in questions 7 through 10.
   a. antisense
   b. clone
   c. library
   d. Southern blot
   e. vector

7. Pieces of human DNA stored in yeast cells.

8. A population of cells carrying a desired plasmid.

9. Self-replicating DNA for transmitting a gene from one organism to another.

10. A gene that hybridizes with mRNA.

Critical Thinking

1. Design an experiment using vaccinia virus to make a vaccine against the AIDS virus (HIV).

2. Why did the use of DNA polymerase from the bacterium *Thermus aquaticus* allow researchers to add the necessary reagents to tubes in a preprogrammed heating block?

3. The following picture shows bacterial colonies growing on X-gal plus ampicillin in a blue-white screening test. Which colonies have the recombinant plasmid? The small satellite colonies do not have the plasmid. Why did they start growing on the medium 48 hours after the larger colonies?

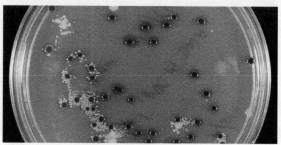

Christine Case

Clinical Applications

1. PCR has been used to examine oysters for the presence of *Vibrio cholerae*. Oysters from different areas were homogenized, and DNA was extracted from the homogenates. The DNA was digested by the restriction enzyme *Hinc*II. A primer for the hemolysin gene of *V. cholerae* was used for the PCR reaction. After PCR, each sample was electrophoresed and stained with a probe for the hemolysin gene. Which of the oyster samples were (was) positive for *V. cholerae*? How can you tell? Why look for *V. cholerae* in oysters? What is the advantage of PCR over conventional biochemical tests to identify the bacteria?

Mike Zeller, Office of Biotechnology, Iowa State Univ

2. Using the restriction enzyme *Eco*RI, the following gel electrophoresis patterns were obtained from digests of various DNA molecules from a transformation experiment. Can you conclude from these data that transformation occurred? Explain why or why not.

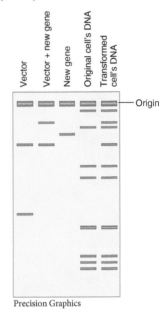

Precision Graphics

Answers to Review and Multiple Choice Study Questions

Review

1. **a.** Both are DNA. cDNA is a segment of DNA made by RNA-dependent DNA polymerase. It is not necessarily a gene; a gene is a transcribable unit of DNA that codes for protein or RNA.
   b. Both are DNA. A restriction fragment is a segment of DNA produced when a restriction endonuclease hydrolyzes DNA. It is not usually a gene; a gene is a transcribable unit of DNA that codes for protein or RNA.
   c. Both are DNA. A DNA probe is a short, single-stranded piece of DNA. It is not a gene; a gene is a transcribable unit of DNA that codes for protein or RNA.
   d. Both are enzymes. DNA polymerase synthesizes DNA one nucleotide at a time using a DNA template; DNA ligase joins pieces (strands of nucleotides) together.
   e. Both are DNA. Recombinant DNA results from joining DNA from two different sources; cDNA results from copying a strand of RNA.
   f. The proteome is the expression of the genome. An organism's genome is one complete copy of its genetic information. The proteins encoded by this genetic material comprise the proteome.

2. In protoplast fusion, two wall-less cells fuse together to combine their DNA. A variety of genotypes can result from this process. In b, c, and d, specific genes are inserted directly into the cell.

3. **a.** *Bam*HI, *Eco*RI, and *Hin*dIII make sticky ends.
   b. Fragments of DNA produced with the same restriction enzyme will spontaneously anneal to each other at their sticky ends.

4. The gene can be spliced into a plasmid and inserted into a bacterial cell. As the cell grows, the number of plasmids will increase. The polymerase chain reaction can make copies of a gene using DNA polymerase and a primer for the gene.

5.

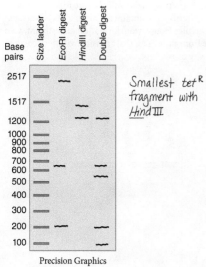

Base pairs

2517
1517
1200
1000
900
800
700
600
500
400
300
200
100

Size ladder | EcoRI digest | HindIII digest | Double digest

Smallest tet^R fragment with Hind III

Precision Graphics

6. In a eukaryotic cell, RNA polymerase copies DNA; RNA processing removes the introns, leaving the exons in the mRNA. cDNA can be made from the mRNA by reverse transcriptase.

7. See Tables 2 and 3.

8. You probably used a few plant cells in a Petri plate for your experiment. You can grow these cells on plant-cell culture media with tetracycline. Only the cells with the new plasmid will grow.

9. In RNAi, siRNA binds mRNA creating double-stranded RNA, which is enzymatically destroyed.

10. Retroviridae

Multiple Choice

| 1. | b | 3. | b | 5. | c | 7. | c | 9. | e |
| 2. | b | 4. | b | 6. | d | 8. | b | 10. | a |

Classification of Microorganisms

From Chapter 10 of *Microbiology: An Introduction*, Eleventh Edition. Gerard J. Tortora, Berdell R. Funke, Christine L. Case.

Classification of
Microorganisms

A. Barry Dowsett/Photo Researchers

The science of classification, especially the classification of living forms, is called *taxonomy* (from the Greek for orderly arrangement). The objective of taxonomy is to classify living organisms—that is, to establish the relationships between one group of organisms and another and to differentiate them. There may be as many as 100 million different living organisms, but fewer than 10% have been discovered, much less classified and identified.

Taxonomy also provides a common reference for identifying organisms already classified. For example, when a bacterium suspected of causing a specific disease is isolated from a patient, characteristics of that isolate are matched to lists of characteristics of previously classified bacteria to identify the isolate. Finally, taxonomy is a basic and necessary tool for scientists, providing a universal language of communication.

Modern taxonomy is an exciting and dynamic field. The ability to rapidly sequence DNA, even entire genomes, has led to new insights into classification and evolution. In this chapter, you will learn the various classification systems, the different criteria used for classification, and tests that are used to identify microorganisms that have already been classified. The contiribution of taxonomy in shedding new light on previously discovered organisms like the *Pneumocystis jirovecii* shown in the photograph will be discussed in this chapter.

Visualize microbiology and check your understanding with a pre-test at www.masteringmicrobiology.com.

The Study of Phylogenetic Relationships

LEARNING OBJECTIVES

1   Define *taxonomy*, *taxon*, and *phylogeny*.
2   Discuss the limitations of a two-kingdom classification system.
3   Identify the contributions of Linnaeus, von Nägeli, Chatton, Whittaker, and Woese.
4   Discuss the advantages of the three-domain system.
5   List the characteristics of the Bacteria, Archaea, and Eukarya domains.

In 2001, an international project called the All Species Inventory was launched. The project's purpose is to identify and record every species of life on Earth in the next 25 years. These researchers have undertaken a challenging goal: whereas biologists have identified more than 1.7 million different organisms thus far, it is estimated that the number of living species ranges from 10 to 100 million.

Among these many and diverse organisms, however, are many similarities. For example, all organisms are composed of cells surrounded by a plasma membrane, use ATP for energy, and store their genetic information in DNA. These similarities are the result of evolution, or descent from a common ancestor. In 1859, the English naturalist Charles Darwin proposed that natural selection was responsible for the similarities as well as the differences among organisms. The differences can be attributed to the survival of organisms with traits best suited to a particular environment.

To facilitate research, scholarship, and communication, we use **taxonomy**—that is, we put organisms into categories, or **taxa** (singular: *taxon*), to show degrees of similarities among organisms. These similarities are due to relatedness—all organisms are related through evolution. **Systematics,** or **phylogeny,** is the study of the evolutionary history of organisms. The hierarchy of taxa reflects evolutionary, or *phylogenetic,* relationships.

From the time of Aristotle, living organisms were categorized in just two ways, as either plants or animals. In 1735, the Swedish botanist Carolus Linnaeus introduced a formal system of classification dividing living organisms into two kingdoms—Plantae and Animalia. He used latinized names to provide one common "language" for systematics. As the biological sciences developed, however, biologists began looking for a *natural* classification system—one that groups organisms based on ancestral relationships and allows us to see the order in life. In 1857, Carl von Nägeli, a contemporary of Pasteur, proposed that bacteria and fungi be placed in the plant kingdom. In 1866, Ernst Haeckel proposed the Kingdom Protista, to include bacteria, protozoa, algae, and fungi. Because of disagreements over the definition of protists, for the next 100 years biologists continued to follow von Nägeli's placement of bacteria and fungi

in the plant kingdom. It is ironic that recent DNA sequencing places fungi closer to animals than plants. Fungi were placed in their own kingdom in 1959.

With the advent of electron microscopy, the physical differences between cells became apparent. The term *prokaryote* was introduced in 1937 by Edouard Chatton to distinguish cells having no nucleus from the nucleated cells of plants and animals. In 1961, Roger Stanier provided the current definition of *prokaryotes*: cells in which the nuclear material (nucleoplasm) is not surrounded by a nuclear membrane. In 1968, Robert G.E. Murray proposed the Kingdom Prokaryotae.

In 1969, Robert H. Whittaker founded the five-kingdom system in which prokaryotes were placed in the Kingdom Prokaryotae, or Monera, and eukaryotes comprised the other four kingdoms. The Kingdom Prokaryotae had been based on microscopic observations. Subsequently, new techniques in molecular biology revealed that there are actually two types of prokaryotic cells and one type of eukaryotic cell.

CHECK YOUR UNDERSTANDING

✓ Of what value is taxonomy and systematics? 1
✓ Why shouldn't bacteria be placed in the plant kingdom? 2, 3

The Three Domains

The discovery of three cell types was based on the observations that ribosomes are not the same in all cells. Ribosomes provide a method of comparing cells because ribosomes are present in all cells. Comparing the sequences of nucleotides in ribosomal RNA from different kinds of cells shows that there are three distinctly different cell groups: the eukaryotes and two different types of prokaryotes—the bacteria and the archaea.

Clinical Case: Full-Flavor Outbreak

Monica Jackson, a 32-year-old production assistant at a Reno, Nevada, television station, has made an appointment with the nurse practitioner at her physician's office. Monica tells the nurse practitioner that she has had diarrhea, nausea, and abdominal cramping for almost 12 hours. She also feels tired and has a low-grade fever. Monica felt fine one minute, and the next she was violently ill. Monica informs the nurse practitioner that she and her good friend, who is also sick, had been at the same luncheon the day before. The nurse practitioner takes a stool sample and sends it to the hospital laboratory for analysis.

What will the laboratory do first to look for a bacterial pathogen? Read on to find out.

The Three-Domain System

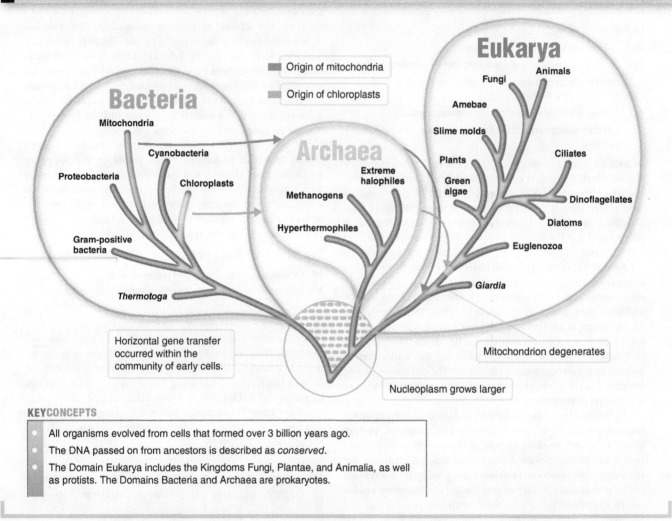

Origin of mitochondria

Origin of chloroplasts

Bacteria

Mitochondria

Cyanobacteria

Proteobacteria

Chloroplasts

Gram-positive
bacteria

Thermotoga

Archaea

Methanogens

Extreme
halophiles

Hyperthermophiles

Eukarya

Fungi

Animals

Amebae

Slime molds

Plants

Ciliates

Green
algae

Dinoflagellates

Diatoms

Euglenozoa

Giardia

Horizontal gene transfer
occurred within the
community of early cells.

Mitochondrion degenerates

Nucleoplasm grows larger

KEYCONCEPTS

- All organisms evolved from cells that formed over 3 billion years ago.
- The DNA passed on from ancestors is described as *conserved*.
- The Domain Eukarya includes the Kingdoms Fungi, Plantae, and Animalia, as well as protists. The Domains Bacteria and Archaea are prokaryotes.

Precision Graphics

In 1978, Carl R. Woese proposed elevating the three cell types to a level above kingdom, called domain. Woese believed that the archaea and the bacteria, although similar in appearance, should form their own separate domains on the evolutionary tree (Figure 1). Organisms are classified by cell type in the three domain systems. In addition to differences in rRNA, the three domains differ in membrane lipid structure, transfer RNA molecules, and sensitivity to antibiotics (Table 1).

In this widely accepted scheme, animals, plants, and fungi are kingdoms in the Domain **Eukarya**. The Domain **Bacteria** includes all of the pathogenic prokaryotes as well as many of the nonpathogenic prokaryotes found in soil and water. The photoautotrophic

prokaryotes are also in this domain. The Domain **Archaea** includes prokaryotes that do not have peptidoglycan in their cell walls. They often live in extreme environments and carry out unusual metabolic processes. Archaea include three major groups:[4]

1. The methanogens, strict anaerobes that produce methane (CH_4) from carbon dioxide and hydrogen.
2. Extreme halophiles, which require high concentrations of salt for survival.
3. Hyperthermophiles, which normally grow in extremely hot environments.

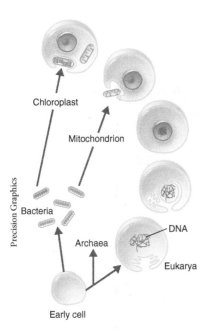

Figure 2 A model of the origin of eukaryotes. Invagination of the plasma membrane may have formed the nuclear envelope and endoplasmic reticulum. Similarities, including rRNA sequences, indicate that endosymbiotic prokaryotes gave rise to mitochondria and chloroplasts.

Q How many membranes make up the nuclear envelope of a eukaryotic cell?

The evolutionary relationship of the three domains is the subject of current research by biologists. Based on rRNA analysis, three cell lineages clearly emerged as cells were forming 3.5 billion years ago. That led to the Archaea, the Bacteria, and what eventually became the nucleoplasm of the eukaryotes. However, the three cell lines were not isolated; horizontal gene transfer appears to have occurred among them. Analysis of complete genomes shows that each domain shares genes with other domains. One-quarter of the genes of the bacterium *Thermotoga* were probably acquired from an archaeon. Gene transfer also has been seen between eukaryotic hosts from their prokaryote symbionts.

The oldest known fossils are the remains of prokaryotes that lived more than 3.5 billion years ago. Eukaryotic cells evolved more recently, about 2.5 billion years ago. According to the endosymbiotic theory, eukaryotic cells evolved from prokaryotic cells living inside one another, as endosymbionts. In fact, the similarities between prokaryotic cells and eukaryotic organelles provide striking evidence for this endosymbiotic relationship (Table 2).

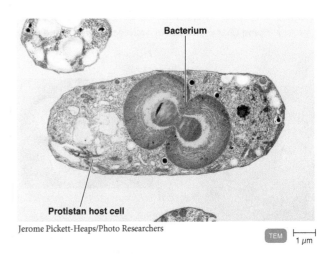

Jerome Pickett-Heaps/Photo Researchers

TEM ⊢—⊣ 1 µm

Figure 3 *Cyanophora paradoxa.* This organism, in which the eukaryotic host and the bacterium require each other for survival, provides a modern example of how eukaryotic cells might have evolved.

Q What features do chloroplasts, mitochondria, and bacteria have in common?

The original nucleoplasmic cell was prokaryotic. However, infoldings in its plasma membrane may have surrounded the nuclear region to produce a true nucleus (Figure 2). Recently, French researchers provided support for this hypothesis with their observations of a true nucleus in *Gemmata* bacteria. Over time, the chromosome of the nucleoplasm may have acquired pieces such as transposons. In some cells, this large chromosome may have fragmented into smaller linear chromosomes. Perhaps cells with linear chromosomes had an advantage in cell division over those with a large, unwieldy circular chromosome.

That nucleoplasmic cell provided the original host in which endosymbiotic bacteria developed into organelles. An example of a modern prokaryote living in a eukaryotic cell is shown in Figure 3. The cyanobacterium-like cell and the eukaryotic host require each other for survival.

Taxonomy provides tools for clarifying the evolution of organisms, as well as their interrelationships. New organisms are being discovered every day, and taxonomists continue to search for a natural classification system that reflects phylogenetic relationships.

A Phylogenetic Hierarchy

In a phylogenetic hierarchy, grouping organisms according to common properties implies that a group of organisms evolved from a common ancestor; each species retains some of the characteristics of the ancestor. Some of the information used to classify and determine phylogenetic relationships in higher

TABLE 1 Some Characteristics of Archaea, Bacteria, and Eukarya

	Archaea	Bacteria	Eukarya
	Sulfolobus SEM ⊢ 1 μm Oliver Meckes/Nicole Ottawa/Photo Researchers;	*E. coli* SEM ⊢ 1 μm Scimat/Photo Researchers;	*Amoeba* SEM ⊢ 5 μm Center for Microscopy and Imaging, Smith College, Northampton, MA
Cell Type	Prokaryotic	Prokaryotic	Eukaryotic
Cell Wall	Varies in composition; contains no peptidoglycan	Contains peptidoglycan	Varies in composition; contains carbohydrates
Membrane Lipids	Composed of branched carbon chains attached to glycerol by ether linkage	Composed of straight carbon chains attached to glycerol by ester linkage	Composed of straight carbon chains attached to glycerol by ester linkage
First Amino Acid in Protein Synthesis	Methionine	Formylmethionine	Methionine
Antibiotic Sensitivity	No	Yes	No
rRNA Loop*	Lacking	Present	Lacking
Common Arm of tRNA†	Lacking	Present	Present

*Binds to ribosomal protein; found in all bacteria.
†A sequence of bases in tRNA found in all eukaryotes and bacteria: guanine-thymine-pseudouridine-cytosine-guanine.

TABLE 2 Prokaryotic Cells and Eukaryotic Organelles Compared

	Prokaryotic Cell	Eukaryotic Cell	Eukaryotic Organelles (Mitochondria and Chloroplasts)
DNA	One circular; some two circular; some linear	Linear	Circular
Histones	In archaea	Yes	No
First Amino Acid in Protein Synthesis	Formylmethionine (bacteria) Methionine (archaea)	Methionine	Formylmethionine
Ribosomes	70S	80S	70S
Growth	Binary fission	Mitosis	Binary fission

Precision Graphics

organisms comes from fossils. Bones, shells, or stems that contain mineral matter or have left imprints in rock that was once mud are examples of fossils.

The structures of most microorganisms are not readily fossilized. Some exceptions are the following:

- A marine protist whose fossilized colonies form the White Cliffs of Dover, England.
- Stromatolites, the fossilized remains of filamentous bacteria and sediments that flourished between 0.5 and 2 billion years ago (Figure 4a and Figure 4b).
- Cyanobacteria-like fossils found in rocks in western Australia that are 3.0 to 3.5 billion years old. These are widely believed to be the oldest known fossils (Figure 4c).

Because fossil evidence is not available for most prokaryotes, their phylogeny must be based on other evidence. But in one notable exception, scientists may have isolated living bacteria and yeast 25 to 40 million years old. In 1995, the American microbiologist Raul Cano and his colleagues reported growing *Bacillus sphaericus* and other as yet unidentified microorganisms that had survived embedded in amber (fossilized plant resin) for millions of years. If confirmed, this discovery should provide more information about the evolution of microorganisms.

Similarities in genomes can be used to group organisms into taxa and to provide a timeline for the emergence of taxa. This is especially important for microorganisms that usually don't leave fossil evidence. This concept of a molecular clock based on the differences in amino acids in hemoglobin among different animals was first proposed in the 1960s. A **molecular clock** for evolution is based on nucleotide sequences in the genomes of organisms. Mutations accumulate in a genome at a constant rate. In some genes, such as the rRNA genes, there are few mutations. These are highly conserved genes. Other regions of a genome, change with no apparent effect on the organism. Comparing the number of mutations between two organisms with the expected rate of change provides an estimate of when the two diverged from a common ancestor. This technique was used to track the path of West Nile virus to the United States.

Conclusions from rRNA sequencing and DNA hybridization studies of selected orders and families of eukaryotes are in agreement with the fossil records. This has encouraged workers to use DNA hybridization and rRNA sequencing to gain an understanding of the evolutionary relationships among prokaryotic groups.

CHECK YOUR UNDERSTANDING

- What evidence supports classifying organisms into three domains? 4
- Compare archaea and bacteria; bacteria and eukarya; and archaea and eukarya. 5

(a) Bacterial communities form rocklike pillars called stromatolites. These began growing about 3000 years ago.

⊢——⊣ 30 cm

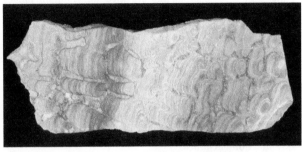

(b) Cut section through a fossilized stomatolite that flourished 2 billion years ago.

⊢—⊣ 2 cm

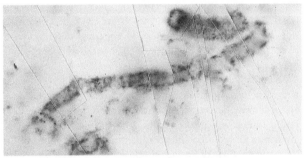

(c) Filamentous prokaryotes from the Early Precambrian (3.5 billion years ago) of western Australia.

TEM ⊢—⊣ 15 μm

Figure 4 Fossilized prokaryotes.

Q What evidence is used to determine the phylogeny of prokaryotes?

Classification of Organisms

LEARNING OBJECTIVES

6   Explain why scientific names are used.

7   List the major taxa.

8   Differentiate *culture*, *clone*, and *strain*.

9   List the major characteristics used to differentiate the three kingdoms of multicellular Eukarya.

10   Define *protist*.

11   Differentiate eukaryotic, prokaryotic, and viral species.

297

Living organisms are grouped according to similar characteristics (classification), and each organism is assigned a unique scientific name. The rules for classifying and naming, which are used by biologists worldwide, are discussed next.

Scientific Nomenclature

In a world inhabited by millions of living organisms, biologists must be sure they know exactly which organism is being discussed. We cannot use common names, because the same name is often used for many different organisms in different locales. For example, there are two different organisms with the common name Spanish moss, and neither one is actually a moss. Plus, local languages are used for common names. Because common names can be misleading and are in different languages, a system of scientific names, referred to as *scientific nomenclature,* was developed in the eighteenth century.

Every organism is assigned two names, or a binomial. These names are the **genus** name and **specific epithet (species),** and both names are printed underlined or italicized. The genus name is always capitalized and is always a noun. The species name is lowercase and is usually an adjective. Because this system gives two names to each organism, the system is called **binomial nomenclature.**

Let's consider some examples. Our own genus and specific epithet are *Homo sapiens* (hō'mō sā'pē-ens). The noun, or genus, means man; the adjective, or specific epithet, means wise. A mold that contaminates bread is called *Rhizopus stolonifer* (rī'zō-pùs stō'ion-i-fèr). *Rhizo-* (root) describes root-like structures on the fungus; *stolo-* (a shoot) describes the long hyphae.

Binomials are used by scientists worldwide, regardless of their native language, which enables them to share knowledge efficiently and accurately. Several scientific entities are responsible for establishing rules governing the naming of organisms. Rules for assigning names for protozoa and parasitic worms are published in the *International Code of Zoological Nomenclature.* Rules for assigning names for fungi and algae are published in the *International Code of Botanical Nomenclature.* Rules for naming newly classified prokaryotes and for assigning prokaryotes to taxa are established by the International Committee on Systematics of Prokaryotes and are published in the *Bacteriological Code.* Descriptions of prokaryotes and evidence for their classifications are published in the *International Journal of Systematic and Evolutionary Microbiology* before being incorporated into a reference called *Bergey's Manual.* According to the *Bacteriological Code,* scientific names are to be taken from Latin (a genus name can be taken from Greek) or latinized by the addition of the appropriate suffix. Suffixes for order and family are *-ales* and *-aceae,* respectively.

As new laboratory techniques make more detailed characterizations of microbes possible, two genera may be reclassified as a single genus, or a genus may be divided into two or more genera. For example, the genera "Diplococcus" and *Streptococcus* were combined in 1974; the only diplococcal species is now called *Streptococcus pneumoniae.* In 1984, DNA hybridization studies indicated that "Streptococcus faecalis" and "Streptococcus faecium" were only distantly related to the other streptococcal species; consequently, a new genus called *Enterococcus* was created, and these species were renamed *E. faecalis* and *E. faecium* (fē' sē-um).

In 2001, based on DNA-DNA hybridization and rRNA studies, some species of *Chlamydia* were moved to a new genus, *Chlamydophila,* based on rRNA analysis. Making the transition to a new name can be confusing, so the old name is often written in parentheses. For example, a physician looking for information on the cause of a patient's pneumonia-like symptoms (melioidosis) would find the bacterial name *Burkholderia (Pseudomonas) pseudomallei* (bèrk'hōld-ér-ē-ä sū-dō-mal'le-ē).

Obtaining the name of the organism is important in determining what treatment to use; antifungal drugs will not work against bacteria, and antibacterial drugs will not work against viruses.

The Taxonomic Hierarchy

All organisms can be grouped into a series of subdivisions that make up the taxonomic hierarchy. Linnaeus developed this hierarchy for his classification of plants and animals. A **eukaryotic species** is a group of closely related organisms that breed among themselves. (Bacterial species will be discussed shortly.) A genus consists of species that differ from each other in certain ways but are related by descent. For example, *Quercus* (kwer'kus), the genus name for oak, consists of all types of oak trees (white oak, red oak, bur oak, velvet oak, and so on). Even though each species of oak differs from every other species, they are all related genetically. Just as a number of species make up a genus, related genera make up a **family.** A group of similar families constitutes an **order,** and a group of similar orders makes up a **class.** Related classes, in turn, make up a **phylum.** Thus, a particular organism (or species) has a genus name and specific epithet and belongs to a family, order, class, and phylum.

All phyla that are related to each other make up a **kingdom,** and related kingdoms are grouped into a **domain** (Figure 5).

CHECK YOUR UNDERSTANDING

✔ Using *Escherichia coli* and *Entamoeba coli* as examples, explain why the genus name must always be written out for the first use. Why is binomial nomenclature preferable to the use of common names? 6

✔ Find the gram-positive bacteria *Staphylococcus.* To which bacteria is this genus more closely related: *Bacillus* or *Streptococcus?* 7

Classification of Prokaryotes

The taxonomic classification scheme for prokaryotes is found in *Bergey's Manual of Systematic Bacteriology,* 2nd edition

Classification of Microorganisms

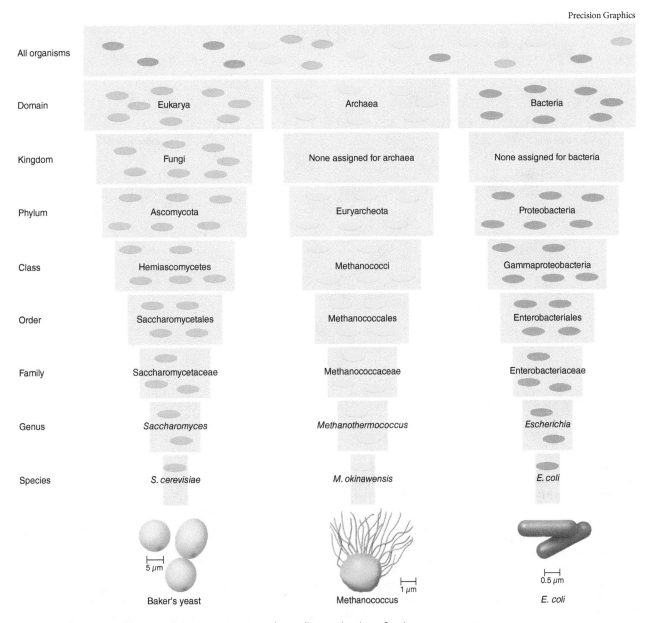

Figure 5 The taxonomic hierarchy. Organisms are grouped according to relatedness. Species that are closely related are grouped into a genus. For example, the baker's yeast belongs to the genus that includes sourdough yeast (*Saccharomyces exiguus*). Related genera, such as *Saccharomyces* and *Candida*, are placed in a family, and so on. Each group is more comprehensive. The domain Eukarya includes all organisms with eukaryotic cells.

Q What is the biological definition of *family*?

In *Bergey's Manual*, prokaryotes are divided into two domains: Bacteria and Archaea. Each domain is divided into phyla. Remember, the classification is based on similarities in nucleotide sequences in rRNA. Classes are divided into orders; orders, into families; families, into genera; and genera, into species.

A prokaryotic species is defined somewhat differently from a eukaryotic species, which is a group of closely related organisms

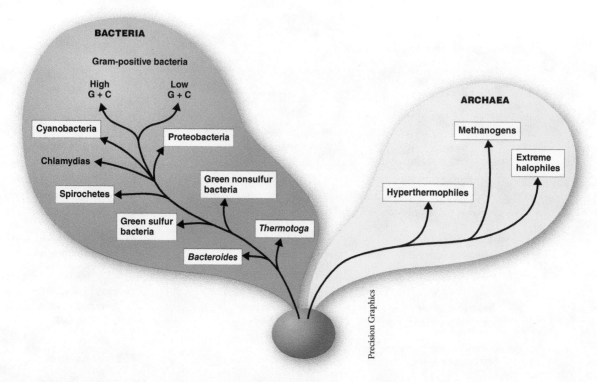

Figure 6 Phylogenetic relationships of prokaryotes. Arrows indicate major lines of descent of bacterial groups. Selected phyla are indicated by the white boxes.

Q Members of which phylum can be identified by Gram staining?

that can interbreed. Unlike reproduction in eukaryotic organisms, cell division in bacteria is not directly tied to sexual conjugation, which is infrequent and does not always need to be species-specific. A **prokaryotic species,** therefore, is defined simply as a population of cells with similar characteristics. (The types of characteristics will be discussed later in this chapter.) The members of a bacterial species are essentially indistinguishable from each other but are distinguishable from members of other species, usually on the basis of several features. As you know, bacteria grown at a given time in media are called a culture. A pure culture is often a **clone,** that is, a population of cells derived from a single parent cell. All cells in the clone should be identical. However, in some cases, pure cultures of the same species are not identical in all ways. Each such group is called a **strain.** Strains are identified by numbers, letters, or names that follow the specific epithet.

Bergey's Manual provides a reference for identifying bacteria in the laboratory, as well as a classification scheme for bacteria. One scheme for the evolutionary relationships of bacteria is shown in Figure 6.

Classification of Eukaryotes

Some kingdoms in the domain Eukarya are shown in Figure 1.

In 1969, simple eukaryotic organisms, mostly unicellular, were grouped as the Kingdom **Protista,** a catchall kingdom for a variety of organisms. Historically, eukaryotic organisms that didn't fit into other kingdoms were placed in the Protista. Approximately 200,000 species of protistans have been identified thus far, and these organisms are nutritionally quite diverse—from photosynthetic to obligate intracellular parasite. Ribosomal RNA sequencing is making it possible to divide protists into groups based on their descent from common ancestors. Consequently, for the time being, the organisms once classified as protists are being divided into **clades,** that is, genetically related groups. For convenience, we will continue to use the term *protist* to refer to unicellular eukaryotes and their close relatives.

Fungi, plants, and animals make up the three kingdoms of more complex eukaryotic organisms, most of which are multicellular.

The Kingdom **Fungi** includes the unicellular yeasts, multicellular molds, and macroscopic species such as mushrooms.

To obtain raw materials for vital functions, a fungus absorbs dissolved organic matter through its plasma membrane. The cells of a multicellular fungus are commonly joined to form thin tubes called *hyphae*. The hyphae are usually divided into multinucleated units by cross-walls that have holes, so that cytoplasm can flow between the cell-like units. Fungi develop from spores or from fragments of hyphae.

The Kingdom **Plantae** (plants) includes some algae and all mosses, ferns, conifers, and flowering plants. All members of this kingdom are multicellular. To obtain energy, a plant uses photosynthesis, the process that converts carbon dioxide and water into organic molecules used by the cell.

The kingdom of multicellular organisms called **Animalia** (animals) includes sponges, various worms, insects, and animals with backbones (vertebrates). Animals obtain nutrients and energy by ingesting organic matter through a mouth of some kind.

Classification of Viruses

Viruses are not classified as part of any of the three domains. Viruses are not composed of cells, and they use the anabolic machinery within living host cells to multiply. A viral genome can direct biosynthesis inside a host cell, and some viral genomes can become incorporated into the host genome. The ecological niche of a virus is its specific host cell, so viruses may be more closely related to their hosts than to other viruses. The International Committee on Taxonomy of Viruses defines a **viral species** as a population of viruses with similar characteristics (including morphology, genes, and enzymes) that occupies a particular ecological niche.

Viruses are obligatory intracellular parasites. Viral genes carried in the genomes of other organisms provide a record of viral evolution. Recent analysis shows that bornavirus genes integrated into mammals, including humans, at least 40 million years ago. There are three hypotheses on the origin of viruses: (1) They arose from independently replicating strands of nucleic acids (such as plasmids). (2) They developed from degenerative cells that, through many generations, gradually lost the ability to survive independently but could survive when associated with another cell. (3) They coevolved with host cells. For example, it has been hypothesized that the bacterial cell wall provided a selection advantage to avoid getting infected. Then mutated viruses that could penetrate the cell wall would be selected.

CHECK YOUR UNDERSTANDING

✔ Use the terms *species, culture, clone,* and strain in one sentence to describe growing methicillin-resistant *Staphylococcus aureus* (MRSA). 8

✔ Assume you discovered a new organism: it is multicellular, is nucleated, is heterotrophic, and has cell walls. To what kingdom does it belong? 9

✔ Write your own definition of *protist.* 10

✔ Why wouldn't the definition of a viral species work for a bacterial species? 11

Methods of Classifying and Identifying Microorganisms

LEARNING OBJECTIVES

12 Compare and contrast classification and identification.

13 Explain the purpose of *Bergey's Manual.*

14 Describe how staining and biochemical tests are used to identify bacteria.

15 Differentiate Western blotting from Southern blotting.

16 Explain how serological tests and phage typing can be used to identify an unknown bacterium.

17 Describe how a newly discovered microbe can be classified by DNA base composition, DNA fingerprinting, and PCR.

18 Describe how microorganisms can be identified by nucleic acid hybridization, Southern blotting, DNA chips, ribotyping, and FISH.

19 Differentiate a dichotomous key from a cladogram.

A classification scheme provides a list of characteristics and a means for comparison to aid in the identification of an organism. Once an organism is identified, it can be placed into a previously devised classification scheme. Microorganisms are *identified* for practical purposes—for example, to determine an appropriate treatment for an infection. They are not necessarily identified by the same techniques by which they are *classified*. Most identification procedures are easily performed in a laboratory and use as few procedures or tests as possible. Protozoa, parasitic worms, and fungi can usually be identified microscopically. Most prokaryotic organisms do not have distinguishing morphological features or even much variation in size and shape. Consequently, microbiologists have developed a variety of methods to test metabolic reactions and other characteristics to identify prokaryotes.

Bergey's Manual of Determinative Bacteriology has been a widely used reference since the first edition was published in 1923. The American bacteriologist David Bergey was chairman of the group who compiled information on the known bacteria from articles published in scientific journals. *Bergey's Manual of Determinative Bacteriology* (9th ed., 1994) does not classify bacteria according to evolutionary relatedness but instead provides identification (determinative) schemes based on such criteria as cell wall composition, morphology, differential staining, oxygen requirements, and biochemical testing.* The majority of Bacteria and Archaea have not been cultured, and scientists estimate that only 1% of these microbes have been discovered.

---

*Both Bergey's *Manual of Systematic Bacteriology* and *Bergey's Manual of Determinative Bacteriology* are referred to simply as *Bergey's Manual;* the complete titles are used when the information under discussion is found in one but not the other, for example, an identification table.

Mass Deaths of Marine Mammals Spur Veterinary Microbiology

Over the past decade, thousands of marine mammals have died unexpectedly all over the world. These deaths occur in outbreaks of a dozen to thousands of mammals, and microbiologists try to determine the cause in each outbreak. The 2010 deaths of over 100 dolphins in the northern Gulf of Mexico is being investigated. These deaths occurred before the *Deepwater Horizon* well blowout in April 2010. Toxoplasmosis has been killing California sea otters in increasing numbers. The current decline in the Southern sea otter population is the result of a 40% mortality rate due to a variety of infectious bacterial diseases. These mortality figures raise concerns that entire populations of marine mammals may ultimately be destroyed.

In 2009, eight dolphin deaths in Australia were attributed to opportunistic infections. Large numbers of opportunistic pathogens, including 55 species of *Vibrio*, have also been found in dolphins. These bacteria are a part of a dolphin's normal microbiota and the biota of coastal waters. They can cause disease only if the animals' immune system, their normal defense against infection, has been weakened. The deaths of lagoon dolphins and sea otters may be due to contaminants in coastal freshwater runoff.

Phocid distemper virus in seals and cetacean morbillivirus (CM) were responsible for the deaths of 20,000 marine mammals in European waters and for recurring mortality episodes in bottlenose dolphins along the Atlantic coast of the United States. Evidence suggests that pilot whales may be responsible for transferring CM virus to other species across wide expanses of ocean.

Information Is Scarce

Such questions are the concern of veterinary microbiology, which until recently has been a neglected branch of medical microbiology. Although the diseases of such animals as cattle, chickens, and mink have been studied, partly because of their availability to researchers, the microbiology of wild animals, especially marine mammals, is a relatively newly emerging field. Gathering samples from animals that live in the open ocean and performing bacteriological analyses on them are very difficult. Currently, the animals being studied are those that have been stranded (**Figure A**) and those that come onto the shore to breed, such as the northern fur sea lion.

Microbiologists are identifying bacteria in marine mammals by using conventional test batteries (**Figure B**) and genomic data of known species. New species of bacteria are being found in marine mammals using the FISH technique.

Veterinary microbiologists hope that increased study of the microbiology of wild animals, including marine mammals, will not only promote improved wildlife management but also provide models for the study of human diseases.

Darryl W. Bush, Marine World/Africa USA, Vallejo, CA

Figure A **Marine mammal researchers examine a Pacific bottlenosed dolphin.**

Gram reaction?

− → Oxidase?
   Yes → Urea hydrolyzed?
     Yes → *Bordetella bronchiseptica*
     No → Indole produced?
       Yes → Acetoin produced? (V-P test)
         Yes → *Aeromonas hydrophila*
         No → *Pasteurella multocida*
       No → *Mannheimia haemolytica*
   No → Citrate utilized?
     Yes → *Klebsiella pneumoniae*
     No → *Yersinia enterocolitica*

+ → Morphology
   Rods → *Erysipelothrix rhusiopathiae*
   Cocci → *Staphylococcus aureus*

Figure B **Biochemical tests used to identify selected species of human pathogens isolated from marine mammals.**

Q Assume you isolated a gram-negative rod that is oxidase-positive, is indole-negative, and does not produce urease or acetoin. What is the bacterium?

MICROBIOLOGY REQUISITION	Date:	Time:	Slip prepared by:
Lab: Date, time received:	Physician name:	Collected by:	Patient ID#:

— DO NOT WRITE BELOW THIS LINE —	**USE SEPARATE SLIP FOR EACH REQUEST**

GRAM STAIN REPORT

- ☐ GRAM POS. COCCI, GROUPS
- ☐ GRAM POS. COCCI, PAIRS/CHAIN
- ☐ GRAM POS. RODS
- ☒ GRAM NEG. COCCI
- ☐ GRAM NEG. RODS
- ☐ GRAM NEG. COCCOBACILLI
- ☐ YEAST
- ☐ OTHER

- ☐ NO GROWTH
- ☐ NO GROWTH IN ___ DAYS
- ☐ MIXED MICROBIOTA
- ☐ SPECIMEN IMPROPERLY COLLECTED OR TRANSPORTED
- ☐ ___ DIFFERENT TYPES OF ORGANISMS
- ☐ NEGATIVE FOR *SALMONELLA*, *SHIGELLA*, AND *CAMPYLOBACTER*
- ☐ NO OVA, CYSTS, OR PARASITES SEEN
- ☒ OXIDASE-POSITIVE GRAM-NEGATIVE DIPLOCOCCI
- ☐ PRESUMPTIVE BETA STREP GROUP A BY BACITRACIN

SOURCE OF SPECIMEN

- ☐ BLOOD
- ☐ CEREBROSPINAL FLUID
- ☐ FLUID (Specify Source) _____
- ☐ THROAT
- ☐ SPUTUM, expectorated
- ☐ OTHER Respiratory (Describe) _____
- ☐ URINE, Clean Catch Midstream
- ☐ URINE, Indwelling Catheter
- ☐ URINE, Straight Catheter
- ☐ URINE, Entire First Morning
- ☐ URINE, Other (Describe) _____
- ☐ STOOL
- ☒ GU (Specify Source) ___ *vag.*
- ☐ ABSCESS (Specify Source) _____
- ☐ TISSUE (Specify Source) _____
- ☐ ULCER (Specify Source) _____
- ☐ WOUND (Specify Source) _____
- ☐ STERILIZER TEST

TEST(S) REQUESTED

Bacterial
- ☐ **Routine culture;** Gram stain, anaerobic culture, susceptibility testing. Throats done for Gp A Strep.
- ☐ *Legionella* culture
- ☐ *Bartonella*
- ☐ Blood Culture

Other Non-Routine Cultures
- ☐ *E. coli* O157:H7
- ☐ *Vibrio*
- ☐ *Yersinia*
- ☒ *H. ducreyi*
- ☐ *B. pertussis*
- ☐ Other _____

Screening Cultures
- ☒ Gonococci
- ☐ Group B Strep
- ☐ Group A Strep
- ☐ Other _____

- ☐ **ACID-FAST BACILLI**

- ☐ **FUNGAL**

VIRAL
- ☐ Routine culture
- ☐ Herpes simplex
- ☐ Direct FA for _____

PARASITOLOGY
- ☐ Exam for intestinal ova and parasites
- ☐ *Giardia* immunoassay
- ☐ *Cryptosporidium*
- ☐ Pinworm prep
- ☐ Blood parasites
- ☐ Filaria concentration
- ☐ *Trichomonas*
- ☐ Other _____

TOXIN ASSAY
- ☐ *Clostridium difficile*

DIRECT (Antigen Detection)
- ☐ Cryptococcal antigen-CSF only
- ☐ Bacterial antigens (Specify)

SPECIAL
- ☒ Antimicrobial tests (MIC)

Filled out by one person | Filled out by different person

Figure 7 A clinical microbiology lab report form. In health care, morphology and differential staining are important in determining the proper treatment for microbial diseases. A clinician completes the form to identify the sample and specific tests. In this case, a genitourinary sample will be examined for sexually transmitted infections. The red notations are the lab technician's report of the Gram stain and culture results.

 What diseases are suspected if the "acid-fast bacilli" box is checked?

Medical microbiology (the branch of microbiology dealing with human pathogens) has dominated the interest in microbes, and this interest is reflected in many identification schemes. However, to put the pathogenic properties of bacteria in perspective, of the more than 2600 species listed in the *Approved Lists of Bacterial Names,* fewer than 10% are human pathogens.

We next discuss several criteria and methods for the classification and routine identification of microorganisms. In addition to properties of the organism itself, the source and habitat of a bacterial isolate are considered as part of the identification processes. In clinical microbiology, a physician will swab a patient's pus or tissue surface. The swab is inserted into a tube of transport medium. **Transport media** are usually not nutritive and are designed to prolong viability of fastidious pathogens. The physician will note the type of specimen and test(s) requested on a lab requisition form (Figure 7). The information returned by the lab technician will help the physician begin treatment.

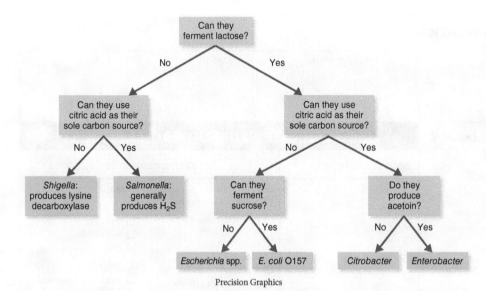

Figure 8 The use of metabolic characteristics to identify selected genera of enteric bacteria.

Q Assume you have a gram-negative bacterium that produces acid from lactose and cannot use citric acid as its sole carbon source. What is the bacterium?

Precision Graphics

Morphological Characteristics

Morphological (structural) characteristics have helped taxonomists classify organisms for 200 years. Higher organisms are frequently classified according to observed anatomical detail. But many microorganisms look too similar to be classified by their structures. Through a microscope, organisms that might differ in metabolic or physiological properties may look alike. Literally hundreds of bacterial species are small rods or small cocci.

Larger size and the presence of intracellular structures do not always mean easy classification, however. *Pneumocystis* (nü-mō-sis′tis) pneumonia is the most common opportunistic infection in AIDS and other immunocompromised patients. Until the AIDS epidemic, the causative agent of this infection, *P. jirovecii* (ye-rō′vet-zē-ē) [formerly "P. carinii" (kär-i′nē-ē)] was rarely seen in humans. *Pneumocystis* lacks structures that can be easily used for identification, and its taxonomic position has been uncertain since its discovery in 1909 by Carlos Chagas in mice. It was originally classified as a protozoan; however, in 1988 rRNA sequencing showed that *Pneumocystis* is actually a member of the Kingdom Fungi. New treatments are being investigated as researchers take into account this organism's relatedness to fungi.

Cell morphology tells us little about phylogenetic relationships. However, morphological characteristics are still useful in identifying bacteria. For example, differences in such structures as endospores or flagella can be helpful.

Differential Staining

One of the first steps in identifying bacteria is differential staining. Most bacteria are either gram-positive or gram-negative. Other differential stains, such as the acid-fast stain, can be useful for a more limited group of microorganisms. Recall that these stains are based on the chemical composition of cell walls and therefore are not useful in identifying either the wall-less bacteria or the archaea with unusual walls. Microscopic examination of a Gram stain or an acid-fast stain is used to obtain information quickly in the clinical environment.

Biochemical Tests

Enzymatic activities are widely used to differentiate bacteria. Even closely related bacteria can usually be separated into distinct species by subjecting them to biochemical tests, such as one to determine their ability to ferment an assortment of selected carbohydrates. For one example of the use of biochemical tests to identify bacteria (in this instance, in marine mammals), see Applications of Microbiology earlier in this chapter. Moreover, biochemical tests can provide insight into a species' niche in the ecosystem. For example, a bacterium that can fix nitrogen gas or oxidize elemental sulfur will provide important nutrients for plants and animals.

Enteric, gram-negative bacteria are a large heterogeneous group of microbes whose natural habitat is the intestinal tract of humans and other animals. This family contains several pathogens that cause diarrheal illness. A number of tests have been developed so that technicians can quickly identify the pathogens, a clinician can then provide appropriate treatment, and epidemiologists can locate the source of an illness. All members of the family Enterobacteriaceae are oxidase-negative. Among the enteric bacteria are members of the genera *Escherichia*, *Enterobacter*, *Shigella*, *Citrobacter*, and *Salmonella*. *Escherichia*, *Enterobacter*, and *Citrobacter*, which ferment lactose to produce acid and gas, can be distinguished from *Salmonella* and *Shigella*, which do not. Further biochemical testing, as represented in Figure 8, can differentiate among the genera.

① One tube containing media for 15 biochemical tests is inoculated with an unknown enteric bacterium.

② After incubation, the tube is observed for results.

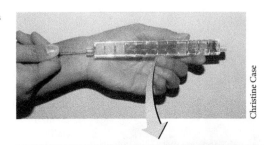

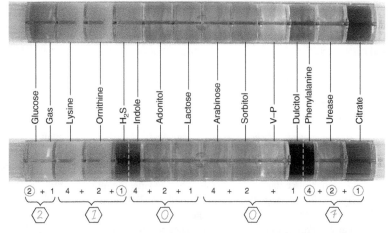

Christine Case

Glucose, Gas, Lysine, Ornithine, H₂S, Indole, Adonitol, Lactose, Arabinose, Sorbitol, V–P, Dulcitol, Phenylalanine, Urease, Citrate

③ The value for each positive test is circled, and the numbers from each group of tests are added to give the ID value.

(2) + 1   4 + 2 + (1)   4 + 2 + 1   4 + 2 + 1   (4) + (2) + (1)

2   1   0   0   7

④ Comparing the resultant ID value with a computerized listing shows that the organism in the tube is *Proteus mirabilis*.

ID Value	Organism	Atypical Test Results	Confirmatory Test
21006	*Proteus mirabilis*	Ornithine⁻	Sucrose
21007	*Proteus mirabilis*	Ornithine⁻	
21020	*Salmonella choleraesuis*	Lysine⁻	

Figure 9 One type of rapid identification method for bacteria: Enterotube II from Becton Dickinson. This example shows results for a typical strain of *P. mirabilis;* however, other strains may produce different test results, which are listed in the Atypical Test Results column. The V-P test is used to confirm an identification.

Q How can one species have two different ID values?

The time needed to identify bacteria can be reduced considerably by the use of selective and differential media or by rapid identification methods. Selective media contain ingredients that suppress the growth of competing organisms and encourage the growth of desired ones, and that differential media allow the desired organism to form a colony that is somehow distinctive.

Bergey's Manual does not evaluate the relative importance of each biochemical test and does not always describe strains. In diagnosing an infection, clinicians must identify a particular species and even a particular strain to proceed with proper treatment. To this end, specific series of biochemical tests have been developed for fast identification in hospital laboratories. Rapid test systems have been developed for yeasts and other fungi, as well as bacteria.

Rapid identification methods are manufactured for groups of medically important bacteria, such as the enterics. Such tools are designed to perform several biochemical tests simultaneously and can identify bacteria within 4 to 24 hours. This is sometimes called **numerical identification** because the results of each test are assigned a number. In the simplest form, a positive test would be assigned a value of 1, and a negative is assigned a value of 0. In most commercial testing kits, test results are assigned numbers ranging from 1 to 4 that are based on the relative reliability and importance of each test, and the resulting total is compared to a database of known organisms.

In the example shown in Figure 9, an unknown enteric bacterium is inoculated into a tube designed to perform 15 biochemical tests. After incubation, results in each compartment

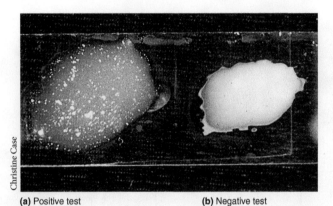

(a) Positive test   **(b)** Negative test

Figure 10 A slide agglutination test. (**a**) In a positive test, the grainy appearance is due to the clumping (agglutination) of the bacteria. (**b**) In a negative test, the bacteria are still evenly distributed in the saline and antiserum.

Q Agglutination results when the bacteria are mixed with _____.

are recorded. Notice that each test is assigned a value; the number derived from scoring all the tests is called the ID value. Fermentation of glucose is important, and a positive reaction is valued at 2, compared with the production of acetoin (V–P test, or the Voges–Proskauer test), which has no value.

A computerized interpretation of the simultaneous test results is essential and is provided by the manufacturer. A limitation of biochemical testing is that mutations and plasmid acquisition can result in strains with different characteristics. Unless a large number of tests is used, an organism could be incorrectly identified.

Clinical Case

The laboratory cannot just Gram stain a stool sample to look for a bacterial pathogen. The large number of gram-negative rods would be indistinguishable in a Gram stain made directly from feces. The stool sample should be cultured on selective and differential media to distinguish among bacteria in the stool. Monica's stool sample is cultured on bismuth sulfite agar. Black colonies are present on the agar after 24 hours.

Can gram-positive bacteria grow on this medium?

Serology

Serology is the science that studies serum and immune responses that are evident in serum. Microorganisms are

antigenic; that is, microorganisms that enter an animal's body stimulate it to form antibodies. Antibodies are proteins that circulate in the blood and combine in a highly specific way with the bacteria that caused their production. For example, the immune system of a rabbit injected with killed typhoid bacteria (antigens) responds by producing antibodies against typhoid bacteria. Solutions of such antibodies used in the identification of many medically important microorganisms are commercially available; such a solution is called an **antiserum** (plural: *antisera*). If an unknown bacterium is isolated from a patient, it can be tested against known antisera and often identified quickly.

In a procedure called a **slide agglutination test,** samples of an unknown bacterium are placed in a drop of saline on each of several slides. Then a different known antiserum is added to each sample. The bacteria agglutinate (clump) when mixed with antibodies that were produced in response to that species or strain of bacterium; a positive test is indicated by the presence of agglutination. Positive and negative slide agglutination tests are shown in **Figure 10**.

Serological testing can differentiate not only among microbial species, but also among strains within species. Strains with different antigens are called **serotypes, serovars,** or **biovars.** Rebecca Lancefield was able to classify serotypes of streptococci by studying serological reactions. She found that the different antigens in the cell walls of various serotypes of streptococci stimulate the formation of different antibodies. In contrast, because closely related bacteria also produce some of the same antigens, serological testing can be used to screen bacterial isolates for possible similarities. If an antiserum reacts with proteins from different bacterial species or strains, these bacteria can be tested further for relatedness.

Serological testing was used to determine whether the increase in number of cases of necrotizing fasciitis in the United States and England since 1987 was due to a common source of the infections. No common source was located, but there has been an increase in two serotypes of *Streptococcus pyogenes* that have been dubbed the "flesh-eating" bacteria.

A test called the **enzyme-linked immunosorbent assay (ELISA)** is widely used because it is fast and can be read by a computer scanner (**Figure 11**). In a direct ELISA, known antibodies are placed in (and adhere to) the wells of a microplate, and an unknown type of bacterium is added to each well. A reaction between the known antibodies and the bacteria provides identification of the bacteria. An ELISA is used in AIDS testing to detect the presence of antibodies against human immunodeficiency virus (HIV), the virus that causes AIDS.

Another serological test, **Western blotting,** is also used to identify antibodies in a patient's serum (**Figure 12**). HIV

Figure 11 An ELISA test.

 What are the similarities between the slide agglutination test and the ELISA test?

(a) A technician uses a micropipette to add samples to a microplate for an ELISA.

(b) ELISA results are then read by the computer scanner.

infection is confirmed by Western blotting, and Lyme disease, caused by *Borrelia burgdorferi,* is often diagnosed by the Western blot.

1. Proteins from a known bacterium or virus are separated by an electric current in electrophoresis.
2. The proteins are then transferred to a filter by blotting.
3. Patient's serum is washed over the filter. If the patient has antibodies to one of the proteins in the filter (in this case, *Borrelia* proteins), the antibodies and protein will combine. Anti-human serum linked to an enzyme is then washed over the filter.
4. This will be made visible as a colored band on the filter after addition of the enzyme's substrate.

Clinical Case

Bismuth sulfite agar inhibits the growth of gram-positive bacteria; it is used to distinguish among gram-negative bacteria. The culture from Monica's stool sample reveals that she has been infected with *Salmonella* bacteria. There are only two species of *Salmonella*: *S. enterica* and *S. bongori*. Monica's infection is caused by *S. enterica*; however, there are over 2500 serovars of *S. enterica* that can infect people. Upon receiving the results from the lab, Monica's nurse practitioner calls the Nevada Department of Health to inform them of her patient's diagnosis and to let them know that Monica's friend has the same symptoms. It is important that the department of health identify the serovar to determine whether there is an outbreak from one source and to trace that source.

How will the department of health identify the correct *S. enterica* serovar?

Phage Typing

Like serological testing, phage typing looks for similarities among bacteria. Both techniques are useful in tracing the origin and course of a disease outbreak. **Phage typing** is a test for determining which phages a bacterium is susceptible to. Bacteriophages (phages) are bacterial viruses and that they usually cause lysis of the bacterial cells they infect. They are highly specialized, in that they usually infect only members of a particular species, or even particular strains within a species. One bacterial strain might be susceptible to two different phages, whereas another strain of the same species might be susceptible to those two phages plus a third phage.

The sources of food-associated infections can be traced by phage typing. One version of this procedure starts with a plate totally covered with bacteria growing on agar. A drop of each different phage type to be used in the test is then placed on the bacteria. Wherever the phages are able to infect and lyse the bacterial cells, clearings in the bacterial growth (called plaques) appear (Figure 13). Such a test might show, for instance, that bacteria isolated from a surgical wound have the same pattern of phage sensitivity as those isolated from the operating surgeon or surgical nurses. This result establishes that the surgeon or a nurse is the source of infection.

Fatty Acid Profiles

Bacteria synthesize a wide variety of fatty acids, and in general, these fatty acids are constant for a particular species. Commercial systems have been designed to separate cellular fatty acids to compare them to fatty acid profiles of known organisms. Fatty acid profiles, called **FAME** (*f*atty *a*cid *m*ethyl *e*ster), are widely used in clinical and public health laboratories.

Flow Cytometry

Flow cytometry can be used to identify bacteria in a sample without culturing the bacteria. In a *flow cytometer,* a moving

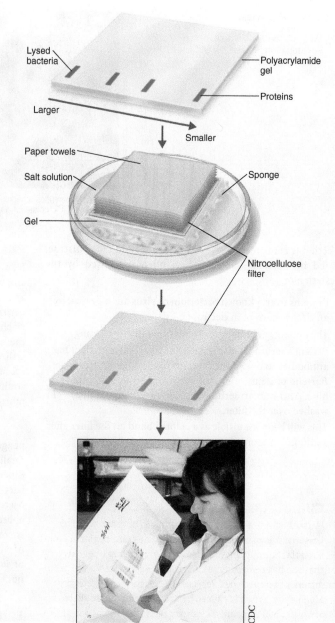

1 If Lyme disease is suspected in a patient: Electrophoresis is used to separate *Borrelia burgdorferi* proteins in the serum. Proteins move at different rates based on their charge and size when the gel is exposed to an electric current.

Lysed bacteria

Polyacrylamide gel

Proteins

Larger

Smaller

2 The bands are transferred to a nitrocellulose filter by blotting. Each band consists of many molecules of a particular protein (antigen). The bands are not visible at this point.

Paper towels

Salt solution

Sponge

Gel

Nitrocellulose filter

3 The proteins (antigens) are positioned on the filter exactly as they were on the gel. The filter is then washed with patient's serum followed by anti-human antibodies tagged with an enzyme. The patient antibodies that combine with their specific antigen are visible (shown here in red) when the enzyme's substrate is added.

4 The test is read. If the tagged antibodies stick to the filter, evidence of the presence of the microorganism in question—in this case, *B. burgdorferi*—has been found in the patient's serum.

CDC

Figure 12 The Western blot. Proteins separated by electrophoresis can be detected by their reactions with antibodies.

Q Name two diseases that may be diagnosed by Western blotting.

fluid containing bacteria is forced through a small opening. The simplest method detects the presence of bacteria by detecting the difference in electrical conductivity between cells and the surrounding medium. If the fluid passing through the opening is illuminated by a laser, the scattering of light provides information about the cell size, shape, density, and surface, which is analyzed by a computer. Fluorescence can be used to detect naturally fluorescent cells, such as *Pseudomonas,* or cells tagged with fluorescent dyes.

Milk can be a vehicle for disease transmission. A proposed test that uses flow cytometry to detect *Listeria* in milk could save time because the bacteria would not need to be cultured for

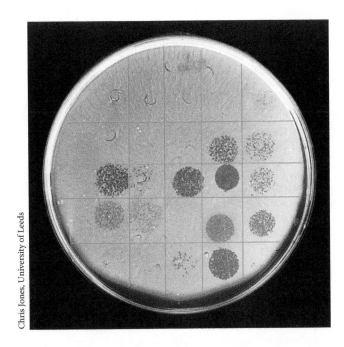

Chris Jones, University of Leeds

Figure 13 Phage typing of a strain of *Salmonella enterica*.
The tested strain was grown over the entire plate. Plaques, or areas of lysis, were produced by bacteriophages, indicating that the strain was sensitive to infection by these phages. Phage typing is used to distinguish *S. enterica* serotypes and *Staphylococcus aureus* types.

Q   What is being identified in phage typing?

identification. Antibodies against *Listeria* can be labeled with a fluorescent dye and added to the milk to be tested. The milk is passed through the flow cytometer, which records the fluorescence of the antibody-labeled cells.

DNA Base Composition

Taxonomists can use an organism's **DNA base composition** to draw conclusions about relatedness. This base composition is usually expressed as the percentage of guanine plus cytosine (G + C). The base composition of a single species is theoretically a fixed property; thus, a comparison of the G + C content in different species can reveal the degree of species relatedness. Each guanine (G) in DNA has a complementary cytosine (C). Similarly, each adenine (A) in the DNA has a complementary thymine (T). Therefore, the percentage of DNA bases that are GC pairs also tells us the percentage that are AT pairs (GC + AT = 100%). Two organisms that are closely related and hence have many identical or similar genes will have similar amounts of the various bases in their DNA. However, if there is a difference of more than 10% in their percentage of GC pairs (for example, if one bacterium's DNA contains 40% GC and another bacterium has 60% GC), then these two organisms are probably not related. Of course, two organisms that have the same percentage of GC are not necessarily closely related; other support-

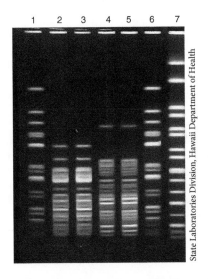

State Laboratories Division, Hawaii Department of Health

Figure 14 DNA fingerprints. DNA from seven different bacteria was digested with the same restriction enzyme. Each digest was put in a different well (origin) in the agarose gel. An electrical current was then applied to the gel to separate the fragments by size and electrical charge. The DNA was made visible by staining with a dye that fluoresces under ultraviolet light. Comparison of the lanes shows that DNA samples (and therefore the bacteria) in lanes 2 and 3; 4 and 5; and 1 and 6 are identical.

Q   What is an RFLP?

ing data are needed to draw conclusions about their phylogenetic relationship.

DNA Fingerprinting

Determining the entire sequence of bases in an organism's DNA is currently impractical for laboratory identification because of the great amount of time required. However, the use of restriction enzymes enables researchers to compare the base sequences of different organisms. Restriction enzymes cut a molecule of DNA everywhere a specific base sequence occurs, producing restriction fragments. For example, the enzyme *Eco*RI cuts DNA at the arrows in the sequence

$$...G^{\downarrow}A\,A\,T\,T\,C...$$
$$...C\,T\,T\,A\,A_{\uparrow}G...$$

In this technique, the DNA from two microorganisms is treated with the same restriction enzyme, and the restriction fragments (RFLPs) produced are separated by electrophoresis producing a **DNA fingerprint**. A comparison of the number and sizes of restriction fragments that are produced from different organisms provides information about their genetic similarities and differences; the more similar the patterns, or *DNA fingerprints,* the more closely related the organisms are expected to be (Figure 14).

DNA fingerprinting is used to determine the source of hospital-acquired infections. In one hospital, patients undergoing coronary-bypass surgery developed infections caused by *Rhodococcus bronchialis* (rō-dō-kok′kus bron-kē′al-is). The DNA fingerprints of the patients' bacteria and the bacteria of one nurse were identical. The hospital was thus able to break the chain of transmission of this infection by encouraging this nurse to use aseptic technique.

This has led to interest in finding a few genes that are present in all species and provide a large variation between species. Primers for these genes would be used for PCR to produce a *DNA bar code* for each species. This was first proposed in 2003 for eukaryotic species, but the necessary six to nine genes for bacterial identification have not been found.

Clinical Case

Salmonella serovars are identified by serotyping with antisera against previously isolated serovars. The department of health identifies the serovar; Monica and her friend are infected with *Salmonella tennessee* bacteria. By now, the department of health has been inundated with calls; 27 additional cases of *Salmonella tennessee* infection have been identified and reported from all over the state of Nevada.

How can the department of health determine whether these 29 cases are related?

Nucleic Acid Amplification Tests (NAATs)

When a microorganism cannot be cultured by conventional methods, the causative agent of an infectious disease might not be recognized. However, **nucleic acid amplification tests (NAATs)** can be used to increase the amount of microbial DNA to levels that can be tested by gel electrophoresis. NAATs use PCR, reverse-transcription PCR, and real-time PCR. If a primer for a specific microorganism is used, the presence of amplified DNA indicates that microorganism is present.

In 1992, researchers used PCR to determine the causative agent of Whipple's disease, which was previously an unknown bacterium now named *Tropheryma whipplei* (trō′fĕr-ē-mä whip′plē-e). Whipple's disease was first described in 1907 by George Whipple as a gastrointestinal and nervous system disorder caused by an unknown bacillus. No one has been able to culture the bacterium to identify it, and thus PCR provides the only reliable methods of diagnosing and treating the disease.

In recent years, PCR made possible several discoveries. For example, in 1992, Raul Cano used PCR to amplify DNA from *Bacillus* bacteria in amber that was 25 to 40 million years

old. These primers were made from rRNA sequences in living *B. circulans* to amplify DNA coding for rRNA in the amber. These primers will cause amplification of DNA from other *Bacillus* species but do not cause amplification of DNA from other bacteria that might have been present, such as *Escherichia* or *Pseudomonas*. The DNA was sequenced after amplification. This information was used to determine the relationships between the ancient bacteria and modern bacteria.

In 1993, microbiologists identified a *Hantavirus* as the cause of an outbreak of hemorrhagic fever in the American Southwest using PCR. The identification was made in record time—less than 2 weeks. PCR was used in 1994 to identify the causative agent of a new tickborne disease (human granulocytic ehrlichiosis) as the bacterium *Ehrlichia chaffeensis* (ėr′lik-ē-ä chaf′fē-en-sis). PCR is used to identify the source of rabies viruses.

In 2009, public health scientists used real-time PCR to identify a new strain of H1N1 influenza virus.

Nucleic Acid Hybridization

If a double-stranded molecule of DNA is subjected to heat, the complementary strands will separate as the hydrogen bonds between the bases break. If the single strands are then cooled slowly, they will reunite to form a double-stranded molecule identical to the original double strand. (This reunion occurs because the single strands have complementary sequences.) When this technique is applied to separated DNA strands from two different organisms, it is possible to determine the extent of similarity between the base sequences of the two organisms. This method is known as **nucleic acid hybridization.** The procedure assumes that if two species are similar or related, a major portion of their nucleic acid sequences will also be similar. The procedure measures the ability of DNA strands from one organism to hybridize (bind through complementary base pairing) with the DNA strands of another organism (Figure 15). The greater the degree of hybridization, the greater the degree of relatedness.

Similar hybridization reactions can occur between any single-stranded nucleic acid chain: DNA-DNA, RNA-RNA, DNA-RNA. An RNA transcript will hybridize with the separated template DNA to form a DNA-RNA hybrid molecule. Nucleic acid hybridization reactions are the basis of several techniques (described below) that are used to detect the presence of microorganisms and to identify unknown organisms.

Southern Blotting

Nucleic acid hybridization can be used to identify unknown microorganisms by **Southern blotting**. In addition, rapid identification methods using **DNA probes** are being developed. One method involves breaking DNA extracted from *Salmonella* into fragments with a restriction enzyme, then selecting a specific fragment as the probe for *Salmonella* (Figure 16). This fragment must be able to hybridize with the DNA of all

Classification of Microorganisms

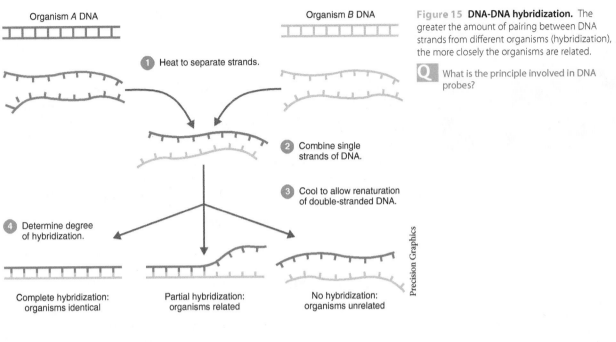

Organism *A* DNA

Organism *B* DNA

Figure 15 DNA-DNA hybridization. The greater the amount of pairing between DNA strands from different organisms (hybridization), the more closely the organisms are related.

Q What is the principle involved in DNA probes?

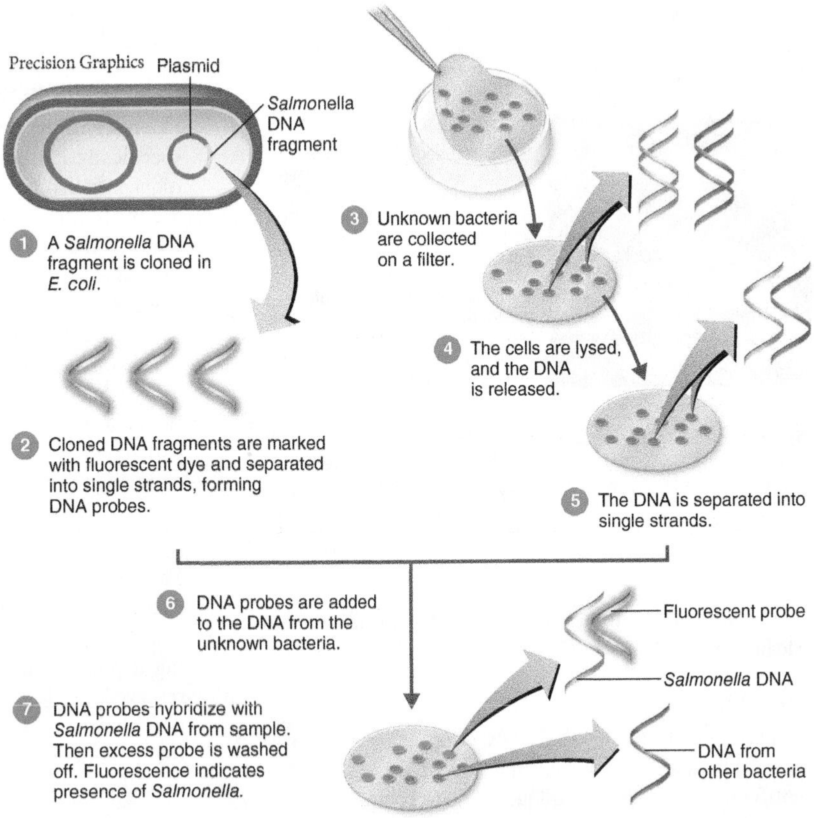

① Heat to separate strands.

② Combine single strands of DNA.

③ Cool to allow renaturation of double-stranded DNA.

④ Determine degree of hybridization.

Precision Graphics

Complete hybridization: organisms identical

Partial hybridization: organisms related

No hybridization: organisms unrelated

Figure 16 A DNA probe used to identify bacteria. Southern blotting is used to detect specific DNA. This modification of the Southern blot is used to detect *Salmonella*.

Q Why do the DNA probe and cellular DNA hybridize?

Precision Graphics   Plasmid

Salmonella DNA fragment

① A *Salmonella* DNA fragment is cloned in *E. coli*.

② Cloned DNA fragments are marked with fluorescent dye and separated into single strands, forming DNA probes.

③ Unknown bacteria are collected on a filter.

④ The cells are lysed, and the DNA is released.

⑤ The DNA is separated into single strands.

⑥ DNA probes are added to the DNA from the unknown bacteria.

⑦ DNA probes hybridize with *Salmonella* DNA from sample. Then excess probe is washed off. Fluorescence indicates presence of *Salmonella*.

Fluorescent probe

Salmonella DNA

DNA from other bacteria

(a) A DNA chip can be manufactured to contain hundreds of thousands of synthetic single-stranded DNA sequences. Assume that each DNA sequence was unique to a different gene.

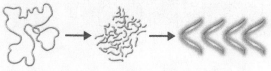

(b) Unknown DNA from a sample is separated into single strands, enzymatically cut, and labeled with a fluorescent dye.

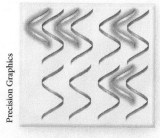

(c) The unknown DNA is inserted into the chip and allowed to hybridize with the DNA on the chip.

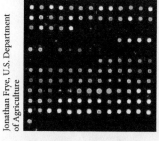

(d) The tagged DNA will bind only to the complementary DNA on the chip. The bound DNA will be detected by its fluorescent dye and analyzed by a computer. In this *Salmonella* antimicrobial resistance gene microarray, *S. typhimurium*-specific antibiotic resistance gene probes are green, *S. typhi*-specific resistance gene probes are red, and antibiotic-resistance genes found in both serovars appear yellow/orange.

Figure 17 DNA chip. This DNA chip contains probes for antibiotic-resistance genes. It is used to detect antibiotic-resistant bacteria in samples collected from animals on a farm or in slaughter facilities.

 What is on the chip to make it specific for a particular microorganism?

Salmonella strains, but not with the DNA of closely related enteric bacteria.

DNA Chips

An exciting new technology is the **DNA chip,** or **microarray,** which can quickly detect a pathogen in a host or the environment by identifying a gene that is unique to that pathogen (Figure 17).

The DNA chip is composed of DNA probes. A sample containing DNA from an unknown organism is labeled with a fluorescent dye and added to the chip. Hybridization between the probe DNA and DNA in the sample is detected by fluorescence.

Ribotyping and Ribosomal RNA Sequencing

Ribotyping is currently being used to determine the phylogenetic relationships among organisms. There are several advantages to using rRNA. First, all cells contain ribosomes. Second, RNA genes have undergone few changes over time so all members of a domain, phylum, and, in some cases, a genus, have the same "signature" sequences in their rRNA. The rRNA used most often is a component of the smaller portion of ribosomes. A third advantage of rRNA sequencing is that cells do not have to be cultured in the laboratory.

DNA can be amplified by PCR using an rRNA primer for specific signature sequences. The amplified fragments are subsequently cut with one or more restriction enzymes and separated by electrophoresis. The resulting band patterns can then be compared. Then the rRNA genes in the amplified fragments can be sequenced to determine evolutionary relationships between organisms. This technique is useful for classifying a newly discovered organism to domain or phylum or to determine the general types of organisms present in one environment. More specific probes are needed to identify individual species, however.

Fluorescent In Situ Hybridization (FISH)

Fluorescent dye-labeled RNA or DNA probes are used to specifically stain microorganisms in place, or in situ. This technique is called **fluorescent in situ hybridization,** or **FISH.** Cells are treated so the probe enters the cells and reacts with target DNA in the cell (in situ). FISH is used to determine the identity, abundance, and relative activity of microorganisms in an environment and can be used to detect bacteria that have not yet been cultured. Using FISH, a tiny bacterium, *Pelagibacter* (pel-aj′ē-bak-tèr), was discovered in the ocean and determined to be related to the rickettsias. As probes are developed, FISH can be used to detect bacteria in drinking water or bacteria in a patient without the normal 24-hour or longer wait required for culturing the bacteria (Figure 18).

Putting Classification Methods Together

Morphological characteristics, differential staining, and biochemical testing were the only identification tools available just a few years ago. Technological advancements are making it possible to use nucleic acid analysis techniques, once reserved for classification, for routine identification. Information obtained about microbes is used to identify and classify the organisms. Two methods of using the information are described on the facing page.

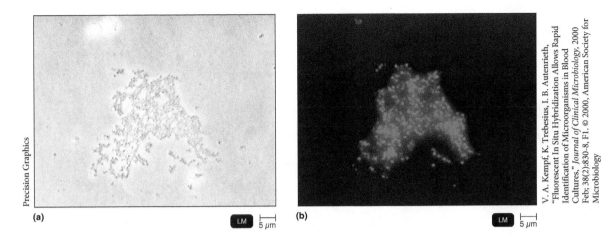

Figure 18 FISH, or fluorescent in situ hybridization. A DNA or RNA probe attached to fluorescent dyes is used to identify chromosomes. Bacteria seen with phase-contrast microscopy (**a**) are identified with a fluorescent-labeled probe that hybridizes with a specific sequence of DNA in *Staphylococcus aureus* (**b**).

Q What is stained using the FISH technique?

V. A. Kempf, K. Trebesius, I. B. Autenrieth, "Fluorescent In Situ Hybridization Allows Rapid Identification of Microorganisms in Blood Cultures," *Journal of Clinical Microbiology*, 2000 Feb; 38(2):830–8, F1. © 2000, American Society for Microbiology

Clinical Case

Salmonella isolates from each of the 29 infected people are sent to the state's public health laboratory for DNA fingerprinting. The DNA fingerprints are then sent to the Centers for Disease Control and Prevention (CDC). At the CDC, computer software compares each of the *Salmonella* DNA fingerprints to determine whether all 29 cases of *Salmonella tennessee* are identical. At this point, the CDC has received over 400 samples from 20 states, indicating a potential nationwide outbreak. Below is a figure of Monica's *Salmonella* DNA fingerprint along with other DNA fingerprint samples.

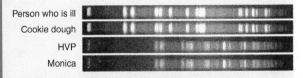

What can the CDC conclude about the outbreak based on these DNA fingerprints?

Canada Communicable Disease Report (CCDR) 2005: Volume 31. Public Health Agency of Canada

Dichotomous Keys

Dichotomous keys are widely used for identification. In a dichotomous key, identification is based on successive questions, and each question has two possible answers (*dichotomous* means cut in two). After answering one question, the investigator is directed to another question until an organism is identified.

Although these keys often have little to do with phylogenetic relationships, they are invaluable for identification. For example, a dichotomous key for bacteria could begin with an easily determined characteristic, such as cell shape, and move on to the ability to ferment a sugar. Dichotomous keys are shown in Figure 8 and in the Applications in Microbiology box earlier in this chapter. **Animations** Dichotomous Keys: Overview, Sample with Flowchart, Practice

Cladograms

Cladograms are maps that show evolutionary relationships among organisms (*clado-* means branch). Cladograms are shown in Figures 1 and 6. Each branch point on the cladogram is defined by a feature shared by various species on that branch. Historically, cladograms for vertebrates were made using fossil evidence; however, rRNA sequences are now being used to confirm assumptions based on fossils. As we said earlier, most microorganisms do not leave fossils; therefore, rRNA sequencing is primarily used to make cladograms for microorganisms. The small rRNA subunit used has 1500 bases, and computer programs do the calculations. The steps for constructing a cladogram are shown in **Figure 19**.

1. Two rRNA sequences are aligned, and
2. the percentage of similarity between the sequences is calculated.
3. Then the horizontal branches are drawn in a length proportional to the calculated percent similarity. All species beyond a node (branch point) have similar rRNA sequences, suggesting that they arose from an ancestor at that node.

1 Determine the sequence of bases in an rRNA molecule for each organism. Only a short sequence of bases is shown for this example.

Lactobacillus brevis	AGUCCAGAGC
L. sanfranciscensis	GUAAAAGAGC
L. acidophilus	AGCGGAGAGC
L. plantarum	ACGUUAGAGC

2 Calculate the percentage of similarity in the nucleotide bases between pairs of species. For example, there is a 70% similarity between the sequences for *L. brevis* and *L. acidophilus*.

	Percent similarity
L. brevis ⟶ *L. sanfranciscensis*	50%
L. brevis ⟶ *L. acidophilus*	70%
L. brevis ⟶ *L. plantarum*	60%
L. sanfranciscensis ⟶ *L. acidophilus*	50%
L. sanfranciscensis ⟶ *L. plantarum*	50%
L. plantarum ⟶ *L. acidophilus*	60%

3 Construct a cladogram. The length of the horizontal lines corresponds to the percent similarity values. Each branch point, or node, in the cladogram represents an ancestor common to all species beyond that node. Each node is defined by a similarity in rRNA present in all species beyond that branch point.

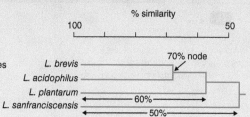

Figure 19 **Building a cladogram.**

Q Why do *L. brevis* and *L. acidophilus* branch from the same node?

Clinical Case Resolved

Early in this outbreak, there was a cluster of *Salmonella tennessee* illness due to consumption of raw eggs. Ill people and randomly chosen uninfected people completed questionnaires about foods they ate. The ill people were significantly more likely than well persons to report eating raw cookie dough, which contains uncooked eggs. However, the CDC soon determines that the cookie dough cluster involves a different strain of *Salmonella tennessee* from the strain involved in the current outbreak. This strain is associated with hydrolyzed vegetable protein (HVP), a flavor enhancer that is commonly used in a variety of foods, including a vegetable dip and chips that Monica and her friend ate the day before they became ill. In conjunction with the CDC and the U.S. Food and Drug Administration, the manufacturer recalls that particular batch of HVP. Monica and her friend fully recover after a few days.

Tracing *Salmonella* infections to their source is essential because *Salmonella* can be transmitted through a variety of foods. It causes an estimated 1.4 million illnesses and 400 deaths annually in the United States.

DNA fingerprinting is currently used worldwide by public health laboratories to distinguish among *Salmonella* strains. NAATs are highly sensitive and specific, but primers or probes would have to be made for every strain. DNA fingerprinting can also detect strains because the RFLPs are made from the entire genome rather than from amplification of a few nucleotide sequences.

CHECK YOUR UNDERSTANDING

✔ What is in *Bergey's Manual*? **13**

✔ Design a rapid test for a *Staphylococcus aureus*. **14**

✔ What is tested in Western blotting and Southern blotting? **15**

✔ What is identified by phage typing? **16**

✔ Why does PCR identify a microbe? **17**

✔ Which techniques involve nucleic acid hybridization? **18**

✔ Is a cladogram used for identification or classification? **12, 19**

Study Outline

Test your understanding with quizzes, microbe review, and a chapter post-test at www.masteringmicrobiology.com.

Introduction

1. Taxonomy is the science of the classification of organisms. Its goal is to show relationships among organisms.
2. Taxonomy also provides a means of identifying organisms.

The Study of Phylogenetic Relationships

1. Phylogeny is the evolutionary history of a group of organisms.
2. The taxonomic hierarchy shows evolutionary, or phylogenetic, relationships among organisms.
3. Bacteria were separated into the Kingdom Prokaryotae in 1968.
4. Living organisms were divided into five kingdoms in 1969.

The Three Domains

5. Living organisms are currently classified into three domains. A domain can be divided into kingdoms.
6. In this system, plants, animals, and fungi belong to the Domain Eukarya.
7. Bacteria (with peptidoglycan) form a second domain.
8. Archaea (with unusual cell walls) are placed in the Domain Archaea.

A Phylogenetic Hierarchy

9. Organisms are grouped into taxa according to phylogenetic relationships (from a common ancestor).
10. Some of the information for eukaryotic relationships is obtained from the fossil record.
11. Prokaryotic relationships are determined by rRNA sequencing.

Classification of Organisms

Scientific Nomenclature

1. According to scientific nomenclature, each organism is assigned two names, or a binomial: a genus and a specific epithet, or species.
2. Rules for assigning names to bacteria are established by the International Committee on Systematics of Prokaryotes.
3. Rules for naming fungi and algae are published in the *International Code of Botanical Nomenclature.*
4. Rules for naming protozoa are found in the *International Code of Zoological Nomenclature.*

The Taxonomic Hierarchy

5. A eukaryotic species is a group of organisms that interbreed with each other but do not breed with individuals of another species.
6. Similar species are grouped into a genus; similar genera are grouped into a family; families, into an order; orders, into a class; classes, into a phylum; phyla, into a kingdom; and kingdoms, into a domain.

Classification of Prokaryotes

7. *Bergey's Manual of Systematic Bacteriology* is the standard reference on bacterial classification.
8. A group of bacteria derived from a single cell is called a strain.
9. Closely related strains constitute a bacterial species.

Classification of Eukaryotes

10. Eukaryotic organisms may be classified into the Kingdom Fungi, Plantae, or Animalia.
11. Protists are mostly unicellular organisms; these organisms are currently being assigned to kingdoms.
12. Fungi are absorptive chemoheterotrophs that develop from spores.
13. Multicellular photoautotrophs are placed in the Kingdom Plantae.
14. Multicellular ingestive heterotrophs are classified as Animalia.

Classification of Viruses

15. Viruses are not placed in a kingdom. They are not composed of cells and cannot grow without a host cell.
16. A viral species is a population of viruses with similar characteristics that occupies a particular ecological niche.

Methods of Classifying and Identifying Microorganisms

1. *Bergey's Manual of Determinative Bacteriology* is the standard reference for laboratory identification of bacteria.
2. Morphological characteristics are useful in identifying microorganisms, especially when aided by differential staining techniques.
3. The presence of various enzymes, as determined by biochemical tests, is used in identifying bacteria and yeasts.
4. Serological tests, involving the reactions of microorganisms with specific antibodies, are useful in determining the identity of strains and species, as well as relationships among organisms. ELISA and Western blotting are examples of serological tests.
5. Phage typing is the identification of bacterial species and strains by determining their susceptibility to various phages.
6. Fatty acid profiles can be used to identify some organisms.
7. Flow cytometry measures physical and chemical characteristics of cells.
8. The percentage of GC base pairs in the nucleic acid of cells can be used in the classification of organisms.
9. The number and sizes of DNA fragments, or DNA fingerprints, produced by restriction enzymes are used to determine genetic similarities.
10. NAATs can be used to amplify a small amount of microbial DNA in a sample. The presence or identification of an organism is indicated by amplified DNA.
11. Single strands of DNA, or of DNA and RNA, from related organisms will hydrogen-bond to form a double-stranded molecule; this bonding is called nucleic acid hybridization.
12. Southern blotting, DNA chips, and FISH are examples of nucleic acid hybridization techniques.
13. The sequence of bases in ribosomal RNA can be used in the classification of organisms.
14. Dichotomous keys are used for the identification of organisms. Cladograms show phylogenetic relationships among organisms.

Study Questions

Answers to the Review and Multiple Choice questions can be found at the end of this chapter.

Review

1. Which of the following organisms are most closely related? Are any two the same species? On what did you base your answer?

Characteristic	A	B	C	D
Morphology	Rod	Coccus	Rod	Rod
Gram Reaction	+	–	–	+
Glucose Utilization	Fermentative	Oxidative	Fermentative	Fermentative
Cytochrome Oxidase	Present	Present	Absent	Absent
GC Moles %	48–52	23–40	50–54	49–53

2. Here is some additional information on the organisms in question 1:

Organism	% DNA Hybridization
A and B	5–15
A and C	5–15
A and D	70–90
B and C	10–20
B and D	2–5

Which of these organisms are most closely related? Compare this answer with your response to review question 1.

3. **DRAW IT** Use the additional information below to construct a cladogram for some of the organisms used in question 4. What is the purpose of a cladogram? How does your cladogram differ from a dichotomous key for these organisms?

	Similarity in rRNA Bases
P. aeruginosa—M. pneumoniae	52%
P. aeruginosa—C. botulinum	52%
P. aeruginosa—E. coli	79%
M. pneumoniae—C. botulinum	65%
M. pneumoniae—E. coli	52%
E. coli—C. botulinum	52%

% similarity

100   50

4. **DRAW IT** Use the information in the table below to complete the dichotomous key to these organisms. What is the purpose of a dichotomous key? Look up each genus, and provide an example of why this organism is of interest to humans.

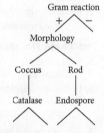

	Morphology	Gram Reaction	Acid from Glucose	Growth in Air (21% O₂)	Motile by Peritrichous Flagella	Presence of Cytochrome Oxidase	Produce Catalase
Staphylococcus aureus	Coccus	+	+	+	–	–	+
Streptococcus pyogenes	Coccus	+	+	+	–	–	–
Mycoplasma pneumoniae	Coccus	–	+	+ (Colonies < 1 mm)	–	–	+
Clostridium botulinum	Rod	+	+	–	+	–	–
Escherichia coli	Rod	–	+	+	+	–	+
Pseudomonas aeruginosa	Rod	–	+	+	–	+	+
Campylobacter fetus	Vibrio	–	–	–	–	+	+
Listeria monocytogenes	Rod	+	+	+	+	–	+

5. **NAME IT** Use the key in the Applications of Microbiology box to identify the gram-negative rod causing pneumonia in a sea otter. It is V–P negative, indole-negative, and urease-positive.

Multiple Choice

1. *Bergey's Manual of Systematic Bacteriology* differs from *Bergey's Manual of Determinative Bacteriology* in that the former
   a. groups bacteria into species.
   b. groups bacteria according to phylogenetic relationships.
   c. groups bacteria according to pathogenic properties.
   d. groups bacteria into 19 species.
   e. all of the above

2. *Bacillus* and *Lactobacillus* are not in the same order. This indicates that which one of the following is *not* sufficient to assign an organism to a taxon?
   a. biochemical characteristics
   b. amino acid sequencing
   c. phage typing
   d. serology
   e. morphological characteristics

3. Which of the following is used to classify organisms into the Kingdom Fungi?
   a. ability to photosynthesize; possess a cell wall
   b. unicellular; possess cell wall; prokaryotic
   c. unicellular; lacking cell wall; eukaryotic
   d. absorptive; possess cell wall; eukaryotic
   e. ingestive; lacking cell wall; multicellular; prokaryotic

4. Which of the following is *false* about scientific nomenclature?
   a. Each name is specific.
   b. Names vary with geographical location.
   c. The names are standardized.
   d. Each name consists of a genus and specific epithet.
   e. It was first designed by Linnaeus.

5. You could identify an unknown bacterium by all of the following *except*
   a. hybridizing a DNA probe from a known bacterium with the unknown's DNA.
   b. making a fatty acid profile of the unknown.
   c. specific antiserum agglutinating the unknown.
   d. ribosomal RNA sequencing.
   e. percentage of guanine + cytosine.

6. The wall-less mycoplasmas are considered to be related to gram-positive bacteria. Which of the following would provide the most compelling evidence for this?
   a. They share common rRNA sequences.
   b. Some gram-positive bacteria and some mycoplasmas produce catalase.
   c. Both groups are prokaryotic.
   d. Some gram-positive bacteria and some mycoplasmas have coccus-shaped cells.
   e. Both groups contain human pathogens.

Use the following choices to answer questions 7 and 8.
   a. Animalia
   b. Fungi
   c. Plantae
   d. Firmicutes (gram-positive bacteria)
   e. Proteobacteria (gram-negative bacteria)

7. Into which group would you place a multicellular organism that has a mouth and lives inside the human liver?

8. Into which group would you place a photosynthetic organism that lacks a nucleus and has a thin peptidoglycan wall surrounded by an outer membrane?

Use the following choices to answer questions 9 and 10.
   1. 9 + 2 flagella
   2. 70S ribosome
   3. fimbria
   4. nucleus
   5. peptidoglycan
   6. plasma membrane

9. Which is (are) found in all three domains?
   a. 2, 6
   b. 5
   c. 2, 4, 6
   d. 1, 3, 5
   e. all six

10. Which is (are) found *only* in prokaryotes?
   a. 1, 4, 6
   b. 3, 5
   c. 1, 2
   d. 4
   e. 2, 4, 5

Critical Thinking

1. The GC content of *Micrococcus* is 66–75 moles %, and of *Staphylococcus*, 30–40 moles %. According to this information, would you conclude that these two genera are closely related?

2. Describe the use of a DNA probe and PCR for:
   a. rapid identification of an unknown bacterium.
   b. determining which of a group of bacteria are most closely related.

3. SF medium is a selective medium, developed in the 1940s, to test for fecal contamination of milk and water. Only certain gram-positive cocci can grow in this medium. Why is it named SF? Using this medium, which genus will you culture?

Clinical Applications

1. A 55-year-old veterinarian was admitted to a hospital with a 2-day history of fever, chest pain, and cough. Gram-positive cocci were detected in his sputum, and he was treated for lobar pneumonia with penicillin. The next day, another Gram stain of his sputum revealed gram-negative rods, and he was switched to ampicillin and gentamicin. A sputum culture showed biochemically inactive gram-negative rods identified as *Pantoea (Enterobacter) agglomerans*. After fluorescent-antibody staining and phage typing, *Yersinia pestis* was identified in the patient's sputum and blood, and chloramphenicol and tetracycline were administered. The patient died 3 days after admission to the hospital. Tetracycline was given to his 220 contacts (hospital personnel, family, and co-workers). What disease did the patient have? Discuss what went wrong in the diagnosis and how his death might have been prevented. Why were the 220 other people treated?

2. A 6-year-old girl was admitted to a hospital with endocarditis. Blood cultures showed a gram-positive, aerobic rod identified by the hospital laboratory as *Corynebacterium xerosis*. The girl died after 6 weeks of treatment with intravenous penicillin and chloramphenicol. The bacterium was tested by another laboratory and identified as *C. diphtheriae*. The following test results were obtained by each laboratory:

	Hospital Lab	Other Lab
Catalase	+	+
Nitrate reduction	+	+
Urea	–	–
Esculin hydrolysis	–	–
Glucose fermentation	+	+
Sucrose fermentation	–	+
Serological test for toxin production	Not done	+

Provide a possible explanation for the incorrect identification. What are the potential public health consequences of mis-identifying *C. diphtheriae*?

3. Using the following information, create a dichotomous key for distinguishing these unicellular organisms. Which cause human disease?

	Mitochondria?	Chlorophyll?	Nutritional Type?	Motile?
Euglena	+	+	Both	+
Giardia	–	–	Heterotroph	+
Nosema	–	–	Heterotroph	–
Pfiesteria	+	+	Autotroph	+
Trichomonas	–	–	Heterotroph	+
Trypanosoma	+	–	Heterotroph	+

Using the additional information shown below, create a dichotomous key for these organisms. Do your two keys differ? Explain why. Which key is more useful for laboratory identification? For classification?

	rRNA base #																			
	1	2	3	4	5	6	7	8	9	10	11	12	13	14	15	16	17	18	19	20
Euglena	C	C	A	G	G	U	U	G	U	U	C	C	A	G	U	U	U	U	A	A
Giardia	C	C	A	U	A	U	U	U	U	U	G	A	C	G	A	A	G	G	U	C
Nosema	C	C	A	U	A	U	U	U	U	U	A	A	C	G	A	A	G	G	C	C
Pfiesteria	C	C	A	A	C	U	U	A	U	U	C	C	A	G	U	U	U	C	A	G
Trichomonas	C	C	A	U	A	U	U	U	U	U	G	A	C	G	A	A	G	G	G	C
Trypanosoma	C	C	A	C	G	U	U	G	U	U	C	C	A	G	U	U	U	A	A	A

Answers to Review and Multiple Choice Study Questions

Review

1. A and D appear to be most closely related because they have similar G-C moles %. No two are the same species.
2. A and D are most closely related.
3.

The purpose of a cladogram is to show the degree of relatedness between organisms. A dichotomous key can be used for identification but doesn't show relatedness like the cladogram. Mycoplasma and Escherichia are on one branch in the key, but the cladogram indicates Mycoplasma is more closely related to Clostridium.

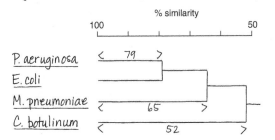

4. One possible key is shown below. Alternative keys could be made starting with morphology or glucose fermentation.

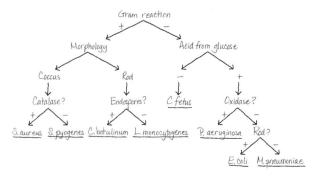

5. *Bordetella bronchiseptica*

Multiple Choice

1. b	**3.** d	**5.** e	**7.** a	**9.** a
2. e	**4.** b	**6.** a	**8.** e	**10.** b

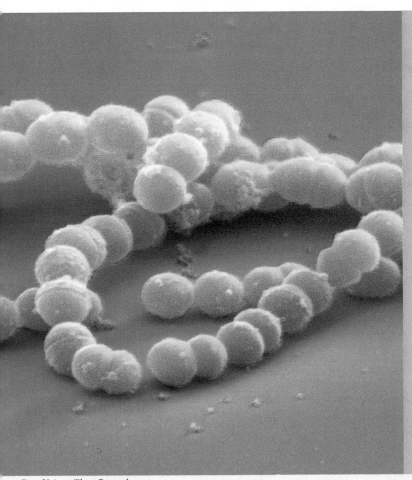

Eye of Science/Photo Researchers

The Prokaryotes: Domains Bacteria and Archaea

Visualize microbiology and check your understanding with a pre-test at www.masteringmicrobiology.com.

When biologists first encountered microscopic bacteria, they were puzzled as to how to classify them. Bacteria were clearly not animals or rooted plants. Attempts to build a taxonomic system for bacteria based on the phylogenetic system developed for plants and animals failed. In the earlier editions of *Bergey's Manual*, bacteria were grouped by morphology (rod, coccus), staining reactions, presence of endospores, and other obvious features. Although this system had its practical uses, it also had many limitations, somewhat like grouping bats and birds together on the basis of their having wings. The knowledge of bacteria at the molecular level has now expanded to such a degree that it is possible to base the latest edition of *Bergey's Manual* on a phylogenetic system. For example, the genera *Rickettsia* and *Chlamydia* are no longer grouped together by their common requirement for intracellular growth. Members of the genus *Chlamydia* are now found in a phylum named Chlamydia, but the rickettsias are now grouped in a distant phylum, Proteobacteria, in the Alphaproteobacteria class. Some microbiologists find such changes upsetting, but they reflect important differences. These differences are primarily in the ribosomal RNA (rRNA) of the microbes, a genetic component that is slow to change and performs the same functions in all organisms.

Pathogenic bacteria isolated from patients, such as the *Streptococcus agalactiae* shown in the photo, must be identified quickly. Laboratory identification of bacterial species usually starts with Gram staining and morphology. Identification of this bacterium is discussed in the Clinical Case.

From Chapter 11 of *Microbiology: An Introduction*, Eleventh Edition. Gerard J. Tortora, Berdell R. Funke, Christine L. Case.

The Prokaryotic Groups

In the second edition of *Bergey's Manual,* the prokaryotes are grouped into two **domains,** the **Archaea** and the **Bacteria.** Both domains consist of prokaryotic cells. Spelled without capitalization, that is, archaea and bacteria, these terms denote organisms that fit into these domains. Each domain is divided into phyla, each phylum into classes, and so on. The phyla discussed in this chapter are summarized in **Table 1.**

Clinical Case: Mercy

Sheree Walker, a neonatologist at a local hospital, is checking on Mercy, a 48-hour-old infant girl. Mercy delivered normally at 39 weeks and gave all indications of being a healthy baby. In the last 2 days, however, she has taken a bad turn and is admitted to the neonatal intensive care unit (NICU). Mercy is limp, has difficulty breathing, and has a body temperature of 35°C; but her lungs are clear, and her heart exam is normal. Dr. Walker speaks with Mercy's mother, who confirms that she received appropriate prenatal care and has no other medical problems. Dr. Walker orders a lumbar puncture for Mercy to check her cerebrospinal fluid (CSF) for possible infection. The report back from the lab shows blood in Mercy's CSF. Dr. Walker diagnoses Mercy with meningitis and then orders a venous blood culture to check for bacteria.

What bacteria could be the cause of Mercy's meningitis? Read on to find out.

TABLE 1 Selected Prokaryotes from *Bergey's Manual of Systemic Bacteriology,* **Second Edition***

Phylum 　Class	Order	Important Genera	Special Features
DOMAIN BACTERIA			
Proteobacteria			
Alphaproteobacteria	Caulobacterales	*Caulobacter*	Stalked
	Rickettsiales	*Anaplasma*	Obligately intracellular human pathogens
		Ehrlichia	Obligately intracellular human pathogens
		Rickettsia	Obligately intracellular human pathogens
		Wolbachia	Symbionts of insects
	Rhizobiales	*Agrobacterium*	Plant pathogens
		Bartonella	Human pathogens
		Beijerinckia	Free-living nitrogen fixers
		Bradyrhizobium	Symbiotic nitrogen fixers
		Brucella	Human pathogens
		Hyphomicrobium	Budding
		Nitrobacter	Nitrifying
		Rhizobium	Symbiotic nitrogen fixers
	Rhodospirillales	*Acetobacter*	Acetic acid producers
		Azospirillum	Nitrogen fixers
		Gluconobacter	Acetic acid producers
		Rhodospirillum	Photosynthetic, anoxygenic
Betaproteobacteria	Burkholderiales	*Burkholderia*	Opportunistic pathogens
		Bordetella	Human pathogens
		Sphaerotilus	Sheathed
	Hydrogenophilales	*Thiobacillus*	Sulfur oxidizers
	Neisseriales	*Neisseria*	Human pathogens

*This table includes prokaryotes mentioned in this text. Descriptions such as *pathogenic* mean that this trait is common in the genus, but not that all members of the genus have this trait.

TABLE 1 (continued)

Phylum Class	Order	Important Genera	Special Features
	Nitrosomonadales	Nitrosomonas	Nitrifying
		Spirillum	Found in stagnant fresh water
	Rhodocyclales	Zoogloea	Sewage treatment
Gammaproteobacteria	Chromatiales	Chromatium	Photosynthetic, anoxygenic
	Thiotrichales	Beggiatoa	Sulfur oxidizers
		Thiomargarita	Giant bacterium
		Francisella	Human pathogens
	Legionellales	Legionella	Human pathogens
		Coxiella	Obligately intracellular human pathogens
	Pseudomonadales	Azomonas	Free-living nitrogen fixers
		Azotobacter	Free-living nitrogen fixers
		Moraxella	Human pathogens
		Pseudomonas	Opportunistic pathogens
	Vibrionales	Vibrio	Human pathogens
	Enterobacteriales	Citrobacter	Opportunistic pathogens
		Enterobacter	Opportunistic pathogens
		Erwinia	Plant pathogens
		Escherichia	Normal intestinal bacteria, some pathogens
		Klebsiella	Opportunistic pathogens
		Proteus	Human intestinal bacteria, occasional pathogens
		Salmonella	Human pathogens
		Serratia	Red pigment, opportunistic infections
		Shigella	Human pathogens
		Yersinia	Human pathogens
	Pasteurellales	Haemophilus	Human pathogens
		Pasteurella	Human pathogens
Deltaproteobacteria	Bdellovibrionales	Bdellovibrio	Parasites of bacteria
	Desulfovibrionales	Desulfovibrio	Sulfate reducers
	Myxococcales	Myxococcus	Gliding, fruiting
		Stigmatella	Gliding, fruiting
Epsilonproteobacteria	Campylobacterales	Campylobacter	Human pathogens
		Helicobacter	Human pathogens, carcinogenic
Firmicutes (The Low G + C Gram-Positive Bacteria)			
	Clostridiales	Clostridium	Anaerobes, endospores, some human pathogens
		Epulopiscium	Giant bacterium
		Sarcina	Occur in cubical packets
	Mycoplasmatales[†]	Mycoplasma	No cell wall, human pathogens
		Spiroplasma	No cell wall, pleomorphic, plant pathogens
		Ureaplasma	No cell wall, ammonia from urea
	Bacillales	Bacillus	Endospores, some pathogens
		Listeria	Human pathogens
		Staphylococcus	Some human pathogens
	Lactobacillales	Enterococcus	Opportunistic pathogens
		Lactobacillus	Lactic acid producers
		Streptococcus	Many human pathogens

[†]The bacteria in the order Mycoplasmatales are genetically related to the low G + C gram-positive bacteria, but they lack a cell wall and stain gram-negative.

(continued)

TABLE 1 Selected Prokaryotes from *Bergey's Manual of Systemic Bacteriology*, Second Edition (continued)

Phylum Class	Order	Important Genera	Special Features
Actinobacteria (The High G + C Gram-Positive Bacteria)			
	Actinomycetales	Actinomyces	Filamentous, branching, some human pathogens
		Corynebacterium	Human pathogens
		Frankia	Symbiotic nitrogen fixers
		Gardnerella	Human pathogens
		Mycobacterium	Acid-fast, human pathogens
		Nocardia	Filamentous, branching, opportunistic pathogens
		Propionibacterium	Propionic acid producers
		Streptomyces	Filamentous branching, many produce antibiotics
Nonproteobacteria, Gram-Negative Bacteria			
Cyanobacteria		Anabaena	Photosynthetic, oxygenic
		Gloeocapsa	Photosynthetic, oxygenic
Chlamydiae	Chlamydiales	Chlamydia	Intracellular parasites, human pathogens
		Chlamydophila	Intracellular parasites, human pathogens
Planctomycetes	Planctomycetales	Planctomyces	No peptidoglycan in cell wall, stalked
		Gemmata	No peptidoglycan in cell wall, internal structure resembles eukaryotic cell
Bacteroidetes	Bacteroidales	Bacteroides	Human intestinal tract
		Prevotella	Human oral cavity
	Sphingobacteriales	Cytophaga	Degrade cellulose in soil
	Flavobacteriales	Capnocytophaga	Mammal oral cavity
Fusobacteria	Fusobacteriales	Fusobacterium	Human intestinal tract
		Streptobacillus	A human pathogen
Purple and Green Photosynthetic Bacteria (The Anoxygenic Photosynthetic Bacteria)			
Chlorobi		Chlorobium	Photosynthetic, anoxygenic
Chloroflexi		Chloroflexus	Photosynthetic, anoxygenic
Spirochaetes	Spirochaetales	Borrelia	Human pathogens
		Leptospira	Human pathogens
		Treponema	Human pathogens
Deinococcus-Thermus	Deinococcales-Thermales	Deinococcus	Radiation-resistant thermophile
		Thermus	Heat-resistant thermophile
DOMAIN ARCHAEA			
Crenarchaeota (Gram-Negative)			
	Desulfurococcales	Pryidictium	Hyperthermophiles
	Sulfolobales	Sulfolobus	Hyperthermophiles
Euryarchaeota (Gram-Positive to Variable)			
	Methanobacteriales	Methanobacterium	Methanogens
	Halobacteriales	Halobacterium	Require high salt concentration
		Halococcus	Require high salt concentration

DOMAIN BACTERIA

Most of us think of bacteria as invisible, potentially harmful little creatures. Actually, relatively few species of bacteria cause disease in humans, animals, plants, or any other organisms. Once you have completed a course in microbiology, you will realize that without bacteria, much of life as we know it would not be possible. In this chapter, you will learn how bacterial groups are differentiated from each other and how important bacteria are in the world of microbiology. Our discussion in this chapter emphasizes bacteria considered to be of practical importance, those that are important in medicine, or those that illustrate biologically unusual or interesting principles.

The Learning Objectives and Check Your Understanding questions throughout this chapter will help you to become familiar with these organisms and to look for similarities and differences between organisms. You will draw a dichotomous key to differentiate the bacteria described in each group.

The Proteobacteria

LEARNING OBJECTIVES

1   Differentiate the alphaproteobacteria described in this chapter by drawing a dichotomous key.

2   Differentiate the betaproteobacteria described in this chapter by drawing a dichotomous key.

3   Differentiate the gammaproteobacteria described in this chapter by drawing a dichotomous key.

4   Differentiate the deltaproteobacteria described in this chapter by drawing a dichotomous key.

5   Differentiate the epsilonproteobacteria described in this chapter by drawing a dichotomous key.

We've drawn the first of these dichotomous keys (for alphaproteobacteria) for you as an example.

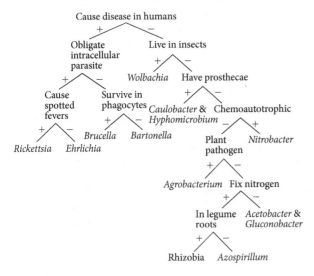

The **proteobacteria**, which includes most of the gram-negative, chemoheterotrophic bacteria, are presumed to have arisen from a common photosynthetic ancestor. They are now the largest taxonomic group of bacteria. However, few are now photosynthetic; other metabolic and nutritional capacities have arisen to replace this characteristic. The phylogenetic relationship in these groups is based upon rRNA studies. The name *Proteobacteria* was taken from the mythological Greek god Proteus, who could assume many shapes. The proteobacteria are separated into five classes designated by Greek letters: alphaproteobacteria, betaproteobacteria, gammaproteobacteria, deltaproteobacteria, and epsilonproteobacteria.

The Alphaproteobacteria

As a group, the alphaproteobacteria includes most of the proteobacteria that are capable of growth at very low levels of nutrients. Some have unusual morphology, including protrusions such as stalks or buds known as **prosthecae**. The alphaproteobacteria also include agriculturally important bacteria capable of inducing nitrogen fixation in symbiosis with plants, and several plant and human pathogens.

Pelagibacter One of the most abundant microorganisms on Earth, certainly in the ocean environment, is *Pelagibacter ubique* (pel-aj′ē-bak-ter u′bēk). It is a member of a group of marine microbes discovered by use of the FISH technique and named SAR 11 because of their original discovery in the Sargasso Sea. *P. ubique* is the first member of this group to be successfully cultivated. Its genome has been sequenced and found to have only 1354 genes. This number is very low for a free-living organism, although several mycoplasmas have even fewer genes. Bacteria in a symbiotic relationship have lower metabolic requirements and have the smallest genomes. The bacterium is extremely small, a little over 0.3 μm diameter. Its small size and minimal genome probably give it a competitive advantage for survival in low-nutrient environments. In fact, it seems to be the most abundant living organism (part of its name, *ubique*, is derived from *ubiquitous*), on the basis of weight, in the oceans, where its sheer numbers must give it an important role in the Earth's carbon cycle.

Azospirillum Agricultural microbiologists have been interested in members of the genus *Azospirillum* (ā-zō-spī′ril-lum), a soil bacterium that grows in close association with the roots of many plants, especially tropical grasses. It uses nutrients excreted by the plants and in return fixes nitrogen from the atmosphere. This form of nitrogen fixation is most significant in some tropical grasses and in sugar cane, although the organism can be isolated from the root system of many temperate-climate

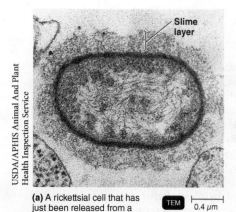

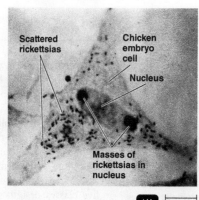

Slime layer

(a) A rickettsial cell that has just been released from a host cell

TEM 0.4 μm

Scattered rickettsias

Chicken embryo cell

Nucleus

Masses of rickettsias in nucleus

LM 5 μm

Figure 1 Rickettsias.

Q How are rickettsias transmitted from one host to another?

(b) Rickettsias grow only within a host cell, such as the chicken embryo cell shown here. Note the scattered rickettsias within the cell and the compact masses of rickettsias in the cell nucleus.

plants, such as corn. The prefix *azo-* is frequently encountered in nitrogen-fixing genera of bacteria. It is derived from *a* (without) and *zo* (life), in reference to the early days of chemistry when oxygen was removed, by a burning candle, from an experimental atmosphere. Presumably, mostly nitrogen remained, and mammalian life was found to be not possible in this atmosphere. Hence, nitrogen came to be associated with absence of life.

Acetobacter and Gluconobacter *Acetobacter* (ä′sē-tō-bak-tėr) and *Gluconobacter* (glü′kon-ō-bak-tėr) are industrially important aerobic organisms that convert ethanol into acetic acid (vinegar).

Rickettsia In earlier editions of *Bergey's Manual,* the genera *Rickettsia, Coxiella,* and *Chlamydia* were grouped closely because they share the common characteristic of being obligate intracellular parasites—that is, they reproduce only within a mammalian cell. In the second edition they are now widely separated.

The rickettsias are gram-negative rod-shaped bacteria, or coccobacilli (**Figure 1a**). One distinguishing feature of most rickettsias is that they are transmitted to humans by bites of insects and ticks, unlike the *Coxiella* (discussed later with gammaproteobacteria). Rickettsia enter their host cell by inducing phagocytosis. They quickly enter the cytoplasm of the cell and begin reproducing by binary fission (**Figure 1b**). They can usually be cultivated artificially in cell culture or chick embryos.

The rickettsias are responsible for a number of diseases known as the spotted fever group. These include epidemic typhus, caused by *Rickettsia prowazekii* (ri-ket′sē-ä prou-wä-ze′kē-ē) and transmitted by lice; endemic murine typhus, caused by *R. typhi* (tī′fē) and transmitted by rat fleas; and Rocky

Mountain spotted fever, caused by *R. rickettsii* (ri-ket′sē-ē) and transmitted by ticks. In humans, rickettsial infections damage the permeability of blood capillaries, which results in a characteristic spotted rash.

Ehrlichia Ehrlichiae are gram-negative, rickettsia-like bacteria that live obligately within white blood cells. *Ehrlichia* (ėr′lik-ē-ä) species are transmitted by ticks to humans and cause ehrlichiosis, a sometimes fatal disease.

Caulobacter and Hyphomicrobium Members of the genus *Caulobacter* (kô-lō-bak′tėr) are found in low-nutrient aquatic environments, such as lakes. They feature stalks that anchor the organisms to surfaces (**Figure 2**). This arrangement increases their nutrient uptake because they are exposed to a continuously changing flow of water and because the stalk increases the surface-to-volume ratio of the cell. Also, if the surface to which they anchor is a living host, these bacteria can use the host's excretions as nutrients. When the nutrient concentration is exceptionally low, the size of the stalk increases, evidently to provide an even greater surface area for nutrient absorption.

Budding bacteria do not divide by binary fission into two nearly identical cells. The budding process resembles the asexual reproductive processes of many yeasts. The parent cell retains its identity while the bud increases in size until it separates as a complete new cell. An example is the genus *Hyphomicrobium* (hī-fō-mī-krō′bē-um), as shown in **Figure 3**. These bacteria, like the caulobacteria, are found in low-nutrient aquatic environments and have even been found growing in laboratory water baths. Both *Caulobacter* and *Hyphomicrobium* produce prominent prosthecae.

Rhizobium, Bradyrhizobium, and Agrobacterium The *Rhizobium* (rī-zō′bē-um) and *Bradyrhizobium* (brăd-ē-rī-zō′bē-um) are two of the more important genera of a group of agriculturally important

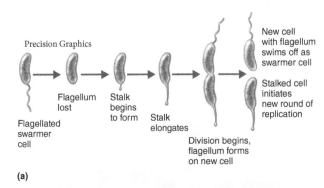

(a)

Yves Brun

(b)

Figure 2 *Caulobacter.*

Q What is the competitive advantage provided by attaching to a surface?

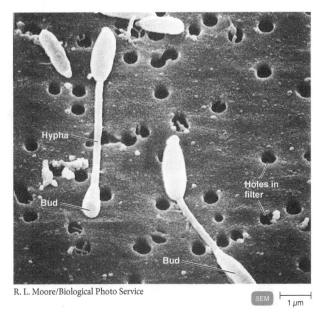

R. L. Moore/Biological Photo Service

SEM | 1 μm

Figure 3 *Hyphomicrobium*, a type of budding bacterium.

Q Most bacteria do not reproduce by budding; what method do they use?

bacteria that specifically infect the roots of leguminous plants, such as beans, peas, or clover. For simplicity these bacteria are known by the common name of **rhizobia.** The presence of rhizobia in the roots leads to formation of nodules in which the rhizobia and plant form a symbiotic relationship, resulting in the fixation of nitrogen from the air for use by the plant.

Like rhizobia, the genus *Agrobacterium* (ag′rō-bak-ti′rē-um) has the ability to invade plants. However, these bacteria do not induce root nodules or fix nitrogen. Of particular interest is *Agrobacterium tumefaciens*. This is a plant pathogen that causes a disease called crown gall; the crown is the area of the plant where the roots and stem merge. The tumorlike gall is induced when *A. tumefaciens* inserts a plasmid containing bacterial genetic information into the plant's chromosomal DNA. For this reason, microbial geneticists are very interested in this organism. Plasmids are the most common vector that scientists use to carry new genes into a cell, and the thick wall of plants is especially difficult to penetrate.

Bartonella The genus *Bartonella* (bär′tō-nel-la) contains several members that are human pathogens. The best known is *Bartonella henselae*, a gram-negative bacillus that causes cat-scratch disease.

Brucella *Brucella* (brü′sel-la) bacteria are small nonmotile coccobacilli. All species of *Brucella* are obligate parasites of mammals and cause the disease brucellosis. Of medical interest is the ability of *Brucella* to survive phagocytosis, an important element of the body's defense against bacteria.

Nitrobacter and Nitrosomonas *Nitrobacter* (nī-trō-bak′tėr) and *Nitrosomonas* (nī-trō-sō-mō′nas) are genera of nitrifying bacteria that are of great importance to the environment and to agriculture. They are chemoautotrophs capable of using inorganic chemicals as energy sources and carbon dioxide as the only source of carbon, from which they synthesize all of their complex chemical makeup. The energy sources of the genera *Nitrobacter* and *Nitrosomonas* (the latter is a member of the betaproteobacteria) are reduced nitrogenous compounds. *Nitrobacter* species oxidize ammonium (NH_4^+) to nitrite (NO_2^-), which is in turn oxidized by *Nitrosomonas* species to nitrates (NO_3^-) in the process of *nitrification*. Nitrate is important to agriculture; it is a nitrogen form that is highly mobile in soil and therefore likely to be encountered and used by plants.

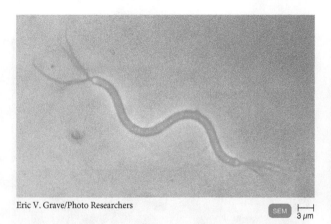

Eric V. Grave/Photo Researchers

SEM | 3 μm

Figure 4 *Spirillum volutans.* These large helical bacteria are found in aquatic environments. Note the polar flagella.

Q Is this bacterium motile? How can you tell?

Wolbachia *Wolbachia* (wol-ba′kē-ä) are probably the most common infectious bacterial genus in the world. Even so, little is known about *Wolbachia*; they live only inside the cells of their hosts, usually insects (a relationship known as *endosymbiosis*). Therefore, *Wolbachia* escape detection by the usual culture methods. This fascinating group of bacteria is described further in the Applications of Microbiology box later in this chapter.

CHECK YOUR UNDERSTANDING

✔ Make a dichotomous key to distinguish the alphaproteobacteria described in this chapter. **1**

The Betaproteobacteria

There is considerable overlap between the betaproteobacteria and the alphaproteobacteria, for example, among the nitrifying bacteria discussed earlier. The betaproteobacteria often use nutrient substances that diffuse away from areas of anaerobic decomposition of organic matter, such as hydrogen gas, ammonia, and methane. Several important pathogenic bacteria are found in this group.

Thiobacillus *Thiobacillus* (thī-ō-bä-sil′lus) species and other sulfur-oxidizing bacteria are important in the sulfur cycle. These chemoautotrophic bacteria are capable of obtaining energy by oxidizing the reduced forms of sulfur, such as hydrogen sulfide (H_2S), or elemental sulfur (S^0), into sulfates (SO_4^{2-}).

Spirillum The habitat of the genus *Spirillum* (spī-ril′lum) is mainly fresh water. An important morphological difference from the helical spirochetes is that *Spirillum* bacteria are motile by conventional polar flagella, rather than axial filaments. The spirilla

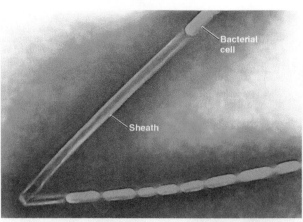

From: "Studies on the filamentous sheathed iron bacterium Sphaerotilus natans." J. L. Stokes. J Bacteriol. 1954 Mar;67(3):278–91

SEM | 6 μm

Figure 5 *Sphaerotilus natans.* These sheathed bacteria are found in dilute sewage and aquatic environments. They form elongated sheaths in which the bacteria live. The bacteria have flagella (not visible here) and can eventually swim free of the sheath.

Q How does the sheath help the cell?

are relatively large, gram-negative, aerobic bacteria. *Spirillum volutans* (vō-lū-tans) is often used as a demonstration slide when microbiology students are first introduced to the operation of the microscope (**Figure 4**).

Sphaerotilus Sheathed bacteria, which include *Sphaerotilus natans* (sfe-rä′ti-lus na′tans), are found in freshwater and in sewage. These gram-negative bacteria with polar flagella form a hollow, filamentous sheath in which to live (**Figure 5**). Sheaths are protective and also aid in nutrient accumulation. *Sphaerotilus* probably contributes to bulking, an important problem in sewage treatment.

Burkholderia The genus *Burkholderia* was formerly grouped with the genus *Pseudomonas,* which is now classified under the gammaproteobacteria. Like the pseudomonads, almost all *Burkholderia* species are motile by a single polar flagellum or tuft of flagella. The best known species is the aerobic, gram-negative rod *Burkholderia cepacia* (berk′hōld-ėr-ē-ä se-pā′se-ä). It has an extraordinary nutritional spectrum and is capable of degrading more than 100 different organic molecules. This capability is often a factor in the contamination of equipment and drugs in hospitals; these bacteria may actually grow in disinfectant solutions. This bacterium is also a problem for persons with the genetic lung disease cystic fibrosis, in whom it metabolizes accumulated respiratory secretions. *Burkholderia pseudomallei* (sūdo-mal′lē-ī) is a resident in moist soils and is the cause of

From: "Type IV Pilus Structure by Cryo-Electron Microscopy and Crystallography: Implications for Pilus Assembly and Functions." L. Craig, et al. *Mol Cell.* 2006 Sep 1;23(5):651–62

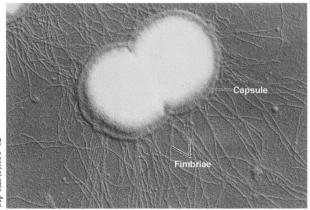

Capsule

Fimbriae

SEM 0.4 µm

Figure 6 The gram-negative coccus *Neisseria gonorrhoeae.* Notice the paired arrangement (diplococci). The fimbriae enable the organism to attach to mucous membranes.

Q How do fimbriae contribute to pathogenicity?

a severe disease (melioidosis) endemic in southeast Asia and northern Australia.

Bordetella Of special importance is the nonmotile, aerobic, gram-negative rod *Bordetella pertussis* (bôr'de-tel-lä pėr-tus'sis). This serious pathogen is the cause of pertussis, or whooping cough.

Neisseria Bacteria of the genus *Neisseria* (nī-se′rē-ä) are aerobic, gram-negative cocci that usually inhabit the mucous membranes of mammals. Pathogenic species include the gonococcus bacterium *Neisseria gonorrhoeae* (go-nôr-rē′ī), the causative agent of gonorrhoea (**Figure 6**), and *N. meningitidis* (men-nin-ji′ti-dis), the agent of meningococcal meningitis.

Zoogloea The genus *Zoogloea* (zō′ ō-glē-ä) is important in the context of aerobic sewage-treatment processes, such as the activated sludge system. As they grow, *Zoogloea* bacteria form fluffy, slimy masses that are essential to the proper operation of such systems.

CHECK YOUR UNDERSTANDING

✔ Make a dichotomous key to distinguish the betaproteobacteria described in this chapter. **2**

The Gammaproteobacteria

The gammaproteobacteria constitute the largest subgroup of the proteobacteria and include a great variety of physiological types.

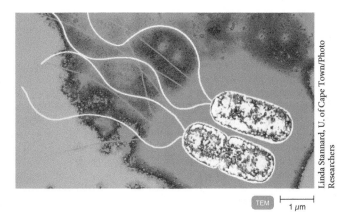

Linda Stannard, U. of Cape Town/Photo Researchers

TEM 1 µm

Figure 7 *Pseudomonas.* This photo of a pair of *Pseudomonas* bacteria shows polar flagella that are a characteristic of the genus. In some species only a single flagellum is present. Note that one cell (on the bottom) is beginning to divide.

Q How does the nutritional diversity of these bacteria make them a problem in hospitals?

Beggiatoa *Beggiatoa alba* (bej′jē-ä-tō-ä al′ba), the only species of this unusual genus, grows in aquatic sediments at the interface between the aerobic and anaerobic layers. Morphologically, it resembles certain filamentous cyanobacteria, but it is not photosynthetic. Motility is by gliding. The mechanism is the production of slime, which attaches to the surface on which movement occurs and also provides lubrication allowing the organism to glide.

Nutritionally *B. alba* uses hydrogen sulfide (H_2S) as an energy source and accumulates internal granules of sulfur. The ability of this organism to obtain energy from an inorganic compound was an important factor in the discovery of autotrophic metabolism.

Francisella *Francisella* (fran′sis-el′lä) is a genus of small, pleomorphic bacteria that grow only on complex media enriched with blood or tissue extracts. *Francisella tularensis* (tü′lär-en-sis) causes the disease tularemia.

Pseudomonadales

Members of the order Pseudomonadales are gram-negative aerobic rods or cocci. The most important genus in this group is *Pseudomonas.*

Pseudomonas A very important genus, *Pseudomonas* (sū-dō-mō′nas) consists of aerobic, gram-negative rods that are motile by polar flagella, either single or tufts (**Figure 7**). Pseudomonads are very common in soil and other natural environments.

APPLICATIONS OF **MICROBIOLOGY**

Bacteria and Insect Sex

***Wolbachia* is quite possibly the most common** infectious bacterial genus on Earth. Although these bacteria were first discovered in 1924, little had been known about them until the 1990s. They escape detection by the usual culture methods because they live as endosymbionts in the cells of insects and other invertebrates (**Figure A**).

Wolbachia infect over a million species of insects and other invertebrates. In all, as many as 75% of species of animals surveyed carry this bacterium. *Wolbachia* is essential to nematodes. If the bacterium is killed with antibiotics, the host worm dies.

In some insects, *Wolbachia* destroys males of its host species. *Wolbachia* can turn males into females by interfering with the male hormone. As shown in **Figure B**, if a male and female insect are uninfected with *Wolbachia*, they produce offspring normally. If only the

male is infected, the insects fail to reproduce. If one or both insects of a mating pair are infected, only the infected females reproduce—and transmit *Wolbachia* in the cytoplasm of their eggs. Offspring produced without fertilization are female. The result is that the bacteria are transmitted to the next generation. This type of reproduction, called parthenogenesis, has been seen in a variety of insects and in some amphibians and reptiles. Thus a question arises: Is *Wolbachia* always responsible?

Eukaryotic species are defined as organisms that reproduce only with members of their own species. This reproductive isolation prevents the production of hybrids and thus maintains the uniqueness of each species. In the laboratory, researchers have found that after antibiotic treatment, wasps of one species will produce hybrid offspring with another species. This raises the question about the influence *Wolbachia* has had on the evolution of insects. Did insects that were not infected reproduce successfully outside their species?

Wolbachia may be evolving into an organelle, much like ancient microbes evolved into mitochondria. Recently researchers discovered that *Wolbachia* can transfer its genes into the host cells and that the genes are expressed. This horizontal gene transfer could provide new traits in the host.

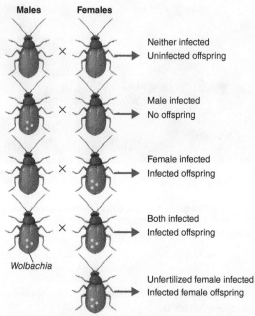

Figure B **In an infected pair, only female hosts can reproduce.**
Precision Graphics

A virulent strain of *Wolbachia* called "popcorn" causes host cells to lyse, or "pop," which eventually kills the host insect. On the one hand, the popcorn strain might be used to kill mosquitoes. On the other hand, eliminating *Wolbachia* from pest insects could result in a lower number of females, thus reducing population growth.

The unique biology of *Wolbachia* has attracted researchers interested in questions that range from the evolutionary implications of infection to commercial uses of *Wolbachia*.

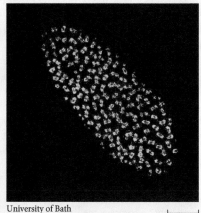

University of Bath

10 µm

Figure A ***Wolbachia* are red inside the cells of this fruit fly embryo.**

Many species of pseudomonads excrete extracellular, water-soluble pigments that diffuse into their media. One species, *Pseudomonas aeruginosa* (ā-rü-ji-nō′sä), produces a soluble, blue-green pigmentation. Under certain conditions, particularly in weakened hosts, this organism can infect the urinary tract, burns, and wounds, and can cause blood infections (sepsis), abscesses, and meningitis. Other pseudomonads produce soluble fluorescent pigments that glow when illuminated by ultraviolet light. One species, *P. syringae* (sėr′in-gī), is an occasional plant pathogen. (Some species of *Pseudomonas* have been

transferred, based upon rRNA studies, to the genus *Burkholderia*, which was discussed previously with the betaproteobacteria.)

Pseudomonads have almost as much genetic capacity as the eukaryotic yeasts and almost half as much as a fruit fly. Although these bacteria are less efficient than some other heterotrophic bacteria in utilizing many of the more common nutrients, they make use of their genetic capacity by compensating for this in other ways. For example, pseudomonads synthesize an unusually large number of enzymes and can metabolize a wide variety of substrates. Therefore, they probably contribute significantly to the decomposition of uncommon chemicals, such as pesticides, that are added to soil.

In hospitals and other places where pharmaceutical agents are prepared, the ability of pseudomonads to grow on minute traces of unusual carbon sources, such as soap residues or cap-liner adhesives found in a solution, has been unexpectedly troublesome. Pseudomonads are even capable of growth in some antiseptics, such as quaternary ammonium compounds. Their resistance to most antibiotics has also been a source of medical concern. This resistance is probably related to the characteristics of the cell wall porins, which control the entrance of molecules through the cell wall. The large genome of pseudomonads also codes for several very efficient efflux pump systems that eject antibiotics from the cell before they can function. Pseudomonads are responsible for about one in ten nosocomial infections (hospital-acquired infections), especially among infections in burn units. Persons with cystic fibrosis are also especially prone to infections by *Pseudomonas* and the closely related *Burkholderia*.

Although pseudomonads are classified as aerobic, some are capable of substituting nitrate for oxygen as a terminal electron acceptor. This process, anaerobic respiration, yields almost as much energy as aerobic respiration. In this way, pseudomonads cause important losses of valuable nitrogen in fertilizer and soil. Nitrate (NO_3^-) is the form of fertilizer nitrogen most easily used by plants. Under anaerobic conditions, as in water-logged soil, pseudomonads eventually convert this valuable nitrate into nitrogen gas (N_2), which is lost to the atmosphere.

Many pseudomonads can grow at refrigerator temperatures. This characteristic, combined with their ability to utilize proteins and lipids, makes them an important contributor to food spoilage.

Azotobacter and Azomonas Some nitrogen-fixing bacteria, such as *Azotobacter* (ā-zō-tō-bak′tėr) and *Azomonas* (ā-zō-mō′nas), are free-living in soil. These large, ovoid, heavily capsulated bacteria are frequently used in laboratory demonstrations of nitrogen fixation. However, to fix agriculturally significant amounts of nitrogen, they would require energy sources, such as carbohydrates, that are in limited supply in soil.

Moraxella Members of the genus *Moraxella* (mô-raks-el′lä) are strictly aerobic coccobacilli—that is, intermediate in shape between cocci and rods. *Moraxella lacunata* (la-kü-nä′tä) is implicated in conjunctivitis, an inflammation of the conjunctiva, the membrane that covers the eye and lines the eyelids.

Acinetobacter The genus *Acinetobacter* (a-si-nē′tō-bak-tėr) is aerobic and in stained preparations typically forms pairs. The bacteria occur naturally in soil and water. A member of this

genus, *Acinetobacter baumanii* (bou′man-ē-ē), is an increasing concern to the medical community because of the rapidity with which it becomes resistant to antibiotics. Some strains are resistant to most available antibiotics. Not yet widespread in the United States, A. *baumanii* is an opportunistic pathogen primarily found in a hospital setting. The antibiotic resistance of the pathogen, combined with the weakened health of infected hospital patients, has resulted in an unusually high mortality rate. A. *baumanii* is primarily a respiratory pathogen, but it also infects skin and soft tissues and wounds and occasionally invades the bloodstream. It is more environmentally hardy than most gram-negative bacteria, and, once established in a hospital, it becomes difficult to eliminate.

Legionellales

The genera *Legionella* and *Coxiella* are closely associated in the second edition of *Bergey's Manual,* where both are placed in the same order, Legionellales. Because the *Coxiella* share an intracellular lifestyle with the rickettsial bacteria, they were previously considered rickettsial in nature and grouped with them. *Legionella* bacteria grow readily on suitable artificial media.

Legionella *Legionella* (lē-jä-nel′lä) bacteria were originally isolated during a search for the cause of an outbreak of pneumonia now known as legionellosis. The search was difficult because these bacteria did not grow on the usual laboratory isolation media then available. After intensive effort, special media were developed that enabled researchers to isolate and culture the first *Legionella*. Microbes of this genus are now known to be relatively common in streams, and they colonize such habitats as warm-water supply lines in hospitals and water in the cooling towers of air conditioning systems. An ability to survive and reproduce within aquatic amoebas often makes them difficult to eradicate in water systems.

Coxiella *Coxiella burnetii* (käks-ē-el′lä bėr-ne′tē-ē), which causes Q fever, was formerly grouped with the rickettsia. Like them, *Coxiella* bacteria require a mammalian host cell to reproduce. Unlike rickettsias, *Coxiella* bacteria are not transmitted among humans by insect or tick bites. Although cattle ticks harbor the organism, it is most commonly transmitted by aerosols or contaminated milk. A sporelike body is present in C. *burnetii*. This might explain the bacterium's relatively high resistance to the stresses of airborne transmission and heat treatment.

Vibrionales

Members of the order Vibrionales are facultatively anaerobic gram-negative rods. Many are slightly curved. They are found mostly in aquatic habitats.

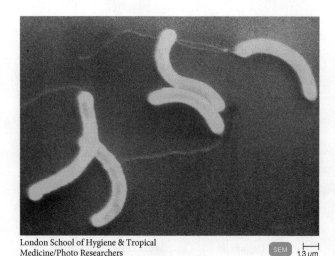

London School of Hygiene & Tropical
Medicine/Photo Researchers

SEM   1.3 μm

Figure 8 *Vibrio cholerae.* Notice the curvature of these rods, which is a characteristic of the genus.

 What disease does *Vibrio cholerae* cause?

Vibrio Members of the genus *Vibrio* (vib′rē-ō) are rods that are often slightly curved (Figure 8). One important pathogen is *Vibrio cholerae* (kol′er-ī), the causative agent of cholera. The disease is characterized by a profuse and watery diarrhea. *V. parahaemolyticus* (pa-rä-hē-mō-li′ti-kus) causes a less serious form of gastroenteritis. Usually inhabiting coastal salt waters, it is transmitted to humans mostly by raw or undercooked shellfish.

Enterobacteriales

The members of the order Enterobacteriales are facultatively anaerobic, gram-negative rods that are, if motile, peritrichously flagellated. Morphologically, the rods are straight. This is an important bacterial group, often commonly called **enterics.** This reflects the fact that they inhabit the intestinal tracts of humans and other animals. Most enterics are active fermenters of glucose and other carbohydrates.

Because of the clinical importance of enterics, there are many techniques to isolate and identify them. An identification method for some enterics incorporates a modern tool using 15 biochemical tests. Biochemical tests are especially important in clinical laboratory work and in food and water microbiology.

Enterics have fimbriae that help them adhere to surfaces or mucous membranes. Specialized sex pili aid in the exchange of genetic information between cells, which often includes antibiotic resistance.

Enterics, like many bacteria, produce proteins called bacteriocins that cause the lysis of closely related species of bacteria.

Bacteriocins may help maintain the ecological balance of various enterics in the intestines.

Escherichia The bacterial species *Escherichia coli* is one of the most common inhabitants of the human intestinal tract and is probably the most familiar organism in microbiology. A great deal is known about the biochemistry and genetics of *E. coli,* and it continues to be an important tool for basic biological research—many researchers consider it almost a laboratory pet. Its presence in water or food is an indication of fecal contamination. *E. coli* is not usually pathogenic. However, it can be a cause of urinary tract infections, and certain strains produce enterotoxins that cause traveler's diarrhea and occasionally cause very serious foodborne disease.

Salmonella Almost all members of the genus *Salmonella* (sal′mön-el-lä) are potentially pathogenic. Accordingly, there are extensive biochemical and serological tests to clinically isolate and identify salmonellae. Salmonellae are common inhabitants of the intestinal tracts of many animals, especially poultry and cattle. Under unsanitary conditions, they can contaminate food.

The nomenclature of the genus *Salmonella* is unusual. Instead of multiple species, members of the genus *Salmonella* that are infectious to warm-blooded animals can be considered for practical purposes to be a single species, *Salmonella enterica* (en-ter′i-kä). This species is divided into more than 2400 **serovars,** that is, *serological varieties.* The term **serotype** is often used to mean the same thing. By way of explanation of these terms, when salmonellae are injected into appropriate animals, their flagella, capsules, and cell walls serve as *antigens* that cause the animals to form *antibodies* in their blood that are specific for each of these structures. Thus, *serological* means are used to differentiate the microorganisms. Serology can be used to differentiate and identify bacteria.

A serovar such as *Salmonella typhimurium* (tī-fi-mur′ē-um) is not a species and should be more properly written as "*Salmonella enterica* serovar Typhimurium." The convention now used by the Centers for Disease Control and Prevention (CDC) is to spell out the entire name at the first mention and then abbreviate it as, for example, *Salmonella* Typhimurium. For simplicity, we will identify serovars of salmonellae in this text as we would species, that is, *S. typhimurium,* etc.

Specific antibodies, which are available commercially, can be used to differentiate *Salmonella* serovars by a system known as the Kauffmann-White scheme. This scheme designates an organism by numbers and letters that correspond to specific antigens on the organism's capsule, cell wall, and flagella, which are identified by the letters K, O, and H, respectively. For example, the antigenic formula for the bacterium *S. typhimurium* is

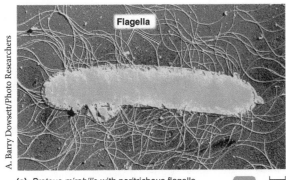

(a) *Proteus mirabilis* with peritrichous flagella

TEM | 0.3 µm

(b) A swarming colony of *Proteus mirabilis*, showing concentric rings of growth

Figure 9 *Proteus mirabilis.* Chemical communication between bacterial cells causes changes from cells adapted to swimming in fluid (few flagella) to cells that are able to move on surfaces (numerous flagella). The concentric growth (**b**) results from periodic synchronized conversion to the highly flagellated form capable of movement on surfaces.

 The photo of the *Proteus* cell is probably a swarmer cell. How would you know?

O1,4,[5],12:H,i,1,2*. Many salmonellae are named only by their antigenic formulas. Serovars can be further differentiated by special biochemical or physiological properties into **biovars,** or **biotypes.**

A recent taxonomic arrangement based upon the latest molecular technology adds another species, *Salmonella bongori* (bon′gôr-ē). This is a resident of "cold-blooded" animals—it was originally isolated from a lizard in the town of Bongor in the African desert nation of Chad—and is rarely found in humans.

Typhoid fever, caused by *Salmonella typhi* (tī′fē), is the most severe illness caused by any member of the genus *Salmonella*. A less severe gastrointestinal disease caused by other salmonellae is called salmonellosis. Salmonellosis is one of the most common forms of foodborne illness.

Shigella Species of *Shigella* (shi-gel′lä) are responsible for a disease called bacillary dysentery, or shigellosis. Unlike salmonellae, they are found only in humans. Some strains of *Shigella* can cause life-threatening dysentery.

Klebsiella Members of the genus *Klebsiella* (kleb-sē-el′lä) are commonly found in soil or water. Many isolates are capable of fixing nitrogen from the atmosphere, which has been proposed as

being a nutritional advantage in isolated populations with little protein nitrogen in their diet. The species *Klebsiella pneumoniae* (nü-mō′nē-ī) occasionally causes a serious form of pneumonia in humans.

Serratia *Serratia marcescens* (ser-rä′ tē-ä mär-ses′sens) is a bacterial species distinguished by its production of red pigment. In hospital situations, the organism can be found on catheters, in saline irrigation solutions, and in other supposedly sterile solutions. Such contamination is probably the cause of many urinary and respiratory tract infections in hospitals.

Proteus Colonies of *Proteus* (prō′ tē-us) bacteria growing on agar exhibit a swarming type of growth. Swarmer cells with many flagella (Figure 9a) move outward on the edges of the colony and then revert to normal cells with only a few flagella and reduced motility. Periodically, new generations of highly motile swarmer cells develop, and the process is repeated. As a result, a *Proteus* colony has the distinctive appearance of a series of concentric rings (Figure 9b). This genus of bacteria is implicated in many infections of the urinary tract and in wounds.

Yersinia *Yersinia pestis* (yėr-sin′ē-ä pes′tis) causes plague, the Black Death of medieval Europe. Urban rats in some parts of the world and ground squirrels in the American Southwest carry these bacteria. Fleas usually transmit the organisms among animals and to humans, although contact with respiratory droplets from infected animals and people can be involved in transmission.

Erwinia *Erwinia* (ėr-wi′nē-ä) species are primarily plant pathogens; some cause plant soft-rot diseases. These species produce

---

*The letters derive from the original German usage: K represents the German for capsule. (Salmonellae with capsules are identified serologically by a particular capsular antigen named Vi, for virulence.) Colonies that spread in a thin film over the agar surface were described by the German word for film, *hauch.* The motility needed to form a film implied the presence of flagella, and the letter H came to be assigned to the antigens of flagella. Nonmotile bacteria were described as *ohne hauch,* without film, and the O came to be assigned to the cell surface or body antigens. This terminology is also used in the naming of *E. coli* O157:H7, *Vibrio cholerae* O:1, and others.

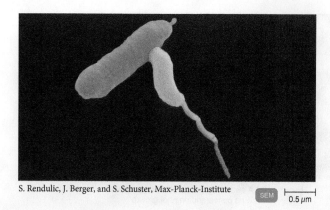

S. Rendulic, J. Berger, and S. Schuster, Max-Planck-Institute

SEM | 0.5 μm

Figure 10 ***Bdellovibrio bacteriovorus.*** The yellow bacterium is *B. bacteriovorus.* It is attacking a bacterial cell shown in blue.

 Would this bacterium attack *Staphylococcus aureus*?

enzymes that hydrolyze the pectin between individual plant cells. This causes the plant cells to separate from each other, a disease that plant pathologists term *plant rot.*

Enterobacter Two *Enterobacter* (en-te-rō-bak′tĕr) species, *E. cloacae* (klō-ā′kī), and *E. aerogenes* (ā-rä′jen-ēz), can cause urinary tract infections and hospital-acquired infections. They are widely distributed in humans and animals, as well as in water, sewage, and soil.

Pasteurellales

The bacteria in the order Pasteurellales are nonmotile; they are best known as human and animal pathogens.

Pasteurella The genus *Pasteurella* (pas-tyĕr-el′ lä) is primarily known as a pathogen of domestic animals. It causes sepsis in cattle, fowl cholera in chickens and other fowl, and pneumonia in several types of animals. The best-known species is *Pasteurella multocida* (mul-tō′si-dä), which can be transmitted to humans by dog and cat bites.

Haemophilus *Haemophilus* (hē-mä′ fil-us) is a very important genus of pathogenic bacteria. These organisms inhabit the mucous membranes of the upper respiratory tract, mouth, vagina, and intestinal tract. The best-known species that affects humans is *Haemophilus influenzae* (in-flü-en′ za), named long ago because of the erroneous belief that it was responsible for influenza.

The name *Haemophilus* is derived from the bacteria's requirement for blood in their culture medium (*hemo* = blood). They are unable to synthesize important parts of the cytochrome system needed for respiration, and they obtain these substances from the heme fraction, known as the **X factor,** of blood hemoglobin. The culture medium must also supply the

cofactor nicotinamide adenine dinucleotide (from either NAD^+ or $NADP^+$), which is known as **V factor.** Clinical laboratories use tests for the requirement of X and V factors to identify isolates as *Haemophilus* species.

Haemophilus influenzae is responsible for several important diseases. It has been a common cause of meningitis in young children and is a frequent cause of earaches. Other clinical conditions caused by *H. influenzae* include epiglotitis (a life-threatening condition in which the epiglottis becomes infected and inflamed), septic arthritis in children, bronchitis, and pneumonia. *Haemophilus ducreyi* (dü-krā′ē) is the cause of the sexually transmitted disease chancroid.

CHECK YOUR UNDERSTANDING

✔ Make a dichotomous key to distinguish the orders of gammaproteobacteria described in this chapter. **3**

The Deltaproteobacteria

The deltaproteobacteria are distinctive in that they include some bacteria that are predators on other bacteria. Bacteria in this group are also important contributors to the sulfur cycle.

Bdellovibrio *Bdellovibrio* (del-lō-vib′rē-ō) is a particularly interesting genus. It attacks other gram-negative bacteria. It attaches tightly (*bdella* = leech; **Figure 10**), and after penetrating the outer layer of gram-negative bacteria, it reproduces within the periplasm. There, the cell elongates into a tight spiral, which then fragments almost simultaneously into several individual flagellated cells. The host cell then lyses, releasing the *Bdellovibrio* cells.

Desulfovibrionales

Members of the order Desulfovibrionales are sulfur-reducing bacteria. They are obligately anaerobic bacteria that use oxidized forms of sulfur, such as sulfates (SO_4^{2-}) or elemental sulfur (S^0) rather than oxygen as electron acceptors. The product of this reduction is hydrogen sulfide (H_2S). (Because the H_2S is not assimilated as a nutrient, this type of metabolism is termed *dissimilatory.*) The activity of these bacteria releases millions of tons of H_2S into the atmosphere every year and plays a key part in the sulfur cycle. Sulfur-oxidizing bacteria such as *Beggiatoa* are able to use H_2S either as part of photosynthesis or as an autotrophic energy source.

Desulfovibrio The best-studied sulfur-reducing genus is *Desulfovibrio* (dē′sul-fō-vib′rē-ō), which is found in anaerobic sediments and in the intestinal tracts of humans and animals. Sulfur-reducing and sulfate-reducing bacteria use organic compounds such as lactate, ethanol, or fatty acids as electron donors. This reduces sulfur or sulfate to H_2S. When H_2S reacts with iron it forms insoluble FeS, which is responsible for the black color of many sediments.

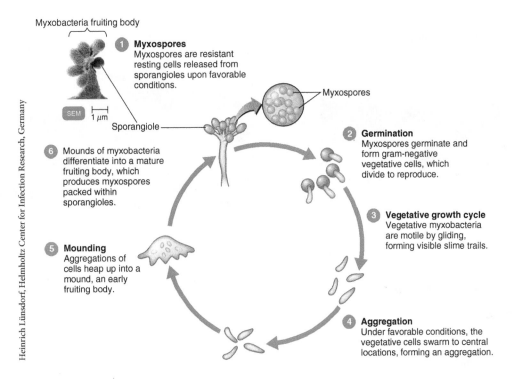

Myxobacteria fruiting body

1 Myxospores
Myxospores are resistant resting cells released from sporangioles upon favorable conditions.

Myxospores

SEM | 1 μm

Sporangiole

2 Germination
Myxospores germinate and form gram-negative vegetative cells, which divide to reproduce.

6 Mounds of myxobacteria differentiate into a mature fruiting body, which produces myxospores packed within sporangioles.

3 Vegetative growth cycle
Vegetative myxobacteria are motile by gliding, forming visible slime trails.

5 Mounding
Aggregations of cells heap up into a mound, an early fruiting body.

4 Aggregation
Under favorable conditions, the vegetative cells swarm to central locations, forming an aggregation.

Heinrich Lünsdorf, Helmholtz Center for Infection Research, Germany

Figure 11 Myxococcales.

 What is the feeding stage of this organism?

Myxococcales

In earlier editions of *Bergey's Manual,* the Myxococcales were classified among the fruiting and gliding bacteria. They illustrate the most complex life cycle of all bacteria, part of which is predatory upon other bacteria.

Myxococcus Vegetative cells of the myxobacteria (*myxo* = nasal mucus) move by gliding and leave behind a slime trail. *Myxococcus xanthus* (micks-ō-kok′kus zan′thus) and *M. fulvus* (ful′vus) are well-studied representatives of the genus. As they move, their source of nutrition is the bacteria they encounter, enzymatically lyse, and digest. Large numbers of these gram-negative microbes eventually aggregate (Figure 11). Where the moving cells aggregate, they differentiate and form a macroscopic stalked fruiting body that contains large numbers of resting cells called *myxospores*. Differentiation is usually triggered by low nutrients. Under proper conditions, usually a change in nutrients, the myxospores germinate and form new vegetative gliding cells. You might note the resemblance to the life cycle of the eukaryotic cellular slime molds.

CHECK YOUR UNDERSTANDING

✔ Make a dichotomous key to distinguish the deltaproteobacteria described in this chapter. 4

The Epsilonproteobacteria

The epsilonproteobacteria are slender gram-negative rods that are helical or curved. We will discuss the two important genera, both of which are motile by means of flagella and are microaerophilic.

Campylobacter Members of the genus *Campylobacter* (kam′pi-lō-bak-tėr) are microaerophilic vibrios; each cell has one polar flagellum. One species of *Campylobacter, C. fetus* (fē′tus), causes spontaneous abortion in domestic animals. Another species, *C. jejuni* (je-ju′ni), is a leading cause of outbreaks of foodborne intestinal disease.

Helicobacter Members of the genus *Helicobacter* are microaerophilic curved rods with multiple flagella. The species *Helicobacter pylori* (hē′lik-ō-bak-tėr pī-lōr′ē) has been identified as the most common cause of peptic ulcers in humans and a cause of stomach cancer (Figure 12).

CHECK YOUR UNDERSTANDING

✔ Make a dichotomous key to distinguish the epsilonproteobacteria described in this chapter. 5

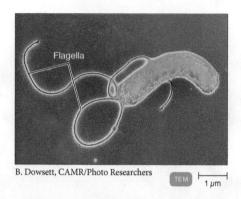

B. Dowsett, CAMR/Photo Researchers

TEM |—————| 1 µm

Figure 12 Helicobacter pylori. *H. pylori*, a curved rod, is an example of a helical bacterium that does not make a complete twist.

 How do helical bacteria differ from spirochetes?

The Gram-Positive Bacteria

LEARNING OBJECTIVES

6   Differentiate the genera of firmicutes described in this chapter by drawing a dichotomous key.

7   Differentiate the actinobacteria described in this chapter by drawing a dichotomous key.

The gram-positive bacteria can be divided into two groups: those that have a high G + C ratio, and those that have a low G + C ratio. To illustrate the variations in G + C ratio, the genus *Streptococcus* has a low G + C content of 33 to 44%; and the genus *Clostridium* has a low content of 21 to 54%. Included with the gram-positive, low G + C bacteria are the mycoplasmas, even though they lack a cell wall and therefore do not have a Gram reaction. Their G + C ratio is 23 to 40%.

By contrast, filamentous actinomycetes of the genus *Streptomyces* have a high G + C content of 69 to 73%. Gram-positive bacteria of a more conventional morphology, such as the genera *Corynebacterium* and *Mycobacterium,* have a G + C content of 51 to 63% and 62 to 70%, respectively.

These bacterial groups are placed into separate phyla, the **Firmicutes (low G + C ratios)** and **Actinobacteria (high G + C ratios).**

Firmicutes (Low G + C Gram-Positive Bacteria)

Low G + C gram-positive bacteria are assigned to the phylum Firmicutes. This group includes important endospore-forming bacteria such as the genera *Clostridium* and *Bacillus.* Also of extreme importance in medical microbiology are the genera *Staphylococcus, Enterococcus,* and *Streptococcus.* In industrial microbiology, the genus *Lactobacillus,* which produces lactic acid, is well known. The mycoplasma, which do not possess a cell wall, are also found in this phylum.

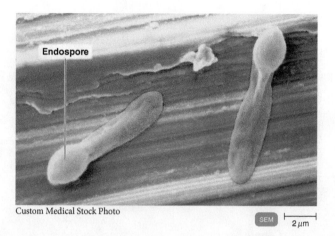

Custom Medical Stock Photo

SEM |—————| 2 µm

Figure 13 Clostridium difficile. The endospores of clostridia usually distend the cell wall, as shown here. The bacterial cell containing the endospore is dehydrated and flattened as a result of preprarion for electron microcopy.

 What physiological characteristic of *Clostridium* makes it a problem in contamination of deep wounds?

Clostridiales

Clostridium Members of the genus *Clostridium* (klôs-tri′ dĕ-um) are obligate anaerobes. The rod-shaped cells contain endospores that usually distend the cell (**Figure 13**). The formation of endospores by bacteria is important to both medicine and the food industry because of the endospore's resistance to heat and many chemicals. Diseases associated with clostridia include tetanus, caused by *C. tetani* (te′tan-e); botulism, caused by *C. botulinum* (bo-tū-lī′num); and gas gangrene, caused by *C. perfringens* (per-frin′jens) and other clostridia. *C. perfringens* is also the cause of a common form of foodborne diarrhea. *C. difficile* (dif′fi-sē-il) is an inhabitant of the intestinal tract that may cause a serious diarrhea. This occurs only when antibiotic therapy alters the normal intestinal microbiota, allowing overgrowth by toxin-producing *C. difficile.*

Epulopiscium Biologists have long considered bacteria to be small by necessity because they lack the nutrient transport systems used by higher, eukaryotic organisms and because they depend on simple diffusion to obtain nutrients. These characteristics would seem to critically limit size. So, when a cigar-shaped organism living symbiotically in the gut of the Red Sea surgeonfish was first observed in 1985, it was considered to be a protozoan. Certainly, its size suggested this: the organism was as large as 80 µm × 600 µm—over half a millimeter in length—large enough to be seen with the unaided eye (**Figure 14**). Compared to the familiar bacterium *E. coli*, which is about 1 µm × 2 µm, this organism would be about a million times larger in volume.

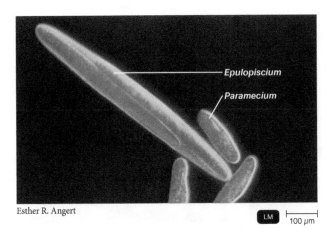

Esther R. Angert

LM | 100 μm

Figure 14 **A giant prokaryote,** *Epulopiscium fishelsoni.*

Q Why is *Epulopiscium* not in the same domain as *Paramecium*?

Further investigation of the new organism showed that certain external structures thought to resemble the cilia of protozoa were actually similar to bacterial flagella, and it did not have a membrane-enclosed nucleus. Ribosomal RNA analysis conclusively placed *Epulopiscium* (ep′ū-lō-pis-ē-um) with the prokaryotes. (The name means "guest at the banquet of a fish." It is literally bathed in semidigested food.) It most closely resembles gram-positive bacteria of the genus *Clostridium*. Strangely, the species *Epulopiscium fishelsoni* (fish-el-sō′nē) does not reproduce

by binary fission. Daughter cells formed within the cell are released through a slit opening in the parent cell. This may be related to the evolutionary development of sporulation.

Recently it was discovered that this bacterium does not rely on diffusion to distribute nutrients. Instead, it makes use of its larger genetic capacity—it has 25 times as much DNA as a human cell and as many as 85,000 copies of at least one gene—to manufacture proteins at internal sites where they are needed. (Another more recently discovered giant bacterium is *Thiomargarita*.)

Bacillales

The order Bacillales includes several important genera of gram-positive rods and cocci.

Bacillus Bacteria of the genus *Bacillus* are typically rods that produce endospores. They are common in soil, and only a few are pathogenic to humans. Several species produce antibiotics.

Bacillus anthracis (bä-sil′lus an-thrā′sis) causes anthrax, a disease of cattle, sheep, and horses that can be transmitted to humans. It is often mentioned as a possible agent of biological warfare. The anthrax bacillus is a nonmotile facultative anaerobe, often forming chains in culture. The centrally located endospore does not distend the walls. *Bacillus thuringiensis* (thur-in-jē-en′sis) is probably the best-known microbial insect pathogen (**Figure 15a**). It produces intracellular crystals when it sporulates. Commercial preparations containing endospores and crystalline toxin (Bt) of this bacterium are sold in gardening

From R.E. Strange and J.R. Hunter, in G.W. Gould and A. Hurst (eds) *The Bacterial Spore,* 1969, p.461, figure 4. (Orlando, FL: Academic Press, 1969)

From Hannay and Fitz James, Canadian Journal of Microbiology 1, 1955/National Researcher Council of Canada

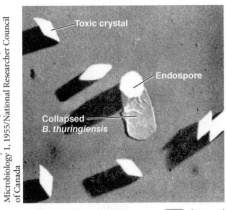

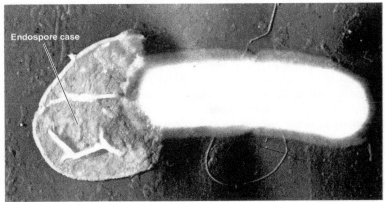

(a) *Bacillus thuringiensis.* The diamond-shaped crystals shown next to the endospore are toxic to insects that ingest them. This electron micrograph was made using the technique of shadow casting.

TEM | 2 μm

(b) This *Bacillus cereus* cell is shown emerging from the endospore.

TEM | 0.5 μm

Figure 15 *Bacillus.*

 What structure is made by both *Clostridium* and *Bacillus*?

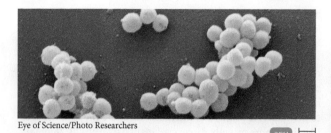

Eye of Science/Photo Researchers

SEM | 1 μm

Figure 16 *Staphylococcus aureus.* Notice the grapelike clusters of these gram-positive cocci.

Q What is an environmental advantage of a pigment?

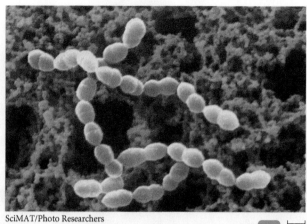

SciMAT/Photo Researchers

SEM | 1 μm

Figure 17 *Streptococcus.* Notice the chains of cells characteristic of most streptococci. Many of the spherical cells are dividing and are somewhat oval in appearance—especially when viewed with a light microscope, which has lower magnification than this electron micrograph.

Q How does the arrangement of *Streptococcus* differ from *Staphylococcus*?

supply shops to be sprayed on plants. *Bacillus cereus* (se'rē-us) (Figure 15b) is a common bacterium in the environment and occasionally is identified as a cause of food poisoning, especially in starchy foods such as rice.

The three species of the genus *Bacillus* that we have just described are dramatically different in important ways, especially their disease-causing properties. However, they are so closely related that taxonomists consider them to be variants of a single species, differing almost entirely in genes carried on plasmids, which are easily transferred from one bacterium to another.

Staphylococcus Staphylococci typically occur in grapelike clusters (Figure 16). The most important staphylococcal species is *Staphylococcus aureus* (staf-i-lō-kok'kus ô'rē-us), which is named for its yellow-pigmented colonies (*aureus* = golden). Members of this species are facultative anaerobes.

Some characteristics of the staphylococci account for their pathogenicity, which takes many forms. They grow comparatively well under conditions of high osmotic pressure and low moisture, which partially explains why they can grow and survive in nasal secretions (many of us carry the bacteria in our nostrils) and on the skin. This also explains how *S. aureus* can grow in some foods with high osmotic pressure (such as ham and other cured meats) or in low-moisture foods that tend to inhibit the growth of other organisms. The yellow pigment probably confers some protection from the antimicrobial effects of sunlight.

S. aureus produces many toxins that contribute to the bacterium's pathogenicity by increasing its ability to invade the body or damage tissue. The infection of surgical wounds by *S. aureus* is a common problem in hospitals. And its ability to develop resistance quickly to such antibiotics as penicillin contributes to its danger to patients in hospital environments. *S. aureus* produces the toxin responsible for toxic shock syndrome, a severe infection characterized by high fever and vomiting, sometimes even death. *S. aureus* also produces an **enterotoxin** that causes vomiting and nausea when ingested; it is one of the most common causes of food poisoning.

Lactobacillales

Several important genera are found in the order Lactobacillales. The genus *Lactobacillus* is a representative of the industrially important lactic acid–producing bacteria. Most lack a cytochrome system and are unable to use oxygen as an electron acceptor. Unlike most obligate anaerobes, though, they are aerotolerant and capable of growth in the presence of oxygen. But compared to oxygen-utilizing microbes, they grow poorly. However, the production of lactic acid from simple carbohydrates inhibits the growth of competing organisms and allows them to grow competitively in spite of their inefficient metabolism. The genus *Streptococcus* shares the metabolic characteristics of the genus *Lactobacillus*. There are several industrially important species, but the streptococci are best known for their pathogenicity. The genera *Enterococcus* and *Listeria* are more conventional metabolically. Both are facultative anaerobes, and several species are important pathogens.

Lactobacillus In humans, bacteria of the genus *Lactobacillus* (lak-tō-bä-sil'lus) are located in the vagina, intestinal tract, and oral cavity. Lactobacilli are used commercially in the production of sauerkraut, pickles, buttermilk, and yogurt. Typically, a succession of lactobacilli, each more acid tolerant than its predecessor, participates in these lactic acid fermentations.

Streptococcus Members of the genus *Streptococcus* (strep-tō-kok'kus) are spherical, gram-positive bacteria that typically appear in chains (Figure 17). They are a taxonomically complex group, probably responsible for more illnesses and causing a greater variety of diseases than any other group of bacteria.

Pathogenic streptococci produce several extracellular substances that contribute to their pathogenicity. Among them are products that destroy phagocytic cells that ingest them. Enzymes produced by some streptococci spread infections by digesting connective tissue of the host, which may also result in extensive tissue destruction. Infections are also allowed to spread from sites of injury by enzymes that lyse the fibrin (a threadlike protein) of blood clots.

A few nonpathogenic species of streptococci are important in the production of dairy products.

Clinical Case

Two species of bacteria that can cause bacterial meningitis are *Neisseria meningitidis* and *Streptococcus pneumoniae*. Dr. Walker then requests that the lab perform a Gram stain of Mercy's CSF and venous blood.

Below is the Gram stain of Mercy's venous blood. What do you see that would cause you to modify your list of possible causes?

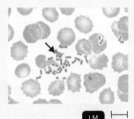

LM 7 µm

The Clinical Chemistry and Hematology Laboratory, Wadsworth Center, NY State Department of Health (www.wadsworth.org)

Beta-hemolytic streptococci. A useful basis for the classification of some streptococci is their colonial appearance when grown on blood agar. The *beta-hemolytic* species produce a hemolysin that forms a clear zone of hemolysis on blood agar. This group includes the principal pathogen of the streptococci, *Streptococcus pyogenes* (pī-äj′en-ēz), also known as the beta-hemolytic group A streptococcus. Group A represents one of an antigenic group (A through G) within the hemolytic streptococci. Among the diseases caused by *S. pyogenes* are scarlet fever, pharyngitis (sore throat), erysipelas, impetigo, and rheumatic fever. The most important virulence factor is the M protein on the bacterial surface by which the bacteria

avoid phagocytosis. Another member of the beta-hemolytic streptococci is *Streptococcus agalactiae* (ā′gal-acī-ē-ī), in the beta-hemolytic group B. It is the only species with the group B antigen and is the cause of an important disease of the newborn, neonatal sepsis.

Non-beta-hemolytic streptococci. Certain streptococci are not beta-hemolytic, but when grown on blood agar, their colonies are surrounded by a distinctive greening. These are the *alpha-hemolytic* streptococci. The greening represents a partial destruction of the red blood cells caused mostly by the action of bacteria-produced hydrogen peroxide, but it appears only when the bacteria grow in the presence of oxygen. The most important pathogen in this group is *Streptococcus pneumoniae*, the cause of pneumococcal pneumonia. Also included among the alpha-hemolytic streptococci are species of streptococci called *viridans streptococci*. However, not all species form the alpha-hemolytic greening (*virescent* = green), so this is not really a satisfactory group name. Probably the most significant pathogen of the group is *Streptococcus mutans* (mū′tans), the primary cause of dental caries.

Enterococcus The enterococci are adapted to areas of the body that are rich in nutrients but low in oxygen, such as the gastrointestinal tract, vagina, and oral cavity. They are also found in large numbers in human stool. Because they are relatively hardy microbes, they persist as contaminants in a hospital environment, on hands, bedding, and even as a fecal aerosol. In recent years they have become a leading cause of nosocomial infections, especially because of their high resistance to most antibiotics. Two species, *Enterococcus faecalis* (en-te-rō-kok′kus fe-kā′lis) and *Enterococcus faecium* (fē′sē-um), are responsible for much of the infections of surgical wounds and the urinary tract. In medical settings they frequently enter the bloodstream through invasive procedures, such as indwelling catheters.

Listeria The pathogenic species of the genus *Listeria*, *Listeria monocytogenes* (lis-te′rē-ä mo-nō-sī-to′je-nēz), can contaminate food, especially dairy products. Important characteristics of *L. monocytogenes* are that it survives within phagocytic cells and is capable of growth at refrigeration temperatures. If it infects a pregnant woman, the organism poses the threat of stillbirth or serious damage to the fetus.

Mycoplasmatales

The mycoplasmas are highly pleomorphic because they lack a cell wall (**Figure 18**) and can produce filaments that resemble fungi, hence their name (*mykes* = fungus, and *plasma* = formed). Cells of the genus *Mycoplasma* (mī-ko-plaz′ma) are very small, ranging in size from 0.1 to 0.25 µm, with a cell volume that is only about 5% of that of a typical bacillus. Because their size and plasticity allowed them to

(a) Individual cells of *M. pneumoniae*. Arrowheads indicate terminal structures that probably aid in attachment to eukaryotic cells, which then become infected.

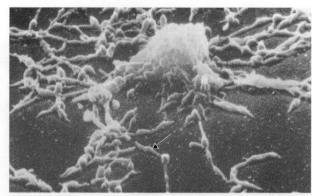

(b) This micrograph shows the filamentous growth of *M. pneumoniae*. Some individual cells can also be seen (arrow). The organism reproduces by fragmentation of the filament at the bulges.

Figure 18 *Mycoplasma pneumoniae.* Bacteria such as *M. pneumoniae* have no cell walls, and their morphology is irregular (pleomorphic)

Q How can the cell structure of mycoplasmas account for their pleomorphism?

(a) From D. C. Krause and D. Taylor-Robinson, 1992. Mycoplasmas which Infect Humans, F1. in J. Maniloff et al., eds., Mycoplasmas: Molecular Biology and Pathogenesis. Reproduced by permission of the American Society for Microbiology. (b) Michael Gabridge/Custom Medical Stock Photo

pass through filters that retained bacteria, they were originally considered to be viruses. Mycoplasmas may represent the smallest self-replicating organisms that are capable of a free-living existence. One species has only 517 genes; the minimum necessary is between 265 and 350. Studies of their DNA suggest that they are genetically related to the gram-positive bacterial group that includes the genera *Bacillus, Streptococcus,* and *Lactobacillus* but have gradually lost genetic material. The term *degenerative evolution* has been used to describe this process.

The most significant human pathogen among the mycoplasmas is *M. pneumoniae* (nu-mō'nē-ī), which is the cause of a common form of mild pneumonia. Other genera in the order Mycoplasmatales are *Spiroplasma* (spī-rō-plaz'mä), cells with a tight corkscrew morphology that are serious plant pathogens and common parasites of plant-feeding insects, and *Ureaplasma* (ū-rē-ä-plaz'mä), so named because they can enzymatically hydrolyze the urea in urine and are occasionally associated with urinary tract infections.

Mycoplasmas can be grown on artificial media that provide them with sterols (if necessary) and other special nutritional or physical requirements. Colonies are less than 1 mm in diameter and have a characteristic "fried egg" appearance when viewed under magnification. For many purposes, cell culture methods are often more satisfactory. In fact, mycoplasmas grow so well by this method that they are a frequent contamination problem in cell culture laboratories.

CHECK YOUR UNDERSTANDING

✔ To which genus is *Enterococcus* more closely related: *Staphylococcus* or *Lactobacilius*? **6**

Clinical Case

The Gram stain of Mercy's venous blood shows gram-positive cocci among the red blood cells. Needing to identify the species of bacteria that is causing Mercy's meningitis, the lab then cultures the cocci on blood agar. See below for the results.

Based on this new information, what bacteria are responsible for Mercy's meningitis?

Hardy Diagnostics (www .HardyDiagnostics.com)

Actinobacteria (High G + C Gram-Positive Bacteria)

High G + C gram-positive bacteria are in the phylum Actinobacteria. Many bacteria in this phylum are highly pleomorphic in their morphology; the genera *Corynebacterium* and *Gardnerella,* for example, and several genera such as *Streptomyces* grow only as extended, often branching filaments. Several important pathogenic genera are found in the Actinobacteria, such as the *Mycobacterium* species causing tuberculosis and leprosy. The genera *Streptomyces, Frankia, Actinomyces,* and *Nocardia* are often informally called actinomycetes (from the Greek *actino* = ray) because they have a radiate, or starlike, form of growth by reason of their often-branching filaments. Superficially, their morphology resembles that of filamentous fungi; however, the actinomycetes are prokaryotic cells, and their filaments have a diameter much smaller than that of the eukaryotic molds. Some actinomycetes further resemble molds by their possession of externally carried asexual spores that are used for reproduction. Filamentous bacteria, like filamentous fungi, are very common inhabitants in soil, where a filamentous pattern of growth has advantages. The filamentous organism can bridge water-free gaps between soil particles to move to a new nutritional site. This morphology also gives the organism a much higher surface-to-volume ratio and improves its ability to absorb nutrients in the highly competitive soil environment.

Mycobacterium The mycobacteria are aerobic, non–endospore-forming rods. The name *myco,* meaning funguslike, was derived from their occasional exhibition of filamentous growth. Many of the characteristics of mycobacteria, such as acid-fast staining, drug resistance, and pathogenicity, are related to their distinctive cell wall, which is structurally similar to gram-negative bacteria. However, the outermost lipopolysaccharide layer in mycobacteria is replaced by mycolic acids, which form a waxy, water-resistant layer. This makes the bacteria resistant to stresses such as drying. Also, few antimicrobial drugs are able to enter the cell. Nutrients enter the cell through this layer very slowly, which is a factor in the slow growth rate of mycobacteria; it sometimes takes weeks for visible colonies to appear. The mycobacteria include the important pathogens *Mycobacterium tuberculosis* (mī-kō-bak-ti′rē-um tü-ber-kū-lō′sis), which causes tuberculosis, and *M. leprae* (lep′rī), which causes leprosy.

The mycobacteria are generally separated into two groups: (1) the slow growers, such as *M. tuberculosis*, and (2) the fast, or rapid, growers, which form visible colonies on appropriate media within 7 days. The slow-growing mycobacteria are more likely to be pathogenic to humans. The rapidly growing group also contains a number of occasional, nontuberculous human pathogens, which most commonly infect wounds. However, these mycobacteria are more likely to be nonpathogenic soil and water microbes.

Corynebacterium The corynebacteria (*coryne* = club-shaped) tend to be pleomorphic, and their morphology often varies with the age of the cells. The best-known species is *Corynebacterium diphtheriae* (kôr′i-nē-bak-ti-rē-um dif-thi′rē-ī), the causative agent of diphtheria.

Propionibacterium The name of the genus *Propionibacterium* (prō-pē-on′ē-bak-ti-rē-um) is derived from the organism's ability to form propionic acid; some species are important in the fermentation of Swiss cheese. *Propionibacterium acnes* (ak′nēz)

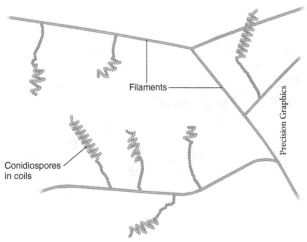

(a) Drawing of a typical streptomycete showing filamentous, branching growth with asexual reproductive conidiospores at the filament tips

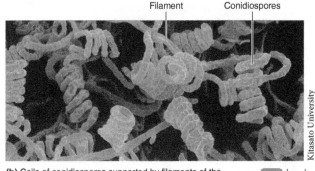

(b) Coils of conidiospores supported by filaments of the streptomycete

SEM   5 μm

Figure 19 *Streptomyces.*

Q   Why is *Streptomyces* not classified with fungi?

are bacteria that are commonly found on human skin and are implicated as the primary bacterial cause of acne.

Gardnerella *Gardnerella vaginalis* (gard-ne-rel′la va-jin-al′is) is a bacterium that causes one of the most common forms of vaginitis. There has always been some difficulty in assigning a taxonomic position in this species, which is gram-variable, and which exhibits a highly pleomorphic morphology.

Frankia The genus *Frankia* (frank′ē-ä) causes nitrogen-fixing nodules to form in alder tree roots, much as rhizobia cause nodules on the roots of legumes.

Streptomyces The genus *Streptomyces* (strep-tō-mī′ses) is the best known of the actinomycetes and is one of the bacteria most commonly isolated from soil (Figure 19). The

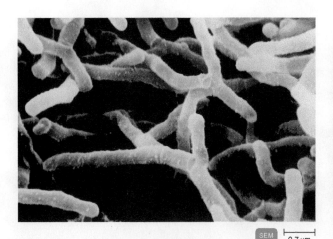

SEM 0.7 μm

Figure 20 *Actinomyces.* Notice the branched filamentous morphology.

Q Why are these bacteria not classified as fungi?

From: *Scanning Electron Micrographs and Gram Stains of Selected Anaerobic Pathogens,* by A.S. Klainer, J.L. LeFrock. Copyright ©: 1976. The Upjohn Company, Kalamazoo, Michigan, USA

reproductive asexual spores of *Streptomyces* are formed at the ends of aerial filaments. If each spore lands on a suitable substrate, it is capable of germinating into a new colony. These organisms are strict aerobes. They often produce extracellular enzymes that enable them to utilize proteins, polysaccharides (such as starch and cellulose), and many other organic materials found in soil. *Streptomyces* characteristically produce a gaseous compound called *geosmin,* which gives fresh soil its typical musty odor. Species of *Streptomyces* are valuable because they produce most of our commercial antibiotics. This has led to intensive study of the genus—there are nearly 500 described species.

Actinomyces The genus *Actinomyces* (ak-tin-ō-mī′sēs) consists of facultative anaerobes that are found in the mouth and throat of humans and animals. They occasionally form filaments that can fragment (**Figure 20**). One species, *Actinomyces israelii* (is-rā′lē-ē), causes actinomycosis, a tissue-destroying disease usually affecting the head, neck, or lungs.

Nocardia The genus *Nocardia* (nō-kär′dē-ä) morphologically resembles *Actinomyces;* however, these bacteria are aerobic. To reproduce, they form rudimentary filaments, which fragment into short rods. The structure of their cell wall resembles that of the mycobacteria; therefore, they are often acid-fast. *Nocardia* species are common in soil. Some species, such as *Nocardia asteroides* (as′ter-oi-dēz), occasionally cause a chronic, difficult-to-treat pulmonary infection. *N. asteroides* is also one of the causative agents of mycetoma, a localized destructive infection of the feet or hands.

CHECK YOUR UNDERSTANDING

✔ What group of bacteria makes most of the commercially important antibiotics? **7**

The Nonproteobacteria Gram-Negative Bacteria

LEARNING OBJECTIVES

8   Differentiate among planctomycetes, chlamydias, Bacteroidetes, *Cytophaga,* and Fusobacteria by drawing a dichotomous key.

9   Compare and contrast purple and green photosynthetic bacteria with the cyanobacteria.

There are a number of important gram-negative bacteria that are not closely related to the gram-negative proteobacteria that were discussed earlier in the chapter. They include several physiologically and morphologically distinctive photosynthesizing bacteria, such as those included in the phyla Cyanobacteria (cyanobacteria), Chlorobi and Chloroflexi. The cyanobacteria produce oxygen during photosynthesis (are *oxygenic*), and the green sulfur and green nonsulfur bacteria do not produce oxygen (are *anoxygenic*). These groups are summarized in **Table 2**.

Cyanobacteria (The Oxygenic Photosynthetic Bacteria)

The cyanobacteria, named for their characteristic blue-green *(cyan)* pigmentation, were once called blue-green algae. Although they resemble the eukaryotic algae and often occupy the same environmental niches, this is a misnomer because they are bacteria; algae are not. However, cyanobacteria do carry out oxygenic photosynthesis, as do the eukaryotic plants and algae.

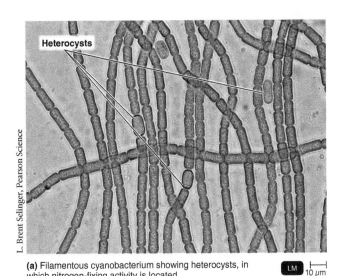

L. Brent Selinger, Pearson Science

(a) Filamentous cyanobacterium showing heterocysts, in which nitrogen-fixing activity is located.

LM ⊢ 10 μm

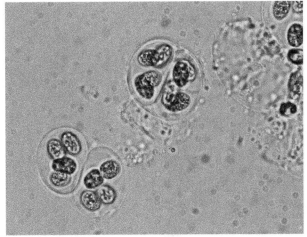

Precision Graphics

(b) A unicellular, nonfilamentous cyanobacterium, *Gloeocapsa*. Groups of these cells, which divide by binary fission, are held together by the surrounding glycocalyx.

LM ⊢ 10 μm

Figure 21 Cyanobacteria.

 How does the photosynthesis of the cyanobacteria differ from that of the purple sulfur bacteria?

Many of the cyanobacteria are capable of fixing nitrogen from the atmosphere. In most cases, this activity is located in specialized cells called **heterocysts,** which contain enzymes that fix nitrogen gas (N_2) into ammonium (NH_4^+) that can be used by the growing cell (Figure 21a). Species that grow in water usually have gas vacuoles that provide buoyancy, helping the cell float at a favorable environment. Cyanobacteria that move about on solid surfaces use gliding motility.

Cyanobacteria are morphologically varied. They range from unicellular forms that divide by simple binary fission (Figure 21b), to colonial forms that divide by multiple fission, to filamentous forms that reproduce by fragmentation of the fila-ments. The filamentous forms usually exhibit some differentiation of cells that are often bound together within an envelope or sheath.

Evidence indicates that oxygenic cyanobacteria played an important part in the development of life on Earth, which originally had very little free oxygen that would support life as we are familiar with it. Fossil evidence indicates that when cyanobacteria first appeared, the atmosphere contained only about 0.1% free oxygen. When oxygen-producing eukaryotic plants appeared millions of years later, the concentration of oxygen was more than 10%. The increase presumably was a result of

TABLE 2 Selected Characteristics of Photosynthesizing Bacteria

Common Name	Example	Phylum	Comments	Electron Donor for CO_2 Reduction	Oxygenic or Anoxygenic
Cyanobacteria	*Anabaena*	Cyanobacteria	Plantlike photosynthesis; some use bacterial photosynthesis under anaerobic conditions	Usually H_2O	Usually oxygenic
Green nonsulfur bacteria	*Chloroflexus*	Chloroflexi	Grow chemoheterotrophically in aerobic environments	Organic compounds	Anoxygenic
Green sulfur bacteria	*Chlorobium*	Chlorobi	Deposit sulfur granules inside cells	Usually H_2S	Anoxygenic
Purple nonsulfur bacteria	*Rhodospirillum*	Proteobacteria	Can grow chemoheterotrophically as well	Organic compounds	Anoxygenic
Purple sulfur bacteria	*Chromatium*	Proteobacteria	Deposit sulfur granules inside cells	Usually H_2S	Anoxygenic

photosynthetic activity by cyanobacteria. The atmosphere we breathe today contains about 20% oxygen.

Cyanobacteria, especially those that fix nitrogen, are extremely important to the environment. They occupy environmental niches similar to those occupied by the eukaryotic algae, but the ability of many of the cyanobacteria to fix nitrogen makes them even more adaptable in nutritionally poor environments.

Chlamydiae

Members of the phylum Chlamydiae are grouped with other genetically similar bacteria that do not contain peptidoglycan in their cell walls. We will discuss only the genera *Chlamydia* and *Chlamydophila.* Earlier editions of *Bergey's Manual of Systematic Bacteriology* grouped these bacteria with the rickettsial bacteria because they all grow intracellularly within host cells. The rickettsia are now classified according to their genetic content with the alphaproteobacteria.

Chlamydia and Chlamydophila *Chlamydia* and *Chlamydophila,* which we will call by the common name of the chlamydias, have a unique developmental cycle that is perhaps their most distinguishing characteristic (Figure 22a). They are gram-negative coccoid bacteria (Figure 22b). The **elementary body** shown in Figure 24 is the infective agent. Unlike the rickettsias, chlamydias do not require insects or ticks for transmission. They are transmitted to humans by interpersonal contact or by airborne respiratory routes. The chlamydias can be cultivated in laboratory animals, cell cultures, or in the yolk sac of embryonated chicken eggs.

There are three species of the chlamydias that are significant pathogens for humans. *Chlamydia trachomatis* (kla-mi′dē-ä trä-kō′mä-tis) is the best known pathogen of the group and responsible for more than one major disease. These include trachoma, one of the most common causes of blindness in humans in the less developed countries. It is also considered to be the primary causative agent of both nongonococcal urethritis, which may be the most common sexually transmitted disease in the United States, and lymphogranuloma venereum, another sexually transmitted disease.

Two members of the genus *Chlamydophila* (kla-mid-o′fil-ä) are well-known pathogens. *Chlamydophila psittaci* (sit′tä-sē) is the causative agent of the respiratory disease psittacosis (ornithosis). *Chlamydophila pneumoniae* (nü-mō′nē-ī) is the cause of a mild form of pneumonia that is especially prevalent in young adults.

Planctomycetes

The planctomycetes, a group of gram-negative, budding bacteria, are said to "blur the definition of what bacteria are."

Although their DNA places them among the bacteria, they resemble the archaea in the makeup of their cell walls, and some even have organelles that resemble the nucleus of a eukaryotic cell. The members of the genus *Planctomyces* are aquatic bacteria that produce stalks resembling Caulobacteria and have cell walls similar to the archaea, that is, without peptidoglycan. One species of planctomycetes, *Gemmata obscuriglobus* (jem′mä-tä ob-sker′ē-glob-us) has a double internal membrane around its DNA, resembling a eukaryotic nucleus (Figure 23). Biologists wonder whether this might make *Gemmata* a model for the origin of the eukaryotic nucleus.

Bacteroidetes

The phylum Bacteroidetes includes several genera of anaerobic bacteria. Included are the genus *Bacteroides,* a common inhabitant of the human intestinal tract, and the genus *Prevotella,* found in the human mouth. Also included in the phylum Bacteroidetes are the important soil bacteria with gliding motility of the genus *Cytophaga.*

Bacteroides Bacteria of the genus *Bacteroides* (bak-tė-roi′dēz) live in the human intestinal tract in numbers approaching 1 billion per gram of feces. Some *Bacteroides* species also reside in anaerobic habitats such as the gingival crevice and are also frequently recovered from deep tissue infections. *Bacteroides* organisms are gram-negative, are nonmotile, and do not form endospores. Infections caused by *Bacteroides* often result from puncture wounds or surgery and are a frequent cause of peritonitis, an inflammation resulting from a perforated bowel.

Cytophaga Members of the genus *Cytophaga* (sī-täf′ag-a) are important in the degradation of cellulose and chitin, which are both abundant in soil. Gliding motility places the microbe in close contact with these substrates so that enzymatic action is very efficient.

Fusobacteria

The fusiform bacteria comprise another phylum of anaerobes. These bacteria are often pleomorphic but, as their name suggests, may be spindle-shaped (*fuso* = spindle).

Fusobacterium Members of the genus *Fusobacterium* (fü-sō-bak-ti′rē-um) are long and slender, gram-negative rods with pointed rather than blunt ends (Figure 24). In humans, they are found most often in the gingival crevice of the gums and may be responsible for some dental abscesses.

CHECK YOUR UNDERSTANDING

✔ Which gram–negative group has a life cycle that includes different stages? 8

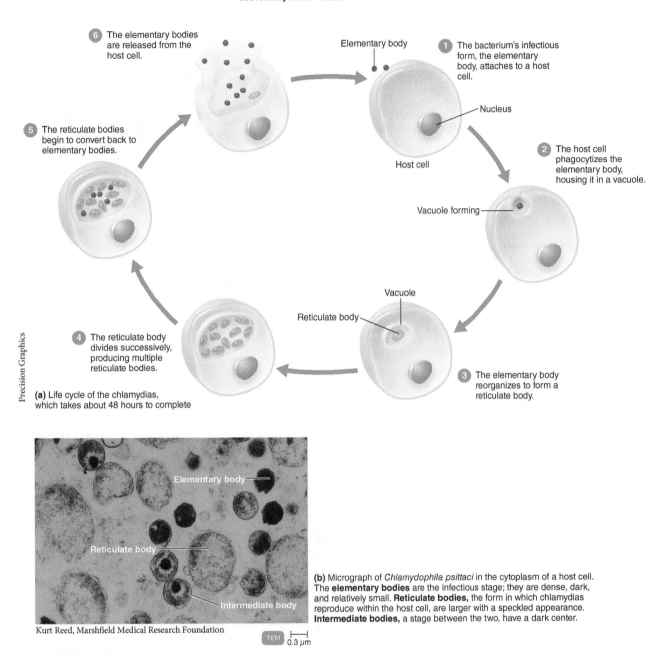

6 The elementary bodies are released from the host cell.

Elementary body

1 The bacterium's infectious form, the elementary body, attaches to a host cell.

Nucleus

Host cell

5 The reticulate bodies begin to convert back to elementary bodies.

2 The host cell phagocytizes the elementary body, housing it in a vacuole.

Vacuole forming

Vacuole

Reticulate body

4 The reticulate body divides successively, producing multiple reticulate bodies.

3 The elementary body reorganizes to form a reticulate body.

(a) Life cycle of the chlamydias, which takes about 48 hours to complete

Precision Graphics

Elementary body

Reticulate body

Intermediate body

(b) Micrograph of *Chlamydophila psittaci* in the cytoplasm of a host cell. The **elementary bodies** are the infectious stage; they are dense, dark, and relatively small. **Reticulate bodies,** the form in which chlamydias reproduce within the host cell, are larger with a speckled appearance. **Intermediate bodies,** a stage between the two, have a dark center.

Kurt Reed, Marshfield Medical Research Foundation

TEM ⊢ 0.3 μm

Figure 22 Chlamydias.

Q Which stage of the life cycle is infectious to humans?

Purple and Green Photosynthetic Bacteria (The Anoxygenic Photosynthetic Bacteria)

The photosynthetic bacteria are taxonomically confusing, but they represent some interesting ecological niches. Few students using this text will have a need to know their complex metabolism in detail, and its presentation is not attempted here.

To begin, the photosynthetic phyla Cyanobacteria, Chlorobi, and Chloroflexi are gram-negative, but they are not genetically included in the proteobacteria. Members of the photosynthetic phyla Chlorobi (representative genus: *Chlorobium*) are called **green sulfur bacteria.** Members of the phyla Chloroflexi (representative genus: *Chloroflexus*) are called **green nonsulfur bacteria.**

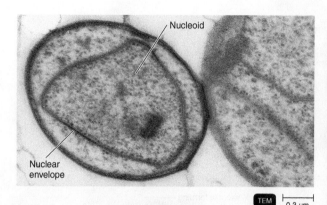

Figure 23 *Gemmata obscuriglobus.* This planctomycete exhibits a double membrane (nuclear envelope) surrounding its nucleoid, which resembles a eukaryotic nucleus.

Q Can you see a resemblance between the double membrane around the nucleoid in this photo and the membrane around the nuclear envelope shown in Figure 4.24?

Jenny Wang, Cheryl Jenkins, Richard I. Webb, and John A. Fuerst. "Isolation of Gemmata-Like and Isosphaera-Like Planctomycete Bacteria from Soil and Freshwater." *Applied and Environmental Microbiology*, January 2002, p. 417–422, Vol. 68, No. 1, Fig. 1c

However, there are photosynthetic gram-negative bacteria that *are* genetically included in the proteobacteria. These are the **purple sulfur bacteria** and the **purple nonsulfur bacteria,** which are placed, respectively, in the alphaproteobacteria and gammaproteobacteria.

In these bacterial groups, the term *sulfur bacteria* indicates that the microbes can use H_2S as an electron donor (see the equations that follow). If classified as *nonsulfur bacteria,* the microbes have at least a limited capability of phototrophic growth, but without the production of oxygen.

Cyanobacteria, as well as eukaryotic plants and algae produce oxygen (O_2) from water (H_2O) as they carry out photosynthesis:

$$(1) \quad 2H_2O + CO_2 \xrightarrow{\text{light}} (CH_2O) + H_2O + O_2$$

The *purple sulfur* and *green sulfur bacteria* use reduced sulfur compounds, such as hydrogen sulfide (H_2S), instead of water, and they produce granules of sulfur (S^0) rather than oxygen, as follows:

$$(2) \quad 2H_2S + CO_2 \xrightarrow{\text{light}} (CH_2O) + H_2O + 2S^0$$

Chromatium (krō-mā′tē-um), shown in **Figure 25,** is a representative genus. At one time, an important question in biology concerned the source of the oxygen produced by plant photosynthesis: was it from CO_2 or from H_2O? Until the introduction of radioisotope tracers, which traced the oxygen in water and carbon dioxide and finally settled the question, comparison of equations 1 and 2 was the best evidence that the oxygen source was

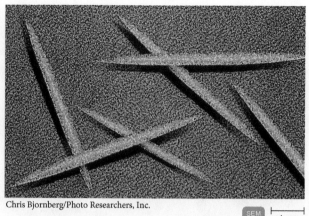

Chris Bjornberg/Photo Researchers, Inc.

Figure 24 *Fusobacterium.* This is a common anaerobic rod found in the human intestine. Notice the characteristic pointed ends.

Q In what other place in the human body do you often find *Fusobacterium?*

from H_2O. It is important, also, to compare these two equations for an understanding of how reduced sulfur compounds, such as H_2S, can substitute for H_2O in photosynthesis.

Other photoautotrophs, the *purple nonsulfur* and *green nonsulfur bacteria,* use organic compounds, such as acids and carbohydrates, for the photosynthetic reduction of carbon dioxide.

Morphologically, the photosynthetic bacteria are very diverse, with spirals, rods, cocci, and even budding forms.

Clinical Case Resolved

GBS is often part of the normal intestinal or genitourinary microbiota, but it can cause disease in immunocompromised individuals. GBS emerged as a major cause of neonatal bacterial sepsis in the 1970s and is a leading infectious cause of neonatal morbidity in the United States. The bacterium, a common colonizer of the maternal genital tract, can infect the fetus during gestation, causing fetal death. GBS can also be acquired by the fetus during passage through the birth canal during delivery. Prevention includes screening all pregnant women for GBS at 35 to 37 weeks' gestation and administering antibiotics to carriers during labor. Although Mercy's mother tested negative during her pregnancy, her results were a rare false negative. Mercy is put on intravenous antibiotics and remains in the hospital for 10 days until the infection clears. She is sent home after 2 weeks and is now a healthy, happy 2-month-old girl.

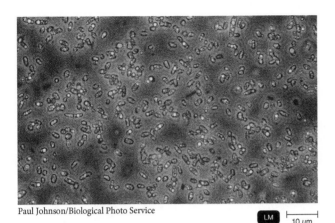

Paul Johnson/Biological Photo Service

LM | 10 μm

Figure 25 Purple sulfur bacteria. This photomicrograph of cells of the genus *Chromatium* shows the intracellular sulfur granules as multicolored refractile objects. The reason the sulfur accumulates can be surmised from inspection of equation 2 in the discussion.

Q What does *anoxygenic* mean?

CHECK YOUR UNDERSTANDING

✔ Both the purple and green photosynthetic bacteria and the photosynthetic cyanobacteria use plantlike photosynthesis to make carbohydrates. In what way does the photosynthesis carried out by these two groups differ from plant photosynthesis? **9**

Spirochaetes

LEARNING OBJECTIVE

10   Describe the features of spirochetes and *Deinococcus*.

The spirochetes have a coiled morphology, resembling a metal spring; some are more tightly coiled than others. The most distinctive characteristic of this order, however, is their method of motility, which makes use of two or more **axial filaments** (or *endoflagella*) enclosed in the space between an outer sheath and the body of the cell. One end of each axial filament is attached near a pole of the cell (see **Figure 26**). By rotating its axial filament, the cell rotates in the opposite direction, like a corkscrew, which is very efficient in moving the organism through liquids. For bacteria, this is more difficult than it might seem. At the scale of a bacterium, water is as viscous as molasses is to a human. However, a bacterium can typically move about 100 times its body length in a second (or about 50 μm/sec), whereas a large, fast fish, such as a tuna, can move only about 10 times its body length in this time.

Many spirochetes are found in the human oral cavity and are probably among the first microorganisms described by van Leeuwenhoek in the 1600s that he found in saliva and tooth scrapings. An extraordinary location for spirochetes is on the surfaces of

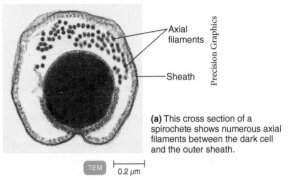

Axial filaments

Sheath

Precision Graphics

(a) This cross section of a spirochete shows numerous axial filaments between the dark cell and the outer sheath.

TEM | 0.2 μm

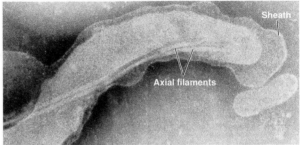

Sheath

Axial filaments

J. A. Breznak and H. S. Pankratz/Biological Photo Service

(b) This micrograph of a portion of *Treponema pallidum* shows the sheath, which has shrunk away from the cell, and two axial filaments attached near one end of the cell under the sheath.

 TEM | 0.5 μm

Figure 26 Spirochetes. Spirochetes are helical and have axial filaments under an outer sheath that enables them to move by a corkscrewlike rotation.

Q How does a spirochete's motility differ from that of *Spirillum* (see Figure 4)?

some of the cellulose-digesting protozoa found in termites, where they may function as substitutes for flagella.

Treponema The spirochetes include a number of important pathogenic bacteria. The best known is the genus *Treponema* (tre-pō-nē′mä), which includes *Treponema pallidum* (pal′ li-dum), the cause of syphilis (**Figure 26b**).

Borrelia Members of the genus *Borrelia* (bôr′rel-ē-ä) cause relapsing fever and Lyme disease, serious diseases that are usually transmitted by ticks or lice.

Leptospira Leptospirosis is a disease usually spread to humans by water contaminated by *Leptospira* (lep-tō-spī′ra) species. The bacteria are excreted in the urine of such animals as dogs, rats, and swine, so domestic dogs and cats are routinely immunized against leptospirosis.

Deinococci

The deinococci include two species of bacteria that have been widely studied because of their resistance to extremes in the environment. They stain Gram-positive but have a cell wall that differs slightly in chemical structure from those of other Gram-positives.

Deinococcus radiodurans (dī'nō-kok-kusra'dē-ō-dür-anz) is exceptionally resistant to radiation, even more than are endospores. They can survive exposure to radiation doses as high as 15,000 Grays. This much radiation is 1500 times the dosage that would kill a human. The mechanism for this extraordinary resistance lies in a unique arrengement of its DNA that facilitates rapid repair of radiation damage. It is similarly resistant to many mutagenic chemicals.

Thermus aquaticus (ther'musa' kwä-ti-kus), another unique member of this group, is a bacterium that is unusually heat stable. It was isolated from a hot spring in Yellowstone National Park and is the source of the heat-resistant enzyme *Taq polymerase,* which is essential to the polymerase chain reaction (PCR). This is the method by which traces of DNA are amplified and used for identification.

CHECK YOUR UNDERSTANDING

✔ The axial filament distinguishes what genera of bacteria? **10**

DOMAIN ARCHAEA

In the late 1970s, a distinctive type of prokaryotic cell was discovered. Most strikingly, the cell walls of these prokaryotes lacked the peptidoglycan common to most bacteria. It soon became clear that they also shared many rRNA sequences, and the sequences were different from either those of the Domain Bacteria or the eukaryotic organisms. These differences were so significant that these organisms now constitute a new taxonomic grouping, the Domain Archaea.

Diversity within the Archaea

LEARNING OBJECTIVE

11 Name a habitat for each group of archaea.

This exceptionally interesting group of prokaryotes is highly diverse. Most archaea are of conventional morphology, that is, rods, cocci, and helixes, but some are of very unusual morphology, as illustrated in Figure 27. Some are gram-positive, others gram-negative; some may divide by binary fission, others by fragmentation or budding; a few lack cell walls. Cultivated members of the archaea (singular: *archaeon*) can be placed into five physiological or nutritional groups.

Physiologically, archaea are found under extreme environmental conditions. **Extremophiles,** as they are known, include halophiles, thermophiles, and acidophiles. There are no known pathogenic archaea. *Halophiles* thrive in salt concentrations of more than 25%, such as found in the Great Salt Lake and solar evaporating ponds. Examples of these are found in the genus *Halobacterium* (ha-lo-bak-ti're-um), some of which may even require such salt concentrations in order to grow. The optimal growth temperatures of extremely *thermophilic* archaea is 80°C or higher. The present record growth temperature is 121°C, established by archaea growing near a hydrothermal vent at 2000 meters deep in the ocean. *Acidophilic* archaea can be found growing at pH values below zero, and frequently at elevated temperatures, as well. An example is *Sulfolobus* (sul' fo-lo-bus), whose optimal pH is about 2 and optimal temperature is more than 70°C.

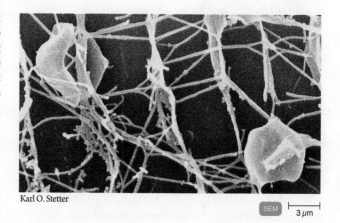

Karl O. Stetter

SEM 3 µm

Figure 27 Archaea. *Pyrodictium abyssi,* an unusual member of the archaea found growing in deep-ocean sediment at a temperature of 110°C. The cells are disk-shaped with a network of tubules (cannulae). Most archaea are more conventional in their morphology.

Q Do the terms included in the name, *pyro* and *abyssi,* suggest a basis for the naming of this bacterium?

Nutritionally, the ocean contains numerous *nitrifying* archaea that oxidize ammonia for energy. Some might also be found in soils. *Methanogens* are strictly anaerobic archaea that produce methane as an end-product by combining hydrogen (H_2) with carbon dioxide (CO_2). There are no known bacterial methanogens. These archaea are of considerable economic importance when they are used in sewage treatment. Methanogens are also part of the microbiota of the human colon, vagina, and mouth.

CHECK YOUR UNDERSTANDING

✔ What kind of archaea would populate solar evaporating ponds? **11**

MICROBIAL DIVERSITY

The Earth provides a seemingly infinite number of environmental niches, and novel life forms have evolved to fill them. Many of the microbes that exist in these niches cannot be cultivated by conventional methods on conventional growth media and have remained unknown. In recent years, however, isolation and identification methods have become much more sophisticated, and microbes that fill these niches are being identified—many without being cultivated. Particularly interesting are bacteria that test the theoretical limits of size for prokaryotes.

Discoveries Illustrating the Range of Diversity

LEARNING OBJECTIVE

12 List two factors that contribute to the limits of our knowledge of microbial diversity.

Earlier in this chapter, we described the giant bacterium *Epulopiscium*. In 1999, another, even larger, giant bacterium was discovered 100 meters deep in the sediments of the coastal waters off Namibia, on the southwestern coast of Africa. Named *Thiomargarita namibiensis* (thī′ō-mär-gär-ē-tá na′mi-bē-èn-sis), meaning "sulfur pearl of Namibia," these spherical organisms, classified with the gammaproteobacteria, are as large as 750 μm in diameter (Figure 28). This is a bit larger than the size of a period at the end of this sentence.

As we have mentioned, a factor that limits the size of prokaryotic cells is that nutrients must enter the cytoplasm by simple diffusion. *T. namibiensis* minimizes this problem by resembling a fluid-filled balloon, the vacuole in the interior being surrounded by a relatively thin outer layer of cytoplasm. This cytoplasm is equal in volume to that of most other prokaryotes. Its energy source is essentially hydrogen sulfide, which is plentiful in the sediments in which it is normally found, and nitrate, which it must extract intermittently from nitrate-rich seawaters when storms stir the loose sediment. The cell's interior vacuole, which makes up about 98% of the bacterium's volume, serves as a storage space to hold the nitrate between recharging of its supply. The cell's energy is derived from the oxidation of hydrogen sulfide; the nitrate, although a source of nutritional nitrogen, primarily serves as an electron acceptor in the absence of oxygen.

The discovery of uniquely large bacteria has raised the question of how large a prokaryotic cell can be and still absorb nutrients. At the other extreme, is there a lower limit for the size of microorganisms—especially their genome? There are reports of bacteria as small as 0.02 to 0.08 μm (nanobacteria) found in deep rock formations and even meteorites. Most microbiologists have concluded that these are nonliving particles that have

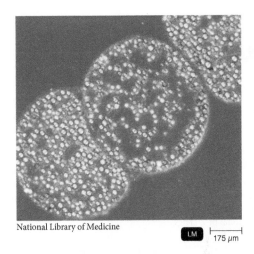

National Library of Medicine

LM 175 μm

Figure 28 *Thiomargarita namibiensis*. *Thiomargarita namibiensis* gets its energy from reduced sulfur compounds such as hydrogen sulfide.

Q Is a bacterium of this size theoretically possible if the interior were cytoplasm rather than a fluid-filled vacuole?

crystallized from minerals and suggest the name **nanons**. Theoretical considerations have been used to calculate that a cell with a significant metabolism would have to have a diameter of at least 0.1 μm. Certain bacteria have extraordinarily small genomes. For example, *Carsonella ruddii* (kar′son-el-lä ru′dē-ē) is a bacterium that lives in a *symbiotic relationship* with its insect host, a sap-eating psyllid (plant louse), and requires less genetic capability than would a free-living microbe. It has only 182 genes, which is close to the 151 genes that is the calculated theoretical minimum even for a microbe in such a symbiotic relationship. (Compare this with the minimal genetic requirements of the *free-living* mycoplasmas). *C. ruddii* is not completely parasitic in its relationship with its host insect, but it supplies the host with some essential amino acids. It is therefore probably in the evolutionary process of becoming an organelle, like the mitochondria of mammalian cells.

Until now, microbiologists have described only about 5000 bacterial species, of which about 3000 are listed in *Bergey's Manual*. The true number may be in the millions. Many bacteria in soil or water, or elsewhere in nature, cannot be cultivated with the media and conditions normally used for bacterial growth. Moreover, some bacteria are part of complex food chains and can grow only in the presence of other microbes that supply specific growth requirements. Recently, researchers have been using the polymerase chain reaction (PCR) to make millions of copies of genes found at random in a soil sample. By comparing the genes found in many repetitions of this process, researchers can estimate the different bacterial species in such a sample. One report indicates that a single gram of soil may contain 10,000 or so bacterial types—about twice as many as have ever been described.

CHECK YOUR UNDERSTANDING

✔ How can you detect the presence of a bacterium that cannot be cultured? 12

Study Outline

MasteringMICROBIOLOGY™

Test your understanding with quizzes, microbe review, and a chapter post-test at www.masteringmicrobiology.com.

Introduction

1. *Bergey's Manual* categorizes bacteria into taxa based on rRNA sequences.
2. *Bergey's Manual* lists identifying characteristics such as Gram stain reaction, cellular morphology, oxygen requirements, and nutritional properties.

The Prokaryotic Groups

1. Prokaryotic organisms are classified into two domains: Archaea and Bacteria.

■ Domain Bacteria

1. Bacteria are essential to life on Earth.

The Proteobacteria

1. Members of the phylum Proteobacteria are gram-negative.
2. Alphaproteobacteria includes nitrogen-fixing bacteria, chemo-autotrophs, and chemoheterotrophs.
3. Betaproteobacteria includes chemoautotrophs and chemo-heterotrophs.
4. Pseudomonadales, Legionellales, Vibrionales, Enterobacteriales, and Pasteurellales are classified as gammaproteobacteria.
5. *Bdellovibrio* and *Myxococcus* in the deltaproteobacteria prey on other bacteria.
6. Epsilonproteobacteria includes *Campylobacter* and *Helicobacter*.

The Gram-Positive Bacteria

1. In *Bergey's Manual*, gram-positive bacteria are divided into those that have low G + C ratio and those that have high G + C ratio.
2. Low G + C gram-positive bacteria include common soil bacteria, the lactic acid bacteria, and several human pathogens.
3. High G + C gram-positive bacteria include mycobacteria, corynebacteria, and actinomycetes.

The Nonproteobacteria Gram-Negative Bacteria

1. Several phyla of gram-negative bacteria are not related phylo-genetically to the Proteobacteria.
2. Cyanobacteria are photoautotrophs that use light energy and CO_2 and do produce O_2.
3. Chemoheterotrophic examples are planctomycetes, chlamydiae, spirochetes, bacteroidetes, and fusobacteria.
4. Purple and green photosynthetic bacteria are photoautotrophs that use light energy and CO_2 and do not produce O_2
5. *Deinococcus* and *Thermus* are resistent to environmental extremes.

■ Domain Archaea

1. Extreme halophiles, extreme thermophiles, and methanogens are included in the archaea.

■ Microbial Diversity

1. Few of the total number of different prokaryotes have been isolated and identified.
2. PCR can be used to uncover the presence of bacteria that can't be cultured in the laboratory.

Study Questions

Answers to the Review and Multiple Choice questions can be found at the end of the chapter.

Review

1. The following outline can be used to identify important bacteria. Fill in a representative genus in the space provided.

                                    Representative Genus
I. Gram-positive
  A. Endospore-forming rod
    1. Obligate anaerobe   (a) _____
    2. Not obligate anaerobe   (b) _____

B. Non–endospore-forming
  1. Cells are rods
    a. Produce conidiospores   (c) _____
    b. Acid-fast   (d) _____
  2. Cells are cocci
    a. Lack cytochrome system   (e) _____
    b. Use aerobic respiration (f) _____

II. Gram-negative
   A. Cells are helical or curved
      1. Axial filament   (g) _____
      2. No axial filament   (h) _____
   B. Cells are rods
      1. Aerobic, nonfermenting   (i) _____
      2. Facultatively anaerobic   (j) _____
III. Lack cell walls   (k) _____
IV. Obligate intracellular parasites
   A. Transmitted by ticks   (l) _____
   B. Reticulate bodies in host cells (m) _____

2. Compare and contrast each of the following:
  a. Cyanobacteria and algae
  b. Actinomycetes and fungi
  c. *Bacillus* and *Lactobacillus*
  d. *Pseudomonas* and *Escherichia*
  e. *Leptospira* and *Spirillum*
  f. *Escherichia* and *Bacteroides*
  g. *Rickettsia* and *Chlamydia*
  h. *Ureaplasma* and *Mycoplasma*

3. DRAW IT Draw a key to differentiate the following bacteria: Cyanobacteria, *Cytophaga*, *Desulfovibrio*, *Frankia*, *Hyphomicrobium*, Methanogens, Myxobacteria, *Nitrobacter*, purple bacteria, *Sphaerotilus*, and *Sulfolobus*.

4. NAME IT These organisms are important in sewage treatment and can produce a fuel used for home heating and for generating electricity.

Multiple Choice

1. If you Gram-stained the bacteria that live in the human intestine, you would expect to find mostly
  a. gram-positive cocci.
  b. gram-negative rods.
  c. gram-positive, endospore-forming rods.
  d. gram-negative, nitrogen-fixing bacteria.
  e. all of the above

2. Which of the following does *not* belong with the others?
  a. Enterobacteriales   **d.** Pasteurellales
  b. Lactobacillales   **e.** Vibrionales
  c. Legionellales

3. Pathogenic bacteria can be
  a. motile.   **d.** anaerobic.
  b. rods.   **e.** all of the above
  c. cocci.

4. Which of the following is an intracellular parasite?
  a. *Rickettsia*   **d.** *Staphylococcus*
  b. *Mycobacterium*   **e.** *Streptococcus*
  c. *Bacillus*

5. Which of the following terms is the most specific?
  a. bacillus
  b. *Bacillus*
  c. gram-positive
  d. endospore-forming rods and cocci
  e. anaerobic

6. Which one of the following does *not* belong with the others?
  a. *Enterococcus*   **d.** *Streptococcus*
  b. *Lactobacillus*   **e.** All are grouped together.
  c. *Staphylococcus*

7. Which of the following pairs is *mismatched*?
  a. anaerobic endospore-forming gram-positive rods—*Clostridium*
  b. facultatively anaerobic gram-negative rods—*Escherichia*
  c. facultatively anaerobic gram-negative rods—*Shigella*
  d. pleomorphic gram-positive rods—*Corynebacterium*
  e. spirochete—*Helicobacter*

8. *Spirillum* is *not* classified as a spirochete because spirochetes
  a. do not cause disease.
  b. possess axial filaments.
  c. possess flagella.
  d. are prokaryotes.
  e. none of the above

9. When *Legionella* was newly discovered, why was it classified with the pseudomonads?
  a. It is a pathogen.
  b. It is an aerobic gram-negative rod.
  c. It is difficult to culture.
  d. It is found in water.
  e. none of the above

10. Unlike purple and green phototrophic bacteria, cyanobacteria
  a. produce oxygen during photosynthesis.
  b. do not require light.
  c. use H_2S as an electron donor.
  d. have a membrane-enclosed nucleus.
  e. all of the above

Critical Thinking

1. Place each phylum listed in Table 1 in the appropriate category:
  a. typical gram-positive cell wall
  b. typical gram-negative cell wall
  c. no peptidoglycan in cell wall
  d. no cell wall

2. To which of the following is the photosynthetic bacterium *Chromatium* most closely related? Briefly explain why.
  a. cyanobacteria
  b. *Chloroflexus*
  c. *Escherichia*

3. Bacteria are single-celled organisms that must absorb their nutrients by simple diffusion. The dimensions of *Thiomargarita namibiensis* are several hundred times larger than those of most bacteria, much too large for simple diffusion to operate. How does the bacterium solve this problem?

Clinical Applications

1. After contact with a patient's spinal fluid, a lab technician developed fever, nausea, and purple lesions on her neck and extremities. A throat culture grew gram-negative diplococci. What is the genus of the bacteria?

2. Between April 1 and May 15 of one year, 22 children in three states developed diarrhea, fever, and vomiting. The children had each received pet ducklings. Gram-negative, facultatively anaerobic bacteria were isolated from both the patients' and the ducks' feces; the bacteria were identified as serovar C2. What is the genus of these bacteria?

3. A woman complaining of lower abdominal pain with a temperature of 39°C gave birth soon after to a stillborn baby. Blood cultures from the infant revealed gram-positive rods. The woman had a history of eating unheated hot dogs during her pregnancy. Which organism is most likely involved?

Answers to Review and Multiple Choice Study Questions

Review

1. **a.** *Clostridium* **g.** *Treponema*
   b. *Bacillus* **h.** *Spirillum*
   c. *Streptomyces* **i.** *Pseudomonas*
   d. *Mycobacterium* **j.** *Escherichia*
   e. *Streptococcus* **k.** *Mycoplasma*
   f. *Staphylococcus* **l.** *Rickettsia*

   m. *Chlamydia*

2. **a.** Both are oxygenic photoautotrophs. Cyanobacteria are prokaryotes; algae are eukaryotes.
   b. Both are chemoheterotrophs capable of forming mycelia; some form conidia. Actinomycetes are prokaryotes; fungi are eukaryotes.
   c. Both are large rod-shaped bacteria. *Bacillus* forms endospores, *Lactobacillus* is a fermentative non–endospore-forming rod.
   d. Both are small rod-shaped bacteria. *Pseudomonas* has an oxidative metabolism; *Escherichia* is fermentative. *Pseudomonas* has polar flagella; *Escherichia* has peritrichous flagella.
   e. Both are helical bacteria. *Leptospira* (a spirochete) has an axial filament. *Spirillum* has flagella.
   f. Both are gram-negative, rod-shaped bacteria. *Escherichia* are facultative anaerobes, and *Bacteroides* are anaerobes.
   g. Both are obligatory intracellular parasites. *Rickettsia* are transmitted by ticks; *Chlamydia* have a unique developmental cycle.
   h. Both lack peptidoglycan cell walls. *Ureaplasma* are archaea; *Mycoplasma* are bacteria.

3. There are many ways to draw a key. Here is one example.

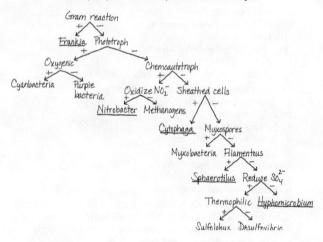

4. Methanogens

Multiple Choice

1.   b   3. e   5. b   7. e   9. b
2. b   4. a   6. c   8. b   10. a

The Eukaryotes: Fungi, Algae, Protozoa, and Helminths

From Chapter 12 of *Microbiology: An Introduction*, Eleventh Edition. Gerard J. Tortora, Berdell R. Funke, Christine L. Case.

The Eukaryotes: Fungi, Algae, Protozoa, and Helminths

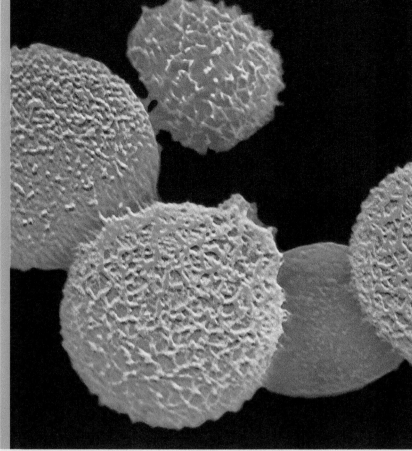

E. Gueho/CNRI/Photo Researchers

O ver half of the world's population is infected with eukaryotic pathogens. The World Health Organization (WHO) ranks six parasitic diseases among the top 20 microbial causes of death in the world. Every year, there are over 5 million new cases of malaria, schistosomiasis, amebiasis, hookworm, African trypanosomiasis, and intestinal parasites reported in developing countries. Emerging eukaryotic pathogens in developed countries include *Pneumocystis,* the leading cause of death in AIDS patients and the protozoan *Cryptosporidium,* which caused disease in 400,000 people in Milwaukee in 1993. In 2001, raccoon roundworm in humans was identified as an emerging disease. In 2011, the CDC announced that bloodborne parasites, *Plasmodium* spp., *Babesia* spp., *Trypanosoma cruzi,* and *Lieshmania* spp., pose a public health threat in the U.S. The emergence of the fungal pathogen *Cryptococcus gattii* (see the photograph) in North America is discussed in the Clinical Case.

In this chapter, we examine the eukaryotic microorganisms that affect humans: fungi, algae, protozoa, parasitic helminths, and the arthropods that transmit diseases. (For a comparison of their characteristics, see Figure 1.)

Visualize microbiology and check your understanding with a pre-test at www.masteringmicrobiology.com.

Exploring Pathogenic Eukaryotes

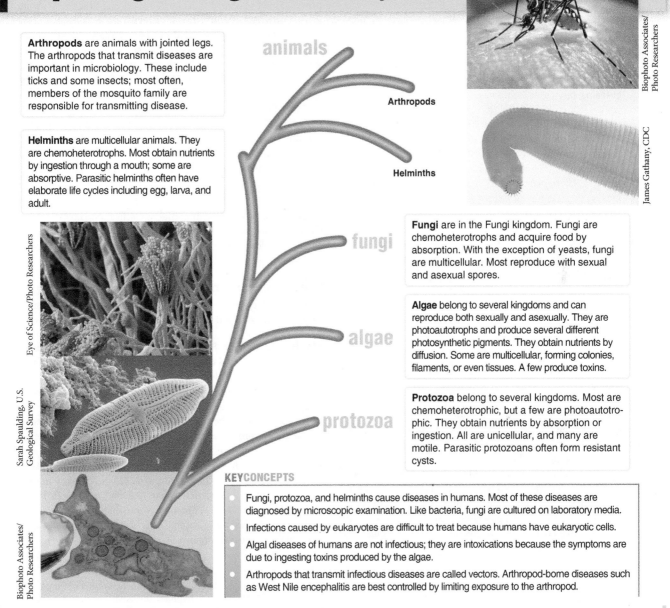

Arthropods are animals with jointed legs. The arthropods that transmit diseases are important in microbiology. These include ticks and some insects; most often, members of the mosquito family are responsible for transmitting disease.

Helminths are multicellular animals. They are chemoheterotrophs. Most obtain nutrients by ingestion through a mouth; some are absorptive. Parasitic helminths often have elaborate life cycles including egg, larva, and adult.

animals

Arthropods

Helminths

fungi

algae

protozoa

Fungi are in the Fungi kingdom. Fungi are chemoheterotrophs and acquire food by absorption. With the exception of yeasts, fungi are multicellular. Most reproduce with sexual and asexual spores.

Algae belong to several kingdoms and can reproduce both sexually and asexually. They are photoautotrophs and produce several different photosynthetic pigments. They obtain nutrients by diffusion. Some are multicellular, forming colonies, filaments, or even tissues. A few produce toxins.

Protozoa belong to several kingdoms. Most are chemoheterotrophic, but a few are photoautotrophic. They obtain nutrients by absorption or ingestion. All are unicellular, and many are motile. Parasitic protozoans often form resistant cysts.

Biophoto Associates/ Photo Researchers

James Gathany, CDC

Eye of Science/Photo Researchers

Sarah Spaulding, U.S. Geological Survey

Biophoto Associates/ Photo Researchers

KEY CONCEPTS

- Fungi, protozoa, and helminths cause diseases in humans. Most of these diseases are diagnosed by microscopic examination. Like bacteria, fungi are cultured on laboratory media.
- Infections caused by eukaryotes are difficult to treat because humans have eukaryotic cells.
- Algal diseases of humans are not infectious; they are intoxications because the symptoms are due to ingesting toxins produced by the algae.
- Arthropods that transmit infectious diseases are called vectors. Arthropod-borne diseases such as West Nile encephalitis are best controlled by limiting exposure to the arthropod.

Fungi

LEARNING OBJECTIVES

1   List the defining characteristics of fungi.
2   Differentiate asexual from sexual reproduction, and describe each of these processes in fungi.
3   List the defining characteristics of the four phyla of fungi described in this chapter.
4   Identify two beneficial and two harmful effects of fungi.

Over the last 10 years, the incidence of serious fungal infections has been increasing. These infections are occurring as health care–associated infections and in people with compromised

Clinical Case: Man's Best Friend

Ethan, a 26-year-old computer programmer, is coaxing his dog, Waldo, into his truck. Waldo is very ill, and Ethan is taking him to the veterinary clinic in Bellingham, Washington, to get Waldo checked out. Waldo not only has nasal discharge, noisy breathing, coughing, and sneezing, but also is losing weight and having difficulty walking. Ethan already had to look all over the property to find Waldo, and by the time Ethan locates Waldo in the barn, carries him to the driveway, and lifts the 60-pound Labrador into the bed of his truck, Ethan has to stop to rest. As a matter of fact, he thinks to himself, he doesn't look much better than Waldo these days! Ethan has been fighting what he thinks is some sort of virus as well.

The veterinarian examines Waldo and prescribes fluconazole, an antibiotic. Ethan, now very tired by this point, takes Waldo home. They both lie down to get some rest.

What type of infection could Waldo have? Read on to find out.

immune systems. In addition, thousands of fungal diseases afflict economically important plants, costing more than $1 billion annually.

Fungi are also beneficial. They are important in the food chain because they decompose dead plant matter, thereby recycling vital elements. Through the use of extracellular enzymes such as cellulases, fungi are the primary decomposers of the hard parts of plants, which cannot be digested by animals. Nearly all plants depend on symbiotic fungi, known as **mycorrhizae,** which help their roots absorb minerals and water from the soil. Fungi are also valuable to animals. Fungi-farming ants cultivate fungi that break down cellulose and lignin from plants, providing glucose that the ants can then digest. Fungi are used by humans for food (mushrooms) and

to produce foods (bread and citric acid) and drugs (alcohol and penicillin). Of the more than 100,000 species of fungi, only about 200 are pathogenic to humans and animals.

The study of fungi is called **mycology.** We will first look at the structures that are the basis of fungal identification in a clinical laboratory, then we will explore their life cycles. A pathogen must be identified to properly treat a disease and to prevent its spread.

We will also examine nutritional needs. All fungi are chemoheterotrophs, requiring organic compounds for energy and carbon. Fungi are aerobic or facultatively anaerobic; only a few anaerobic fungi are known.

Table 1 lists the basic differences between fungi and bacteria.

Characteristics of Fungi

Yeast identification, like bacterial identification, involves biochemical tests. However, multicellular fungi are identified on the basis of physical appearance, including colony characteristics and reproductive spores.

Vegetative Structures

Fungal colonies are described as **vegetative** structures because they are composed of the cells involved in catabolism and growth.

Molds and Fleshy Fungi The **thallus** (body) of a mold or fleshy fungus consists of long filaments of cells joined together; these filaments are called **hyphae** (singular: *hypha*). Hyphae can grow to immense proportions. The hyphae of a single fungus in Oregon extend across 3.5 miles.

In most molds, the hyphae contain cross-walls called **septa** (singular: *septum*), which divide them into distinct, uninucleate (one-nucleus) cell-like units. These hyphae are called **septate hyphae** (Figure 2a). In a few classes of fungi, the hyphae contain no septa and appear as long, continuous cells with many nuclei. These are called **coenocytic hyphae** (Figure 2b). Even in fungi with septate hyphae, there are usually openings in the septa that make the cytoplasm of adjacent "cells" continuous; these fungi are actually coenocytic organisms, too.

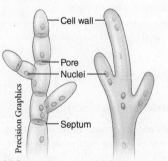

(a) Septate hypha **(b)** Coenocytic hypha

Precision Graphics

Cell wall
Pore
Nuclei
Septum

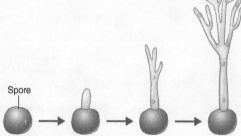

Spore

(c) Growth of a hypha from a spore

Figure 2 Characteristics of fungal hyphae. (a) Septate hyphae have cross-walls, or septa, dividing the hyphae into cell-like units. **(b)** Coenocytic hyphae lack septa. **(c)** Hyphae grow by elongating at the tips.

Q What is a hypha? A mycelium?

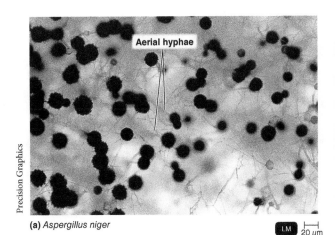

(a) *Aspergillus niger*

LM ⊢——⊣ 20 µm

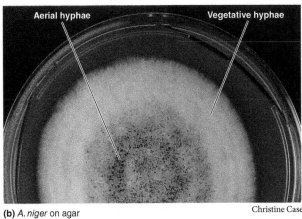

(b) *A. niger* on agar

Christine Case

Precision Graphics

Figure 3 Aerial and vegetative hyphae. (a) A photomicrograph of aerial hyphae, showing reproductive spores. **(b)** A colony of *Aspergillus niger* grown on a glucose agar plate, showing both vegetative and aerial hyphae.

Q How do fungal colonies differ from bacterial colonies?

Hyphae grow by elongating at the tips (Figure 2c). Each part of a hypha is capable of growth, and when a fragment breaks off, it can elongate to form a new hypha. In the laboratory, fungi are usually grown from fragments obtained from a fungal thallus.

The portion of a hypha that obtains nutrients is called the *vegetative hypha;* the portion concerned with reproduction is the *reproductive* or *aerial hypha,* so named because it projects above the surface of the medium on which the fungus is growing. Aerial hyphae often bear reproductive spores (Figure 3a), discussed later. When environmental conditions are suitable, the hyphae grow to form a filamentous mass called a **mycelium,** which is visible to the unaided eye (Figure 3b).

Yeasts Yeasts are nonfilamentous, unicellular fungi that are typically spherical or oval. Like molds, yeasts are widely distributed in nature; they are frequently found as a white powdery coating on fruits and leaves. **Budding yeasts,** such as *Saccharomyces* (sak-ä-rō-mi'sēs), divide unevenly.

In budding (Figure 4), the parent cell forms a protuberance (bud) on its outer surface. As the bud elongates, the parent cell's nucleus divides, and one nucleus migrates into the bud. Cell wall material is then laid down between the bud and parent cell, and the bud eventually breaks away.

One yeast cell can in time produce up to 24 daughter cells by budding. Some yeasts produce buds that fail to detach themselves; these buds form a short chain of cells called a **pseudohypha.** *Candida albicans* (kan'did-ä al'bi-kanz) attaches to human epithelial cells as a yeast but usually requires pseudohyphae to invade deeper tissues.

Fission yeasts, such as *Schizosaccharomyces* (skiz-ō-sak-ä-rō-mī'sēs), divide evenly to produce two new cells. During fission, the parent cell elongates, its nucleus divides, and two offspring

TABLE 1 Selected Features of Fungi and Bacteria Compared

	Fungi	Bacteria
Cell Type	Eukaryotic	Prokaryotic
Cell Membrane	Sterols present	Sterols absent, except in *Mycoplasma*
Cell Wall	Glucans; mannans; chitin (no peptidoglycan)	Peptidoglycan
Spores	Sexual and asexual reproductive spores	Endospores (not for reproduction); some asexual reproductive spores
Metabolism	Limited to heterotrophic; aerobic, facultatively anaerobic	Heterotrophic, autotrophic; aerobic, facultatively anaerobic, anaerobic

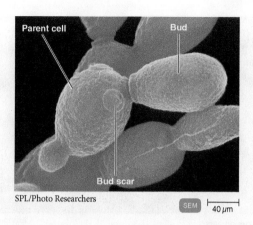

SPL/Photo Researchers

SEM | 40 μm

Figure 4 A budding yeast. A micrograph of *Saccharomyces cerevisiae* in various stages of budding.

 How does a bud differ from a spore?

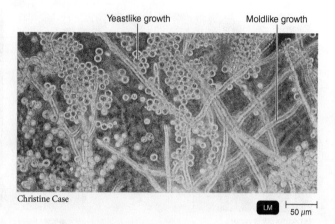

Christine Case

LM | 50 μm

Figure 5 Fungal dimorphism. Dimorphism in the fungus *Mucor indicus* depends on CO_2 concentration. On the agar surface, *Mucor* exhibits yeastlike growth, but in the agar it is moldlike.

 What is fungal dimorphism?

cells are produced. Increases in the number of yeast cells on a solid medium produce a colony similar to a bacterial colony.

Yeasts are capable of facultative anaerobic growth. Yeasts can use oxygen or an organic compound as the final electron acceptor; this is a valuable attribute because it allows these fungi to survive in various environments. If given access to oxygen, yeasts perform aerobic respiration to metabolize carbohydrates to carbon dioxide and water; denied oxygen, they ferment carbohydrates and produce ethanol and carbon dioxide. This fermentation is used in the brewing, wine-making, and baking industries. *Saccharomyces* species produce ethanol in brewed beverages and carbon dioxide for leavening bread dough.

Dimorphic Fungi Some fungi, most notably the pathogenic species, exhibit **dimorphism**—two forms of growth. Such fungi can grow either as a mold or as a yeast. The moldlike forms produce vegetative and aerial hyphae; the yeastlike forms reproduce by budding. Dimorphism in pathogenic fungi is temperature-dependent: at 37°C, the fungus is yeastlike, and at 25°C, it is moldlike. However, the appearance of the dimorphic (in this instance, nonpathogenic) fungus shown in Figure 5 changes with CO_2 concentration.

Life Cycle

Filamentous fungi can reproduce asexually by fragmentation of their hyphae. In addition, both sexual and asexual reproduction in fungi occurs by the formation of **spores.** In fact, fungi are usually identified by spore type.

Fungal spores, however, are quite different from bacterial endospores. Bacterial endospores allow a bacterial cell to survive adverse environmental conditions. A single vegetative bacterial cell forms one endospore, which eventually germinates

to produce a single vegetative bacterial cell. This process is not reproduction because it does not increase the total number of bacterial cells. But after a mold forms a spore, the spore detaches from the parent and germinates into a new mold (see Figure 2c). Unlike the bacterial endospore, this is a true reproductive spore; a second organism grows from the spore. Although fungal spores can survive for extended periods in dry or hot environments, most do not exhibit the extreme tolerance and longevity of bacterial endospores.

Spores are formed from aerial hyphae in a number of different ways, depending on the species. Fungal spores can be either asexual or sexual. **Asexual spores** are formed by the hyphae of one organism. When these spores germinate, they become organisms that are genetically identical to the parent. **Sexual spores** result from the fusion of nuclei from two opposite mating strains of the same species of fungus. Fungi produce sexual spores less frequently than asexual spores. Organisms that grow from sexual spores will have genetic characteristics of both parental strains. Because spores are of considerable importance in identifying fungi, we will next look at some of the various types of asexual and sexual spores.

Asexual Spores Asexual spores are produced by an individual fungus through mitosis and subsequent cell division; there is no fusion of the nuclei of cells. Two types of asexual spores are produced by fungi. One type is a **conidiospore,** or **conidium** (plural: *conidia*), a unicellular or multicellular spore that is not enclosed in a sac (Figure 6a). Conidia are produced in a chain at the end of a **conidiophore.** Such spores are produced by *Aspergillus* (a-spėr-jil'lus). Conidia formed by the fragmentation of a septate hypha into single, slightly thickened cells are called **arthroconidia** (Figure 6b).

BSIP/Photo Researchers

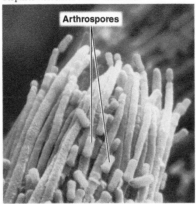

(a) Conidia are arranged in chains at the end of an *Aspergillus niger* conidiophore.

SEM ⊢―⊣ 12 μm

Biophoto Associates/Photo Researchers

(b) Fragmentation of hyphae results in the formation of arthroconidia in *Ceratocystis ulmi*.

SEM ⊢―⊣ 2.5 μm

David M. Phillips/Photo Researchers

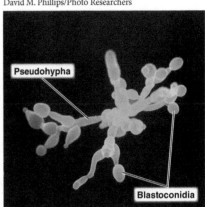

(c) Blastoconidia are formed from the buds of a parent cell of *Candida albicans*.

SEM ⊢―⊣ 13 μm

David M. Phillips/Photo Researchers

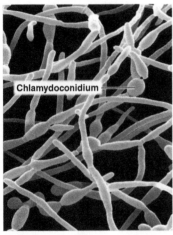

(d) Chlamydoconidia are thick-walled cells within hyphae of this *Candida albicans*.

SEM ⊢―⊣ 5 μm

Jeremy Burgess/Photo Researchers

(e) Sporangiospores are formed within a sporangium of *Rhizopus stolonifer*.

SEM ⊢―⊣ 5 μm

Figure 6 Representative asexual spores.

Q What are the green powdery structures on moldy food?

One species that produces such spores is *Coccidioides immitis* (kok-sid-ē-oi′dēz im′mi-tis). Another type of conidium, **blastoconidia,** consists of buds coming off the parent cell (Figure 6c). Such spores are found in some yeasts, such as *Candida albicans* and *Cryptococcus.* A **chlamydoconidium** is a thick-walled spore formed by rounding and enlargement within a hyphal segment (Figure 6d). A fungus that produces chlamydoconidia is the yeast *C. albicans*.

The other type of asexual spore is a **sporangiospore,** formed within a **sporangium,** or sac, at the end of an aerial hypha called a **sporangiophore.** The sporangium can contain hundreds of sporangiospores (Figure 6e). Such spores are produced by *Rhizopus.*

Sexual Spores A fungal sexual spore results from sexual reproduction, which consists of three phases:

1. **Plasmogamy.** A haploid nucleus of a donor cell (+) penetrates the cytoplasm of a recipient cell (−).
2. **Karyogamy.** The (+) and (−) nuclei fuse to form a diploid zygote nucleus.
3. **Meiosis.** The diploid nucleus gives rise to haploid nuclei (sexual spores), some of which may be genetic recombinants.

The sexual spores produced by fungi characterize the phyla. In laboratory settings, most fungi exhibit only asexual spores. Consequently, clinical identification is based on microscopic examination of asexual spores.

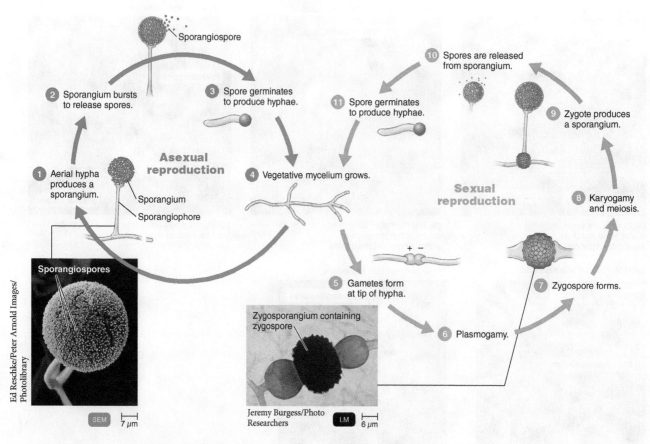

Figure 7 The life cycle of *Rhizopus*, a zygomycete. This fungus will reproduce asexually most of the time. Two opposite mating strains (designated + and −) are necessary for sexual reproduction.

Q   What is an opportunistic mycosis?

Nutritional Adaptations

Fungi are generally adapted to environments that would be hostile to bacteria. Fungi are chemoheterotrophs, and, like bacteria, they absorb nutrients rather than ingesting them as animals do. However, fungi differ from bacteria in certain environmental requirements and in the following nutritional characteristics:

- Fungi usually grow better in an environment with a pH of about 5, which is too acidic for the growth of most common bacteria.

- Almost all molds are aerobic. Most yeasts are facultative anaerobes.

- Most fungi are more resistant to osmotic pressure than bacteria; most can therefore grow in relatively high sugar or salt concentrations.

- Fungi can grow on substances with a very low moisture content, generally too low to support the growth of bacteria.

- Fungi require somewhat less nitrogen than bacteria for an equivalent amount of growth.

- Fungi are often capable of metabolizing complex carbohydrates, such as lignin (a component of wood), that most bacteria cannot use for nutrients.

These characteristics enable fungi to grow on such unlikely substrates as bathroom walls, shoe leather, and discarded newspapers.

CHECK YOUR UNDERSTANDING

- Assume you isolated a single-celled organism that has a cell wall. How would you determine that it is a fungus and not a bacterium? 1

- Contrast the mechanism of conidiospore and ascospore formation. 2

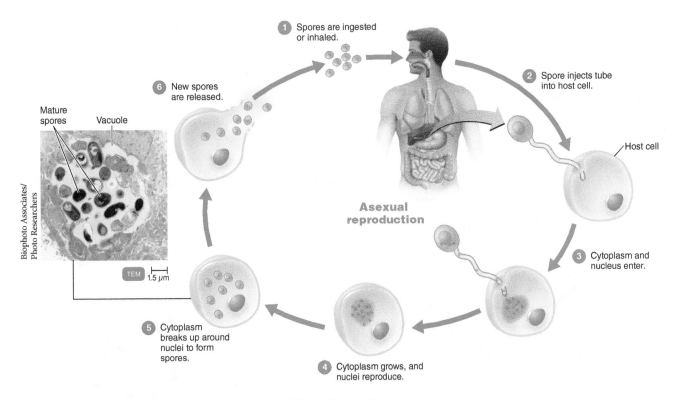

Figure 8 **The life cycle of *Encephalitozoon*, a microsporidian.** Microsporidiosis is an emerging opportunistic infection in immunocompromised patients and the elderly. *E. intestinalis* causes diarrhea. Sexual reproduction has not been observed.

Q Why were microsporidia so difficult to classify?

Medically Important Fungi

This section provides an overview of medically important phyla of fungi. Note that not all fungi cause disease.

The genera named in the following phyla include many that are readily found as contaminants in foods and in laboratory bacterial cultures. Although these genera are not all of primary medical importance, they are typical examples of their respective groups.

Zygomycota

The Zygomycota, or conjugation fungi, are saprophytic molds that have coenocytic hyphae. An example is *Rhizopus stolonifer,* the common black bread mold. The asexual spores of *Rhizopus* are sporangiospores (Figure 7, lower left). The dark sporangiospores inside the sporangium give *Rhizopus* its descriptive common name. When the sporangium breaks open, the sporangiospores are dispersed. If they fall on a suitable medium, they will germinate into a new mold thallus.

The sexual spores are zygospores. A **zygospore** is a large spore enclosed in a thick wall (Figure 7, lower right). This type of spore results from the fusion of the nuclei of two cells that are morphologically similar to each other.

Microsporidia

Microsporidia are unusual eukaryotes because they lack mitochondria. Microsporidia do not have microtubules, and they are obligate intracellular parasites. In 1857, when they were discovered, microsporidians were classified as fungi. They were reclassified as protists in 1983 because they lack mithochondria. Recent genome sequencing, however, reveals that the microsporidians are fungi. Sexual reproduction has not been observed but probably occurs within the host (Figure 8). Microsporidia have been reported since 1984 to be the cause of a number of human diseases, including chronic diarrhea and keratoconjunctivitis (inflammation of the conjunctiva near the cornea), most notably in AIDS patients.

Ascomycota

The Ascomycota, or sac fungi, include molds with septate hyphae and some yeasts. Their asexual spores are usually

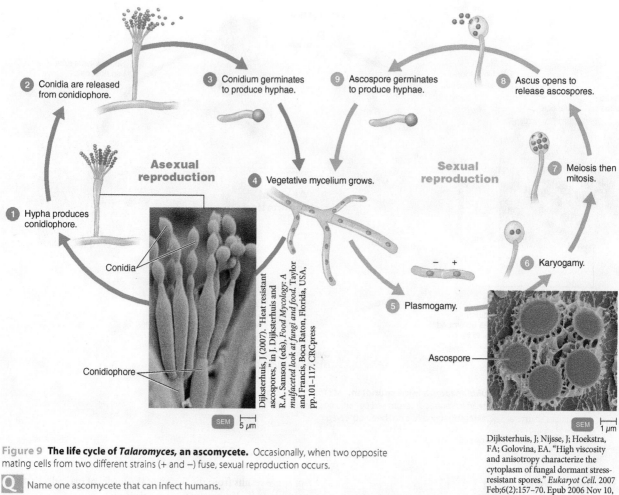

2 Conidia are released from conidiophore.

3 Conidium germinates to produce hyphae.

9 Ascospore germinates to produce hyphae.

8 Ascus opens to release ascospores.

Asexual reproduction

1 Hypha produces conidiophore.

4 Vegetative mycelium grows.

Sexual reproduction

7 Meiosis then mitosis.

Conidia

Conidiophore

Dijksterhuis, J (2007). "Heat resistant ascospores," in J. Dijksterhuis and R.A. Samson (eds), *Food Mycology: A multifaceted look at fungi and food.* Taylor and Francis, Boca Raton, Florida, USA, pp.101–117. CRCpress

SEM   5 μm

− +

6 Karyogamy.

5 Plasmogamy.

Ascospore

SEM   1 μm

Dijksterhuis, J; Nijsse, J; Hoekstra, FA; Golovina, EA. "High viscosity and anisotropy characterize the cytoplasm of fungal dormant stress-resistant spores." *Eukaryot Cell.* 2007 Feb;6(2):157–70. Epub 2006 Nov 10, Fig. 7

Figure 9 The life cycle of *Talaromyces,* an ascomycete. Occasionally, when two opposite mating cells from two different strains (+ and −) fuse, sexual reproduction occurs.

Q Name one ascomycete that can infect humans.

conidia produced in long chains from the conidiophore. The term *Conidia* means dust, and these spores freely detach from the chain at the slightest disturbance and float in the air like dust.

An **ascospore** results from the fusion of the nuclei of two cells that can be either morphologically similar or dissimilar. These spores are produced in a saclike structure called an **ascus** (Figure 9, lower right). The members of this phylum are called sac fungi because of the ascus.

Basidiomycota

The Basidiomycota, or club fungi, also possess septate hyphae. This phylum includes fungi that produce mushrooms. **Basidiospores** are formed externally on a base pedestal called a **basidium** (Figure 10). (The common name of the fungus is derived from the club shape of the basidium.) There are usually

four basidiospores per basidium. Some of the basidiomycota produce asexual conidiospores.

* * *

The fungi we have looked at thus far are **teleomorphs;** that is, they produce both sexual and asexual spores. Some ascomycetes have lost the ability to reproduce sexually. These asexual fungi are called **anamorphs.** *Penicillium* is an example of an anamorph that arose from a mutation in a teleomorph. Historically, fungi whose sexual cycle had not been observed were put in a "holding category" called *Deuteromycota.* Now, mycologists are using rRNA sequencing to classify these organisms. Most of these previously unclassified deuteromycetes are anamorph phases of Ascomycota, and a few are basidiomycetes.

Table 2 lists some fungi that cause human diseases. Two generic names are given for some of the fungi because medically important fungi that are well known by their anamorph, or asexual, name are often referred to by that name.

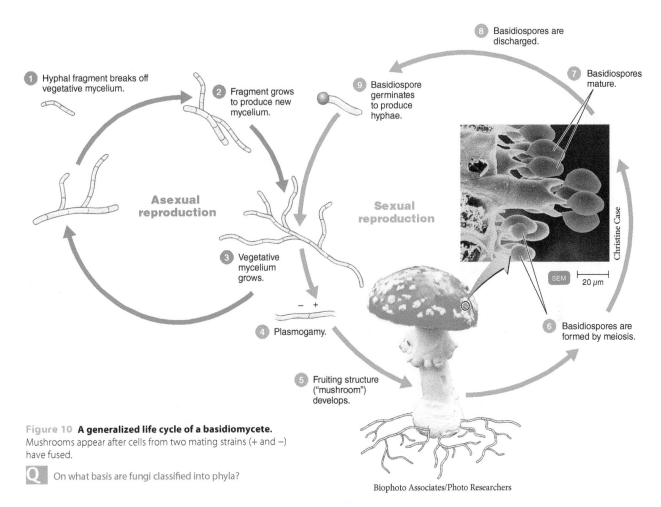

Figure 10 A generalized life cycle of a basidiomycete.
Mushrooms appear after cells from two mating strains (+ and −) have fused.

Q On what basis are fungi classified into phyla?

Biophoto Associates/Photo Researchers

Fungal Diseases

Any fungal infection is called a **mycosis**. Mycoses are generally chronic (long-lasting) infections because fungi grow slowly. Mycoses are classified into five groups according to the degree of tissue involvement and mode of entry into the host: systemic, subcutaneous, cutaneous, superficial, or opportunistic. Fungi are related to animals. Consequently, drugs that affect fungal cells may also affect animal cells. This fact makes fungal infections of humans and other animals often difficult to treat.

Systemic mycoses are fungal infections deep within the body. They are not restricted to any particular region of the body but can affect a number of tissues and organs. Systemic mycoses are usually caused by fungi that live in the soil. Inhalation of spores is the route of transmission; these infections typically begin in the lungs and then spread to other body tissues. They are not contagious from animal to human or from human to human.

Clinical Case

Five days later, Ethan's doctor sends him to the hospital. For the past week Ethan has had shortness of breath, fever, chills, headache, night sweats, loss of appetite, nausea, and muscle pain. He has no other symptoms and is treated with amoxicillin for a presumed lower respiratory tract infection. Three days later, Ethan's condition deteriorates; his respiratory rate increases, but no other systemic symptoms are apparent. Based on Ethan's respiratory symptoms, his doctor orders a chest X-ray exam. The X-ray film shows that Ethan has a mass in his lungs.

Both Ethan and his dog seem to have acquired the same infection. Make a short list of possible pathogens based on this new information.

TABLE 2 Characteristics of Some Pathogenic Fungi

Phylum	Growth Characteristics	Asexual Spore Types	Human Pathogens	Habitat	Type of Mycosis
Zygomycota	Nonseptate hyphae	Sporangiospores	*Rhizopus*	Ubiquitous	Systemic
			Mucor	Ubiquitous	Systemic
Microsporidia	No hyphae	Nonmotile spores	*Encephalitozoon, Nosema*	Humans, other animals	Diarrhea, keratoconjunctivitis
Ascomycota	Dimorphic	Conidia	*Aspergillus*	Ubiquitous	Systemic
			Blastomyces* (Ajellomyces†) dermatitidis	Unknown	Systemic
			Histoplasma* (Ajellomyces†) capsulatum	Soil	Systemic
	Septate hyphae, strong affinity for keratin	Conidia	*Microsporum*	Soil, animals	Cutaneous
		Arthroconidia Chlamydoconidia	*Trichophyton* (Arthroderma†)*	Soil, animals	Cutaneous
Anamorphs	Septate hyphae	Conidia	*Epidermophyton*	Soil, humans	Cutaneous
	Dimorphic		*Sporothrix schenckii, Stachybotrys*	Soil	Subcutaneous
		Arthroconidia	*Coccidioides immitis*	Soil	Systemic
	Yeastlike, pseudohyphae	Chlamydoconidia	*Candida albicans*	Human normal microbiota	Cutaneous, systemic, mucocutaneous
	Unicellular	None	*Pneumocystis*	Ubiquitous	Systemic
Basidiomycota	Septate hyphae; includes rusts and smuts, and plant pathogens; yeastlike encapsulated cells	Conidia	*Cryptococcus* (Filobasidiella†)*	Soil, bird feces	Systemic
			Malassezia	Human skin	Cutaneous

*Anamorph name.
†Teleomorph name.

Subcutaneous mycoses are fungal infections beneath the skin caused by saprophytic fungi that live in soil and on vegetation. Sporotrichosis is a subcutaneous infection acquired by gardeners and farmers. Infection occurs by direct implantation of spores or mycelial fragments into a puncture wound in the skin.

Fungi that infect only the epidermis, hair, and nails are called **dermatophytes,** and their infections are called *dermatomycoses* or **cutaneous mycoses.** Dermatophytes secrete keratinase, an enzyme that degrades **keratin,** a protein found in hair, skin, and nails. Infection is transmitted from human to human or from animal to human by direct contact or by contact with infected hairs and epidermal cells (as from barber shop clippers or shower room floors).

The fungi that cause **superficial mycoses** are localized along hair shafts and in superficial (surface) epidermal cells. These infections are prevalent in tropical climates.

An **opportunistic pathogen** is generally harmless in its normal habitat but can become pathogenic in a host who is seriously debilitated or traumatized, who is under treatment with broad-spectrum antibiotics, whose immune system is suppressed by drugs or by an immune disorder, or who has a lung disease.

Pneumocystis is an opportunistic pathogen in individuals with compromised immune systems and is the most common life-threatening infection in AIDS patients. It was first classified as a protozoan, but recent studies of its RNA indicate it is a unicellular anamorphic fungus. Another example of an opportunistic pathogen is the fungus *Stachybotrys* (sta′ke-botris), which normally grows on cellulose found in dead plants but in recent years has been found growing on water-damaged walls of homes.

Mucormycosis is an opportunistic mycosis caused by *Rhizopus* and *Mucor* (mū′kôr); the infection occurs mostly in patients who have diabetes mellitus, have leukemia, or are undergoing treatment with immunosuppressive drugs. Aspergillosis is also an opportunistic mycosis; it is caused by *Aspergillus* (see Figure 3). This disease occurs in people who have debilitating lung diseases or cancer and have inhaled *Aspergillus* spores. Opportunistic infections by *Cryptococcus* and *Penicillium* can cause fatal diseases in AIDS patients. These opportunistic fungi may be transmitted from one person to an uninfected person but do not usually infect immunocompetent people. **Yeast infection,** or candidiasis, is most frequently caused by *Candida albicans* and may occur as vulvovaginal candidiasis or thrush, a mucocutaneous candidiasis. Candidiasis frequently occurs in newborns, in people with AIDS, and in people being treated with broad-spectrum antibiotics.

Some fungi cause disease by producing toxins.

Clinical Case

Ethan's physician, suspecting that Ethan has a fungal infection, orders a biopsy of the lung mass. Figure A and Figure B show the microscopic examination and a culture from the biopsied tissue.

Based on the figures, what is the most likely pathogen?

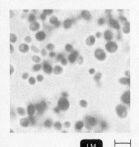

LM 25 μm

Figure A **Microscopic examination from lung mass.**
Lucille K. Georg, CDC.

LM 30 μm

Figure B **Microscopic appearance of culture.**
Connie Nichols, Duke University Medical Center

Economic Effects of Fungi

Fungi have been used in biotechnology for many years. *Aspergillus niger* (nī-jér), for example, has been used to produce citric acid for foods and beverages since 1914. The yeast *Saccharomyces cerevisiae* is used to make bread and wine. It is also genetically modified to produce a variety of proteins, including hepatitis B vaccine. *Trichoderma* is used commercially to produce the enzyme cellulase, which is used to remove plant cell walls to produce a clear fruit juice. When the anticancer drug taxol, which is produced by yew trees, was discovered, there was concern that the yew forests of the U.S. Northwest coast would be decimated to harvest the drug. However, the fungus *Taxomyces* (tax′ō-mī′sēs) also produces taxol.

Fungi are used as biological controls of pests. In 1990, the fungus *Entomophaga* (en′tō-mo-fäg-ä) unexpectedly proliferated and killed gypsy moths that were destroying trees in the eastern United States. Scientists are investigating the use of several fungi to kill pests:

- The fungus *Coniothyrium minitans* (kon′ē-oth-rē-um mi′ni-tanz) feeds on fungi that destroy soybeans and other bean crops.
- A foam filled with *Paecilomyces fumosoroseus* is being used as a biological alternative to chemicals to kill termites hiding inside tree trunks and other hard-to-reach places.

In contrast to these beneficial effects, fungi can have undesirable effects for agriculture because of their nutritional adaptations. As most of us have observed, mold spoilage of fruits, grains, and vegetables is relatively common, but bacterial spoilage of such foods is not. There is little moisture on the unbroken surfaces of such foods, and the interiors of fruits are too acidic for many bacteria to grow there. Jams and jellies also tend to be acidic, and they have a high osmotic pressure from the sugars they contain. These factors all discourage bacterial growth but readily support the growth of molds. A paraffin layer on top of a jar of homemade jelly helps deter mold growth because molds are aerobic and the paraffin layer keeps out the oxygen. However, fresh meats and certain other foods are such good substrates for bacterial growth that bacteria not only will outgrow molds but also will actively suppress mold growth in these foods.

The spreading chestnut tree, of which Longfellow wrote, no longer grows in the United States except in a few widely isolated locations; a fungal blight killed virtually all of them. This blight was caused by the ascomycete *Cryphonectria parasitica* (kri-fō-nek′trē-ä par-ä-si′ti-kä), which was introduced from China around 1904. The fungus allows the tree roots to live and put forth shoots regularly, but then it kills the shoots just as regularly. *Cryphonectria*-resistant chestnuts are being developed. Another imported fungal plant disease is Dutch elm disease, caused by *Ceratocystis ulmi* (sē-rä-tō-sis'tis ul'me). Carried from tree to tree by a bark beetle, the fungus blocks the afflicted tree's circulation. The disease has devastated the American elm population.

CHECK YOUR UNDERSTANDING

✔ List the asexual and sexual spores made by Zygomycetes, Ascomycetes, and Basidiomycetes. 3

✔ Why are microsporidia classified as fungi? 4

✔ Are yeasts beneficial or harmful? 4

Clinical Case Resolved

Cryptococcus gattii, an emerging fungal infection in the United States, is a dimorphic fungus found in the soil. It grows as a yeast at 37°C and produces hyphae at 25°C. Based on the yeastlike appearance and presence of hyphae, the lab confirms the presence of *C. gattii* in Ethan's lung mass. Ethan regularly takes Waldo hiking in the Douglas fir forest of the Northwest, so it isn't possible to know exactly where or when they contracted their infections. Since the first reported case in 1999, over 200 cases have been reported in British Columbia alone. In the United States Pacific Northwest, 60 people and 50 companion animal cases have been confirmed since 2004.

Ethan is placed on intravenous therapy with the antifungal agents amphotericin B and flucytosine. After a 6-week hospital stay, Ethan and Waldo are back at home and almost ready to go hiking again.

Lichens

LEARNING OBJECTIVES

5 List the distinguishing characteristics of lichens, and describe their nutritional needs.

6 Describe the roles of the fungus and the alga in a lichen.

A **lichen** is a combination of a green alga (or a cyanobacterium) and a fungus. Lichens are placed in the Kingdom Fungi and are classified according to the fungal partner, most often an ascomycete. The two organisms exist in a *mutualistic* relationship, in which each partner benefits. The lichen is very different from either the alga or fungus growing alone, and if the partners are separated, the lichen no longer exists. Approximately 13,500 species of lichens occupy quite diverse habitats. Because they can inhabit areas in which neither fungi nor algae could survive alone, lichens are often the first life forms to colonize newly exposed soil or rock. Lichens secrete organic acids that chemically weather rock, and they accumulate nutrients needed for plant growth. Also found on trees, concrete structures, and rooftops, lichens are some of the slowest-growing organisms on Earth.

Lichens can be grouped into three morphologic categories (Figure 11a). *Crustose lichens* grow flush or encrusting onto the substratum, *foliose lichens* are more leaflike, and *fruticose lichens* have fingerlike projections. The lichen's thallus, or body, forms when fungal hyphae grow around algal cells to become the **medulla** (Figure 11b). Fungal hyphae project below the lichen body to form **rhizines,** or holdfasts. Fungal hyphae also form a **cortex,** or protective covering, over the algal layer and sometimes under it as well. After incorporation into a lichen thallus, the alga continues to grow, and the growing hyphae can incorporate new algal cells.

When the algal partner is cultured separately in vitro, about 1% of the carbohydrates produced during photosynthesis are released into the culture medium; however, when the alga is associated with a fungus, the algal plasma membrane is more permeable, and up to 60% of the products of photosynthesis are released to the fungus or are found as end-products of fungal metabolism. The fungus clearly benefits from this association. The alga, while giving up valuable nutrients, is in turn compensated; it receives from the fungus both attachment (rhizines) and protection from desiccation (cortex).

Lichens had considerable economic importance in ancient Greece and other parts of Europe as dyes for clothing. Usnic acid from *Usnea* is used as an antimicrobial agent in China. Erythrolitmin, the dye used in litmus paper to indicate changes in pH, is extracted from a variety of lichens. Some lichens or their acids can cause allergic contact dermatitis in humans.

Populations of lichens readily incorporate cations (positively charged ions) into their thalli. Therefore, the concentrations and types of cations in the atmosphere can be determined by chemical analyses of lichen thalli. In addition, the presence or absence of species that are quite sensitive to pollutants can be used to ascertain air quality. A 1985 study in the Cuyahoga Valley in Ohio revealed that 81% of the 172 lichen species that were present in 1917 were gone. Because this area is severely affected by air pollution, the inference is that air pollutants, primarily sulfur dioxide (the major contributor to acid precipitation), caused the death of sensitive species.

Lichens are the major food for tundra herbivores such as caribou and reindeer. After the 1986 Chernobyl nuclear disaster, 70,000 reindeer in Lapland that had been raised for food had to be destroyed because of high levels of radiation. The lichens on which the reindeer fed had absorbed radioactive cesium-137, which had spread in the air.

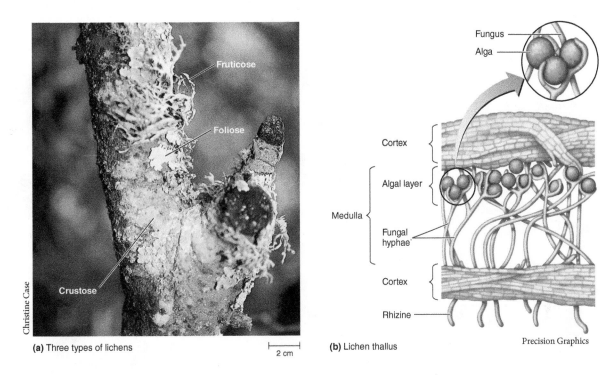

(a) Three types of lichens

Fruticose

Foliose

Crustose

2 cm

Christine Case

(b) Lichen thallus

Fungus

Alga

Cortex

Algal layer

Medulla

Fungal hyphae

Cortex

Rhizine

Precision Graphics

Figure 11 Lichens. The lichen medulla is composed of fungal hyphae surrounding the algal layer. The protective cortex is a layer of fungal hyphae that covers the surface and sometimes the bottom of the lichen.

Q In what ways are lichens unique?

CHECK YOUR UNDERSTANDING

✔ What is the role of lichens in nature? **5**

✔ What is the role of the fungus in a lichen? **6**

Algae

LEARNING OBJECTIVES

7 List the defining characteristics of algae.

8 List the outstanding characteristics of the five phyla of algae discussed in this chapter.

9 Identify two beneficial and two harmful effects of algae.

Algae are familiar as the large brown kelp in coastal waters, the green scum in a puddle, and the green stains on soil or on rocks. A few algae are responsible for food poisonings. Some algae are unicellular; others form chains of cells (are filamentous); and a few have thalli.

"Algae" is not a taxonomic group; it is a way to describe photoautotrophs that lack the roots and stems of plants. Algae are mostly aquatic, although some are found in soil or on trees when sufficient moisture is available there. Unusual algal habitats include the hair of both the sedentary South American sloth and the polar bear. Water is necessary for physical support, reproduction, and the diffusion of nutrients. Generally, algae are found in cool temperate waters, although the large floating mats of the brown alga *Sargassum* (sär-gas′sum) are found in the subtropical Sargasso Sea. Some species of brown algae grow in antarctic waters.

Characteristics of Algae

Algae are relatively simple eukaryotic photoautotrophs that lack the tissues (roots, stem, and leaves) of plants. The identification of unicellular and filamentous algae requires microscopic examination. Most algae are found in the ocean. Their locations depend on the availability of appropriate nutrients, wavelengths of light, and surfaces on which to grow. Probable locations for representative algae are shown in **Figure 12a**.

Vegetative Structures

The body of a multicellular alga is called a thallus. Thalli of the larger multicellular algae, those commonly called seaweeds, consist of branched **holdfasts** (which anchor the alga to

367

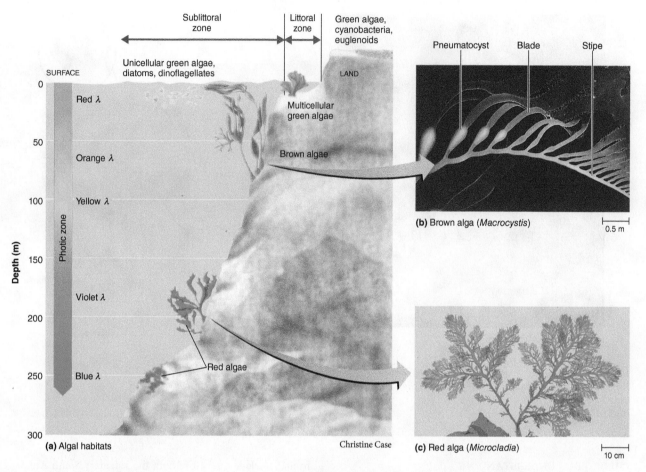

(a) Algal habitats

Christine Case

Sublittoral zone

Littoral zone

Green algae, cyanobacteria, euglenoids

Unicellular green algae, diatoms, dinoflagellates

SURFACE

Depth (m)

Photic zone

Red λ

Orange λ

Yellow λ

Violet λ

Blue λ

LAND

Multicellular green algae

Brown algae

Red algae

Pneumatocyst   Blade   Stipe

(b) Brown alga (*Macrocystis*)   0.5 m

(c) Red alga (*Microcladia*)   10 cm

Figure 12 Algae and their habitats.
(**a**) Although unicellular and filamentous algae can be found on land, they frequently exist in marine and freshwater environments as plankton. Multicellular green, brown, and red algae require a suitable attachment site, adequate water for support, and light of the appropriate wavelengths. (**b**) *Macrocystis porifera*, a brown alga. The hollow stipe and gas-filled pneumatocysts hold the thallus upright ensuring that sufficient sunlight is received for growth. (**c**) *Microcladia*, a red alga. The delicately branched red algae get their color from phycobiliprotein accessory pigments.

Q What red alga is toxic for humans?

a rock), stemlike and often hollow **stipes,** and leaflike **blades** (**Figure 12b**). The cells covering the thallus can carry out photosynthesis. The thallus lacks the conductive tissue (xylem and phloem) characteristic of vascular plants; algae absorb nutrients from the water over their entire surface. The stipe is not lignified or woody, so it does not offer the support of a plant's stem; instead, the surrounding water supports the algal thallus; some algae are also buoyed by a floating, gas-filled bladder called a *pneumatocyst.*

Life Cycle

All algae can reproduce asexually. Multicellular algae with thalli and filamentous forms can fragment; each piece is capable of forming a new thallus or filament. When a unicellular alga divides, its nucleus divides (mitosis), and the two nuclei move to opposite parts of the cell. The cell then divides into two complete cells (cytokinesis).

Sexual reproduction occurs in algae (**Figure 13**). In some species, asexual reproduction may occur for several generations and then, under different conditions, the same species reproduce sexually. Other species alternate generations so that the offspring resulting from sexual reproduction reproduce asexually, and the next generation then reproduces sexually.

Nutrition

Algae is a common name that includes several phyla (**Table 3**). Most algae are photosynthetic; however, the oomycotes, or fungal-like algae, are chemoheterotrophs. Photosyn-

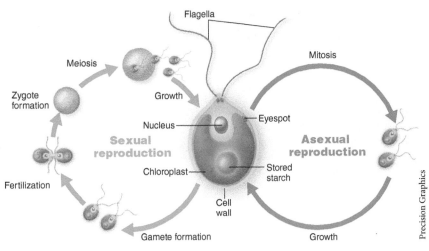

(a) Multicellular green alga (*Ulva*) |——————| 10 cm

(b) Life cycle of a unicellular green alga (*Chlamydomonas*)

Figure 13   Green algae. (**a**) The multicellular green alga *Ulva*. (**b**) The life cycle of the unicellular green alga *Chlamydomonas*. Two whiplike flagella propel this cell.

Q   What is the primary role of algae in the ecosystem?

thetic algae are found throughout the photic (light) zone of bodies of water. Chlorophyll *a* (a light-trapping pigment) and accessory pigments involved in photosynthesis are responsible for the distinctive colors of many algae.

Algae are classified according to their rRNA sequences, structures, pigments, and other qualities (see Table 3). Following are descriptions of some phyla of algae.

Selected Phyla of Algae

The *brown algae,* or kelp, are macroscopic; some reach lengths of 50 m (see Figure 12b). Most brown algae are found in coastal waters. Brown algae have a phenomenal growth rate. Some grow at rates exceeding 20 cm per day and therefore can be harvested regularly. **Algin,** a thickener used in many foods (such as ice cream and cake decorations), is extracted from their cell walls. Algin is

TABLE 3   Characteristics of Selected Phyla of Algae

	Brown Algae	**Red Algae**	**Green Algae**	**Diatoms**	**Dinoflagellates**	**Water Molds**
Phylum	Phaeophyta	Rhodophyta	Chlorophyta	Bacillariophyta	Dinoflagellata	Oomycota
Color	Brownish	Reddish	Green	Brownish	Brownish	Colorless, white
Cell Wall	Cellulose and alginic acid	Cellulose	Cellulose	Pectin and silica	Cellulose in membrane	Cellulose
Cell Arrangement	Multicellular	Most are multicellular	Unicellular and multicellular	Unicellular	Unicellular	Multicellular
Photosynthetic Pigments	Chlorophyll *a* and *c*, xanthophylls	Chlorophyll *a* and *d*, phycobiliproteins	Chlorophyll *a* and *b*	Chlorophyll *a* and *c*, carotene, xanthophylls	Chlorophyll *a* and *c*, carotene, xanthins	None
Sexual Reproduction	Yes	Yes	Yes	Yes	In a few	Yes (similar to the Zygomycota)
Storage Material	Carbohydrate	Glucose polymer	Glucose polymer	Oil	Starch	None
Pathogenicity	None	A few produce toxins	None	Toxins	Toxins	Parasitic

Steve Gshmeissner/SPL/Photo Researchers

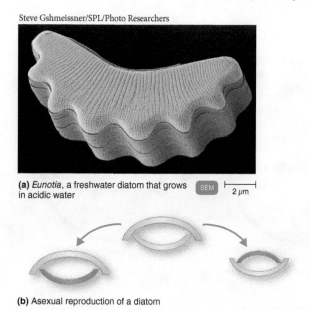

(a) *Eunotia*, a freshwater diatom that grows in acidic water   SEM   2 µm

(b) Asexual reproduction of a diatom

Figure 14 Diatoms. (a) In this micrograph of *Eunotia Serra*, notice how the two parts of the cell wall fit together. (b) Asexual reproduction in a diatom. During mitosis, each daughter cell retains one-half of the cell wall from the parent (yellow) and must synthesize the remaining half (pink).

Q What human disease is caused by diatoms?

also used in the production of a wide variety of nonfood goods, including rubber tires and hand lotion. The brown alga *Laminaria japonica* is used to induce vaginal dilation before surgical entry into the uterus through the vagina.

Most *red algae* have delicately branched thalli and can live at greater ocean depths than other algae (see Figure 12c). The thalli of a few red algae form crustlike coatings on rocks and shells. The red pigments enable red algae to absorb the blue light that penetrates deepest into the ocean. The agar used in microbiological media is extracted from many red algae. Another gelatinous material, carrageenan, comes from a species of red algae commonly called Irish moss. Carrageenan and agar can be a thickening ingredient in evaporated milk, ice cream, and pharmaceutical agents. *Gracilaria* species, which grow in the Pacific Ocean, are used by humans for food. However, members of this genus can produce a lethal toxin.

Green algae have cellulose cell walls, contain chlorophyll *a* and *b*, and store starch, as plants do (see Figure 13a). Green algae are believed to have given rise to terrestrial plants. Most green algae are microscopic, although they may be either unicellular or multicellular. Some filamentous kinds form grass-green scum in ponds.

Diatoms, dinoflagellates, and water molds are grouped into the kingdom Stramenopila. *Diatoms* (Figure 14) are unicellular or

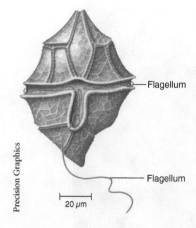

— Flagellum

— Flagellum

20 µm

Precision Graphics

Figure 15 *Peridinium*, a dinoflagellate. Like some other dinoflagellates, *Peridinium* has two flagella in perpendicular, opposing grooves. When the two flagella beat simultaneously, they cause the cell to spin.

Q What human diseases are caused by dinoflagellates?

filamentous algae with complex cell walls that consist of pectin and a layer of silica. The two parts of the wall fit together like the halves of a Petri dish. The distinctive patterns of the walls are a useful tool in diatom identification. Diatoms store energy captured through photosynthesis in the form of oil.

The first reported outbreak of a neurological disease caused by diatoms was reported in 1987 in Canada. Affected people ate mussels that had been feeding on diatoms. The diatoms produced *domoic acid*, a toxin that was then concentrated in the mussels. Symptoms included diarrhea and memory loss. The fatality rate was less than 4%. Since 1991, hundreds of marine birds and sea lions have died from the same **domoic acid intoxication** in California.

Dinoflagellates are unicellular algae collectively called **plankton,** or free-floating organisms (Figure 15). Their rigid structure is due to cellulose embedded in the plasma membrane. Some dinoflagellates produce neurotoxins. In the last 20 years, a worldwide increase in toxic marine algae has killed millions of fish, hundreds of marine mammals, and even some humans. When fish swim through large numbers of the dinoflagellate *Karenia brevis* (kăr′en-ē-ä brev′is), the algae trapped in the gills of the fish release a neurotoxin that stops the fish from breathing. Dinoflagellates in the genus *Alexandrium* (a′leks-an-drē-um) produce neurotoxins (called **saxitoxins**) that cause **paralytic shellfish poisoning (PSP).** The toxin is concentrated when large numbers of dinoflagellates are eaten by mollusks, such as mussels or clams. Humans who eat these mollusks develop PSP. Large concentrations of *Alexandrium* give the ocean a deep red color, from which the name **red tide** originates. Mollusks should not be harvested

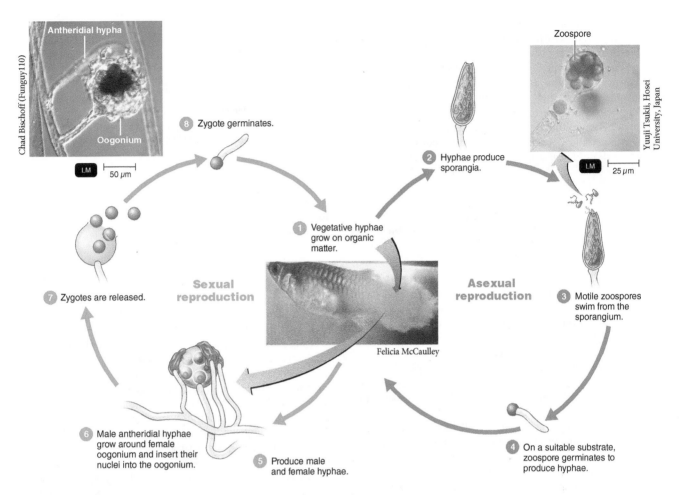

Figure 16 Oomycotes. These funguslike algae are common decomposers in fresh water. A few cause diseases of fish and terrestrial plants. Note the fuzzy mass of *Saprolegnia ferax* on the fish.

Q Is this oomycote more closely related to *Penicillium* or to diatoms?

for consumption during a red tide. A disease called **ciguatera** occurs when the dinoflagellate *Gambierdiscus toxicus* (gam′bē-er-dis-kus toks′i-kus) passes up the food chain and is concentrated in large fish. Ciguatera is endemic (constantly present) in the south Pacific Ocean and the Caribbean Sea. An emerging disease associated with *Pfiesteria* (fē′ster-ē-ä) is responsible for periodic massive fish deaths along the Atlantic Coast.

Most *water molds,* or *Oomycota,* are decomposers. They form the cottony masses on dead algae and animals, usually in fresh water (**Figure 16**). Asexually, the oomycotes resemble the zygomycete fungi in that they produce spores in a sporangium (spore sac). However, oomycote spores, called **zoospores** (**Figure 16**, top right), have two flagella; fungi do not have flagella. Because of

their superficial similarity to fungi, oomycotes were previously classified with the fungi. Their cellulose cell walls always raised the question about their relationship to algae, and recent DNA analyses have confirmed that oomycotes are more closely related to diatoms and dinoflagellates than to fungi. Many of the terrestrial oomycotes are plant parasites. The USDA inspects imported plants for white rust and other parasites. Often travelers, or even commercial plant importers, do not realize that one little blossom or seedling could carry a pest that is capable of causing millions of dollars' worth of damage to U.S. agriculture.

In Ireland during the mid-1800s, 1 million people died when the country's potato crop failed. The fungus that caused the great potato blight, *Phytophthora infestans* (fī-tof′thô-rä in-fes′tans), was one of the first microorganisms to be associated with a disease. Today, *Phytophthora* infects soybeans, potatoes, and cocoa worldwide. Vegetative hyphae produce motile zoospores as well as specialized sex hyphae (see Figure 16). All of the U.S. strains were one mating type ("sex") called A1. In the 1990s, the other mating type, A2, was identified in the United States. When in close proximity, A1 and A2 will differentiate to produce haploid gametes that can mate to form a zygote. When the zygote germinates, the resulting alga will have genes from both parents.

In Australia, *P. cinnamoni* has infected about 20% of one species of *Eucalyptus* tree. *Phytophthora* was introduced into the United States in the 1990s and caused widespread damage to fruit and vegetable crops. When California oak trees suddenly started dying in 1995, University of California scientists identified the cause of this "sudden oak death" to be a new species, *P. ramorum*. *P. ramorum* also infects redwood trees.

Roles of Algae in Nature

Algae are an important part of any aquatic food chain because they fix carbon dioxide into organic molecules that can be consumed by chemoheterotrophs. Using the energy produced in photophosphorylation, algae convert carbon dioxide in the atmosphere into carbohydrates. Molecular oxygen (O_2) is a by-product of their photosynthesis. The top few meters of any body of water contain planktonic algae. As 75% of the Earth is covered with water, it is estimated that 80% of the Earth's O_2 is produced by planktonic algae.

Seasonal changes in nutrients, light, and temperature cause fluctuations in algal populations; periodic increases in numbers of planktonic algae are called **algal blooms.** Blooms of dinoflagellates are responsible for seasonal red tides. Blooms of a certain few species indicate that the water in which they grow is polluted because these algae thrive in high concentrations of organic materials that exist in sewage or industrial wastes. When algae die, the decomposition of the large numbers of cells associated with an algal bloom depletes the level of dissolved oxygen in the water.

Much of the world's petroleum was formed from diatoms and other planktonic organisms that lived several million years ago. When such organisms died and were buried by sediments, the organic molecules they contained did not decompose to be returned to the carbon cycle as CO_2. Heat and pressure resulting from the Earth's geologic movements altered the oil stored in the cells, as well as the cell membranes. Oxygen and other elements were eliminated, leaving a residue of hydrocarbons in the form of petroleum and natural gas deposits.

Many unicellular algae are symbionts in animals. The giant clam *Tridacna* (trī-dak′nä) has evolved special organs that host dinoflagellates. As the clam sits in shallow water, the algae proliferate in these organs when they are exposed to the sun. The algae release glycerol into the clam's bloodstream, thus supplying the clam's carbohydrate requirement. In addition, evidence suggests that the clam gets essential proteins by phagocytizing old algae.

CHECK YOUR UNDERSTANDING

☞ How do algae differ from bacteria? From fungi? 7

☞ List the cell wall composition and diseases caused by the following algae: diatoms, dinoflagellates, oomycotes. 8, 9

Protozoa

LEARNING OBJECTIVE

10 List the defining characteristics of protozoa.

11 Describe the outstanding characteristics of the seven phyla of protozoa discussed in this chapter, and give an example of each.

12 Differentiate an intermediate host from a definitive host.

Protozoa are unicellular, eukaryotic organisms. Among the protozoa are many variations on this cell structure, as we shall see. Protozoa inhabit water and soil. The feeding and growing stage, or **trophozoite,** feeds upon bacteria and small particulate nutrients. Some protozoa are part of the normal microbiota of animals. *Nosema locustae* (nō′sē-mä lō′kus-tī), an insect pathogen, is sold commercially as a nontoxic insecticide to kill grasshoppers. Because the protozoa are specific for grasshoppers, they will not affect humans or animals that eat grasshoppers. Fire ants cause millions of dollars in agricultural damage each year and can cause painful stings. Researchers at the U.S. Department of Agriculture are studying an apicomplexan protozoan that reduces egg production by fire ants. Of the nearly 20,000 species of protozoa, relatively few cause human disease. Those few, however, have significant health and economic impact. Malaria is the fourth leading cause of death in children in Africa.

Characteristics of Protozoa

The term *protozoan* means "first animal," which generally describes its animal-like nutrition. In addition to getting food, a protozoan must reproduce, and parasitic species must be able to get from one host to another.

Life Cycle

Protozoa reproduce asexually by fission, budding, or schizogony. **Schizogony** is multiple fission; the nucleus undergoes multiple divisions before the cell divides. After many nuclei are formed, a small portion of cytoplasm concentrates around each nucleus, and then the single cell separates into daughter cells.

Sexual reproduction has been observed in some protozoa. The ciliates, such as *Paramecium,* reproduce sexually by **conjugation** (Figure 17), which is very different from the bacterial process of the same name. During protozoan conjugation, two cells fuse, and a haploid nucleus (the micronucleus) from each cell migrates to the other cell. This haploid micronucleus fuses with the haploid micronucleus within the cell. The parent cells separate, each now a fertilized cell. When the cells later divide, they produce daughter cells with recombined DNA. Some protozoa produce **gametes (gametocytes),** haploid sex cells. During reproduction, two gametes fuse to form a diploid zygote.

Encystment Under certain adverse conditions, some protozoa produce a protective capsule called a **cyst.** A cyst permits the organism to survive when food, moisture, or oxygen are lacking, when temperatures are not suitable, or when toxic chemicals are present. A cyst also enables a parasitic species to survive outside a host. This is important because parasitic protozoa may have to be excreted from one host in order to get to a new host. The cyst form in members of the phylum Apicomplexa is called an **oocyst.** It is a reproductive structure in which new cells are produced asexually.

Nutrition

Protozoa are mostly aerobic heterotrophs, although many intestinal protozoa are capable of anaerobic growth. Two chlorophyll-containing groups, dinoflagellates and euglenoids, are often studied with algae.

All protozoa live in areas with a large supply of water. Some protozoa transport food across the plasma membrane. However, some have a protective covering, or *pellicle,* and thus require specialized structures to take in food. Ciliates take in food by waving their cilia toward a mouthlike opening called a **cytostome.** Amebas engulf food by surrounding it with pseudopods and phagocytizing it. In all protozoa, digestion takes place in membrane-enclosed **vacuoles,** and waste may be eliminated through the plasma membrane or through a specialized **anal pore.**

Medically Important Protozoa

The biology of protozoa is discussed in this chapter. Diseases caused by protozoa are described in Part Four.

Protozoa are a large and diverse group. Current schemes of classifying protozoan species into phyla are based on DNA data and morphology. As more information is obtained, some of the phyla discussed here may be grouped to form kingdoms.

Feeding Grooves

Single-celled eukaryotes with a feeding groove in the cytoskeleton have been placed in the Excavata superkingdom. Most are spindle-shaped and possess flagella (**Figure 18a**). This superkingdom includes two phyla that lack mitochondria and the phylum Euglenozoa.

A parasite without mitochondria is *Giardia lamblia* (jē-är′d ē-ä lam′lē-ä), sometimes called *G. intestinalis* or

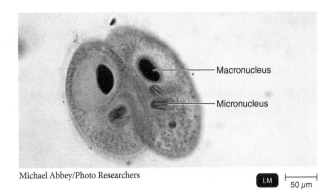

Michael Abbey/Photo Researchers

LM   50 μm

Figure 17 Conjugation in the ciliate protozoan *Paramecium*. Sexual reproduction in ciliates is by conjugation. Each cell has two nuclei: a micronucleus and a macronucleus. The micronucleus is haploid and is specialized for conjugation. One micronucleus from each cell will migrate to the other cell during conjugation. Both cells will then go on to produce two daughter cells. Condensed chromosomes are visible in the micronuclei.

Q   Does conjugation result in more cells?

G. duodenalis. The parasite (**Figure 18b**) is found in the small intestine of humans and other mammals. It is excreted in the feces as a cyst (**Figure 18c**) and survives in the environment before being ingested by the next host. Diagnosis of giardiasis, the disease caused by *G. lamblia,* is often based on the identification of cysts in feces.

Another human parasite that lacks mitochondria is *Trichomonas vaginalis* (trik-ō-mōn′as va-jin-al′is), shown in **Figure 18d.** Like some other flagellates, *T. vaginalis* has an **undulating membrane,** which consists of a membrane bordered by a flagellum. *T. vaginalis* does not have a cyst stage and must be transferred from host to host quickly before desiccation occurs. *T. vaginalis* is found in the vagina and in the male urinary tract. It is usually transmitted by sexual intercourse but can also be transmitted by toilet facilities or towels.

Euglenozoa

Two groups of flagellated cells are included in the **Euglenozoa** based on common rRNA sequences, disk-shaped mitochondria, and absence of sexual reproduction.

Euglenoids are photoautotrophs (**Figure 18e**). Euglenoids have a semirigid plasma membrane called a pellicle, and they move by means of a flagellum at the anterior end. Most euglenoids also have a red *eyespot* at the anterior end. This carotenoid-containing organelle senses light and directs the cell in the appropriate direction by using a *preemergent flagellum.* Some euglenoids are facultative chemoheterotrophs. In the dark, they ingest organic matter through a cytostome. Euglenoids are frequently studied with algae because they can photosynthesize.

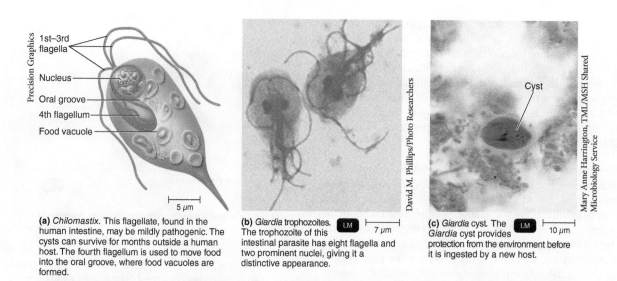

(a) *Chilomastix.* This flagellate, found in the human intestine, may be mildly pathogenic. The cysts can survive for months outside a human host. The fourth flagellum is used to move food into the oral groove, where food vacuoles are formed.

1st–3rd flagella
Nucleus
Oral groove
4th flagellum
Food vacuole
5 µm

Precision Graphics

(b) *Giardia* trophozoites. The trophozoite of this intestinal parasite has eight flagella and two prominent nuclei, giving it a distinctive appearance. LM 7 µm

David M. Phillips/Photo Researchers

(c) *Giardia* cyst. The *Giardia* cyst provides protection from the environment before it is ingested by a new host. LM 10 µm

Cyst

Mary Anne Harrington, TML/MSH Shared Microbiology Service

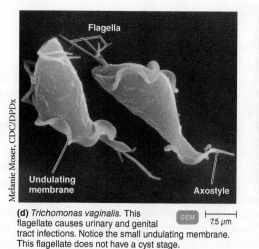

Flagella
Undulating membrane
Axostyle

Melanie Moser, CDC/DPDx

(d) *Trichomonas vaginalis.* This flagellate causes urinary and genital tract infections. Notice the small undulating membrane. This flagellate does not have a cyst stage. SEM 7.5 µm

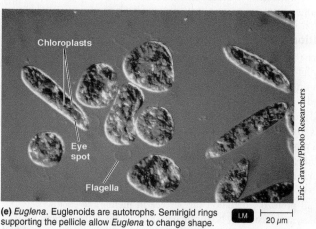

Chloroplasts
Eye spot
Flagella

Eric Graves/Photo Researchers

(e) *Euglena.* Euglenoids are autotrophs. Semirigid rings supporting the pellicle allow *Euglena* to change shape. LM 20 µm

Figure 18 Members of the super kingdom Excavata.

Q How does *Giardia* obtain energy without mitochondria?

The **hemoflagellates** (blood parasites) are transmitted by the bites of blood-feeding insects and are found in the circulatory system of the bitten host. To survive in this viscous fluid, hemoflagellates usually have long, slender bodies and an undulating membrane. The genus *Trypanosoma* (tri-pa′nō-sō-mä) includes the species that causes African sleeping sickness, *T. brucei* (brüs′ē), which is transmitted by the tsetse fly. *T. cruzi* (kruz′ē), the causative agent of Chagas' disease, is transmitted by the "kissing bug," so named because it bites on the face (see Figure 33d). After entering the insect, the trypanosome rapidly multiplies by schizogony. If the insect then defecates while

biting a human, it can release trypanosomes that can contaminate the bite wound.

Amebae

The **amebae** move by extending blunt, lobelike projections of the cytoplasm called **pseudopods** (Figure 19a). Any number of pseudopods can flow from one side of the ameba, and the rest of the cell will flow toward the pseudopods.

Entamoeba histolytica (en-ta-me′ba his-to-li′ti-ka) is the only pathogenic ameba found in the human intestine. As many as 10% of the human population may be colonized by this ameba. New techniques, including DNA analyses and lectin binding, have revealed that the ameba thought to be *E. histo-lytica* are actually two distinct species. The nonpathogenic species, *E. dispar* (dis'par) is most common. The invasive *E. histolytica* (**Figure 19b**) causes amebic dysentery. In the human intestine, *E. histolytica* uses proteins called lectins to attach to the galactose of the plasma membrane and causes cell lysis. *E. dispar* does not have galactose-binding lectins. *Entamoeba* is transmitted between humans through ingestion of the cysts that are excreted in the feces of the infected person. *Acanthamoeba* (a-kan-thä-mē'bä) growing in water, including tap water, can infect the cornea and cause blindness.

Since 1990, *Balamuthia* (bal'am-üth-ē-ä) has been reported as the cause of brain abscesses called granulomatous amebic encephalitis in the United States and other countries. The ameba most often infects immunocompromised people. Like *Acanthamoeba*, *Balamuthia* is a free-living ameba found in water and is not transmitted from human to human.

Apicomplexa

The **Apicomplexa** are not motile in their mature forms and are obligate intracellular parasites. Apicomplexans are characterized by the presence of a complex of special organelles at the apexes (tips) of their cells (hence the phylum name). The organelles in these apical complexes contain enzymes that penetrate the host's tissues.

Apicomplexans have a complex life cycle that involves transmission between several hosts. An example of an apicomplexan is *Plasmodium* (plaz-mō'dē-um), the causative agent of malaria. Malaria affects 10% of the world's population, with 300 to 500 million new cases each year. The complex life cycle makes it difficult to develop a vaccine against malaria.

Plasmodium grows by sexual reproduction in the *Anopheles* (an-of'el-ēz) mosquito (**Figure 20**). When an *Anopheles* carrying the infective stage of *Plasmodium*, called a **sporozoite**, bites a human, sporozoites can be injected into the human. The sporozoites undergo schizogony in liver cells and produce thousands of progeny called **merozoites**, which infect red blood cells. The young trophozoite looks like a ring in which the nucleus and cytoplasm are visible. This is called a **ring stage** . The red blood cells eventually rupture and release more merozoites. Upon release of the merozoites, their waste products, which cause fever and chills, are also released. Most of the merozoites infect new red blood cells and perpetuate their cycle of asexual reproduction. However, some develop into male and female sexual forms (gametocytes). Even though the gametocytes themselves cause no further damage, they can be picked up by the bite of another *Anopheles* mosquito; they then enter the mosquito's intestine and begin their sexual cycle. Their progeny can then be injected into a new human host by the biting mosquito.

The mosquito is the **definitive host** because it harbors the sexually reproducing stage of *Plasmodium*. The host in which

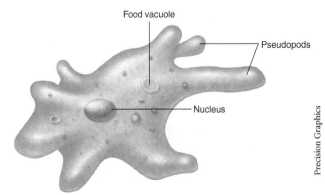

(a) *Amoeba proteus*

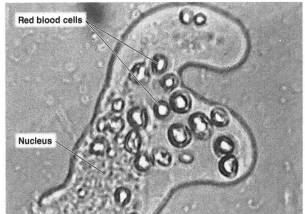

(b) *Entamoeba histolytica*

LM   5 μm

Figure 19 Amebae. (**a**) To move and to engulf food, amebae (such as this *Amoeba proteus*) extend cytoplasmic structures called pseudopods. Food vacuoles are created when pseudopods surround food and bring it into the cell. (**b**) *Entamoeba histolytica*. The presence of ingested red blood cells is diagnostic for *Entamoeba*.

Q How do amebic dysentery and bacillary dysentery differ?

From: "Alteration of isoenzyme patterns of a cloned culture of non pathogenic Entamoeba histolytica upon changes in growth conditions." D. Mirelman, et al. *Arch Invest Med* (Mex). 1986;17 Suppl 1:187–93. Copyright Elsevier 1986

Precision Graphics

the parasite undergoes asexual reproduction (in this case, the human) is the **intermediate host.**

Malaria is diagnosed in the laboratory by microscopic observation of thick blood smears for the presence of *Plasmodium*. A peculiar characteristic of malaria is that the interval between periods of fever caused by the release of merozoites is always the same for a given species of *Plasmodium* and is always a multiple of 24 hours. The reason and mechanism for such precision have intrigued scientists. After all, why should a parasite need a biological clock? *Plasmodium*'s development is regulated by the host's body temperature, which normally fluctuates over a 24-hour period. The parasite's careful timing ensures that gametocytes are mature at night, when *Anopheles* mosquitoes are

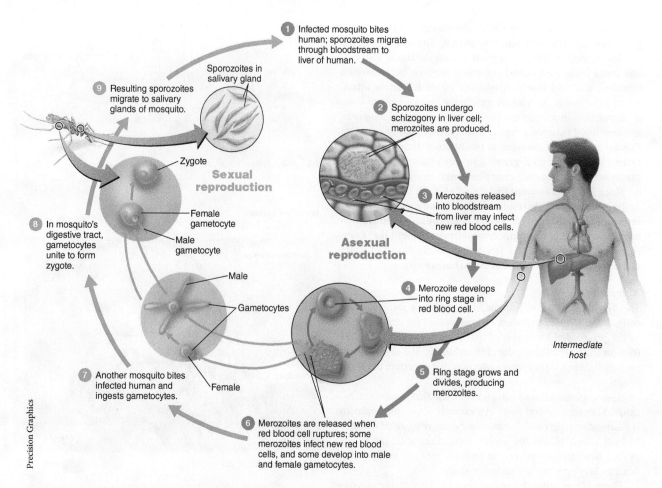

1 Infected mosquito bites human; sporozoites migrate through bloodstream to liver of human.

2 Sporozoites undergo schizogony in liver cell; merozoites are produced.

3 Merozoites released into bloodstream from liver may infect new red blood cells.

4 Merozoite develops into ring stage in red blood cell.

5 Ring stage grows and divides, producing merozoites.

6 Merozoites are released when red blood cell ruptures; some merozoites infect new red blood cells, and some develop into male and female gametocytes.

7 Another mosquito bites infected human and ingests gametocytes.

8 In mosquito's digestive tract, gametocytes unite to form zygote.

9 Resulting sporozoites migrate to salivary glands of mosquito.

Sporozoites in salivary gland

Zygote

Sexual reproduction

Female gametocyte

Male gametocyte

Male

Gametocytes

Female

Asexual reproduction

Intermediate host

Precision Graphics

Figure 20 The life cycle of *Plasmodium vivax*, the apicomplexan that causes malaria.
Asexual reproduction (schizogony) of the parasite takes place in the liver and in the red blood cells of a human host. Sexual reproduction occurs in the intestine of an *Anopheles* mosquito after the mosquito has ingested gametocytes.

Q What is the definitive host for *Plasmodium*?

feeding, and thereby facilitates transmission of the parasite to a new host.

Another apicomplexan parasite of red blood cells is *Babesia microti* (ba-bē′sē-ä mī-krō′tē). *Babesia* causes fever and anemia in immunosuppressed individuals. In the United States, it is transmitted by the tick *Ixodes scapularis* (iks-ō′ dēs skap-ū-lār′is).

Toxoplasma gondii (toks-ō-plaz′mä gon′dē-ē) is another apicomplexan intracellular parasite of humans. The life cycle of this parasite involves domestic cats. The trophozoites, called **tachyzoites,** reproduce sexually and asexually in an infected cat, and **oocysts,** each containing eight sporozoites, are excreted with feces. If the oocysts are ingested by humans or other animals, the sporozoites emerge as trophozoites, which can reproduce in the tissues of the new host. *T. gondii* is dangerous to

pregnant women because it can cause congenital infections in utero. Tissue examination and observation of *T. gondii* are used for diagnosis. Antibodies may be detected by ELISA and by indirect fluorescent-antibody tests.

Cryptosporidium (krip-tō-spô-ri′dē-um) lives inside the cells lining the small intestine and can be transmitted to humans through the feces of cows, rodents, dogs, and cats. Inside the host cell, each *Cryptosporidium* organism forms four oocysts, each containing four sporozoites. When the oocyst ruptures, sporozoites may infect new cells in the host or be released with the feces. See the Clinical Focus later in this chapter.

During the 1980s, epidemics of waterborne diarrhea were identified on every continent except Antarctica. The causative agent was misidentified as a cyanobacterium because the outbreaks occurred during warm months, and the disease agent looked like a prokaryotic cell. In 1993, the organism was identified as an apicomplexan similar to *Cryptosporidium*. In 2004, the new parasite, named *Cyclospora cayetanensis* (sĭ′klō-spô-rä kī′ē-tan-en-sis), was responsible for 300 cases of diarrhea associated with snowpeas in the United States and Canada.

Ciliates

Ciliates have cilia that are similar to but shorter than flagella. The cilia are arranged in precise rows on the cell (Figure 21). They are moved in unison to propel the cell through its environment and to bring food particles to the mouth.

The only ciliate that is a human parasite is *Balantidium coli* (bal-an-tid′ē-um kō′lī), the causative agent of a severe, though rare, type of dysentery. When the host ingests cysts, they enter the large intestine, into which the trophozoites are released. The trophozoites produce proteases and other substances that destroy host cells. The trophozoite feeds on host cells and tissue fragments. Its cysts are excreted with feces.

Table 4 lists some typical parasitic protozoa and the diseases they cause.

CHECK YOUR UNDERSTANDING

✔ Identify three differences between protozoa and animals. 10

✔ Do protozoa have mitochondria? 11

✔ Where does *Plasmodium* undergo sexual reproduction? 12

Slime Molds

LEARNING OBJECTIVE

13 Compare and contrast cellular slime molds and plasmodial slime molds.

Slime molds are closely related to amebae and are placed in the phylum Amoebozoa. There are two taxa of slime molds: cellular and plasmodial. **Cellular slime molds** are typical eukaryotic cells that resemble amebae. In the life cycle of cellular slime molds (Figure 22), the ameboid cells live and grow by ingesting fungi and bacteria by phagocytosis. Cellular slime molds are of interest to biologists who study cellular migration and aggregation, because when conditions are unfavorable, large numbers of ameboid cells aggregate to form a single structure. This aggregation occurs because some individual amebae produce the chemical cyclic AMP (cAMP), toward which the other amebae migrate. Some of the ameboid cells form a stalk; others swarm up the stalk to form a spore cap, and most of these differentiate into spores. When spores are released under favorable conditions, they germinate to form single amebae.

In 1973, a Dallas resident discovered a pulsating red blob in his backyard. The news media claimed that a "new life form" had been found. For some people, the "creature" evoked spine-chilling recollections of an old science fiction movie. Before

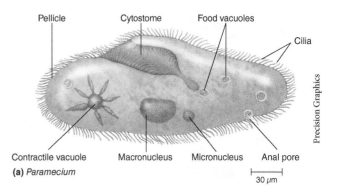

(a) *Paramecium*

Labels: Pellicle, Cytostome, Food vacuoles, Cilia, Contractile vacuole, Macronucleus, Micronucleus, Anal pore

30 µm

Precision Graphics

Frank Fox/Photo Researchers

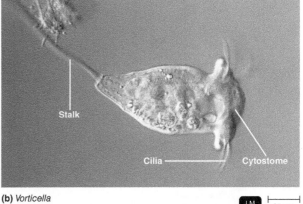

(b) *Vorticella*

Labels: Stalk, Cilia, Cytostome

 LM · 25 µm

Figure 21 Ciliates. **(a)** *Paramecium* is covered with rows of cilia. It has specialized structures for ingestion (mouth), elimination of wastes (anal pore), and the regulation of osmotic pressure (contractile vacuoles). The macronucleus is involved with protein synthesis and other ongoing cellular activities. The micronucleus functions in sexual reproduction. **(b)** *Vorticella* attaches to objects in water by the base of its stalk. The springlike stalk can expand allowing *Vorticella* to feed in different areas. Cilia surround its cytostome.

Q What ciliate can cause disease in humans?

imaginations got carried away too far, biologists calmed everyone's worst fears (or highest hopes). The amorphous mass was merely a plasmodial slime mold, they explained. But its unusually large size—46 cm in diameter—startled even scientists.

Plasmodial slime molds were first scientifically reported in 1729. A plasmodial slime mold exists as a mass of protoplasm with many nuclei (it is multinucleated). This mass of protoplasm is called a **plasmodium** (Figure 23). The entire plasmodium moves as a giant ameba; it engulfs organic debris and bacteria. Biologists have found that musclelike proteins forming microfilaments account for the movement of the plasmodium.

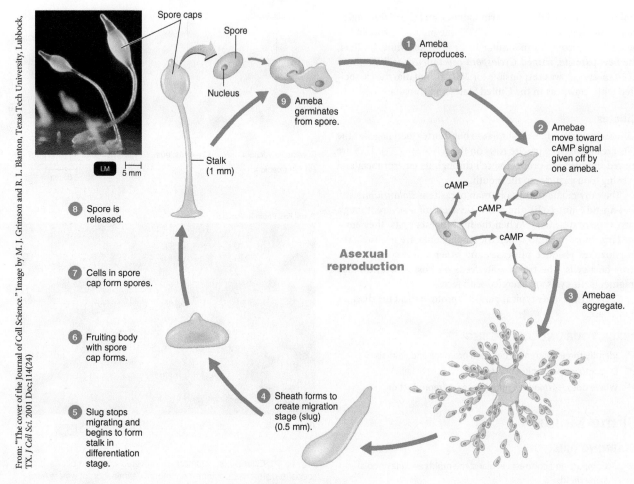

From: "The cover of the Journal of Cell Science." Image by M. J. Grimson and R. L. Blanton, Texas Tech University, Lubbock, TX. *J Cell Sci.* 2001 Dec;114(24)

Figure 22 **The generalized life cycle of a cellular slime mold.** The micrograph shows a spore cap of *Dictyostelium.*

Q What characteristics do slime molds share with protozoa? With fungi?

When plasmodial slime molds are grown in laboratories, a phenomenon called **cytoplasmic streaming** is observed, during which the protoplasm within the plasmodium moves and changes both its speed and direction so that the oxygen and nutrients are evenly distributed. The plasmodium continues to grow as long as there is enough food and moisture for it to thrive.

When either is in short supply, the plasmodium separates into many groups of protoplasm; each of these groups forms a stalked sporangium, in which haploid spores (a resistant, resting form of the slime mold) develop. When conditions improve, these spores germinate, fuse to form diploid cells, and develop into a multinucleated plasmodium.

CHECK YOUR UNDERSTANDING

✔ Why are slime molds classified with amebae and not fungi? **13**

Helminths

LEARNING OBJECTIVES

14 List the distinguishing characteristics of parasitic helminths.

15 Provide a rationale for the elaborate life cycle of parasitic worms.

16 List the characteristics of the two classes of parasitic platyhelminths, and give an example of each.

17 Describe a parasitic infection in which humans serve as a definitive host, as an intermediate host, and as both.

18 List the characteristics of parasitic nematodes, and give an example of infective eggs and infective larvae.

19 Compare and contrast platyhelminths and nematodes.

A number of parasitic animals spend part or all of their lives in humans. Most of these animals belong to two phyla:

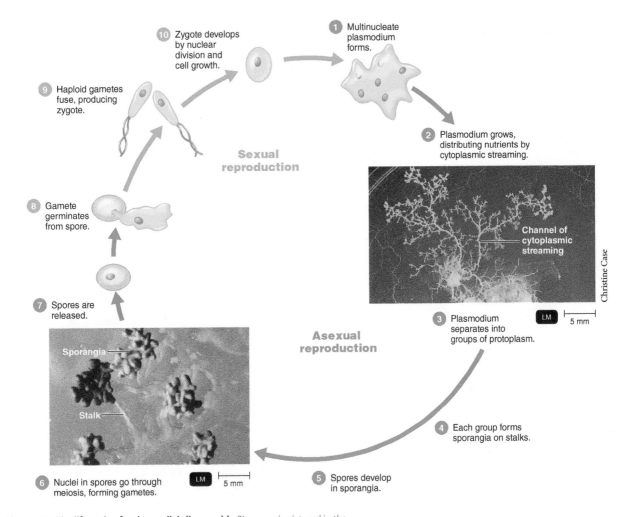

10 Zygote develops by nuclear division and cell growth.

1 Multinucleate plasmodium forms.

9 Haploid gametes fuse, producing zygote.

Sexual reproduction

2 Plasmodium grows, distributing nutrients by cytoplasmic streaming.

8 Gamete germinates from spore.

Channel of cytoplasmic streaming

Christine Case

LM 5 mm

7 Spores are released.

3 Plasmodium separates into groups of protoplasm.

Asexual reproduction

Sporangia

Stalk

6 Nuclei in spores go through meiosis, forming gametes.

LM 5 mm

5 Spores develop in sporangia.

4 Each group forms sporangia on stalks.

Figure 23 The life cycle of a plasmodial slime mold. *Physarum* is pictured in the photomicrographs.

Q How do cellular and acellular slime molds differ?

Platyhelminthes (flatworms) and Nematoda (roundworms). These worms are commonly called **helminths**. There are also free-living species in these phyla, but we will limit our discussion to the parasitic species. Diseases caused by parasitic worms are discussed in Part Four.

Characteristics of Helminths

Helminths are multicellular eukaryotic animals that generally possess digestive, circulatory, nervous, excretory, and reproductive systems. Parasitic helminths must be highly specialized to live inside their hosts. The following generalizations distinguish parasitic helminths from their free-living relatives:

1. *They may lack a digestive system.* They can absorb nutrients from the host's food, body fluids, and tissues.
2. *Their nervous system is reduced.* They do not need an extensive nervous system because they do not have to search for food or respond much to their environment. The environment within a host is fairly constant.
3. *Their means of locomotion is occasionally reduced or completely lacking.* Because they are transferred from host to host, they do not need to search actively for a suitable habitat.
4. *Their reproductive system is often complex.* An individual produces large numbers of eggs, by which a suitable host is infected.

TABLE **4** **Some Representative Parasitic Protozoa**

Phylum	Human Pathogens	Distinguishing Features	Disease	Source of Human Infections
Diplomonads	*Giardia lamblia*	Two nuclei, eight flagella	Giardial enteritis	Fecal contamination of drinking water
Parabasalids	*Trichomonas vaginalis*	No encysting stage	Urethritis, vaginitis	Contact with vaginal-urethral discharge
Euglenozoa	*Leishmania*	Flagellated form in sand fly; ovoid form in vertebrate host	Leishmaniasis	Bite of sand fly (*Phlebotomus*)
	Naegleria fowleri	Flagellated and ameboid forms	Meningoencephalitis	Water in which people swim
	Trypanosoma cruzi	Undulating membrane	Chagas' disease	Bite of *Triatoma* (kissing bug)
	T. brucei gambiense, T.b. rhodesiense		African trypanosomiasis	Bite of tsetse fly
Amebae	*Acanthamoeba*	Pseudopods	Keratitis	Water
	Entamoeba histolytica, E. dispar		Amebic dysentery	Fecal contamination of drinking water
	Balamuthia		Encephalitis	Water
Apicomplexa	*Babesia microti*	Complex	Babesiosis	Domestic animals, ticks
	Cryptosporidium	Life cycles may require more than one host	Diarrhea	Humans, other animals, water
	Cyclospora	—	Diarrhea	Water
	Plasmodium	—	Malaria	Bite of *Anopheles* mosquito
	Toxoplasma gondii	—	Toxoplasmosis	Cats, beef; congenital
Dinoflagellates	*Alexandrium, Pfiesteria*	Photosynthetic, (see Table 3)	Paralytic shellfish poisoning; ciguatera	Ingestion of dinoflagellates in mollusks, fish
Ciliates	*Balantidium coli*	Only parasitic ciliate of humans	Balantidial dysentery	Fecal contamination of drinking water

Life Cycle

The life cycle of parasitic helminths can be extremely complex, involving a succession of intermediate hosts for completion of each **larval** (developmental) stage of the parasite and a definitive host for the adult parasite.

Adult helminths may be **dioecious;** male reproductive organs are in one individual, and female reproductive organs are in another. In those species, reproduction occurs only when two adults of the opposite sex are in the same host.

Adult helminths may also be **monoecious,** or **hermaphroditic**—one animal has both male and female reproductive organs. Two hermaphrodites may copulate and simultaneously fertilize each other. A few types of hermaphrodites fertilize themselves.

CHECK YOUR UNDERSTANDING

🖎 Why are the drugs used to treat parasitic helminths often toxic to the host? 14

🖎 Of what value is the complicated life cycle of parasitic helminths? 15

Platyhelminths

Members of the phylum Platyhelminthes, the **flatworms,** are dorsoventrally flattened. The classes of parasitic flatworms include the trematodes and cestodes. These parasites cause disease or developmental disturbances in a wide variety of animals (Figure 24).

Trematodes

Trematodes, or **flukes,** often have flat, leaf-shaped bodies with a ventral sucker and an oral sucker (Figure 25). The suckers hold the organism in place. Flukes obtain food by absorbing it through their nonliving outer covering, called the **cuticle.** Flukes are given common names according to the tissue of the definitive host in which the adults live (for example, lung fluke, liver fluke, blood

The Most Frequent Cause of Recreational Waterborne Diarrhea

Melanie Moser, CDC/DPDx

As you read through this box, you will encounter a series of questions that microbiologists ask themselves as they try to diagnose a disease. Try to answer each question before going on to the next one.

1. One week after her birthday party, 8-year-old Chloe had watery diarrhea, vomiting, and abdominal cramping. Her mother took her to the pediatrician because Chloe's symptoms were not going away on their own.
   What diseases are possible?

2. Possible diseases included giardiasis, cryptosporidiosis, *Cyclospora* diarrheal infection, and amebic dysentery. Chloe's pediatrician took a stool sample from Chloe and sent it to the lab for testing. The result of acid-fast staining of her stool is shown in **Figure A**.
   What is the disease?

3. The acid-fast staining stains the *Cryptosporidium* oocysts red, therefore making them easy to identify. In this case, the sporozoites are made visible inside the oocyst at the arrow. The oocysts are infectious immediately upon being excreted in feces.
   What else do you need to know?

4. Chloe's birthday party was held at a community water park. Chloe's mother immediately followed up with the parents of the other children who attended the party. She found out that the other 20 children also had watery diarrhea, vomiting, or abdominal cramps. All the children recovered from the infection 2 to 10 days after becoming ill.
   How is this disease transmitted?

5. *Cryptosporidium* infection is transmitted by the fecal-oral route. It results from ingesting *Cryptosporidium* oocysts through the

consumption of fecally contaminated food or water or through direct person-to-person or animal-to-person contact. The infectious dose is low; feeding studies have demonstrated that ingesting as few as 10 to 30 oocysts can cause infection in healthy persons. Infected persons have been reported to shed 10^8 to 10^9 oocysts in a single bowel movement and to excrete oocysts for up to 50 days after cessation of diarrhea.

Cryptosporidium has emerged as the most frequently recognized cause of recreational water-associated outbreaks of gastroenteritis, even in venues with disinfected water. It became a reportable disease in 1994 (**Figure B**).

How Can *Cryptosporidium* Outbreaks Be Prevented?
Cryptosporidium species are known to be resistant to most chemical disinfectants, such as chlorine. Recommendations to reduce the risk of infection include the following:

Figure A Acid-fast stain of Chloe's feces.

- Do not swim during and for 2 weeks after diarrheal illness.
- Avoid swallowing pool water.
- Wash hands after using the restroom or changing diapers.

Source: Adapted from *MMWR* 58(22):615–618, June 12, 2009.

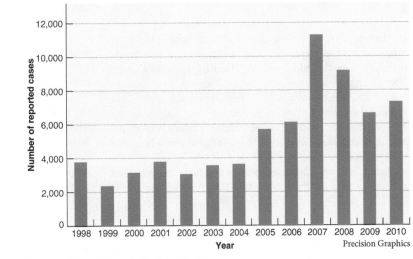

Figure B Reported cases in the United States.

fluke). The Asian liver fluke *Clonorchis sinensis* (klo-nôr′kis si-nen′sis) is occasionally seen in immigrants in the United States, but it cannot be transmitted because its intermediate hosts are not in the United States.

To exemplify a fluke's life cycle, let's look at the lung fluke, *Paragonimus*, spp (păr-ä-gŏn′e-mus). *Paragonimus* species occur throughout the world. *P. kellicotti* (kel′li-kot-tē), endemic in the United States, has been associated with eating raw

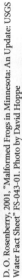

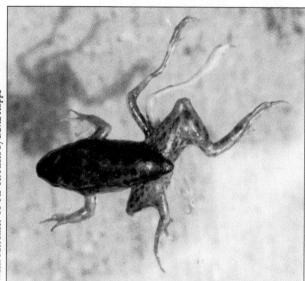

Figure 24 Infection by a parasitic platyhelminth. An increase in the trematode *Ribeiroia* in recent years has caused deformed frogs. Frogs with multiple limbs have been found from Minnesota to California. Cercaria of the trematode infect tadpoles. The encysted metacercariae displace developing limb buds, causing abnormal limb development. The increase in the parasite may be due to fertilizer runoff that increases algae, which are food for the parasite's intermediate host snail.

Q What tailed stage of the parasite lives in a snail?

crayfish on river raft trips. The adult lung fluke lives in the bronchioles of humans and other mammals and is approximately 6 mm wide and 12 mm long. The hermaphroditic adults liberate eggs into the bronchi. Because sputum that contains eggs is frequently swallowed, the eggs are usually excreted in feces of the definitive host. If the life cycle is to continue, the eggs must reach a body of water. A series of steps occurs that ensure adult flukes can mature in the lungs of a new host. The life cycle is shown in Figure 26.

In a laboratory diagnosis, sputum and feces are examined microscopically for fluke eggs. Infection results from eating

undercooked freshwater crustaceans, and the disease can be prevented by thoroughly cooking crayfish and freshwater crabs.

The cercariae of the blood fluke *Schistosoma* (shis-tō-sō′ma) are not ingested. Instead, they burrow through the skin of the human host and enter the circulatory system. The adults are found in certain abdominal and pelvic veins. The disease schistosomiasis is a major world health problem.

Cestodes

Cestodes, or **tapeworms**, are intestinal parasites. Their structure is shown in Figure 27. The head, or **scolex** (plural: *scoleces*), has suckers for attaching to the intestinal mucosa of the definitive host; some species also have small hooks for attachment. Tapeworms do not ingest the tissues of their hosts; in fact, they completely lack a digestive system. To obtain nutrients from the small intestine, they absorb food through their cuticle. The body consists of segments called **proglottids**. Proglottids are continually produced by the neck region of the scolex, as long as the scolex is attached and alive. Each mature proglottid contains both male and female reproductive organs. The proglottids farthest away from the scolex are the mature ones containing eggs. Mature proglottids are essentially bags of eggs, each of which is infective to the proper intermediate host.

Humans as Definitive Hosts The adults of *Taenia saginata* (te′nē-ä sa-ji-nä′tä), the beef tapeworm, live in humans and can reach a length of 6 m. The scolex is about 2 mm long and is followed by a thousand or more proglottids. The feces of an infected human contain mature proglottids, each of which contains thousands of eggs. As the proglottids wriggle away from the fecal material, they increase their chances of being ingested by an animal that is grazing. Upon ingestion by cattle, the larvae hatch from the eggs and bore through the intestinal wall. The larvae migrate to muscle (meat), in which they encyst as **cysticerci**. When the cysticerci are ingested by humans, all but the scolex is digested. The scolex anchors itself in the small intestine and begins producing proglottids.

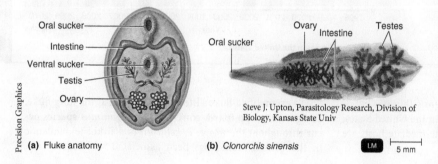

Oral sucker
Intestine
Ventral sucker
Testis
Ovary

Oral sucker

Ovary
Intestine
Testes

Steve J. Upton, Parasitology Research, Division of Biology, Kansas State Univ

(a) Fluke anatomy

(b) *Clonorchis sinensis*

LM 5 mm

Precision Graphics

Figure 25 Flukes. (a) General anatomy of an adult fluke, shown in cross section. The oral and ventral suckers attach the fluke to the host. The mouth is located in the center of the oral sucker. Flukes are hermaphroditic; each animal contains both testes and ovaries. **(b)** The Asian liver fluke *Clonorchis sinensis*. Notice the incomplete digestive system. Heavy infestations may block bile ducts from the liver.

Q Why is the flatworm digestive system called "incomplete"?

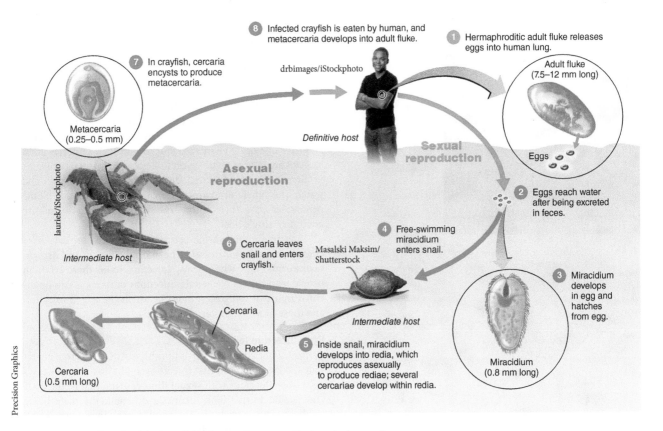

Figure 26 The life cycle of the lung fluke, *Paragonimus*, spp. The trematode reproduces sexually in a human and asexually in a snail, its first intermediate host. Larvae encysted in the second intermediate host, freshwater crabs and crayfish, infect humans and other mammals when ingested.

Q Of what value is this complex life cycle to *Paragonimus*?

Diagnosis of tapeworm infection in humans is based on the presence of mature proglottids and eggs in feces. Cysticerci can be seen macroscopically in meat; their presence is referred to as "measly beef." Inspecting beef that is intended for human consumption for "measly" appearance is one way to prevent infections by beef tapeworm. Another method of prevention is to avoid the use of untreated human sewage as fertilizer in grazing pastures.

Humans are the only known definitive host of the pork tapeworm, *Taenia solium*. Adult worms living in the human intestine produce eggs, which are passed out in feces. When eggs are eaten by pigs, the larval helminth encysts in the pig's muscles; humans become infected when they eat undercooked pork. The human-pig-human cycle of *T. solium* is common in Latin America, Asia, and Africa. In the United States, however, *T. solium* is virtually nonexistent in pigs; the parasite is transmitted from human to human. Eggs shed by one person and ingested by another person

hatch, and the larvae encyst in the brain and other parts of the body, causing cysticercosis. The human hosting *T. solium*'s larvae is serving as an intermediate host. Approximately 7% of the few hundred cases reported in recent years were acquired by people who had never been outside the United States. They may have become infected through household contact with people who were born in or had traveled in other countries.

Humans as Intermediate Hosts Humans are the intermediate hosts for *Echinococcus granulosus* (ē-kīn-ō-kok'kus gra-nū-lō'sus), shown in **Figure 28**. Dogs and coyotes are the definitive hosts for this minute (2–8 mm) tapeworm.

1 Eggs are excreted with feces.

2 Eggs are ingested by deer, sheep, or humans. Humans can also become infected by contaminating their hands with dog feces or saliva from a dog that has licked itself.

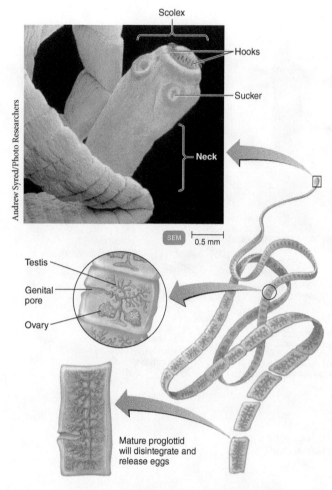

Figure 27 **General anatomy of an adult tapeworm.** The scolex, shown in the micrograph, consists of suckers and hooks that attach to the host's tissues. The body lengthens as new proglottids form at the neck. Each mature proglottid contains both testes and ovaries.

Q What are the similarities between tapeworms and flukes?

③ The eggs hatch in the human's small intestine, and the larvae migrate to the liver or lungs.

④ The larva develops into a **hydatid cyst.** The cyst contains "brood capsules," from which thousands of scoleces might be produced.

⑤ Humans are a dead-end for the parasite, but in the wild, the cysts might be in a deer that is eaten by a wolf.

⑥ The scoleces would be able to attach themselves in the wolf's intestine and produce proglottids.

Diagnosis of hydatid cysts is frequently made only on autopsy, although X rays can detect the cysts.

CHECK YOUR UNDERSTANDING

✔ Differentiate *Paragonimus* and *Taenia.* 16

Nematodes

Members of the Phylum Nematoda, the **roundworms,** are cylindrical and tapered at each end. Roundworms have a *complete* digestive system, consisting of a mouth, an intestine, and an anus. Most species are dioecious. Males are smaller than females and have one or two hardened **spicules** on their posterior ends. Spicules are used to guide sperm to the female's genital pore.

Some species of nematodes are free-living in soil and water, and others are parasites on plants and animals. Some nematodes pass their entire life cycle, from egg to mature adult, in a single host.

Intestinal roundworms are the most common causes of chronic infectious diseases. The most common are *Ascaris,* hookworms, and whipworms, infecting more than 2 billion people world wide. Nematode infections of humans can be divided into two categories: those in which the egg is infective, and those in which the larva is infective.

Eggs Infective for Humans

Ascaris lumbricoides (as'kar-is lum-bri-koi'dēz) is a large nematode (30 cm in length) that infects over 1 billion people worldwide. It is dioecious with **sexual dimorphism;** that is, the male and female worms look distinctly different, the male being smaller with a curled tail. The adult *Ascaris* lives in the small intestines of humans exclusively; it feeds primarily on semidigested food. Eggs, excreted with feces, can survive in the soil for long periods until accidentally ingested by another host. The eggs hatch in the small intestine of the host. The larvae then burrow out of the intestine and enter the blood. They are carried to the lungs, where they grow. The larvae will then be coughed up, swallowed, and returned to the small intestine, where they mature into adults.

Raccoon roundworm, *Baylisascaris procyonis,* is an emerging roundworm in North America. Raccoons are the definitive host, although the adult roundworm can also live in domestic dogs. Eggs are shed with feces and ingested by an intermediate host, usually a rabbit. The ingested eggs hatch in the intestines of rabbits and humans. The larvae migrate through a variety of tissues, causing a condition called *larva migrans.* Infection often results in severe neurological symptom or death. Larva migrans can also be caused by *Toxocara canis* (from dogs) and *T. cati* (from cats). These companion animals are the intermediate and definitive hosts, but humans can become infected by ingesting *Toxocara* eggs shed in the animals' feces. It is estimated that 14% of the U.S. population has been infected. Children are most likely to be infected probably because they play in soil and sandboxes, where animal feces can be found.

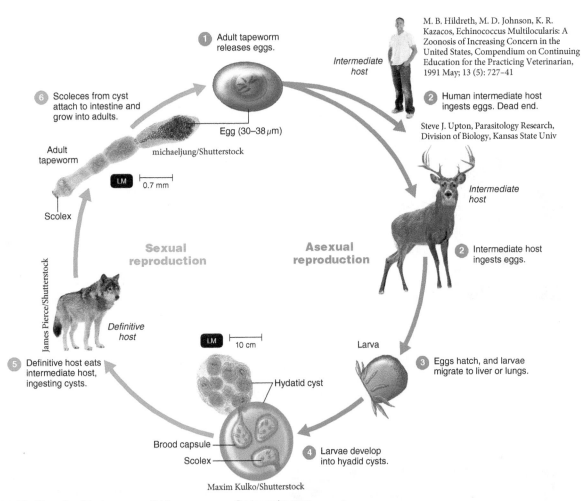

① Adult tapeworm releases eggs.

Egg (30–38 μm)

michaeljung/Shutterstock

LM 0.7 mm

⑥ Scoleces from cyst attach to intestine and grow into adults.

Adult tapeworm

Scolex

Sexual reproduction

James Pierce/Shutterstock

Definitive host

⑤ Definitive host eats intermediate host, ingesting cysts.

LM 10 cm

Hydatid cyst

Brood capsule

Scolex

Maxim Kulko/Shutterstock

Asexual reproduction

Intermediate host

M. B. Hildreth, M. D. Johnson, K. R. Kazacos, Echinococcus Multilocularis: A Zoonosis of Increasing Concern in the United States, Compendium on Continuing Education for the Practicing Veterinarian, 1991 May; 13 (5): 727–41

② Human intermediate host ingests eggs. Dead end.

Steve J. Upton, Parasitology Research, Division of Biology, Kansas State Univ

Intermediate host

② Intermediate host ingests eggs.

Larva

③ Eggs hatch, and larvae migrate to liver or lungs.

④ Larvae develop into hyadid cysts.

Figure 28 The life cycle of the tapeworm, *Echinococcus*, spp. Dogs are the most common definitive host of *E. granulosus*. *E. multilocularis* infections in humans are rare. The parasite can complete its life cycle only if the cysts are ingested by a definitive host that eats the intermediate host.

Q Why isn't being in a human of benefit to *Echinococcus*?

One billion people worldwide are infected with *Trichuris trichiura*, or whipworm. The worms are spread from person to person by fecal–oral transmission or through feces-contaminated food. The disease occurs most often in areas with tropical weather and poor sanitation practices and among children.

The pinworm *Enterobius vermicularis* (en-te-rō′bē-us ver-mi-kū-lar′is) spends its entire life in a human host (Figure 29). Adult pinworms are found in the large intestine. From there, the female pinworm migrates to the anus to deposit her eggs on the perianal skin. The eggs can be ingested by the host or by another person exposed through contaminated clothing or bedding.

Larvae Infective for Humans

Adult hookworms, *Necator americanus* (ne-kā′tôr ä-me-ri-ka′nus) and *Ancylostoma duodenale* (an-sil-os′toma dü′o-den-al-ē), live in the small intestine of humans; the eggs are excreted in feces. The larvae hatch in the soil, where they feed on bacteria. A larva enters its host by penetrating the host's skin. It then enters a blood or lymph vessel, which carries it to the lungs. It is coughed up in sputum, swallowed, and finally carried to the small intestine.

Trichinellosis is caused by a nematode that the host acquires by eating encysted larvae in undercooked meat of infected animals. The nematode, *Dirofilaria immitis* (dir′ō-fi-lār-ē-ä im′mi-tis), is spread from host to host through the bites

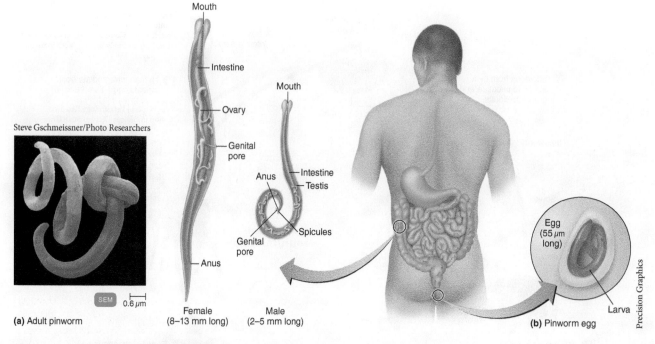

Steve Gschmeissner/Photo Researchers

(a) Adult pinworm

Mouth

Intestine

Ovary

Genital pore

Anus

Female
(8–13 mm long)

Mouth

Intestine

Testis

Anus

Spicules

Genital pore

Male
(2–5 mm long)

Egg
(55 μm long)

Larva

(b) Pinworm egg

Precision Graphics

Figure 29 The pinworm *Enterobius vermicularis*. **(a)** Adult pinworms live in the large intestine of humans. Most roundworms are dioecious, and the female (left and photomicrograph) is often distinctly larger than the male (right). **(b)** Pinworm eggs are deposited by the female on the perianal skin at night.

Q Are humans the definitive or intermediate host for pinworms?

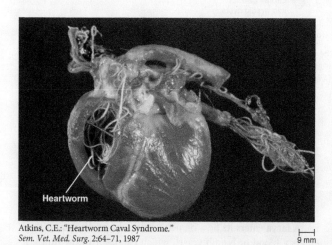

Heartworm

Atkins, C.E.: "Heartworm Caval Syndrome."
Sem. Vet. Med. Surg. 2:64–71, 1987

9 mm

Figure 30 The heartworm *Dirofilaria immitis*. Four adult *D. immitis* in the right ventricle of a dog's heart. Each worm is 12–30 cm long.

Q How do roundworms and flatworms differ?

of *Aedes* mosquitoes. It primarily affects dogs and cats, but it can infest human skin, conjunctiva, or lungs. Larvae injected by the mosquito migrate to various organs, where they mature into adults. The parasitic worm is called a **heartworm** because the adult stage is often in the animal host's heart, where it can kill its host through congestive heart failure (**Figure 30**). The disease occurs on every continent except Antarctica. *Wolbachia* bacteria appear to be essential to development of the worm embryos.

Four genera of roundworms called *anisakines*, or wriggly worms, can be transmitted to humans from infected fish and squid. Anisakine larvae are in the fish's intestinal mesenteries and migrate to the muscle when the fish dies. Freezing or thorough cooking will kill the larvae.

Table 5 lists representative parasitic helminths of each phylum and class and the diseases they cause.

CHECK YOUR UNDERSTANDING

✔ What is the definitive host for *Enterobius*? **17**

✔ What stage of *Dirofilaria immitis* is infectious for dogs and cats? **18**

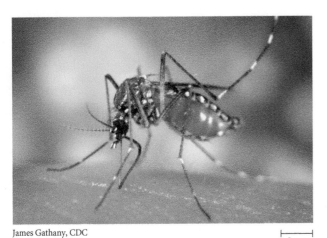

James Gathany, CDC

2 mm

Figure 31 Mosquito. A female mosquito sucking blood from human skin. Mosquitoes transmit several pathogens from person to person, including the yellow fever and West Nile viruses.

Q When is a vector also a definitive host?

✔ You find a parasitic worm in a baby's diapers. How would you know whether it's a *Taenia* or a *Necator*? **19**

Arthropods as Vectors

LEARNING OBJECTIVES

20 Define *arthropod vector*.

21 Differentiate a tick from a mosquito, and name a disease transmitted by each.

Arthropods are animals characterized by segmented bodies, hard external skeletons, and jointed legs. With nearly 1 million

Tom Murray/BugGuide.Net.

LM 0.7 mm

Figure 32 Tick. *Ixodes pacificus* is the Lyme disease vector on the West Coast.

Q Why aren't ticks classified as insects?

species, this is the largest phylum in the animal kingdom. Although arthropods are not microbes themselves, we will briefly describe them here because a few suck the blood of humans and other animals and can transmit microbial diseases while doing so. Arthropods that carry pathogenic microorganisms are called **vectors.** Scabies and pediculosis are diseases that are caused by arthropods.

Representative classes of arthropods include the following:

- Arachnida (eight legs): spiders, mites, ticks
- Crustacea (four antennae): crabs, crayfish
- Insecta (six legs): bees, flies, lice

Table 6 lists those arthropods that are important vectors, and **Figures 31, 32**, and **33** illustrate some of them. These insects and ticks reside on an animal only when they are feeding. An

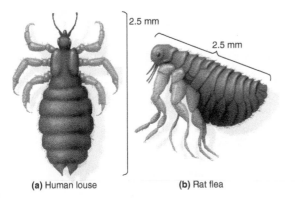
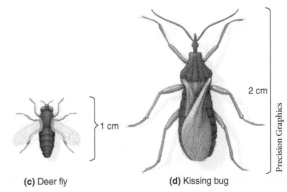

2.5 mm

2.5 mm

1 cm

2 cm

Precision Graphics

(a) Human louse **(b)** Rat flea **(c)** Deer fly **(d)** Kissing bug

Figure 33 Arthropod vectors. **(a)** The human louse, *Pediculus*. **(b)** The rat flea, *Xenopsylla*. **(c)** The deer fly, *Chrysops*. **(d)** The kissing bug, *Triatoma*.

Q Name one pathogen carried by each of these vectors.

TABLE 5 Representative Parasitic Helminths

Phylum	Class	Human Parasites	Intermediate Host	Definitive Host Site	Stage Passed to Humans; Method	Disease	Figure Reference
Platyhelminthes	Trematodes	*Paragonimus,* spp.	Freshwater snails and crayfish	Humans; lungs	Metacercaria in crustaceans; ingested	Paragonimiasis (lung fluke)	12.26
		Schistosoma	Freshwater snails	Humans	Cercariae; through skin	Schistosomiasis	
	Cestodes	*Echinococcus granulosus*	Humans	Dogs and other animals; intestines	Eggs from other animals; ingested	Hydatidosis	12.28
		Taenia saginata	Cattle	Humans; small intestine	Cysticerci in beef; ingested	Tapeworm	—
		Taenia solium	Humans; pigs	Humans	Eggs; ingested	Neurocysti-cercosis	
Nematoda		*Ancylostoma duodenale*	—	Humans; small intestine	Larvae; through skin	Hookworm	
		Anisakines	Marine fish and squid	Marine mammals	Larvae in fish; ingested	Anisakiasis (sashimi worms)	—
		Ascaris lumbricoides	—	Humans; small intestine	Eggs; ingested	Ascariasis	
		Baylisascaris procyonis	Rabbits	Raccoons; large intestine	Eggs; ingested	Raccoon roundworm	—
		Enterobius vermicularis	—	Humans; large intestine	Eggs; ingested	Pinworm	12.29
		Necator americanus	—	Humans; small intestine	Larvae; through skin	Hookworm	
		Trichinella spiralis	Humans and other mammals	Humans small intestine	Eggs; ingested	Whipworm	
		Trichuris trichiura	—	Humans, pigs, and other mammals; small intestine	Larvae; ingested	Trichinellosis	
		Toxocara canis, T. cati	Dogs, cats	Dogs, cats; small instestine	Eggs; ingested	Toxocariasis	—

TABLE 6 Important Arthropod Vectors of Human Diseases

Class	Order	Vector	Disease	Figure Reference
Arachnida	Mites and ticks	*Dermacentor* (tick)	Rocky Mountain spotted fever	—
		Ixodes (tick)	Lyme disease, babesiosis, ehrlichiosis	12.32
		Ornithodorus (tick)	Relapsing fever	—
Insecta	Sucking lice	*Pediculus* (human louse)	Epidemic typhus, relapsing fever	12.33a
	Fleas	*Xenopsylla* (rat flea)	Endemic murine typhus, plague	12.33b
	True flies	*Chrysops* (deer fly)	Tularemia	12.33c
		Aedes (mosquito)	Dengue fever, yellow fever, heartworm	12.31
		Anopheles (mosquito)	Malaria	—
		Culex (mosquito)	Arboviral encephalitis	—
		Glossina (tsetse fly)	African trypanosomiasis	—
	True bugs	*Triatoma* (kissing bug)	Chagas' disease	12.33d

exception to this is the louse, which spends its entire life on its host and cannot survive for long away from a host.

Some vectors are just a mechanical means of transport for a pathogen. For example, houseflies lay their eggs on decaying organic matter, such as feces. While doing so, a housefly can pick up a pathogen on its feet or body and transport the pathogen to our food.

Some parasites multiply in their vectors. When this happens, the parasites can accumulate in the vector's feces or saliva. Large numbers of parasites can then be deposited on or in the host while the vector is feeding there. The spirochete that causes Lyme disease is transmitted by ticks in this manner, and the West Nile virus is transmitted in the same way by mosquitoes.

As discussed earlier, *Plasmodium* is an example of a parasite that requires that its vector also be the definitive host. *Plasmodium* can sexually reproduce only in the gut of an *Anopheles* mosquito. *Plasmodium* is introduced into a human host with the mosquito's saliva, which acts as an anticoagulant that keeps blood flowing.

To eliminate vectorborne diseases, health workers focus on eradicating the vectors.

CHECK YOUR UNDERSTANDING

- Vectors can be divided into three major types, according to the roles they play for the parasite. List the three types of vectors and a disease transmitted by each. 20

- Assume you see an arthropod on your arm. How will you determine whether it is a tick or a flea? 21

Study Outline

Test your understanding with quizzes, microbe review, and a chapter post-test at www.masteringmicrobiology.com.

Fungi

1. Mycology is the study of fungi.
2. The number of serious fungal infections is increasing.
3. Fungi are aerobic or facultatively anaerobic chemoheterotrophs.
4. Most fungi are decomposers, and a few are parasites of plants and animals.

Characteristics of Fungi

5. A fungal thallus consists of filaments of cells called hyphae; a mass of hyphae is called a mycelium.
6. Yeasts are unicellular fungi. To reproduce, fission yeasts divide symmetrically, whereas budding yeasts divide asymmetrically.
7. Buds that do not separate from the parent cell form pseudohyphae.
8. Pathogenic dimorphic fungi are yeastlike at 37°C and moldlike at 25°C.
9. Fungi are classified according to rRNA.
10. Sporangiospores and conidiospores are produced asexually.
11. Sexual spores are usually produced in response to special circumstances, often changes in the environment.
12. Fungi can grow in acidic, low-moisture, aerobic environments.
13. They are able to metabolize complex carbohydrates.

Medically Important Fungi

14. The Zygomycota have coenocytic hyphae and produce sporangiospores and zygospores.
15. Microsporidia lack mitochondria and microtubules; they cause diarrhea in AIDS patients.
16. The Ascomycota have septate hyphae and produce ascospores and frequently conidiospores.

17. Basidiomycota have septate hyphae and produce basidiospores; some produce conidiospores.
18. Teleomorphic fungi produce sexual and asexual spores; anamorphic fungi produce asexual spores only.

Fungal Diseases

19. Systemic mycoses are fungal infections deep within the body that affect many tissues and organs.
20. Subcutaneous mycoses are fungal infections beneath the skin.
21. Cutaneous mycoses affect keratin-containing tissues such as hair, nails, and skin.
22. Superficial mycoses are localized on hair shafts and superficial skin cells.
23. Opportunistic mycoses are caused by fungi that are not usually pathogenic.
24. Opportunistic mycoses can infect any tissues. However, they are usually systemic.

Economic Effects of Fungi

25. *Saccharomyces* and *Trichoderma* are used in the production of foods.
26. Fungi are used for the biological control of pests.
27. Mold spoilage of fruits, grains, and vegetables is more common than bacterial spoilage of these products.
28. Many fungi cause diseases in plants.

Lichens

1. A lichen is a mutualistic combination of an alga (or a cyanobacterium) and a fungus.
2. The alga photosynthesizes, providing carbohydrates for the lichen; the fungus provides a holdfast.
3. Lichens colonize habitats that are unsuitable for either the alga or the fungus alone.
4. Lichens may be classified on the basis of morphology as crustose, foliose, or fruticose.

Algae

1. Algae are unicellular, filamentous, or multicellular (thallic).
2. Most algae live in aquatic environments.

Characteristics of Algae

3. Algae are eukaryotic; most are photoautotrophs.
4. The thallus of multicellular algae usually consists of a stipe, a holdfast, and blades.
5. Algae reproduce asexually by cell division and fragmentation.
6. Many algae reproduce sexually.
7. Photoautotrophic algae produce oxygen.
8. Algae are classified according to their structures and pigments.

Selected Phyla of Algae

9. Brown algae (kelp) may be harvested for algin.
10. Red algae grow deeper in the ocean than other algae.
11. Green algae have cellulose and chlorophyll *a* and *b* and store starch.
12. Diatoms are unicellular and have pectin and silica cell walls; some produce a neurotoxin.
13. Dinoflagellates produce neurotoxins that cause paralytic shellfish poisoning and ciguatera.
14. The oomycotes are heterotrophic; they include decomposers and pathogens.

Roles of Algae in Nature

15. Algae are the primary producers in aquatic food chains.
16. Planktonic algae produce most of the molecular oxygen in the Earth's atmosphere.
17. Petroleum is the fossil remains of planktonic algae.
18. Unicellular algae are symbionts in such animals as *Tridacna*.

Protozoa

1. Protozoa are unicellular, eukaryotic chemoheterotrophs.
2. Protozoa are found in soil and water and as normal microbiota in animals.

Characteristics of Protozoa

3. The vegetative form is called a trophozoite.
4. Asexual reproduction is by fission, budding, or schizogony.
5. Sexual reproduction is by conjugation.
6. During ciliate conjugation, two haploid nuclei fuse to produce a zygote.
7. Some protozoa can produce a cyst that provides protection during adverse environmental conditions.
8. Protozoa have complex cells with a pellicle, a cytostome, and an anal pore.

Medically Important of Protozoa

9. *Trichomonas* and *Giardia* lack mitochondria and have flagella.
10. Euglenozoa move by means of flagella and lack sexual reproduction; they include *Trypanosoma*.
11. Amebae include *Entamoeba* and *Acanthamoeba*.
12. Apicomplexa have apical organelles for penetrating host tissue; they include *Plasmodium* and *Cryptosporidium*.
13. Ciliates move by means of cilia; *Balantidium coli* is the human parasitic ciliate.

Slime Molds

1. Cellular slime molds resemble amebae and ingest bacteria by phagocytosis.
2. Plasmodial slime molds consist of a multinucleated mass of protoplasm that engulfs organic debris and bacteria as it moves.

Helminths

1. Parasitic flatworms belong to the phylum Platyhelminthes.
2. Parasitic roundworms belong to the phylum Nematoda.

Characteristics of Helminths

3. Helminths are multicellular animals; a few are parasites of humans.
4. The anatomy and life cycle of parasitic helminths are modified for parasitism.
5. The adult stage of a parasitic helminth is found in the definitive host.
6. Each larval stage of a parasitic helminth requires an intermediate host.
7. Helminths can be monoecious or dioecious.

Platyhelminths

8. Flatworms are dorsoventrally flattened animals; parasitic flatworms may lack a digestive system.
9. Adult trematodes, or flukes, have an oral and ventral sucker with which they attach to host tissue.
10. Eggs of trematodes hatch into free-swimming miracidia that enter the first intermediate host; two generations of rediae develop; the rediae become cercariae that bore out of the first intermediate host and penetrate the second intermediate host; cercariae encyst as metacercariae; the metacercariae develop into adults in the definitive host.
11. A cestode, or tapeworm, consists of a scolex (head) and proglottids.
12. Humans serve as the definitive host for the beef tapeworm, and cattle are the intermediate host.
13. Humans serve as the definitive host and can be an intermediate host for the pork tapeworm.
14. Humans serve as the intermediate host for *Echinococcus granulosus;* the definitive hosts are dogs, wolves, and foxes.

Nematodes

15. .Roundworms have a complete digestive system.
16. The nematodes that infect humans with their eggs include and *Ascaris, Trichuris*, and *Enterobius.*
17. The nematodes that infect humans with their larvae include hookworms and *Trichinella.*

Arthropods as Vectors

1. Jointed-legged animals, including ticks and insects, belong to the phylum Arthropoda.
2. Arthropods that carry diseases are called vectors.
3. Vectorborne diseases are most effectively eliminated by controlling or eradicating the vectors.

Study Questions

Answers to the Review and Multiple Choice questions can be found at the end of this chapter.

Review

1. Following is a list of fungi, their methods of entry into the body, and sites of infections they cause. Categorize each type of mycosis as cutaneous, opportunistic, subcutaneous, superficial, or systemic.

Genus	Method of Entry	Site of Infection	Mycosis
Blastomyces	Inhalation	Lungs	(a) _____
Sporothrix	Puncture	Ulcerative lesions	(b) _____
Microsporum	Contact	Fingernails	(c) _____
Trichosporon	Contact	Hair shafts	(d) _____
Aspergillus	Inhalation	Lungs	(e) _____

2. A mixed culture of *Escherichia coli* and *Penicillium chrysogenum* is inoculated onto the following culture media. On which medium would you expect each to grow? Why?
   a. 0.5% peptone in tap water
   b. 10% glucose in tap water

3. Briefly discuss the importance of lichens in nature. Briefly discuss the importance of algae in nature.

4. Differentiate cellular and plasmodial slime molds. How does each survive adverse environmental conditions?

5. Complete the following table.

Phylum	Method of Motility	One Human Parasite
Diplomonads	(a) _____	(b) _____
Microsporidia	(c) _____	(d) _____
Amebae	(e) _____	(f) _____
Apicomplexa	(g) _____	(h) _____
Ciliates	(i) _____	(j) _____
Euglenozoa	(k) _____	(l) _____
Parabasalids	(m) _____	(n) _____

6. Why is it significant that *Trichomonas* does not have a cyst stage? Name a protozoan parasite that does have a cyst stage.

7. By what means are helminthic parasites transmitted to humans?

8. Most nematodes are dioecious. What does this term mean? To what phylum do nematodes belong?

9. NAME IT Identify the structures of this eukaryote, which has an affinity for keratin.

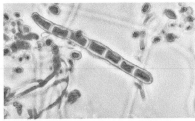

SeDmi/Shutterstock

LM ⊢ 12 μm ⊣

10. DRAW IT A generalized life cycle of the liver fluke *Clonorchis sinensis* is shown below Label the fluke's stages. Identify the intermediate host(s). Identify the definitive host(s). To what phylum and class does this animal belong?

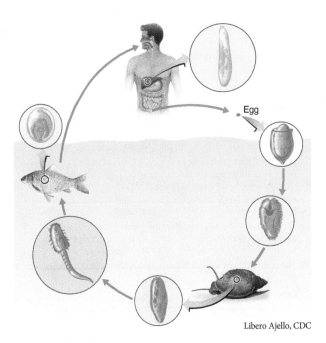

Egg

Libero Ajello, CDC

Multiple Choice

1. How many phyla are represented in the following list of organisms: *Echinococcus, Cyclospora, Aspergillus, Taenia, Toxoplasma, Trichinella?*
   a. 1   d. 4
   b. 2   e. 5
   c. 3

Use the following choices to answer questions 2 and 3:
   (1) metacercaria   (4) miracidium
   (2) redia   (5) cercaria
   (3) adult

2. Put the above stages in order of development, beginning with the egg.
   a. 5, 4, 1, 2, 3   d. 3, 4, 5, 1, 2
   b. 4, 2, 5, 1, 3   e. 2, 4, 5, 1, 3
   c. 2, 5, 4, 3, 1

3. If a snail is the first intermediate host of a parasite with these stages, which stage would be found in the snail?
   a. 1   d. 4
   b. 2   e. 5
   c. 3

4. Which of the following statements about yeasts are true?
   (**1**) Yeasts are fungi.
   (**2**) Yeasts can form pseudohyphae.
   (**3**) Yeasts reproduce asexually by budding.
   (**4**) Yeasts are facultatively anaerobic.
   (**5**) All yeasts are pathogenic.
   (**6**) All yeasts are dimorphic.
   a. 1, 2, 3, 4   **d.** 1, 3, 5, 6
   b. 3, 4, 5, 6   **e.** 2, 3, 4
   c. 2, 3, 4, 5

5. Which of the following events follows cell fusion in an ascomycete?
   a. conidiophore formation
   b. conidiospore germination
   c. ascus opening
   d. ascospore formation
   e. conidiospore release

6. The definitive host for *Plasmodium vivax* is
   a. human.   **c.** a sporocyte.
   b. *Anopheles*.   **d.** a gametocyte.

7. Fleas are the intermediate host for *Dipylidium caninum* tapeworm, and dogs are the definitive host. Which stage of the parasite could be found in the flea?
   a. cysticerus larva   **c.** scolex
   b. proglottids   **d.** adult

Use the following choices to answer questions 8–10:
   a. Apicomplexa   **c.** dinoflagellates
   b. ciliates   **d.** Microsporidia

8. These are obligate intracellular parasites that lack mitochondria.

9. These are nonmotile parasites with special organelles for penetrating host tissue.

10. These photosynthetic organisms can cause paralytic shellfish poisoning.

Critical Thinking

1. The size of a cell is limited by its surface-to-volume ratio; that is, if the volume becomes too great, internal heat cannot be dissipated, and nutrients and wastes cannot be efficiently transported. How do plasmodial slime molds manage to circumvent the surface-to-volume rule?

2. The life cycle of the fish tapeworm *Diphyllobothrium* is similar to that of *Taenia saginata*, except that the intermediate host is fish. Describe the life cycle and method of transmission to humans. Why are freshwater fish more likely to be a source of tapeworm infection than marine fish?

3. *Trypanosoma brucei gambiense*—part (a) in the figure—is the causative agent of African sleeping sickness. To what phylum does it belong? Part (b) shows a simplified life cycle for *T. b. gambiense*. Identify the host and vector of this parasite.

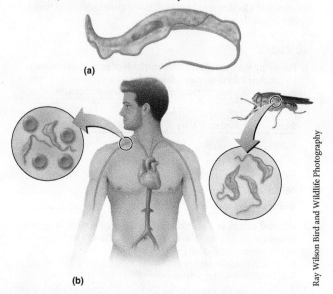

(a)

(b)

Ray Wilson Bird and Wildlife Photography

Clinical Applications

1. A girl developed generalized seizures. A CT scan revealed a single brain lesion consistent with a tumor. Biopsy of the lesion showed a cysticercus. The patient lived in South Carolina and had never traveled outside the state. What parasite caused her disease? How is this disease transmitted? How might it be prevented?

2. A California farmer developed a low-grade fever, myalgia, and cough. A chest X-ray exam revealed an infiltrate in the lung. Microscopic examination of the sputum revealed round, budding cells. A sputum culture grew mycelia and arthroconidia. What organism is most likely the cause of the symptoms? How is this disease transmitted? How might it be prevented?

3. A teenaged male in California complained of remittent fever, chills, and headaches. A blood smear revealed ring-shaped cells in his red blood cells. He was successfully treated with primaquine and chloroquine. The patient lives near the San Luis Rey River and has no history of foreign travel, blood transfusion, or intravenous drug use. What is the disease? How was it acquired?

Answers to Review and Multiple Choice Study Questions

Review

1. **a.** Systemic
   b. Subcutaneous
   c. Cutaneous
   d. Superficial
   e. Systemic

2. **a.** *E. coli*
   b. *P. chrysogenum*

3. As the first colonizers on newly exposed rock or soil, lichens are responsible for the chemical weathering of large inorganic particles and the consequent accumulation of soil.

4. Cellular slime molds exist as individual ameboid cells. Plasmodial slime molds are multinucleate masses of protoplasm. Both survive adverse environmental conditions by forming spores.

5. **a.** Flagella
   b. *Giardia*
   c. None
   d. *Nosema*
   e. Pseudopods
   f. *Entamoeba*
   g. None
   h. *Plasmodium*
   i. Cilia
   j. *Balantidium*
   k. Flagella
   l. *Trypanosoma*
   m. Flagella
   n. *Trichomonas*

6. *Trichomonas* cannot survive for long outside a host because it does not form a protective cyst. *Trichomonas* must be transferred from host to host quickly.

7. Ingestion.

8. The male reproductive organs are in one individual, and the female reproductive organs in another. Nematodes belong to the Phylum Aschelminthes.

9. Arthroconidia *(Trichophyton)*

10.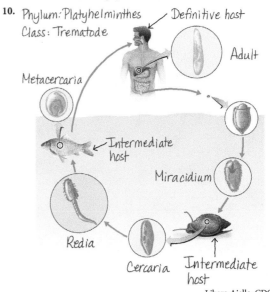
Libero Ajello, CDC

Multiple Choice

1. d   3. b   5. e   7. a   9. a
2. b   4. a   6. b   8. d   10. c

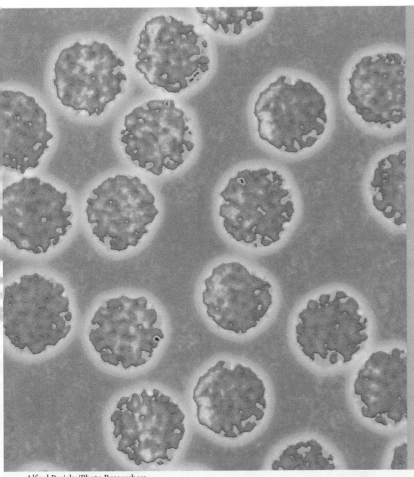

Alfred Pasieka/Photo Researchers

Viruses, Viroids, and Prions

Visualize microbiology and check your understanding with a pre-test at www.masteringmicrobiology.com.

V iruses are too small to be seen with a light microscope and cannot be cultured outside their hosts. Therefore, although viral diseases are not new, the viruses themselves could not be studied until the twentieth century. In 1886, the Dutch chemist Adolf Mayer showed that tobacco mosaic disease (TMD) was transmissible from a diseased plant to a healthy plant. In 1892, in an attempt to isolate the cause of TMD, the Russian bacteriologist Dimitri Iwanowski filtered the sap of diseased plants through a porcelain filter that was designed to retain bacteria. He expected to find the microbe trapped in the filter; instead, he found that the infectious agent had passed through the minute pores of the filter. When he infected healthy plants with the filtered fluid, they contracted TMD. The first human disease associated with a filterable agent was yellow fever.

Advances in molecular biological techniques in the 1980s and 1990s led to the recognition of several new viruses, including human immunodeficiency virus (HIV) and SARS-associated coronavirus. Viral hepatitis is one of the most common infectious diseases in the world. Several different hepatitis viruses have been identified, including the bloodborne hepatitis B virus (shown in the photo) and hepatitis C virus, and the foodborne hepatitis A virus discussed in the Clinical Case. In this chapter, we will study the biology of viruses.

From Chapter 13 of *Microbiology: An Introduction*, Eleventh Edition. Gerard J. Tortora, Berdell R. Funke, Christine L. Case.

General Characteristics of Viruses

LEARNING OBJECTIVE

1   Differentiate a virus from a bacterium.

One hundred years ago, researchers could not imagine sub-microscopic particles, and thus they described the infectious agent as *contagium vivum fluidum*—a contagious fluid. By the 1930s, scientists had begun using the word *virus,* the Latin word for poison, to describe these filterable agents. The nature of viruses, however, remained elusive until 1935, when Wendell Stanley, an American chemist, isolated tobacco mosaic virus, making it possible for the first time to carry out chemical and structural studies on a purified virus. At about the same time, the invention of the electron microscope made it possible to see viruses.

The question of whether viruses are living organisms has an ambiguous answer. Life can be defined as a complex set of processes resulting from the actions of proteins specified by nucleic acids. The nucleic acids of living cells are in action all the time. Because viruses are inert outside living host cells, in this sense they are not considered to be living organisms. However, once viruses enter a host cell, the viral nucleic acids become active, and viral multiplication results. In this sense, viruses are alive when they multiply in the host cells they infect. From a clinical point of view, viruses can be considered alive because they cause infection and disease, just as pathogenic bacteria, fungi, and protozoa do. Depending on one's viewpoint, a virus may be regarded as an exceptionally complex aggregation of nonliving chemicals, or as an exceptionally simple living microorganism.

How, then, do we define *virus*? Viruses were originally distinguished from other infectious agents because they are especially small (filterable) and because they are **obligatory**

TABLE 1 Viruses and Bacteria Compared

	Bacteria		Viruses
	Typical Bacteria	Rickettsias/ Chlamydias	
Intracellular Parasite	No	Yes	Yes
Plasma Membrane	Yes	Yes	No
Binary Fission	Yes	Yes	No
Pass through Bacteriological Filters	No	No/Yes	Yes
Possess Both DNA and RNA	Yes	Yes	No
ATP-Generating Metabolism	Yes	Yes/No	No
Ribosomes	Yes	Yes	No
Sensitive to Antibiotics	Yes	Yes	No
Sensitive to Interferon	No	No	Yes

intracellular parasites—that is, they absolutely require living host cells in order to multiply. However, both of these properties are shared by certain small bacteria, such as some rickettsias. Viruses and bacteria are compared in Table 1.

The truly distinctive features of viruses are now known to relate to their simple structural organization and their mechanism of multiplication. Accordingly, **viruses** are entities that

- Contain a single type of nucleic acid, either DNA or RNA.
- Contain a protein coat (sometimes itself enclosed by an envelope of lipids, proteins, and carbohydrates) that surrounds the nucleic acid.
- Multiply inside living cells by using the synthesizing machinery of the cell.
- Cause the synthesis of specialized structures that can transfer the viral nucleic acid to other cells.

Viruses have few or no enzymes of their own for metabolism; for example, they lack enzymes for protein synthesis and ATP generation. To multiply, viruses must take over the metabolic machinery of the host cell. This fact has considerable medical significance for the development of antiviral drugs, because most drugs that would interfere with viral multiplication would also interfere with the functioning of the host cell and therefore are too toxic for clinical use.

Host Range

The **host range** of a virus is the spectrum of host cells the virus can infect. There are viruses that infect invertebrates, vertebrates, plants, protists, fungi, and bacteria. However, most viruses are able to infect specific types of cells of only one host species. In rare cases, viruses cross the host-range barrier, thus expanding

Clinical Case: An Inconvenient Outbreak

Tina Markham, a 42-year-old pharmaceutical sales representative, has been home from work because of a very high, persistent fever (40°C). She is taking medications to reduce the fever, but they work only for a few hours. Tina makes an appointment to see her physician; he notices right away that Tina's skin is jaundiced. When he palpates her abdomen, she winces in pain; it is very tender. Sensing an issue with her liver, Tina's physician sends a blood sample to the local laboratory for a liver function test (LFT). The results show abnormal findings.

What disease could be causing Tina's symptoms? Read on to find out.

their host range. An example is described in the Clinical Focus later in this chapter. In this chapter, we are concerned mainly with viruses that infect either humans or bacteria. Viruses that infect bacteria are called **bacteriophages,** or **phages.**

The particular host range of a virus is determined by the virus's requirements for its specific attachment to the host cell and the availability within the potential host of cellular factors required for viral multiplication. For the virus to infect the host cell, the outer surface of the virus must chemically interact with specific receptor sites on the surface of the cell. The two complementary components are held together by weak bonds, such as hydrogen bonds. The combination of many attachment and receptor sites leads to a strong association between host cell and virus. For some bacteriophages, the receptor site is part of the cell wall of the host; in other cases, it is part of the fimbriae or flagella. For animal viruses, the receptor sites are on the plasma membranes of the host cells.

The potential to use viruses to treat diseases is intriguing because of their narrow host range and their ability to kill their host cells. The idea of *phage therapy*—using bacteriophages to treat bacterial infections—has been around for 100 years. Recent advances in our understanding of virus-host interactions have fueled new studies in the field of phage therapy.

Experimentally induced viral infections in cancer patients during the 1920s suggested that viruses might have antitumor activity. These tumor-destroying, or *oncolytic,* viruses may selectively infect and kill tumor cells or cause an immune response against tumor cells. Some viruses naturally infect tumor cells, and other viruses can be genetically modified to infect tumor cells. At present several studies are underway to determine the killing mechanism of oncolytic viruses and the safety of using viral therapy.

Viral Size

Viral sizes are determined with the aid of electron microscopy. Different viruses vary considerably in size. Although most are quite a bit smaller than bacteria, some of the larger viruses (such as the vaccinia virus) are about the same size as some very small bacteria (such as the mycoplasmas, rickettsias, and chlamydias). Viruses range from 20 to 1000 nm in length. The comparative sizes of several viruses and bacteria are shown in Figure 1.

CHECK YOUR UNDERSTANDING

✔ How could the small size of viruses have helped researchers detect viruses before the invention of the electron microscope? 1

Viral Structure

LEARNING OBJECTIVE

2   Describe the chemical and physical structure of both an enveloped and a nonenveloped virus.

A **virion** is a complete, fully developed, infectious viral particle composed of nucleic acid and surrounded by a protein coat outside of a host cell, and is a vehicle of transmission from one host cell to another. Viruses are classified by their nucleic acid and by differences in the structures of their coats.

Nucleic Acid

In contrast to prokaryotic and eukaryotic cells, in which DNA is always the primary genetic material (and RNA plays an auxiliary role), a virus can have either DNA or RNA—but never both. The nucleic acid of a virus can be single-stranded or double-stranded. Thus, there are viruses with the familiar double-stranded DNA, with single-stranded DNA, with double-stranded RNA, and with single-stranded RNA. Depending on the virus, the nucleic acid can be linear or circular. In some viruses (such as the influenza virus), the nucleic acid is in several separate segments.

The percentage of nucleic acid in relation to protein is about 1% for the influenza virus and about 50% for certain bacteriophages. The total amount of nucleic acid varies from a few thousand nucleotides (or pairs) to as many as 250,000 nucleotides. (*E. coli*'s chromosome consists of approximately 4 million nucleotide pairs.)

Capsid and Envelope

The nucleic acid of a virus is protected by a protein coat called the **capsid** (Figure 2a). The structure of the capsid is ultimately determined by the viral nucleic acid and accounts for most of the mass of a virus, especially of small ones. Each capsid is composed of protein subunits called **capsomeres.** In some viruses, the proteins composing the capsomeres are of a single type; in other viruses, several types of protein may be present. Individual capsomeres are often visible in electron micrographs (see Figure 2b for an example). The arrangement of capsomeres is characteristic of a particular type of virus.

In some viruses, the capsid is covered by an **envelope** (Figure 3a), which usually consists of some combination of lipids, proteins, and carbohydrates. Some animal viruses are released from the host cell by an extrusion process that coats the virus with a layer of the host cell's plasma membrane; that layer becomes the viral envelope. In many cases, the envelope contains proteins determined by the viral nucleic acid and materials derived from normal host cell components.

Depending on the virus, envelopes may or may not be covered by **spikes,** which are carbohydrate-protein complexes that project from the surface of the envelope. Some viruses attach to host cells by means of spikes. Spikes are such a reliable characteristic of some viruses that they can be used as a means of identification. The ability of certain viruses, such as the influenza virus (Figure 3b), to clump red blood cells is associated with spikes. Such viruses bind to red blood cells and form bridges between them. The resulting clumping is called *hemagglutination* and is the basis for several useful laboratory tests.

Viruses whose capsids are not covered by an envelope are known as **nonenveloped viruses** (see Figure 2). The capsid of a nonenveloped virus protects the nucleic acid from nuclease

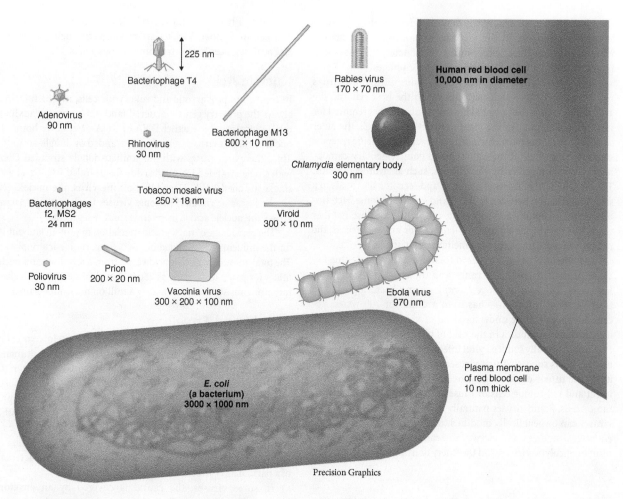

Precision Graphics

Figure 1 Virus sizes. The sizes of several viruses (teal blue) and bacteria (brown) are compared with a human red blood cell, shown to the right of the microbes. Dimensions are given in nanometers (nm) and are either diameters or length by width.

Q How do viruses differ from bacteria?

R. C. Valentine and H. G. Pereira, Journal of Molecular Biology/Biological Photo Service

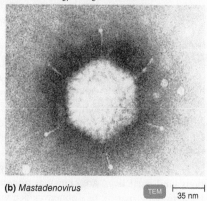

(a) A polyhedral virus

(b) *Mastadenovirus*   TEM   35 nm

Figure 2 Morphology of a nonenveloped polyhedral virus. (**a**) A diagram of a polyhedral (icosahedral) virus. (**b**) A micrograph of the adenovirus *Mastadenovirus*. Individual capsomeres are visible.

Q What is the chemical composition of a capsid?

Figure 3 **Morphology of an enveloped helical virus.** (**a**) A diagram of an enveloped helical virus. (**b**) A micrograph of *Influenzavirus* A2. Notice the halo of spikes projecting from the outer surface of each envelope.

 What is the nucleic acid in a virus?

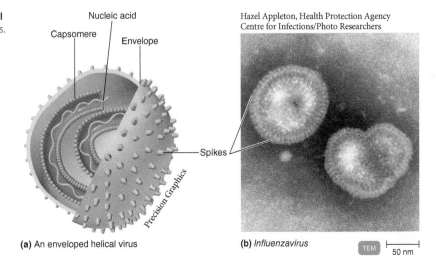

(**a**) An enveloped helical virus

(**b**) *Influenzavirus*

TEM 50 nm

Hazel Appleton, Health Protection Agency Centre for Infections/Photo Researchers

enzymes in biological fluids and promotes the virus's attachment to susceptible host cells.

When the host has been infected by a virus, the host immune system is stimulated to produce antibodies (proteins that react with the surface proteins of the virus). This interaction between host antibodies and virus proteins should inactivate the virus and stop the infection. However, some viruses can escape antibodies because regions of the genes that code for these viruses' surface proteins are susceptible to mutations. The progeny of mutant viruses have altered surface proteins, such that the antibodies are not able to react with them. Influenza virus frequently undergoes such changes in its spikes. This is why you can get influenza more than once. Although you may have produced antibodies to one influenza virus, the virus can mutate and infect you again.

General Morphology

Viruses may be classified into several different morphological types on the basis of their capsid architecture. The structure of these capsids has been revealed by electron microscopy and a technique called X-ray crystallography.

Helical Viruses

Helical viruses resemble long rods that may be rigid or flexible. The viral nucleic acid is found within a hollow, cylindrical capsid that has a helical structure (Figure 4). The viruses that cause rabies and Ebola hemorrhagic fever are helical viruses.

Polyhedral Viruses

Many animal, plant, and bacterial viruses are polyhedral, or many-sided, viruses. The capsid of most polyhedral viruses is in the shape of an *icosahedron*, a regular polyhedron with 20 triangular faces and 12 corners (see Figure 2a). The capsomeres of each face form an equilateral triangle. An example of a polyhedral virus in the shape of an icosahedron is the adenovirus (shown in Figure 2b). Another icosahedral virus is the poliovirus.

Enveloped Viruses

As noted earlier, the capsid of some viruses is covered by an envelope. Enveloped viruses are roughly spherical. When helical or polyhedral viruses are enclosed by envelopes, they are called *enveloped helical* or *enveloped polyhedral viruses*. An example of

Figure 4 **Morphology of a helical virus.** (**a**) A diagram of a portion of a helical virus. A row of capsomeres has been removed to reveal the nucleic acid. (**b**) A micrograph of Ebola virus, a filovirus, showing a helical rod.

 What is the chemical composition of a capsomere?

(**a**) A helical virus   Precision Graphics

(**b**) Ebola virus

TEM 160 nm

Frederick A. Murphy, CDC

Influenza: Crossing the Species Barrier

Influenza A viruses are found in many different animals, including birds, pigs, whales, horses, and seals. Sometimes influenza A viruses seen in one species can cross over and cause illness in another species. For example, up until 1998, only H1N1 viruses circulated widely in the U.S. pig population. In 1998, H3N2 viruses from humans were introduced into the pig population and caused widespread disease among pigs. The subtypes differ because of certain proteins on the surface of the virus (hemagglutinin [HA] and neuraminidase [NA] proteins). There are 16 different HA subtypes and 9 different NA subtypes of influenza A viruses.

How many different combinations of H and N proteins are possible?

Each combination is a different subtype. When we talk about "human flu viruses," we are referring to those subtypes that occur widely in humans. There are only three known subtypes of human influenza viruses (H1N1, H1N2, and H3N2).

What's different about bird flu?

H5 and H7 subtypes occur mainly in birds. Avian influenza (bird flu) viruses do not usually infect humans. All human cases of avian flu can be attributed to outbreaks in poultry, except one noteworthy probable transmission from a daughter to her mother. Avian influenza viruses may be transmitted to humans: (1) directly from birds or from avian-virus-contaminated environments or (2) through an intermediate host, such as a pig.

Why are pigs important?

Pigs can be infected with both human and avian flu. The influenza virus genome is composed of eight separate segments. A segmented genome allows virus genes to mix and create a new influenza A virus if viruses from two different species infect the same person or animal (see the figure). This is known as *antigenic shift*.

The 2009 H1N1 virus was originally referred to as "swine flu" because laboratory testing showed that many of the genes in the virus were very similar to influenza viruses that normally occur in North American pigs. But further study has shown that the 2009 H1N1 is very different from that which normally circulates in North American pigs. It has two genes from flu viruses that normally circulate in pigs in Europe and Asia, avian influenza genes, and human genes. This is called a *quadruple reassortant* virus (see the figure).

Pandemics

During the last 100 years, the emergence of new influenza A virus subtypes caused three pandemics, all of which spread around the world within one year of being detected (see the table). Some genetic parts of all of these influenza A strains originally came from birds.

Source: Adapted from *MMWR* sources.

Influenza A Pandemics During the Past 100 Years	
1918–19	H1N1 caused up to 50 million deaths worldwide. Virus has avian flu–like genes.
1957–58	H2N2 caused about 70,000 deaths in the United States. First identified in China in late February 1957. Viruses contained a combination of genes from a human influenza virus and an avian influenza virus.
1968–69	H3N2 caused about 34,000 deaths in the United States. This virus contained genes from a human influenza virus and an avian influenza virus.
2009–10	H1N1 caused at least 14,000 deaths worldwide, A vaccine was available in developed and developing countries 3 months after the first cases.

an enveloped helical virus is the influenza virus (see Figure 3b). An example of an enveloped polyhedral (icosahedral) virus is the herpes simplex virus (see Figure 16b).

Complex Viruses

Some viruses, particularly bacterial viruses, have complicated structures and are called **complex viruses.** One example of a complex virus is a bacteriophage. Some bacteriophages have capsids to which additional structures are attached (Figure 5a). In this figure, notice that the capsid (head) is polyhedral and that the tail sheath is helical. The head contains the nucleic acid. Later in the chapter, we will discuss the functions of the other structures, such as the tail sheath, tail fibers, plate, and pin. Another

example of complex viruses are poxviruses, which do not contain clearly identifiable capsids but have several coats around the nucleic acid (Figure 5b).

CHECK YOUR UNDERSTANDING

✔ Diagram a nonenveloped polyhedral virus that has spikes. 2

Taxonomy of Viruses

LEARNING OBJECTIVES

3   Define *viral species.*

4   Give an example of a family, genus, and common name for a virus.

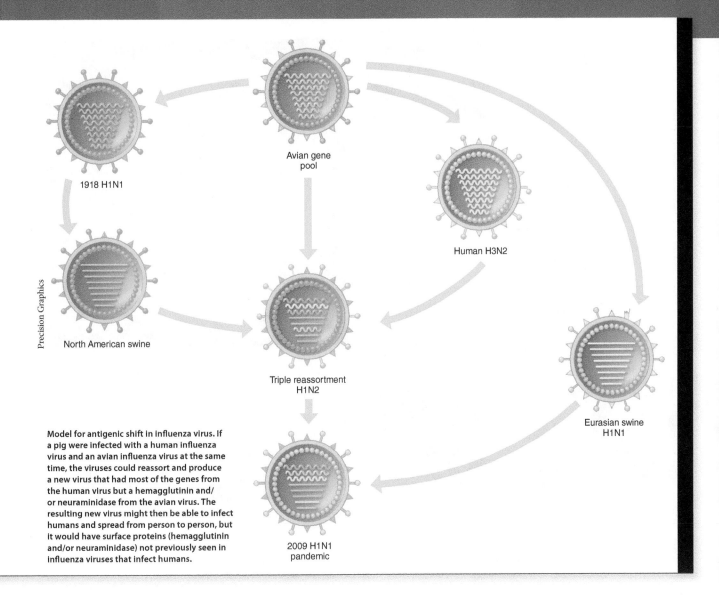

Model for antigenic shift in influenza virus. If a pig were infected with a human influenza virus and an avian influenza virus at the same time, the viruses could reassort and produce a new virus that had most of the genes from the human virus but a hemagglutinin and/or neuraminidase from the avian virus. The resulting new virus might then be able to infect humans and spread from person to person, but it would have surface proteins (hemagglutinin and/or neuraminidase) not previously seen in influenza viruses that infect humans.

Just as we need taxonomic categories of plants, animals, and bacteria, we need viral taxonomy to help us organize and understand newly discovered organisms. The oldest classification of viruses is based on symptomatology, such as for diseases that affect the respiratory system. This system was convenient but not scientifically acceptable because the same virus may cause more than one disease, depending on the tissue affected. In addition, this system artificially grouped viruses that do not infect humans.

New, fast DNA sequencing allows the International Committee on Taxonomy of Viruses to group viruses into families based on genomics and structure. The suffix *-virus* is used for genus names; family names end in *-viridae;* and order names end in *-ales.* In formal usage, the family and genus names are used in the following manner: Family Herpesviridae, genus *Simplexvirus,* human herpesvirus 2.

A **viral species** is a group of viruses sharing the same genetic information and ecological niche (host range). Specific epithets for viruses are not used. Thus, viral species are designated by descriptive common names, such as human immunodeficiency virus (HIV), with subspecies (if any) designated by a number (HIV-1). **Table 2** presents a summary of the classification of viruses that infect humans.

CHECK YOUR UNDERSTANDING

✔ How does a virus species differ from a bacterial species? **3**

✔ Attach the proper endings to *Papilloma-* to show the family and genus that includes HPV, the cause of cervical cancer. **4**

Eye of Science/Photo Researchers

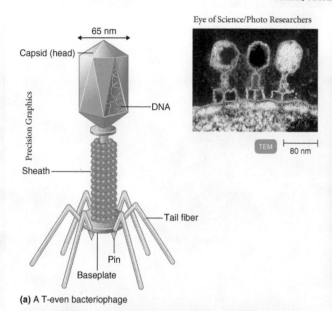

65 nm

Capsid (head)

DNA

Sheath

Tail fiber

Pin

Baseplate

(a) A T-even bacteriophage

TEM 80 nm

Precision Graphics

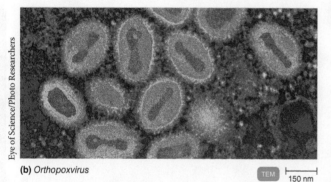

Eye of Science/Photo Researchers

(b) *Orthopoxvirus*

TEM 150 nm

Figure 5 **Morphology of complex viruses.** **(a)** A diagram and micrograph of a T-even bacteriophage. **(b)** A micrograph of variola virus, a species in the genus *Orthopoxvirus*, which causes smallpox.

Q What is the value of a capsid to a virus?

Isolation, Cultivation, and Identification of Viruses

LEARNING OBJECTIVES

5 Describe how bacteriophages are cultured.

6 Describe how animal viruses are cultured.

7 List three techniques used to identify viruses.

The fact that viruses cannot multiply outside a living host cell complicates their detection, enumeration, and identification. Viruses must be provided with living cells instead of a fairly simple chemical medium. Living plants and animals are difficult and expensive to maintain, and pathogenic viruses that grow only

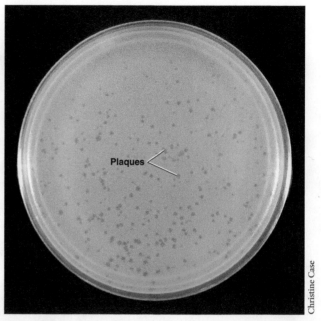

Plaques

Christine Case

Figure 6 **Viral plaques formed by bacteriophages.** Clear viral plaques of various sizes have been formed by bacteriophage λ (lambda) on a lawn of *E. coli*.

Q What is a plaque-forming unit?

in higher primates and human hosts cause additional complications. However, viruses that use bacterial cells as a host (bacteriophages) are rather easily grown on bacterial cultures. This is one reason so much of our understanding of viral multiplication has come from bacteriophages.

Growing Bacteriophages in the Laboratory

Bacteriophages can be grown either in suspensions of bacteria in liquid media or in bacterial cultures on solid media. The use of solid media makes possible the *plaque method* for detecting and counting viruses. A sample of bacteriophage is mixed with host bacteria and melted agar. The agar containing the bacteriophages and host bacteria is then poured into a Petri plate containing a hardened layer of agar growth medium. The virus-bacteria mixture solidifies into a thin top layer that contains a layer of bacteria approximately one cell thick. Each virus infects a bacterium, multiplies, and releases several hundred new viruses. These newly produced viruses infect other bacteria in the immediate vicinity, and more new viruses are produced. Following several viral multiplication cycles, all the bacteria in the area surrounding the original virus are destroyed. This produces a number of clearings, or **plaques,** visible against a lawn of bacterial growth on the surface of the agar (Figure 6). While the plaques form, uninfected bacteria elsewhere in the Petri plate multiply rapidly and produce a turbid background.

TABLE 2 Families of Viruses That Affect Humans

Characteristics/ Dimensions	Viral Family	Important Genera	Clinical or Special Features
Single-Stranded DNA Nonenveloped			
18–25 nm	Parvoviridae	Human parvovirus B19	Fifth disease; anemia in immunocompromised patients.
Double-Stranded DNA Nonenveloped			
70–90 nm	Adenoviridae	*Mastadenovirus*	Medium-sized viruses that cause various respiratory infections in humans; some cause tumors in animals.
40–57 nm	Papovaviridae	*Papillomavirus* (human wart virus) *Polyomavirus*	Small viruses that cause warts and cervical and anal cancer in humans belong to this family.
Double-Stranded DNA Enveloped			
200–350 nm	Poxviridae	*Orthopoxvirus* (vaccinia and smallpox viruses) *Molluscipoxvirus*	Very large, complex, brick-shaped viruses that cause smallpox (variola), molluscum contagiosum (wartlike skin lesion), and cowpox.
150–200 nm	Herpesviridae	*Simplexvirus* (HHV-1 and -2) *Varicellovirus* (HHV-3) *Lymphocryptovirus* (HHV-4) *Cytomegalovirus* (HHV-5) *Roseolovirus* (HHV-6 and HHV-7) *Rhadinovirus* (HHV-8)	Medium-sized viruses that cause various human diseases: fever blisters, chickenpox, shingles, and infectious mononucleosis; cause a type of human cancer called Burkitt's lymphoma.
42 nm	Hepadnaviridae	*Hepadnavirus* (hepatitis B virus)	After protein synthesis, hepatitis B virus uses reverse transcriptase to produce its DNA from mRNA; causes hepatitis B and liver tumors.
Single-Stranded RNA, + Strand Nonenveloped			
28–30 nm	Picornaviridae	*Enterovirus* *Rhinovirus* (common cold virus) Hepatitis A virus	At least 70 human enteroviruses are known, including the polio-, coxsackie-, and echoviruses; more than 100 rhinoviruses exist and are the most common cause of colds.
35–40 nm	Caliciviridae	Hepatitis E virus *Norovirus*	Includes causes of gastroenteritis and one cause of human hepatitis.
Single-Stranded RNA, + Strand Enveloped			
60–70 nm	Togaviridae	*Alphavirus* *Rubivirus* (rubella virus)	Included are many viruses transmitted by arthropods (*Alphavirus*); diseases include eastern equine encephalitis (EEE), western equine encephalitis (WEE), and chikungunya. Rubella virus is transmitted by the respiratory route.
40–50 nm	Flaviviridae	*Flavivirus* *Pestivirus* Hepatitis C virus	Can replicate in arthropods that transmit them; diseases include yellow fever, dengue and St. Louis and West Nile encephalitis.

(continued)

TABLE 2 Families of Viruses That Affect Humans *(continued)*

Characteristics/ Dimensions	Viral Family	Important Genera	Clinical or Special Features
80–160 nm	Coronaviridae	*Coronavirus*	Associated with upper respiratory tract infections and the common cold; SARS virus.
– Strand, One Strand of RNA			
70–180 nm	Rhabdoviridae	*Vesiculovirus* (vesicular stomatatis virus) *Lyssavirus* (rabies virus)	Bullet-shaped viruses with a spiked envelope; cause rabies and numerous animal diseases.
80–14,000 nm	Filoviridae	*Filovirus*	Enveloped, helical viruses; Ebola and Marburg viruses are filoviruses.
150–300 nm	Paramyxoviridae	*Paramyxovirus* *Morbillivirus* (measles virus)	Paramyxoviruses cause parainfluenza, mumps, and Newcastle disease in chickens.
32 nm	Deltaviridae	Hepatitis D	Depend on coinfection with hepadnavirus.
– Strand, Multiple Strands of RNA			
80–200 nm	Orthomyxoviridae	Influenza virus A, B, and C	Envelope spikes can agglutinate red blood cells.
90–120 nm	Bunyaviridae	*Bunyavirus* (California encephalitis virus) *Hantavirus*	Hantaviruses cause hemorrhagic fevers such as Korean hemorrhagic fever and *Hantavirus* pulmonary syndrome; associated with rodents.
110–130 nm	Arenaviridae	*Arenavirus*	Helical capsids contain RNA-containing granules; cause lymphocytic choriomeningitis, Venezuelan hemorrhagic fever, and Lassa fever.
Produce DNA			
100–120 nm	Retroviridae	Oncoviruses *Lentivirus* (HIV)	Includes all RNA tumor viruses. Oncoviruses cause leukemia and tumors in animals; the *Lentivirus* HIV causes AIDS.
Double-Stranded RNA Nonenveloped			
60–80 nm	Reoviridae	*Reovirus* *Rotavirus*	Generally mild respiratory infections transmitted by arthropods; Colorado tick fever is the best-known.

Derived from material in *Archives of Virology*: Supplementum 2: Classification and Nomenclature of Viruses, Fifth Report of the International Committee on Taxonomy of Viruses ed. by R. I. B. Franki et al., 1991, Springer-Verlag AND *Virus Taxonomy*: Classification and Nomenclature of Viruses, 8th Report of the International Commitee on Taxonomy of Viruses by C. Fauquet, et al., 2005, Elsevier.

Each plaque theoretically corresponds to a single virus in the initial suspension. Therefore, the concentrations of viral suspensions measured by the number of plaques are usually given in terms of **plaque-forming units (PFU)**.

Growing Animal Viruses in the Laboratory

In the laboratory, three methods are commonly used for culturing animal viruses. These methods involve using living animals, embryonated eggs, or cell cultures.

In Living Animals

Some animal viruses can be cultured only in living animals, such as mice, rabbits, and guinea pigs. Most experiments to study the immune system's response to viral infections must also be performed in virally infected live animals. Animal inoculation may be used as a diagnostic procedure for identifying and isolating a virus from a clinical specimen. After the animal is inoculated with the specimen, the animal is observed for signs of disease or is killed so that infected tissues can be examined for the virus.

Some human viruses cannot be grown in animals or can be grown but do not cause disease. The lack of natural animal models for AIDS has slowed our understanding of its disease process and prevented experimentation with drugs that inhibit growth of the virus in vivo. Chimpanzees can be infected with one subspecies of human immunodeficiency virus (HIV-1, genus *Lentivirus*), but because they do not show symptoms of the disease, they cannot be used to study the effects of viral growth and disease treatments. AIDS vaccines are presently being tested in humans, but the disease progresses so slowly in humans that it can take years to determine the effectiveness of these vaccines. In 1986, simian AIDS (an immunodeficiency disease of green monkeys) was reported, followed in 1987 by feline AIDS (an immunodeficiency disease of domestic cats). These diseases are caused by lentiviruses, which are closely related to HIV, and the diseases develop within a few months, thus providing a model for studying viral growth in different tissues. In 1990, a way to infect mice with HIV was found when immunodeficient mice were grafted to produce human T cells and human gamma globulin. The mice provide a reliable model for studying viral replication, although they do not provide models for vaccine development.

In Embryonated Eggs

If the virus will grow in an *embryonated egg,* this can be a fairly convenient and inexpensive form of host for many animal viruses. A hole is drilled in the shell of the embryonated egg, and a viral suspension or suspected virus-containing tissue is injected into the fluid of the egg. There are several membranes in an egg, and the virus is injected near the one most appropriate for its growth (Figure 7). Viral growth is signaled by the death of the embryo, by embryo cell damage, or by the formation of typical pocks or lesions on the egg membranes. This method was once the most

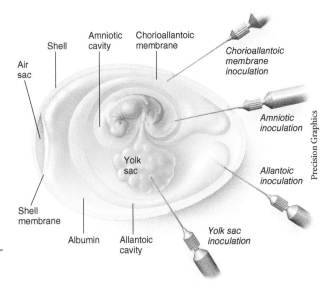

Figure 7 Inoculation of an embryonated egg. The injection site determines the membrane on which the viruses will grow.

Q Why are viruses grown in eggs and not in culture media?

widely used method of viral isolation and growth, and it is still used to grow viruses for some vaccines. For this reason, you may be asked if you are allergic to eggs before receiving a vaccination, because egg proteins may be present in the viral vaccine preparations.

In Cell Cultures

Cell cultures have replaced embryonated eggs as the preferred type of growth medium for many viruses. Cell cultures consist of cells grown in culture media in the laboratory. Because these cultures are generally rather homogeneous collections of cells and can be propagated and handled much like bacterial cultures, they are more convenient to work with than whole animals or embryonated eggs.

Cell culture lines are started by treating a slice of animal tissue with enzymes that separate the individual cells (Figure 8). These cells are suspended in a solution that provides the osmotic pressure, nutrients, and growth factors needed for the cells to grow. Normal cells tend to adhere to the glass or plastic container and reproduce to form a monolayer. Viruses infecting such a monolayer sometimes cause the cells of the monolayer to deteriorate as they multiply. This cell deterioration, called **cytopathic effect (CPE),** is illustrated in Figure 9. CPE can be detected and counted in much the same way as plaques caused by bacteriophages on a lawn of bacteria and reported as PFU/ml.

Viruses may be grown in primary or continuous cell lines. **Primary cell lines,** derived from tissue slices, tend to die out after only a few generations. Certain cell lines, called **diploid**

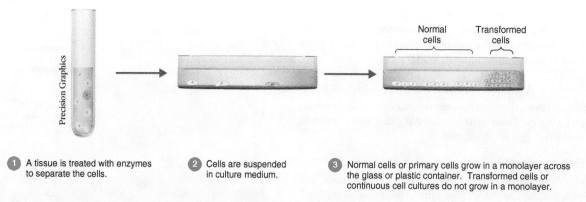

① A tissue is treated with enzymes to separate the cells.

② Cells are suspended in culture medium.

③ Normal cells or primary cells grow in a monolayer across the glass or plastic container. Transformed cells or continuous cell cultures do not grow in a monolayer.

Figure 8 Cell cultures. Transformed cells can be grown indefinitely in laboratory culture.

Q Why are transformed cells referred to as "immortal"?

cell lines, developed from human embryos can be maintained for about 100 generations and are widely used for culturing viruses that require a human host. Cell lines developed from embryonic human cells are used to culture rabies virus for a rabies vaccine called human diploid culture vaccine.

When viruses are routinely grown in a laboratory, **continuous cell lines** are used. These are transformed (cancerous) cells that can be maintained through an indefinite number of generations, and they are sometimes called immortal cell lines (see the discussion of transformation later in this chapter). One of these, the HeLa cell line, was isolated from the cancer of a woman (**He**nrietta **La**cks) who died in 1951. After years of laboratory cultivation, many such cell lines have lost almost all the original characteristics of the cell, but these changes have not interfered with the use of the cells for viral propagation. In spite of the success of cell culture in viral isolation and growth, there are still some viruses that have never been successfully cultivated in cell culture.

The idea of cell culture dates back to the end of the nineteenth century, but it was not a practical laboratory technique until the development of antibiotics in the years following World War II. A major problem with cell culture is that the cell lines must be kept free of microbial contamination. The maintenance of cell culture lines requires trained technicians with considerable experience working on a full-time basis. Because of these difficulties, most hospital laboratories and many state health laboratories do not isolate and identify viruses in clinical work. Instead, the tissue or serum samples are sent to central laboratories that specialize in such work.

Viral Identification

Identifying viral isolates is not an easy task. For one thing, viruses cannot be seen at all without the use of an electron microscope. Serological methods, such as Western blotting, are the most commonly used means of identification. In these tests, the virus is detected and identified by its reaction with antibodies. Observation of cytopathic effects is also useful for identifying a virus.

Virologists can identify and characterize viruses by using such modern molecular methods as use of restriction fragment length polymorphisms (RFLPs) and the polymerase chain reaction (PCR). PCR was used to amplify viral RNA to identify the West Nile virus in 1999 in the United States and the SARS-associated coronavirus in China in 2002.

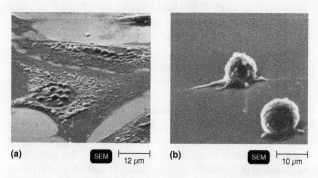

(a) SEM ⊢ 12 μm ⊣ (b) SEM ⊢ 10 μm ⊣

Figure 9 The cytopathic effect of viruses. (a) Uninfected mouse cells align next to each other, forming a monolayer. **(b)** The same cells 24 hours after infection with vesicular stomatitis virus (VSV). Notice the cells pile up and "round up."

Q How did VSV infection affect the cells?

From: "A novel cytotoxin from Clostridium difficile serogroup F is a functional hybrid between two other large clostridial cytotoxins." E. Chaves-Olarte, et al. *J Biol Chem.* 1999 Apr 16;274(16):11046–52

CHECK YOUR UNDERSTANDING

✓ What is the plaque method? 5

✓ Why are continuous cell lines of more practical use than primary cell lines for culturing viruses? 6

✓ What tests could you use to identify influenza virus in a patient? 7

Viral Multiplication

LEARNING OBJECTIVES

8   Describe the lytic cycle of T-even bacteriophages.

9   Describe the lysogenic cycle of bacteriophage lambda.

10   Compare and contrast the multiplication cycle of DNA and RNA-containing animal viruses.

The nucleic acid in a virion contains only a few of the genes needed for the synthesis of new viruses. These include genes for the virion's structural components, such as the capsid proteins, and genes for a few of the enzymes used in the viral life cycle. These enzymes are synthesized and functional only when the virus is within the host cell. Viral enzymes are almost entirely concerned with replicating or processing viral nucleic acid. Enzymes needed for protein synthesis, ribosomes, tRNA, and energy production are supplied by the host cell and are used for synthesizing viral proteins, including viral enzymes. Although the smallest nonenveloped virions do not contain any preformed enzymes, the larger virions may contain one or a few enzymes, which usually function in helping the virus penetrate the host cell or replicate its own nucleic acid.

Thus, for a virus to multiply, it must invade a host cell and take over the host's metabolic machinery. A single virion can give rise to several or even thousands of similar viruses in a single host cell. This process can drastically change the host cell and usually causes its death. In a few viral infections, cells survive and continue to produce viruses indefinitely.

The multiplication of viruses can be demonstrated with a **one-step growth curve** (Figure 10). The data are obtained by infecting every cell in a culture and then testing the culture medium and cells for virions and viral proteins and nucleic acids.

Multiplication of Bacteriophages

Although the means by which a virus enters and exits a host cell may vary, the basic mechanism of viral multiplication is similar for all viruses. Bacteriophages can multiply by two alternative mechanisms: the lytic cycle or the lysogenic cycle. The **lytic cycle** ends with the lysis and death of the host cell, whereas the host cell remains alive in the **lysogenic cycle.** Because the *T-even bacteriophages* (T2, T4, and T6) have been studied most extensively, we will describe the multiplication of T-even bacteriophages in their host, *E. coli,* as an example of the lytic cycle.

T-Even Bacteriophages: The Lytic Cycle

The virions of T-even bacteriophages are large, complex, and non-enveloped, with a characteristic head-and-tail structure shown in Figure 5a and Figure 11. The length of DNA contained in these bacteriophages is only about 6% of that contained in *E. coli,* yet the phage has enough DNA for over 100 genes. The multiplication cycle of these phages, like that of all viruses, occurs in five distinct stages: attachment, penetration, biosynthesis, maturation, and release.

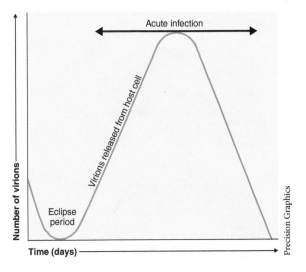

Figure 10 **A viral one-step growth curve.** No new infective virions are found in a culture until after biosynthesis and maturation have taken place. Most infected cells die as a result of infection; consequently, new virions will not be produced.

Q What can be found in the cell during biosynthesis and maturation?

Attachment ❶ After a chance collision between phage particles and bacteria, *attachment,* or *adsorption,* occurs. During this process, an attachment site on the virus attaches to a complementary receptor site on the bacterial cell. This attachment is a chemical interaction in which weak bonds are formed between the attachment and receptor sites. T-even bacteriophages use fibers at the end of the tail as attachment sites. The complementary receptor sites are on the bacterial cell wall.

Penetration ❷ After attachment, the T-even bacteriophage injects its DNA (nucleic acid) into the bacterium. To do this, the bacteriophage's tail releases an enzyme, **phage lysozyme,** which breaks down a portion of the bacterial cell wall. During the process of *penetration,* the tail sheath of the phage contracts, and the tail core is driven through the cell wall. When the tip of the core reaches the plasma membrane, the DNA from the bacteriophage's head passes through the tail core, through the plasma membrane, and enters the bacterial cell. The capsid remains outside the bacterial cell. Therefore, the phage particle functions like a hypodermic syringe to inject its DNA into the bacterial cell.

Biosynthesis ❸ Once the bacteriophage DNA has reached the cytoplasm of the host cell, the biosynthesis of viral nucleic acid and protein occurs. Host protein synthesis is stopped by virus-induced degradation of the host DNA, viral proteins that interfere with transcription, or the repression of translation.

Initially, the phage uses the host cell's nucleotides and several of its enzymes to synthesize many copies of phage DNA. Soon after,

407

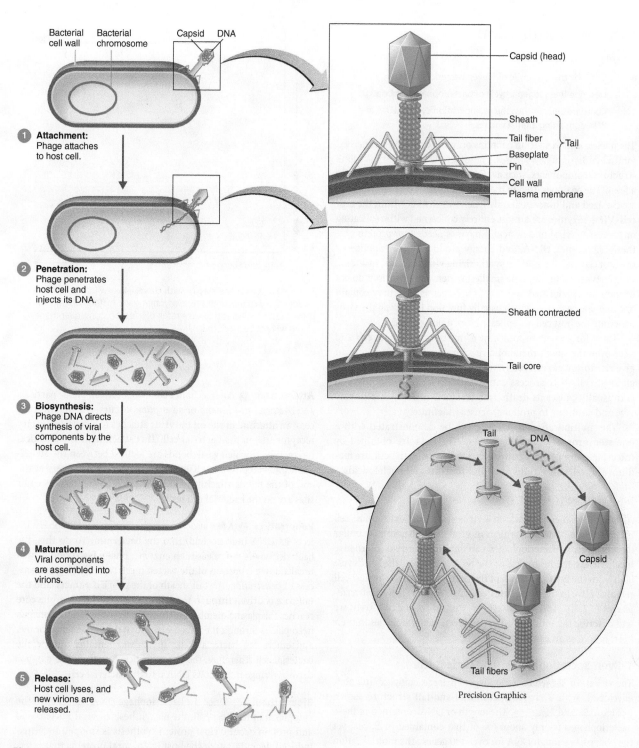

Figure 11 **The lytic cycle of a T-even bacteriophage.**

Q What is the result of the lytic cycle?

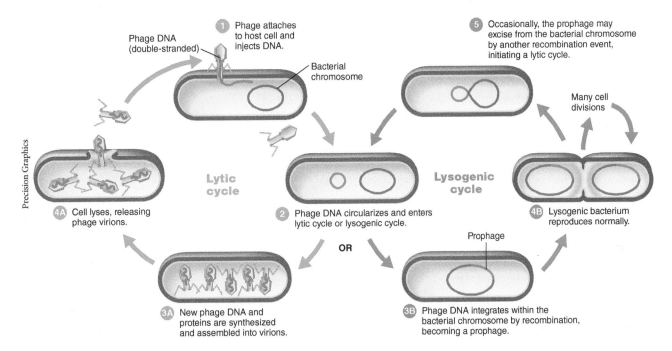

Figure 12 **The lysogenic cycle of bacteriophage λ in *E. coli*.**

Q How does lysogeny differ from the lytic cycle?

the biosynthesis of viral proteins begins. Any RNA transcribed in the cell is mRNA transcribed from phage DNA for the biosynthesis of phage enzymes and capsid proteins. The host cell's ribosomes, enzymes, and amino acids are used for translation. Genetic controls regulate when different regions of phage DNA are transcribed into mRNA during the multiplication cycle. For example, early messages are translated into early phage proteins, the enzymes used in the synthesis of phage DNA. Also, late messages are translated into late phage proteins for the synthesis of capsid proteins.

For several minutes following infection, complete phages cannot be found in the host cell. Only separate components— DNA and protein—can be detected. The period during viral multiplication when complete, infective virions are not yet present is called the **eclipse period.**

Maturation ④ In the next sequence of events, *maturation* occurs. In this process, bacteriophage DNA and capsids are assembled into complete virions. The viral components essentially assemble into a viral particle spontaneously, eliminating the need for many nonstructural genes and gene products. The phage heads and tails are separately assembled from protein subunits, and the head is filled with phage DNA and attached to the tail.

Release ⑤ The final stage of viral multiplication is the *release* of virions from the host cell. The term **lysis** is generally used for

this stage in the multiplication of T-even phages because in this case, the plasma membrane actually breaks open (lyses). Lysozyme, which is encoded by a phage gene, is synthesized within the cell. This enzyme causes the bacterial cell wall to break down, and the newly produced bacteriophages are released from the host cell. The released bacteriophages infect other susceptible cells in the vicinity, and the viral multiplication cycle is repeated within those cells.

Bacteriophage Lambda (λ): The Lysogenic Cycle

In contrast to T-even bacteriophages, some viruses do not cause lysis and death of the host cell when they multiply. These *lysogenic phages* (also called *temperate phages*) may indeed proceed through a lytic cycle, but they are also capable of incorporating their DNA into the host cell's DNA to begin a lysogenic cycle. In **lysogeny,** the phage remains latent (inactive). The participating bacterial host cells are known as *lysogenic cells*.

We will use the bacteriophage λ (lambda), a well-studied lysogenic phage, as an example of the lysogenic cycle (**Figure 12**).

① Upon penetration into an *E. coli* cell,

② the originally linear phage DNA forms a circle.

③Ⓐ This circle can multiply and be transcribed,

④Ⓐ leading to the production of new phage and to cell lysis (the lytic cycle).

Alternatively, the circle can recombine with and become part of the circular bacterial DNA (the lysogenic cycle). The inserted phage DNA is now called a **prophage.** Most of the prophage genes are repressed by two repressor proteins that are the products of phage genes. These repressors stop transcription of all the other phage genes by binding to operators. Thus, the phage genes that would otherwise direct the synthesis and release of new virions are turned off, in much the same way that the genes of the *E. coli lac* operon are turned off by the *lac* repressor.

Every time the host cell's machinery replicates the bacterial chromosome,

it also replicates the prophage DNA. The prophage remains latent within the progeny cells.

However, a rare spontaneous event, or the action of UV light or certain chemicals, can lead to the excision (popping-out) of the phage DNA, and to initiation of the lytic cycle.

There are three important results of lysogeny. First, the lysogenic cells are immune to reinfection by the same phage. (However, the host cell is not immune to infection by other phage types.) The second result of lysogeny is **phage conversion;** that is, the host cell may exhibit new properties. For example, the bacterium *Corynebacterium diphtheriae*, which causes diphtheria, is a pathogen whose disease-producing properties are related to the synthesis of a toxin. The organism can produce toxin only when it carries a lysogenic phage, because the prophage carries the gene coding for the toxin. As another example, only streptococci carrying a lysogenic phage are capable of causing toxic shock syndrome. The toxin produced by *Clostridium botulinum*, which causes botulism, is encoded by a prophage gene, as is the Shiga toxin produced by pathogenic strains of *E. coli*.

The third result of lysogeny is that it makes **specialized transduction** possible. Bacterial genes can be picked up in a phage coat and transferred to another bacterium in a process called generalized transduction. Any bacterial genes can be transferred by generalized transduction because the host chromosome is broken down into fragments, any of which can be packaged into a phage coat. In specialized transduction, however, only certain bacterial genes can be transferred.

Specialized transduction is mediated by a lysogenic phage, which packages bacterial DNA *along with* its own DNA in the same capsid. When a prophage is excised from the host chromosome, adjacent genes from either side may remain attached to the phage DNA. In Figure 13, bacteriophage λ has picked up the *gal* gene for galactose fermentation from its galactose-positive host. The phage carries this gene to a galactose-negative cell, which then becomes galactose-positive.

Certain animal viruses can undergo processes very similar to lysogeny. Animal viruses that can remain latent in cells for

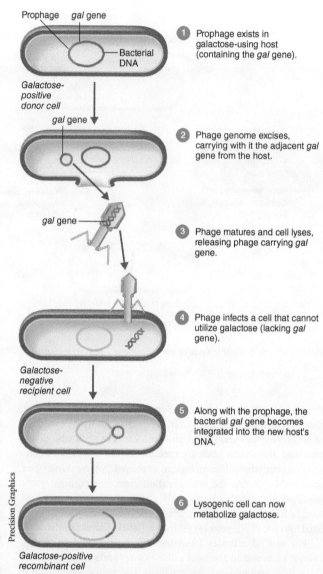

1. Prophage exists in galactose-using host (containing the *gal* gene).

2. Phage genome excises, carrying with it the adjacent *gal* gene from the host.

3. Phage matures and cell lyses, releasing phage carrying *gal* gene.

4. Phage infects a cell that cannot utilize galactose (lacking *gal* gene).

5. Along with the prophage, the bacterial *gal* gene becomes integrated into the new host's DNA.

6. Lysogenic cell can now metabolize galactose.

Figure 13 Specialized transduction. When a prophage is excised from its host chromosome, it can take with it a bit of the adjacent DNA from the bacterial chromosome.

Q How does specialized transduction differ from the lytic cycle?

long periods without multiplying or causing disease may become inserted into a host chromosome or remain separate from host DNA in a repressed state (as some lysogenic phages). Cancer-causing viruses may also be latent, as will be discussed later in the chapter. **Animations** Viral Replication: Virulent Bacteriophages; Temperate Bacteriophages; Transduction: Specialized Transduction

TABLE 3 Bacteriophage and Animal Viral Multiplication Compared

Stage	Bacteriophages	Animal Viruses
Attachment	Tail fibers attach to cell wall proteins.	Attachment sites are plasma membrane proteins and glycoproteins.
Entry	Viral DNA is injected into host cell.	Capsid enters by receptor-mediated endocytosis or fusion.
Uncoating	Not required	Enzymatic removal of capsid proteins
Biosynthesis	In cytoplasm	In nucleus (DNA viruses) or cytoplasm (RNA viruses)
Chronic infection	Lysogeny	Latency; slow viral infections; cancer
Release	Host cell is lysed.	Enveloped viruses bud out; nonenveloped viruses rupture plasma membrane.

CHECK YOUR UNDERSTANDING

✔ How do bacteriophages get nucleotides and amino acids if they don't have any metabolic enzymes? **8**

✔ *Vibrio cholerae* produces toxin and is capable of causing cholera only when it is lysogenic. What does this mean? **9**

Multiplication of Animal Viruses

The multiplication of animal viruses follows the basic pattern of bacteriophage multiplication but has several differences, summarized in **Table 3**. Animal viruses differ from phages in their mechanism of entering the host cell. Also, once the virus is inside, the synthesis and assembly of the new viral components are somewhat different, partly because of the differences between prokaryotic cells and eukaryotic cells. Animal viruses may have certain types of enzymes not found in phages. Finally, the mechanisms of maturation and release, and the effects on the host cell, differ in animal viruses and phages.

In the following discussion of the multiplication of animal viruses, we will consider the processes that are shared by both DNA- and RNA-containing animal viruses. These processes are attachment, entry, uncoating, and release. We will also examine how DNA- and RNA-containing viruses differ with respect to their processes of biosynthesis.

Attachment

Like bacteriophages, animal viruses have attachment sites that attach to complementary receptor sites on the host cell's surface. However, the receptor sites of animal cells are proteins and glycoproteins of the plasma membrane. Moreover, animal viruses do not possess appendages like the tail fibers of some bacteriophages. The attachment sites of animal viruses are distributed over the surface of the virus. The sites themselves vary from one group of viruses to another. In adenoviruses, which are icosahedral viruses, the attachment sites are small fibers at the corners of the icosahedron (see Figure 2b). In many of the enveloped viruses, such as influenza virus, the attachment sites are spikes located on the surface of the envelope (see Figure 3b). As soon as one spike attaches to a host receptor, additional receptor sites on the same cell migrate to the virus. Attachment is completed when many sites are bound.

Receptor sites are inherited characteristics of the host. Consequently, the receptor for a particular virus can vary from person to person. This could account for the individual differences in susceptibility to a particular virus. For example, people who lack the cellular receptor (called P antigen) for parvovirus B19, are naturally resistant to infection and do not get fifth disease. Understanding the nature of attachment can lead to the development of drugs that prevent viral infections. Monoclonal antibodies that combine with a virus's attachment site or the cell's receptor site may soon be used to treat some viral infections.

Entry

Following attachment, entry occurs. Many viruses enter into eukaryotic cells by **receptor-mediated endocytosis**. A cell's plasma membrane continuously folds inward to form vesicles. These vesicles contain elements that originate outside the cell and are brought into the interior of the cell to be digested. If a virion attaches to the plasma membrane of a potential host cell, the host cell will enfold the virion into a fold of plasma membrane, forming a vesicle (Figure 14a).

Enveloped viruses can enter by an alternative method called **fusion,** in which the viral envelope fuses with the plasma membrane and releases the capsid into the cell's cytoplasm. For example, HIV penetrates cells by this method (Figure 14b).

Uncoating

Viruses disappear during the eclipse period of an infection because they are taken apart inside the cell. **Uncoating** is the separation of the viral nucleic acid from its protein coat once the virion is enclosed within the vesicle. The capsid is digested when the cell attempts to digest the vesicle's contents, or the nonenveloped capsid may be released into the cytoplasm of the host cell. This process varies with the type of virus. Some animal viruses accomplish uncoating by the action of lysosomal enzymes of the

From: Medical Virology, 4th ed. D. O. White and F. J. Fenner. Academic Press California (1994)

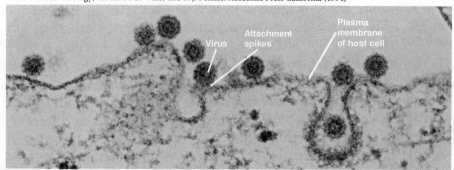

(a) Entry of togavirus by receptor-mediated endocytosis

TEM | 85 nm

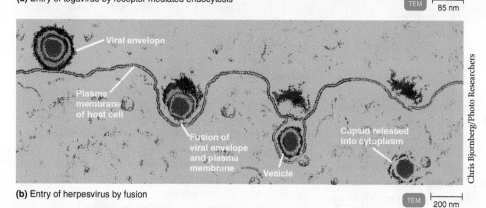

Chris Bjornberg/Photo Researchers

(b) Entry of herpesvirus by fusion

TEM | 200 nm

Figure 14 The entry of viruses into host cells. After attachment, viruses enter host cells by (**a**) receptor-mediated endocytosis or (**b**) fusion of the viral envelope and cell membrane, followed by endocytosis of the capsid.

Q In which process is the cell actively taking in the virus?

host cell. These enzymes degrade the proteins of the viral capsid. The uncoating of poxviruses is completed by a specific enzyme encoded by the viral DNA and synthesized soon after infection. For other viruses, uncoating appears to be exclusively caused by enzymes in the host cell cytoplasm. For at least one virus, the poliovirus, uncoating seems to begin while the virus is still attached to the host cell's plasma membrane.

The Biosynthesis of DNA Viruses

Generally, DNA-containing viruses replicate their DNA in the nucleus of the host cell by using viral enzymes, and they synthesize their capsid and other proteins in the cytoplasm by using host cell enzymes. Then the proteins migrate into the nucleus and are joined with the newly synthesized DNA to form virions. These virions are transported along the endoplasmic reticulum to the host cell's membrane for release. Herpesviruses, papovaviruses, adenoviruses, and hepadnaviruses all follow this pattern of biosynthesis (Table 4). Poxviruses are an exception because all of their components are synthesized in the cytoplasm.

As an example of the multiplication of a DNA virus, the sequence of events in papovavirus is shown in Figure 15.

①–② Following attachment, entry, and uncoating, the viral DNA is released into the nucleus of the host cell.

③ Transcription of a portion of the viral DNA—the "early" genes—occurs next. Translation follows. The products of

these genes are enzymes that are required for the multiplication of viral DNA. In most DNA viruses, early transcription is carried out with the host's transcriptase (RNA polymerase); poxviruses, however, contain their own transcriptase.

④ Sometime after the initiation of DNA replication, transcription and translation of the remaining "late" viral genes occur. Late proteins include capsid and other structural proteins.

⑤ This leads to the synthesis of capsid proteins, which occurs in the cytoplasm of the host cell.

⑥ After the capsid proteins migrate into the nucleus of the host cell, maturation occurs; the viral DNA and capsid proteins assemble to form complete viruses.

⑦ Complete viruses are then released from the host cell.

Some DNA viruses are described below.

Adenoviridae Named after adenoids, from which they were first isolated, adenoviruses cause acute respiratory diseases—the common cold (Figure 16a).

Poxviridae All diseases caused by poxviruses, including smallpox and cowpox, include skin lesions. *Pox* refers to pus-filled lesions. Viral multiplication is started by viral transcriptase; the viral components are synthesized and assembled in the cytoplasm of the host cell.

Replication of a DNA-Containing Animal Virus

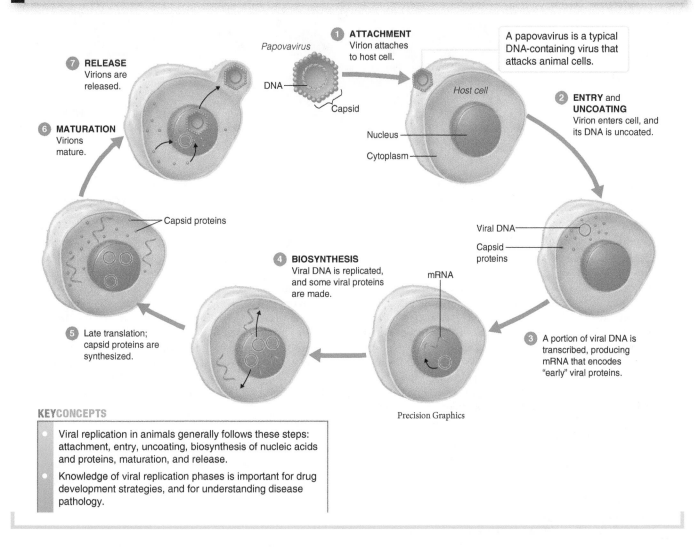

1 ATTACHMENT
Virion attaches to host cell.

Papovavirus

DNA

Capsid

A papovavirus is a typical DNA-containing virus that attacks animal cells.

Host cell

2 ENTRY and **UNCOATING**
Virion enters cell, and its DNA is uncoated.

Nucleus

Cytoplasm

7 RELEASE
Virions are released.

6 MATURATION
Virions mature.

Capsid proteins

Viral DNA

Capsid proteins

4 BIOSYNTHESIS
Viral DNA is replicated, and some viral proteins are made.

mRNA

5 Late translation; capsid proteins are synthesized.

3 A portion of viral DNA is transcribed, producing mRNA that encodes "early" viral proteins.

Precision Graphics

KEYCONCEPTS

- Viral replication in animals generally follows these steps: attachment, entry, uncoating, biosynthesis of nucleic acids and proteins, maturation, and release.

- Knowledge of viral replication phases is important for drug development strategies, and for understanding disease pathology.

Herpesviridae Nearly 100 herpesviruses are known (Figure 16b). They are named after the spreading *(herpetic)* appearance of cold sores. Species of human herpesviruses (HHV) include HHV-1 and HHV-2, both in the genus *Simplexvirus,* which cause cold sores; HHV-3, genus *Varicellovirus,* which cause chickenpox; HHV-4, genus *Lymphocryptovirus,* which causes infectious mononucleosis; HHV-5, genus *Cytomegalovirus,* which causes CMV inclusion disease; HHV-6, genus *Roseolovirus,* which causes roseola; HHV-7, *Roseolovirus,* which infects most infants, causing measleslike rashes; and HHV-8, *Rhadinovirus,* which causes Kaposi's sarcoma, primarily in AIDS patients.

Papovaviridae Papovaviruses are named for *pa*pillomas (warts), *po*lyomas (tumors), and *va*cuolation (cytoplasmic vacuoles produced by some of these viruses). Warts are caused by members of the genus *Papillomavirus*. Some *Papillomavirus* species are capable of transforming cells and causing cancer. Viral DNA is replicated in the host cell's nucleus along with host cell chromosomes. Host cells may proliferate, resulting in a tumor.

Hepadnaviridae Hepadnaviridae are so named because they cause *hepa*titis and contain *DNA*. The only genus in this family causes hepatitis B. (Hepatitis A, C, D, E, F, and G viruses, although not related to each other, are RNA viruses.) Hepadnaviruses differ from other DNA viruses because they synthesize

C. Garon and J.Rose, CDC

Linda Stannard, U. of Cape Town/Photo Researchers

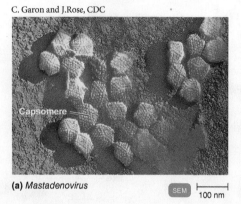

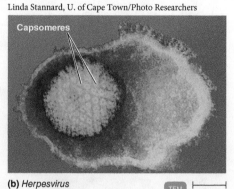

Figure 16 DNA-containing animal viruses. (**a**) Negatively stained adenoviruses that have been concentrated in a centrifuge gradient. The individual capsomeres are clearly visible. (**b**) The envelope around this herpes simplex virus capsid has broken, giving a "fried egg" appearance.

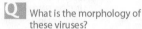 What is the morphology of these viruses?

(a) *Mastadenovirus*   SEM |—————| 100 nm

(b) *Herpesvirus*   TEM |——| 50 nm

DNA by copying RNA, using viral reverse transcriptase. This enzyme is discussed later with the retroviruses, the only other family with reverse transcriptase.

The Biosynthesis of RNA Viruses

The multiplication of RNA viruses is essentially the same as that of DNA viruses, except that several different mechanisms of mRNA formation occur among different groups of RNA viruses (see Table 4). Although the details of these mechanisms are beyond the scope of this text, for comparative purposes we will trace the multiplication cycles of the four nucleic acid types of RNA viruses (three of which are shown in Figure 17). RNA viruses multiply in the host cell's cytoplasm. The major differences among the multiplication processes of these viruses lie in how mRNA and viral RNA are produced. Once viral RNA and viral proteins are synthesized, maturation occurs by similar means among all animal viruses, as will be discussed shortly.**20**

Picornaviridae Picornaviruses, such as enteroviruses and poliovirus, are single-stranded RNA viruses. They are the smallest

viruses; and the prefix *pico-* (small) plus *RNA* gives these viruses their name. The RNA within the virion is called a **sense strand** (or **+ strand**), because it can act as mRNA. After attachment, penetration, and uncoating are completed, the single-stranded viral RNA (Figure 17a) is translated into two principal proteins, which inhibit the host cell's synthesis of RNA and protein and which form an enzyme called *RNA-dependent RNA polymerase*. This enzyme catalyzes the synthesis of another strand of RNA, which is complementary in base sequence to the original infecting strand. This new strand, called an **antisense strand** (or **− strand**), serves as a template to produce additional + strands. The + strands may serve as mRNA for the translation of capsid proteins, may become incorporated into capsid proteins to form a new virus, or may serve as a template for continued RNA multiplication. Once viral RNA and viral protein are synthesized, maturation occurs.

Togaviridae Togaviruses, which include *arthropod-borne arbo* viruses or alphaviruses, also contain a single + strand of RNA. Togaviruses are enveloped viruses; their name is from the Latin word for covering, *toga*. Keep in mind that these are not the only enveloped viruses. After a − strand is made

---

TABLE 4 The Biosynthesis of DNA and RNA Viruses Compared

Viral Nucleic Acid	Virus Family	Special Features of Biosynthesis
DNA, single-stranded	Parvoviridae	Cellular enzyme transcribes viral DNA in nucleus.
DNA, double-stranded	Herpesviridae Papovaviridae	Cellular enzyme transcribes viral DNA in nucleus.
	Poxviridae	Viral enzyme transcribes viral DNA in virion, in cytoplasm.
DNA, reverse transcriptase	Hepadnaviridae	Cellular enzyme transcribes viral DNA in nucleus; reverse transcriptase copies mRNA to make viral DNA.
RNA, + strand	Picornaviridae Togaviridae	Viral RNA functions as a template for synthesis of RNA polymerase, which copies − strand RNA to make mRNA in cytoplasm.
RNA, − strand	Rhabdoviridae	Viral enzyme copies viral RNA to make mRNA in cytoplasm.
RNA, double-stranded	Reoviridae	Viral enzyme copies − strand RNA to make mRNA in cytoplasm.
RNA, reverse transcriptase	Retroviridae	Viral enzyme copies viral RNA to make DNA in cytoplasm; DNA moves to nucleus.

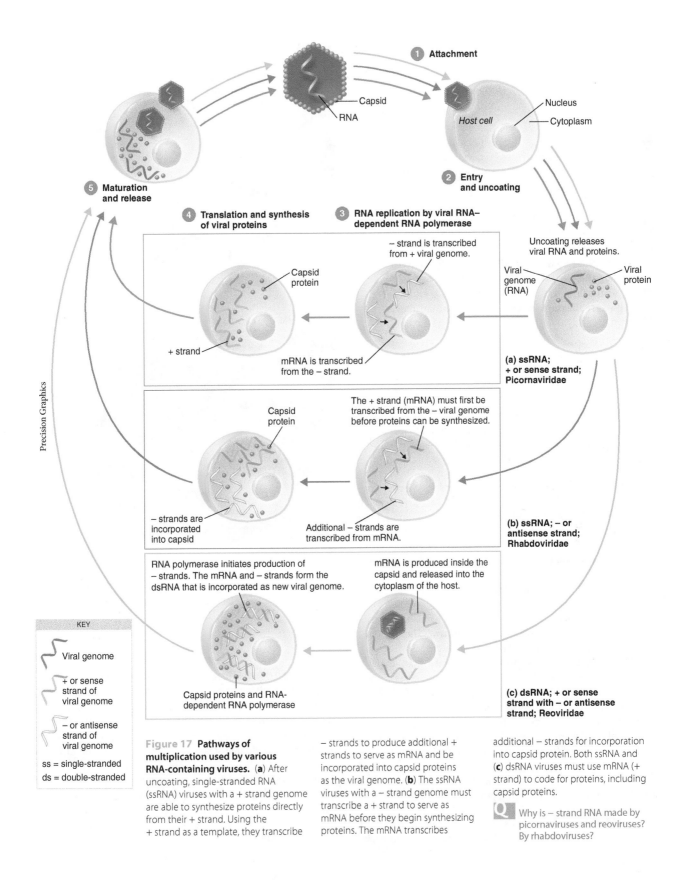

① Attachment

Capsid

RNA

Host cell

Nucleus

Cytoplasm

② Entry and uncoating

⑤ Maturation and release

④ Translation and synthesis of viral proteins

③ RNA replication by viral RNA–dependent RNA polymerase

Uncoating releases viral RNA and proteins.

− strand is transcribed from + viral genome.

Capsid protein

Viral genome (RNA)

Viral protein

+ strand

mRNA is transcribed from the − strand.

(a) ssRNA; + or sense strand; Picornaviridae

Capsid protein

The + strand (mRNA) must first be transcribed from the − viral genome before proteins can be synthesized.

− strands are incorporated into capsid

Additional − strands are transcribed from mRNA.

(b) ssRNA; − or antisense strand; Rhabdoviridae

RNA polymerase initiates production of − strands. The mRNA and − strands form the dsRNA that is incorporated as new viral genome.

mRNA is produced inside the capsid and released into the cytoplasm of the host.

Capsid proteins and RNA-dependent RNA polymerase

(c) dsRNA; + or sense strand with − or antisense strand; Reoviridae

Precision Graphics

KEY

Viral genome

+ or sense strand of viral genome

− or antisense strand of viral genome

ss = single-stranded
ds = double-stranded

Figure 17 Pathways of multiplication used by various RNA-containing viruses. (a) After uncoating, single-stranded RNA (ssRNA) viruses with a + strand genome are able to synthesize proteins directly from their + strand. Using the + strand as a template, they transcribe − strands to produce additional + strands to serve as mRNA and be incorporated into capsid proteins as the viral genome. **(b)** The ssRNA viruses with a − strand genome must transcribe a + strand to serve as mRNA before they begin synthesizing proteins. The mRNA transcribes additional − strands for incorporation into capsid protein. Both ssRNA and **(c)** dsRNA viruses must use mRNA (+ strand) to code for proteins, including capsid proteins.

Q Why is − strand RNA made by picornaviruses and reoviruses? By rhabdoviruses?

415

Clinical Case

Based on the abnormal LFT, Tina's physician diagnoses her with infectious hepatitis. This isn't the first case he's seen this month. As a matter of fact, the local health department has received reports of 31 other people with hepatitis. For a town of 4000 people, this is not a small number. The health department needs to know what type of hepatitis they are dealing with. *Hepatitis* describes any inflammation of the liver. Infectious hepatitis can be caused by a member of the Picornaviridae, Hepadnaviridae, or Flaviviridae.

The health department will need to differentiate among these viral families. List the method of transmission, morphology, nucleic acid, and type of replication for these three viral families.

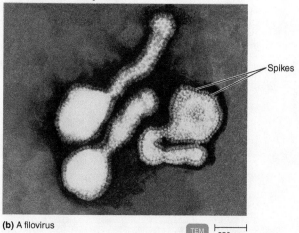

Frederick A. Murphy, Univ. of Texas Medical Branch, Galveston

RNA
Capsid
Envelope

(a) A rhabdovirus   TEM   75 nm

Linda Stannard, U. of Cape Town/Photo Researchers

Spikes

(b) A filovirus   TEM   250 nm

Figure 18 RNA-containing animal viruses. (a) Vesicular stomatitis viruses, a member of the family Rhabdoviridae. **(b)** Marburg virus, found in African cave bats, causes hemorrhagic fever in humans.

Q Why do viruses with a + strand of RNA make a − strand of RNA?

from the + strand, two types of mRNA are transcribed from the − strand. One type of mRNA is a short strand that codes for envelope proteins; the other, longer strand serves as mRNA for capsid proteins and can become incorporated into a capsid.

Rhabdoviridae Rhabdoviruses, such as rabies virus (genus *Lyssavirus*), are usually bullet-shaped (Figure 18a). *Rhabdo-* is from the Greek word for rod, which is not really an accurate description of their morphology. They contain a single − strand of RNA (Figure 17b). They also contain an *RNA-dependent RNA polymerase* that uses the − strand as a template from which to produce a + strand. The + strand serves as mRNA and as a template for synthesis of new viral RNA.

Reoviridae Reoviruses were named for their habitats: the respiratory and enteric (digestive) systems of humans. They were not associated with any diseases when first discovered, so they were considered orphan viruses. Their name comes from the first letters of *respiratory, enteric,* and *orphan.* Three serotypes are now known to cause respiratory tract and intestinal tract infections.

The capsid containing the double-stranded RNA is digested upon entering a host cell. Viral mRNA is produced in the cytoplasm, where it is used to synthesize more viral proteins (Figure 17c). One of the newly synthesized viral proteins acts as *RNA-dependent RNA polymerase* to produce more − strands of RNA. The mRNA and − strand form the double-stranded RNA that is then surrounded by capsid proteins.

Retroviridae Many retroviruses infect vertebrates (Figure 18b). One genus of retrovirus, *Lentivirus,* includes the subspecies

HIV-1 and HIV-2, which cause AIDS. The retroviruses that cause cancer will be discussed later in this chapter.

The formation of mRNA and RNA for new retrovirus virions is shown in Figure 19. These viruses carry **reverse transcriptase,** which uses the viral RNA as a template to produce complementary double-stranded DNA. This enzyme also degrades the original viral RNA. The name *retrovirus* is derived from the first letters of *reverse transcriptase.* The viral DNA is then integrated into a host cell chromosome as a **provirus.** Unlike a prophage, the provirus never comes out of the chromosome. As a provirus, HIV is protected from the host's immune system and antiviral drugs.

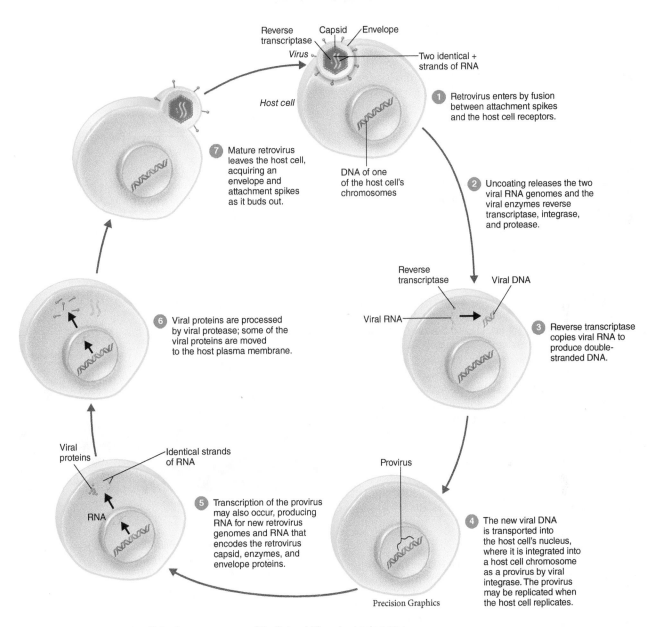

Figure 19 Multiplication and inheritance processes of the Retroviridae. A retrovirus may become a provirus that replicates in a latent state, and it may produce new retroviruses.

Q How does the biosynthesis of a retrovirus differ from that of other RNA viruses?

Sometimes the provirus simply remains in a latent state and replicates when the DNA of the host cell replicates. In other cases, the provirus is expressed and produces new viruses, which may infect adjacent cells. Mutagens such as gamma radiation can induce expression of a provirus. In oncogenic retroviruses, the provirus can also convert the host cell into a tumor cell; possible mechanisms for this phenomenon will be discussed later.

Maturation and Release

The first step in viral maturation is the assembly of the protein capsid; this assembly is usually a spontaneous process. The capsids of many animal viruses are enclosed by an envelope consisting of protein, lipid, and carbohydrate, as noted earlier. Examples of such viruses include orthomyxoviruses and paramyxoviruses.

Clinical Case

Hepatitis A virus, a nonenveloped + stranded RNA virus, is transmitted via the fecal-oral route. Hepatitis B virus is an enveloped double-stranded DNA virus. It has reverse transcriptase and is transmitted by the parenteral route (intravenous injection) or through sexual contact. Hepatitis C virus is also transmitted parenterally and is an enveloped + stranded RNA virus.

Based on this information, what conclusion can the health department make about which hepatitis virus is most likely infecting Tina and the other 31 people in this town?

(a) Release by budding

The envelope protein is encoded by the viral genes and is incorporated into the plasma membrane of the host cell. The envelope lipid and carbohydrate are encoded by host cell genes and are present in the plasma membrane. The envelope actually develops around the capsid by a process called **budding** (Figure 20).

After the sequence of attachment, entry, uncoating, and biosynthesis of viral nucleic acid and protein, the assembled capsid containing nucleic acid pushes through the plasma membrane. As a result, a portion of the plasma membrane, now the envelope, adheres to the virus. This extrusion of a virus from a host cell is one method of release. Budding does not immediately kill the host cell, and in some cases the host cell survives.

Nonenveloped viruses are released through ruptures in the host cell plasma membrane. In contrast to budding, this type of release usually results in the death of the host cell. (MM) Animations Viral Replication: Overview; Animal Viruses

CHECK YOUR UNDERSTANDING

✔ Describe the principal events of attachment, entry, uncoating, biosynthesis, maturation, and release of an enveloped DNA-containing virus. 10

Viruses and Cancer

LEARNING OBJECTIVES

11 Define *oncogene* and *transformed cell*.

12 Discuss the relationship between DNA- and RNA-containing viruses and cancer.

Several types of cancer are now known to be caused by viruses. Molecular biological research shows that the mechanisms of the diseases are similar, even when a virus does not cause the cancer.

The relationship between cancers and viruses was first demonstrated in 1908, when virologists Wilhelm Ellerman and Olaf

(b) *Lentivirus* · TEM · 50 nm

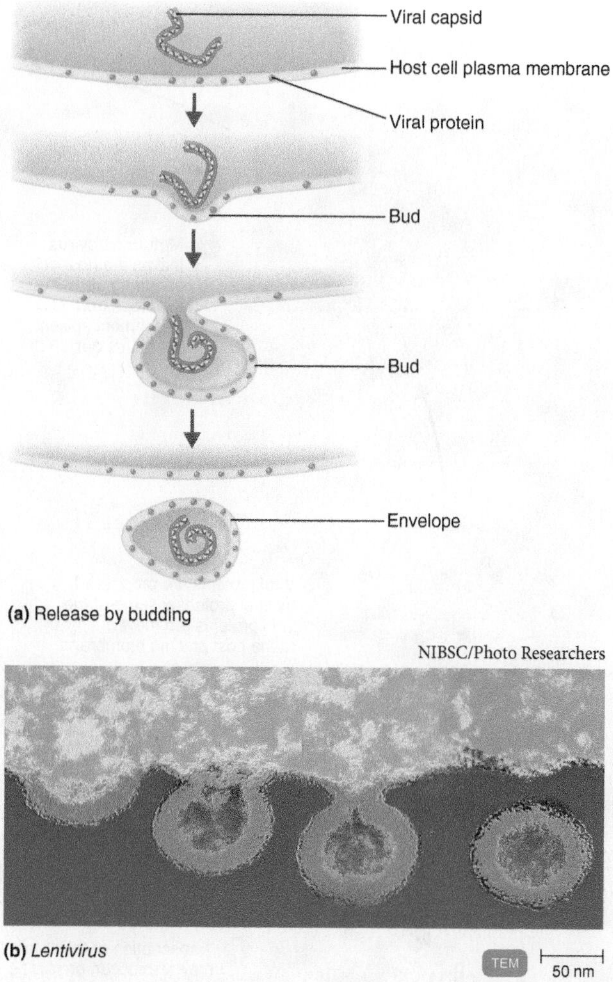

Figure 20 Budding of an enveloped virus. (a) A diagram of the budding process. **(b)** HIV budding from a T cell. Notice that the four budding viruses acquire their coats from the host plasma membrane.

Q Of what is a viral envelope composed?

Bang, working in Denmark, were trying to isolate the causative agent of chicken leukemia. They found that leukemia could be transferred to healthy chickens by cell-free filtrates that contained viruses. Three years later, F. Peyton Rous, working at the Rockefeller Institute in New York, found that a chicken **sarcoma** (cancer of connective tissue) can be similarly transmitted. Virus-induced **adenocarcinomas** (cancers of glandular epithelial tissue) in mice were discovered in 1936. At that time, it was clearly shown that mouse mammary gland tumors are transmitted from mother to offspring through the mother's milk. A human cancer-causing virus was discovered and isolated in 1972 by American bacteriologist Sarah Stewart.

Clinical Case

It is improbable that over 30 people of different ages and backgrounds are all IV drug users, so the most likely virus is hepatitis A. To investigate the source of the viral infection, the health department compares foods eaten by the 32 ill people with asymptomatic household members. All 32, including Tina, had eaten an ice-slush beverage purchased from a local convenience store. The health department determines that the convenience store clerk, unknowingly infected with hepatitis A virus, transferred the virus to the machine that makes the icy beverage. Over the next several months, Tina's symptoms subside, and her liver function returns to normal.

How can knowing the identity of the virus affect the health department's recommendation for treatment and for prevention of future outbreaks?

The viral cause of cancer can often go unrecognized for several reasons. First, most of the particles of some viruses infect cells but do not induce cancer. Second, cancer might not develop until long after viral infection. Third, cancers do not seem to be contagious, as viral diseases usually are.

The Transformation of Normal Cells into Tumor Cells

Almost anything that can alter the genetic material of a eukaryotic cell has the potential to make a normal cell cancerous. These cancer-causing alterations to cellular DNA affect parts of the genome called **oncogenes.** Oncogenes were first identified in cancer-causing viruses and were thought to be a part of the normal viral genome. However, American microbiologists J. Michael Bishop and Harold E. Varmus received the 1989 Nobel Prize in Medicine for proving that the cancer-inducing genes carried by viruses are actually derived from animal cells. Bishop and Varmus showed that the cancer-causing *src* gene in avian sarcoma viruses is derived from a normal part of chicken genes.

Oncogenes can be activated to abnormal functioning by a variety of agents, including mutagenic chemicals, high-energy radiation, and viruses. Viruses capable of inducing tumors in animals are called **oncogenic viruses,** or *oncoviruses.* Approximately 10% of cancers are known to be virus-induced. An outstanding feature of all oncogenic viruses is that their genetic material integrates into the host cell's DNA and replicates along with the host cell's chromosome. This mechanism is similar to the phenomenon of lysogeny in bacteria, and it can alter the host cell's characteristics in the same way.

Tumor cells undergo **transformation;** that is, they acquire properties that are distinct from the properties of uninfected cells or from infected cells that do not form tumors. After being transformed by viruses, many tumor cells contain a virus-specific antigen on their cell surface, called **tumor-specific transplantation antigen (TSTA),** or an antigen in their nucleus, called the **T antigen.** Transformed cells tend to be less round than normal cells, and they tend to exhibit certain chromosomal abnormalities, such as unusual numbers of chromosomes and fragmented chromosomes.

DNA Oncogenic Viruses

Oncogenic viruses are found within several families of DNA-containing viruses. These groups include the Adenoviridae, Herpesviridae, Poxviridae, Papovaviridae, and Hepadnaviridae. Among the papovaviruses, papillomaviruses cause uterine (cervical) cancer.

Virtually all cervical and anal cancers are caused by human papillomavirus (HPV). A vaccine against four HPVs, including HPV-16, is recommended for 11- to 12-year-old girls and boys.

Epstein-Barr (EB) virus was isolated from Burkitt's lymphoma cells in 1964 by Michael Epstein and Yvonne Barr. The proof that EB virus can cause cancer was accidentally demonstrated in 1985 when a 12-year-old boy known only as David received a bone marrow transplant. Several months after the transplant, he died of cancer. An autopsy revealed that the virus had been unwittingly introduced into the boy with the bone marrow transplant.

Another DNA virus that causes cancer is hepatitis B virus (HBV). Many animal studies have been performed that have clearly indicated the causal role of HBV in liver cancer. In one human study, virtually all people with liver cancer had previous HBV infections.

RNA Oncogenic Viruses

Among the RNA viruses, only the oncoviruses in the family Retroviridae cause cancer. The human T-cell leukemia viruses (HTLV-1 and HTLV-2) are retroviruses that cause adult T-cell leukemia and lymphoma in humans. (T cells are a type of white blood cell involved in the immune response.)

Sarcoma viruses of cats, chickens, and rodents, and the mammary tumor viruses of mice, are also retroviruses. Another retrovirus, feline leukemia virus (FeLV), causes leukemia in cats and is transmissible among cats. There is a test to detect the virus in cat serum.

The ability of retroviruses to induce tumors is related to their production of a reverse transcriptase by the mechanism described earlier (see Figure 19). The provirus, which is the double-stranded DNA molecule synthesized from the viral RNA, becomes integrated into the host cell's DNA; new genetic material is thereby introduced into the host's genome, and this is the key reason retroviruses can contribute to cancer. Some retroviruses contain oncogenes; others contain promoters that turn on oncogenes or other cancer-causing factors.

CHECK YOUR UNDERSTANDING

✔ What is a provirus? 11

✔ How can an RNA virus cause cancer if it doesn't have DNA to insert into a cell's genome? 12

Clinical Case Resolved

Drugs and vaccines work against specific viruses. There are no special treatments for hepatitis, but the preventive measures are different. For example, in this case, the health department recommends that everyone who ate at this convenience store in the previous 2 weeks receive hepatitis A vaccine and hepatitis A immunoglobulin.

Viruses were originally named for the symptoms they caused, hence the name "hepatitis virus" for a virus that affects the liver (from Latin *hepaticus*). This naming convention is imprecise but was the only method available until recently.

Molecular tools now allow viruses to be classified on the basis of genomes and morphology. Thus, related viruses, which may affect different tissues, are grouped into the same families. Differentiating viruses based on their genetic information provides valuable information for treatment and prevention.

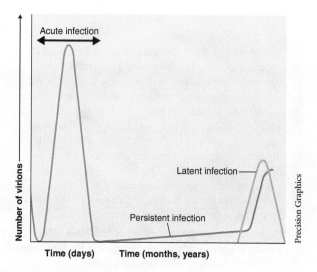

Figure 21 **Latent and persistent viral infections.**

Q How do latent and persistent infections differ?

The chickenpox virus *(Varicellovirus)* can also exist in a latent state. Chickenpox (varicella) is a skin disease that is usually acquired in childhood. The virus gains access to the skin via the blood. From the blood, some viruses may enter nerves, where they remain latent. Later, changes in the immune (T-cell) response can activate these latent viruses, causing shingles (zoster). The shingles rash appears on the skin along the nerve in which the virus was latent. Shingles occurs in 10–20% of people who have had chickenpox.

Latent Viral Infections

LEARNING OBJECTIVE

13 Provide an example of a latent viral infection.

A virus can remain in equilibrium with the host and not actually produce disease for a long period, often many years. The oncogenic viruses just discussed are examples of such latent infections. All of the human herpesviruses can remain in host cells throughout the life of an individual. When herpesviruses are reactivated by immunosuppression (for example, AIDS), the resulting infection may be fatal. The classic example of such a **latent infection** is the infection of the skin by *Simplexvirus,* which produces cold sores. This virus inhabits the host's nerve cells but causes no damage until it is activated by a stimulus such as fever or sunburn— hence the term *fever blister.*

In some individuals, viruses are produced, but symptoms never appear. Even though a large percentage of the human population carries *Simplexvirus,* only 10–15% of people carrying the virus exhibit the disease. The virus of some latent infections can exist in a lysogenic state within host cells.

Persistent Viral Infections

LEARNING OBJECTIVE

14 Differentiate persistent viral infections from latent viral infections.

A **persistent** or **chronic viral infection** occurs gradually over a long period. Typically, persistent viral infections are fatal.

A number of persistent viral infections have in fact been shown to be caused by conventional viruses. For example, several years after causing measles, the measles virus can be responsible for a rare form of encephalitis called subacute sclerosing panencephalitis (SSPE). A persistent viral infection is apparently different from a latent viral infection in that, in most persistent viral infections, detectable infectious virus gradually builds up over a long period, rather than appearing suddenly (Figure 21).

Several examples of latent and persistent viral infections are listed in **Table 5.**

CHECK YOUR UNDERSTANDING

✔ Is shingles a persistent or latent infection? 13,14

Prions

LEARNING OBJECTIVE

15 Discuss how a protein can be infectious.

A few infectious diseases are caused by prions. In 1982, American neurobiologist Stanley Prusiner proposed that infectious proteins caused a neurological disease in sheep called scrapie. The infectivity of scrapie-infected brain tissue is reduced by treatment with proteases but not by treatment with radiation, suggesting that the infectious agent is pure protein. Prusiner coined the name **prion** for *prot*einaceous *in*fectious particle.

Nine animal diseases now fall into this category, including the "mad cow disease" that emerged in cattle in Great Britain in 1987. All nine are neurological diseases called spongiform encephalopathies because large vacuoles develop in the brain. The human diseases are kuru, Creutzfeldt-Jakob disease (CJD), Gerstmann-Sträussler-Scheinker syndrome, and fatal familial insomnia. These diseases run in families, which indicates a possible genetic cause. However, they cannot be purely inherited, because mad cow disease arose from feeding scrapie-infected sheep meat to cattle, and the new (bovine) variant was transmitted to humans who ate undercooked beef from infected cattle. Additionally, CJD has been transmitted with transplanted nerve tissue and contaminated surgical instruments.

These diseases are caused by the conversion of a normal host glycoprotein called PrP^C (for cellular prion protein) into an infectious form called PrP^{Sc} (for scrapie protein). The gene for PrP^C is located on chromosome 20 in humans. Recent evidence suggests that PrP^C is involved in regulating cell death. One hypothesis for how an infectious agent that lacks any nucleic acid can reproduce is shown in **Figure 22**.

The actual cause of cell damage is not known. Fragments of PrP^{Sc} molecules accumulate in the brain, forming plaques; these plaques are used for postmortem diagnosis, but they do not appear to be the cause of cell damage. (MM) **Animations** Prion Reproduction: Overview, Characteristics, Diseases

Plant Viruses and Viroids

LEARNING OBJECTIVES

16 Differentiate virus, viroid, and prion.

17 Describe the lytic cycle for a plant virus.

Plant viruses resemble animal viruses in many respects: plant viruses are morphologically similar to animal viruses, and they have similar types of nucleic acid (**Table 6**). In fact, some plant viruses can multiply inside insect cells. Plant viruses cause many diseases of economically important crops, including beans (bean mosaic virus), corn and sugarcane (wound tumor virus), and potatoes (potato yellow dwarf virus). Viruses can cause color

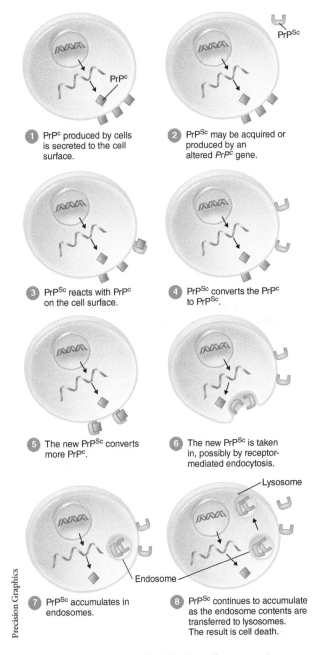

1 PrP^c produced by cells is secreted to the cell surface.

2 PrP^{Sc} may be acquired or produced by an altered *PrP^c* gene.

3 PrP^{Sc} reacts with PrP^c on the cell surface.

4 PrP^{Sc} converts the PrP^c to PrP^{Sc}.

5 The new PrP^{Sc} converts more PrP^c.

6 The new PrP^{Sc} is taken in, possibly by receptor-mediated endocytosis.

7 PrP^{Sc} accumulates in endosomes.

8 PrP^{Sc} continues to accumulate as the endosome contents are transferred to lysosomes. The result is cell death.

Precision Graphics

Figure 22 How a protein can be infectious. If an abnormal prion protein (PrP^{Sc}) enters a cell, it changes a normal prion protein to PrP^{Sc}, which now can change another normal PrP^C, resulting in an accumulation of the abnormal PrP^{Sc}.

Q How do prions differ from viruses?

TABLE 5 Examples of Latent and Persistent Viral Infections in Humans

Disease	Primary Effect	Causative Virus
Latent	**No symptoms during latency; viruses not usually released**	
Cold sores	Skin and mucous membrane lesions; genital lesions	Herpes simplex 1 and 2
Leukemia	Increased white blood cell growth	HTLV-1 and -2
Shingles	Skin lesions	*Varicellovirus* (Herpesvirus)
Persistent	**Viruses continuously released**	
Cervical cancer	Increased cell growth	Human papillomavirus
HIV/AIDS	Decreased CD$_4$+T cells	HIV-1 and -2 (*Lentivirus*)
Liver cancer	Increased cell growth	Hepatitis B virus
Persistent enterovirus infection	Mental deterioration associated with AIDS	Echoviruses
Progressive encephalitis	Rapid mental deterioration	Rubella virus
Subacute sclerosing panencephalitis (SSPE)	Mental deterioration	Measles virus

change, deformed growth, wilting, and stunted growth in their plant hosts. Some hosts, however, remain symptomless and only serve as reservoirs of infection.

Plant cells are generally protected from disease by an impermeable cell wall. Viruses must enter through wounds or be assisted by other plant parasites, including nematodes, fungi, and, most often, insects that suck the plant's sap. Once one plant is infected, it can spread infection to other plants in its pollen.

In laboratories, plant viruses are cultured in protoplasts (plant cells with the cell walls removed) and in insect cell cultures.

Some plant diseases are caused by **viroids,** short pieces of naked RNA, only 300 to 400 nucleotides long, with no protein coat. The nucleotides are often internally paired, so the molecule has a closed, folded, three-dimensional structure that presumably helps protect it from attack by cellular enzymes. The RNA does not code for any proteins. Thus far, viroids have been conclusively identified as pathogens only of plants. Annually, infections by viroids, such as potato spindle tuber viroid, result in losses of millions of dollars from crop damage (Figure 23).

TABLE 6 Classification of Some Major Plant Viruses

Characteristic	Viral Family	Viral Genus or Unclassified Members	Morphology	Method of Transmission
Double-stranded DNA, nonenveloped	Papovaviridae	Cauliflower mosaic virus		Aphids
Single-stranded RNA, + strand, nonenveloped	Potyviridae	Watermelon wilt		Whiteflies
	Tetraviridae	*Tobamovirus*		Wounds
Single-stranded RNA, – strand, enveloped	Rhabdoviridae	Potato yellow dwarf virus		Leafhoppers and aphids
Double-stranded RNA, nonenveloped	Reoviridae	Wound tumor virus		Leafhoppers

Current research on viroids has revealed similarities between the base sequences of viroids and introns. Introns are sequences of genetic material that do not code for polypeptides. This observation has led to the hypothesis that viroids evolved from introns, leading to speculation that future researchers may discover animal viroids.

CHECK YOUR UNDERSTANDING

☞ Contrast viroids and prions, and for each name a disease it causes. 15, 16

☞ How do plant viruses enter host cells? 17

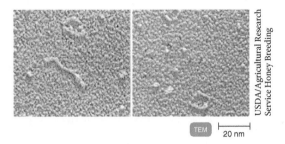

Figure 23 Linear and circular potato spindle tuber viroid (PSTV).

Q How do viroids differ from prions?

Study Outline

Test your understanding with quizzes, microbe review, and a chapter post-test at www.masteringmicrobiology.com.

General Characteristics of Viruses

1. Depending on one's viewpoint, viruses may be regarded as exceptionally complex aggregations of nonliving chemicals or as exceptionally simple living microbes.
2. Viruses contain a single type of nucleic acid (DNA or RNA) and a protein coat, sometimes enclosed by an envelope composed of lipids, proteins, and carbohydrates.
3. Viruses are obligatory intracellular parasites. They multiply by using the host cell's synthesizing machinery to cause the synthesis of specialized elements that can transfer the viral nucleic acid to other cells.

Host Range

4. *Host range* refers to the spectrum of host cells in which a virus can multiply.
5. Most viruses infect only specific types of cells in one host species.
6. Host range is determined by the specific attachment site on the host cell's surface and the availability of host cellular factors.

Viral Size

7. Viral size is ascertained by electron microscopy.
8. Viruses range from 20 to 1000 nm in length.

Viral Structure

1. A virion is a complete, fully developed viral particle composed of nucleic acid surrounded by a coat.

Nucleic Acid

2. Viruses contain either DNA or RNA, never both, and the nucleic acid may be single- or double-stranded, linear or circular, or divided into several separate molecules.
3. The proportion of nucleic acid in relation to protein in viruses ranges from about 1% to about 50%.

Capsid and Envelope

4. The protein coat surrounding the nucleic acid of a virus is called the capsid.
5. The capsid is composed of subunits, capsomeres, which can be a single type of protein or several types.
6. The capsid of some viruses is enclosed by an envelope consisting of lipids, proteins, and carbohydrates.
7. Some envelopes are covered with carbohydrate-protein complexes called spikes.

General Morphology

8. Helical viruses (for example, Ebola virus) resemble long rods, and their capsids are hollow cylinders surrounding the nucleic acid.
9. Polyhedral viruses (for example, adenovirus) are many-sided. Usually the capsid is an icosahedron.
10. Enveloped viruses are covered by an envelope and are roughly spherical but highly pleomorphic. There are also enveloped helical viruses (for example, influenza virus) and enveloped polyhedral viruses (for example, *Simplexvirus*).
11. Complex viruses have complex structures. For example, many bacteriophages have a polyhedral capsid with a helical tail attached.

Taxonomy of Viruses

1. Classification of viruses is based on type of nucleic acid, strategy for replication, and morphology.
2. Virus family names end in -*viridae*; genus names end in -*virus*.
3. A viral species is a group of viruses sharing the same genetic information and ecological niche.

Isolation, Cultivation, and Identification of Viruses

1. Viruses must be grown in living cells.
2. The easiest viruses to grow are bacteriophages.

Growing Bacteriophages in the Laboratory

3. The plaque method mixes bacteriophages with host bacteria and nutrient agar.

4. After several viral multiplication cycles, the bacteria in the area surrounding the original virus are destroyed; the area of lysis is called a plaque.

5. Each plaque originates with a single viral particle; the concentration of viruses is given as plaque-forming units.

Growing Animal Viruses in the Laboratory

6. Cultivation of some animal viruses requires whole animals.

7. Simian AIDS and feline AIDS provide models for studying human AIDS.

8. Some animal viruses can be cultivated in embryonated eggs.

9. Cell cultures are cells growing in culture media in the laboratory.

10. Primary cell lines and embryonic diploid cell lines grow for a short time in vitro.

11. Continuous cell lines can be maintained in vitro indefinitely.

12. Viral growth can cause cytopathic effects in the cell culture.

Viral Identification

13. Serological tests are used most often to identify viruses.

14. Viruses may be identified by RFLPs and PCR.

Viral Multiplication

1. Viruses do not contain enzymes for energy production or protein synthesis.

2. For a virus to multiply, it must invade a host cell and direct the host's metabolic machinery to produce viral enzymes and components.

Multiplication of Bacteriophages

3. During the lytic cycle, a phage causes the lysis and death of a host cell.

4. Some viruses can either cause lysis or have their DNA incorporated as a prophage into the DNA of the host cell. The latter situation is called lysogeny.

5. During the attachment phase of the lytic cycle, sites on the phage's tail fibers attach to complementary receptor sites on the bacterial cell.

6. In penetration, phage lysozyme opens a portion of the bacterial cell wall, the tail sheath contracts to force the tail core through the cell wall, and phage DNA enters the bacterial cell. The capsid remains outside.

7. In biosynthesis, transcription of phage DNA produces mRNA coding for proteins necessary for phage multiplication. Phage DNA is replicated, and capsid proteins are produced. During the eclipse period, separate phage DNA and protein can be found.

8. During maturation, phage DNA and capsids are assembled into complete viruses.

9. During release, phage lysozyme breaks down the bacterial cell wall, and the new phages are released.

10. During the lysogenic cycle, prophage genes are regulated by a repressor coded for by the prophage. The prophage is replicated each time the cell divides.

11. Exposure to certain mutagens can lead to excision of the prophage and initiation of the lytic cycle.

12. Because of lysogeny, lysogenic cells become immune to reinfection with the same phage and may undergo phage conversion.

13. A lysogenic phage can transfer bacterial genes from one cell to another through transduction. Any genes can be transferred in generalized transduction, and specific genes can be transferred in specialized transduction.

Multiplication of Animal Viruses

14. Animal viruses attach to the plasma membrane of the host cell.

15. Entry occurs by receptor-mediated endocytosis or fusion.

16. Animal viruses are uncoated by viral or host cell enzymes.

17. The DNA of most DNA viruses is released into the nucleus of the host cell. Transcription of viral DNA and translation produce viral DNA and, later, capsid proteins. Capsid proteins are synthesized in the cytoplasm of the host cell.

18. DNA viruses include members of the families Adenoviridae, Poxviridae, Herpesviridae, Papovaviridae, and Hepadnaviridae.

19. Multiplication of RNA viruses occurs in the cytoplasm of the host cell. RNA-dependent RNA polymerase synthesizes a double-stranded RNA.

20. Picornaviridae + strand RNA acts as mRNA and directs the synthesis of RNA-dependent RNA polymerase.

21. Togaviridae + strand RNA acts as a template for RNA-dependent RNA polymerase, and mRNA is transcribed from a new – RNA strand.

22. Rhabdoviridae – strand RNA is a template for viral RNA-dependent RNA polymerase, which transcribes mRNA.

23. Reoviridae are digested in host cell cytoplasm to release mRNA for viral biosynthesis.

24. Retroviridae reverse transcriptase (RNA-dependent DNA polymerase) transcribes DNA from RNA.

25. After maturation, viruses are released. One method of release (and envelope formation) is budding. Nonenveloped viruses are released through ruptures in the host cell membrane.

Viruses and Cancer

1. The earliest relationship between cancer and viruses was demonstrated in the early 1900s, when chicken leukemia and chicken sarcoma were transferred to healthy animals by cell-free filtrates.

The Transformation of Normal Cells Into Tumor Cells

2. When activated, oncogenes transform normal cells into cancerous cells.

3. Viruses capable of producing tumors are called oncogenic viruses.

4. Several DNA viruses and retroviruses are oncogenic.

5. The genetic material of oncogenic viruses becomes integrated into the host cell's DNA.

6. Transformed cells lose contact inhibition, contain virus-specific antigens (TSTA and T antigen), exhibit chromosome abnormalities, and can produce tumors when injected into susceptible animals.

DNA Oncogenic Viruses

7. Oncogenic viruses are found among the Adenoviridae, Herpesviridae, Poxviridae, Papovaviridae, and Hepadnaviridae.

RNA Oncogenic Viruses

8. Among the RNA viruses, only retroviruses seem to be oncogenic.

9. HTLV-1 and HTLV-2 have been associated with human leukemia and lymphoma.

10. The virus's ability to produce tumors is related to the production of reverse transcriptase. The DNA synthesized from the viral RNA becomes incorporated as a provirus into the host cell's DNA.

11. A provirus can remain latent, can produce viruses, or can transform the host cell.

Latent Viral Infections

1. A latent viral infection is one in which the virus remains in the host cell for long periods without producing an infection.
2. Examples are cold sores and shingles.

Persistent Viral Infections

1. Persistent viral infections are disease processes that occur over a long period and are generally fatal.
2. Persistent viral infections are caused by conventional viruses; viruses accumulate over a long period.

Prions

1. Prions are infectious proteins first discovered in the 1980s.

2. Prion diseases, such as CJD and mad cow disease, all involve the degeneration of brain tissue.
3. Prion diseases are the result of an altered protein; the cause can be a mutation in the normal gene for PrP^C or contact with an altered protein (PrP^{Sc}).

Plant Viruses and Viroids

1. Plant viruses must enter plant hosts through wounds or with invasive parasites, such as insects.
2. Some plant viruses also multiply in insect (vector) cells.
3. Viroids are infectious pieces of RNA that cause some plant diseases, such as potato spindle tuber disease.

Study Questions

Answers to the Review and Multiple Choice questions can be found at the end of this chapter.

Review

1. Why do we classify viruses as obligatory intracellular parasites?
2. List the four properties that define a virus. What is a virion?
3. Describe the four morphological classes of viruses, then diagram and give an example of each.
4. **DRAW IT** Label the principal events of attachment, biosynthesis, entry, and maturation of a + stranded RNA virus. Draw in uncoating.

Precision Graphics

5. Compare biosynthesis of a + stranded RNA and a − stranded RNA virus.
6. Some antibiotics activate phage genes. MRSA releasing Panton-Valentine leukocidin causes a life-threatening disease. Why can this happen following antibiotic treatment?
7. Koch's postulates are used to determine the etiology of a disease. Why is it difficult to determine the etiology of
   a. a viral infection, such as influenza?
   b. cancer?
8. Persistent viral infections such as (a) _____ might be caused by (b) _____ that are (c) _____.
9. Plant viruses cannot penetrate intact plant cells because (a) _____; therefore, they enter cells by (b) _____. Plant viruses can be cultured in (c) _____.
10. **NAME IT** Identify the viral family that infects skin, mucosa, and nerve cells; causes infections that can recur because of latency, and has polyhedral geometry.

Multiple Choice

1. Place the following in the most likely order for biosynthesis of a bacteriophage: (1) phage lysozyme; (2) mRNA; (3) DNA; (4) viral proteins; (5) DNA polymerase.
   a. 5, 4, 3, 2, 1
   b. 1, 2, 3, 4, 5
   c. 5, 3, 4, 2, 1
   d. 3, 5, 2, 4, 1
   e. 2, 5, 3, 4, 1
2. The molecule serving as mRNA can be incorporated in the newly synthesized virus capsids of all of the following *except*
   a. + strand RNA picornaviruses.
   b. + strand RNA togaviruses.
   c. − strand RNA rhabdoviruses.
   d. double-stranded RNA reoviruses.
   e. *Rotavirus*.
3. A virus with RNA-dependent RNA polymerase
   a. synthesizes DNA from an RNA template.
   b. synthesizes double-stranded RNA from an RNA template.
   c. synthesizes double-stranded RNA from a DNA template.
   d. transcribes mRNA from DNA.
   e. none of the above
4. Which of the following would be the first step in the biosynthesis of a virus with reverse transcriptase?
   a. A complementary strand of RNA must be synthesized.
   b. Double-stranded RNA must be synthesized.
   c. A complementary strand of DNA must be synthesized from an RNA template.
   d. A complementary strand of DNA must be synthesized from a DNA template.
   e. none of the above
5. An example of lysogeny in animals could be
   a. slow viral infections.
   b. latent viral infections.
   c. T-even bacteriophages.
   d. infections resulting in cell death.
   e. none of the above

6. The ability of a virus to infect an organism is regulated by
   a. the host species.
   b. the type of cells.
   c. the availability of an attachment site.
   d. cell factors necessary for viral replication.
   e. all of the above

7. Which of the following statements is *false?*
   a. Viruses contain DNA or RNA.
   b. The nucleic acid of a virus is surrounded by a protein coat.
   c. Viruses multiply inside living cells using viral mRNA, tRNA, and ribosomes.
   d. Viruses cause the synthesis of specialized infectious elements.
   e. Viruses multiply inside living cells.

8. Place the following in the order in which they are found in a host cell: (1) capsid proteins; (2) infective phage particles; (3) phage nucleic acid.
   a. 1, 2, 3
   b. 3, 2, 1
   c. 2, 1, 3
   d. 3, 1, 2
   e. 1, 3, 2

9. Which of the following does *not* initiate DNA synthesis?
   a. a double-stranded DNA virus (Poxviridae)
   b. a DNA virus with reverse transcriptase (Hepadnaviridae)
   c. an RNA virus with reverse transcriptase (Retroviridae)
   d. a single-stranded RNA virus (Togaviridae)
   e. none of the above

10. A viral species is *not* defined on the basis of the disease symptoms it causes. The best example of this is
    a. polio.
    b. rabies.
    c. hepatitis.
    d. chickenpox and shingles.
    e. measles.

Critical Thinking

1. Discuss the arguments for and against the classification of viruses as living organisms.

2. In some viruses, capsomeres function as enzymes as well as structural supports. Of what advantage is this to the virus?

3. Why was the discovery of simian AIDS and feline AIDS important?

4. Prophages and proviruses have been described as being similar to bacterial plasmids. What similar properties do they exhibit? How are they different?

Clinical Applications

1. A 40-year-old man who was seropositive for HIV experienced abdominal pain, fatigue, and low-grade fever (38°C) for 2 weeks. A chest X-ray examination revealed lung infiltrates. Gram and acid-fast stains were negative. A viral culture revealed the cause of his symptoms: a large, enveloped polyhedral virus with double-stranded DNA. What is the disease? Which virus causes it? Why was a viral culture done after the Gram and acid-fast stain results were obtained?

2. A newborn female developed extensive vesicular and ulcerative lesions over her face and chest. What is the most likely cause of her symptoms? How would you determine the viral cause of this disease without doing a viral culture?

3. By May 14, two people living in the same household had died within 5 days of each other. Their illnesses were characterized by abrupt onset of fever, muscle pain, headache, and cough, followed by the rapid development of respiratory failure. By the end of the year, 36 cases of this disease, with a 50% mortality rate, had been confirmed. A member of the Orthomyxoviridae, Bunyaviridae, or Adenoviridae could cause this disease. Differentiate among these families by method of transmission, morphology, nucleic acid, and type of replication. The reservoir for this disease is mice. Name the disease.

Answers to Review and Multiple Choice Study Questions

Review

1. Viruses absolutely require living host cells to multiply.

2. A virus
   - contains DNA or RNA;
   - has a protein coat surrounding the nucleic acid;
   - multiplies inside a living cell using the synthetic machinery of the cell; and
   - causes the synthesis of virions.
     A virion is a fully developed virus particle that transfers the viral nucleic acid to another cell and initiates multiplication.

3. Polyhedral (Figure 2); helical (Figure 4); enveloped (Figure 3); complex (Figure 5).

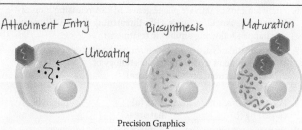

Precision Graphics

5. Both produce double-stranded RNA with the − strand being the template for more + strands. + strands act as mRNA in both virus groups.

6. Antibiotic treatment of *S. aureus* can activate phage genes that encode P-V leukocidin.

7. a. Viruses cannot easily be observed in host tissues. Viruses cannot easily be cultured in order to be inoculated into a new host. Additionally, viruses are specific for their hosts and cells, making it difficult to substitute a laboratory animal for the third step of Koch's postulates.

   b. Some viruses can infect cells without inducing cancer. Cancer may not develop until long after infection. Cancers do not seem to be contagious.

8. a. Subacute sclerosing panencephalitis

   b. Common viruses

   c. Answers will vary. One example of a possible mechanism is latent, in an abnormal tissue.

9. a. of the rigid cell walls

   b. vectors such as sap-sucking insects

   c. plant protoplasts and insect cell cultures

10. Herpesviridae

Multiple Choice

1. e	**3.** b	**5.** b	**7.** c	**9.** d
2. c	**4.** c	**6.** e	**8.** d	**10.** c

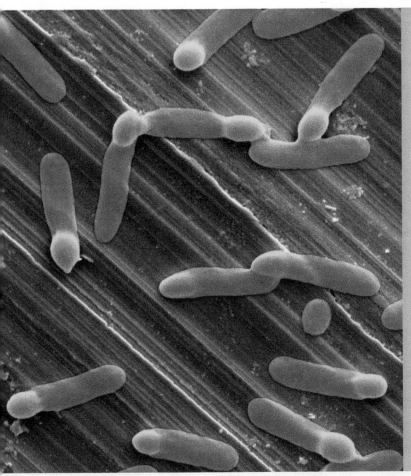

Principles of Disease and Epidemiology

Visualize microbiology and check your understanding with a pre-test at www.masteringmicrobiology.com.

Now that you have a basic understanding of the structures and functions of microorganisms and some idea of the variety of microorganisms that exist, we can consider how the human body and various microorganisms interact in terms of health and disease.

We all have defenses to keep us healthy. In spite of these, however, we are still susceptible to **pathogens** (disease-causing microorganisms). A rather delicate balance exists between our defenses and the pathogenic mechanisms of microorganisms. When our defenses resist these pathogenic capabilities, we maintain our health—when the pathogen's capability overcomes our defenses, disease results. After the disease has become established, an infected person may recover completely, suffer temporary or permanent damage, or die.

We will examine some of the principles of infection and disease, the mechanisms by which pathogens cause disease, the body's defenses against disease, and the ways that microbial diseases can be prevented by immunization and controlled by drugs. This chapter discusses the general principles of disease, starting with a discussion of the meaning and scope of pathology. Later, you will learn how these principles are useful in studying and controlling disease. Understanding of these principles is vital to prevent disease transmission to patients. Health care-associated infection by the *Clostridium difficile* bacteria shown in the photograph is discussed in the Clinical Case.

From Chapter 14 of *Microbiology: An Introduction*, Eleventh Edition. Gerard J. Tortora, Berdell R. Funke, Christine L. Case.
Copyright © 2013 by Pearson Education, Inc. All rights reserved.

Pathology, Infection, and Disease

LEARNING OBJECTIVE

1 Define *pathology, etiology, infection,* and *disease.*

Pathology is the scientific study of disease (*pathos* = suffering; *logos* = science). Pathology is first concerned with the cause, or **etiology,** of disease. Second, it deals with **pathogenesis,** the manner in which a disease develops. Third, pathology is concerned with the *structural* and *functional changes* brought about by disease and with their final effects on the body.

Although the terms *infection* and *disease* are sometimes used interchangeably, they differ somewhat in meaning. **Infection** is the invasion or colonization of the body by pathogenic microorganisms; **disease** occurs when an infection results in any change from a state of health. Disease is an abnormal state in which part or all of the body is not properly adjusted or incapable of performing its normal functions. An infection may exist in the absence of detectable disease. For example, the body may be infected with the virus that causes AIDS but experience no symptoms of the disease.

The presence of a particular type of microorganism in a part of the body where it is not normally found is also called an infection—and may lead to disease. For example, although large numbers of *E. coli* are normally present in the healthy intestine, their infection of the urinary tract usually results in disease.

Few microorganisms are pathogenic. In fact, the presence of some microorganisms can even benefit the host. Therefore, before we discuss the role of microorganisms in causing disease, let's examine the relationship of the microorganisms to the healthy human body.

CHECK YOUR UNDERSTANDING

✔ What are the objectives of pathology? 1

Clinical Case: Bathroom Break

Jamil Carter is in the bathroom, again. Ever since he was hospitalized for a urinary tract infection (UTI) 6 months ago, Jamil has been plagued with fever, chills, and severe diarrhea. He has lost 15 pounds since his hospitalization. Jamil is 75 years old, is retired, and lives with his wife and adult son. He does not smoke and rarely drinks alcohol. While in the hospital, Jamil was treated with the antibiotics ceftriaxone and ciprofloxacin for the UTI. He developed diarrhea 3 days after being discharged from the hospital and has had it ever since.

What could be causing Jamil's diarrhea and other symptoms? Read on to find out.

Normal Microbiota

LEARNING OBJECTIVES

2 Define *normal* and *transient microbiota.*

3 Compare commensalism, mutualism, and parasitism, and give an example of each.

4 Contrast normal microbiota and transient microbiota with opportunistic microorganisms.

Animals, including humans, are generally free of microbes in utero. At birth, however, normal and characteristic microbial populations begin to establish themselves. Just before a woman gives birth, lactobacilli in her vagina multiply rapidly. The newborn's first contact with microorganisms is usually with these lactobacilli, and they become the predominant organisms in the newborn's intestine. More microorganisms are introduced to the newborn's body from the environment when breathing begins and feeding starts. After birth, *E. coli* and other bacteria acquired from foods begin to inhabit the large intestine. These microorganisms remain there throughout life and, in response to altered environmental conditions, may increase or decrease in number and contribute to disease.

Many other usually harmless microorganisms establish themselves inside other parts of the normal adult body and on its surface. A typical human body contains 1×10^{13} body cells, yet harbors an estimated 1×10^{14} bacterial cells (10 times more bacterial cells than human cells). This gives you an idea of the abundance of microorganisms that normally reside in the human body. The **Human Microbiome Project** began in 2007 to analyze microbial communities called *microbiomes* that live in and on the human body. Its goal is to determine the relationship between changes in the human microbiome and human health and disease. The human microbiome is more diverse than previously thought. Currently, researchers are comparing the microbiomes of healthy volunteers and volunteers with specific diseases. The microorganisms that establish more or less permanent residence (colonize) but that do not produce disease under normal conditions are members of the body's **normal microbiota,** or **normal flora** (Figure 1). Others, called **transient microbiota,** may be present for several days, weeks, or months and then disappear. Microorganisms are not found throughout the entire human body but are localized in certain regions, as shown in Table 1.

Many factors determine the distribution and composition of the normal microbiota. Among these are nutrients, physical and chemical factors, defenses of the host, and mechanical factors. Microbes vary with respect to the types of nutrients that they can use as an energy source. Accordingly, microbes can colonize only those body sites that can supply the appropriate nutrients. These nutrients may be derived from secretory and excretory products of cells, substances in body fluids, dead cells, and foods in the gastrointestinal tract.

Juergen Berger/Photo Researchers

SPL/Photo Researchers

Stephanie Schuller/Photo Researchers

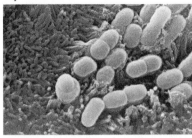

(a) Bacteria (orange spheres) on the surface of the nasal epithelium · SEM · ⊢—⊣ 2 μm

(b) Bacteria (brown) on the lining of the stomach · SEM · ⊢—⊣ 2.5 μm

(c) Bacteria (orange) in the small intestine · SEM · ⊢—⊣ 1 μm

Figure 1 Representative normal microbiota for different regions of the body.

 Of what value are normal microbiota?

A number of physical and chemical factors affect the growth of microbes and thus the growth and composition of the normal microbiota. Among these are temperature, pH, available oxygen and carbon dioxide, salinity, and sunlight.

The human body has certain defenses against microbes. These defenses include a variety of molecules and activated cells that kill microbes, inhibit their growth, prevent their adhesion to host cell surfaces, and neutralize toxins that microbes produce. Although these defenses are extremely important against pathogens, their role in determining and regulating the normal microbiota is unclear.

Certain regions of the body are subjected to mechanical forces that may affect colonization by the normal microbiota. For example, the chewing actions of the teeth and tongue movements can dislodge microbes attached to tooth and mucosal surfaces. In the gastrointestinal tract, the flow of saliva and digestive secretions and the various muscular movements of the throat, esophagus, stomach, and intestines can remove unattached microbes. The flushing action of urine also removes unattached microbes. In the respiratory system, mucus traps microbes, which cilia then propel toward the throat for elimination.

The conditions provided by the host at a particular body site vary from one person to another. Among the factors that also affect the normal microbiota are age, nutritional status, diet, health status, disability, hospitalization, emotional state, stress, climate, geography, personal hygiene, living conditions, occupation, and lifestyle.

The principal normal microbiota in different regions of the body and some distinctive features of each region are listed in **Table 1**. Normal microbiota are also discussed more specifically in Part Four.

Animals with no microbiota whatsoever can be reared in the laboratory. Most germfree mammals used in research are obtained by breeding them in a sterile environment. On the one hand, research with germfree animals has shown that microbes are not absolutely essential to animal life. On the other hand, this research has shown that germfree animals have undeveloped immune systems and are unusually susceptible to infection and serious disease. Germfree animals also require more calories and vitamins than do normal animals.

Relationships between the Normal Microbiota and the Host

Once established, the normal microbiota can benefit the host by preventing the overgrowth of harmful microorganisms. This phenomenon is called **microbial antagonism,** or **competitive exclusion.** Microbial antagonism involves competition among microbes. One consequence of this competition is that the normal microbiota protect the host against colonization by potentially pathogenic microbes by competing for nutrients, producing substances harmful to the invading microbes, and affecting conditions such as pH and available oxygen. When this balance between normal microbiota and pathogenic microbes is upset, disease can result. For example, the normal bacterial microbiota of the adult human vagina maintains a local pH of about 4. The presence of normal microbiota inhibits the overgrowth of the yeast *Candida albicans,* which can grow when the balance between normal microbiota and pathogens is upset and when pH is altered. If the bacterial population is eliminated by antibiotics, excessive douching, or deodorants, the pH of the vagina reverts to nearly neutral, and *C. albicans* can flourish and become the dominant microorganism there. This condition can lead to a form of vaginitis (vaginal infection).

Another example of microbial antagonism occurs in the large intestine. *E. coli* cells produce *bacteriocins,* proteins that inhibit the growth of other bacteria of the same or closely related species, such as pathogenic *Salmonella* and *Shigella.* A bacterium that makes a particular bacteriocin is not killed by that bacteriocin but may be killed by other ones. Bacteriocins are used in medical microbiology to help identify different strains of bacteria. Such identification helps determine whether

TABLE **1** Representative Normal Microbiota by Body Region

Region	Principal Components	Comments
Skin	*Propionibacterium, Staphylococcus, Corynebacterium, Micrococcus, Acinetobacter, Brevibacterium; Candida* (fungus), *Malassezia* (fungus)	• Most of the microbes in direct contact with skin do not become residents because secretions from sweat and oil glands have antimicrobial properties. • Keratin is a resistant barrier, and the low pH of the skin inhibits many microbes. • The skin also has a relatively low moisture content.
Eyes (Conjunctiva)	*Staphylococcus epidermidis, S. aureus,* diphtheroids, *Propionibacterium, Corynebacterium,* streptococci, *Micrococcus*	• The conjunctiva, a continuation of the skin or mucous membrane, contains basically the same microbiota found on the skin. • Tears and blinking also eliminate some microbes or inhibit others from colonizing.

Nose and throat
(upper respiratory
system)

Eyes (conjunctiva)

Mouth

Skin

Large intestine

Urinary and reproductive systems (lower urethra in both sexes and vagina in females)

Precision Graphics

Precision Graphics

Region	Principal Components	Comments
Nose and Throat (Upper Respiratory System)	*Staphylococcus aureus, S. epidermidis,* and aerobic diphtheroids in the nose; *S. epidermidis, S. aureus,* diphtheroids, *Streptococcus pneumoniae, Haemophilus,* and *Neisseria* in the throat	• Although some normal microbiota are potential pathogens, their ability to cause disease is reduced by microbial antagonism. • Nasal secretions kill or inhibit many microbes, and mucus and ciliary action remove many microbes.
Mouth	*Streptococcus, Lactobacillus, Actinomyces, Bacteroides, Veillonella, Neisseria, Haemophilis, Fusobacterium, Treponema, Staphylococcus, Corynebacterium,* and *Candida* (fungus)	• Abundant moisture, warmth, and the constant presence of food make the mouth an ideal environment that supports very large and diverse microbial populations on the tongue, cheeks, teeth, and gums. • Biting, chewing, tongue movements, and salivary flow dislodge microbes. Saliva contains several antimicrobial substances.
Large Intestine	*Escherichia coli, Bacteroides, Fusobacterium, Lactobacillus, Enterococcus, Bifidobacterium, Enterobacter, Citrobacter, Proteus, Klebsiella, Candida* (fungus)	• The large intestine contains the largest numbers of resident microbiota in the body because of its available moisture and nutrients. • Mucus and periodic shedding of the lining prevent many microbes from attaching to the lining of the gastrointestinal tract, and the mucosa produces several antimicrobiol chemicals. • Diarrhea also flushes out some of the normal microbiota.
Urinary and Reproductive Systems	*Staphylococcus, Micrococcus, Enterococcus, Lactobacillus, Bacteroides,* aerobic diphtheroids, *Pseudomonas, Klebsiella,* and *Proteus* in urethra; lactobacilli, *Streptococcus, Clostridium, Candida albicans* (fungus), and *Trichomonas vaginalis* (protozoan) in vagina	• The lower urethra in both sexes has a resident population; the vagina has its acid-tolerant population of microbes because of the nature of its secretions. • Mucus and periodic shedding of the lining prevent microbes from attaching to the lining; urine flow mechanically removes microbes, and the pH of urine and urea are antimicrobial. • Cilia and mucus expel microbes from the cervix of the uterus into the vagina, and the acidity of the vagina inhibits or kills microbes.

several outbreaks of an infectious disease are caused by one or more strains of a bacterium.

A final example involves another bacterium, *Clostridium difficile* (dif' fi-sē-il), also in the large intestine. The normal microbiota of the large intestine effectively inhibit *C. difficile,* possibly by making host receptors unavailable, competing for available nutrients, or producing bacteriocins. However, if the normal microbiota are eliminated (for example, by antibiotics), *C. difficile* can become a problem. This microbe is responsible for nearly all gastrointestinal infections that follow antibiotic therapy, from mild diarrhea to severe or even fatal colitis (inflammation of the colon).

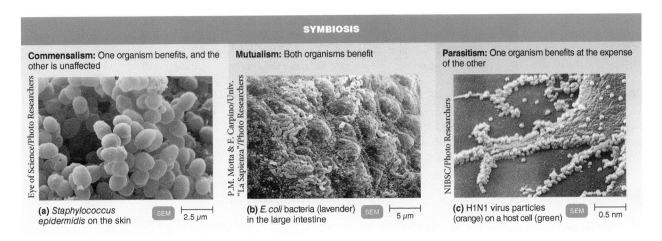

SYMBIOSIS

Commensalism: One organism benefits, and the other is unaffected

Mutualism: Both organisms benefit

Parasitism: One organism benefits at the expense of the other

(a) *Staphylococcus epidermidis* on the skin   SEM   2.5 μm

(b) *E. coli* bacteria (lavender) in the large intestine   SEM   5 μm

(c) H1N1 virus particles (orange) on a host cell (green)   SEM   0.5 nm

Figure 2 Symbiosis.

Which type of symbiosis is best represented by the relationship between humans and *E. coli?*

The relationship between the normal microbiota and the host is called **symbiosis,** a relationship between two organisms in which at least one organism is dependent on the other (Figure 2). In the symbiotic relationship called **commensalism,** one of the organisms benefits, and the other is unaffected. Many of the microorganisms that make up our normal microbiota are commensals; these include *staphylococcus epidermidis* that inhabit the surface of the skin, the corynebacteria that inhabit the surface of the eye, and certain saprophytic mycobacteria that inhabit the ear and external genitals. These bacteria live on secretions and sloughed-off cells, and they bring no apparent benefit or harm to the host.

Mutualism is a type of symbiosis that benefits both organisms. For example, the large intestine contains bacteria, such as *E. coli,* that synthesize vitamin K and some B vitamins. These vitamins are absorbed into the bloodstream and distributed for use by body cells. In exchange, the large intestine provides nutrients used by the bacteria, resulting in their survival.

Recent genetics studies have found hundreds of antibiotic-resistance genes in the intestinal bacteria. It may seem desirable to have these bacteria survive while a person is taking antibiotics for an infectious disease; however, these beneficial bacteria may be able to transfer antibiotic-resistance genes to pathogens.

In still another kind of symbiosis, one organism benefits by deriving nutrients at the expense of the other; this relationship is called **parasitism.** Many disease-causing bacteria are parasites.

Opportunistic Microorganisms

Although categorizing symbiotic relationships by type is convenient, keep in mind that under certain conditions the relationship can change. For example, given the proper circumstances, a mutualistic organism, such as *E. coli,* can become harmful. *E. coli* is generally harmless as long as it remains in the large intestine; but if it gains access to other body sites, such as the urinary bladder, lungs, spinal cord, or wounds, it may cause urinary tract infections, pulmonary infections, meningitis, or abscesses, respectively. Microbes such as *E. coli* are called **opportunistic pathogens.** They ordinarily do not cause disease in their normal habitat in a healthy person but may do so in a different environment. For example, microbes that gain access through broken skin or mucous membranes can cause opportunistic infections. Or, if the host is already weakened or compromised by infection, microbes that are usually harmless can cause disease. AIDS is often accompanied by a common opportunistic infection, *Pneumocystis* pneumonia, caused by the opportunistic organism *Pneumocystis jirovecii.* This secondary infection can develop in AIDS patients because their immune systems are suppressed. Before the AIDS epidemic, this type of pneumonia was rare. Opportunistic pathogens possess other features that contribute to their ability to cause disease. For example, they are present in or on the body or in the external environment in relatively large numbers. Some opportunistic pathogens may be found in locations in or on the body that are somewhat protected from the body's defenses, and some are resistant to antibiotics.

In addition to the usual symbionts, many people carry other microorganisms that are generally regarded as pathogenic but that may not cause disease in those people. Among the pathogens that are frequently carried in healthy individuals are echoviruses (*echo* comes from *e*nteric *c*ytopathogenic *h*uman *o*rphan), which can cause intestinal diseases, and adenoviruses, which can cause respiratory diseases. *Neisseria meningitidis,*

433

which often resides benignly in the respiratory tract, can cause meningitis, a disease that inflames the coverings of the brain and spinal cord. *Streptococcus pneumoniae,* a normal resident of the nose and throat, can cause a type of pneumonia.

Cooperation among Microorganisms

It is not only competition among microbes that can cause disease; cooperation among microbes can also be a factor in causing disease. For example, pathogens that cause periodontal disease and gingivitis have been found to have receptors, not for the teeth, but for the oral streptococci that colonize the teeth.

CHECK YOUR UNDERSTANDING

✔ How do normal microbiota differ from transient microbiota? 2

✔ Give several examples of microbial antagonism. 3

✔ How can opportunistic pathogens cause infections? 4

The Etiology of Infectious Diseases

LEARNING OBJECTIVE

5 List Koch's postulates.

Some diseases—such as polio, Lyme disease, and tuberculosis—have a well-known etiology. Some have an etiology that is not completely understood, for example, the relationship between certain viruses and cancer. For still others, such as Alzheimer disease, the etiology is unknown. Of course, not all diseases are caused by microorganisms. For example, the disease hemophilia is an *inherited (genetic) disease;* osteoarthritis and cirrhosis are considered *degenerative diseases.* There are several other categories of disease, but here we will discuss only *infectious diseases,* those caused by microorganisms. To see how microbiologists determine the etiology of an infectious disease, we will discuss in greater detail the work of Robert Koch.

Koch's Postulates

Koch was a German physician who played a major role in establishing that microorganisms cause specific diseases. In 1877, he published some early papers on anthrax, a disease of cattle that can also occur in humans. Koch demonstrated that certain bacteria, today known as *Bacillus anthracis,* were always present in the blood of animals that had the disease and were not present in healthy animals. He knew that the mere presence of the bacteria did not prove that they had caused the disease; the bacteria could have been there as a result of the disease. Thus, he experimented further.

He took a sample of blood from a sick animal and injected it into a healthy one. The second animal developed the same disease and died. He repeated this procedure many times, always with the same results. (A key criterion in the validity of any

scientific proof is that experimental results be repeatable.) Koch also cultivated the microorganism in fluids outside the animal's body, and he demonstrated that the bacterium would cause anthrax even after many culture transfers.

Koch showed that a specific infectious disease (anthrax) is caused by a specific microorganism *(B. anthracis)* that can be isolated and cultured on artificial media. He later used the same methods to show that the bacterium *Mycobacterium tuberculosis* is the causative agent of tuberculosis.

Koch's research provides a framework for the study of the etiology of any infectious disease. Today, we refer to Koch's experimental requirements as **Koch's postulates** (Figure 3). They are summarized as follows:

1. The same pathogen must be present in every case of the disease.

2. The pathogen must be isolated from the diseased host and grown in pure culture.

3. The pathogen from the pure culture must cause the disease when it is inoculated into a healthy, susceptible laboratory animal.

4. The pathogen must be isolated from the inoculated animal and must be shown to be the original organism.

Exceptions to Koch's Postulates

Although Koch's postulates are useful in determining the causative agent of most bacterial diseases, there are some exceptions. For example, some microbes have unique culture requirements. The bacterium *Treponema pallidum* is known to cause syphilis, but virulent strains have never been cultured on artificial media. The causative agent of leprosy, *Mycobacterium leprae,* has also never been grown on artificial media. Moreover, many rickettsial and viral pathogens cannot be cultured on artificial media because they multiply only within cells.

The discovery of microorganisms that cannot grow on artificial media has necessitated some modifications of Koch's postulates and the use of alternative methods of culturing and detecting certain microbes. For example, when researchers looking for the microbial cause of legionellosis (Legionnaires' disease) were unable to isolate the microbe directly from a victim, they took the alternative step of inoculating a victim's lung tissue into guinea pigs. These guinea pigs developed the disease's pneumonia-like symptoms, whereas guinea pigs inoculated with tissue from an unafflicted person did not. Then tissue samples from the diseased guinea pigs were cultured in yolk sacs of chick embryos, a method that reveals the growth of extremely small microbes. After the embryos were incubated, electron microscopy revealed rod-shaped bacteria in the chick embryos. Finally, modern immunological techniques were used to show that the bacteria in the chick embryos were the same bacteria as those in the guinea pigs and in afflicted humans.

Koch's Postulates: Understanding Disease

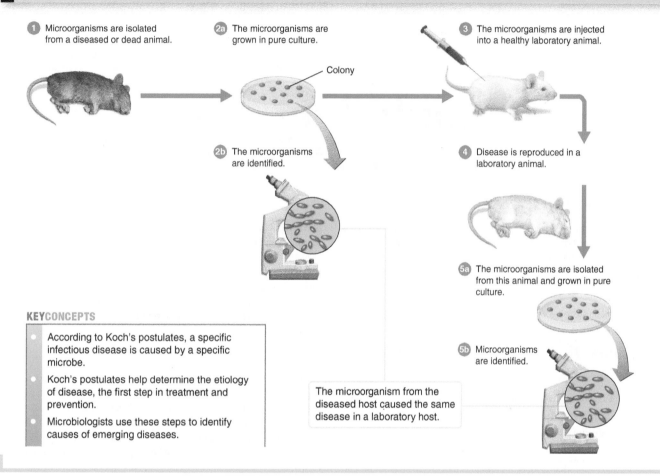

① Microorganisms are isolated from a diseased or dead animal.

②a The microorganisms are grown in pure culture.

Colony

③ The microorganisms are injected into a healthy laboratory animal.

②b The microorganisms are identified.

④ Disease is reproduced in a laboratory animal.

⑤a The microorganisms are isolated from this animal and grown in pure culture.

⑤b Microorganisms are identified.

The microorganism from the diseased host caused the same disease in a laboratory host.

KEY CONCEPTS

- According to Koch's postulates, a specific infectious disease is caused by a specific microbe.
- Koch's postulates help determine the etiology of disease, the first step in treatment and prevention.
- Microbiologists use these steps to identify causes of emerging diseases.

Precision Graphics

In a number of situations, a human host exhibits certain signs and symptoms that are associated only with a certain pathogen and its disease. For example, the pathogens responsible for diphtheria and tetanus cause distinguishing signs and symptoms that no other microbe can produce. They are unequivocally the only organisms that produce their respective diseases. But some infectious diseases are not as clear-cut and provide another exception to Koch's postulates. For example, nephritis (inflammation of the kidneys) can involve any of several different pathogens, all of which cause the same signs and symptoms. Thus, it is often difficult to know which particular microorganism is causing a disease. Other infectious diseases that sometimes have poorly defined etiologies are pneumonia, meningitis, and peritonitis (inflammation of the peritoneum, the membrane that lines the abdomen and covers the organs within them).

Still another exception to Koch's postulates results because some pathogens can cause several disease conditions. *Mycobac-*

terium tuberculosis, for example, is implicated in diseases of the lungs, skin, bones, and internal organs. *Streptococcus pyogenes* can cause sore throat, scarlet fever, skin infections (such as erysipelas), and osteomyelitis (inflammation of bone), among other diseases. When clinical signs and symptoms are used together with laboratory methods, these infections can usually be distinguished from infections of the same organs by other pathogens.

Ethical considerations may also impose an exception to Koch's postulates. For example, some agents that cause disease in humans have no other known host. An example is human immunodeficiency virus (HIV), the cause of AIDS. This poses the ethical question of whether humans can be intentionally inoculated with infectious agents. In 1721, King George I told several condemned prisoners they could be inoculated with smallpox to test a smallpox vaccine. He promised their freedom if they lived. Human experiments with untreatable diseases

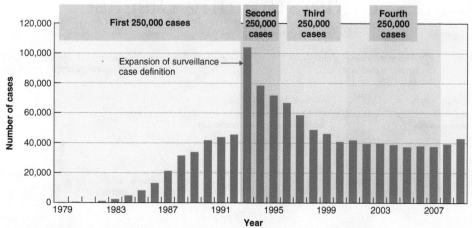

Figure 4 Reported AIDS cases in the United States. Notice that the first 250,000 cases occurred over a 12-year period, whereas the second through fourth 250,000 cases in this epidemic occurred in just 3 to 6 years. Much of the increase shown for 1993 is due to an expanded definition of AIDS cases adopted in that year. *Source:* CDC.

Q What was the incidence of AIDS in 2004?

Precision Graphics

are not acceptable today. Sometimes accidental inoculation does occur. A contaminated red bone marrow transplant satisfied the third Koch's postulate to prove that a herpesvirus caused cancer.

CHECK YOUR UNDERSTANDING

✔ Explain some exceptions to Koch's postulates. 5

Classifying Infectious Diseases

LEARNING OBJECTIVES

6   Differentiate a communicable from a noncommunicable disease.

7   Categorize diseases according to frequency of occurrence.

8   Categorize diseases according to severity.

9   Define *herd immunity*.

Every disease that affects the body alters body structures and functions in particular ways, and these alterations are usually indicated by several kinds of evidence. For example, the patient may experience certain **symptoms,** or changes in body function, such as pain and *malaise* (a vague feeling of body discomfort). These *subjective* changes are not apparent to an observer. The patient can also exhibit **signs,** which are *objective* changes the physician can observe and measure. Frequently evaluated signs include lesions (changes produced in tissues by disease), swelling, fever, and paralysis. A specific group of symptoms or signs may always accompany a particular disease; such a group is called a **syndrome.** The diagnosis of a disease is made by evaluation of the signs and symptoms, together with the results of laboratory tests.

Diseases are often classified in terms of how they behave within a host and within a given population. Any disease that spreads from one host to another, either directly or indirectly, is said to be a **communicable disease.** Chickenpox, measles, genital herpes, typhoid fever, and tuberculosis are examples. Chickenpox and measles are also examples of **contagious**

diseases, that is, diseases that are *easily* spread from one person to another. A **noncommunicable disease** is not spread from one host to another. These diseases are caused by microorganisms that normally inhabit the body and only occasionally produce disease or by microorganisms that reside outside the body and produce disease only when introduced into the body. An example is tetanus: *Clostridium tetani* produces disease only when it is introduced into the body via abrasions or wounds.

Occurrence of a Disease

To understand the full scope of a disease, we should know something about its occurrence. The **incidence** of a disease is the number of people in a population who develop a disease during a particular time period. It is an indicator of the spread of the disease. The **prevalence** of a disease is the number of people in a population who develop a disease at a specified time, regardless of when it first appeared. Prevalence takes into account both old and new cases. It's an indicator of how seriously and how long a disease affects a population. For example, the incidence of AIDS in the United States in 2007 was 56,300 whereas the prevalence in that same year was estimated to be about 1,185,000. Knowing the incidence and the prevalence of a disease in different populations (for example, in populations representing different geographic regions or different ethnic groups) enables scientists to estimate the range of the disease's occurrence and its tendency to affect some groups of people more than others.

Frequency of occurrence is another criterion that is used in the classification of diseases. If a particular disease occurs only occasionally, it is called a **sporadic disease;** typhoid fever in the United States is such a disease. A disease constantly present in a population is called an **endemic disease;** an example of such a disease is the common cold. If many people in a given area acquire a certain disease in a relatively short period, it is called an **epidemic disease;** influenza is an example of a disease that often achieves epidemic status. Figure 4 shows the epidemic incidence of AIDS in the United States. Some authorities consider gonorrhea and certain other sexually transmitted infections to be epidemic at this time as well. An epidemic disease that occurs worldwide is called a **pandemic disease.** We experience pandemics of influenza from time to time. AIDS is another example of a pandemic disease.

Severity or Duration of a Disease

Another useful way of defining the scope of a disease is in terms of its severity or duration. An **acute disease** is one that develops rapidly but lasts only a short time; a good example is influenza. A **chronic disease** develops more slowly, and the body's reactions may be less severe, but the disease is likely to continue or recur for long periods. Infectious mononucleosis, tuberculosis, and hepatitis B fall into this category. A disease that is intermediate between acute and chronic is described as a **subacute disease;** an example is subacute sclerosing panencephalitis, a rare brain disease characterized by diminished intellectual function and loss of nervous function. A **latent disease** is one in which the causative agent remains inactive for a time but then becomes active to produce symptoms of the disease; an example is shingles, one of the diseases caused by varicella virus.

The rate at which a disease or an epidemic spreads and the number of individuals involved are determined in part by the immunity of the population. Vaccination can provide long-lasting and sometimes lifelong protection of an individual against certain diseases. People who are immune to an infectious disease will not be carriers, thereby reducing the occurrence of the disease. Immune individuals act as a barrier to the spread of infectious agents. Even though a highly communicable disease may cause an epidemic, many nonimmune people will be protected because of the unlikelihood of their coming into contact with an infected person. A great advantage of vaccination is that enough individuals in a population will be protected from a disease to prevent its rapid spread to those in the population who are not vaccinated. When many immune people are present in a community, **herd immunity** exists.

Extent of Host Involvement

Infections can also be classified according to the extent to which the host's body is affected. A **local infection** is one in which the invading microorganisms are limited to a relatively small area of the body. Some examples of local infections are boils and abscesses. In a **systemic (generalized) infection,** microorganisms or their products are spread throughout the body by the blood or lymph. Measles is an example of a systemic infection. Very often, agents of a local infection enter a blood or lymphatic vessel and spread to other specific parts of the body, where they are confined to specific areas of the body. This condition is called a **focal infection.** Focal infections can arise from infections in areas such as the teeth, tonsils, or sinuses.

Sepsis is a toxic inflammatory condition arising from the spread of microbes, especially bacteria or their toxins, from a focus of infection. **Septicemia,** also called blood poisoning, is a systemic infection arising from the multiplication of pathogens in the blood. Septicemia is a common example of sepsis. The presence of bacteria in the blood is known as **bacteremia.** **Toxemia** refers to the presence of toxins in the blood (as occurs in tetanus), and **viremia** refers to the presence of viruses in blood.

The state of host resistance also determines the extent of infections. A **primary infection** is an acute infection that causes the initial illness. A **secondary infection** is one caused by an opportunistic pathogen after the primary infection has weakened the body's defenses. Secondary infections of the skin and respiratory tract are common and are sometimes more dangerous than the primary infections. *Pneumocystis* pneumonia as a consequence of AIDS is an example of a secondary infection; streptococcal bronchopneumonia following influenza is an example of a secondary infection that is more serious than the primary infection. A **subclinical (inapparent) infection** is one that does not cause any noticeable illness. Poliovirus and hepatitis A virus, for example, can be carried by people who never develop the illness.

CHECK YOUR UNDERSTANDING

- Does *Clostridium perfringens* cause a communicable disease? 6
- Distinguish the incidence from the prevalence of a disease. 7
- List two examples of acute and chronic diseases. 8
- How does herd immunity develop? 9

Patterns of Disease

LEARNING OBJECTIVES

10   Identify four predisposing factors for disease.

11   Put the following in proper sequence, according to the pattern of disease: period of decline, period of convalescence, period of illness, prodromal period, incubation period.

A definite sequence of events usually occurs during infection and disease. As you will learn shortly, for an infectious disease to occur, there must be a reservoir of infection as a source of pathogens. Next, the pathogen must be transmitted to a susceptible host by direct contact, by indirect contact, or by vectors. Transmission is followed by invasion, in which the microorganism enters the host and multiplies. Following invasion, the microorganism injures the host through a process called pathogenesis. The extent of injury depends on the degree to which host cells are damaged, either directly or by toxins. Despite the effects of all these factors, the occurrence of disease ultimately depends on the resistance of the host to the activities of the pathogen.

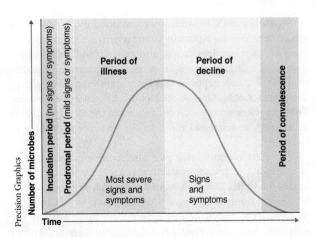

Figure 5 The stages of a disease.

Q During which periods can a disease be transmitted?

Predisposing Factors

Certain predisposing factors also affect the occurrence of disease. A **predisposing factor** makes the body more susceptible to a disease and may alter the course of the disease. Gender is sometimes a predisposing factor; for example, females have a higher incidence of urinary tract infections than males, whereas males have higher rates of pneumonia and meningitis. Other aspects of genetic background may play a role as well. For example, sickle cell disease is a severe, life-threatening form of anemia that occurs when the genes for the disease are inherited from both parents. Individuals who carry only one sickle cell gene have a condition called sickle cell trait and are normal unless specially tested. However, they are relatively resistant to the most serious form of malaria. The potential that individuals in a population might inherit a life-threatening disease is more than counterbalanced by protection from malaria among carriers of the gene for sickle cell trait. Of course, in countries where malaria is not present, sickle cell trait is an entirely negative condition.

Climate and weather seem to have some effect on the incidence of infectious diseases. In temperate regions, the incidence of respiratory diseases increases during the winter. This increase may be related to the fact that when people stay indoors, the closer contact with one other facilitates the spread of respiratory pathogens.

Other predisposing factors include inadequate nutrition, fatigue, age, environment, habits, lifestyle, occupation, preexisting illness, chemotherapy, and emotional disturbances. It is often difficult to know the exact relative importance of the various predisposing factors.

Development of Disease

Once a microorganism overcomes the defenses of the host, development of the disease follows a certain sequence that tends to be similar whether the disease is acute or chronic (Figure 5).

Incubation Period

The **incubation period** is the interval between the initial infection and the first appearance of any signs or symptoms. In some diseases, the incubation period is always the same; in others, it is quite variable. The time of incubation depends on the specific microorganism involved, its virulence (degree of pathogenicity), the number of infecting microorganisms, and the resistance of the host.

Prodromal Period

The **prodromal period** is a relatively short period that follows the period of incubation in some diseases. The prodromal period is characterized by early, mild symptoms of disease, such as general aches and malaise.

Period of Illness

During the **period of illness,** the disease is most severe. The person exhibits overt signs and symptoms of disease, such as fever, chills, muscle pain (myalgia), sensitivity to light (photophobia), sore throat (pharyngitis), lymph node enlargement (lymphadenopathy), and gastrointestinal disturbances. During the period of illness, the number of white blood cells may increase or decrease. Generally, the patient's immune response and other defense mechanisms overcome the pathogen, and the period of illness ends. If the disease is not successfully overcome (or successfully treated), the patient dies during this period.

Period of Decline

During the **period of decline,** the signs and symptoms subside. The fever decreases, and the feeling of malaise diminishes. During this phase, which may take from less than 24 hours to several days, the patient is vulnerable to secondary infections.

Period of Convalescence

During the **period of convalescence,** the person regains strength and the body returns to its prediseased state. Recovery has occurred.

We all know that during the period of illness, people can serve as reservoirs of disease and can easily spread infections to other people. However, you should also know that people can spread infection during incubation and convalescence as well. This is especially true of diseases such as typhoid fever and cholera, in which the convalescing person carries the pathogenic microorganism for months or even years.

CHECK YOUR UNDERSTANDING

✔ What is a predisposing factor? **10**

✔ The incubation period for a cold is 3 days, and the period of disease is usually 5 days. If the person next to you has a cold, when will you know whether you contracted it? **11**

The Spread of Infection

LEARNING OBJECTIVES

12 Define *reservoir of infection.*

13 Contrast human, animal, and nonliving reservoirs, and give one example of each.

14 Explain three methods of disease transmission.

Now that you have an understanding of normal microbiota, the etiology of infectious diseases, and the types of infectious diseases, we will examine the sources of pathogens and how diseases are transmitted.

Reservoirs of Infection

For a disease to perpetuate itself, there must be a continual source of the disease organisms. This source can be either a living organism or an inanimate object that provides a pathogen with adequate conditions for survival and multiplication and an opportunity for transmission. Such a source is called a **reservoir of infection.** These reservoirs may be human, animal, or nonliving.

Human Reservoirs

The principal living reservoir of human disease is the human body itself. Many people harbor pathogens and transmit them directly or indirectly to others. People with signs and symptoms of a disease may transmit the disease; in addition, some people can harbor pathogens and transmit them to others without exhibiting any signs of illness. These people, called **carriers,** are important living reservoirs of infection. Some carriers have inapparent infections for which no signs or symptoms are ever exhibited. Other people, such as those with latent diseases, carry a disease during its symptom-free stages—during the incubation period (before symptoms appear) or during the convalescent period (recovery). Typhoid Mary is an example of a carrier. Human carriers play an important role in the spread of such diseases as AIDS, diphtheria, typhoid fever, hepatitis, gonorrhea, amebic dysentery, and streptococcal infections.

Animal Reservoirs

Both wild and domestic animals are living reservoirs of microorganisms that can cause human diseases. Diseases that occur primarily in wild and domestic animals and can be transmitted to humans are called **zoonoses** (zō-ō-no′sēz) (singular: *zoonosis*). Rabies (found in bats, skunks, foxes, dogs, and coyotes), and Lyme disease (found in field mice) are examples of zoonoses. Other representative zoonoses are presented in **Table 2.**

About 150 zoonoses are known. The transmission of zoonoses to humans can occur via one of many routes: by direct contact with infected animals; by direct contact with domestic pet waste (such as cleaning a litter box or bird cage); by contamination of food and water; by air from contaminated hides, fur, or feathers; by consuming infected animal products; or by insect vectors (insects that transmit pathogens).

Nonliving Reservoirs

The two major nonliving reservoirs of infectious disease are soil and water. Soil harbors such pathogens as fungi, which cause mycoses such as ringworm and systemic infections; *Clostridium botulinum,* the bacterium that causes botulism; and *C. tetani,* the bacterium that causes tetanus. Because both species of clostridia are part of the normal intestinal microbiota of horses and cattle, the bacteria are found especially in soil where animal feces are used as fertilizer.

Water that has been contaminated by the feces of humans and other animals is a reservoir for several pathogens, notably those responsible for gastrointestinal diseases. These include *Vibrio cholerae,* which causes cholera, and *Salmonella typhi,* which causes typhoid fever. Other nonliving reservoirs include foods that are improperly prepared or stored. They may be sources of diseases such as trichinellosis and salmonellosis.

Transmission of Disease

The causative agents of disease can be transmitted from the reservoir of infection to a susceptible host by three principal routes: contact, vehicles, and vectors.

Contact Transmission

Contact transmission is the spread of an agent of disease by direct contact, indirect contact, or droplet transmission. **Direct contact transmission,** also known as *person-to-person transmission,* is the direct transmission of an agent by physical contact between its source and a susceptible host; no intermediate object is involved (**Figure 6a**). The most common forms of direct contact transmission are touching, kissing, and sexual intercourse. Among the diseases that can be transmitted by direct contact are viral respiratory tract diseases (the common cold and influenza), staphylococcal infections, hepatitis A, measles, scarlet fever, and sexually transmitted infections (syphilis, gonorrhea, and genital herpes). Direct contact is also one way to spread AIDS and infectious mononucleosis. To guard against person-to-person transmission, health care workers use gloves and other protective measures (**Figure 6b**). Potential pathogens can also be transmitted by direct contact from animals (or animal products) to humans. Examples are the pathogens causing rabies and anthrax.

Indirect contact transmission occurs when the agent of disease is transmitted from its reservoir to a susceptible host by means of a nonliving object. The general term for any nonliving object involved in the spread of an infection is a **fomite.** Examples of fomites are tissues, handkerchiefs, towels, bedding, diapers, drinking cups, eating utensils, toys, money, and thermometers (**Figure 6c**). Contaminated syringes serve as fomites in transmitting AIDS and hepatitis B. Other fomites may transmit diseases such as tetanus.

Droplet transmission is a third type of contact transmission in which microbes are spread in *droplet nuclei* (mucus drop-

Monkey Business Images/Shutterstock

Levent Konuk/Shutterstock

Stockbyte Platinum/Alamy

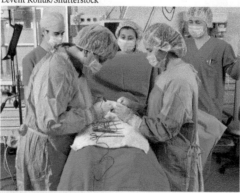

(a) Direct contact transmission

(b) Preventing direct contact transmission through the use of gloves, masks, and face shields

(c) Indirect contact transmission

Andrew Davidhazy, Photo Arts and Sciences at Rochester Institute of Technology

Figure 6 Contact transmission.

Q Name a disease transmitted by direct contact, a disease transmitted by indirect contact, and a disease transmitted by droplet transmission.

(d) Droplet transmission

lets) that travel only short distances (**Figure 6d**). These droplets are discharged into the air by coughing, sneezing, laughing, or talking and travel less than 1 meter from the reservoir to the host. One sneeze may produce 20,000 droplets. Disease agents that travel such short distances are not regarded as airborne (airborne transmission is discussed shortly). Examples of diseases spread by droplet transmission are influenza, pneumonia, and pertussis (whooping cough).

Vehicle Transmission

Vehicle transmission is the transmission of disease agents by a medium, such as water, food, or air (**Figure 7**). Other media include blood and other body fluids, drugs, and intravenous fluids. Here we will discuss water, food, and air as vehicles of transmission.

iStockphoto

iStockphoto

iStockphoto

(a) Water

(b) Food

(c) Air

Figure 7 Vehicle transmission.

Q How does vehicle transmission differ from contact transmission?

TABLE **2** **Selected Zoonoses**

Disease	Causative Agent	Reservoir	Transmission Due To
Viral			
Influenza (some types)	*Influenzavirus*	Swine, birds	Direct contact
Rabies	*Lyssavirus*	Bats, skunks, foxes, dogs, raccoons	Direct contact (bite)
West Nile encephalitis	*Flavivirus*	Horses, birds	*Aedes* and *Culex* mosquito bite
Hantavirus pulmonary syndrome	*Hantavirus*	Rodents (primarily deer mice)	Direct contact with rodent saliva, feces, or urine
Bacterial			
Anthrax	*Bacillus anthracis*	Domestic livestock	Direct contact with contaminated hides or animals; air; food
Brucellosis	*Brucella* spp.	Domestic livestock	Direct contact with contaminated milk, meat, or animals
Plague	*Yersinia pestis*	Rodents	Flea bites
Cat-scratch disease	*Bartonella henselae*	Domestic cats	Direct contact
Ehrlichiosis	*Ehrlichia* spp.	Deer, rodents	Tick bites
Leptospirosis	*Leptospira* spp.	Wild mammals, domestic dogs and cats	Direct contact with urine, soil, water
Lyme disease	*Borrelia burgdorferi*	Field mice	Tick bites
Psittacosis (ornithosis)	*Chlamydophila psittaci*	Birds, especially parrots	Direct contact
Rocky Mountain spotted fever	*Rickettsia rickettsii*	Rodents	Tick bites
Salmonellosis	*Salmonella enterica*	Poultry, reptiles	Ingestion of contaminated food and water and putting hands in mouth
Endemic typhus	*Rickettsia typhi*	Rodents	Flea bites
Fungal			
Ringworm	*Trichophyton* *Microsporum* *Epidermophyton*	Domestic mammals	Direct contact; fomites (nonliving objects)
Protozoan			
Malaria	*Plasmodium* spp.	Monkeys	*Anopheles* mosquito bite
Toxoplasmosis	*Toxoplasma gondii*	Cats and other mammals	Ingestion of contaminated meat or by direct contact with infected tissues or fecal matter
Helminthic			
Tapeworm (pork)	*Taenia solium*	Pigs	Ingestion of undercooked contaminated pork
Trichinellosis	*Trichinella spiralis*	Pigs, bears	Ingestion of undercooked contaminated meat

In *waterborne transmission,* pathogens are usually spread by water contaminated with untreated or poorly treated sewage. Diseases transmitted via this route include cholera, waterborne shigellosis, and leptospirosis. In *foodborne transmission,* pathogens are generally transmitted in foods that are incompletely cooked, poorly refrigerated, or prepared under unsanitary conditions. Foodborne pathogens cause diseases such as food poisoning and tapeworm infestation.

Airborne transmission refers to the spread of agents of infection by droplet nuclei in dust that travel more than 1 meter from the reservoir to the host. For example, microbes are spread by droplets, which may be discharged in a fine spray from the mouth and nose during coughing and sneezing (see Figure 6d).

These droplets are small enough to remain airborne for prolonged periods. The virus that causes measles and the bacterium that causes tuberculosis can be transmitted via airborne droplets. Dust particles can harbor various pathogens. Staphylococci and streptococci can survive on dust and be transmitted by the airborne route. Spores produced by certain fungi are also transmitted by the airborne route and can cause such diseases as histoplasmosis, coccidioidomycosis, and blastomycosis.

Vectors

Arthropods are the most important group of disease **vectors**—animals that carry pathogens from one host to another. Arthropod vectors transmit disease by two general methods.

Imagebroker/Alamy

Figure 8 Mechanical transmission.

 How do mechanical transmission and biological transmission by vectors differ?

Mechanical transmission is the passive transport of the pathogens on the insect's feet or other body parts (Figure 8). If the insect makes contact with a host's food, pathogens can be transferred to the food and later swallowed by the host. Houseflies, for instance, can transfer the pathogens of typhoid fever and bacillary dysentery (shigellosis) from the feces of infected people to food.

Biological transmission is an active process and is more complex. The arthropod bites an infected person or animal and ingests some of the infected blood. The pathogens then reproduce in the vector, and the increase in the number of pathogens increases the possibility that they will be transmitted to another host. Some parasites reproduce in the gut of the arthropod; these can be passed with feces. If the arthropod defecates or vomits while biting a potential host, the parasite can enter the wound. Other parasites reproduce in the vector's gut and migrate to the salivary gland; these are directly injected into a bite. Some protozoan and helminthic parasites use the vector as a host for a developmental stage in their life cycle.

Table 3 lists a few important arthropod vectors and the diseases they transmit.

CHECK YOUR UNDERSTANDING

✔ Why are carriers important reservoirs of infection? 12

✔ How are zoonoses transmitted to humans? 13

✔ Give an example of contact transmission, vehicle transmission, mechanical transmission, and biological transmission. 14

Nosocomial (Hospital-Acquired) Infections

LEARNING OBJECTIVES

15 Define *nosocomial infections,* and explain their importance.

16 Define *compromised host.*

17 List several methods of disease transmission in hospitals.

18 Explain how nosocomial infections can be prevented.

A **nosocomial** (nōs-ō-kō′mē-al) **infection** does not show any evidence of being present or incubating at the time of admission

TABLE 3 Representative Arthropod Vectors and the Diseases They Transmit

Disease	Causative Agent	Arthropod Vector
Malaria	*Plasmodium* spp. (protozoan)	*Anopheles* (mosquito)
African trypanosomiasis	*Trypanosoma brucei gambiense* and *T. b. rhodesiense* (protozoan)	*Glossina* (tsetse fly)
Chagas' disease	*T. cruzi* (protozoan)	*Triatoma* (kissing bug)
Yellow fever	*Alphavirus* (yellow fever virus)	*Aedes* (mosquito)
Dengue	*Alphavirus* (dengue fever virus)	*A. aegypti* (mosquito)
Arthropod-borne encephalitis	*Alphavirus* (encephalitis virus)	*Culex* (mosquito)
Ehrlichiosis	*Ehrlichia* spp.	*Ixodes* spp. (tick)
Epidemic typhus	*Rickettsia prowazekii*	*Pediculus humanus* (louse)
Endemic murine typhus	*R. typhi*	*Xenopsylla cheopis* (rat flea)
Rocky Mountain spotted fever	*R. rickettsii*	*Dermacentor andersoni* and other species (tick)
Plague	*Yersinia pestis*	*X. cheopis* (rat flea)
Relapsing fever	*Borrelia* spp.	*Ornithodorus* spp. (soft tick)
Lyme disease	*B. burgdorferi*	*Ixodes* spp. (tick)

to a hospital; it is acquired as a result of a hospital stay. (The word *nosocomial* is derived from the Greek word for hospital; the term also includes infections acquired in nursing homes and other health care facilities.)

In recent years, the term **health care–associated infection (HAI)** has been introduced to include infections acquired in settings other than just hospitals. These include same-day surgical centers, ambulatory outpatient health care clinics, nursing homes, rehabilitation facilities, and in-home health care environments.

The Centers for Disease Control and Prevention (CDC) estimates that 5–15% of all hospital patients acquire some type of nosocomial infection. The work of pioneers in aseptic techniques such as Lister and Semmelweis decreased the rate of nosocomial infections considerably. However, despite modern advances in sterilization techniques and disposable materials, the rate of nosocomial infections has increased 36% during the last 20 years. In the United States, about 2 million people per year contract nosocomial infections, and nearly 20,000 die as a result. Nosocomial infections represent the eighth leading cause of death in the United States (the top three are heart disease, cancer, and strokes).

Nosocomial infections result from the interaction of several factors: (1) microorganisms in the hospital environment, (2) the compromised (or weakened) status of the host, and (3) the chain of transmission in the hospital. Figure 9 illustrates that the presence of any one of these factors alone is generally not enough to cause infection; it is the interaction of all three factors that poses a significant risk of nosocomial infection.

Microorganisms in the Hospital

Although every effort is made to kill or check the growth of microorganisms in the hospital, the hospital environment is a major reservoir for a variety of pathogens. One reason is that certain normal microbiota of the human body are opportunistic and present a particularly strong danger to hospital patients. In fact, most of the microbes that cause nosocomial infections do not cause disease in healthy people but are pathogenic only for individuals whose defenses have been weakened by illness or therapy (see the Clinical Focus later in this chapter).

In the 1940s and 1950s, most nosocomial infections were caused by gram-positive microbes. At one time, the gram-positive *Staphylococcus aureus* was the primary cause of nosocomial infections. In the 1970s, gram-negative rods, such as *E. coli* and *Pseudomonas aeruginosa*, were the most common causes of nosocomial infections. Then, during the 1980s, antibiotic-resistant gram-positive bacteria, *Staphylococcus aureus*, coagulase-negative staphylococci, and *Enterococcus* spp., emerged as nosocomial pathogens. By the 1990s, these gram-positive bacteria accounted for 34% of nosocomial infections, and four gram-negative pathogens accounted for 32%. In the 2000s, antibiotic resistance in nosocomial infections is a major concern. The principal microorganisms involved in nosocomial infections are summarized in Table 4.

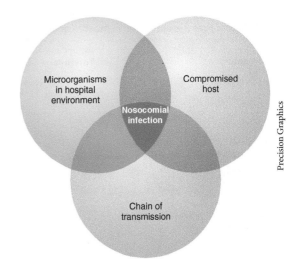

Figure 9 Nosocomial infections.

Q What is a nosocomial infection?

Precision Graphics

Clinical Case

Jamil calls his physician to discuss his symptoms and makes an appointment for that afternoon. His wife, Charlene, drives Jamil to the appointment; he is not sure he can make it that far without stopping. Initially, Jamil's physician thinks he has noroviral gastroenteritis, but the symptoms have gone on too long. She orders a stool sample to be sent to the local laboratory for culturing. The results return positive for *C. difficile*.

Where could Jamil have contracted *C. difficile*?

In addition to being opportunistic, some microorganisms in the hospital become resistant to antimicrobial drugs, which are commonly used there. For example, *P. aeruginosa* and other such gram-negative bacteria tend to be difficult to control with antibiotics because of their R factors, which carry genes that determine resistance to antibiotics. As the R factors recombine, new and multiple resistance factors are produced. These strains become part of the microbiota of patients and hospital personnel and become progressively more resistant to antibiotic therapy. In this way, people become part of the reservoir (and chain of transmission) for antibiotic-resistant strains of bacteria. Usually, if the host's resistance is high, the new strains are not much of a problem. However, if disease, surgery, or trauma has weakened the host's defenses, secondary infections may be difficult to treat.

TABLE **4** Microorganisms Involved in Most Nosocomial Infections

Microorganism	Percentage of Total Infections	Percentage Resistant to Antibiotics	Infections Caused
Coagulase-negative staphylococci	15%	89%	Most common cause of sepsis
Staphylococcus aureus	15%	50%	Most frequent cause of pneumonia
Enterococcus spp.	10%	4–71%	Most common cause of surgical wound infections
Escherichia coli, *Pseudomonas aeruginosa*, *Enterobacter*, and *Klebsiella pneumoniae*	23%	3–32%	Pneumonia and surgical wound infections
Clostridium difficile	15–25%	Not reported	Causes nearly half of all nosocomial diarrhea
Candida albicans (fungus)	7%	Not reported	Urinary tract infections and sepsis
Other gram-negative bacteria (*Acinetobacter*, *Citrobacter*, *Haemophilus*)	7%	Not reported	Urinary tract infections and surgical wound infections

Source: Data from CDC, National Nosocomial Infections Surveillance.

Compromised Host

A **compromised host** is one whose resistance to infection is impaired by disease, therapy, or burns. Two principal conditions can compromise the host: broken skin or mucous membranes, and a suppressed immune system.

As long as the skin and mucous membranes remain intact, they provide formidable physical barriers against most pathogens. Burns, surgical wounds, trauma (such as accidental wounds), injections, invasive diagnostic procedures, ventilators, intravenous therapy, and urinary catheters (used to drain urine) can all break the first line of defense and make a person more susceptible to disease in hospitals. Burn patients are especially susceptible to nosocomial infections because their skin is no longer an effective barrier to microorganisms.

The risk of infection is also related to other invasive procedures, such as administering anesthesia, which may alter breathing and contribute to pneumonia, and tracheotomy, in which an incision is made into the trachea to assist breathing. Patients who require invasive procedures usually have a serious underlying disease, which further increases susceptibility to infections. Invasive devices provide a pathway for microorganisms in the environment to enter the body; they also help transfer microbes from one part of the body to another. Pathogens can also proliferate on the devices themselves.

In healthy individuals, white blood cells called T cells (T lymphocytes) provide resistance to disease by killing pathogens directly, mobilizing phagocytes and other lymphocytes, and secreting chemicals that kill pathogens. White blood cells called B cells (B lymphocytes), which develop into antibody-producing cells, also protect against infection. Antibodies provide immunity by such actions as neutralizing toxins, inhibiting the attachment of a pathogen to host cells, and helping to lyse pathogens. Drugs, radiation therapy, steroid therapy, burns,

diabetes, leukemia, kidney disease, stress, and malnutrition can all adversely affect the actions of T and B cells and compromise the host. In addition, the AIDS virus destroys certain T cells.

A summary of the principal sites of nosocomial infections is presented in **Table 5**.

Chain of Transmission

Given the variety of pathogens (and potential pathogens) in the hospital and the compromised state of the host, routes of transmission are a constant concern. The principal routes of transmission of nosocomial infections are (1) direct contact transmission from hospital staff to patient and from patient to patient and (2) indirect contact transmission through fomites and the hospital's ventilation system (airborne transmission).

Because hospital personnel are in direct contact with patients, they can often transmit disease. For example, a physician or nurse may transmit microbes to a patient when changing a dressing, or a kitchen worker who carries *Salmonella* can contaminate a food supply.

Certain areas of a hospital are reserved for specialized care; these include the burn, hemodialysis, recovery, intensive care, and oncology units. Unfortunately, these units also group patients together and provide environments for the epidemic spread of nosocomial infections from patient to patient.

Many diagnostic and therapeutic hospital procedures provide a fomite route of transmission. The urinary catheter used to drain urine from the urinary bladder is a fomite in many nosocomial infections. Intravenous catheters, which pass through the skin and into a vein to provide fluids, nutrients, or medication, can also transmit nosocomial infections. Respiratory aids can introduce contaminated fluids into the lungs. Needles may introduce pathogens into muscle or blood, and surgical dressings can become contaminated and promote disease.

TABLE 5   Principal Sites of Nosocomial Infections

Type of Infection	Comment
Urinary tract infections	Most common, usually accounts for about 32% of all nosocomial infections. Typically related to urinary catheterization.
Surgical site infections (cutaneous and subcutaneous)	Ranks second in infection incidence (about 22%). An estimated 5–12% of all surgical patients develop postoperative infections; the percentage can reach 30% for certain surgeries, such as colon surgery and amputations.
Lower respiratory infections	Nosocomial pneumonias account for about 15% and have high mortality rates (13–55%). Most of these pneumonias are related to respiratory devices that aid breathing or administer medications.
Bacteremia, caused primarily by intravenous catheterizations	Bacteremias account for about 14% of nosocomial infections. Intravenous catheterization is implicated in nosocomial infections of the bloodstream, particularly infections caused by bacteria and fungi.
Other	All other infection sites account for about 17% of nosocomial infections.

Source: Data from CDC, National Nosocomial Infection Surveillance.

- Urinary tract infections
- Surgical site infections
- Lower respiratory infections
- Bloodstream infections
- Other

Control of Nosocomial Infections

Control measures aimed at preventing nosocomial infections vary from one institution to another, but certain procedures are generally implemented. It is important to reduce the number of pathogens to which patients are exposed by using aseptic techniques, handling contaminated materials carefully, insisting on frequent and thorough handwashing, educating staff members about basic infection control measures, and using isolation rooms and wards.

According to the CDC, handwashing is the single most important means of preventing the spread of infection. Nevertheless, the CDC reports that adherence of health care workers to recommended hand-washing procedures has been poor. On average, health care workers wash their hands before interacting with patients only 40% of the time.

In addition to handwashing, tubs used to bathe patients should be disinfected between uses so that bacteria from the previous patient will not contaminate the next one. Respirators and humidifiers provide both a suitable growth environment for some bacteria and a method of airborne transmission. These sources of nosocomial infections must be kept scrupulously clean and disinfected, and materials used for bandages and intubation (insertion of tubes into organs, such as the trachea) should be single-use disposable or sterilized before use. Packaging used to maintain sterility should be removed aseptically. Physicians can help improve patients' resistance to infection by prescribing antibiotics only when necessary, avoiding invasive procedures if possible, and minimizing the use of immunosuppressive drugs.

Accredited hospitals should have an infection control committee. Most hospitals have at least an infection control nurse or epidemiologist (an individual who studies disease in populations). The role of these staff members is to identify problem sources, such as antibiotic-resistant strains of bacteria and improper sterilization techniques. The infection control officer should make periodic examinations of hospital equipment to determine the extent of microbial contamination. Samples should be taken from tubing, catheters, respirator reservoirs, and other equipment.

(MM) **Animations** Nosocomial Infections: Overview, Prevention

Clinical Case

C. difficile is a bacterium that is involved in 15–25% of all nosocomial infections and almost half of all nosocomial diarrhea. It was first identified in 1935 as part of the normal intestinal microbiota. *C. difficile* was associated with diarrhea in 1977. *C. difficile* infection can range from asymptomatic colonization of patients to diarrhea or colitis. Mortality in older patients is 10–20%. After making sure Jamil is not taking any antibiotics, his physician prescribes the antibiotic metronidazole to treat the *C. difficile*.

Why does Jamil's physician make sure he is not taking antibiotics before she treats the *C. difficile* infection? (Hint: See page 403).

CHECK YOUR UNDERSTANDING

✔ What interacting factors result in nosocomial infections? 15

✔ What is a compromised host? 16

✔ How are nosocomial infections primarily transmitted, and how can they be prevented? 17, 18

Emerging Infectious Diseases

LEARNING OBJECTIVE

19   List several probable reasons for emerging infectious diseases, and name one example for each reason.

Emerging infectious diseases (EIDs) are ones that are new or changing, showing an increase in incidence in the recent past, or a potential to increase in the near future. An emerging disease can be caused by a virus, a bacterium, a fungus, a protozoan, or a helminth. About 75% of emerging infectious diseases are zoonotic, mainly of viral origin, and are likely to be vector-borne. Several criteria are used for identifying an EID. For example, some diseases present symptoms that are clearly distinctive from all other diseases. Some are recognized because improved diagnostic techniques allow the identification of a new pathogen. Others are identified when a local disease becomes widespread, a rare disease becomes common, a mild disease becomes more severe, or an increase in life span permits a slow disease to develop. Examples of emerging infectious diseases are listed in **Table 6**.

A variety of factors contribute to the emergence of new infectious diseases:

- New strains, such as *E. coli* O157:H7 and avian influenza (H5N1), may result from genetic recombination between organisms.

- A new serovar, such as *Vibrio cholerae* O139, may result from changes in or the evolution of existing microorganisms.

- The widespread, and sometimes unwarranted, use of antibiotics and pesticides encourages the growth of more resistant populations of microbes and the insects (mosquitoes and lice) and ticks that carry them.

- Global warming and changes in weather patterns may increase the distribution and survival of reservoirs and vectors, resulting in the introduction and dissemination of diseases such as malaria and *Hantavirus* pulmonary syndrome.

- Known diseases, such as cholera and West Nile virus, may spread to new geographic areas by modern transportation. This was less likely 100 years ago, when travel took so long that infected travelers either died or recovered during passage.

- Previously unrecognized infections may appear in individuals living or working in regions undergoing ecological changes brought about by natural disaster, construction, wars, and expanding human settlement. In California, the incidence of coccidioidomycosis increased tenfold following the Northridge earthquake of 1994. Workers clearing South American forests are now contracting Venezuelan hemorrhagic fever.

- Even animal control measures may affect the incidence of a disease. The increase in Lyme disease in recent years could be due to rising deer populations resulting from the killing of deer predators.

- Failures in public health measures may be a contributing factor to the emergence of previously controlled infections. For example, the failure of adults to get a diphtheria booster vaccination led to a diphtheria epidemic in the newly independent republics of the former Soviet Union in the 1990s.

The CDC, the National Institutes of Health (NIH), and the World Health Organization (WHO) have developed plans to address issues relating to EIDs. Their priorities include:

1. To detect, promptly investigate, and monitor emerging infectious pathogens, the diseases they cause, and factors that influence their emergence

2. To expand basic and applied research on ecological and environmental factors, microbial changes and adaptations, and host interactions that influence EIDs

3. To enhance the communication of public health information and the prompt implementation of prevention strategies regarding EIDs

4. To establish plans to monitor and control EIDs worldwide

The importance of emerging infectious diseases to the scientific community resulted in a 1995 publication, *Emerging Infectious Diseases,* devoted exclusively to the topic.

CHECK YOUR UNDERSTANDING

✔ Give several examples of emerging infectious diseases. 19

Clinical Case

Antibiotics can kill competing bacteria, thus allowing growth of *C. difficile*. When Jamil's physician learns of the cause of Jamil's diarrhea, she checks with the hospital to see whether any other patients have developed *C. difficile* diarrhea and colitis. It turns out that 20 other patients are also infected with *C. difficile*. The local health department completes an epidemiological study of the outbreak and releases the following information:

Rate of infection for patients	
Single room	7%
Double room	17%
Triple room	26%

Rate of environmental isolations of *C. difficile*	
Bed rail	10%
Commode	1%
Floor	18%
Call button	6%
Toilet	3%

C. difficile on hands of hospital personnel after contact with patients who were culture-positive for *C. difficile*	
Used gloves	0%
Did not use gloves	59%
Had *C. difficile* before patient contact	3%
Washed with nondisinfectant soap	40%
Washed with disinfectant soap	3%
Did not wash hands	20%

What is the most likely mode of transmission, and how can transmission be prevented?

TABLE **6** Emerging Infectious Diseases

Microorganism	Year of Emergence	Disease Caused
Bacteria		
Bacillus anthracis	2001	Anthrax
Bordetella pertussis	2000	Whooping cough
Mycobacterium ulcerans	1998	Buruli ulcer
Methicillin-resistant *Staphylococcus aureus*	1997	Bacteremia, pneumonia
Vancomycin-resistant *Staphylococcus aureus*	1996	Bacteremia, pneumonia
Streptococcus pneumoniae	1995	Antibiotic-resistant pneumonia
Streptococcus pyogenes	1995	Streptococcal toxic shock syndrome
Corynebacterium diphtheriae	1994	Diphtheria epidemic, eastern Europe
Vibrio cholerae O139	1992	New serovar of cholera, Asia
Vancomycin-resistant enterococci	1988	Urinary tract infections, bacteremia, endocarditis
Bartonella henselae	1983	Cat-scratch disease
Escherichia coli O157:H7	1982	Hemorrhagic diarrhea
Legionella pneumophila	1976	Legionellosis (Legionnaires' disease)
Borrelia burgdorferi	1975	Lyme disease
Fungi		
Coccidioides immitis	1993	Coccidioidomycosis
Pneumocystis jirovecii	1981	Pneumonia in immunocompromised individuals
Protozoa		
Trypanosoma cruzi	2007	Chagas' disease in United States
Cyclospora cayetanensis	1993	Severe diarrhea and wasting syndrome
Cryptosporidium spp.	1976	Cryptosporidiosis
Helminths		
Baylisascaris procyonis	2001	Raccoon roundworm encephalitis, in humans
Viruses		
SARS-associated coronavirus	2002	Severe acute respiratory syndrome (SARS)
Ebola virus	2002, 1995, 1975	Ebola hemorrhagic fever
West Nile virus	1999	West Nile encephalitis
Nipah virus	1998	Encephalitis, Malaysia
Influenza A virus	1997, 2009	Avian influenza (H5N1), Swine flu (H1N1)
Hendra virus	1994	Encephalitis-like symptoms, Australia
Hantavirus	1993	*Hantavirus* pulmonary syndrome
Venezuelan hemorrhagic fever	1991	Hemorrhagic fever, South America
Hepatitis C virus	1989	Hepatitis
Monkeypox virus	1985	Chickenpox-like disease
Dengue virus	1984	Dengue fever and dengue hemorrhagic fever
HIV	1983	AIDS
Prions		
Bovine spongiform encephalitis agent	1996	Mad cow disease, Great Britain

Epidemiology

LEARNING OBJECTIVES

20 Define *epidemiology*, and describe three types of epidemio-
logic investigations.

21 Identify the function of the CDC.

22 Define the following terms: *morbidity*, *mortality*, and *notifiable
infectious diseases*.

In today's crowded, overpopulated world, in which frequent travel
and the mass production and distribution of food and other goods

are a way of life, diseases can spread rapidly. A contaminated food or water supply, for example, can affect many thousands of people very quickly. Identifying the causative agent of a disease is desirable so that it can be effectively controlled and treated. It is also desirable to understand the mode of transmission and geographical distribution of the disease. The science that studies when and where diseases occur and how they are transmitted in populations is called **epidemiology** (ep-i-dē-mē-ol′ ō-jē).

Modern epidemiology began in the mid-1800s with three now-famous investigations. John Snow, a British physician, conducted a series of investigations related to outbreaks of cholera in London. As the cholera epidemic of 1848 to 1849 raged, Snow analyzed the death records attributed to cholera, gathered information about the victims, and interviewed survivors who lived in the neighborhood. Using the information he compiled, Snow made a map showing that most individuals who died of cholera drank or brought water from the Broad Street pump; those who used other pumps (or drank beer, like the workers at a nearby brewery) did not get cholera. He concluded that contaminated water from the Broad Street pump was the source of the epidemic. When the pump's handle was removed and people could no longer get water from this location, the number of cholera cases dropped significantly.

Between 1846 and 1848, Ignaz Semmelweis meticulously recorded the number of births and maternal deaths at Vienna General Hospital. The First Maternity Clinic had become a source of gossip throughout Vienna because the death rate due to puerperal sepsis ranged between 13% and 18%, four times that of the Second Maternity Clinic. Puerperal sepsis (childbirth fever) is a nosocomial infection that begins in the uterus as a result of childbirth or abortion. It is frequently caused by *Streptococcus pyogenes*. The infection progresses to the abdominal cavity (peritonitis) and in many cases to septicemia (proliferation of microbes in the blood). Wealthy women did not go to the clinic, and poor women had learned they had a better chance of surviving childbirth if they gave birth elsewhere before going to the hospital. Looking at his data, Semmelweis identified a common factor among the wealthy women and the poor women who had given birth prior to entering the clinic: they were not examined by the medical students, who had spent their mornings dissecting cadavers. In May 1847, he ordered all medical students to wash their hands with chloride of lime before entering the delivery room, and the mortality rate dropped to under 2%.

Florence Nightingale recorded statistics on epidemic typhus in the English civilian and military populations. In 1858, she published a thousand-page report using statistical comparisons to demonstrate that diseases, poor food, and unsanitary conditions were killing the soldiers. Her work resulted in reforms in the British Army and to her admission to the Statistical Society, their first female member.

These three careful analyses of where and when a disease occurs and how it is transmitted within a population constituted a new approach to medical research and demonstrated the importance of epidemiology. The works of Snow, Semmelweis, and Nightingale resulted in changes that lowered the incidence of diseases even though knowledge of the causes of infectious disease was limited. Most physicians believed that the symptoms they saw were the causes of the disease, not the result of disease. Koch's work on the germ theory of disease was still 30 years in the future.

An epidemiologist not only determines the etiology of a disease but also identifies other possibly important factors and patterns concerning the people affected. An important part of the epidemiologist's work is assembling and analyzing such data as age, sex, occupation, personal habits, socioeconomic status, history of immunization, presence of any other diseases, and the common history of affected individuals (such as eating the same food or visiting the same doctor's office). Also important for the prevention of future outbreaks is knowledge of the site at which a susceptible host came into contact with the agent of infection. In addition, the epidemiologist considers the period during which the disease occurs, either on a seasonal basis (to indicate whether the disease is prevalent during the summer or winter) or on a yearly basis (to indicate the effects of immunization or an emerging or reemerging disease).

An epidemiologist is also concerned with various methods for controlling a disease. The strategies controlling diseases include the use of drugs (chemotherapy) and vaccines (immunization). Other methods include the control of human, animal, and nonliving reservoirs of infection, water treatment, proper sewage disposal (enteric diseases), cold storage, pasteurization, food inspection, adequate cooking (foodborne diseases), improved nutrition to bolster host defenses, changes in personal habits, and screening of transfused blood and transplanted organs.

Figure 10 contains graphs indicating the incidence of selected diseases. Such graphs provide information about whether disease outbreaks are sporadic or epidemic and, if epidemic, how the disease might have spread. By establishing the frequency of a disease in a population and identifying the factors responsible for its transmission, an epidemiologist can provide physicians with information that is important in determining the prognosis and treatment of a disease. Epidemiologists also evaluate how effectively a disease is being controlled in a community—by a vaccination program, for example. Finally, epidemiologists can provide data to help in evaluating and planning overall health care for a community.

Epidemiologists use three basic types of investigations when analyzing the occurrence of a disease: descriptive, analytical, and experimental.

Descriptive Epidemiology

Descriptive epidemiology entails collecting all data that describe the occurrence of the disease under study. Relevant information usually includes information about the affected individuals and the place and period in which the disease occurred. Snow's search for the cause of the cholera outbreak in London is an example of descriptive epidemiology.

Figure 10 Epidemiological graphs. (a) Lyme disease cases, showing the annual occurrence of the disease during the covered period. **(b)** A different perspective of Lyme disease that enabled epidemiologists to draw some conclusions about the disease's epidemiology. This graph records the number of cases per 100,000 people, rather than the total number of cases. **(c)** A graph of the incidence of tuberculosis shows a rapid decrease in the rate of infection from 1948 to 1957.
Source: Data from CDC.

Q What does graph (b) indicate about transmission of Lyme disease? What can you conclude from graph (c)?

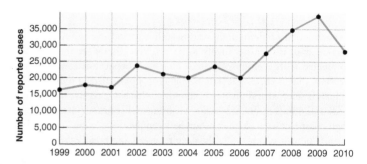

(a) Lyme disease cases, 1999–2010

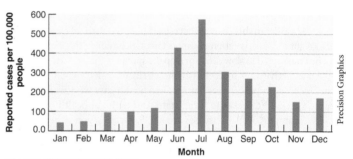

(b) Lyme disease by month, 2009

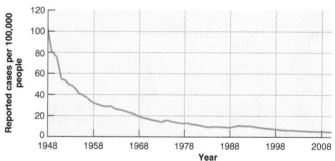

(c) Reported tuberculosis cases, 1948–2010

Such a study is generally *retrospective* (looking backward after the episode has ended). In other words, the epidemiologist backtracks to the cause and source of the disease. The search for the cause of toxic shock syndrome is an example of a fairly recent retrospective study. In the initial phase of an epidemiological study, retrospective studies are more common than *prospective* (looking forward) studies, in which an epidemiologist chooses a group of people who are free of a particular disease to study. The group's subsequent disease experiences are then recorded for a given period. Prospective studies were used to test the Salk polio vaccine in 1954 and 1955.

Analytical Epidemiology

Analytical epidemiology analyzes a particular disease to determine its probable cause. This study can be done in two ways. With the *case control method,* the epidemiologist looks for factors that might have preceded the disease. A group of people who have the disease is compared with another group of people who are free of the disease. For example, one group with meningitis and one without the disease might be matched by age, sex, socioeconomic status, and location. These statistics are compared to determine which of all the possible factors—genetic, environmental, nutritional, and so forth—might be responsible for the meningitis. Nightingale's work was an example of analytical epidemiology, in which she compared disease in soldiers and civilians. With the *cohort method,* the epidemiologist studies two populations: one that has had contact with the agent causing a disease and another that has not (both groups are called *cohort groups*). For example, a comparison of one group composed of people who have received blood transfusions and one composed of people who have not could reveal an association between blood transfusions and the incidence of hepatitis B virus.

Experimental Epidemiology

Experimental epidemiology begins with a hypothesis about a particular disease; experiments to test the hypothesis are then conducted with a group of people. One such hypothesis could be the assumed effectiveness of a drug. A group of infected individuals is selected and divided randomly so that some receive the drug and others receive a *placebo,* a substance that has no effect. If all other factors are kept constant between the two groups, and if those people who received the drug recover more rapidly than those who received the placebo, it can be concluded that the drug was the experimental factor (variable) that made the difference.

Case Reporting

We noted earlier in this chapter that establishing the chain of transmission for a disease is extremely important. Once known, the chain can be interrupted to slow down or stop the spread of the disease.

An effective way to establish the chain of transmission is *case reporting,* a procedure that requires health care workers to report specified diseases to local, state, and national health officials. Examples of such diseases are AIDS, measles, gonorrhea, tetanus, and typhoid fever. Case reporting provides epidemiologists with an approximation of the incidence and prevalence of a disease. This information helps officials decide whether or not to investigate a given disease.

Case reporting provided epidemiologists with valuable leads regarding the origin and spread of AIDS. In fact, one of the first clues about AIDS came from reports of young men with Kaposi's sarcoma, formerly a disease of older men. Using these reports, epidemiologists began various studies of the patients. If an epidemiological study shows that a large enough segment of the population is affected by a disease, an attempt is then made to isolate and identify its causative agent. Identification is accomplished by a number of different microbiological methods. Identifying the causative agent often provides valuable information regarding the reservoir for the disease.

Once the chain of transmission is discovered, it is possible to apply control measures to stop the disease from spreading. These might include elimination of the source of infection, isolation and segregation of infected people, the development of vaccines, and, as in the case of AIDS, education.

The Centers for Disease Control and Prevention (CDC)

Epidemiology is a major concern of state and federal public health departments. The **Centers for Disease Control and Prevention (CDC),** a branch of the U.S. Public Health Service located in Atlanta, Georgia, is a central source of epidemiological information in the United States.

Clinical Case Resolved

Transmission of *C. difficile* can be prevented by wearing gloves for contact with all body substances, using disposable rectal thermometers, and stopping antibiotic overuse. *C. difficile* is acquired by ingesting the bacteria or its endospores from direct contact between people or indirect contact via fomites; it is the most common nosocomial infection and is considered an epidemic. Jamil responds well to treatment; he is gaining most of his weight back and no longer spends most of his time in the bathroom.

The CDC issues a publication called the *Morbidity and Mortality Weekly Report* (www.cdc.gov). The *MMWR,* as it is called, is read by microbiologists, physicians, and other hospital and public health professionals. The *MMWR* contains data on **morbidity,** the incidence of specific notifiable diseases, and **mortality,** the number of deaths from these diseases. These data are usually organized by state. **Notifiable infectious diseases** shown in **Table 7,** are diseases for which physicians are required by law to report cases to the U.S. Public Health Service. As of 2011, a total of 62 infectious diseases were reported at the national level. **Morbidity rate** is the number of people affected by a disease in a given period of time in relation to the total population. **Mortality rate** is the number of deaths resulting from a disease in a population in a given period of time in relation to the total population.

MMWR articles include reports of disease outbreaks, case histories of special interest, and summaries of the status of particular diseases during a recent period. These articles often include recommendations for procedures for diagnosis, immunization, and treatment. Several graphs and other data in this text are from the *MMWR,* and the Clinical Focus boxes are adapted from reports from this publication. See the Clinical Focus on the following page, for example. (MM) **Animations** Epidemiology: Overview, Occurrence of Disease, Transmission of Disease

CHECK YOUR UNDERSTANDING

✔ After learning that 40 hospital employees developed nausea and vomiting, the hospital infection control officer determined that 39 ill people ate green beans in the hospital cafeteria, compared to 34 healthy people who ate in the cafeteria the same day but did not eat green beans in the hospital cafeteria. What type of epidemiology is this? 20

✔ What is the CDC's function? 21

✔ In 2003, the morbidity of hemolytic uremic syndrome was 176, and the mortality was 29. The morbidity of listeriosis was 696; the mortality was 33. Which disease is more likely to be fatal? 22

* * *

Nosocomial Infections

In this box, you will encounter a series of questions the epidemiologist asks himself as he tries to trace an outbreak to its source. Try to answer each question before going to the next one.

1. Dwayne Jackson, the epidemiologist at a city hospital, would like to find out why during one year, 5287 patients developed bacteremia during their hospital stays. All patients had a fever (>38°C), chills, and low blood pressure; 14% had severe necrotizing fasciitis. Dr. Jackson looks at the results of the blood cultures, which were grown on mannitol-salt agar; the bacteria are identified as coagulase-positive, gram-positive cocci (Figure A).
   What organisms are possible agents of infection?

2. The biochemical tests confirm that *Staphylococcus aureus* is the culprit. Antibiotic-sensitivity testing shows that all the isolates are methicillin-resistant. Six are vancomycin-intermediate resistant, and one is vancomycin-resistant. Methicillin-resistant *S. aureus* (MRSA) can cause a life-threatening, necrotizing illness due to a leukocidin toxin.
   What else does Dr. Jackson need to know?

3. Polymerase chain reaction (PCR) is used to determine that strain USA100 caused 80% of the MRSA cases in Dr. Jackson's hospital. USA100 is the cause of 92% of health care–acquired strains. The majority (89%) of community-acquired MRSA infections are the USA300 strain. The incidence of MRSA in the community (not hospitalized) is 0.02–0.04%. Dr. Jackson compares the number of patients with MRSA to the procedures performed and cross-references that information with the antibiotic use of the patients (see table).
   Based on the information in the table, which procedure increases the likelihood of infection most?

4. Each year, an estimated 250,000 cases of bloodstream infections occur in hospitals in the United States from inserting needles into veins to deliver intravenous (IV) solutions, and the estimated mortality for these infections is 12–25%. Dr. Jackson sees that people receiving hemodialysis are especially vulnerable to infections because they require access to veins for prolonged periods and undergo frequent punctures of the access site (Figure B).
   How does antimicrobial therapy contribute?

5. The first VRSA (vancomycin-resistant *S. aureus*) infection in the United States occurred in a dialysis patient in 2002. The patient had been treated with vancomycin for a MRSA infection.

Christine Case

Figure B Hemodialysis procedure.

The VRSA isolate contained the *vanA* vancomycin-resistance gene from enterococci. VRSA are always methicillin resistant. Only six VRSA cases have been reported in the United States; however, 63 VISA (vancomycin-intermediate *S. aureus*) cases were reported in 2008. Antimicrobial therapy for hemodialysis-associated infections increases the prevalence of antimicrobial resistance. Susceptible bacteria are killed, and bacteria with a mutation that confers resistance are able to grow without competition.

Source: Adapted from *MMWR* 56(9):197–199, March 9, 2007. and *MMWR* 57(54), June 25, 2010.

Precision Graphics

Figure A The gram-positive cocci grown on mannitol-salt agar.

Procedure	MRSA-Infected Patients	Total Number of Patients Receiving Procedure
Hemodialysis	813	1807
Intravenous (IV) catheter	1057	16,516
Surgery	945	5659
Urinary bladder catheter	1750	7919
Ventilator (invasive airway)	722	7367
Antibiotic use during the 6 months prior to infection		
Vancomycin	21	41
Fluoroquinolone	49	113
Ceftriaxone	14	41

TABLE 7 Nationally Notifiable Infectious Diseases, 2011

Anthrax	Hepatitis A, B, C	Severe acute respiratory syndrome-associated coronavirus (SARS-CoV)
Arboviral disease	HIV infection	Shiga toxin-producing E. coli
Babesiosis	Influenza A novel strains	Shigellosis
Botulism	Influenza-associated pediatric mortality	Smallpox
Brucellosis	Legionellosis	Spotted fever rickettsiosis
Chancroid	Listeriosis	Streptococcal toxic shock syndrome
Chlamydia trachomatis infections	Lyme disease	S. pneumoniae, invasive disease
Cholera	Malaria	Syphilis
Coccidioidomycosis	Measles	Tetanus
Cryptosporidiosis	Meningococcal disease	Toxic shock syndrome (nonstreptococcal)
Cyclosporiasis	Mumps	Trichinellosis
Dengue	Pertussis	Tuberculosis
Diphtheria	Plague	Tularemia
Ehrlichiosis/Anaplasmosis	Poliomyelitis	Typhoid fever
Giardiasis	Psittacosis	Vancomycin-intermediate resistant Staphylococcus aureus (VISA)
Gonorrhea	Q fever	Vancomycin-resistant Staphylococcus aureus (VRSA)
Haemophilus influenzae invasive disease	Rabies, animal and human	Varicella
Hansen's disease (Leprosy)	Rubella	Vibriosis
Hantavirus pulmonary syndrome	Rubella, congenital syndrome	Viral hemorrhagic fevers
Hemolytic uremic syndrome, postdiarrheal	Salmonnellosis	Yellow fever

Study Outline

MasteringMICROBIOLOGY™

Test your understanding with quizzes, microbe review, and a chapter post-test at www.masteringmicrobiology.com.

Introduction

1. Disease-causing microorganisms are called pathogens.
2. Pathogenic microorganisms have special properties that allow them to invade the human body or produce toxins.
3. When a microorganism overcomes the body's defenses, a state of disease results.

Pathology, Infection, and Disease

1. Pathology is the scientific study of disease.
2. Pathology is concerned with the etiology (cause), pathogenesis (development), and effects of disease.
3. Infection is the invasion and growth of pathogens in the body.
4. A host is an organism that shelters and supports the growth of pathogens.
5. Disease is an abnormal state in which part or all of the body is not properly adjusted or is incapable of performing normal functions.

Normal Microbiota

1. Animals, including humans, are usually germfree in utero.
2. Microorganisms begin colonization in and on the surface of the body soon after birth.
3. Microorganisms that establish permanent colonies inside or on the body without producing disease make up the normal microbiota.
4. Transient microbiota are microbes that are present for various periods and then disappear.

Relationships between the Normal Microbiota and the Host

5. The normal microbiota can prevent pathogens from causing an infection; this phenomenon is known as microbial antagonism.
6. Normal microbiota and the host exist in symbiosis (living together).
7. The three types of symbiosis are commensalism (one organism benefits, and the other is unaffected), mutualism (both organisms benefit), and parasitism (one organism benefits, and one is harmed).

Opportunistic Microorganisms

8. Opportunistic pathogens do not cause disease under normal conditions but cause disease under special conditions.

Cooperation among Microorganisms

9. In some situations, one microorganism makes it possible for another to cause a disease or produce more severe symptoms.

The Etiology of Infectious Diseases

Koch's Postulates

1. Koch's postulates are criteria for establishing that specific microbes cause specific diseases.
2. Koch's postulates have the following requirements: (1) the same pathogen must be present in every case of the disease; (2) the pathogen must be isolated in pure culture; (3) the pathogen isolated from pure culture must cause the same disease in a healthy, susceptible laboratory animal; and (4) the pathogen must be reisolated from the inoculated laboratory animal.

Exceptions to Koch's Postulates

3. Koch's postulates are modified to establish etiologies of diseases caused by viruses and some bacteria, which cannot be grown on artificial media.
4. Some diseases, such as tetanus, have unequivocal signs and symptoms.
5. Some diseases, such as pneumonia and nephritis, may be caused by a variety of microbes.
6. Some pathogens, such as *S. pyogenes*, cause several different diseases.
7. Certain pathogens, such as HIV, cause disease in humans only.

Classifying Infectious Diseases

1. A patient may exhibit symptoms (subjective changes in body functions) and signs (measurable changes), which a physician uses to make a diagnosis (identification of the disease).
2. A specific group of symptoms or signs that always accompanies a specific disease is called a syndrome.

3. Communicable diseases are transmitted directly or indirectly from one host to another.
4. A contagious disease is one that is easily spread from one person to another.
5. Noncommunicable diseases are caused by microorganisms that normally grow outside the human body and are not transmitted from one host to another.

Occurrence of a Disease

6. Disease occurrence is reported by incidence (number of people contracting the disease) and prevalence (number of cases at a particular time).
7. Diseases are classified by frequency of occurrence: sporadic, endemic, epidemic, and pandemic.

Severity or Duration of a Disease

8. The scope of a disease can be defined as acute, chronic, subacute, or latent.
9. Herd immunity is the presence of immunity to a disease in most of the population.

Extent of Host Involvement

10. A local infection affects a small area of the body; a systemic infection is spread throughout the body via the circulatory system.
11. A primary infection is an acute infection that causes the initial illness.
12. A secondary infection can occur after the host is weakened from a primary infection.
13. An inapparent, or subclinical, infection does not cause any signs of disease in the host.

Patterns of Disease

Predisposing Factors

1. A predisposing factor is one that makes the body more susceptible to disease or alters the course of a disease.
2. Examples include gender, climate, age, fatigue, and inadequate nutrition.

Development of Disease

3. The incubation period is the interval between the initial infection and the first appearance of signs and symptoms.
4. The prodromal period is characterized by the appearance of the first mild signs and symptoms.
5. During the period of illness, the disease is at its height, and all disease signs and symptoms are apparent.
6. During the period of decline, the signs and symptoms subside.
7. During the period of convalescence, the body returns to its prediseased state, and health is restored.

The Spread of Infection

Reservoirs of Infection

1. A continual source of infection is called a reservoir of infection.
2. People who have a disease or are carriers of pathogenic microorganisms are human reservoirs of infection.
3. Zoonoses are diseases that affect wild and domestic animals and can be transmitted to humans.
4. Some pathogenic microorganisms grow in nonliving reservoirs, such as soil and water.

Transmission of Disease

5. Transmission by direct contact involves close physical contact between the source of the disease and a susceptible host.
6. Transmission by fomites (inanimate objects) constitutes indirect contact.
7. Transmission via saliva or mucus in coughing or sneezing is called droplet transmission.
8. Transmission by a medium such as water, food, or air is called vehicle transmission.
9. Airborne transmission refers to pathogens carried on water droplets or dust for a distance greater than 1 meter.
10. Arthropod vectors carry pathogens from one host to another by both mechanical and biological transmission.

Nosocomial (Hospital-Acquired) Infections

1. A nosocomial infection is any infection that is acquired during the course of stay in a hospital. Health care–associated infections (HAIs) include those acquired in a setting other than a hospital.
2. About 5–15% of all hospitalized patients acquire nosocomial infections.

Microorganisms in the Hospital

3. Certain normal microbiota are often responsible for nosocomial infections when they are introduced into the body through such medical procedures as surgery and catheterization.
4. Opportunistic, drug-resistant gram-negative bacteria are the most frequent causes of nosocomial infections.

Compromised Host

5. Patients with burns, surgical wounds, and suppressed immune systems are the most susceptible to nosocomial infections.

Chain of Transmission

6. Nosocomial infections are transmitted by direct contact between staff members and patients and between patients.

7. Fomites such as catheters, syringes, and respiratory devices can transmit nosocomial infections.

Control of Nosocomial Infections

8. Aseptic techniques can prevent nosocomial infections.
9. Hospital infection control staff members are responsible for overseeing the proper cleaning, storage, and handling of equipment and supplies.

Emerging Infectious Diseases

1. New diseases and diseases with increasing incidences are called emerging infectious diseases (EIDs).
2. EIDs can result from the use of antibiotics and pesticides, climatic changes, travel, the lack of vaccinations, and improved case reporting.
3. The CDC, NIH, and WHO are responsible for surveillance and responses to emerging infectious diseases.

Epidemiology

1. The science of epidemiology is the study of the transmission, incidence, and frequency of disease.
2. Modern epidemiology began in the mid-1800s with the works of Snow, Semmelweis, and Nightingale.
3. In descriptive epidemiology, data about infected people are collected and analyzed.
4. In analytical epidemiology, a group of infected people is compared with an uninfected group.
5. In experimental epidemiology, controlled experiments designed to test hypotheses are performed.
6. Case reporting provides data on incidence and prevalence to local, state, and national health officials.
7. The Centers for Disease Control and Prevention (CDC) is the main source of epidemiological information in the United States.
8. The CDC publishes the *Morbidity and Mortality Weekly Report* to provide information on morbidity (incidence) and mortality (deaths).

Study Questions

Answers to the Review and Multiple Choice questions can be found at the end of this chapter.

Review

1. Differentiate the terms in each of the following pairs:
   a. etiology and pathogenesis
   b. infection and disease
   c. communicable disease and noncommunicable disease
2. Define *symbiosis*. Differentiate commensalism, mutualism, and parasitism, and give an example of each.
3. Indicate whether each of the following conditions is typical of subacute, chronic, or acute infections.
   a. The patient experiences a rapid onset of malaise; symptoms last 5 days.
   b. The patient experiences cough and breathing difficulty for months.
   c. The patient has no apparent symptoms and is a known carrier.

4. Of all the hospital patients with infections, one-third do not enter the hospital with an infection. How do they acquire these infections? What is the method of transmission of these infections? What is the reservoir of infection?
5. Distinguish symptoms from signs as signals of disease.
6. How can a local infection become a systemic infection?
7. Why are some organisms that constitute the normal microbiota described as commensals, whereas others are described as mutualistic?
8. Put the following in the correct order to describe the pattern of disease: period of convalescence, prodromal period, period of decline, incubation period, period of illness.
9. NAME IT This microbe is acquired by humans as infants and is essential for good health. Acquiring a closely related strain causes severe stomach cramps, bloody diarrhea, and vomiting. What is the microbe?

10. DRAW IT Using the data below, draw a graph showing the incidence of influenza during a typical year. Indicate the endemic and epidemic levels.

Month	Percentage of Physician Visits for Influenza-like Symptoms
Jan	2.33
Feb	3.21
Mar	2.68
Apr	1.47
May	0.97
Jun	0.30
Jul	0.30
Aug	0.20
Sep	0.20
Oct	1.18
Nov	1.54
Dec	2.39

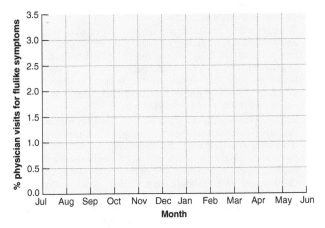

Multiple Choice

1. The emergence of new infectious diseases is probably due to all of the following *except*
   a. the need of bacteria to cause disease.
   b. the ability of humans to travel by air.
   c. changing environments (e.g., flood, drought, pollution).
   d. a pathogen crossing the species barrier.
   e. the increasing human population.

2. All members of a group of ornithologists studying barn owls in the wild have had salmonellosis (*Salmonella* gastroenteritis). One birder is experiencing her third infection. What is the most likely source of their infections?
   a. The ornithologists are eating the same food.
   b. They are contaminating their hands while handling the owls and nests.
   c. One of the workers is a *Salmonella* carrier.
   d. Their drinking water is contaminated.

3. Which of the following statements is *false*?
   a. *E. coli* never causes disease.
   b. *E. coli* provides vitamin K for its host.
   c. *E. coli* often exists in a mutualistic relationship with humans.
   d. *E. coli* gets nutrients from intestinal contents.

4. Which of the following is *not* one of Koch's postulates?
   a. The same pathogen must be present in every case of the disease.
   b. The pathogen must be isolated and grown in pure culture from the diseased host.
   c. The pathogen from pure culture must cause the disease when inoculated into a healthy, susceptible laboratory animal.
   d. The disease must be transmitted from a diseased animal to a healthy, susceptible animal by direct contact.
   e. The pathogen must be isolated in pure culture from an experimentally infected lab animal.

5. Which one of the following diseases is *not* correctly matched to its reservoir?
   a. influenza—human
   b. rabies—animal
   c. botulism—nonliving
   d. anthrax—nonliving
   e. toxoplasmosis—cats

Use the following information to answer questions 6–7.

On September 6, a 6-year-old boy experienced fever, chills, and vomiting. On September 7, he was hospitalized with diarrhea and swollen lymph nodes under both arms. On September 3, the boy had been scratched and bitten by a cat. The cat was found dead on September 5, and *Yersinia pestis* was isolated from the cat. Chloramphenicol was administered to the boy from September 7, when *Y. pestis* was isolated from him. On September 17, the boy's temperature returned to normal; and on September 22, he was released from the hospital.

6. Identify the incubation period for this case of bubonic plague.
   a. September 3–5.
   b. September 3–6.
   c. September 6–7.
   d. September 6–17.

7. Identify the prodromal period for this disease.
   a. September 3–5.
   b. September 3–6.
   c. September 6–7.
   d. September 6–17.

Use the following information to answer questions 8–10.

A Maryland woman was hospitalized with dehydration; *Vibrio cholerae* and *Plesiomonas shigelloides* were isolated from the patient. She had neither traveled outside the United States nor eaten raw shell fish during the preceding month. She had attended a party 2 days before her hospitalization. Two other people at the party had acute diarrheal illness and elevated levels of serum antibodies against *Vibrio*. Everyone at the party ate crabs and rice pudding with coconut milk. Crabs left over from this party were served at a second party. One of the 20 people at the second party had onset of mild diarrhea; specimens from 14 of these people were negative for vibriocidal antibodies.

8. This is an example of
   a. vehicle transmission.
   b. airborne transmission.
   c. transmission by fomites.
   d. direct contact transmission.
   e. nosocomial transmission.

9. The etiologic agent of the disease is
   a. *Plesiomonas shigelloides.*
   b. crabs.
   c. *Vibrio cholerae.*
   d. coconut milk.
   e. rice pudding.

10. The source of the disease was
   a. *Plesiomonas shigelloides.*
   b. crabs.
   c. *Vibrio cholerae.*
   d. coconut milk.
   e. rice pudding.

Critical Thinking

1. Ten years before Robert Koch published his work on anthrax, Anton De Bary showed that potato blight was caused by the alga *Phytophthora infestans.* Why do you suppose we use Koch's postulates instead of something called "De Bary's postulates"?

2. Florence Nightingale gathered the following data in 1855.

Population Sampled	Deaths from Contagious Diseases
Englishmen (in general population)	0.2%
English soldiers (in England)	18.7%
English soldiers (in Crimean War)	42.7%
English soldiers (in Crimean War) after Nightingale's sanitary reforms	2.2%

Discuss how Nightingale used the three basic types of epidemiological investigation. The contagious diseases were primarily cholera and typhus; how are these diseases transmitted and prevented?

3. Name the method of transmission of each of the following diseases:
   a. malaria
   b. tuberculosis
   c. nosocomial infections
   d. salmonellosis
   e. streptococcal pharyngitis
   f. mononucleosis
   g. measles
   h. hepatitis A
   i. tetanus
   j. hepatitis B
   k. chlamydial urethritis

4. The following graph shows the incidence of typhoid fever in the United States from 1954 through 2010. Mark the graph to show when this disease occurred sporadically and epidemically. What appears to be the endemic level? What would have to be shown to indicate a pandemic of this disease? How is typhoid fever transmitted?

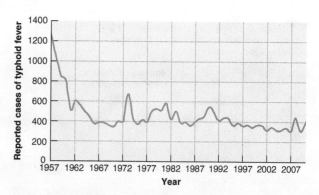

Clinical Applications

1. Three days before a nurse developed meningococcemia, she assisted with intubation of a patient with a *Neisseria meningitidis* infection. Of the 24 medical personnel involved, only this nurse became ill. The nurse recalled that she was exposed to nasopharyngeal secretions and did not receive antibiotic prophylaxis. What two mistakes did the nurse make? How is meningitis transmitted?

2. Three patients in a large hospital acquired infections of *Burkholderia cepacia* during their stay. All three patients received cryoprecipitate, which is prepared from blood that has been frozen in a standard plastic blood transfer pack. The transfer pack is then placed in a water bath to thaw. What is the probable origin of the infections? What characteristics of *Burkholderia* would allow it to be involved in this type of infection?

3. Following is a case history of a 49-year-old man. Identify each period in the pattern of disease that he experienced. On February 7, he handled a parakeet with a respiratory illness. On March 9, he experienced intense pain in his legs, followed by severe chills and headaches. On March 16, he had chest pains, cough, and diarrhea, and his temperature was 40°C. Appropriate antibiotics were administered on March 17, and his fever subsided within 12 hours. He continued taking antibiotics for 14 days. (*Note:* The disease is psittacosis. Can you find the etiology?)

4. *Mycobacterium avium-intracellulare* is prevalent in AIDS patients. In an effort to determine the source of this infection, hospital water systems were sampled. The water contained chlorine.

Percentage of Samples with *M. avium*

Hot Water		Cold Water	
February	88%	February	22%
June	50%	June	11%

What is the usual method of transmission for *Mycobacterium*? What is a probable source of infection in hospitals? How can such nosocomial infections be prevented?

Answers to Review and Multiple Choice Study Questions

Review

1. a. Etiology is the study of the cause of a disease, whereas pathogenesis is the manner in which the disease develops.

  b. Infection refers to the colonization of the body by a microorganism. Disease is any change from a state of health. A disease may, but does not always, result from infection.

  c. A communicable disease is a disease that is spread from one host to another, whereas a noncommunicable disease is not transmitted from one host to another.

2. Symbiosis refers to different organisms living together. Commensalism—one of the organisms benefits and the other is unaffected; e.g., corynebacteria living on the surface of the eye. Mutualism—both organisms benefit; e.g., *E. coli* receives nutrients and a constant temperature in the large intestine and produces vitamin K and certain B vitamins that are useful for the human host. Parasitism—one organism benefits while the other is harmed; e.g., *Salmonella enterica* receives nutrients and warmth in the large intestine, and the human host experiences gastroenteritis or typhoid fever.

3. a. Acute
  b. Chronic
  c. Subacute

4. Hospital patients may be in a weakened condition and therefore predisposed to infection. Pathogenic microorganisms are generally transmitted to patients by contact and airborne transmission. The reservoirs of infection are the hospital staff, visitors, and other patients.

5. Changes in body function that the patient feels are called *symptoms*. Symptoms such as weakness or pain are not measurable by a physician. Objective changes that the physician can observe and measure are called *signs*.

6. When microorganisms causing a local infection enter a blood or lymph vessel and are spread throughout the body, a systemic infection can result.

7. Mutualistic microorganisms are providing a chemical or environment that is essential for the host. Commensal organisms are not essential; another microorganism might serve the function as well.

8. Incubation period, prodromal period, period of illness, period of decline (may be crisis), period of convalescence.

9. *Escherichia coli*

10.

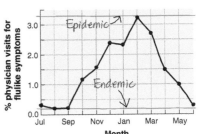

Multiple Choice

1. a	**3.** a	**5.** a	**7.** c	**9.** c
2. b	**4.** d	**6.** a	**8.** a	**10.** b

APPENDIX

Metabolic Pathways

Figure 1 **The Calvin-Benson cycle for photosynthetic carbon metabolism.**
①–③ The initial fixation and reduction of carbon occurs, generating the three-carbon compounds glyceraldehyde 3-phosphate and dihydroxyacetone phosphate, **④** which are interconvertible.
Ⓐ–Ⓓ On average, 2 of every 12 three-carbon molecules are used in the synthesis of glucose.
⑤ Ten of every 12 three-carbon molecules are used to generate ribulose 5-phosphate by a complex series of reactions.
⑥ The ribulose 5-phosphate is then phosphorylated at the expense of ATP, forming ribulose 1,5-diphosphate, the acceptor molecule with which the sequence began.

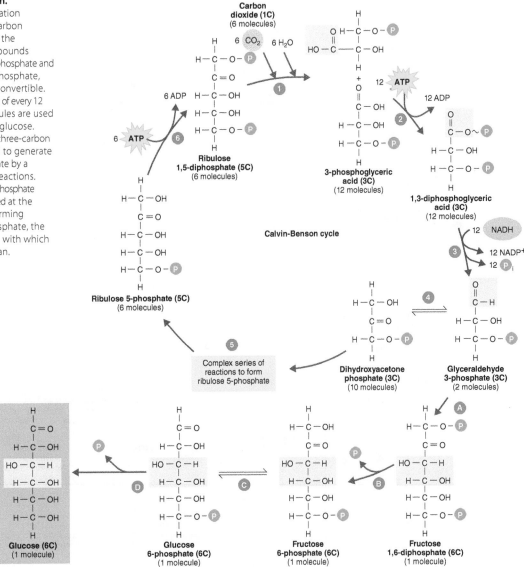

Figure 2 **Glycolysis (Embden-Meyerhof pathway).** Each of the ten steps of glycolysis is catalyzed by a specific enzyme, which is named under each step number.

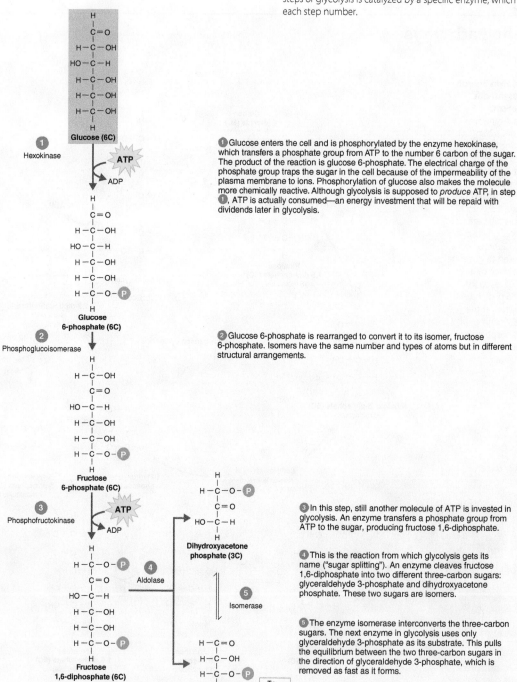

① Glucose enters the cell and is phosphorylated by the enzyme hexokinase, which transfers a phosphate group from ATP to the number 6 carbon of the sugar. The product of the reaction is glucose 6-phosphate. The electrical charge of the phosphate group traps the sugar in the cell because of the impermeability of the plasma membrane to ions. Phosphorylation of glucose also makes the molecule more chemically reactive. Although glycolysis is supposed to *produce* ATP, in step ①, ATP is actually consumed—an energy investment that will be repaid with dividends later in glycolysis.

② Glucose 6-phosphate is rearranged to convert it to its isomer, fructose 6-phosphate. Isomers have the same number and types of atoms but in different structural arrangements.

③ In this step, still another molecule of ATP is invested in glycolysis. An enzyme transfers a phosphate group from ATP to the sugar, producing fructose 1,6-diphosphate.

④ This is the reaction from which glycolysis gets its name ("sugar splitting"). An enzyme cleaves fructose 1,6-diphosphate into two different three-carbon sugars: glyceraldehyde 3-phosphate and dihydroxyacetone phosphate. These two sugars are isomers.

⑤ The enzyme isomerase interconverts the three-carbon sugars. The next enzyme in glycolysis uses only glyceraldehyde 3-phosphate as its substrate. This pulls the equilibrium between the two three-carbon sugars in the direction of glyceraldehyde 3-phosphate, which is removed as fast as it forms.

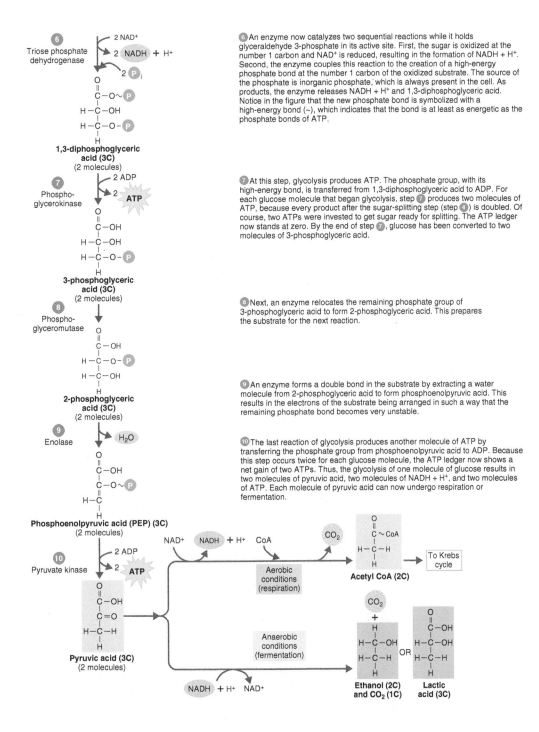

6 Triose phosphate dehydrogenase

2 NAD⁺

2 NADH + H⁺

2 Pᵢ

1,3-diphosphoglyceric acid (3C)
(2 molecules)

6 An enzyme now catalyzes two sequential reactions while it holds glyceraldehyde 3-phosphate in its active site. First, the sugar is oxidized at the number 1 carbon and NAD⁺ is reduced, resulting in the formation of NADH + H⁺. Second, the enzyme couples this reaction to the creation of a high-energy phosphate bond at the number 1 carbon of the oxidized substrate. The source of the phosphate is inorganic phosphate, which is always present in the cell. As products, the enzyme releases NADH + H⁺ and 1,3-diphosphoglyceric acid. Notice in the figure that the new phosphate bond is symbolized with a high-energy bond (~), which indicates that the bond is at least as energetic as the phosphate bonds of ATP.

7 Phospho-glycerokinase

2 ADP

2 ATP

3-phosphoglyceric acid (3C)
(2 molecules)

7 At this step, glycolysis produces ATP. The phosphate group, with its high-energy bond, is transferred from 1,3-diphosphoglyceric acid to ADP. For each glucose molecule that began glycolysis, step **7** produces two molecules of ATP, because every product after the sugar-splitting step (step **4**) is doubled. Of course, two ATPs were invested to get sugar ready for splitting. The ATP ledger now stands at zero. By the end of step **7**, glucose has been converted to two molecules of 3-phosphoglyceric acid.

8 Phospho-glyceromutase

2-phosphoglyceric acid (3C)
(2 molecules)

8 Next, an enzyme relocates the remaining phosphate group of 3-phosphoglyceric acid to form 2-phosphoglyceric acid. This prepares the substrate for the next reaction.

9 Enolase

H₂O

Phosphoenolpyruvic acid (PEP) (3C)
(2 molecules)

9 An enzyme forms a double bond in the substrate by extracting a water molecule from 2-phosphoglyceric acid to form phosphoenolpyruvic acid. This results in the electrons of the substrate being arranged in such a way that the remaining phosphate bond becomes very unstable.

10 Pyruvate kinase

2 ADP

2 ATP

10 The last reaction of glycolysis produces another molecule of ATP by transferring the phosphate group from phosphoenolpyruvic acid to ADP. Because this step occurs twice for each glucose molecule, the ATP ledger now shows a net gain of two ATPs. Thus, the glycolysis of one molecule of glucose results in two molecules of pyruvic acid, two molecules of NADH + H⁺, and two molecules of ATP. Each molecule of pyruvic acid can now undergo respiration or fermentation.

Pyruvic acid (3C)
(2 molecules)

NAD⁺ → NADH + H⁺   CoA   CO₂

Aerobic conditions (respiration)

Acetyl CoA (2C)

To Krebs cycle

Anaerobic conditions (fermentation)

NADH + H⁺ → NAD⁺

CO₂ +

Ethanol (2C) and CO₂ (1C)   OR   **Lactic acid (3C)**

Appendix

Figure 3 The pentose phosphate pathway.
This pathway, which operates simultaneously with glycolysis, provides an alternate route for the oxidation of glucose and plays a role in the synthesis of biological molecules, depending on the needs of the cell. Possible fates of the various intermediates are shown in the boxes on the right.

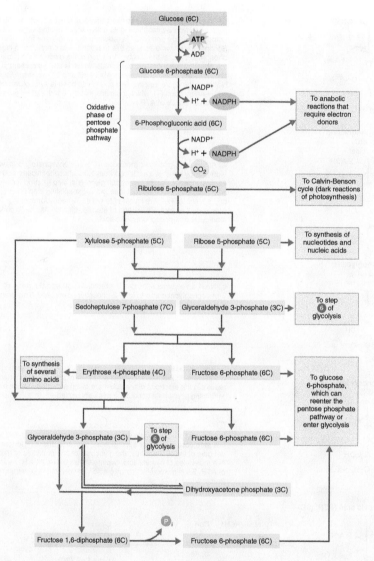

Figure 4 **The Entner-Doudoroff pathway.** This pathway is an alternate to glycolysis for the oxidation of glucose to pyruvic acid.

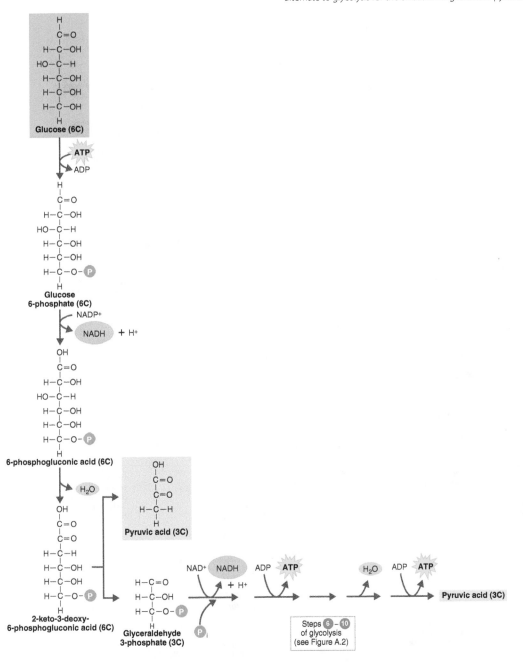

Figure 5 The Krebs cycle.

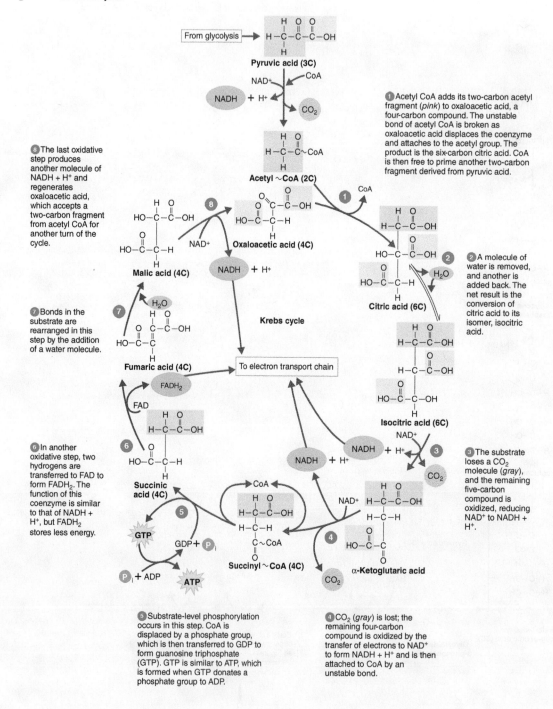

Pyruvic acid (3C)

From glycolysis

NAD⁺

NADH + H⁺

CoA

CO₂

Acetyl ~CoA (2C)

❶ Acetyl CoA adds its two-carbon acetyl fragment (*pink*) to oxaloacetic acid, a four-carbon compound. The unstable bond of acetyl CoA is broken as oxaloacetic acid displaces the coenzyme and attaches to the acetyl group. The product is the six-carbon citric acid. CoA is then free to prime another two-carbon fragment derived from pyruvic acid.

❽ The last oxidative step produces another molecule of NADH + H⁺ and regenerates oxaloacetic acid, which accepts a two-carbon fragment from acetyl CoA for another turn of the cycle.

CoA

❶

Oxaloacetic acid (4C)

NAD⁺

NADH + H⁺

Malic acid (4C)

❷ A molecule of water is removed, and another is added back. The net result is the conversion of citric acid to its isomer, isocitric acid.

H₂O

Citric acid (6C)

Krebs cycle

❼ Bonds in the substrate are rearranged in this step by the addition of a water molecule.

❼

H₂O

Fumaric acid (4C)

To electron transport chain

FADH₂

FAD

Isocitric acid (6C)

NAD⁺

NADH + H⁺

❸

CO₂

❸ The substrate loses a CO₂ molecule (*gray*), and the remaining five-carbon compound is oxidized, reducing NAD⁺ to NADH + H⁺.

❻ In another oxidative step, two hydrogens are transferred to FAD to form FADH₂. The function of this coenzyme is similar to that of NADH + H⁺, but FADH₂ stores less energy.

❻

Succinic acid (4C)

NADH + H⁺

CoA

GTP

❺

GDP + Pᵢ

Pᵢ + ADP

ATP

NAD⁺

Succinyl ~CoA (4C)

❹

CO₂

α-Ketoglutaric acid

❺ Substrate-level phosphorylation occurs in this step. CoA is displaced by a phosphate group, which is then transferred to GDP to form guanosine triphosphate (GTP). GTP is similar to ATP, which is formed when GTP donates a phosphate group to ADP.

❹ CO₂ (*gray*) is lost; the remaining four-carbon compound is oxidized by the transfer of electrons to NAD⁺ to form NADH + H⁺ and is then attached to CoA by an unstable bond.

APPENDIX

Exponents, Exponential Notation, Logarithms, and Generation Time

Exponents and Exponential Notation

Very large and very small numbers, such as 4,650,000,000 and 0.00000032, are cumbersome to work with. It is more convenient to express such numbers in exponential notation—that is, as a power of 10. For example, 4.65×10^9 is in standard exponential notation, or **scientific notation:** 4.65 is the *coefficient,* and 9 is the power or *exponent.* In standard exponential notation, the coefficient is always a number between 1 and 10, and the exponent can be positive or negative.

To change a number into exponential notation, follow two steps. First, determine the coefficient by moving the decimal point so there is only one nonzero digit to the left of it. For example,

0.0000003 2

The coefficient is 3.2. Second, determine the exponent by counting the number of places you moved the decimal point. If you moved it to the left, the exponent is positive. If you moved it to the right, the exponent is negative. In the example, you moved the decimal point seven places to the right, so the exponent is −7. Thus

$$0.00000032 = 3.2 \times 10^{-7}$$

Now suppose you are working with a larger number instead of a very small number. The same rules apply, but the exponential value will be positive rather than negative. For example,

$$4,650,000,000 = 4.65 \times 10^9$$

To multiply numbers written in exponential notation, multiply the coefficients and *add* the exponents. For example,

$$(3 \times 10^4) \times (2 \times 10^3) =$$
$$(3 \times 2) \times (10^{4+3}) = 6 \times 10^7$$

To divide, divide the coefficient and *subtract* the exponents. For example,

$$\frac{3 \times 10^4}{2 \times 10^3} = \frac{3}{2} \times 10^{4-3} = 1.5 \times 10^1$$

Microbiologists use exponential notation in many situations. For instance, exponential notation is used to describe the number of microorganisms in a population. Such numbers are often very large. Another application of exponential notation is to express concentrations of chemicals in a solution—chemicals such as media components, disinfectants, or antibiotics. Such numbers are often very small. Converting from one unit of measurement to another in the metric system requires multiplying or dividing by a power of 10, which is easiest to carry out in exponential notation.

Logarithms

A **logarithm (log)** is the power to which a base number is raised to produce a given number. Usually we work with logarithms to the base 10, abbreviated $\log_{10}$. The first step in finding the $\log_{10}$ of a number is to write the number in standard exponential notation. If the coefficient is exactly 1, the $\log_{10}$ is simply equal to the exponent. For example

$$\log_{10} 0.00001 = \log_{10} (1 \times 10^{-5})$$
$$= -5$$

If the coefficient is not 1, as is often the case, the logarithm function on a calculator must be used to determine the logarithm.

Microbiologists use logs for calculating pH levels and for graphing the growth of microbial populations in culture.

Calculating Generation Time

As a cell divides, the population increases exponentially. Numerically this is equal to 2 (because one cell divides into two) raised to the number of times the cell divided (generations);

$$2^{\text{number of generations}}$$

To calculate the final concentration of cells:

$$\text{Initial number of cells} \times 2^{\text{number of generations}} = \text{Number of cells}$$

For example, if 5 cells were allowed to divide 9 times, this would result in

$$5 \times 2^9 = 2560 \text{ cells}$$

To calculate the number of generations a culture has undergone, cell numbers must be converted to logarithms. Standard logarithm values are based on 10. The log of 2 (0.301) is used because one cell divides into two.

$$\text{Number of generations} = \frac{\text{log number of cells (end)} - \text{log number of cells (beginning)}}{0.301}$$

To calculate the generation of time for a population:

$$\frac{60 \text{ min/hr} \times \text{hours}}{\text{number of generations}} = \text{minutes/generation}$$

As an example, we will calculate the generation time if 100 bacterial cells growing for 5 hours produced 1,720,320 cells:

$$\frac{\log 1,720,320 - \log 100}{0.301} = 14 \text{ generations}$$

$$\frac{60 \text{ min/hr} \times 5 \text{ hours}}{14 \text{ generations}} = 21 \text{ minutes/generation}$$

A practical application of the calculation is determining the effect of a newly developed food preservative on the culture. Suppose 900 of the same species were grown under the same conditions as the previous example, except that the preservative was added to the culture medium. After 15 hours, there were 3,276,800 cells. Calculate the generation time, and decide whether the preservative inhibited growth.

Answer: 75 minutes/generation. The preservative did inhibit growth.

From Appendix B of *Microbiology: An Introduction*, Eleventh Edition. Gerard J. Tortora, Berdell R. Funke, Christine L. Case.

Appendix

APPENDIX

Methods for Taking Clinical Samples

To diagnose a disease, it is often necessary to obtain a sample of material that may contain the pathogenic microorganism. Samples must be taken aseptically. The sample container should be labeled with the patient's name, room number (if hospitalized), date, time, and medications being taken. Samples must be transported to the laboratory immediately for culture. Delay in transport may result in the growth of some organisms, and their toxic products may kill other organisms. Pathogens tend to be fastidious and die if not kept in optimum environmental conditions.

In the laboratory, samples from infected tissues are cultured on differential and selective media in an attempt to isolate and identify any pathogens or organisms that are not normally found in association with that tissue.

Universal Precautions*

The following procedures should be used by all health care workers, including students, whose activities involve contact with patients or with blood or other body fluids. These procedures were developed to minimize the risk of transmitting HIV or AIDS in a health care environment, but adherence to these guidelines will minimize the transmission of *all* nosocomial infections.

1. Gloves should be worn when touching blood and body fluids, mucous membranes, and nonintact skin and when handling items or surfaces soiled with blood or body fluids. Gloves should be changed after contact with each patient.
2. Hands and other skin surfaces should be washed immediately and thoroughly if contaminated with blood or other body fluids. Hands should be washed immediately after gloves are removed.
3. Masks and protective eyewear or face shields should be worn during procedures that are likely to generate droplets of blood or other body fluids.
4. Gowns or aprons should be worn during procedures that are likely to generate splashes of blood or other body fluids.
5. To prevent needlestick injuries, needles should not be recapped, purposely bent or broken, or otherwise manipulated by hand. After disposable syringes and needles, scalpel blades, and other sharp items are used, they should be placed in puncture-resistant containers for disposal.
6. Although saliva has not been implicated in HIV transmission, mouthpieces, resuscitation bags, and other ventilation devices should be available for use in areas in which the need for resuscitation is predictable. Emergency mouth-to-mouth resuscitation should be minimized.
7. Health care workers who have exudative lesions or weeping dermatitis should refrain from all direct patient care and from handling patient-care equipment.
8. Pregnant health care workers are not known to have a greater risk of contracting HIV infection than health care workers who are not pregnant; however, if a health care worker develops HIV infection during pregnancy, the infant is at risk of infection. Because of this risk, pregnant health care workers should be especially familiar with, and strictly adhere to, precautions to minimize the risk of HIV transmission.

Instructions for Specific Sampling Procedures

Wound or Abscess Culture

1. Cleanse the area with a sterile swab moistened in sterile saline.
2. Disinfect the area with 70% ethanol or iodine solution.

3. If the abscess has not ruptured spontaneously, a physician will open it with a sterile scalpel.
4. Wipe the first pus away.
5. Touch a sterile swab to the pus, taking care not to contaminate the surrounding tissue.
6. Replace the swab in its container, and properly label the container.

Ear Culture

1. Clean the skin and auditory canal with 1% tincture of iodine.
2. Touch the infected area with a sterile cotton swab.
3. Replace the swab in its container.

Eye Culture

This procedure is often performed by an ophthalmologist.
1. Anesthetize the eye with topical application of a sterile anesthetic solution.
2. Wash the eye with sterile saline solution.
3. Collect material from the infected area with a sterile cotton swab. Return the swab to its container.

Blood Culture

1. Close the room's windows to avoid contamination.
2. Clean the skin around the selected vein with 2% tincture of iodine on a cotton swab.
3. Remove dried iodine with gauze moistened with 80% isopropyl alcohol.
4. Draw a few milliliters of venous blood.
5. Aseptically bandage the puncture.

Urine Culture

1. Provide the patient with a sterile container.
2. Instruct the patient to first void a small volume from the urinary bladder before collection (to wash away extraneous bacteria of the skin microbiota) then to collect a midstream sample.
3. A urine sample may be stored under refrigeration (4–6°C) for up to 24 hours.

Fecal Culture

For bacteriological examination, only a small sample is needed. This may be obtained by inserting a sterile swab into the rectum or feces. The swab is then placed in a tube of sterile enrichment broth for transport to the laboratory. For examination for parasites, a small sample may be taken from a morning stool. The sample is placed in a preservative (polyvinyl alcohol, buffered glycerol, saline, or formalin) for microscopic examination for eggs and adult parasites.

Sputum Culture

1. A morning sample is best because microorganisms will have accumulated while the patient is sleeping.
2. The patient should rinse his or her mouth thoroughly to remove food and normal microbiota.
3. The patient should cough deeply from the lungs and expectorate into a sterile glass wide-mouth jar.
4. Care should be taken to avoid contaminating health care workers.
5. In cases such as tuberculosis in which there is little sputum, stomach aspiration may be necessary.
6. Infants and children tend to swallow sputum. A fecal sample may be of some value in these cases.

---

*Source: Centers for Disease Control and Prevention and National Institutes of Health. *Biosafety in Microbiological and Biomedical Laboratories*.

From Appendix C of *Microbiology: An Introduction*, Eleventh Edition. Gerard J. Tortora, Berdell R. Funke, Christine L. Case.

Appendix

APPENDIX

Pronunciation of Scientific Names

Rules of Pronunciation

The easiest way to learn new material is to talk about it, and that requires saying scientific names. Scientific names may look difficult at first glance, but keep in mind that generally every *syllable* is pronounced. The primary requirement in saying a scientific name is to communicate it.

The rules for the pronunciation of scientific names depend, in part, on the derivation of the root word and its vowel sounds. We have provided some general guidelines here. Pronunciations frequently do not follow the rules because a common usage has become "accepted" or the derivation of the name cannot be determined. For many scientific names there are alternative correct pronunciations.

Vowels

Pronounce all the vowels in scientific names. Two vowels written together and pronounced as one sound are called a *diphthong* (for example, the *ou* in *sound*). A special comment is needed about the pronunciation of the vowel endings *-i* and *-ae*: There are two alternative ways to pronounce each of these. We usually give the pronunciation of a long *e* (*ē*) to the *-i* ending, and a long *i* (*ī*) to the *-ae* ending. However, the reverse pronunciations are also correct and in some cases are preferred. For example, *coli* is usually pronounced kō′lī.

Consonants

When *c* or *g* is followed by *ae, e, oe, i,* or *y,* it has a soft sound. When *c* or *g* is followed by *a, o, oi,* or *u,* it has a hard sound. When a double *c* is followed by *e, i,* or *y,* it is pronounced as *ks* (e.g., *cocci*).

Accent

The accented syllable is usually the next-to-last or third-to-last syllable.

1. The accent is on the next-to-last syllable:
   a. When the name contains only two syllables. Example: pes′tis.
   b. When the next-to-last syllable is a diphthong. Example: a-kan-thä-mē′bä.
   c. When the vowel of the next-to-last syllable is long. Example: tre-pō-nē′mä. The vowel in the next-to-last syllable is long in words ending in the following suffixes:

Suffix	Example
-ales	Orders such as Eubacteriales
-ina	Sarcina
-anus,-anum	pasteurianum
-uta	diminuta

   d. When the word ends in one of the following suffixes:

Suffix	Example
-atus,-atum	caudatum
-ella	Salmonella

2. The accent is on the third-to-last syllable in family names. Families end in *-aceae*, which is always pronounced *-ā′sē-ē.*

From Appendix D of *Microbiology: An Introduction*, Eleventh Edition. Gerard J. Tortora, Berdell R. Funke, Christine L. Case.
Copyright © 2013 by Pearson Education, Inc. All rights reserved.

Pronunciation of Microorganisms in this Text

Pronunciation key:

a	hat	ē	see	o	hot	th	thin
ā	age	ė	term	ō	go	u	cup
ã	care	g	go	ô	order	ủ	put
ä	father	i	sit	oi	oil	ü	rule
ch	child	ī	ice	ou	out	û	use
e	let	ng	long	sh	she	zh	seizure

Acanthamoeba polyphaga　a-kan-thä-mē′bä pol′if-ä-gä
Acetobacter　a-sē′tō-bak-tėr
Acinetobacter baumanii　a′sin-ē-tō-bak-tėr bou′man-ē-ē
Actinomyces israelii　ak-tin-ō-mī′sēs is-rä′lē-ē
Aedes aegypti　ā′ē-dēz ē-jip′tē
A. albopictus　al-bō-pik′tus
Aeromonas hydrophilia　ãr′ō-mō-nas hī′dro-fil-ē-ä
Agrobacterium tumefaciens　ag′rō-bak-ti′rē-um tü′me-fãsh-enz
Ajellomyces capsulata　ä′jel-lō-mī-sēs kap′sü-lä-ta̱
A. dermatitidis　dėr′mä-tit-i-dis
Alcaligenes　al′kä-li-gen-ēs
Alexandrium　a′leks-an-drē-um
Aliivibrio fischeri　a′lē-ē-vib-rē-ō fish′ėr-ē
Amanita phalloides　am-an-ī′ta fal-loi′dēz
Anabaena azollae　an-ä-bē′nä ä′zō-lī
Anaplasma phagocytophilum　an′ä-plaz-mä fãg′o sī-to-fil-um
Ancylostoma duodenale　an-sil-os′tō-mä dü′o-den-al-ē
Anopheles　an-of′e-lēz
Aquaspirillum serpens　ä-kwä-spī-ril′lum sėr′penz
Arcanobacterium phocae　är′kä-nō-bak-ti-rē-um fō′sī
Arthroderma　är′thrō-dėr-mä
Ascaris lumbricoides　as′kar-is lum-bri-koi′dēz
Ashbya gossypii　ash′bē-ä gos-sip′ē-ē
Aspergillus flavus　a-spėr-jil′lus flä′vus
A. fumigatus　fü′mi-gä-tus
A. niger　nī′jer
A. rouxii　rō′ē-ē
Azolla　ā-zō′lä
Azomonas　ā-zō-mō′nas
Azospirillum　ā-zō-spī′ril-lum
Azotobacter　ä-zo′tō-bak-tėr
Babesia microti　ba-bē′sē-ä mī-krō′tē
Bacillus amyloliquefaciens　bä-sil′lus a′mil-ō-li-kwi-fa-shens
B. anthracis　an-thrä′sis
B. cereus　se′rē-us
B. circulans　sėr′ku-lans
B. coagulans　kō-ag′ū-lanz
B. licheniformis　lī-ken-i-fôr′mis
B. sphaericus　sfe′ri-kus
B. subtilis　su′til-us
B. thuringiensis　thůr-in-jē-en′sis
Bacteroides　bak-tė-roi′dēz
Balamuthia mandrillaris　bal′am-üth-ē-ä man′dril-lãr-is
Balantidium coli　bal-an-tid′ē-um kō′lī (or kō′lē)
Bartonella henselae　bär′tō-nel-lä hen′sel-ī
Baylisascaris procyonis　bä′lis-as-kar-is prō′sē-on-is
Bdellovibrio bacteriovorus　del-lō-vib′rē-ō bak-tė-rē-o′vô-rus
Beggiatoa alba　bej′jē-ä-tō-ä al′bä
Beijerinckia　bī-yė-rink′ē-ä

Bifidobacterium   bī-fĭ-dō-bak-ti′rē-um
Blastomyces dermatitidis   blas-tō-mī′sēz dėr-mä-tit′i-dis
Bordetella bronchiseptica   bron′kē-sep-ti-kä
B. pertussis   bôr′de-tel-lä pėr-tus′sis
Borrelia burgdorferi   bôr′rel-ē-ä burg-dôr′fėr-ē
Bradyrhizobium   brad-ē-rī-zō′bē-um
Brevibacterium   bre′vē-bak-ti-rē′um
Brucella abortus   brü′sel-lä ä-bôr′tus
B. melitensis   me-li-ten′sis
B. suis   sü′is
Burkholderia   bėrk′hōld-ėr-ē-ä
B. cepacia   se-pä′sē-ä
B. pseudomallei   sū-dō-mal′le-ē
Byssochlamys fulva   bis-sō-klam′is fŭl′vä
Campylobacter fetus   kam′pi-lō-bak-tėr fē′tus
C. jejuni   jē-ju′nē
Candida albicans   kan′did-ä al′bi-kanz
Capnocytophaga canimorsus   kap′no-sī-tâf-äg-ä ka′ni-môr-sus
Carsonella rudii   kar′son-el-lä ru′dē-ē
Caulobacter   kô-lō-bak′tėr
Cephalosporium   sef-ä-lō-spô′rē-um
Ceratocystis ulmi   sē-rä-tō-sis′tis ul′mē
Chilomastix   kē′lō-ma-sticks
Chlamydia trachomatis   kla-mi′dē-ä trä-kō′mä-tis
Chlamydomonas   klam-i-dō-mō′näs
Chlamydophila pneumoniae   kla-mi-do′fĭl-ä nü-mō′nē-ī
C. psittaci   sit′tä-sē
Chlorobium   klō-rō′bē-um
Chloroflexus   klō-rō-flex′us
Chromatium   krō-mä′tē-um
Chrysops   krī′sops
Citrobacter   sit′rō-bak-tėr
Claviceps purpurea   kla′vi-seps pûr-pú-rē′ä
Clonorchis sinensis   klo-nôr′kis si-nen′sis
Clostridium acetobutylicum   klôs-trī′dē-um a-sē-tō-bū-til′i-kum
C. botulinum   bo-tū-lī′num
C. difficile   dif fi-sil
C. pasteurianum   pas-tyėr-ē-ā′num
C. perfringens   pėr-frin′jens
C. sporogenes   spô-rä′jen-ēz
C. tetani   te′tan-ē
Coccidioides immitis   kok-sid-ē-oi′dēz im′mi-tis
Coniothyrium minitans   kon′ē-ō-ther-ē-um mi′ni-tanz
Corynebacterium diphtheriae   kôr′ī-nē-bak-ti-rē-um dif-thi′rē-ī
C. xerosis   ze-rō′sis
Coxiella burnetii   käks′ē-el-lä bėr-ne′tē-ē
Cryphonectria parasitica   kri-fō-nek′trē-ä par-ä-si′ti-kä
Cryptococcus gattii   krip′tō-kok-kus gat′tē-ē
C. grubii   grub′ē-ē
C. neoformans   nē-ō-fôr′manz
Cryptosporidium hominis   krip′tō-spô-ri-dē-um ho′min-is
C. parvum   pär′vum
Culex   kū′leks
Culiseta   kū-li′se-tä
Cupriavidus   kü′prē-ä-vid-us
Cyanophora paradoxa   sī′an-o-fôr-ä par′ä -docks ä
Cyclospora cayetanensis   sī′klō-spô-rä kī′ē-tan-en-sis
Cytophaga   sī′tâf-äg-ä
Deinococcus radiodurans   dē′nō-kok-kus rä′dē-ō-dür-anz
Dermacentor andersoni   dėr-mä-sen′tôr an-dėr-sôn′ē
D. variabilis   vär-ē-a′bil-is
Desulfovibrio desulfuricans   dē′sul-fō-vib-rē-ō dē-sul-fėr′i-kans
Dictyostelium   dik′tē-ō-stel-ē-um
Diphyllobothrium latum   dī-fĭl-lō-bo′thrē-um lä′tum
Dipylidium caninum   dī′pil-i-dē-um kan-i-num
Dirofilaria immitis   dī′rō-fi-lär-ē-ä im′mi-tis
Dracunculus medininsis   dra-kun′ku-lus med-in′in-sis
Echinococcus granulosus   ē-kīn-ō-kok′kus gra′nū-lō-sus
E. multilocularis   mul′tē-lok-ū-lär-is
Ectothiorhodospira mobilis   ek′tō-thī-rō-dō-spī-rä mō′bil-is
Ehrlichia chaffeensis   ėr′lik-ē-ä chaf fē-en-sis
Encephalitozoon intestinalis   en′sef-ä-lit-ō-zō-on in′tes-tin-al-is

Entamoeba coli   en-tä-mē′bä kō′lē
E. dispar   dis′par
E. histolytica   his-tō-li′ti-kä
Enterobacter aerogenes   en-te-rō-bak′tėr ā-rä′jen-ēz
E. cloacae   klō-ä′kē
Enterobius vermicularis   en-te-rō′bē-us ver-mi-kū-lar′is
Enterococcus faecalis   en-te-rō-kok′kus fē-kä′lis
E. faecium   fē′sē-um
Entomophaga   en′tō-mo-fäg-ä
Epidermophyton   ep-i-dėr-mō-fī′ton
Epulopiscium fishelsoni   ep′ū-lō-pis-sē-um fish′el-sō-nē
Erwinia amylovora   ėr-wi′nē-ä am′i-lo-vôr-ä
Erysipelothrix rhusiopathiae   är-i-si-pel′ō-thrix rus-ē-ō-path′ē-ī
Escherichia coli   esh-ė-rik′ē-ä kō′lī (or kō′lē)
Eucalyptus   ū′kal-ip-tus
Euglena   ū-glē′nä
Eunotia serra   ū′nō-tē-ä ser′rä
Filobasidiella   fi-lō-ba-si-dē-el′lä
Francisella tularensis   fran′sis-el-lä tü′lä-ren-sis
Frankia   frank′ē-ä
Fusarium   fu′sär-ē-um
Fusobacterium   fü-sō-bak-ti′rē-um
Gambierdiscus toxicus   gam′bē-ėr-dis-kus toks′i-kus
Gardnerella vaginalis   gärd-nė-rel′lä va-jin-al′is
Gemmata obscuriglobus   jem′mä-tä ob′skėr-ē-glob-us
Geobacillus stearothermophilus   gē′ō-bä-sil-lus ste-rō-thėr-mä′fil-us
Giardia duodenalis   jē-är′dē-ä dü′ō-den-al-is
G. intestinalis   in′tes-tin-al-is
G. lamblia   lam′lē-ä
Gloeocapsa   glē-ō-kap′sä
Glossina   gläs-sē′nä
Gluconacetobacter xylinus   glü′kon-a-sē-tō-bak-tėr zy′lin-us
Gluconobacter   glü′kon-ō-bak-tėr
Gracilaria   gra′sil-är-ē-ä
Gymnoascus   jim-nō-as′kus
Haemophilus aegyptius   hē-mä′fil-us e′jip-tē-us
H. ducreyi   dü-krä′ē
H. influenzae   in-flü-en′zī
Haloarcula   hä′lō-är-kü-lä
Halobacterium   ha-lō-bak-ti′rē-um
Halococcus   hä′lō-kok-kus
Helicobacter pylori   hē′lik-ō-bak-tėr pī′lô-rē
Histoplasma capsulatum   his-tō-plaz′mä kap-su-lä′tum
Homo sapiens   hō′mō sä′pē-ens
Hyphomicrobium   hī-fō-mī-krō′bē-um
Isospora   ī-so′spô-rä
Isthmia nervosa   isth′mē-ä nėr′vō-sä
Ixodes scapularis   iks-ō′dēs skap-ū-lär′is
I. pacificus   pas-i′fi-kus
Karenia brevis   kär′en-ē-ä brev′ is
Klebsiella pneumoniae   kleb-sē-el′lä nü-mō′nē-ī
Komagataella pastoris   kō′mä-gä-tä-el-kä pas′tôr-is
Lactobacillus acidophilus   lak-tō-bä-sil′lus a′sid-o-fil-us
L. delbrueckii bulgaricus   del-brúk′ē-ē bul′gä-ri-kus
L. plantarum   plan-tä′rum
L. sanfranciscensis   san-fran-si′sken-sis
Lactococcus   lak-tō-kok′kus
Laminaria japonica   lam′i-när-e-ä ja-pon′i-kä
Legionella pneumophila   lē-jä-nel′lä nü-mō′fi-lä
Leishmania braziliensis   lish′mä-nē-ä brä-sil′ē-en-sis
L. donovani   don′ō-van-ē
L. tropica   trop′i-kä
Leptospira interrogans   lep-tō-spī′rä in-tėr′rä-ganz
Leuconostoc mesenteroides   lü-kō-nos′tok mes-en-ter-oi′dēz
Limulus polyphemus   lim′ū-lus pol-if′ī-mus
Listeria monocytogenes   lis-te′rē-ä mo-nō-sī-tô′je-nēz
Macrocystis   ma′krō-sis-tis
Magnetospirillum magnetotacticum   mag-nē-tō-spī-ril-lum mag-ne-tō-tak′ti-kum
Malassezia furfur   mal′as-sēz-ē-ä fur′fur
Mannheimia haemolytica   man-hī′me-ä hē′mō-li-ti-kä
Metarrhizium   me′tär-rī-zē-um
Methanobacterium   meth′an-ō-bak-ti-rē-um

470

Methanococcus　meth′an-ō-kok-kus
Methanosarcina　meth′an-ō-sär-sī-nä
Methanothermococcus okinawensis　meth′an-ō-thêrm-ō-kok-kus ō′ki-nä-wen-sis
Methylophilus methylotrophus　meth-i-lo′fi-lus meth-i-lō-trōf′us
Microcladia　mī-krō-klād′ē-ä
Micrococcus luteus　mī-krō-kok′kus lū′tē-us
Micromonospora purpurea　mī-krō-mo-nä′spō-rä pů-pů-rē′ä
Microcystis aeruginosa　mī-krō-sis-tis ā-rü-ji-nō′sä
Microsporum　mī-krō-spō′rum
Mixotricha　mix-ō-trik′ä
Moraxella catarrhalis　mô-raks-el′lä ka-tär′al-is
M. lacunata　la-kü-nä′tä
Mucor indicus　mū′ kôr in′di-kus
Mycobacterium abscessus　mi-kō-bak-ti′rē-um ab′ses-sus
M. avium-intracellulare　ā′vē-um-in′trä-cel-ū-lä-rē
M. bovis　bō′vis
M. leprae　lep′rī
M. lepromatosis　lep′rō-mä-tō-sis
M. tuberculosis　tü-bêr-kū-lō′sis
M. ulcerans　ul′sèr-anz
Mycoplasma　mī-kō-plaz′mä
M. capricolum　kap′ri-kō-lum
M. mycoides　mī′koi-dēz
M. pneumoniae　nu-mō′nē-ī
Myxococcus fulvus　micks-ō-kok′kus ful′vus
M. xanthus　zan′thus
Naegleria fowleri　nī-gle′rē-ä fou′lèr-ē
Necator americanus　ne-kā′tôr ä-me-ri-ka′nus
Neisseria gonorrhoeae　nī-se′rē-ä go-nôr-rē′ī
N. meningitidis　me-nin-ji′ti-dis
Nitrobacter　nī-trō-bak′tèr
Nitrosomonas　nī-trō-sō-mō′näs
Nocardia　nō-kär′dē-ä
Nosema locustae　nō′sē-mä lō′kus-tē
Oocystis　ō-ō-sis′tis
Ornithodorus　ôr-nith-ō′dō-rus
Paecilomyces fumosoroseus　pī′sil-ō-mī-cēs fū′mō-sō-rō-sē-us
Paenibacillus polymixa　pi′nē-bä-sil-lus po-lē-miks′ä
Pantoea agglomerans　pan′tō-ē-ä äg′glom-ér-anz
Paracoccus denitrificans　pär-ä-kok′kus dē-nī-tri′fi-kanz
Paragonimus kellicotti　pär-ä-gōn′e-mus kel′li-kot-tē
Paramecium multimicronucleatum　pär-ä-mē′sē-um mul′tē-mī-krō-nü-clē-ä-tum
Pasteurella multocida　pas-tyèr-el′lä mul-tō′si-dä
Pediculus humanus capitis　ped-ik′ū-lus hü′ma-nus kap′i tis
P. humanus corporis　hü′ma-nus kôr′pō-ris
Pediococcus　pe-dē-ō-kok′kus
Pelagibacter ubique　pel-aj′ē-bak-tèr ū′bēk
Penicillium chrysogenum　pen-i-sil′lē-um krī-so′jen-um
P. griseofulvum　gri-sē-ō-fůl′vum
P. notatum　nō′ta-tum
Peridinium　per-i-din′ē-um
Pfiesteria　fē′ster-ē-ä
Phlebotomus　fle′bo-to-mus
Photobacterium　fō′tō-bak-ti-rē-um
Photoplepharon palpebratus　fō′tō-ble-fèr-on pal′pi-brä-tus
Physarum　fī′sär-um
Phytophthora cinnamoni　fī-tof′thô-rä cin′nä-mō-nē
P. infestans　in-fes′tans
P. ramorum　ra ′môr-um
Planctomyces　plänk′tō-mī-sēs
Plasmodium falciparum　plaz-mō′dē-um fal-sip′är-um
P. malariae　mä-lä′rē-ī
P. ovale　ō-vä′lē
P. vivax　vī′vaks
Plesiomonas shigelloides　ple-sē-ō-mō′nas shi-gel-loi′des
Pleurotus multilus　plür′ō-tus mů′til-us
Pneumocystis jirovecii　nü-mō-sis′tis ye-rō′vet-zē-ē
Porphyromonas　pôr′fi-rō-mō-nas
Prevotella intermedia　prev′ō-tel-la in′tèr-mē-dē-ä
Prochlorococcus　prō-klôr′ō-kok-kus
Propionibacterium acnes　prō-pē-on′ē-bak-ti-rē-um ak′nēz

P. freudenreichii　froi-den-rīk′ē-ē
Proteus mirabilis　prō′tē-us mi-ra′bi-lis
Pseudomonas aeruginosa　sū-dō-mō′nas ā-rü-ji-nō′sä
P. carboxydohydrogena　kär′boks-i-dō-hī-drō-je-nä
P. fluorescens　flōr-es′ens
P. putida　pü′tē-dä
P. syringae　sèr-in′jī
Pyrococcus furiosus　pī′rō-kok-kus fīr′ē-ō-sus
Pyrodictium abyssi　pī′rō-dik-tē-um a-bis′sē
Quercus　kwer′kus
Ralostonia mannitolilytica　räl′stō-nē-ä man′ni-tōl-li-li-ti-kä
Rhizobium meliloti　rī-zō′bē-um mel′li-lo-tē
Rhizopus stolonifer　rī′zō-půs stō′lon-i-fèr
Rhodococcus bronchialis　rō-dō-kok′kus bron-kē′al-is
Rhodopseudomonas　rō-dō-su-dō-mō′nas
Rhodospirillum rubrum　rō-dō-spī-ril′um rüb′rum
Ribeiroia　rī′bèr-oi-ä
Rickettsia prowazekii　ri-ket′sē-ä prou-wä-ze′kē-ē
R. rickettsii　ri-ket′sē-ē
R. typhi　tī′fē
Saccharomyces carlsbergensis　sak-ä-rō-mī′sēs kärls′bérg-en-sis
S. cerevisiae　se-ri-vis′ē-ī
S. ellipsoideus　ē′lip-soi-dē-us
S. exiguus　egz-ij′ū-us
S. uvarum　ü′vår-um
Salmonella bongori　sal′mön-el-lä bon′gôr-ē
S. enterica　en-ter′i-kä
Saprolegnia ferax　sa′prō-leg-nē-ä fe′raks
Sarcina　sär′sī-nä
Sarcoptes scabiei　sär-kop′tēs skä′bē-ē
Sargassum　sär-gas′sum
Schistosoma haemotobium　shis-tō-sō′mä (or skis-tō-sō′mä) hē′mō-tō-bē-um
S. japonicum　ja-pon′i-kum
S. mansoni　man′son-ē
Schizosaccharomyces　skiz-ō-sak-ä-rō-mī′sēs
Serratia　ser-rä′tē-ä
Shigella boydii　shi-gel′lä boi′dē-ē
S. dysenteriae　dis-en-te′rē-ī
S. flexneri　fleks′nèr-ē
S. sonnei　sōn′ne-ē
Sphaerotilus natans　sfe-rä′ti-lus nä′tans
Spirillum minus　spī′ril-lum mī′nus
S. volutans　vō′lů-tans
Spiroplasma　spī-rō-plaz′mä
Spirulina　spī-rü-lī′nä
Sporothrix schenkii　spô-rō′thriks shen′kē-ē
Stachybotrys　stak′ē-bo-tris
Staphylococcus aureus　staf′i-lō-kok′-kus ô′rē-us
S. epidermidis　e-pi-der′mi-dis
S. saprophyticus　sa′prō-fi-ti-kus
Stella　stel′lä
Stigmatella　stig′mä-tel-lä
Streptobacillus moniliformis　strep′tō-bä-sil-lus mon′il-i-fôr-mis
Streptococcus agalactiae　strep′tō-kok-kus ā′gal-act-ē-ī
S. equisimilis　e′kwi-si-mi-lis
S. mutans　mūtans
S. pneumoniae　nü-mō′nē-ī
S. pyogenes　pī-äj′en-ēz
S. salivarius　sal′vår-e-us
S. sobrinus　so′brī-nus
S. thermophilus　thèr-mo′fil-us
Streptomyces aureofaciens　strep′tō-mī′sēs ô-rē-ō-fa′si-ens
S. erythraea　ā-rith′rē-ä
S. fradiae　frä′dē-ī
S. griseus　gri′sē-us
S. nodosus　nō-dō′sus
S. venezuelae　ve-ne-zü-e′lī
Sulfolobus　sul′fō-lō-bus
Synechococcus　sin′ē-kō-kok′kus
Taenia saginata　te′nē-ä sa′ji-nä-tä

T. solium   sō'lē-um
Talaromyces   ta-lä-rŏ-mī'sēs
Taxomyces   tacks'ō-mī-sēs
Tetrahymena   tet-rä-hī'me-nä
Thermoactinomyces vulgaris   thèr-mŏ-ak-tin-ō-mī'sēs vul-ga'ris
Thermoanaerobium thermosaccharolyticum   thèr'mŏ-an-e-rŏ-bē-um thèr-mŏ-sak-kär-ō-li'ti-kum
Thermococcus litoralis   thér'mŏ-kok-kus lit'ôr-al-is
Thermoplasma   thèr-mŏ-plaz'mä
Thermotoga   thèr'mŏ-tō-gä
Thermovibrio ammonificans   thèr'mŏ-vib-rē-ō am'mŏ-ni-fi-kanz
Thermus aquaticus   thèr'mus ä'kwä-ti-kus
Thiobacillus ferrooxidans   thī-ō-bä-sil'lus fer-rŏ-oks'i-danz
T. thiooxidans   thī-ō-oks'i-danz
Thiomargarita namibiensis   thī'ō-mär-gär-ē-tä na'mi-bē-en-sis
Toxocara canis   toks'ō-kär-a kä'nis
Toxoplasma cati   toks-ō-plaz'mä kat'ē
Treponema pallidum pertenue   trep'ō-nē-mä pal'li-dum pèr'ten-ū
Tribonema vulgare   trī'bō-nē-mä vul'gär-ē
Trichinella nativa   trik-in-el'lä na'tē-vä
T. spiralis   spī-ra'lis
Trichoderma viride   trik'ō-dèr-mä vir'i-dä
Trichodesmium   trik'ō-des-mē-um
Trichomonas vaginalis   trik-ō-mōn'as va-jin-al'is
Trichonympha sphaerica   trik-ō-nimf'ä sfe'ri-kä

Trichophyton   trik-ō-fī'ton
Trichosporon   trik-ō-spôr'on
Trichuris trichiura   trik'èr-is trik-ē-yèr'a
Tridacna   trī-dak'nä
Tropheryma whipplei   trō-fer-ē'mä whip'plē-ī
Trypanosoma brucei gambiense   tri-pa'nō-sō-mä brüs'ē gam-bē-ens'
T. brucei rhodesiense   rō-dē-sē-ens'
T. cruzi   kruz'ē
Ulva   ul'vä
Ureaplasma urealyticum   ū-rē-ä-plaz'mä ū-rē-ä-lit'i-kum
Usnea   üs'nē-ä
Veillonella   vī'yo-nel-lä
Vibrio cholerae   vib'rē-ō kol'èr-ī
V. parahaemolyticus   pa-rä-hē-mō-li'ti-kus
V. vulnificus   vul'ni-fi-kus
Volvox   vol'voks
Vorticella   vòr'ti-sel-lä
Wolbachia   wol-ba'kē-ä
Xanthomonas campestris   zan'thō-mō-nas kam'pe-stris
Xenopsylla cheopis   ze-nop'sil-lä kē-ō'pis
Yersinia enterocolitica   yèr-sin'ē-ä en'tèr-ō-kōl-it-ik-ä
Y. pestis   pes'tis
Y. Pseudotuberculosis   sū'dō-tü-bèr-kū-lō-sis
Zoogloea   zō'ō-glē-ä

APPENDIX

Word Roots Used in Microbiology

The Latin rules of grammar pertain to singular and plural forms of scientific names.

	Gender		
	Feminine	Masculine	Neuter
Singular	-a	-us	-um
Plural	-ae	-i	-a
Examples	alga, algae	fungus, fungi	bacterium, bacteria

a-, an- absence, lack. Examples: abiotic, in the absence of life; anaerobic, in the absence of air.

-able able to, capable of. Example: viable, having the ability to live or exist.

actino- ray. Example: actinomycetes, bacteria that form star-shaped (with rays) colonies.

aer- air. Examples: aerobic, in the presence of air; aerate, to add air.

albo- white. Example: *Streptomyces albus* produces white colonies.

ameb- change. Example: ameboid, movement involving changing shapes.

amphi- around. Example: amphitrichous, tufts of flagella at both ends of a cell.

amyl- starch. Example: amylase, an enzyme that degrades starch.

ana- up. Example: anabolism, building up.

ant-, anti- opposed to, preventing. Example: antimicrobial, a substance that prevents microbial growth.

archae- ancient. Example: archaeobacteria, "ancient" bacteria, thought to be like the first form of life.

asco- bag. Example: ascus, a baglike structure holding spores.

aur- gold. Example: *Staphylococcus aureus*, gold-pigmented colonies.

aut-, auto- self. Example: autotroph, self-feeder.

bacillo- a little stick. Example: bacillus, rod-shaped.

basid- base, pedestal. Example: basidium, a cell that bears spores.

bdell- leech. Example: *Bdellovibrio*, a predatory bacterium.

bio- life. Example: biology, the study of life and living organisms.

blast- bud. Example: blastospore, spores formed by budding.

bovi- cattle. Example: *Mycobacterium bovis*, a bacterium found in cattle.

brevi- short. Example: *Lactobacillus brevis*, a bacterium with short cells.

butyr- butter. Example: butyric acid, formed in butter, responsible for rancid odor.

campylo- curved. Example: *Campylobacter*, curved rod.

carcin- cancer. Example: carcinogen, a cancer-causing agent.

caseo- cheese. Example: caseous, cheeselike.

caul- a stalk. Example: *Caulobacter*, appendaged or stalked bacteria.

cerato- horn. Example: keratin, the horny substance making up skin and nails.

chlamydo- covering. Example: chlamydoconidia, conidia formed inside hypha.

chloro- green. Example: chlorophyll, green-pigmented molecule.

chrom- color. Examples: chromosome, readily stained structure; metachromatic, intracellular colored granules.

chryso- golden. Example: *Streptomyces chryseus*, golden colonies.

-cide killing. Example: bactericide, an agent that kills bacteria.

cili- eyelash. Example: cilia, a hairlike organelle.

cleisto- closed. Example: cleistothecium, completely closed ascus.

co-, con- together. Example: concentric, having a common center, together in the center.

cocci- a berry. Example: coccus, a spherical cell.

coeno- shared. Example: coenocyte, a cell with many nuclei not separated by septa.

col-, colo- colon. Examples: colon, large intestine; *Escherichia coli*, a bacterium found in the large intestine.

conidio- dust. Example, conidia, spores developed at the end of aerial hypha, never enclosed.

coryne- club. Example: *Corynebacterium*, club-shaped cells.

-cul small form. Example: particle, a small part.

-cut the skin. Example: Firmicutes, bacteria with a firm cell wall, gram-positive.

cyano- blue. Example: cyanobacteria, blue-green pigmented organisms.

cyst- bladder. Example: cystitis, inflammation of the urinary bladder.

cyt- cell. Example: cytology, the study of cells.

de- undoing, reversal, loss, removal. Example: deactivation, becoming inactive.

di-, diplo- twice, double. Example: diplococci, pairs of cocci.

dia- through, between. Example: diaphragm, the wall through or between two areas.

dys- difficult, faulty, painful. Example: dysfunction, disturbed function.

ec-, ex-, ecto- out, outside, away from. Example: excrete, to remove materials from the body.

en-, em- in, inside. Example: encysted, enclosed in a cyst.

entero- intestine. Example: *Enterobacter*, a bacterium found in the intestine.

eo- dawn, early. Example: *Eobacterium*, a 3.4-billion-year-old fossilized bacterium.

epi- upon, over. Example: epidemic, number of cases of a disease over the normally expected number.

erythro- red. Example: erythema, redness of the skin.

eu- well, proper. Example: eukaryote, a proper cell.

exo- outside, outer layer. Example: exogenous, from outside the body.

extra- outside, beyond. Example: extracellular, outside the cells of an organism.

firmi- strong. Example: *Bacillus firmus* forms resistant endospores.

flagell- a whip. Example: flagellum, a projection from a cell; in eukaryotic cells, it pulls cells in a whiplike fashion.

flav- yellow. Example: *Flavobacterium* cells produce yellow pigment.

fruct- fruit. Example: fructose, fruit sugar.

-fy to make. Example: magnify, to make larger.

galacto- milk. Example: galactose, monosaccharide from milk sugar.

gamet- to marry. Example: gamete, a reproductive cell.

gastr- stomach. Example: gastritis, inflammation of the stomach.

gel- to stiffen. Example: gel, a solidified colloid.

-gen an agent that initiates. Example: pathogen, any agent that produces disease.

-genesis formation. Example: pathogenesis, production of disease.

germ, germin- bud. Example: germ, part of an organism capable of developing.

-gony reproduction. Example: schizogony, multiple fission producing many new cells.

gracili- thin. Example: *Aquaspirillum gracile*, a thin cell.

halo- salt. Example: halophile, an organism that can live in high salt concentrations.

haplo- one, single. Example: haploid, half the number of chromosomes or one set.

hema-, hemato-, hemo- blood. Example: *Haemophilus*, a bacterium that requires nutrients from red blood cells.

hepat- liver. Example: hepatitis, inflammation of the liver.

herpes creeping. Example: herpes, or shingles, lesions appear to creep along the skin.

hetero- different, other. Example: heterotroph, obtains organic nutrients from other organisms; other feeder.

hist- tissue. Example: histology, the study of tissues.

hom-, homo- same. Example: homofermenter, an organism that produces only lactic acid from fermentation of a carbohydrate.

From Appendix E of *Microbiology: An Introduction*, Eleventh Edition. Gerard J. Tortora, Berdell R. Funke, Christine L. Case.

Appendix

hydr-, hydro- water. Example: dehydration, loss of body water.

hyper- excess. Example: hypertonic, having a greater osmotic pressure in comparison with another.

hypo- below, deficient. Example: hypotonic, having a lesser osmotic pressure in comparison with another.

im- not, in. Example: impermeable, not permitting passage.

inter- between. Example: intercellular, between the cells.

intra- within, inside. Example: intracellular, inside the cell.

io- violet. Example: iodine, a chemical element that produces a violet vapor.

iso- equal, same. Example: isotonic, having the same osmotic pressure when compared with another.

-itis inflammation of. Example: colitis, inflammation of the large intestine.

-karyo, -caryo a nut. Example: eukaryote, a cell with a membrane-enclosed nucleus.

kin- movement. Example: streptokinase, an enzyme that lyses or moves fibrin.

lacti- milk. Example: lactose, the sugar in milk.

lepis- scaly. Example: leprosy, disease characterized by skin lesions.

lepto- thin. Example: *Leptospira*, thin spirochete.

leuko- whiteness. Example: leukocyte, a white blood cell.

lip-, lipo- fat, lipid. Example: lipase, an enzyme that breaks down fats.

-logy the study of. Example: pathology, the study of changes in structure and function brought on by disease.

lopho- tuft. Example: lophotrichous, having a group of flagella on one side of a cell.

luc-, luci- light. Example: luciferin, a substance in certain organisms that emits light when acted upon by the enzyme luciferase.

lute-, luteo- yellow. Example: *Micrococcus luteus*, yellow colonies.

-lysis loosening, to break down. Example: hydrolysis, chemical decomposition of a compound into other compounds as a result of taking up water.

macro- largeness. Example: macromolecules, large molecules.

mendosi- faculty. Example: mendosicutes, archaeobacteria lacking peptidoglycan.

meningo- membrane. Example: meningitis, inflammation of the membranes of the brain.

meso- middle. Example: mesophile, an organism whose optimum temperature is in the middle range.

meta- beyond, between, transition. Example: metabolism, chemical changes occurring within a living organism.

micro- smallness. Example: microscope, an instrument used to make small objects appear larger.

-mnesia memory. Examples: amnesia, loss of memory; anamnesia, return of memory.

molli- soft. Example: Mollicutes, a class of wall-less eubacteria.

-monas a unit. Example: *Methylomonas*, a unit (bacterium) that utilizes methane as its carbon source.

mono- singleness. Example: monotrichous, having one flagellum.

morpho- form. Example: morphology, the study of the form and structure of organisms.

multi- many. Example: multinuclear, having several nuclei.

mur- wall. Example: murein, a component of bacterial cell walls.

mus-, muri- mouse. Example: murine typhus, a form of typhus endemic in mice.

mut- to change. Example: mutation, a sudden change in characteristics.

myco-, -mycetoma, -myces a fungus. Example: *Saccharomyces*, sugar fungus, a genus of yeast.

myxo- slime, mucus. Example: Myxobacteriales, an order of slime-producing bacteria.

necro- a corpse. Example: necrosis, cell death or death of a portion of tissue.

-nema a thread. Example: *Treponema* has long, threadlike cells.

nigr- black. Example: *Aspergillus niger*, a fungus that produces black conidia.

ob- before, against. Example: obstruction, impeding or blocking up.

oculo- eye. Example: monocular, pertaining to one eye.

-oecium, -ecium a house. Examples: perithecium, an ascus with an opening that encloses spores; ecology, the study of the relationships among organisms and between an organism and its environment (household).

-oid like, resembling. Example: coccoid, resembling a coccus.

oligo- small, few. Example: oligiosaccharide, a carbohydrate composed of a few (7–10) monosaccharides.

-oma tumor. Example: lymphoma, a tumor of the lymphatic tissues.

-ont being, existing. Example: schizont, a cell existing as a result of schizogony.

ortho- straight, direct. Example: orthomyxovirus, a virus with a straight, tubular capsid.

-osis, -sis condition of. Examples: lysis, the condition of loosening; symbiosis, the condition of living together.

pan- all, universal. Example: pandemic, an epidemic affecting a large region.

para- beside, near. Example: parasite, an organism that "feeds beside" another.

peri- around. Example: peritrichous, projections from all sides.

phaeo- brown. Example: Phaeophyta, brown algae.

phago- eat. Example: phagocyte, a cell that engulfs and digests particles or cells.

philo-, -phil liking, preferring. Example: thermophile, an organism that prefers high temperatures.

-phore bears, carries. Example: conidiophore, a hypha that bears conidia.

-phyll leaf. Example: chlorophyll, the green pigment in leaves.

-phyte plant. Example: saprophyte, a plant that obtains nutrients from decomposing organic matter.

pil- a hair. Example: pilus, a hairlike projection from a cell.

plankto- wandering, roaming. Example: plankton, organisms drifting or wandering in water.

plast- formed. Example: plastid, a formed body within a cell.

-pnoea, -pnea breathing. Example: dyspnea, difficulty in breathing.

pod- foot. Example: pseudopod, a footlike structure.

poly- many. Example: polymorphism, many forms.

post- after, behind. Example: posterior, a place behind a (specific) part.

pre-, pro- before, ahead of. Examples: prokaryote, a cell with the first nucleus; pregnant, before birth.

pseudo- false. Example: pseudopod, false foot.

psychro- cold. Example: psychrophile, an organism that grows best at low temperatures.

-ptera wing. Example: Diptera, the order of true flies, insects with two wings.

pyo- pus. Example: pyogenic, pus-forming.

rhabdo- stick, rod. Example: rhabdovirus, an elongated, bullet-shaped virus.

rhin- nose. Example: rhinitis, inflammation of mucous membranes in the nose.

rhizo- root. Examples: *Rhizobium*, a bacterium that grows in plant roots; mycorrhiza, a fungus that grows in or on plant roots.

rhodo- red. Example: *Rhodospirillum*, a red-pigmented, spiral-shaped bacterium.

rod- gnaws. Example: rodents, the class of mammals with gnawing teeth.

rubri- red. Example: *Clostridiium rubrum*, red-pigmented colonies.

rumin- throat. Example: *Ruminococcus*, a bacterium associated with a rumen (modified esophagus).

saccharo- sugar. Example: disaccharide, a sugar consisting of two simple sugars.

sapr- rotten. Example: *Saprolegnia*, a fungus that lives on dead animals.

sarco- flesh. Example: sarcoma, a tumor of muscle or connective tissues.

schizo- split. Example: schizomycetes, organisms that reproduce by splitting and an early name for bacteria.

scolec- worm. Example: scolex, the head of a tapeworm.

-scope, -scopic watcher. Example: microscope, an instrument used to watch small things.

semi- half. Example: semicircular, having the form of half a circle.

sept- rotting. Example: septic, presence of bacteria that could cause decomposition.

septo- partition. Example: septum, a cross-wall in a fungal hypha.

serr- notched. Example: serrate, with a notched edge.

sidero- iron. Example: *Siderococcus*, a bacterium capable of oxidizing iron.

siphon- tube. Example: Siphonaptera, the order of fleas, insects with tubular mouths.

soma- body. Example: somatic cells, cells of the body other than gametes.

speci- particular things. Examples: species, the smallest group of organisms with similar properties; specify, to indicate exactly.

spiro- coil. Example: spirochete, a bacterium with a coiled cell.

sporo- spore. Example: sporangium, a structure that holds spores.

staphylo- grapelike cluster. Example: *Staphylococcus,* a bacterium that forms clusters of cells.

-stasis arrest, fixation. Example: bacteriostasis, cessation of bacterial growth.

strepto- twisted. Example: *Streptococcus,* a bacterium that forms twisted chains of cells.

sub- beneath, under. Example: subcutaneous, just under the skin.

super- above, upon. Example: superior, the quality or state of being above others.

sym-, syn- together, with. Examples: synapse, the region of communication between two neurons; synthesis, putting together.

-taxi to touch. Example: chemotaxis, response to the presence (touch) of chemicals.

taxis- orderly arrangement. Example: taxonomy, the science dealing with arranging organisms into groups.

tener- tender. Example: Tenericutes, the phylum containing wall-less eubacteria.

thallo- plant body. Example: thallus, an entire macroscopic fungus.

therm- heat. Example: *Thermus,* a bacterium that grows in hot springs (to 75°C).

thio- sulfur. Example: *Thiobacillus,* a bacterium capable of oxidizing sulfur-containing compounds.

-thrix See trich-.

-tome, -tomy to cut. Example: appendectomy, surgical removal of the appendix.

-tone, -tonic strength. Example: hypotonic, having less strength (osmotic pressure).

tox- poison. Example: antitoxin, effective against poison.

trans- across, through. Example: transport, movement of substances.

tri- three. Example: trimester, three-month period.

trich- a hair. Example: peritrichous, hairlike projections from cells.

-trope turning. Example: geotropic, turning toward the Earth (pull of gravity).

-troph food, nourishment. Example: trophic, pertaining to nutrition.

-ty condition of, state. Example: immunity, the condition of being resistant to disease or infection.

undul- wavy. Example: undulating, rising and falling, presenting a wavy appearance.

uni- one. Example: unicellular, pertaining to one cell.

vaccin- cow. Example: vaccination, injection of a vaccine (originally pertained to cows).

vacu- empty. Example: vacuoles, an intracellular space that appears empty.

vesic- bladder. Example: vesicle, a bubble.

vitr- glass. Example: in vitro, in culture media in a glass (or plastic) container.

-vorous eat. Example: carnivore, an animal that eats other animals.

xantho- yellow. Example: *Xanthomonas,* produces yellow colonies.

xeno- strange. Example: axenic, sterile, free of strange organisms.

xero- dry. Example: xerophyte, any plant that tolerates dry conditions.

xylo- wood. Example: xylose, a sugar obtained from wood.

zoo- animal. Example: zoology, the study of animals.

zygo- yoke, joining. Example: zygospore, a spore formed from the fusion of two cells.

-zyme ferment. Example: enzyme, any protein in living cells that catalyzes chemical reactions.

APPENDIX

Classification of Prokaryotes According to *Bergey's Manual**

Domain: Archaea
  Phylum Crenarchaeota
    Class: Thermoprotei
      Order: Desulfurococcales
        Family: Desulfurococcaceae
          Desulfurococcus
        Family: Pyrodictiaceae
          Pyrodictium
      Order: Sulfolobales
        Family: Sulfolobaceae
          Sulfolobus
  Phylum Euryarchaeota
    Class: Methanobacteria
      Order: Methanobacteriales
        Family: Methanobacteriaceae
          Methanobacterium
    Class: Methanococci
      Order: Methanococcales
        Family: Methaococcaceae
          Methanothermococcus
    Class: Halobacteria
      Order: Halobacteriales
        Family: Halobacteriaceae
          Haloarcula
          Halobacterium
          Halococcus
    Class: Thermoplasmata
      Order: Thermoplasmatales
        Family: Thermoplasmataceae
          Thermoplasma
    Class: Thermococci
      Order: Thermococcales
        Family: Thermococcaceae
          Pyrococcus
          Thermococcus
Domain: Bacteria
    Unclassified
      Thermovibrio
  Phylum Thermotogae
    Class: Thermotogae
      Order: Thermotogales
        Family: Thermotogaceae
          Thermotoga
  Phylum Deinococcus-Thermus
    Class: Deinococci
      Order: Deinococcales
        Family: Deinococcaceae
          Deinococcus
      Order: Thermales
          Thermus
  Phylum Chrysiogenetes
  Phylum Chloroflexi
    Class: Chloroflexi
      Order: Chloroflexales
        Family: Chloroflexaceae
          Chloroflexus
  Phylum Cyanobacteria
    Class: Cyanobacteria
      Gloeocapsa
      Prochlorococcus
      Synechococcus
      Spirulina
      Anabaena

Phylum Chlorobi
  Class: Chlorobia
    Order: Chlorobiales
      Family: Chlorobiaceae
        Chlorobium
Phylum Proteobacteria
  Class: Alphaproteobacteria
    Order: Rhodospirillales
      Family: Rhodospirillaceae
        Azospirillum
        Magnetospirillum
        Rhodospirillum
      Family: Acetobacteraceae
        Acetobacter
        Gluconacetobacter
        Gluconobacter
        Stella
    Order: Rickettsiales
      Family: Rickettsiaceae
        Rickettsia
      Family: *Anaplasmataceae*
        Anaplasma
        Ehrlichia
        Wolbachia
      Unclassified
        Pelagibacter
    Order: Rhodobacterales
      Family: Rhodobacteraceae
        Paracoccus
    Order: Caulobacterales
      Family: Caulobacteraceae
        Caulobacter
    Order: Rhizobiales
      Family: Rhizobiaceae
        Agrobacterium
        Rhizobium
      Family: Bartonellaceae
        Bartonella
      Family: Brucellaceae
        Brucella
      Family: Beijerinckiaceae
        Beijerinckia
      Family: Bradyrhizobiaceae
        Bradyrhizobium
        Nitrobacter
        Rhodopseudomonas
      Family: Hyphomicrobiaceae
        Hyphomicrobium
  Class: Betaproteobacteria
    Order: Burkholderiales
      Family: Burkholderiaceae
        Burkholderia
        Cupriavidus
        Ralstonia
      Family: Alcaligenaceae
        Alcaligenes
        Bordetella
      Unclassified
        Sphaerotilus
    Order: Hydrogenophilales
      Family: Hydrogenophilaceae
        Thiobacillus

    Order: Methylophilales
      Family: Methylophilaceae
        Methylophilus
    Order: Neisseriales
      Family: Neisseriaceae
        Aquaspirillum
        Neisseria
    Order: Nitrosomonadales
      Family: Nitrosomonadaceae
        Nitrosomonas
      Family: Spirillaceae
        Spirillum
    Order: Rhodocyclales
      Family: Rhodocyclaceae
        Propionibacter
        Zoogloea
  Class: Gammaproteobacteria
    Order: Chromatiales
      Family: Chromatiaceae
        Chromatium
        Thiocapsa
      Family: Ectothiorhodospiraceae
        Ectothiorhodospira
    Order: Xanthomonadales
      Family: Xanthomonadaceae
        Xanthomonas
    Order: Thiotrichales
      Family: Thiotrichaceae
        Beggiatoa
        Thiomargarita
      Family: Francisellaceae
        Francisella
    Order: Legionellales
      Family: Legionellaceae
        Legionella
      Family: Coxiellaceae
        Coxiella
    Order: Pseudomonadales
      Family: Pseudomonadaceae
        Azomonas
        Azotobacter
        Pseudomonas
      Family: Moraxellaceae
        Acinetobacter
        Moraxella
    Order: Vibrionales
      Family: Vibrionaceae
        Aliivibrio
        Photobacterium
        Vibrio
    Order: Aeromonadales
      Family: Aeromonadaceae
        Aeromonas
    Order: Enterobacteriales
      Family: Enterobacteriaceae
        Citrobacter
        Enterobacter
        Erwinia
        Escherichia
        Klebsiella
        Pantoea
        Plesiomonas
        Proteus

Bergey's Manual of Systematic Bacteriology, 2nd ed., 5 vols. (2004), is the reference for classification. *Bergey's Manual of Determinative Bacteriology*, 9th ed. (1994), should be used for identifying culturable bacteria and archaea.

Appendix

Salmonella
Serratia
Shigella
Yersinia
Order: Pasteurellales
  Family: Pasteurellaceae
    Haemophilus
    Pasteurella
    Mannheimia
Unclassified
  Carsonella
Class: Deltaproteobacteria
  Order: Desulfovibrionales
    Family: Desulfovibrionaceae
      Desulfovibrio
  Order: Bdellovibrionales
    Family: Bdellovibrionaceae
      Bdellovibrio
  Order: Myxococcales
    Family: Myxococcaceae
      Myxococcus
Class: Epsilonproteobacteria
  Order: Campylobacterales
    Family: Campylobacteraceae
      Campylobacter
    Family: Helicobacteraceae
      Helicobacter

Phylum Firmicutes
Class: Bacilli
  Order: Bacillales
    Family: Bacillaceae
      Bacillus
      Geobacillus
    Family: Listeriaceae
      Listeria
    Family: Paenibacillaceae
      Paenibacillus
    Family: Staphylococcaceae
      Staphylococcus
    Family: Thermoactinomycetaceae
      Thermoactinomyces
  Order: Lactobacillales
    Family: Lactobacillaceae
      Lactobacillus
      Pediococcus
    Family: Leuconostocaceae
      Leuconostoc
    Family: Streptococcaceae
      Lactococcus
      Streptococcus

Class: Clostridia
  Order: Clostridiales
    Family: Clostridiaceae
      Clostridium
    Family: Peptococcaceae
      Desulfotomaculum
    Family: Veillonellaceae
      Veillonella
    Unclassified
      Epulopiscium
  Order: Thermoanaerobacteriales
    Family: Thermoanaerobacteriaceae
      Thermoanaerobacterium

Phylum Tenericutes
Order: Mycoplasmatales
  Family: Mycoplasmataceae
    Mycoplasma
    Ureaplasma
Order: Entomoplasmatales
  Family: Spiroplasmataceae
    Spiroplasma
Order: Anaeroplasmatales
  Family: Erysipelotrichidae
    Erysipelothrix

Phylum Actinobacteria
Class: Actinobacteria
  Order: Actinomycetales
    Family: Actinomycetaceae
      Actinomyces
      Arcanobacterium
    Suborder: Micrococcineae
    Family: Micrococcaceae
      Micrococcus
    Family: Brevibacteriaceae
      Brevibacterium
    Family: Cellulomonadaceae
      Tropheryma
    Family: Corynebacteriaceae
      Corynebacterium
    Family: Mycobacteriaceae
      Mycobacterium
    Family: Nocardiaceae
      Nocardia
      Rhodococus
    Family: Micromonosporaceae
      Micromonospora
    Family: Streptomycetaceae
      Streptomyces
    Family: Frankiaceae
      Frankia

Order: Bifidobacteriales
  Family: Bifidobacteriaceae
    Bifidobacterium
    Gardnerella

Phylum Planctomycetes
Order: Planctomycetales
  Family: Planctomycetaceae
    Gemmata

Phylum Chlamydiae
Order: Chlamydiales
  Family: Chlamydiaceae
    Chlamydia
    Chlamydophila

Phylum Spirochaetes
Class: Spirochaetes
  Order: Spirochaetales
    Family: Spirochaetaceae
      Treponema
    Family: Leptospiraceae
      Leptospira

Phylum Bacteroidetes
Class: Bacteroidetes
  Order: Bacteroidales
    Family: Bacteroidaceae
      Bacteroides
    Family: Porphyromonadaceae
      Porphyromonas
    Family: Prevotellaceae
      Prevotella
Class: Flavobacteria
  Order: Flavobacteriales
    Family: Flavobacteriaceae
    Family: Blattabacteriaceae
      Blattabacterium
Class: Sphingobacteria
  Order: Sphingobacteriales
    Family: Flexibacteraceae
      Cytophaga

Phylum Fusobacteria
Class: Fusobacteria
  Order: Fusobacteriales
    Family: Fusobacteriaceae
      Fusobacterium
      Streptobacillus

Appendix

GLOSSARY

9 + 2 array Attachment of microtubules in eukaryotic flagella and cilia; 9 pairs of microtubules plus two microtubules.

12D treatment A sterilization process that would result in a decrease of the number of *Clostridium botulinum* endospores by 12 logarithmic cycles.

ABO blood group system The classification of red blood cells based on the presence or absence of A and B carbohydrate antigens.

abscess A localized accumulation of pus.

A-B toxin Bacterial exotoxins consisting of two polypeptides.

acellular vaccine A vaccine consisting of antigenic parts of cells.

acetyl group

$$H_3C-\overset{\overset{\displaystyle O}{\|}}{C}-$$

acid A substance that dissociates into one or more hydrogen ions (H^+) and one or more negative ions.

acid-fast stain A differential stain used to identify bacteria that are not decolorized by acid-alcohol.

acidic dye A salt in which the color is in the negative ion; used for negative staining.

acidophile A bacterium that grows below pH 4.

acquired immunodeficiency The inability, obtained during the life of an individual, to produce specific antibodies or T cells, due to drugs or disease.

activated macrophage A macrophage that has increased phagocytic ability and other functions after exposure to mediators released by T cells after stimulation by antigens.

activated sludge system A process used in secondary sewage treatment in which batches of sewage are held in highly aerated tanks; to ensure the presence of microbes efficient in degrading sewage, each batch is inoculated with portions of sludge from a precious batch.

activation energy The minimum collision energy required for a chemical reaction to occur.

active site A region on an enzyme that interacts with the substrate.

active transport Net movement of a substance across a membrane against a concentration gradient; requires the cell to expend energy.

acute disease A disease in which symptoms develop rapidly but last for only a short time.

acute-phase proteins Serum proteins whose concentration changes by at least 25% during inflammation.

adaptive immunity The ability, obtained during the life of the individual, to produce specific antibodies and T cells.

adenosarcoma Cancer of glandular epithelial tissue.

adenosine diphosphate (ADP) The substance formed when ATP is hydrolyzed and energy is released.

adenosine triphosphate (ATP) An important intracellular energy source.

adherence Attachment of a microbe or phagocyte to another's plasma membrane or other surface.

adhesin A carbohydrate-specific binding protein that projects from prokaryotic cells; used for adherence, also called a ligand.

adjuvant A substance added to a vaccine to increase its effectiveness.

aerobe An organism requiring molecular oxygen (O_2) for growth.

aerobic respiration Respiration in which the final electron acceptor in the electron transport chain is molecular oxygen (O_2).

aerotolerant anaerobe An organism that does not use molecular oxygen (O_2) but is not affected by its presence.

aflatoxin A carcinogenic toxin produced by *Aspergillus flavus*.

agar A complex polysaccharide derived from a marine alga and used as a solidifying agent in culture media.

agglutination A joining together or clumping of cells.

agranulocyte A leukocyte without visible granules in the cytoplasm; includes monocytes and lymphocytes.

alarmone A chemical signal that promotes a cell's response to environmental stress.

alcohol An organic molecule with the functional group—OH.

alcohol fermentation A catabolic process, beginning with glycolysis, that produces ethyl alcohol to reoxidize NADH.

aldehyde An organic molecule with the functional group

alga (plural: **algae**) A photosynthetic eukaryote; may be unicellular, filamentous, or multicellular but lack the tissues found in plants.

algal bloom An abundant growth of microscopic algae producing visible colonies in nature.

algin A sodium salt of mannuronic acid ($C_6H_8O_6$); found in brown algae.

allergen An antigen that evokes a hypersensitivity response.

allergy *See* hypersensitivity.

allograft A tissue graft that is not from a genetically identical donor (i.e., not from self or an identical twin).

allosteric inhibition The process in which an enzyme's activity is changed because of binding to the allosteric site.

allosteric site The site on an enzyme at which a noncompetitive inhibitor binds.

allylamines Antifungal agents that interfere with sterol synthesis.

amanitin A polypeptide toxin produced by *Amanita* spp., inhibits RNA polymerase.

Ames test A procedure using bacteria to identify potential carcinogens.

amination The addition of an amino group.

amino acid An organic acid containing an amino group and a carboxyl group. In alpha-amino acids the amino and carboxyl groups are attached to the same carbon atom called the alpha-carbon.

aminoglycoside An antibiotic consisting of amino sugars and an aminocyclitol ring; for example, streptomycin.

amino group —NH_2.

ammonification The release of ammonia from nitrogen-containing organic matter by the action of microorganisms.

amphibolic pathway A pathway that is both anabolic and catabolic.

amphitrichous Having flagella at both ends of a cell.

anabolism All synthesis reactions in a living organism; the building of complex organic molecules from simpler ones.

anaerobe An organism that does not require molecular oxygen (O_2) for growth.

anaerobic respiration Respiration in which the final electron acceptor in the electron transport chain is an inorganic molecule other than molecular oxygen (O_2); for example, a nitrate ion or CO_2.

anaerobic sludge digester Anaerobic digestion used in secondary sewage treatment.

anal pore A site in certain protozoa for elimination of waste.

analytical epidemiology Comparison of a diseased group and a healthy group to determine the cause of the disease.

anamnestic response *See* memory response.

anamorph Ascomycete fungi that have lost the ability to reproduce sexually; the asexual stage of a fungus.

anaphylaxis A hypersensitivity reaction involving IgE antibodies, mast cells, and basophils.

Angstrom (Å) A unit of measurement equal to 10^{-10} m, or 0.1 nm.

Animalia The kingdom composed of multicellular eukaryotes lacking cell walls.

anion An ion with a negative charge.

anoxygenic Not producing molecular oxygen; typical of cyclic photophosphorylation.

antagonism Active opposition; (1) When two drugs are less effective than either one alone. (2) Competition among microbes.

antibiogram   Report of antibiotic susceptibility of a bacterium.

antibiotic   An antimicrobial agent, usually produced naturally by a bacterium or fungus.

antibody   A protein produced by the body in response to an antigen, and capable of combining specifically with that antigen.

antibody-dependent cell-mediated cytotoxicity (ADCC)   The killing of antibody-coated cells by natural killer cells and leukocytes.

antibody titer   The amount of antibody in serum.

anticodon   The three nucleotides by which a tRNA recognizes an mRNA codon.

antigen   Any substance that causes antibody formation; also called immunogen.

antigen–antibody complex   The combination of an antigen with the antibody that is specific for it; the basis of immune protection and many diagnostic tests.

antigen-binding sites   A site on an antibody that binds to an antigenic determinant.

antigenic determinant   A specific region on the surface of an antigen against which antibodies are formed; also called epitope.

antigenic drift   A minor variation in the antigenic makeup of influenza viruses that occurs with time.

antigenic shift   A major genetic change in influenza viruses causing changes in H and N antigens.

antigenic variation   Changes in surface antigens that occur in a microbial population.

antigen-presenting cell (APC)   A macrophage, dendritic cell, or B cell that engulfs an antigen and presents fragments to T cells.

anti-human immune serum globulin (anti-HISG)   An antibody that reacts specifically with human antibodies.

antimetabolite   A competitive inhibitor.

antimicrobial peptide   An antibiotic that is bactericidal and has a broad spectrum of activity; *see* bacteriocin.

antisense DNA   DNA that is complementary to the DNA encoding a protein; the antisense RNA transcript will hybridize with the mRNA encoding the protein and inhibit synthesis of the protein.

antisense strand (– strand)   Viral RNA that cannot act as mRNA.

antisepsis   A chemical method for disinfection of the skin or mucous membranes; the chemical is called an antiseptic.

antiserum   A blood-derived fluid containing antibodies.

antitoxin   A specific antibody produced by the body in response to a bacterial exotoxin or its toxoid.

antiviral protein (AVP)   A protein made in response to interferon that blocks viral multiplication.

apoenzyme   The protein portion of an enzyme, which requires activation by a coenzyme.

apoptosis   The natural programmed death of a cell; the residual fragments are disposed of by phagocytosis.

aquatic microbiology   The study of microorganisms and their activities in natural waters.

arbuscule   Fungal mycelia in plant root cells.

archaea   Domain of prokaryotic cells lacking peptidoglycan; one of the three domains.

arthroconidia   An asexual fungal spore formed by fragmentation of a septate hypha.

Arthus reaction   Inflammation and necrosis at the site of injection of foreign serum, due to immune complex formation.

artificially acquired active immunity   The production of antibodies by the body in response to a vaccination.

artificially acquired passive immunity   The transfer of humoral antibodies formed by one individual to a susceptible individual, accomplished by the injection of antiserum.

artificial selection   Choosing one organism from a population to grow because of its desirable traits.

ascospore   A sexual fungal spore produced in an ascus, formed by the ascomycetes.

ascus   A saclike structure containing ascospores; found in the ascomycetes.

asepsis   The absence of contamination by unwanted organisms.

aseptic packaging   Commercial food preservation by filling sterile containers with sterile food.

aseptic surgery   Techniques used in surgery to prevent microbial contamination of the patient.

aseptic techniques   Laboratory techniques used to minimize contamination.

asexual spore   A reproductive cell produced by mitosis and cell division (eukaryotes) or binary fission (actinomycetes).

atom   The smallest unit of matter that can enter into a chemical reaction.

atomic force microscopy   *See* scanned-probe microscopy.

atomic number   The number of protons in the nucleus of an atom.

atomic weight   The total number of protons and neutrons in the nucleus of an atom.

atrichous   Bacteria that lack flagella.

attenuated vaccine   A vaccine containing live, attenuated (weakened) microorganisms.

autoclave   Equipment for sterilization by steam under pressure, usually operated at 15 psi and 121°C.

autograft   A tissue graft from one's self.

autoimmune disease   Damage to one's own organs due to action of the immune system.

autotroph   An organism that uses carbon dioxide (CO_2) as its principal carbon source. chemoautotroph, photoautotroph.

auxotroph   A mutant microorganism with a nutritional requirement that is absent in the parent.

axial filament   The structure for motility found in spirochetes; also called endoflagellum.

azole   Antifungal agents that interfere with sterol synthesis.

bacillus (plural: bacilli)   (1) Any rod-shaped bacterium. (2) When written as a genus (*Bacillus*) refers to rod-shaped, endospore-forming, facultatively anaerobic, gram-positive bacteria.

bacteremia   A condition in which there are bacteria in the blood.

bacteria   Domain of prokaryotic organisms, characterized by peptidoglycan cell walls; **bacterium** (singular) when referring to a single organism.

bacterial growth curve   A graph indicating the growth of a bacterial population over time.

bactericide   A substance capable of killing bacteria.

bacteriocin   An antimicrobial peptide produced by bacteria that kills other bacteria.

bacteriochlorophyll   A photosynthetic pigment that transfers electrons for photophosphorylation; found in anoxygenic photosynthetic bacteria.

bacteriology   The scientific study of prokaryotes, including bacteria and archaea.

bacteriophage (phage)   A virus that infects bacterial cells.

bacteriostasis   A treatment capable of inhibiting bacterial growth.

base   A substance that dissociates into one or more hydroxide ions (OH^-) and one or more positive ions.

base pairs   The arrangement of nitrogenous bases in nucleic acids based on hydrogen bonding; in DNA, base pairs are A-T and G-C; in RNA, base pairs are A-U and G-C.

base substitution   The replacement of a single base in DNA by another base, causing a mutation; also called point mutation.

basic dye   A salt in which the color is in the positive ion; used for bacterial stains.

basidiospore   A sexual fungal spore produced in a basidium, characteristic of the basidiomycetes.

basidium   A pedestal that produces basidiospores; found in the basidiomycetes.

basophil   A granulocyte (leukocyte) that readily takes up basic dye and is not phagocytic; has receptors for IgE Fc regions.

batch production   An industrial process in which cells are grown for a period of time after which the product is collected.

B cell   A type of lymphocyte; differentiates into antibody-secreting plasma cells and memory cells.

BCG vaccine   A live, attenuated strain of *Mycobacterium bovis* used to provide immunity to tuberculosis.

beer   Alcoholic beverage produced by fermentation of starch.

benthic zone   The sediment at the bottom of a body of water.

Bergey's Manual   *Bergey's Manual of Systematic Bacteriology*, the standard taxonomic reference on bacteria; also refers to *Bergey's Manual of Determinative Bacteriology*, the standard laboratory identification reference on bacteria.

β-lactam   Core structure of penicillins.

beta oxidation   The removal of two carbon units from a fatty acid to form acetyl CoA.

binary fission   Prokaryotic cell reproduction by division into two daughter cells.

binomial nomenclature   The system of having two names (genus and specific epithet) for each organism; also called scientific nomenclature.

bioaugmentation   The use of pollutant-acclimated microbes or genetically engineered microbes for bioremediation.

biochemical oxygen demand (BOD)   A measure of the biologically degradable organic matter in water.

biocide   A substance capable of killing microorganisms.

bioconversion   Changes in organic matter brought about by the growth of microorganisms.

bioenhancer   Nutrients such as nitrate and phosphate that promote microbial growth.

biofilm   A microbial community that usually forms as a slimy layer on a surface.

biofuels   Energy resources made by living organisms, usually from biomass, e.g., ethanol, methane.

biogenesis   The theory that living cells arise only from preexisting cells.

biogeochemical cycle   The recycling of chemical elements by microorganisms for use by other organisms.

bioinformatics   The science of determining the function of genes through computer-assisted analysis.

biological transmission   The transmission of a pathogen from one host to another when the pathogen reproduces in the vector.

bioluminescence   The emission of light from the electron transport chain; requires the enzyme luciferase.

biomass   Organic matter produced by living organisms and measured by weight.

bioreactor   A fermentation vessel with controls for environmental conditions, e.g., temperature and pH.

bioremediation   The use of microbes to remove an environmental pollutant.

Biosafety Level (BSL)   Safety guidelines for working with live microorganisms in a laboratory, four levels called BSL-1 through BSL-4.

biosynthetic   *See* anabolism.

biotechnology   The industrial application of microorganisms, cells, or cell components to make a useful product.

bioterrorism   Use of a living organism or its product to intimidate.

biotype   *See* biovar.

biovar   A subgroup of a serovar based on biochemical or physiological properties; also called biotype.

bioweapon   Living organism or its product used to inflict harm.

bisphenol   Phenolic that contains two phenol groups connected by a bridge.

blade   A flat leaflike structure of multicellular algae.

blastoconidium   An asexual fungal spore produced by budding from the parent cell.

blebbing   Bulging of plasma membrane as a cell dies.

blood–brain barrier   Cell membranes that allow some substances to pass from the blood to the brain but restrict others.

brightfield microscope   A microscope that uses visible light for illumination; the specimens are viewed against a white background.

broad-spectrum antibiotic   An antibiotic that is effective against a wide range of both gram-positive and gram-negative bacteria.

broth dilution test   A method of determining the minimal inhibitory concentration by using serial dilutions of an antimicrobial drug.

bubo   An enlarged lymph node caused by inflammation.

budding   (1) Asexual reproduction beginning as a protuberance from the parent cell that grows to become a daughter cell. (2) Release of an enveloped virus through the plasma membrane of an animal cell.

budding yeast   Following mitosis, a yeast cell that divides unevenly to produce a small cell (bud) from the parent cell.

buffer   A substance that tends to stabilize the pH of a solution.

bulking   A condition arising when sludge floats rather than settles in secondary sewage treatment.

bullae (singular: **bulla**)   Large serum-filled vesicles in the skin.

bursa of Fabricius   An organ in chickens responsible for maturation of the immune system.

Calvin-Benson cycle   The fixation of CO_2 into reduced organic compounds; used by autotrophs.

capnophile   A microorganism that grows best at relatively high CO_2 concentrations.

capsid   The protein coat of a virus that surrounds the nucleic acid.

capsomere   A protein subunit of a viral capsid.

capsule   An outer, viscous covering on some bacteria composed of a polysaccharide or polypeptide.

carbapenems   Antibiotics that contain a β-lactam antibiotic and cilastatin.

carbohydrate   An organic compound composed of carbon, hydrogen, and oxygen, with the hydrogen and oxygen present in a 2:1 ratio; carbohydrates include starches, sugars, and cellulose.

carbon cycle   The series of processes that converts CO_2 to organic substances and back to CO_2 in nature.

carbon fixation   The synthesis of sugars by using carbons from CO_2. *See also* Calvin-Benson cycle.

carbon skeleton   The basic chain or ring of carbon atoms in a molecule; for example,

carboxyl group

carboxysome   A prokaryotic inclusion containing ribulose 1,5-diphosphate carboxylase.

carcinogen   Any cancer-causing substance.

carrier   Organism (usually refers to humans) that harbors pathogens and transmits them to others.

casein   Milk protein.

catabolism   All decomposition reactions in a living organism; the breakdown of complex organic compounds into simpler ones.

catabolite repression   Inhibition of the metabolism of alternate carbon sources by glucose.

catalase   An enzyme that breaks down hydrogen peroxide: $2H_2O_2 \rightarrow 2H_2O + O_2$

catalyst   A substance that increases the rate of a chemical reaction but is not altered itself.

cation   A positively charged ion.

CD (cluster of differentiation)   Number assigned to an epitope on a single antigen, for example, CD4 protein, which is found on T helper cells.

cDNA (complementary DNA)   DNA made in vitro from an mRNA template.

cell culture   Eukaryotic cells grown in culture media; also called tissue culture.

cell theory   All living organisms are composed of cells and arise from preexisting cells.

cellular immunity   An immune response that involves T cells binding to antigens presented on antigen-presenting cells; T cells then differentiate into several types of effector T cells.

cellular respiration   *See* respiration.

cell wall   The outer covering of most bacterial, fungal, algal, and plant cells; in bacteria, it consists of peptidoglycan.

Centers for Disease Control and Prevention (CDC)   A branch of the U.S. Public Health Service that serves a central source of epidemiological information.

central nervous system (CNS)   The brain and the spinal cord. *See also* peripheral nervous system.

centriole   A structure consisting of nine microtubule triplets, found in eukaryotic cells.

centrosome   Region in a eukaryotic cell consisting of a pericentriolar area (protein fibers) and a pair of centrioles; involved in formation of the mitotic spindle.

cercaria   A free-swimming larva of trematodes.

CFU (colony-forming unit)   Visible bacterial colonies on solid media.

chancre   A hard sore, the center of which ulcerates.

chemical bond   An attractive force between atoms forming a molecule.

chemical element   A fundamental substance composed of atoms that have the same atomic number and behave the same way chemically.

chemical energy   The energy of a chemical reaction.

chemical reaction   The process of making or breaking bonds between atoms.

chemically defined medium A culture medium in which the exact chemical composition is known.

chemiosmosis A mechanism that uses a proton gradient across a cytoplasmic membrane to generate ATP.

chemistry The science of the interactions between atoms and molecules.

chemoautotroph An organism that uses an inorganic chemical as an energy source and CO_2 as a carbon source.

chemoheterotroph An organism that uses organic molecules as a source of carbon and energy.

chemokine A cytokine that induces, by chemotaxis, the migration of leukocytes into infected areas.

chemotaxis Movement in response to the presence of a chemical.

chemotherapy Treatment of disease with chemical substances.

chemotroph An organism that uses oxidation-reduction reactions as its primary energy source.

chimeric monoclonal antibody A genetically engineered antibody made of human constant regions and mouse variable regions.

chlamydoconidium An asexual fungal spore formed within a hypha.

chlorophyll *a* A photosynthetic pigment that transfers electrons for photophosphorylation; found in plant, algae, and cyanobacteria.

chloroplast The organelle that performs photosynthesis in photoautotrophic eukaryotes.

chlorosome Plasma membrane folds in green sulfur bacteria containing bacteriochlorophylls.

chromatin Threadlike, uncondensed DNA in an interphase eukaryotic cell.

chromatophore An infolding in the plasma membrane where bacterio-chlorophyll is located in photoautotrophic bacteria; also known as thylakoids.

chromosome The structure that carries hereditary information, chromosomes contain genes.

chronic infection An illness that develops slowly and is likely to continue or recur for long periods.

ciliary escalator Ciliated mucosal cells of the lower respiratory tract that move inhaled particulates away from the lungs.

cilium (plural: cilia) A relatively short cellular projection from some eukaryotic cells, composed of nine pairs plus two microtubules. *See* flagellum.

cis Hydrogen atoms on the same side across a double bond in a fatty acid. *See* trans.

cistern A flattened membranous sac in endoplasmic reticulum and the Golgi complex.

clade A group of organisms that share a particular common ancestor; a branch on a cladogram.

cladogram A dichotomous phylogenetic tree that branches repeatedly, suggesting the classification of organisms based on the time sequence in which evolutionary branches arose.

class A taxonomic group between phylum and order.

class switching Ability of a B cell to produce a different class of antibody against one antigen.

clonal deletion The elimination of B and T cells that react with self.

clonal selection The development of clones of B and T cells against a specific antigen.

clone A population of cells arising from a single parent cell.

clue cells Sloughed-off vaginal cells covered with *Gardnerella vaginalis*.

coagulase A bacterial enzyme that causes blood plasma to clot.

coccobacillus (plural: coccobacilli) A bacterium that is an oval rod.

coccus (plural: cocci) A spherical or ovoid bacterium.

codon A sequence of three nucleotides in mRNA that specifies the insertion of an amino acid into a polypeptide.

coenocytic hypha A fungal filament that is not divided into uninucleate cell-like units because it lacks septa.

coenzyme A nonprotein substance that is associated with and that activates an enzyme.

coenzyme A (CoA) A coenzyme that functions in decarboxylation.

coenzyme Q *See* ubiquinone.

cofactor (1) The nonprotein component of an enzyme. (2) A microorganism or molecule that acts with others to synergistically enhance or cause disease.

coliforms Aerobic or facultatively anaerobic, gram-negative, non–endospore-forming, rod-shaped bacteria that ferment lactose with acid and gas formation within 48 hours at 35°C.

collagenase An enzyme that hydrolyzes collagen.

collision theory The principle that chemical reactions occur because energy is gained as particles collide.

colony A visible mass of microbial cells arising from one cell or from a group of the same microbes.

colony hybridization The identification of a colony containing a desired gene by using a DNA probe that is complementary to that gene.

colony-stimulating factor (CSF) A substance that induces certain cells to proliferate or differentiate.

commensalism A symbiotic relationship in which two organisms live in association and one is benefited while the other is neither benefited nor harmed.

commercial sterilization A process of treating canned goods aimed at destroying the endospores of *Clostridium botulinum*.

communicable disease Any disease that can be spread from one host to another.

competence The physiological state in which a recipient cell can take and incorporate a large piece of donor DNA.

competitive exclusion Growth of some microbes prevents the growth of other microbes.

competitive inhibitor A chemical that competes with the normal substrate for the active site of an enzyme. *See also* noncompetitive inhibitor.

complement A group of serum proteins involved in phagocytosis and lysis of bacteria.

complementary DNA (cDNA) DNA made in vitro from an mRNA template.

complement fixation The process in which complement combines with an antigen–antibody complex.

complex medium A culture medium in which the exact chemical composition is not known.

complex virus A virus with a complicated structure, such as a bacteriophage.

composting A method of solid waste disposal, usually plant material, by encouraging its decomposition by microbes.

compound A substance composed of two or more different chemical elements.

compound light microscope (LM) An instrument with two sets of lenses that uses visible light as the source of illumination.

compromised host A host whose resistance to infection is impaired.

condensation reaction A chemical reaction in which a molecule of water is released; also called dehydration synthesis.

condenser A lens system located below the microscope stage that directs light rays through the specimen.

confocal microscopy A light microscope that uses fluorescent stains and laser to make two- and three-dimensional images.

congenital Refers to a condition existing at birth; may be inherited or acquired in utero.

congenital immunodeficiency The inability, due to an individual's genotype, to produce specific antibodies or T cells.

conidiophore An aerial hypha bearing conidiospores.

conidiospore *See* conidium.

conidium An asexual spore produced in a chain from a conidiophore.

conjugated monoclonal antibody *See* immunotoxin.

conjugated vaccine A vaccine consisting of the desired antigen and other proteins.

conjugation The transfer of genetic material from one cell to another involving cell-to-cell contact.

conjugative plasmid A prokaryotic plasmid that carries genes for sex pili and for transfer of the plasmid to another cell.

constitutive enzyme An enzyme that is produced continuously.

contact inhibition The cessation of animal cell movement and division as a result of contact with other cells.

contact transmission The spread of disease by direct or indirect contact or via droplets.

contagious disease A disease that is easily spread from one person to another.

continuous cell line Animal cells that can be maintained through an indefinite number of generations in vitro.

continuous flow An industrial fermentation in which cells are grown indefinitely with continual addition of nutrients and removal of waste and products.

corepressor A molecule that binds to a repressor protein, enabling the repressor to bind to an operator.

cortex The protective fungal covering of a lichen.

counterstain A second stain applied to a smear, provides contrast to the primary stain.

covalent bond A chemical bond in which the electrons of one atom are shared with another atom.

crisis The phase of a fever characterized by vasodilation and sweating.

crista (plural: cristae) Folding of the inner membrane of a mitochondrion.

crossing over The process by which a portion of one chromosome is exchanged with a portion of another chromosome.

CTL (cytotoxic T lymphocytes) An activated T_C cell; kills cells presenting endogenous antigens.

culture Microorganisms that grow and multiply in a container of culture medium.

culture medium The nutrient material prepared for growth of microorganisms in a laboratory.

curd The solid part of milk that separates from the liquid (whey) in the making of cheese, for example.

cutaneous mycosis A fungal infection of the epidermis, nails, or hair.

cuticle The outer covering of helminths.

cyanobacteria Oxygen-producing photoautotrophic prokaryotes.

cyclic AMP (cAMP) A molecule derived from ATP, in which the phosphate group has a cyclic structure; acts as a cellular messenger.

cyclic photophosphorylation The movement of an electron from chlorophyll through a series of electron acceptors and back to chlorophyll; anoxygenic; purple and green bacterial photophosphorylation.

cyst A sac with a distinct wall containing fluid or other material; also, a protective capsule of some protozoa.

cysticercus An encysted tapeworm larva.

cytochrome A protein that functions as an electron carrier in cellular respiration and photosynthesis.

cytochrome c oxidase An enzyme that oxidizes cytochrome *c*.

cytokine A small protein released from human cells that regulates the immune response; directly or indirectly may induce fever, pain, or T cell proliferation.

cytokine storm Overproduction of cytokines; can cause damage to the human body.

cytolysis The destruction of cells, resulting from damage to their cell membrane, that causes cellular contents to leak out.

cytopathic effect (CPE) A visible effect on a host cell, caused by a virus, that may result in host cell damage or death.

cytoplasm In a prokaryotic cell, everything inside the plasma membrane; in a eukaryotic cell, everything inside the plasma membrane and external to the nucleus.

cytoplasmic streaming The movement of cytoplasm in a eukaryotic cell.

cytoskeleton Microfilaments, intermediate filaments, and microtubules that provide support and movement for eukaryotic cytoplasm.

cytosol The fluid portion of cytoplasm.

cytostome The mouthlike opening in some protozoa.

cytotoxin A bacterial toxin that kills host cells or alters their functions.

darkfield microscope A microscope that has a device to scatter light from the illuminator so that the specimen appears white against a black background.

deamination The removal of an amino group from an amino acid to form ammonia. *See also* ammonification.

death phase The period of logarithmic decrease in a bacterial population; also called logarithmic decline phase.

debridement Surgical removal of necrotic tissue.

decarboxylation The removal of CO_2 from an amino acid.

decimal reduction time (DRT) The time (in minutes) required to kill 90% of a bacterial population at a given temperature; also called D value.

decolorizing agent A solution used in the process of removing a stain.

decomposition reaction A chemical reaction in which bonds are broken to produce smaller parts from a large molecule.

deep-freezing Preservation of bacterial cultures at −50°C to −95°C.

defensins Small peptide antibiotics made by human cells.

definitive host An organism that harbors the adult, sexually mature form of a parasite.

degeneracy Redundancy of the genetic code; that is, most amino acids are encoded by several codons.

degerming The removal of microorganisms in an area; also called degermation.

degranulation The release of contents of secretory granules from mast cells or basophils during anaphylaxis.

dehydration synthesis *See* condensation reaction.

dehydrogenation The loss of hydrogen atoms from a substrate.

delayed hypersensitivity Cell-mediated hypersensitivity.

denaturation A change in the molecular structure of a protein, usually making it nonfunctional.

dendritic cell A type of antigen-presenting cell characterized by long finger like extensions; found in lymphatic tissue and skin.

denitrification The reduction of nitrogen in nitrate to nitrite or nitrogen gas.

dental plaque A combination of bacterial cells, dextran, and debris adhering to the teeth.

deoxyribonucleic acid (DNA) The nucleic acid of genetic material in all cells and some viruses.

deoxyribose A five-carbon sugar contained in DNA nucleotides.

dermatomycosis A fungal infection of the skin; also known as tinea or ringworm.

dermatophyte A fungus that causes a cutaneous mycosis.

dermis The inner portion of the skin.

descriptive epidemiology The collection and analysis of all data regarding the occurrence of a disease to determine its cause.

desensitization The prevention of allergic inflammatory responses.

desiccation The removal of water.

diapedesis The process by which phagocytes move out of blood vessels.

dichotomous key An identification scheme based on successive paired questions; answering one question leads to another pair of questions, until an organism is identified.

differential interference contrast (DIC) microscope An instrument that provides a three-dimensional, magnified image.

differential medium A solid culture medium that makes it easier to distinguish colonies of the desired organism.

differential stain A stain that distinguishes objects on the basis of reactions to the staining procedure.

differential white blood cell count The number of each kind of leukocyte in a sample of 100 leukocytes.

diffusion The net movement of molecules or ions from an area of higher concentration to an area of lower concentration.

dimorphism The property of having two forms of growth. *See also* sexual dimorphism.

dioecious Referring to organisms in which organs of different sexes are located in different individuals.

diplobacilli (singular: diplobacillus) Rods that divide and remain attached in pairs.

diplococci (singular: diplococcus) Cocci that divide and remain attached in pairs.

diploid cell A cell having two sets of chromosomes; diploid is the normal state of a eukaryotic cell.

diploid cell line Eukaryotic cells grown in vitro.

direct agglutination test The use of known antibodies to identify an unknown cell-bound antigen.

direct contact transmission A method of spreading infection from one host to another through some kind of close association between the hosts.

direct FA test A fluorescent-antibody test to detect the presence of an antigen.

direct microscopic count Enumeration of cells by observation through a microscope.

disaccharide A sugar consisting of two simple sugars, or monosaccharides.

disease An abnormal state in which part or all of the body is not properly adjusted or is incapable of performing normal functions; any change from a state of health.

disinfection Any treatment used on inanimate objects to kill or inhibit the growth of microorganisms; a chemical used is called a disinfectant.

disk-diffusion method An agar-diffusion test to determine microbial susceptibility to chemotherapeutic agents; also called Kirby-Bauer test.

D-isomer Arrangement of four different atoms or groups around a carbon atom. *See* L-isomer.

dissimilation A metabolic process in which nutrients are not assimilated but are excreted as ammonia, hydrogen sulfide, and so on.

dissimilation plasmid A plasmid containing genes encoding production of enzymes that trigger the catabolism of certain unusual sugars and hydrocarbons.

dissociation The separation of a compound into positive and negative ions in solution. *See also* ionization.

disulfide bond A covalent bond that holds together two atoms of sulfur.

DNA base composition The moles-percentage of guanine plus cytosine in an organism's DNA.

DNA chip (microassay) A silica wafer that holds DNA probes; used to recognize DNA in samples being tested.

DNA fingerprinting Analysis of DNA by electrophoresis of restriction enzyme fragments of the DNA.

DNA gyrase *See* topoisomerase.

DNA ligase An enzyme that covalently bonds a carbon atom of one nucleotide with the phosphate of another nucleotide.

DNA polymerase Enzyme that synthesizes DNA by copying a DNA template.

DNA probe A short, labeled, single strand of DNA or RNA used to locate its complementary strand in a quantity of DNA.

DNA sequencing A process by which the nucleotide sequence of DNA is determined.

domain A taxonomic classification based on rRNA sequences; above the kingdom level.

donor cell A cell that gives DNA to a recipient cell during genetic recombination.

droplet transmission The transmission of infection by small liquid droplets carrying microorganisms.

DTaP vaccine A combined vaccine used to provide active immunity, containing diphtheria and tetanus toxoids and *Bordetella pertussis* cell fragments.

D value *See* decimal reduction time.

dysentery A disease characterized by frequent, watery stools containing blood and mucus.

eclipse period The time during viral multiplication when complete, infective virions are not present.

ecology The study of the interrelationships between organisms and their environment.

edema An abnormal accumulation of interstitial fluid in body parts or tissues, causing swelling.

electron A negatively charged particle in motion around the nucleus of an atom.

electron acceptor An ion that picks up an electron that has been lost from another atom.

electron donor An ion that gives up an electron to another atom.

electronic configuration The arrangement of electrons in shells or energy levels in an atom.

electron microscope A microscope that uses electrons instead of light to produce an image.

electron shell A region of an atom where electrons orbit the nucleus, corresponding to an energy level.

electron transport chain, electron transport system A series of compounds that transfer electrons from one compound to another, generating ATP by oxidative phosphorylation.

electroporation A technique by which DNA is inserted into a cell using an electrical current.

elementary body The infectious form of chlamydiae.

ELISA (enzyme-linked immunosorbent assay) A group of serological tests that use enzyme reactions as indicators.

embryonic stem cell (ESC) A cell from an embryo that has the potential to become a wide variety of specialized cell types.

emerging infectious disease (EID) A new or changing disease that is increasing or has the potential to increase in incidence in the near future.

Embden-Meyerhof pathway *See* glycolysis.

enanthem Rash on mucous membranes. *See also* exanthem.

encephalitis Infection of the brain.

encystment Formation of a cyst.

endemic disease A disease that is constantly present in a certain population.

endergonic reaction A chemical reaction that requires energy.

endocarditis Infection of the lining of the heart (endocardium).

endocytosis The process by which material is moved into a eukaryotic cell.

endoflagellum *See* axial filament.

endogenous (1) Infection caused by an opportunistic pathogen from an individual's own normal microbiota. (2) Surface antigens on human cells produced as a result of infection.

endolith An organism that lives inside rock.

endoplasmic reticulum (ER) A membranous network in eukaryotic cells connecting the plasma membrane with the nuclear membrane.

endospore A resting structure formed inside some bacteria.

endosymbiotic theory A model for the evolution of eukaryotes which states that organelles arose from prokaryotic cells living inside a host prokaryote.

endotoxic shock *See* gram-negative sepsis.

endotoxin Part of the outer portion of the cell wall (lipid A) of most gram-negative bacteria; released on destruction of the cell.

end-product inhibition *See* feedback inhibition.

energy level Potential energy of an electron in an atom. *See also* electron shell.

enrichment culture A culture medium used for preliminary isolation that favors the growth of a particular microorganism.

enteric The common name for a bacterium in the family Enterobacteriaceae.

enterotoxin An exotoxin that causes gastroenteritis, such as those produced by *Staphylococcus*, *Vibrio*, and *Escherichia*.

Entner-Doudoroff pathway An alternate pathway for the oxidation of glucose to pyruvic acid.

envelope An outer covering surrounding the capsid of some viruses.

enzyme A molecule that catalyzes biochemical reactions in a living organism, usually a protein. *See also* ribozyme.

enzyme immunoassay (EIA) *See* ELISA

enzyme-linked immunosorbent assay *See* ELISA.

enzyme–substrate complex A temporary union of an enzyme and its substrate.

eosinophil A granulocyte whose granules take up the stain eosin.

epidemic disease A disease acquired by many hosts in a given area in a short time.

epidemiology The science that studies when and where diseases occur and how they are transmitted.

epidermis The outer portion of the skin.

epitope *See* antigenic determinant.

equilibrium The point of even distribution.

equivalent treatments Different methods that have the same effect on controlling microbial growth.

ergot A toxin produced in sclerotia by the fungus *Claviceps purpurea* that causes ergotism.

ester linkage Bonding between fatty acids and glycerol in bacterial and eukaryotic phospholipids:

$$\cdots\text{C}-\text{O}-\overset{\overset{\text{O}}{\|}}{\text{C}}\cdots$$

E test An agar diffusion test to determine antibiotic sensitivity using a plastic strip impregnated with varying concentrations of an antibiotic.

ethambutol A synthetic antimicrobial agent that interferes with the synthesis of RNA.

ethanol

$$\text{H}-\overset{\overset{\text{H}}{|}}{\underset{\underset{\text{H}}{|}}{\text{C}}}-\overset{\overset{\text{H}}{|}}{\underset{\underset{\text{H}}{|}}{\text{C}}}-\text{OH}$$

ether linkage Bonding between fatty acids and glycerol in archaeal phospholipids: $\cdots\text{C}-\text{O}-\text{C}\cdots$

etiology The study of the cause of a disease.

eukarya All eukaryotes (animals, plants, fungi, and protists); members of the Domain Eukarya.

eukaryote A cell having DNA inside a distinct membrane-enclosed nucleus.

eukaryotic species A group of closely related organisms that can interbreed.

eutrophication The addition of organic matter and subsequent removal of oxygen from a body of water.

exanthem Skin rash. *See also* enanthem.

exchange reaction A chemical reaction that has both synthesis and decomposition components.

exergonic reaction A chemical reaction that releases energy.

exon A region of a eukaryotic chromosome that encodes a protein.

exotoxin A protein toxin released from living, mostly gram-positive bacterial cells.

experimental epidemiology The study of a disease using controlled experiments.

exponential growth phase *See* log phase.

extracellular polymeric substance (EPS) A glycocalyx that permits bacteria to attach to various surfaces.

extreme thermophile *See* hyperthermophile.

extremophile A microorganism that lives in environmental extremes of temperature, acidity, alkalinity, salinity, or pressure.

extremozymes Enzymes produced by extremophiles.

facilitated diffusion The movement of a substance across a plasma membrane from an area of higher concentration to an area of lower concentration, mediated by transporter proteins.

facultative anaerobe An organism that can grow with or without molecular oxygen (O_2).

facultative halophile An organism capable of growth in, but not requiring, 1–2% salt.

FAD Flavin adenine dinucleotide; a coenzyme that functions in the removal and transfer of hydrogen ions (H^+) and electrons from substrate molecules.

FAME Fatty acid methyl ester; identification of microbes by the presence of specific fatty acids.

family A taxonomic group between order and genus.

feedback inhibition Inhibition of an enzyme in a particular pathway by the accumulation of the end-product of the pathway; also called end-product inhibition.

fermentation The enzymatic degradation of carbohydrates in which the final electron acceptor is an organic molecule, ATP is synthesized by substrate-level phosphorylation, and O_2 is not required.

fermentation test Method used to determine whether a bacterium or yeast ferments a specific carbohydrate; usually performed in a peptone broth containing the carbohydrate, a pH indicator, and an inverted tube to trap gas.

fever An abnormally high body temperature.

F factor (fertility factor) A plasmid found in the donor cell in bacterial conjugation.

fibrinolysin A kinase produced by streptococci.

filtration The passage of a liquid or gas through a screenlike material; a 0.45-μm filter removes most bacteria.

fimbria (plural: fimbriae) An appendage on a bacterial cell used for attachment.

FISH Fluorescent in situ hybridization; use of rRNA probes to identify microbes without cuturing.

fission yeast Following mitosis, a yeast cell that divides evenly to produce two new cells.

fixed macrophage A macrophage that is located in a certain organ or tissue (e.g., liver, lungs, spleen, or lymph nodes); also called a histiocyte.

fixing (1) In slide preparation, the process of attaching a specimen to a slide. (2) Regarding chemical elements, combining elements so that a critical element can enter the food chain. *See also* Calvin-Benson cycle; nitrogen fixation.

flaccid paralysis Loss of muscle movement, loss of muscle tone.

flagellum (plural: flagella) A thin appendage from the surface of a cell; used for cellular locomotion; composed of flagellin in prokaryotic cells, composed of 9 + 2 microtubules in eukaryotic cells.

flaming The process of sterilizing an inoculating loop by holding it in an open flame.

flat sour spoilage Thermophilic spoilage of canned goods not accompanied by gas production.

flatworm An animal belonging to the phylum Platyhelminthes.

flavoprotein A protein containing the coenzyme flavin; functions as an electron carrier in electron transport chains.

flocculation The removal of colloidal material during water purification by adding a chemical that causes colloidal particles to coalesce.

flow cytometry A method of counting cells using a flow cytometer, which detects cells by the presence of a fluorescent tag on the cell surface.

fluid mosaic model A way of describing the dynamic arrangement of phospholipids and proteins comprising the plasma membrane.

fluke A flatworm belonging to the class Trematoda.

fluorescence The ability of a substance to give off light of one color when exposed to light of another color.

fluorescence-activated cell sorter (FACS) A modification of a flow cytometer that counts and sorts cells labeled with fluorescent antibodies.

fluorescence microscope A microscope that uses an ultraviolet light source to illuminate specimens that will fluoresce.

fluorescent-antibody (FA) technique A diagnostic tool using antibodies labeled with fluorochromes and viewed through a fluorescence microscope; also called immunofluorescence.

FMN Flavin mononucleotide; a coenzyme that functions in the transfer of electrons in the electron transport chain.

focal infection A systemic infection that began as an infection in one place.

folliculitis An infection of hair follicles, often occurring as pimples.

fomite A nonliving object that can spread infection.

forespore A structure consisting of chromosome, cytoplasm, and endospore membrane inside a bacterial cell.

frameshift mutation A mutation caused by the addition or deletion of one or more bases in DNA.

free radical A compound with an unpaired electron. *See* superoxide.

free wandering macrophage A macrophage that leaves the blood and migrates to infected tissue.

freeze-drying *See* lyophilization.

FTA-ABS test An indirect fluorescent-antibody test used to detect syphilis.

fulminating A condition that develops quickly and rapidly increases in severity.

functional group An arrangement of atoms in an organic molecule that is responsible for most of the chemical properties of that molecule.

fungus (plural: fungi) An organism that belongs to the Kingdom Fungi; a eukaryotic absorptive chemoheterotroph.

furuncle An infection of a hair follicle.

fusion The merging of plasma membranes of two different cells, resulting in one cell containing cytoplasm from both original cells.

gamete A male or female reproductive cell.

gametocyte A male or female protozoan cell.

gamma globulin The serum fraction containing immunoglobulins (antibodies); also called immune serum globulin.

gastroenteritis Inflammation of the stomach and intestine.

gas vacuole A prokaryotic inclusion for buoyancy compensation.

gel electrophoresis The separation of substances (such as serum proteins or DNA) by their rate of movement through an electrical field.

gene A segment of DNA (a sequence of nucleotides in DNA) encoding a functional product.

gene silencing A mechanism to inhibit gene expression. *See* RNAi.

gene therapy Treating a disease by replacing abnormal genes.

generalized transduction The transfer of bacterial chromosome fragments from one cell to another by a bacteriophage.

generation time The time required for a cell or population to double in number.

genetic code The mRNA codons and the amino acids they encode.

genetic engineering *See* recombinant DNA technology.

genetic recombination The process of joining pieces of DNA from different sources.

genetics The science of heredity and gene function.

genetic testing Techniques for determining which genes are in a cell's genome.

genome One complete copy of the genetic information in a cell.

genomic library A collection of cloned DNA fragments created by inserting restriction enzyme fragments in a bacterium, yeast, or phage.

genomics The study of genes and their function.

genotype The genetic makeup of an organism.

genus (plural: genera) The first name of the scientific name (binomial); the taxon between family and species.

germicide *See* biocide.

germination The process of starting to grow from a spore or endospore.

germ theory of disease   The principle that microorganisms cause disease.

global warming   Retention of solar heat by gases in the atmosphere.

globulin   The class of globular proteins that includes antibodies. *See also* immunoglobulin.

glycocalyx   A gelatinous polymer surrounding a cell.

glycolysis   The main pathway for the oxidation of glucose to pyruvic acid; also called Embden-Meyerhof pathway.

Golgi complex   An organelle involved in the secretion of certain proteins.

graft-versus-host (GVH) disease   A condition that occurs when a transplanted tissue has an immune response to the tissue recipient.

gram-negative bacteria   Bacteria that lose the crystal violet color after decolorizing by alcohol; they stain red after treatment with safranin.

gram-negative sepsis   Septic shock caused by gram-negative endotoxins.

gram-positive bacteria   Bacteria that retain the crystal violet color after decolorizing by alcohol; they stain dark purple.

gram-positive sepsis   Septic shock caused by gram-positive bacteria.

Gram stain   A differential stain that classifies bacteria into two groups, gram-positive and gram-negative.

granulocyte   A leukocyte with visible granules in the cytoplasm; includes neutrophils, basophils, and eosinophils.

granuloma   A lump of inflamed tissue containing macrophages.

granum   Stack of thylakoid membrane.

granzymes   Proteases that induce apoptosis.

green nonsulfur bacteria   Gram-negative, nonproteobacteria; anaerobic and phototrophic; use reduced organic compounds as electron donors for CO_2 fixation.

green sulfur bacteria   Gram-negative, nonproteobacteria; strictly anaerobic and phototrophic; no growth in dark; use reduced sulfur compounds as electron donors for CO_2 fixation.

group translocation   In prokaryotes, active transport in which a substance is chemically altered during transport across the plasma membrane.

gumma   A rubbery mass of tissue characteristic of tertiary syphilis.

HAART (highly active antiretroviral therapy)   A combination of drugs used to treat HIV infection.

halogen   One of the following elements: fluorine, chlorine, bromine, iodine, or astatine.

halophile   An organism that requires a high salt concentration for growth.

H antigen   Flagella antigens of enterics, identified by serological testing.

haploid cell   A eukaryotic cell or organism with one of each type of chromosome.

hapten   A substance of low molecular weight that does not cause the formation of antibodies by itself but does so when combined with a carrier molecule.

HA (hemagglutinin) spike   Antigenic projections from the outer lipid bilayer of *Influenzavirus*.

Hazard Analysis and Critical Control Point (HACCP)   System of prevention of hazards, for food safety.

health care–associated infection (HAI)   *See* nosocomial infection.

helminth   A parasitic roundworm or flatworm.

hemagglutination   The clumping of red blood cells.

hematopoietic cytokines   Cytokines that control development of hematopoietic (blood) stem cells.

hemoflagellate   A parasitic flagellate found in the circulatory system of its host.

hemolysin   An enzyme that lyses red blood cells.

herd immunity   The presence of immunity in most of a population.

hermaphroditic   Having both male and female reproductive capacities.

heterocyst   A large cell in certain cyanobacteria; the site of nitrogen fixation.

heterolactic   Describing an organism that produces lactic acid and other acids or alcohols as end-products of fermentation; e.g., *Escherichia*.

heterotroph   An organism that requires an organic carbon source; also called organotroph.

Hfr cell   A bacterial cell in which the F factor has become integrated into the chromosome; Hfr stands for high frequency of recombination.

high-efficiency particulate air (HEPA) filter   A screenlike material that removes particles larger than 0.3 μm from air.

high-temperature short-time (HTST) pasteurization   Pasteurizing at 72°C for 15 seconds.

histamine   A substance released by tissue cells that causes vasodilation, capillary permeability, and smooth muscle contraction.

histocompatibility antigen   An antigen on the surface of human cells.

histone   A protein associated with DNA in eukaryotic chromosomes.

holdfast   The branched base of an algal stipe.

holoenzyme   An enzyme consisting of an apoenzyme and a cofactor.

homolactic   Describing an organism that produces only lactic acid from fermentation; e.g., *Streptococcus*.

horizontal gene transfer   Transfer of genes between two organisms in the same generation. *See also* vertical gene transfer.

host   An organism infected by a pathogen. *See also* definitive host; intermediate host.

host range   The spectrum of species, strains, or cell types that a pathogen can infect.

hot-air sterilization   Sterilization by the use of an oven at 170°C for approximately 2 hours.

human leukocyte antigen (HLA) complex   Human cell surface antigens. *See also* major histocompatibility complex.

Human Microbiome Project   A project to characterize the microbial communities found on the human body.

humanized antibody   Human antibodies produced by genetically modified mice.

humoral immunity   Immunity produced by antibodies dissolved in body fluids, mediated by B cells; also called antibody-mediated immunity.

hyaluronidase   An enzyme secreted by certain bacteria that hydrolyzes hyaluronic acid and helps spread microorganisms from their initial site of infection.

hybridoma   A cell made by fusing an antibody-producing B cell with a cancer cell.

hydrogen bond   A bond between a hydrogen atom covalently bonded to oxygen or nitrogen and another covalently bonded oxygen or nitrogen atom.

hydrolysis   A decomposition reaction in which chemicals react with the H^+ and OH^- of a water molecule.

hydroxide OH^-; the anion that forms a base.

hydroxyl   —OH; covalently bonded to a molecule forms an alcohol.

hydroxyl radical   A toxic form of oxygen (OH·) formed in cytoplasm by ionizing radiation and aerobic respiration.

hyperacute rejection   Very rapid rejection of transplanted tissue, usually in the case of tissue from nonhuman sources.

hyperbaric chamber   An apparatus to hold materials at pressures greater than 1 atmosphere.

hypersensitivity   An altered, enhanced immune reaction leading to pathological changes; also called allergy.

hyperthermophile   An organism whose optimum growth temperature is at least 80°C; also called extreme thermophile.

hypertonic solution   A solution that has a higher concentration of solutes than an isotonic solution.

hypha   A long filament of cells in fungi or actinomycetes.

hypotonic solution   A solution that has a lower concentration of solutes than an isotonic solution.

ID$_{50}$ The number of microorganisms required to produce a demonstrable infection in 50% of the test host population.

idiophase   The period in the production curve of an industrial cell population in which secondary metabolites are produced; a period of stationary growth following the phase of rapid growth. *See also* trophophase.

IgA   The class of antibodies found in secretions.

IgD   The class of antibodies found on B cells.

IgE   The class of antibodies involved in hypersensitivities.

IgG   The most abundant class of antibodies in serum.

IgM   The first class of antibodies to appear after exposure to an antigen.

immune complex   A circulating antigen-antibody aggregate capable of fixing complement.

immune serum globulin   *See* gamma globulin.

immune surveillance   The body's immune response to cancer.

immunity   *See* adaptive immunity, innate immunity.

immunization   *See* vaccination.

immunodeficiency   The absence of an adequate immune response; may be congenital or acquired.

Glossary

immunodiffusion test   A test consisting of precipitation reactions carried out in an agar gel medium.

immunoelectrophoresis   The identification of proteins by electrophoretic separation followed by serological testing.

immunofluorescence   *See* fluorescent-antibody technique.

immunogen   *See* antigen.

immunoglobulin (Ig)   A protein (antibody) formed in response to an antigen and can react with that antigen. *See also* globulin.

immunology   The study of a host's defenses to a pathogen.

immunosuppression   Inhibition of the immune response.

immunotherapy   Making use of the immune system to attack tumor cells, either by enhancing the normal immune response or by using toxin-bearing specific antibodies. *See also* immunotoxin.

immunotoxin   An immunotherapeutic agent consisting of a poison bound to a monoclonal antibody.

inapparent infection   *See* subclinical infection.

incidence   The fraction of the population that contracts a disease during a particular period of time.

inclusion   Material held inside a cell, often consisting of reserve deposits.

inclusion body   A granule or viral particle in the cytoplasm or nucleus of some infected cells; important in the identification of viruses that cause infection.

incubation period   The time interval between the actual infection and first appearance of any signs or symptoms of disease.

indicator organism   A microorganism, such as a coliform, whose presence indicates conditions such as fecal contamination of food or water.

indirect (passive) agglutination test   An agglutination test using soluble antigens attached to latex or other small particles.

indirect contact transmission   The spread of pathogens by fomites (nonliving objects).

indirect FA test   A fluorescent-antibody test to detect the presence of specific antibodies.

inducer   A chemical or environmental stimulus that causes transcription of specific genes.

induction   The process that turns on the transcription of a gene.

infection   The growth of microorganisms in the body.

infectious disease   A disease in which pathogens invade a susceptible host and carry out at least part of their life cycle in the host.

inflammation   A host response to tissue damage characterized by redness, pain, heat, and swelling; and sometimes loss of function.

innate immunity   Host defenses that afford protection against any kind of pathogen. *See also* adaptive immunity.

inoculum   Microbes introduced into a culture medium to initiate growth.

inorganic compound   A small molecule that does not contain carbon and hydrogen.

insertion sequence (IS)   The simplest kind of transposon.

integrase   An enzyme produced by HIV that allows the integration of HIV DNA into the host cell's DNA.

interferon (IFN)   A specific group of cytokines. Alpha- and beta-IFNs are antiviral proteins produced by certain animal cells in response to a viral infection. Gamma-IFN stimulates macrophage activity.

interleukin (IL)   A chemical that causes T-cell proliferation. *See also* cytokine.

intermediate host   An organism that harbors the larval or asexual stage of a helminth or protozoan.

intoxication   A condition resulting from the ingestion of a microbially produced toxin.

intron   A region in a eukaryotic gene that does not code for a protein or mRNA.

intubation   Placing a tube into the body; tracheal intubation provides access for air to the lungs.

invasin   A surface protein produced by *Salmonella typhimurium* and *Escherichia coli* that rearranges nearby actin filaments in the cytoskeleton of a host cell.

iodophor   A complex of iodine and a detergent.

ion   A negatively or positively charged atom or group of atoms.

ionic bond   A chemical bond formed when atoms gain or lose electrons in the outer energy levels.

ionization   The separation (dissociation) of a molecule into ions.

ionizing radiation   High-energy radiation with a wavelength less than 1nm; causes ionization. X rays and gamma rays are examples.

ischemia   Localized decreased blood flow.

isograft   A tissue graft from a genetically identical source (i.e., from an identical twin).

isomer   One or two molecules with the same chemical formula but different structures.

isotonic solution   A solution in which, after immersion of a cell, osmotic pressure is equal across the cell's membrane.

isotope   A form of a chemical element in which the number of neutrons in the nucleus is different from the other forms of that element.

karyogamy   Fusion of the nuclei of two cells; occurs in the sexual stage of a fungal life cycle.

kelp   A multicellular brown alga.

keratin   A protein found in epidermis, hair, and nails.

ketolide   Semi-synthetic macrolide antibiodies; effective against macrolide resistant bacteria.

kinase   (1) An enzyme that removes a P from ATP and attaches it to another molecule. (2) A bacterial enzyme that breaks down fibrin (blood clots).

kingdom   A taxonomic classification between domain and phylum.

kinin   A substance released from tissue cells that causes vasodilation.

Kirby-Bauer test   *See* disk-diffusion method.

Koch's postulates   Criteria used to determine the causative agent of infectious diseases.

koji   A microbial fermentation on rice; usually *Aspergillus oryzae;* used to produce amylase.

Krebs cycle   A pathway that converts two-carbon compounds to CO_2, transferring electrons to NAD^+ and other carriers; also called tricarboxylic acid (TCA) cycle or critic acid cycle.

lactic acid fermentation   A catabolic process, beginning with glycolysis, that produces lactic acid to reoxidize NADH.

lagging strand   During DNA replication, the daughter strand that is synthesized discontinuously.

lag phase   The time interval in a bacterial growth curve during which there is no growth.

larva   The sexually immature stage of a helminth or arthropod.

latent disease   A disease characterized by a period of no symptoms when the pathogen is inactive.

latent infection   A condition in which a pathogen remains in the host for long periods without producing disease.

LD$_{50}$ The lethal dose for 50% of the inoculated hosts within a given period.

leading strand   During DNA replication, the daughter strand that is synthesized continuously.

lectin   Carbohydrate-binding proteins on a cell, not an antibody.

lepromin test   A skin test to determine the presence of antibodies to *Mycobacterium leprae*, the cause of leprosy.

leukocidins   Substances produced by some bacteria that can destroy neutrophils and macrophages.

leukocyte   A white blood cell.

leukotriene   A substance produced by mast cells and basophils that causes increased permeability of blood vessels and helps phagocytes attach to pathogens.

L form   Prokaryotic cells that lack a cell wall; can return to walled state.

lichen   A mutualistic relationship between a fungus and an alga or a cyanobacterium.

ligand   *See* adhesin.

light-dependent (light) reaction   The process by which light energy is used to convert ADP and phosphate to ATP. *See also* photophosphorylation.

light-independent (dark) reactions   The process by which electrons and energy from ATP are used to reduce CO_2 to sugar. *See also* Calvin-Benson cycle.

light-repair enzyme   *See* photolyase.

limnetic zone   The surface zone of an inland body of water away from the shore.

Limulus amebocyte lysate (LAL) assay   A test to detect the presence of bacterial endotoxins.

lipase   An enzyme that breaks down triglycerides into their component glycerol and fatty acids.

lipid   A non–water-soluble organic molecule, including triglycerides, phospholipids, and sterols.

lipid A   A component of the gram-negative outer membrane; endotoxin.

lipid inclusion   *See* inclusion.

lipopolysaccharide (LPS)   A molecule consisting of a lipid and a polysaccharide, forming the outer membrane of gram-negative cell walls.

L-isomer   Arrangement of four different atoms or groups around a carbon atom. *See* D-isomer.

lithotroph   *See* autotroph.

littoral zone   The region along the shore of the ocean or a large lake where there is considerable vegetation and where light penetrates to the bottom.

local infection   An infection in which pathogens are limited to a small area of the body.

localized anaphylaxis   An immediate hypersensitivity reaction that is restricted to a limited area of skin or mucous membrane; for example, hayfever, a skin rash, or asthma. *See also* systemic anaphylaxis.

logarithmic decline phase   *See* death phase.

log phase   The period of bacterial growth or logarithmic increase in cell numbers; also called exponential growth phase.

lophotrichous   Having two or more flagella at one end of a cell.

luciferase   An enzyme that accepts electrons from flavoproteins and emits a photon of light in bioluminescence.

lymphangitis   Inflammation of lymph vessels.

lymphocyte   A leukocyte involved in specific immune responses.

lyophilization   Freezing a substance and sublimating the ice in a vacuum; also called freeze-drying.

lysis   (1) Destruction of a cell by the rupture of the plasma membrane, resulting in a loss of cytoplasm. (2) In disease, a gradual period of decline.

lysogenic conversion   The acquisition of new properties by a host cell infected by a lysogenic phage.

lysogenic cycle   Stages in viral development that result in the incorporation of viral DNA into host DNA.

lysogeny   A state in which phage DNA is incorporated into the host cell without lysis.

lysosome   An organelle containing digestive enzymes.

lysozyme   An enzyme capable of hydrolyzing bacterial cell walls.

lytic cycle   A mechanism of phage multiplication that results in host cell lysis.

macrolide   An antibiotic that inhibits protein synthesis; for example, erythromycin.

macromolecule   A large organic molecule.

macrophage   A phagocytic cell; a mature monocyte. *See* fixed macrophage, free wandering macrophage.

macule   A flat, reddened skin lesion.

maculopapular   A rash with macules and papules.

magnetosome   An iron oxide inclusion, produced by some gram-negative bacteria, that acts like a magnet.

major histocompatibility complex (MHC)   The genes that code for histocompatibility antigens; also known as human leukocyte antigen (HLA) complex.

malolactic fermentation   The conversion of malic acid to lactic acid by lactic acid bacteria.

malt   Germinated barley grains containing maltose, glucose, and amylase.

malting   The germination of starchy grains resulting in glucose and maltose production.

margination   The process by which phagocytes stick to the lining of blood vessels.

mast cell   A type of cell found throughout the body that contains histamine and other substances that stimulate vasodilation.

matrix   Fluid in mitochondria.

maximum growth temperature   The highest temperature at which a species can grow.

M (microfold) cell   Cells that take up and transfer antigens to lymphocytes, on Peyer's patches.

mechanical transmission   The process by which arthropods transmit infections by carrying pathogens on their feet and other body parts.

medulla   A lichen body consisting of algae (or cyanobacteria) and fungi.

meiosis   A eukaryotic cell replication process that results in cells with half the chromosome number of the original cell.

membrane attack complex (MAC)   Complement proteins C5–C9, which together make lesions in cell membranes that lead to cell death.

membrane filter   A screenlike material with pores small enough to retain microorganisms; a 0.45-µm filter retains most bacteria.

memory cell   A long-lived B or T cell responsible for the memory, or secondary, response.

memory response   A rapid rise in antibody titer following exposure to an antigen after the primary response to that antigen; also called anamestic response or secondary response.

meningitis   Inflammation of the meninges, the three membranes covering the brain and spinal cord.

merozoite   A trophozoite of *Plasmodium* found in red blood cells or liver cells.

mesophile   An organism that grows between about 10°C and 50°C; a moderate-temperature–loving microbe.

mesosome   An irregular fold in the plasma membrane of a prokaryotic cell that is an artifact of preparation for microscopy.

messenger RNA (mRNA)   The type of RNA molecule that directs the incorporation of amino acids into proteins.

metabolic pathway   A sequence of enzymatically catalyzed reactions occurring in a cell.

metabolism   The sum of all the chemical reactions that occur in a living cell.

metabolomics   The study of small molecules in and around growing cells.

metacercaria   The encysted stage of a fluke in its final intermediate host.

metachromatic granule   A granule that stores inorganic phosphate and stains red with certain blue dyes; characteristic of *Corynebacterium diphtheriae*. Collectively known as volutin.

metagenomics   The study of the genomes of uncultured organisms by the collection and sequencing of DNA from environmental samples.

methane   The hydrocarbon CH_4, a flammable gas formed by the microbial decomposition of organic matter; natural gas.

methylase   An enzyme that attaches methyl groups ($—CH_3$) to a molecule; methylated cytosine is protected from digestion by restriction enzymes.

microaerophile   An organism that grows best in an environment with less molecular oxygen (O_2) than is normally found in air.

microarray   DNA probes attached to a glass surface, used to identify nucleotide sequences in a sample of DNA.

micrometer (µm)   A unit of measurement equal to 10^{-6}m.

microorganism   A living organism too small to be seen with the naked eye; includes bacteria, fungi, protozoa, and microscopic algae; also includes viruses.

microRNA (miRNA)   Small, single-stranded RNA that prevent translation of a complementary mRNA.

microtubule   A hollow tube made of the protein tubulin; the structural unit of eukaryotic flagella and centrioles.

microwave   Electromagnetic radiation with wavelength between 10^{-1} and 10^{-3} m.

minimal bactericidal concentration (MBC)   The lowest concentration of chemotherapeutic agent that will kill test microorganisms.

minimal inhibitory concentration (MIC)   The lowest concentration of a chemotherapeutic agent that will prevent growth of the test microorganisms.

minimum growth temperature   The lowest temperature at which a species will grow.

miracidium   The free-swimming, ciliated larva of a fluke that hatches from the egg.

missense mutation   A mutation that results in the substitution of an amino acid in a protein.

mitochondrion (plural: **mitochondria**)   An organelle containing Krebs cycle enzymes and the electron transport chain.

mitosis   A eukaryotic cell replication process in which the chromosomes are duplicated; usually followed by division of the cytoplasm of the cell.

mitosome   Eukaryotic organelle derived form degenrate mitochondria, found in *Trichomonas* and *Giardia*.

MMWR   *Morbidity and Mortality Weekly Report*; a CDC publication containing data on notifiable diseases and topics of special interest.

mole   An amount of a chemical equal to the atomic weights of all the atoms in a molecule of the chemical.

molecular biology   The science dealing with DNA and protein synthesis of living organisms.

molecular clock   An evolution timeline based on nucleotide sequences in organisms.

molecular weight   The sum of the atomic weights of all atoms making up a molecule.

molecule   A combination of atoms forming a specific chemical compound.

monoclonal antibody (Mab)   A specific antibody produced in vitro by a clone of B cells hybridized with cancerous cells.

monocyte   A leukocyte that is the precursor of a macrophage.

monoecious   Having both male and female reproductive capacities.

monomer   A small molecule that collectively combines to form polymers.

monomorphic   Having a single shape; most bacteria always present with a genetically determined shape. *See also* pleomorphic.

mononuclear phagocytic system   A system of fixed macrophages located in the spleen, liver, lymph nodes, and red bone marrow.

monosaccharide   A simple sugar consisting of 3–7 carbon atoms.

monotrichous   Having a single flagellum.

morbidity   (1) The incidence of a specific disease. (2) The condition of being diseased.

morbidity rate   The number of people affected by a disease in a given period of time in relation to the total population.

mordant   A substance added to a staining solution to make it stain more intensely.

mortality   The number of deaths from a specific notifiable disease.

mortality rate   The number of deaths resulting from a disease in a given period of time in relation to the total population.

most probable number (MPN) method   A statistical determination of the number of coliforms per 100 ml of water or 100 g of food.

motility   The ability of an organism to move by itself.

M protein   A heat- and acid-resistant protein of streptococcal cell walls and fibrils.

mucous membranes   Membranes that line body openings, including the intestinal tract, open to the exterior; also called mucosa.

mutagen   An agent in the environment that brings about mutations.

mutation   Any change in the nitrogenous base sequence of DNA.

mutation rate   The probability that a gene will mutate each time a cell divides.

mutualism   A type of symbiosis in which both organisms or populations are benefited.

mycelium   A mass of long filaments of cells that branch and intertwine, typically found in molds.

mycolic acid   Long-chained, branched fatty acids characteristic of members of the genus *Mycobacterium*.

mycology   The scientific study of fungi.

mycorrhiza   A fungus growing in symbiosis with plant roots.

mycosis   A fungal infection.

mycotoxin   A toxin produced by a fungus.

NAD⁺   A coenzyme that functions in the removal and transfer of hydrogen ion (H^+) and electrons from substrate molecules.

NADP⁺   A coenzyme similar to NAD⁺.

nanobacteria   Hypothesized bacteria well below the generally accepted lower limit diameter (about 200 nm) for bacteria.

nanometer (nm)   A unit of measurement equal to 10^{-9} m, 10^{-3} μm.

nanotechnology   Making molecular- or atomic-sized products.

NA (neuraminidase) spikes   Antigenic projections from the outer lipid bilayer of *Influenzavirus*.

natural killer (NK) cell   A lymphoid cell that destroys tumor cells and virus-infected cells.

naturally acquired active immunity   Antibody production in response to an infectious disease.

naturally acquired passive immunity   The natural transfer of humoral antibodies, for example, transplacental transfer.

natural selection   Process by which organisms with certain inherited characteristics are more likely to survive and reproduce than organisms with other characteristics.

necrosis   Tissue death.

negative (indirect) selection   The process of identifying mutations by selecting cells that do not grow using replica plating.

negative staining   A procedure that results in colorless bacteria against a stained background.

neurotoxin   An exotoxin that interferes with normal nerve impulse conduction.

neutralization   An antigen–antibody reaction that inactivates a bacterial exotoxin or virus.

neutron   An uncharged particle in the nucleus of an atom.

neutrophil   A highly phagocytic granulocyte; also called polymorphonuclear leukocyte (PMN) or polymorph.

nitrification   The oxidation of nitrogen in ammonia to produce nitrate.

nitrogen cycle   The series of processes that converts nitrogen (N_2) to organic substances and back to nitrogen in nature.

nitrogen fixation   The conversion of nitrogen (N_2) into ammonia.

nitrosamine   A carcinogen formed by the combination of nitrite and amino acids.

noncommunicable disease   A disease that is not transmitted from one person to another.

noncompetitive inhibitor   An inhibitory chemical that does not compete with the substrate for an enzyme's active site. *See also* allosteric inhibition; competitive inhibitor.

noncyclic photophosphorylation   The movement of an electron from chlorophyll to NAD⁺; plant and cyanobacterial photophosphorylation.

nonionizing radiation   Short-wavelength radiation that does not cause ionization; ultraviolet (UV) radiation is an example.

non-nucleoside reverse transcriptase inhibitor   A drug that binds with and inhibits the action of the HIV reverse transcriptase enzyme.

nonsense codon   A codon that does not encode any amino acid.

nonsense mutation   A base substitution in DNA that results in a nonsense codon.

normal microbiota   The microorganisms that colonize a host without causing disease; also called normal flora.

nosocomial infection   An infection that develops during a hospital stay and was not present at the time the patient was admitted; infection associated with any health care facility.

notifiable infectious disease   A disease that physicians must report to the U.S. Public Health Service; also called reportable disease.

nuclear envelope   The double membrane that separates the nucleus from the cytoplasm in a eukaryotic cell.

nuclear pore   An opening in the nuclear envelope through which materials enter and exit the nucleus.

nucleic acid   A macromolecule consisting of nucleotides; DNA and RNA are nucleic acids.

nucleic acid amplification test (NAAT)   Test to identify an organism without culturing by making copies (amplifying) nucleic acid sequences that are specific for the organism being detected.

nucleic acid hybridization   The process of combining single complementary strands of DNA.

nucleic acid vaccine   A vaccine made up of DNA, usually in the form of a plasmid.

nucleoid   The region in a bacterial cell containing the chromosome.

nucleolus (plural: nucleoli)   An area in a eukaryotic nucleus where rRNA is synthesized.

nucleoside   A compound consisting of a purine or pyrimidine base and a pentose sugar.

nucleoside reverse transcriptase inhibitor   A nucleoside analog antiretroviral drug.

nucleotide   A compound consisting of a purine or pyrimidine base, a five- carbon sugar, and a phosphate.

nucleotide (or nucleoside) analog   A chemical that is structurally similar to the normal nucleotide or nucleoside in nucleic acids but with altered base-pairing properties.

nucleotide excision repair   The repair of DNA involving removal of defective nucleotides and replacement with functional ones.

nucleus   (1) The part of an atom consisting of the protons and neutrons. (2) The part of a eukaryotic cell that contains the genetic material.

numerical identification   Bacterial identification schemes in which test values are assigned a number.

nutrient agar   Nutrient broth containing agar.

nutrient broth   A complex medium made of beef extract and peptone.

O antigen   Polysaccharide antigens in the outer membrane of gram-negative bacteria, identified by serological testing.

objective lenses   In a compound light microscope, the lenses closest to the specimen.

obligate aerobe   An organism that requires molecular oxygen (O_2) to live.

obligate anaerobe   An organism that does not use molecular oxygen (O_2) and is killed in the presence of O_2.

obligate halophile   An organism that requires high osmotic pressures such as high concentrations of NaCl.

ocular lens   In a compound light microscope, the lens closest to the viewer; also called the eyepiece.

oligodynamic action   The ability of small amounts of a heavy metal compound to exert antimicrobial activity.

oligosaccharide   A carbohydrate consisting of 2 to approximately 20 monosaccharides.

oncogene   A gene that can bring about malignant transformation.

oncogenic virus   A virus that is capable of producing tumors; also called oncovirus.

oocyst   An encysted apicomplexan zygote in which cell division occurs to form the next infectious stage.

Opa   A bacterial outer membrane protein; cells with Opa form opaque colonies.

operator   The region of DNA adjacent to structural genes that controls their transcription.

operon   The operator and promoter sites and structural genes they control.

opportunistic pathogen   A microorganism that does not ordinarily cause a disease but can become pathogenic under certain circumstances.

opsonization   The enhancement of phagocytosis by coating microorganisms with certain serum proteins (opsonins); also called immune adherence.

optimum growth temperature   The temperature at which a species grows best.

order   A taxonomic classification between class and family.

organotroph   *See* heterotroph.

organelle   A membrane-enclosed structure within eukaryotic cells.

organic compound   A molecule that contains carbon and hydrogen.

organic growth factor   An essential organic compound that an organism is unable to synthesize.

osmosis   The net movement of solvent molecules across a selectively permeable membrane from an area of lower solute concentration to an area of higher solute concentration.

osmotic lysis   Rupture of the plasma membrane resulting from movement of water into the cell.

osmotic pressure   The force with which a solvent moves from a solution of lower solute concentration to a solution of higher solute concentration.

oxidation   The removal of electrons from a molecule.

oxidation pond   A method of secondary sewage treatment by microbial activity in a shallow standing pond of water.

oxidation-reduction   A coupled reaction in which one substance is oxidized and one is reduced; also called redox reaction.

oxidative phosphorylation   The synthesis of ATP coupled with electron transport.

oxygenic   Producing oxygen, as in plant and cyanobacterial photosynthesis.

ozone O_3.

PAMP (pathogen-associated molecular patterns)   Molecules present on pathogens and not self.

pandemic disease   An epidemic that occurs worldwide.

papule   Small, solid elevation of the skin.

parasite   An organism that derives nutrients from a living host.

parasitism   A symbiotic relationship in which one organism (the parasite) exploits another (the host) without providing any benefit in return.

parasitology   The scientific study of parasitic protozoa and worms.

parenteral route   A portal of entry for pathogens by deposition directly into tissues beneath the skin and mucous membranes.

pasteurization   The process of mild heating to kill particular spoilage microorganisms or pathogens.

pathogen   A disease-causing organism.

pathogenesis   The manner in which a disease develops.

pathogenicity   The ability of a microorganism to cause disease by overcoming the defenses of a host.

pathology   The scientific study of disease.

pellicle   (1) The flexible covering of some protozoa. (2) Scum on the surface of a liquid medium.

penicillins   A group of antibiotics produced either by *Penicillium* (natural penicillins) or by adding side chains to the β-lactam ring (semisynthetic penicillins).

pentose phosphate pathway   A metabolic pathway that can occur simultaneously with glycolysis to produce pentoses and NADH without ATP production; also called hexose monophosphate shunt.

peptide bond   A bond joining the amino group of one amino acid to the carboxyl group of a second amino acid with the loss of a water molecule.

peptidoglycan   The structural molecule of bacterial cell walls consisting of the molecules N-acetylglucosamine, N-acetylmuramic acid, tetrapeptide side chain, and peptide side chain.

perforin   Protein that makes a pore in a target cell membrane, released by cytotoxic T lymphocytes.

pericarditis   Inflammation of the pericardium, the sac around the heart.

period of convalescence   The recovery period, when the body returns to its predisease state.

peripheral nervous system (PNS)   The nerves that connect the outlying parts of the body with the central nervous system.

periplasm   The region of a gram-negative cell wall between the outer membrane and the cytoplasmic membrane.

peritrichous   Having flagella distributed over the entire cell.

peroxidase   An enzyme that destroys hydrogen peroxide: $H_2O_2 + 2 H^+ \rightarrow 2 H_2O$

peroxide anion   An oxygen anion consisting of two atoms of oxygen (O_2^{2-}).

peroxisome   Organelle that oxidizes amino acids, fatty acids, and alcohol.

peroxygen   A class of oxidizing-type sterilizing disinfectants.

persistent viral infection   A disease process that occurs gradually over a long period.

Peyer's patches   Lymphoid organs on the intestinal wall.

PFU (plaque-forming units)   Visible clearing in a bacterial culture caused by lysis of bacterial cells by bacteriophages.

pH   The symbol for hydrogen ion (H^+) concentration; a measure of the relative acidity or alkalinity of a solution.

phage   *See* bacteriophage.

phage conversion   Genetic change in the host cell resulting from infection by a bacteriophage.

phage typing   A method of identifying bacteria using specific strains of bacteriophages.

phagocyte   A cell capable of engulfing and digesting particles that are harmful to the body.

phagocytosis   The ingestion of particles by eukaryotic cells.

phagolysosome   A digestive vacuole.

phagosome   A food vacuole of a phagocyte; also called a phagocytic vesicle.

phalloidin   A peptide toxin produced by *Amanita phalloides*, affects plasma membrane function.

phase-contrast microscope   A compound light microscope that allows examination of structures inside cells through the use of a special condenser.

phenol OH Also called carbolic acid.

phenolic   A derivative of phenol used as a disinfectant.

phenotype   The external manifestations of an organism's genotype, or genetic makeup.

phosphate group   A portion of a phosphoric acid molecule attached to some other molecule, (P),

$$PO_4^{3-}, \quad {}^-O-\overset{\displaystyle O}{\underset{\displaystyle O^-}{\overset{\|}{\underset{|}{P}}}}-O^-$$

phospholipid   A complex lipid composed of glycerol, two fatty acids, and a phosphate group.

phosphorous cycle   The various solubility stages of phosphorus in the environment.

phosphorylation The addition of a phosphate group to an organic molecule.

photoautotroph An organism that uses light as its energy source and carbon dioxide (CO_2) as its carbon source.

photoheterotroph An organism that uses light as its energy source and an organic carbon source.

photolyase An enzyme that splits thymine dimers in the presence of visible light.

photophosphorylation The production of ATP in a series of redox reactions; electrons from chlorophyll initiate the reactions.

photosynthesis The conversion of light energy from the sun into chemical energy; the light-fueled synthesis of carbohydrate from carbon dioxide (CO_2).

phototaxis Movement in response to the presence of light.

phototroph An organism that uses light at its primary energy source.

phylogeny The evolutionary history of a group of organisms; phylogenetic relationships are evolutionary relationships.

phylum A taxonomic classification between kingdom and class.

phytoplankton Free-floating photoautotrophs.

pilus (plural: **pili**) An appendage on a bacterial cell used for conjugation and gliding motility.

pinocytosis Taking in molecules by infolding of the plasma membrane, in eukaryotes.

plankton Free-floating aquatic organisms.

Plantae The kingdom composed of multicellular eukaryotes with cellulose cell walls.

plaque A clearing in a bacterial lawn resulting from lysis by phages. *See also* dental plaque.

plasma (1) The liquid portion of blood in which the formed elements are suspended. (2) Excited gases used for sterilizing.

plasma cell A cell that an activated B cell differentiates into; plasma cells manufacture specific antibodies.

plasma (cytoplasmic) membrane The selectively permeable membrane enclosing the cytoplasm of a cell; the outer layer in animal cells, internal to the cell wall in other organisms.

plasmid A small circular DNA molecule that replicates independently of the chromosome.

plasmodium (1) A multinucleated mass of protoplasm, as in plasmodial slime molds. (2) When written as a genus, refers to the causative agent of malaria.

plasmogamy Fusion of the cytoplasm of two cells; occurs in the sexual stage of a fungal life cycle.

plasmolysis Loss of water from a cell in a hypertonic environment.

plate count A method of determining the number of bacteria in a sample by counting the number of colony-forming units on a solid culture medium.

pleomorphic Having many shapes, characteristic of certain bacteria.

pluripotent A cell that can differentiate into a many different types of tissue cells.

pneumonia Inflammation of the lungs.

point mutation *See* base substitution.

polar flagella Having flagella at one or both ends of a cell.

polar molecule A molecule with an unequal distribution of charges.

polymer A molecule consisting of a sequence of similar molecules, or monomers.

polymerase chain reaction (PCR) A technique using DNA polymerase to make multiple copies of a DNA template in vitro. *See also* cDNA.

polymorphonuclear leukocyte (PMN) *See* neutrophil.

polypeptide (1) A chain of amino acids. (2) A group of antibiotics.

polysaccharide A carbohydrate consisting of 8 or more monosaccharides joined through dehydration synthesis.

porins A type of protein in the outer membrane of gram-negative cell walls that permits the passage of small molecules.

portal of entry The avenue by which a pathogen gains access to the body.

portal of exit The route by which a pathogen leaves the body.

positive (direct) selection A procedure for picking out mutant cells by growing them.

pour plate method A method of inoculating a solid nutrient medium by mixing bacteria in the melted medium and pouring the medium into a Petri dish to solidify.

prebiotics Chemicals that promote growth of beneficial bacteria in the body.

precipitation reaction A reaction between soluble antigens and multivalent antibodies to form visible aggregates.

precipitin ring test A precipitation test performed in a capillary tube.

predisposing factor Anything that makes the body more susceptible to a disease or alters the course of a disease.

prevalence The fraction of a population having a specific disease at a given time.

primary cell line Human tissue cells that grow for only a few generations in vitro.

primary infection An acute infection that causes the initial illness.

primary metabolite A product of an industrial cell population produced during the time of rapid logarithmic growth. *See also* secondary metabolite.

primary producer An autotrophic organism, either chemotroph or phototroph, that converts carbon dioxide into organic compounds.

primary response Antibody production in response to the first contact with an antigen. *See also* memory response.

primary sewage treatment The removal of solids from sewage by allowing them to settle out and be held temporarily in tanks or ponds.

prion An infectious agent consisting of a self-replicating protein, with no detectable nucleic acids.

privileged site (tissue) An area of the body (or a tissue) that does not elicit an immune response.

probiotics Microbes inoculated into a host to occupy a niche and prevent growth of pathogens.

prodromal period The time following the incubation period when the first symptoms of illness appear.

profundal zone The deeper water under the limnetic zone in an inland body of water.

proglottid A body segment of a tapeworm containing both male and female organs.

prokaryote A cell whose genetic material is not enclosed in a nuclear envelope.

prokaryotic species A population of cells that share certain rRNA sequences; in conventional biochemical testing, it is a population of cells with similar characteristics.

promoter The starting site on a DNA strand for transcription of RNA by RNA polymerase.

prophage Phage DNA inserted into the host cell's DNA.

prophylactic Anything used to prevent disease.

prostaglandin A hormonelike substance that is released by damaged cells, intensifies inflammation.

prostheca A stalk or bud protruding from a prokaryotic cell.

protease An enzyme that digests protein (proteolytic enzymes).

protein A large molecule containing carbon, hydrogen, oxygen, and nitrogen (and sulfur); some proteins have a helical structure and others are pleated sheets.

protein kinase An enzyme that activates another protein by adding a Ⓟ from ATP.

proteobacteria Gram-negative, chemoheterotrophic bacteria that possess a signature rRNA sequence.

proteomics The science of determining all of the proteins expressed in a cell.

protist Term used for unicellular and simple multicellular eukaryotes; usually protozoa and algae.

proton A positively charged particle in the nucleus of an atom.

protoplast A gram-positive bacterium or plant cell treated to remove the cell wall.

protoplast fusion A method of joining two cells by first removing their cell walls; used in genetic engineering.

protozoan (plural: **protozoa**) Unicellular eukaryotic organisms; usually chemoheterotrophic.

provirus Viral DNA that is integrated into the host cell's DNA.

pseudohypha A short chain of fungal cells that results from the lack of separation of daughter cells after budding.

pseudopod An extension of a eukaryotic cell that aids in locomotion and feeding.

psychrophile An organism that grows best at about 15°C and does not grow above 20°C; a cold-loving microbe.

pscyhrotroph An organism that is capable of growth between about 0°C and 30°C.

purines The class of nucleic acid bases that includes adenine and guanine.

purple nonsulfur bacteria Alphaproteobacteria; strictly anaerobic and phototrophic; grow on yeast extract in dark; use reduced organic compounds as electron donors for CO_2 fixation.

purple sulfur bacteria   Gammaproteobacteria; strictly anaerobic and phototrophic; use reduced sulfur compounds as electron donors for CO_2 fixation.

pus   An accumulation of dead phagocytes, dead bacterial cells, and fluid.

pustule   A small pus-filled elevation of skin.

pyocyanin   A blue-green pigment produced by *Pseudomonas aeruginosa*.

pyrimidines   The class of nucleic acid bases that includes uracil, thymine, and cytosine.

quaternary ammonium compound (quat)   A cationic detergent with four organic groups attached to a central nitrogen atom; used as a disinfectant.

quorum sensing   The ability of bacteria to communicate and coordinate behavior via signaling molecules.

R   Used to represent nonfunctional groups of a molecule. *See also* resistance factor.

rapid diagnostic test (RDT)   A test that allows diagnosis of a disease within a few minutes.

rapid identification methods   Bacterial identification tools that perform several biochemical tests simultaneously.

rapid plasma reagin (RPR) test   A serological test for syphilis.

r-determinant   A group of genes for antibiotic resistance carried on R factors.

RecA   Catalyzes joining of DNA strands, facilitates recombination of DNA.

receptor   An attachment for a pathogen on a host cell.

receptor-mediated endocytosis   A type of pinocytosis in which molecules bound to proteins on the plasma membrane are taken in by infolding of the membrane.

recipient cell   A cell that receives DNA from a donor cell during genetic recombination.

recombinant DNA (rDNA)   A DNA molecule produced by combining DNA from two different sources.

recombinant DNA (rDNA) technology   Manufacturing and manipulating genetic material in vitro; also called genetic engineering.

recombinant vaccine   A vaccine made by recombinant DNA techniques.

redia   A trematode larval stage that reproduces asexually to produce cercariae.

redox reaction   *See* oxidation-reduction.

red tide   A bloom of planktonic dinoflagellates.

reducing medium   A culture medium containing ingredients that will remove dissolved oxygen from the medium to allow the growth of anaerobes.

reduction   The addition of electrons to a molecule.

refractive index   The relative velocity with which light passes through a substance.

relative risk   A comparison of the risk of disease in two groups.

rennin   An enzyme that forms curds as part of any dairy fermentation product; originally from calves' stomachs, now produced by molds and bacteria.

replica plating   A method of inoculating a number of solid minimal culture media from an original plate to produce the same pattern of colonies on each plate.

replication fork   The point where DNA strands separate and new strands will be synthesized.

repression   The process by which a repressor protein can stop the synthesis of a protein.

repressor   A protein that binds to the operator site to prevent transcription.

reservoir of infection   A continual source of infection.

resistance   The ability to ward off diseases through innate and adaptive immunity.

resistance (R) factor   A bacterial plasmid carrying genes that determine resistance to antibiotics.

resistance transfer factor (RTF)   A group of genes for replication and conjugation on the R factor.

resolution   The ability to distinguish fine detail with a magnifying instrument; also called resolving power.

respiration   A series of redox reactions in a membrane that generates ATP; the final electron acceptor is usually an inorganic molecule.

restriction enzyme   An enzyme that cuts double-stranded DNA at specific sites between nucleotides.

reticulate body   The intracellular growing stage of chlamydiae.

reticuloendothelial system   *See* mononuclear phagocytic system.

retort   A device for commercially sterilizing canned food by using steam under pressure; operates on the same principle as an autoclave but is much larger.

reverse genetics   Genetic analysis that begins with a piece of DNA and proceeds to find out what it does.

reverse transcriptase   An RNA-dependent DNA polymerase; an enzyme that synthesizes a complementary DNA from an RNA template.

reversible reaction   A chemical reaction in which the end-products can readily revert to the original molecules.

RFLP   Restriction fragment length polymorphism; a fragment resulting from restriction-enzyme digestion of DNA.

Rh factor   An antigen on red blood cells of rhesus monkeys and most humans; possession makes the cells Rh^+.

rhizine   A rootlike hypha that anchors a fungus to a surface.

ribonucleic acid (RNA)   The class of nucleic acids that comprises messenger RNA, ribosomal RNA, and transfer RNA.

ribose   A five-carbon sugar that is part of ribonucleotide molecules and RNA.

ribosomal RNA (rRNA)   The type of RNA molecule that forms ribosomes.

ribosomal RNA (rRNA) sequencing   Determination of the order of nucleotide bases in rRNA.

ribosome   The site of protein synthesis in a cell, composed of RNA and protein.

ribotyping   Classification or identification of bacteria based on rRNA genes.

ribozyme   An enzyme consisting of RNA that specifically acts on strands of RNA to remove introns and splice together the remaining exons.

ring stage   A young *Plasmodium* trophozoite that looks like a ring in a red blood cell.

RNAi   RNA interference; stops gene expression at transcription by using a short interfering RNA to make double-stranded RNA.

RNA-induced silencing complex (RISC)   A complex consisting of a protein and siRNA or miRNA that binds complementary mRNA, preventing transcription of the mRNA.

RNA primer   A short strand of RNA used to start synthesis of the lagging strand of DNA, and to start the polymerase chain reaction.

root nodule   A tumorlike growth on the roots of certain plants containing symbiotic nitrogen-fixing bacteria.

rotating biological contactor   A method of secondary sewage treatment in which large disks are rotated while partially submerged in a sewage tank exposing sewage to microorganisms and aerobic conditions.

rough ER   Endoplasmic reticulum with ribosomes on its surface.

roundworm   An animal belonging to the phylum Nematoda.

S (Svedberg unit)   Notes the relative rate of sedimentation during ultra-high speed centrifugation.

salt   A substance that dissolves in water to cations and anions, neither of which is H^+ or OH^-.

sanitization   The removal of microbes from eating utensils and food preparation areas.

saprophyte   An organism that obtains its nutrients from dead organic matter.

sarcina (plural: sarcinae)   (1) A group of eight bacteria that remain in a packet after dividing. (2) When written as a genus, refers to gram-positive, anaerobic cocci.

saturation   (1) The condition in which the active site on an enzyme is occupied by the substrate or product at all times. (2) In a fatty acid, having no double bonds.

saxitoxin   A neurotoxin produced by some dinoflagellates.

scanned-probe microscopy   Microscopic technique used to obtain images of molecular shapes, to characterize chemical properties, and to determine temperature variations within a specimen.

scanning acoustic microscope (SAM)   A microscope that uses high-frequency ultrasound waves to penetrate surfaces.

scanning electron microscope (SEM)   An electron microscope that provides three-dimensional views of the specimen magnified 1000–10,000×.

scanning tunneling microscopy   *See* scanned-probe microscopy.

schizogony   The process of multiple fission, in which one organism divides to produce many daughter cells.

scientific nomenclature   *See* binomial nomenclature.

sclerotia   The compact mass of hardened mycelia of the fungus *Claviceps purpurea* that fills infected rye flowers; produces the toxin ergot.

scolex The head of a tapeworm, containing suckers and possibly hooks.

secondary infection An infection caused by an opportunistic microbe after a primary infection has weakened the host's defenses.

secondary metabolite A product of an industrial cell population produced after the microorganism has largely completed its period of rapid growth and is in a stationary phase of the growth cycle. *See also* primary metabolite.

secondary response *See* memory response.

secondary sewage treatment Biological degradation of the organic matter in wastewater following primary treatment.

secretory vesicle A membrane-enclosed sac produced by the ER; transports synthesized material into cytoplasm.

selective medium A culture medium designed to suppress the growth of unwanted microorganisms and encourage the growth of desired ones.

selective permeability The property of a plasma membrane to allow certain molecules and ions to move through the membrane while restricting others.

selective toxicity The property of some antimicrobial agents to be toxic for a microorganism and nontoxic for the host.

self Host tissue.

semiconservative replication The process of DNA replication in which each double-stranded DNA molecule contains one original strand and one new strand.

sense codon A codon that codes for an amino acid.

sense strand (+ strand) Viral RNA that can act as mRNA.

sensitivity Percentage of positive samples correctly detected by a diagnostic test.

sentinel animal An organism in which changes can be measured to assess the extent of environmental contamination and its implication for human health.

sepsis The presence of a toxin or pathogenic organism in blood and tissue.

septate hypha A hypha consisting of uninucleate cell-like units.

septicemia The proliferation of pathogens in the blood, accompanied by fever; sometimes causes organ damage.

septic shock A sudden drop in blood pressure induced by bacterial toxins.

septum A cross-wall in a fungal hypha.

serial dilution The process of diluting a sample several times.

seroconversion A change in a person's response to an antigen in a serological test.

serological testing Techniques for identifying a microorganism based on its reaction with antibodies.

serology The branch of immunology that studies blood serum and antigen–antibody reactions in vitro.

serotype *See* serovar.

serovar A variation within a species; also called serotype.

serum The liquid remaining after blood plasma is clotted; contains antibodies (immunoglobulins).

sexual dimorphism The distinctly different appearance of adult male and female organisms.

sexual spore A spore formed by sexual reproduction.

Shiga toxin An exotoxin produced by *Shigella dysenteriae* and entero-hemorrhagic *E. coli*.

shock Any life-threatening loss of blood pressure. *See also* septic shock.

short tandem repeats (STRs) Repeating sequences of 2- to 5-nucleotides.

shotgun sequencing A technique for determining the nucleotide sequence in an organism's genome.

shuttle vector A plasmid that can exist in several different species; used in genetic engineering.

siderophore Bacterial iron-binding proteins.

sign A change due to a disease that a person can observe and measure.

simple stain A method of staining microorganisms with a single basic dye.

singlet oxygen Highly reactive molecular oxygen (O_2^-).

siRNA Small interfering RNA; An intermediate in the RNAi process in which the long double-stranded RNA has been cut up into short (~21 nucleotides) double-stranded RNA.

site-directed mutagenesis Techniques used to modify a gene in a specific location to produce the desired polypeptide.

slide agglutination test A method of identifying an antigen by combining it with a specific antibody on a slide.

slime layer A glycocalyx that is unorganized and loosely attached to the cell wall.

sludge Solid matter obtained from sewage.

smear A thin film of material containing microorganisms, spread over the surface of a slide.

smooth ER Endoplasmic reticulum without ribosomes.

SNP Single nucleotide polymorphism (pronounced "snip"). Single base-pair variations in the genomes of a population, found in at least 1% of the population.

snRNP Small nuclear ribonucleoprotein (pronounced "snurp"). Short RNA transcript plus protein that combines with pre-mRNA to remove introns and join exons together.

solute A substance dissolved in another substance.

solvent A dissolving medium.

Southern blotting A technique that uses DNA probes to detect the presence of specific DNA in restriction fragments separated by electrophoresis.

specialized transduction The process of transferring a piece of cell DNA adjacent to a prophage to another cell.

species The most specific level in the taxonomic hierarchy. *See also* bacterial species; eukaryotic species; viral species.

specific epithet The second or species name in a scientific binomial. *See also* species.

specificity Percentage of false positive results given by a diagnostic test.

spectrum of microbial activity The range of distinctly different types of microorganisms affected by an antimicrobial drug; a wide range is referred to as a broad spectrum of activity.

spheroplast A gram-negative bacterium treated to damage the cell wall, resulting in a spherical cell.

spicule One of two external structures on the male roundworm used to guide sperm.

spike A carbohydrate-protein complex that projects from the surface of certain viruses.

spiral *See* spirillum and spirochete.

spirillum (plural: spirilla) (1) A helical or corkscrew-shaped bacterium. (2) When written as a genus, refers to aerobic, helical bacteria with clumps of polar flagella.

spirochete A corkscrew-shaped bacterium with axial filaments.

spontaneous generation The idea that life could arise spontaneously from nonliving matter.

spontaneous mutation A mutation that occurs without a mutagen.

sporadic disease A disease that occurs occasionally in a population.

sporangiophore An aerial hypha supporting a sporangium.

sporangiospore An asexual fungal spore formed within a sporangium.

sporangium A sac containing one or more spores.

spore A reproductive structure formed by fungi and actinomycetes. *See also* endospore.

sporogenesis *See* sporulation.

sporozoite A trophozoite of *Plasmodium* found in mosquitoes, infective for humans.

sporulation The process of spore and endospore formation; also called sporogenesis.

spread plate method A plate count method in which inoculum is spread over the surface of a solid culture medium.

staining Colorizing a sample with a dye to view through a microscope or to visualize specific structures.

staphylococci (singular: staphylococcus) Cocci in a grapelike cluster or broad sheet.

stationary phase The period in a bacterial growth curve when the number of cells dividing equals the number dying.

stem cell An undifferentiated cell that gives rise to a variety of specialized cells.

stereoisomers Two molecules consisting of the same atoms, arranged in the same manner but differing in their relative positions; mirror images; also called D-isomer and L-isomer.

sterile Free of microorganisms.

sterilization The removal of all microorganisms, including endospores.

steroid A specific group of lipids, including cholesterol and hormones.

stipe A stemlike supporting structure of multicellular algae and basidiomycetes.

storage vesicle Organelles that form from the Golgi complex; contain proteins made in the rough ER and processed in the Golgi complex.

strain Genetically different cells within a clone. *See* serovar.

streak plate method   A method of isolating a culture by spreading microorganisms over the surface of a solid culture medium.

streptobacilli (singular: **streptobacillus**)   Rods that remain attached in chains after cell division.

streptococci (singular: **streptococcus**)   (1) Cocci that remain attached in chains after cell division. (2) When written as a genus, refers to gram-positive, catalase-negative bacteria.

streptokinase   A blood-clot dissolving enzyme, produced by beta-hemolytic streptococci.

streptolysin   A hemolytic enzyme, produced by streptococci.

structural gene   A gene that determines the amino acid sequence of a protein.

subacute disease   A disease with symptoms that are intermediate between acute and chronic.

subclinical infection   An infection that does not cause a noticeable illness; also called inapparent infection.

subcutaneous mycosis   A fungal infection of tissue beneath the skin.

substrate   Any compound with which an enzyme reacts.

substrate-level phosphorylation   The synthesis of ATP by direct transfer of a high-energy phosphate group from an intermediate metabolic compound to ADP.

subunit vaccine   A vaccine consisting of an antigenetic fragment.

sulfhydryl group   —SH.

sulfur cycle   The various oxidation and reduction stages of sulfur in the environment, mostly due to the action of microorganisms.

sulfur granule   *See* inclusion.

superantigen   An antigen that activates many different T cells, thereby eliciting a large immune response.

superbug   Bacterium resistant to a large number of antibiotics.

superficial mycosis   A fungal infection localized in surface epidermal cells and along hair shafts.

superinfection   The growth of a pathogen that has developed resistance to an antimicrobial drug being used; the growth of an opportunistic pathogen.

superoxide dismutase (SOD)   An enzyme that destroys superoxide: $O_2^- + O_2^- + 2\,H^+ \rightarrow H_2O_2 + O_2$

superoxide radical   A toxic anion (O_2^-) with an unpaired electron.

surface-active agent   Any compound that decreases the tension between molecules lying on the surface of a liquid; also called surfactant.

susceptibility   The lack of resistance to a disease.

symbiosis   The living together of two different organisms or populations.

symptom   A change in body function that is felt by a patient as a result of a disease.

syncytium   A multinucleated giant cell resulting from certain viral infections.

syndrome   A specific group of signs or symptoms that accompany a disease.

synergism   The principle whereby the effectiveness of two drugs used simultaneously is greater than that of either drug used alone.

synthesis reaction   A chemical reaction in which two or more atoms combine to form a new, larger molecule.

synthetic drug   A chemotherapeutic agent that is prepared from chemicals in a laboratory.

systematics   The science organizing groups of organisms into a hierarchy.

systemic anaphylaxis   A hypersensitivity reaction causing vasodilation and resulting in shock; also called anaphylactic shock.

systemic (generalized) infection   An infection throughout the body.

systemic mycosis   A fungal infection in deep tissues.

tachyzoite   A rapidly growing trophozoite form of a protozoan.

T antigen   An antigen in the nucleus of a tumor cell.

tapeworm   A flatworm belonging to the class Cestoda.

target cell   An infected body cell to which defensive cells of the immune system bind.

taxa   Subdivisions used to classify organisms, e.g., domain, kingdom, phylum.

taxis   Movement in response to an environmental stimulus.

taxonomy   The science of the classification of organisms.

T cell   A type of lymphocyte, which develops from a stem cell processed in the thymus gland, that is responsible for cell-mediated immunity. *See also* T cytotoxic cells, T helper cells, T regulatory cells.

TCRs (T cell receptors)   Molecules on T cells that recognize antigens.

T cytotoxic (T_C) cells   A precursor to a cytotoxic T lymphocyte.

T helper (T_H) cell   A specialized T cell that often interacts with an antigen before B cells interact with the antigen.

T regulatory (T_{reg}) cells   Lymphocytes that appear to suppress other T cells.

T-dependent antigen   An antigen that will stimulate the formation of antibodies only with the assistance of T helper cells. *See also* T-independent antigen.

teichoic acid   A polysaccharide found in gram-positive cell walls.

telomere   Noncoding regions of DNA at the ends of eukaryotic chromosomes.

teleomorph   The sexual stage in the life cycle of a fungus; also refers to a fungus that produces both sexual and asexual spores.

temperate phage   A phage capable of lysogeny.

temperature abuse   Improper food storage at a temperature that allows bacteria to grow.

terminator   The site on a DNA strand at which transcription ends.

tertiary sewage treatment   A method of waste treatment that follows conventional secondary sewage treatment; nonbiodegradable pollutants and mineral nutrients are removed, usually by chemical or physical means.

tetrad   A group of four cocci.

thallus   The entire vegetative structure or body of a fungus, lichen, or alga.

thermal death point (TDP)   The temperature required to kill all the bacteria in a liquid culture in 10 minutes.

thermal death time (TDT)   The length of time required to kill all bacteria in a liquid culture at a given temperature.

thermoduric   Heat resistant.

thermophile   An organism whose optimum growth temperature is between 50°C and 60°C; a heat loving microbe.

thermophilic anaerobic spoilage   Spoilage of canned foods due to the growth of thermophilic bacteria.

thylakoid   A chlorophyll-containing membrane in a chloroplast. A bacterial thylakoid is also known as a chromatophore.

thymus   A mammalian organ responsible for maturation of the immune system.

thymic selection   Elimination of T cells that don't recognize self antigens (major histocompatibility complex).

tincture   A solution in aqueous alcohol.

T-independent antigen   An antigen that will stimulate the formation of antibodies without the assistance of T helper cells. *See also* T-dependent antigen.

tinea   Fungal infection of hair, skin, or nails.

Ti plasmid   A tumor-inducing plasmid that can be incorporated into a host plant chromosome; found in *Agrobacterium*.

titer   An estimate of the amount of antibodies or viruses in a solution; determined by serial dilution and expressed as the reciprocal of the dilution.

TLR (Toll-like receptor)   Transmembrane protein of immune cells that recognizes pathogens and activates an immune response directed against those pathogens.

topoisomerase   Enzyme that relaxes supercoiling of DNA ahead of replication form; separates DNA circles at the end of DNA replication.

total magnification   The magnification of a microscopic specimen, determined by multiplying the ocular lens magnification by the objective lens magnification.

toxemia   The presence of toxins in the blood.

toxigenicity   The capacity of a microorganism to produce a toxin.

toxin   Any poisonous substance produced by a microorganism.

toxoid   An inactivated toxin.

T plasmid   An *Agrobacterium* plasmid carrying genes for tumor induction in plants.

trace element   A chemical element required in small amounts for growth.

trans   Hydrogen atoms on opposite side across a double bond in a fatty acid. *See* cis.

transamination   The transfer of an amino group from an amino acid to another organic acid.

transcription   The process of synthesizing RNA from a DNA template.

transduction   The transfer of DNA from one cell to another by a bacteriophage. *See also* generalized transduction; specialized transduction.

transferrin   One of several human iron-binding proteins that reduce iron available to a pathogen.

transfer RNA (tRNA)   The type of RNA molecule that brings amino acids to the ribosomal site where they are incorporated into proteins.

transfer vesicle Membrane-bound sacs that move proteins from the Golgi complex to specific areas in the cell.

transformation (1) The process in which genes are transferred from one bacterium to another as "naked" DNA in solution. (2) The changing of a normal cell into a cancerous cell.

transient microbiota The microorganisms that are present in an animal for a short time without causing a disease.

translation The use of mRNA as a template in the synthesis of protein.

transmission electron microscope (TEM) An electron microscope that provides high magnifications ($10,000$–$100,000\times$) of thin sections of a specimen.

transport media Media used to keep microorganisms alive between sample collection and laboratory testing; usually used for clinical samples.

transport vesicle Membrane-bound sacs that move proteins from the rough ER to the Golgi complex.

transporter protein A carrier protein in the plasma membrane.

transposon A small piece of DNA that can move from one DNA molecule to another.

trickling filter A method of secondary sewage treatment in which sewage is sprayed out of rotating arms onto a bed of rocks or similar materials, exposing the sewage to highly aerobic conditions and microorganisms.

triglyceride A simple lipid consisting of glycerol and three fatty acids.

triplex agent A short segment of DNA that binds to a target area on a double strand of DNA blocking transcription.

trophophase The period in the production curve of an industrial cell population in which the primary metabolites are formed; a period of rapid, logarithmic growth. *See also* idiophase.

trophozoite The vegetative form of a protozoan.

tuberculin skin test A skin test used to detect the presence of antibodies to *Mycobacterium tuberculosis*.

tumor necrosis factor (TNF) A polypeptide released by phagocytes in response to bacterial endotoxins.

tumor-specific transplantation antigen (TSTA) A viral antigen on the surface of a transformed cell.

turbidity The cloudiness of a suspension.

turnover number The number of substrate molecules acted on per enzyme molecule per second.

two-photon microscope A light microscope that uses fluorescent stains and long wavelength light.

ubiquinone A low–molecular weight, nonprotein carrier in an electron transport chain; also called coenzyme Q.

ultra-high-temperature (UHT) treatment A method of treating food with high temperatures (140–$150°C$) for very short times to make the food sterile so that it can be stored at room temperature.

uncoating The separation of viral nucleic acid from its protein coat.

undulating membrane A highly modified flagellum on some protozoa.

unsaturated A fatty acid with one or more double bonds.

use-dilution test A method of determining the effectiveness of a disinfectant using serial dilutions.

vaccination The process of conferring immunity by administering a vaccine; also called immunization.

vaccine A preparation of killed, inactivated, or attenuated microorganisms or toxoids to induce artificially acquired active immunity.

vacuole An intracellular inclusion, in eukaryotic cells, surrounded by a plasma membrane; in prokaryotic cells, surrounded by a proteinaceous membrane.

valence The combining capacity of an atom or a molecule.

vancomycin An antibiotic that inhibits cell wall synthesis.

variolation An early method of vaccination using infected material from a patient.

vasodilation Dilation or enlargement of blood vessels.

VDRL test A rapid screening test to detect the presence of antibodies against *Treponema pallidum*. (VDRL stands for Venereal Disease Research Laboratory.)

vector (1) A plasmid or virus used in genetic engineering to insert genes into a cell. (2) An arthropod that carries disease-causing organisms from one host to another.

vegetative Referring to cells involved with obtaining nutrients, as opposed to reproduction.

vehicle transmission The transmission of a pathogen by an inanimate reservoir.

vertical gene transfer Transfer of genes from an organism or cell to its offspring.

vesicle (1) A small serum-filled elevation of the skin. (2) Smooth oval bodies formed in plant roots by mycorrhizae.

V factor NAD^+ or $NADP^+$.

vibrio (1) A curved or comma-shaped bacterium. (2) When written as a genus (*Vibrio*), a gram-negative, motile, facultatively anaerobic curved rod.

viral hemagglutination The ability of certain viruses to cause the clumping of red blood cells in vitro.

viral hemagglutination inhibition test A neutralization test in which antibodies against particular viruses prevent the viruses from clumping red blood cells in vitro.

viral species A group of viruses sharing the same genetic information and ecological niche.

viremia The presence of viruses in the blood.

virion A complete, fully developed viral particle.

viroid Infectious RNA.

virology The scientific study of viruses.

virulence The degree of pathogenicity of a microorganism.

virus A submicroscopic, parasitic, filterable agent consisting of a nucleic acid surrounded by a protein coat.

volutin Stored inorganic phosphate in a prokaryotic cell. *See also* metachromatic granule.

Western blotting A technique that uses antibodies to detect the presence of specific proteins separated by electrophoresis.

whey The fluid portion of milk that separates from curd.

xenobiotics Synthetic chemicals that are not readily degraded by microorganisms.

xenodiagnosis A method of diagnosis based on exposing a parasite-free normal host to the parasite and then examining the host for parasites.

xenotransplantation product A tissue graft from another species; also called xenograft.

X factor Substances from the heme fraction of blood hemoglobin.

yeast Nonfilamentous, unicellular fungi.

yeast infection Disease caused by growth of certain yeasts in a susceptible host.

zone of inhibition The area of no bacterial growth around an antimicrobial agent in the disk-diffusion method.

zoonosis A disease that occurs primarily in wild and domestic animals but can be transmitted to humans.

zoospore An asexual algal spore; has two flagella.

zygospore A sexual fungal spore characteristic of the zygomycetes.

zygote A diploid cell produced by the fusion of two haploid gametes.

Index

filamentous branching, 324
gas vesicles, 103
heterocyst, 486
photosynthesis of, 343
terrestrial, 169
thylakoids of, 148
Cyanophora paradoxa, 295, 470
Cyclic AMP, 237, 377, 483
cyclic AMP (cAMP)
catabolite repression, 238
cyclic compounds, 51
Cyclic photophosphorylation, 479
cyclic structure, 483
Cyclospora cayetanensis, 377, 447, 470
Cyclospora diarrheal infection, 381
Cyclosporiasis, 452
Cystic fibrosis
pathogens affecting patients with
Pseudomonas aeruginosa, 62, 330
Cysticerci, 382-383
cysticercosis, 383
Cystitis, 473
cysts of protozoa
resistance to chemical biocides, 214
Cytochrome a, 161, 483
Cytochrome b, 137
cytochrome c oxidase, 147, 483
Cytochrome oxidase, 124-125, 316
Cytochrome oxidase complex, 139
Cytochromes, 137-138
Cytokine, 482
Cytokines, 483
hematopoietic, 486
immune response, 483
Cytokine(s)
immune system, 481
Cytokines
phagocytosis and, 482
Cytomegalovirus (HHV-5), 403
Cytopathic effect, 405-406, 483
Cytophaga, 342, 470, 478
Cytoplasm
halophilic, 86
of prokaryotic and eukaryotic cells, 83-86
Cytoplasmic membrane
mycoplasma, 97, 202, 316, 336, 357
psychrophile, 191, 491
selective barrier, 98
Cytoplasmic streaming, 102, 378-379, 483
Cytotoxin, 483

D

d forms, 88
Dairy products
fermented, 26, 144, 172
spoilage, 3, 143-144, 168, 201, 365, 485
Darkfield microscope, 63, 483
Dead Sea, 6, 170
Death phase, 183, 483
debridement, 483
Decarboxylase, 125, 304
Decimal reduction time, 199, 483-484
Decimeter (dm), 60
Decolorizing agent
gram stain, 74-75, 303-304, 340, 486
Decomposition reactions, 36, 481
Decontamination, 213
deep-freezing
to control microbial growth, 205
Deep-sea hydrothermal vents, 168
DEET (N,N-diethyl-m-toluamide), in disease
prevention
tularemia, 329, 452
Defined medium, 174, 482
Definitive host
of Plasmodium vivax, 376
of Taenia saginata, 382
degenerative evolution, 340
Degerming, 196-197, 483
degradation of synthetic chemicals
bioremediation, 24
degranulation, 483
Dehydration synthesis
in transcription, 234
of sucrose, 36, 123
peptide bond formation by, 48
dehydrogenases, 124
Dehydrogenation reactions, 130
Deinococcus, 324, 470, 477

Deinococcus radiodurans, 348, 470
Denaturation, 48, 127, 198-199, 483
Dendritic cells
phagocytosis by, 88, 490
Dengue fever, 388, 442
Dengue hemorrhagic fever, 447
Dental abscesses, 344
Dermatitis
allergic, 366
allergic contact, 366
Descriptive epidemiology, 448, 483
desensitization, 483
Desiccation, 105, 173, 199, 366, 483
in food preservation, 198
Desiccation, in microbial control
food preservation and, 182, 198
Desulfotomaculum, 478
Desulfovibrio, 140, 323, 470, 478
Desulfovibrio desulfuricans, 470
Desulfurococcales, 324, 477
Desulfurococcus, 477
detergent (SDS), 274
Detergents
cationic, 210
Deuteromycetes, 362
Deuteromycota, 362
devescovinids, 114
Dextrose, 177
D-glucose, 45
d-Glutamic acid, 47-48, 88
Diabetes
diabetes mellitus, 365
Diabetes mellitus
atherosclerosis and, 18
Diagnostic methods
ELISA, 306, 376, 484
diagnostic tools
Western blotting, 306, 406
Dialysis, 220
diapedesis, 483
Diarrhea
cholera and, 446
Diatoms
neurological disease caused by, 370
Dicer, 276
Dictyostelium, 378, 470
differential interference contrast (DIC) microscope, 483
Differential interference contrast (DIC) microscopy, 65
Differential media, 173, 305-306
Differential medium, 177-178, 483
Differential staining
acid-fast stain, 70, 304, 479
Differential stains
Gram, 70, 93-95, 177-178, 300, 341-342, 426,
480-482
Differential white blood cell count, 483
diffusion methods (to evaluate antibiotic sensitivity)
disk-diffusion method, 204, 483
E test, 484
Digestion
intracellular, 176, 238, 479
digestive aids, 4
Dihydroxyacetone, 132, 459-460
Dilution tests, 204
Dimers
repair of, 244
Dimorphic forms of fungi
thalli, 366-368
dimorphic fungi, 358
Dipeptide, 47-48
dipicolinic acid, 48, 105
diplobacilli, 85, 483
Diplobacillus, 483
Diplococci, 85, 303, 329, 483
diploid cell lines, 424
Diploid cell(s)
eukaryotic
algal, 270, 355, 486
Diplomonads, 380
Diptera, 474
Direct agglutination, 483
Direct ELISA, 306
Direct microscopic count, 187, 483
direct microscopic count of bacteria, 187
disease
fulminating, 485
general principles of
etiology, 430
hospital-acquired, 442

spread of infection, 439
germ theory of, 16, 448, 486
manifestations of, 490
noncommunicable diseases, 453
pandemic, 20, 401, 437, 474, 490
predisposing factors, 437
severity or duration of, 437
signs and symptoms, 435-436
sporadic, 20, 436, 493
viroid, 422, 495
Disease process, 405, 490
disease reservoirs
animal and human, 452
Disease(s)
etiology of, 425, 435
soilborne, 167
Diseases and disorders
pathogens causing, 439
Diseases and disorders, human
diagnosis and treatment of, 278
hypercholesterolemia, 18
xeroderma pigmentosum, 244
Diseases, plant
plant pathogens and, 340
Disinfectant, 24, 105, 196, 328, 446, 483
Disinfectants
formaldehyde, 211
sulfur dioxide, 211
surface-active agents, 205
use-dilution tests, 204
Disinfectants/disinfection
water, 79, 97-99, 196, 380, 480-484
principles of, 206
water treatment, 208
Disinfection/disinfectants
chemical agents, 195
dissimilation, 251, 484
dissimilation plasmids, 251
Dissimilation metabolism
nitrate reduction, 152
Disulfide bond, 484
DNA
amplification of, 269, 310
bent, 11, 63
blunt ends, 265, 344
denaturation, 48, 198-199, 483
in transformation, 250
ionizing radiation, 172, 203, 243, 486-487
melting, 54, 180
naked, 258, 286, 422, 488
nucleotide bases in, 234, 265, 492
probes, 70, 269, 310-312, 484-485
relaxed, 226
supercoiled, 225
variations in, 85, 248, 336, 493
DNA base composition, 301, 484
DNA chips, 279, 301
DNA (deoxyribonucleic acid)
and retroviruses, 276, 424
damage
by antimicrobial agents, 98
by radiation, 203
double-stranded (dsDNA)
provirus, 417, 491
G + C ratio, 350
histones, 102, 296
in bacteria, 12, 101, 154, 180, 232, 275-276, 300,
419, 481
in chromosomes, 243
methylation, 258
molecular structure, 205, 483
nucleotide sequences
terminator, 234, 494
recombinant DNA technology, 12, 263, 485
repair mechanisms, 259
restriction sites, 272
transposons, 247, 276, 295
DNA fingerprinting
for animals, 17
to identify microbes, 485
DNA ligase, 125, 227-228, 266, 484
in making recombinant DNA, 263
DNA polymerase
Pfu, 405, 490
proofreading capability of, 230
DNA polymerase I, 124
DNA polymerases, 169, 229
DNA probes
by Southern blotting, 310

509